BOTANY

FOR DEGREE STUDENTS

Sixth Edition

A. C. DUTTA M. SC.
Formerly Head of the Departments of
Botany and Biology, Cotton College,
Gauhati

Revised by
T. C. DUTTA
Head of the Department of Botany
St. Anthony's College
Shillong

OXFORD
UNIVERSITY PRESS

OXFORD
UNIVERSITY PRESS

YMCA Library Building, Jai Singh Road, New Delhi 110001

Oxford University Press is a department of the University of Oxford.
It furthers the University's objective of excellence in research, scholarship,
and education by publishing worldwide in

Oxford New York
Auckland Cape Town Dar es Salaam Hong Kong Karachi
Kuala Lumpur Madrid Melbourne Mexico City Nairobi
New Delhi Shanghai Taipei Toronto

With offices in
Argentina Austria Brazil Chile Czech Republic France Greece
Guatemala Hungary Italy Japan Poland Portugal Singapore
South Korea Switzerland Thailand Turkey Ukraine Vietnam

Oxford is a registered trade mark of Oxford University Press
in the UK and in certain other countries.

Published in India
by Oxford University Press

First published 1964
Twenty-eighth impression 2010

ISBN-13: 978-0-19-563748-9
ISBN-10: 0-19-563748-8

Printed in India by Sai Printopack, New Delhi 110020
and published by Oxford University Press
YMCA Library Building, Jai Singh Road, New Delhi 110001

PREFACE TO THE SIXTH EDITION

The sixth edition of 'BOTANY for Degree Students', has been brought out with a thorough revision of the whole text including the rewriting of many portions and addition of several new topics on the basis of recent researches, thereby covering as far as possible the prescribed syllabi of several universities.

In this text, Morphology and Embryology have been dealt together. Several new topics such as Morphology of stamen, Morphology of carpel, Phyllode theory have been included. Topics like Megagametogenesis and Embryogeny have been thoroughly modified and rewritten. A new chapter on Ecosystem (structural and functional aspects) with reference to food chain and food web has been added. Special mentions have also been made about Desertification, Eutrophication. On the basis of recent researches in Biochemistry, the mechanism of photosynthesis and that of respiration in Physiology, have been elaborated and some new topics added. Likewise, the readers will notice many necessary changes and new additions in other sections of the text.

Thus, this improved and enlarged sixth edition of 'BOTANY for Degree Students' will definitely meet the needs of degree students in our country as well as abroad.

EXTRACT FROM THE
PREFACE TO THE FIRST EDITION

BOTANY for Degree Students is an enlarged version of the author's *A Class-book of Botany*, eleventh edition, with necessary modifications and considerable additions. The book, as the name implies, is meant to meet the needs of students preparing for the three-year or two-year degree examination (pass standard) of Indian universities. With this end in view, an attempt has been made to cover as far as possible the syllabuses for the above courses. The author has tried to present the subject-matter in an easily understandable way without sacrificing the essential details and general principles and yet avoiding redundant matter and unnecessary complications. The book, as it stands, is expected to meet adequately the needs of the students for whom it is meant.

The illustrations, as incorporated in the book, are mostly the author's own drawings and photographs, either from *A Class-book of Botany*, eleventh edition, or drawn afresh; while others as listed below, have been adapted from the following publications with the permission of the publishers to whom sincere thanks of the author are due. Thus, with the permission of McGraw-Hill Book Company, Inc., FIG. II/11 has been redrawn from *Introduction to Plant Anatomy* by A. J. Eames and L. H. MacDaniels; edition and copyright 1925; FIGS. II/19, II/20 and II/21 redrawn from *Fundamentals of Cytology* by L. W. Sharp, edition and copyright 1943; FIGS. V/13 and V/14 redrawn from *Cryptogamic Botany* by G. M. Smith, edition and copyright 1938; and FIGS. V/44, V/49, V/126, V/154, V/160-1 and VI/16 from *Plant Morphology* by A. W. Haupt, edition and copyright 1953. with the premission of The University of Chicago Press. FIGS. VI/14, VI/15, VI/20D, VI/22 and VI/23A-F have been redrawn from *Gymnosperms: Structure and Evolution* by C. J. Chamberlain, edition and copyright 1935.

Satribari Road   **A.C.D.**
Gauhati, Assam
May, 1963

11.1.2.

CONTENTS

INTRODUCTION

1. Botany. The science that deals with the study of living objects goes by the general name of **biology** (*bios*, life; *logos*, discourse or science). Since both animals and plants are living, biology includes a study of both. Biology is, therefore, divided into two branches: **botany** (*botane*, herb) which deals with plants, and **zoology** (*zoon*, animal) which deals with animals.

2. Scope of Botany. Botany deals with the study of plants from many points of view. This science investigates the internal and external structures of plants, their functions in regard to nutrition, growth, movement and reproduction, their adaptations to varying conditions of the environment, their distribution in space and time, their life history, relationships and classification, the laws involved in their evolution from lower and simpler forms to higher and more complex ones, the laws of heredity, the uses that plants may be put to and, lastly, the different methods that can be adopted to improve plants for the use of mankind.

3. Origin and Continuity of Life. Life itself is mysterious, and its origin still remains shrouded in mystery. It is assumed, however, that many millions of years ago, life first came into existence in water as a speck of protoplasm (*protos,* first; *plasma,* form)from inorganic or non-living materials as a result of certain chemical and physical changes in them under adventitious circumstances. Protoplasm is, therefore, the first living substance. It is interesting to note that protoplasm is not formed afresh and, therefore, no new life comes into being and nor can it be created. Protoplasm is, however, continuous from generation to generation through reproduction. Thus, but for evolution, life would have still remained at the one-celled stage. [see also pp. 610-11].

4. Importance of Green Plants. Green plants are essential for the existence of all kinds of life, including human life. Their importance in this respect lies, *first,* in the fact that they are the only natural agents which are able to purify the atmosphere by absorbing carbon dioxide from it and releasing (by the breaking down of water) an almost equal volume of pure oxygen into it; and *second*, that green plants prepare food, such as starch (the chief constituent of rice, wheat, millets, etc.) using carbon dioxide from the air, and water and inorganic salts from the soil. Both these functions, viz. purification of the atmosphere and manufacture of food, are the monopoly of green plants and are performed by the green corpuscles or chloroplasts of the leaf during the day, sunlight being the source of energy. Animals, being devoid of chloroplasts, have no such power. It is evident, therefore, that animals, including human beings, are deeply indebted to plants for their basic needs, viz. oxygen for respiration and food for nutrition and energy. In this respect chloroplasts may be said to hold a strategic position so far as the living world is concerned.

5. Uses of Plants. The primary necessities of man are food, clothing and shelter. All these are met by plants. Food comes primarily from plants in the form of cereals (rice, wheat, maize, oat, rye and barley), millets (smaller grains), pulses, vegetables, fruit, vegetable oils, etc. Plants are indispensable sources of fibres for the manufacture of garments. The value of wood, bamboo, cane reed, thatch grass, etc. has been inestimable in providing shelter. Man has also tried to tap plants as sources for his comfort and used them to improve the quality of his life. (see Part IX Economic Botany).

6. Characteristics of Living Objects. We do not know what life really is. It is something mysterious and we are not in a position to define it. All living organisms have, however, certain characteristics by which they can be distinguished from non-living objects. These characteristics are as follows:

(1) **Life-cycle.** All living objects follow a definite life-cycle of birth, growth, reproduction, old age (senescence) and death.

(2) **Cellular Structure.** All living organisms are composed of characteristic types of structural units, called cells. A cell is an organized mass of living substance, called protoplasm, with a nucleus in it, surrounded by a membrane or wall. This cellular structure is an exclusive feature of all living organisms.

(3) **Protoplasm.** Life cannot exist without protoplasm. It is the actual living substance in both plants and animals, and it is, as Huxley defined it, the physical basis of life. It performs all the vital functions. Protoplasm is a highly complex mixture of proteins and a variety of other chemical compounds occurring in particular proportions and in particular patterns and interacting in a harmonious and consistent manner. The property we call life depends on the co-ordinated action of all these substances.

(4) **Respiration.** All living beings—plants and animals—respire continously day and night, and for the process of respiration they take in oxygen from the atmosphere and give out an almost equal volume of carbon dioxide. Respiration is an *energy-releasing* process, i.e. the energy that is stored up in food is released by this process and made use of by the protoplasm for its manifold activities.

(5) **Reproduction.** Living beings—plants and animals—possess the power of reproduction, i.e. of giving rise to new young ones like themselves. Non-living objects have no such power. They may mechanically break down into a number of irregular parts. Living beings follow certain definite modes of reproduction and give rise to offspring of the same kind.

(6) **Metabolism.** Metabolism is a phenomenon of life. It includes constructive (or anabolic) and destructive (or catabolic) changes that the protoplasm is constantly undergoing.

(7) **Nutrition.** A living organism requires food. The chemical constituents of food are much the same in plants and animals. These are ultimately digested and assimilated by the protoplasm for its own nutrition and growth.

(8) **Growth.** All living beings—plants and animals—grow. Certain non-living bodies may also grow, as does a crystal. But this growth is different from the growth of a living being. The growth of non-living objects is external, while that of living beings is internal.

(9) **Movements.** Movements are comonly regarded as a sign of life. Movements in plants, however, are restricted as most of them are fixed to the ground, while most animals move freely. Moving plants and fixed animals are not, however, uncommon among the lower organisms. Movements in plants and animals may be *spontaneous* or *induced.*

(a) *Spontaneous movement* is the movement of an organism or of an organ of a plant or an animal of its own accord, i.e. without any external influence. This kind of movement is regarded as a characteristic sign of life. Spontaneous movement is evident in animals, and in plants it is exhibited by many algae, e.g. *Euglena, Chlamydomonas, Volvox,* many desmids and diatoms, *Oscillatoria,* etc. Among 'flowering' plants the best example of spontaneous movement is exhibited by the Indian telegraph plant (*Desmodium gyrans;* see FIG. III/47). Besides, the streaming movements of protoplasm in the cells of many higher plants are distinctly visible under the microscope.

(b) *Induced movement or irritability,* on the other hand, is the movement of living organisms, or of their organs in response to external stimuli. Protoplasm is sensitive to a variety of external stimuli, and when a particular stimulus is applied, the reaction is usually in the form of a movement, as seen in sensitive plant (*Mimosa*), sensitive wood-sorrel (*Biophytum*), sundew (*Drosera*), Venus' fly-trap (*Dionaea*), etc. Leaves of many plants close in the evening and open again in the morning. This is spoken of as 'sleep' movement. Irritability, however, is more pronounced in animals than in plants.

7. Differences between the Living and the Non-living. It is very difficult to trace the absolute differences between the living and the non-living. Certain points, however, may be cited as general differences between the two. Protoplasm is the physical basis of life; so all objects containing protoplasm are regarded as living. Non-living objects do not have protoplasm. Thus, the presence or absence of protoplasm is a fundamental difference between the animate and the inanimate, and the various life-processes carried on by the protoplasm, such as respiration, metabolism, nutrition, growth, movements and reproduction, are characteristics of the living beings. Non-living objects may show movements and growth in a certain sense. Thus, non-living objects like machines are seen to move when induced by external forces. Very minute particles embedded in a liquid are also seen to vibrate with great rapidity; this vibration is called **Brownian movement** as it was first observed by **Robert Brown** in 1828 while he was examining poll grains under the microscope. Non-living objects like crystals and corals may also grow, but there is a diference in the mode of growth of the living, and the non-living as already discussed. All nerves and tissu undergo fatigue on repeated stimulation, from which they recover after a period of rest. Nonliving objects like metals may also undergo similar fatigue when worked for a prolonged period, and they can be poisoned or stimulated by drugs, as the late Sir J. C. Bose proved. Thus, no hard and fast line of distinction can be drawn between the living and the non-living.

8. Distinctions between Plants and Animals. The higher plants and animals are readily distinguished from one another by their possession of definite organs or members, particularly organs of locomotion in the latter case, for the discharge of definite functions. But difficulty is experienced in the case of lower, *unicellular* plants and animals. In fact, no hard and fast line of distinction can be drawn between lower plants and animals. However, the distinguishing features in general are as follows :

(1) **Growth.** The regions of growth are localized in the case of plants, lying primarily at the extremities—root-apex and stem-apex—and also in the interior, i.e. growth is both apical and intercalary. In the case of animals, growth is not localized to any definite region i.e. all parts grow simultaneously. Moreover, in plants growth proceeds until death; while in animals growth ceases long before death.

(2) **Chlorophyll.** Chlorophyll is present in all plants with the exception of fungi and total parasites. Chlorophyll and plastids are absent in animal cells.

(3) **Cell-wall.** Both plants and animals are cellular in composition. Each plant cell, however, is surrounded by a distinct but dead wall, called the *cell-wall*. The cell-wall is almost universally present in all plants and is the most conspicuous part of the cell. The cell-wall, however, is always absent in an animal cell. An extremely thin membrane called the *plasma membrane*, made of fat and protein, covers every cell in both plants and animals.

(4) **Cellulose.** The cell-wall of the plant cell is made of a chemical substance, called *cellulose*. Pure cellulose, however, is not found in fungi. Cellulose is altogether absent in the animal body.

(5) **Food.** Green plants absorb raw food material from outside—water and inorganic salts from the soil and carbon dioxide from the air—and prepare organic food substances out of them, primarily in the leaf, with the help of chlorophyll and in the presence of sunlight. Animals, being devoid of chlorophyll, cannot manufacture their own food. They have to depend on plants for this primary need. It is also to be noted that plants take in food in the form of solution, whereas animals can ingest solid food.

(6) **Utilization of Carbon dioxide.** Plants possess the power to utilize carbon dioxide of the atmosphere. It is only the green cells that have this power. Thus, during the day the green cells of the leaf absorb a volume of carbon dioxide from the surrounding air, manufacture sugar, starch, etc. out of this carbon dioxide, inorganic salts and water, and give out an almost equal volume of oxygen by the breakdown of the water, H_2O (and not carbon dioxide, CO_2). Animals do not possess this power.

(7) **Movements.** Plants grow fixed to the ground or attached to some support, and as such they cannot move bodily from one place to another, except some lower plants, while animals move freely in search of food and shelter, and manoeuvre when attacked. Some animals, of course, grow attached to some object.

(8) **Organs.** Various organs such as the organs of locomotion, respiration, excretion, etc. have reached a stage of perfection in animals, while in plants the corresponding organs are simple or even altogether absent.

9. Divisions of the Plant Kingdom. Various schemes have been formulated from time to time for classifying the vast plant kingdom, comprising all categories of plants, into several groups. Each of these schemes has its merits and demerits. The early researchers divided the plant kingdom into two main groups, viz 'flowerless' or 'seedless' plants, called **Cryptogamia** (*kryptos*, concealed; *gamos*, marriage) and 'flowering' or 'seed-bearing' plants, called **Phanerogamia** (*phaneros*, visible) or **Spermatophyta** (*sperma*, seed). Cryptogams have been further divided into three groups, viz. **Thallophyta, Bryophyta** and **Pteridophyta,** and phanerogams into two groups, viz. **Gymnospermae** (naked-seeded plants), e.g. cycads and conifers, and **Angiospermae** (closed-seeded plants). The latter have been divided into **Dicotyledonae** (embryo with two cotyledons) and **Monocotyledonae** (embryo with one cotyledon). A tentative scheme based on modern natural classifications, satisfying our needs, is as follows. It may be noted that the use of the terms *sub-kingdom*, *division* and *class* to represent the bigger groups of plants is somewhat aribitrary—in fact, these are matters of opinion and convenience.

Sub-kingdom A. **Thallophyta** (plants not forming embryos)

Division I. **Phycophyta** or **Algae**. Class (1) Cyanophyta or blue-green algae; class (2) Euglenophyta or euglenoids; class (3) Bacillariophyta or diatoms; class (4) Chlorophyta or green algae; class (5) Phaeophyta or brown algae; and class (6) Rhodophyta or red algae.

Division II. **Mycophyta** or **Fungi**: Class (1) Schizomycophyta or bacteria; class (2) Myxomycophyta or slime fungi; class (3) Eumycophyta or true fungi; (*a*) Phycomycetes or alga-like fungi, (*b*) Ascomycetes or sac fungi, and (*c*) Basidiomycetes or club fungi.

Sub-kingdom B. **Embryophyta** (plants forming embryos)

Division I. **Bryophyta** (plants without vascular tissues). Class (1) Hepaticae or liverworts; class (2) Anthocerotae or horned liverworts; and class (3) Musci or mosses.

Division II. **Tracheophyta** (plants with vascular tissues).

Class (1) Psilotopsida, e.g. *Psilotum* ;	
Class (2) Lycopsida, e.g. *Lycopodium*;	
Class (3) Sphenopsida e.g. *Equisetum*;	Pteridophyta
Class (4) Pteropsida. (a) Filicinae	
(b) Gymnospermae	Spermatophyta
(c) Angiospermae	

Dicotyledons and Monocotyledons. Angiosperms have been divided into two big classes: dicotyledons (*di*, two) and monocotyledons (*monos*, single), primarily on the basis of the number of cotyledons (first introduced by John Ray of Cambridge in 1686 and later followed by others). Other morphological distinctions are: in dicotyledons the primary root persists and gives rise to the tap root, while in monocotyledons the primary root soon perishes and is replaced by a cluster of fibrous roots; as a rule the venation of the leaf is reticulate (net-like) in dicotyledons, while it is parallel in monocotyledons (with a few exceptions in both); and the dicotyledonous flower mostly has a pentamerous symmetry, while the monocotyledonous flower a trimerous symmetry (see also pp. 539-40).

10. Number of Species on Record.

1	Algae	20,000
2	Fungi	90,000
3	Bacteria	2,000
4	Lichens	15,000
5	Bryophyta	23,725
	(*a*) Liverworts (8,750)	
	(*b*) Mosses (14,975)	
6	Pteridophyta (ferns & allies)	9,000
7	Gymnosperms	700
8	Angiosperms	199,000
	(*a*) Dicotyledons (159,000)	
	(*b*) Monocotyledons (40,000)	
	T O T A L	**359,425** species

11. Branches of Botany. Botany, like every other science, may be studied from two angles—the *pure* and the *applied* or *economic*. Pure botany deals with the study of plants as they form a part of nature and applied botany as it is applied to the well-being of mankind. The subject as a whole may be divided into the following branches.

(1) **Morphology** (*morphe*, form; *logos*, discourse or study). This deals with the study of forms and features of different plant organs such as roots, stems, leaves, flowers, seeds and fruits. The study of the external structures of such organs is otherwise known as *external morphology*, and that of internal structures as *internal morphology*. The latter may be histology or anatomy.

(2) **Histology** (*histos*, tissue). The study of the detailed structure of tissues making up a particular organ is called **histology**. The study of the gross internal strucure of a plant organ, as seen in a section, is called **anatomy**. **Cytology** (*kytos*, cell), dealing with the cell-structure with special reference to the behaviour of the nucleus, is a comparatively newer branch of histology.

(3) **Physiology** (*physis*, nature of life). This deals with the various functions that plants perform. Functions may be *vital* or *mechanical*. Vital functions are performed by the living matter, i.e. the protoplasm, and mechanical functions by certain dead tissues, without the intervention of the protoplasm, for example, bark and cork protect the plant body, and certain hard tissues strengthen it. It is to be noted that structure and function are correlated, i.e. a particular structure develops in response to a particular function.

(4) **Ecology** (*oikos*, home). This deals with the inter-relationships between plants and the environment they live in.

(5) **Plant Geography.** This deals with the distribution of plants over the surface of the earth and the factors responsible for this distribution.

(6) **Taxonomy or Systematic Botany.** This deals with the description and identification of plants, and their classification into various natural groups according to the similarities and differences between their morphological characteristics.

(7) **Organic Evolution.** This deals with the sequence of descent of more complex, more recent and more advanced types of plants (and animals) from the simpler, earlier and more primitive types through successive stages over the centuries.

(8) **Genetics.** This deals with the facts and laws of inheritance (variation and heredity) of parental characteristics by the offspring.

(9) **Palaeobotany** (*palaios*, ancient). This deals with the ancient forms of plants preserved in the form of fossils in various strata of the earth during past geological ages.

(10) **Applied** or **Economic Botany.** This deals with the utilization of plants and plant products for the well-being of mankind, and the various scientific methods employed for the improvement of plants from the point of view of their utility (see Part IX). It has several branches: (*a*) **agronomy** deals with the cultivation of field crops for food and industry; (*b*) **horticulture** deals with the cultivation of garden plants for flowers and fruit; (*c*) **plant pathology** deals with the diagnosis, cure and prevention of plant diseases (mainly in field crops and other useful plants), commonly caused by fungi and bacteria, and also deficiency diseases; (*d*) **pharmacognosy** deals with the study of medicinal plants with special reference to preparation and preservation of drugs; (*e*) **forestry** deals with the study and utilization of forest plants for timber and other forest products; and (*f*) **plant breeding** deals with the crossbreeding of plants to evolve improved types with desired characteristics, e.g. higher yield and better quality.

12. Parts of an Angiospermic Plant (FIG. 1). The parts of the plant body mainly concerned with nutrition and growth are called the *vegetative parts*. They comprise the root system and the shoot system (partly). The root system performs two primary functions: fixation and absorption. The shoot system, on the other hand, may be vegetative or reproductive. The vegetative shoot, consisting of the main stem, branches and leaves, has mainly three functions: support, conduction, and food manufacture (primarily by leaves). The reproductive shoot is the flower with its differentiated organs, and is essentially concerned with the reproduction of the plant.

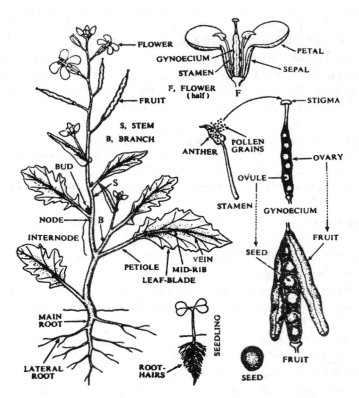

FIG. 1. Parts of an angiospermic plant (mustard plant)

13. A Short History of Botany. Botany as a subject developed out of the study of agriculture and medicine. It was from the 16th century that several attempts were made to systematize the knowledge of the plant kingdom by classifying plants on scientific lines. From the 18th century, classification began to take a definite shape. The 19th century was specially remarkable for the development of the science of Botany.

Ancient History. From the records available, meagre though they are, it is known that early civilized men, especially the Assyrians and the Egyptians, as long ago as 5,000 to 3,400 B.C., possibly earlier, were acquainted with the uses of certain plants, particularly those with agricultural and medicinal values. They used to cultivate wheat, barley, etc. and grow roses, grapes, pomegranates, dates, figs, etc. and also certain medicinal plants. They also knew the art of pollinating date-palms. **Herodotus,** a Greek historian, who travelled to Egypt about 465 B.C., gave a good account of Egyptian agriculture. It is also known that the Chinese, as early as 2,500 B.C. or even earlier, used to grow rice, tea, oranges and some medicinal plants. In Greece, about 340 B.C., a considerable advance was made in the study of plants, particularly by **Theophrastus** (372 to 287 B.C.), a disciple of Aristotle (384 to 322 B.C.). In his book, *History of Plants,* Theophrastus described about 500 plants of food and medicinal value and other economic uses, with their morphological characteristics, particularly the habit of—herbs, shrubs and trees, and annuals, biennials, and perennials. Mention may also be made of **Dioscorides,** a Cicilian Greek, and **Pliny**, a meritorious Roman writer, both of 1st century A.D. The former, a learned physician, described about 600 plants in his *Materia Medica*, while the latter wrote *Natural History*, in 37 volumes. Pliny died at the age of 56, while watching the eruption of the Vesuvius in 79 A. D. A period of great upheavals—religious, political and social—followed and there was a definite setback in the pursuit of scientific knowledge. In ancient India, the system of Ayurvedic medicine may be traced back to the Vedic period (6,000 B.C.). There is mention of SOMA and of vegetable drugs for the cure of pthisis and leprosy in the *Rig Veda* which is the earliest book in the library of man (3,000 B.C.). The Vedic Aryans were acquainted with about 100 medicinal plants (2,000 B.C.). Records show again that the Indo-Aryans were acquainted with seveal medicinal plants, and that surgery was highly developed then. The rise of Buddhism (5th century B.C.) gave further impetus to the study of medicine in ancient India, but because of AHIMSA preached by Lord Buddha, surgery suffered a setback. The edict of Aṣhoka (2nd century B.C.) provided for the establishment of hospitals in all the principal towns and cities of India. The works of **Sushruta** (5th century B.C.) and **Charaka** (1st century A.D.), deserve special mention. The writings of these two ancient celebrites are considered to be standard works on Hindu medicine, anatomy and surgery. **Sushruta** was a specialist in surgery, but his works also included medicine (he mentioned 700 medicinal plants) pathology, midwifery, opthalmology, etc. **Charaka** was a specialist in drugs and their uses. The Ayurvedic system further flourished under the care of eminent scholars such as Nagarjuna, Bagbhatta, Madhaba, Chakrapani Dutta and others, and attained its full glory between the 5th and the 11th centuries A.D. The agricultural system was also fairly advanced in India during 3,500 to 2,000 B.C.

16th Century. Medical botany dominated the study of plants during the Renaissance period. **Brunfels** (1464-1534), a German botanist, wrote his book on medicinal plants in three volumes in 1530. His work was a link between ancient and modern botany. **Fuchs** (1501-66), a German medical botanist, wrote *Historia of Plants* in 1542. **Turner** (1515-68), an English physician and botanist, wrote *A New Herbal* in three volumes in 1551, 1562 and 1568. He was regarded as the father of botany in England at that time. Caesalpino (1519-1603), an Italian botanist and medical man, wrote *De Plants* in 1583, describing about 1,520 plants. In 1596, Kaṣpar Bauhin (1560-1624), an Italian botanist, described about 2,700 plants.

17th Century. In 1620 and 1623, **Bauhin** published his life-long work in the form of two books, containing 6,000 species. He introduced binomial names for several species and formulated a system of classification largely based on the natural affinities of plants, mainly depending on texture and form. He was the first to get rid of medical superstition in classifying plants. He could not recognize, however, the importance of flowers as a basis of classification. **John Ray** (1627-1705) of Cambridge showed outstanding merit in classifying plants in 1686 and later into (a)Imperfectae (algae, fungi, mosses and ferns) and (b) Perfectae (dicotyledons and monocotyledons). Ray also published *Flora of British Isles* in 1690. In 1695, **Tournefort** (1656-1708), a French botanist and contemporary of Ray, for the first time classified plants according to certain characteristic of flowers and fruits without, however, ignoring the habit, and revived the concept of genera and species. About 8,000 species were known then.

18th Century. A very prominent figure of this century was the Swedish botanist **Carolus Linnaeus** (1707-78), professor of botany at Uppsala. His monumental work on taxonomy and binomial nomenclature (1735 and later) proved to be invaluable to future generations. He is regarded as the father of botany. His *Sexual System of Classification* published in 1735, artificial though it is, is a brilliant piece of work on taxonomic botany. His great achievement, however, lay in the foundation of a precise binary system of nomenclature for each and every species of plants. In 1789, **De Jussieu** (1748-1836), a French botanist, introduced several changes in the Linnaean system. He classified plants into 100 orders (families) and placed them under (a) Acotyledons (cryptogams of today including, however, some aquatic 'flowering' plants), (b) Monocotyledons and Dicotyledons, and introduced the terms hypogyny, perigyny and epigyny. His system formed a basis for subsequent progress.

19th Century. In the earlier part of this century the systems of classification proposed were those of **De Candolle** in 1819, **Robert Brown** in 1827, **Radilicheran** 1836, **Lindley** in 1845. Then two great English botanists, **Bentham** (1800-84) and **Hooker** (1817-1911), came together and laid the foundation of a natural system of classification known as the 'Bentham and Hooker's System' (1862-83) which is still widely followed. They have given an account of 202 families of angiosperms. *The Flora of British India* published by them over a long period (1872-97) is a masterpiece on Indian flora. Some years after the publication of Darwin's *Origin of Species by Natural Selection* in 1859, attempts were made to classify plants on the basis of evolution and to establish a phylogenetic tree. Thus, many new systems of classification were formulated, particularly in Germany; for example, **Prantl's** in 1883, **Eichler's** in the same year, **Engler's** in 1886. Engler and Prantl published *Die Naturlichen Pflanzenfamilien* (1887-1909) and Engler and Gilg's very useful publication *Syllabus der Pflanzenfamilien* (1892) gives a comprehensive account of 297 families of 'flowering' plants, in addition to a systematic classification of cryptogams.

20th Century. In the present century, **Hutchinson's** (an English botanist, born in 1884) phylogenetic system appeared in 1926 (Dicotyledons) and 1934 (Monocotyledons) with several modifications of Engler's system. In his revised second edition of *Families of Flowering Plants* published in 1959, Hutchinson described 411 families (342 of dicotyledons and 69 of monocotyledons). Other important systems that have appeared during the current century are those of **Wettstein,** an Austrian, in 1901 and later a posthumous improved edition in 1930-35; of **Bessey,** an American, in 1915; of **Rendle,** an Englishman, in 1904 (1st volume) and 1925 (2nd volume); and of **Tippo,** an American, in 1942.

1 MORPHOLOGY & EMBRYOLOGY

THE ROOT

TAP ROOT SYSTEM

The primary root and its branches form the tap root system of the plant. The primary or tap root normally grows vertically downwards to a shorter or longer depth, while the branched roots (secondary, tertiary, etc.) grow obliquely downwards, apex by a sort of cap or thimble known as the root-cap, which protects the tender apex of the root as it makes its way through the soil. Due to the impact of the hard soil particles the outer part of the root-cap wears away and newer cells formed by the underlying growing tissue are added to it. The root-cap is, however, usually absent in the aquatic plant.

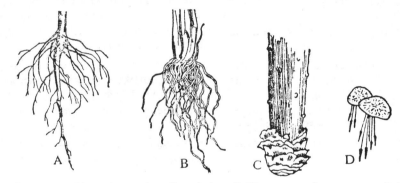

FIG. 2. *A*, tap and lateral roots in a dicotyledon; *B*, fibrous roots in a monocotyledon; *C*, multiple root-cap in screwpine (*Pandanus*); *D*, root-pocket in duckweed (*Lemna*)

or in many cases spread horizontally outwards. The primary root may be sparingly or profusely branched according to the need of the plant. The tap root system is normally meant to absorb water and mineral salts from the soil, to conduct them upwards to the stem and to give proper anchorage to the plant, but in order to perform some specialized functions it becomes modified into distinct shapes.

REGIONS OF THE ROOT (FIG. 3). The following regions may be distinguished in a root from the apex upwards. There is, of course, no line of demarcation between one region and another and each tends to merge into the next.

(1) **Root-cap.** Each root is covered over at the

(2) **Region of Cell Division.** This is the growing apex of the root lying within and a little beyond the root-cap and extends to a length of one to a few millimetres. The cells of this region are very small and thin-walled, and contain a dense mass of protoplasm. The characteristic feature of this region is that the cells undergo repeated divisions and hence, this region is otherwise called the **meristematic region** (*meristos*, divided). Some of the newly formed cells contribute to the formation of the root-cap and others to the next upper region.

(3) **Region of Elongation.** This lies above the meristematic region and extends to a length of a few millimetres (1 to 5 mm. or a little more). The cells of this region undergo rapid elongation and

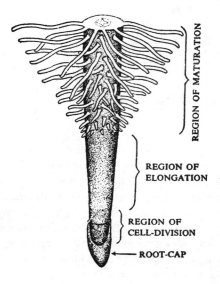

FIG. 3. Regions of the root

water and mineral salts from the soil. Internally, the cells of this region are seen to undergo maturation and differentiation into various kinds of primary tissues. Higher up, it gradually merges into the region of secondary tissues. Above the root-hair region, lateral roots are produced in *acropetal* succession.

CHARACTERISTICS OF THE ROOT. There are certain distinctive characteristics of the root by which it can be distinguished from the stem. These are as follows:

(1) The root is the descending portion of the axis of the plant and is not normally green in colour.

(2) The root does not commonly bear **buds** except in sweet potato (*Batatas*), wood-apple (*Aegle*), *Trichosanthes* (B. PATAL; H. PARWAL), Indian redwood (*Dalbergia*), lemon and ipecac. Such plants are sometimes propagated by root-cuttings, e.g. ipecac.

(3) The root ends in and is protected by a cap or thimble-like structure known as the **root-cap** (FIG. 3) while the stem ends in a bud. A distinct multiple root-cap is seen in the aerial root of screwpine (*Pandanus*; FIG. 2C).

In water plants like duckweed (*Lemna*), water lettuce (*Pistia*), water hyacinth (*Eichhornia*), etc.,

enlargement, and are responsible for growth in the length of the root.

(4) **Region of Maturation.** This region lies above the region of elongation and extends upwards. Externally, often extending to a length of a few millimetres and sometimes a few centimetres, this region produces a cluster of very fine and delicate thread-like structures known as root-hairs. These hairs are essentially meant to absorb

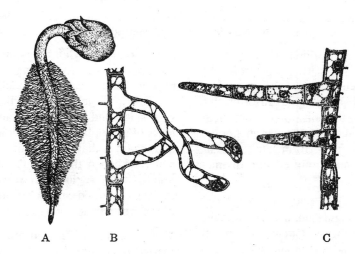

A   B   C

FIG. 4. *A*, root-hairs in mustard seedling; *B*, two root-hairs (magnified) unicelluar; *C*, two shoot-hairs (magnified)—multicellular

a loose sheath which comes off easily is distinctly seen at the apex of each root. This is an anomalous root-cap, called the root-pocket (FIG. 2D).

(4) The root bears **unicellular hairs** (FIG. 4B), while the stem or the shoot bears mostly **multicellular hairs** (FIG. 4C). Root-hairs occur in a cluster in the tender part of the root a little behind the apex. Shoot-hairs, on the other hand, are of various kinds and they remain scattered all over the surface of the shoot. Root-hairs absorb water and mineral salts from the soil, while shoot-hairs prevent evaporation of water from the surface of the plant body and afford protection.

(5) Lateral roots always develop from an inner layer (pericycle; see FIG. II/66), so they are said to be **endogenous** (*endo*, inner; *gen*, producing). Branches, on the other hand, develop from a few outer layers, so they are said to be **exogenous** (*exo*, outer).

(6) **Nodes** and **internodes** are always present in the stem, although they may not often be quite distinct. However, in the root these are absent.

ADVENTITIOUS ROOT SYSTEM

Roots that grow from any part of the plant body other than the radicle are called **adventitious roots**. They may develop from the base of the stem, replacing the primary root or in addition to it, or from any node or internode of the stem or the branch, or even from the leaf, under special circumstances. Adventitious roots are of various kinds and have diverse functions—normal and specialized. Those with normal functions may be of the following types :

(1) **Fibrous Roots** (FIG. 2B). Fibrous roots of monocotyledons are all adventitious roots. They may be given off in clusters from the base of the stem, as in onion, tuberose, etc., or from the nodes and sometimes inter-nodes of branches creeping along the ground, as in many grasses, or from the lower nodes of the stem, as in maize, sugarcane, bamboo, etc.

(2) **Foliar Roots** (FIG. 5). Foliar roots are those that come directly out of the leaf, mainly from the petiole or the vein. Such roots may sometimes

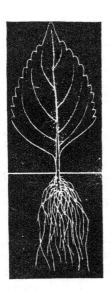

FIG. 5. Foliar (adventitious) roots in *Pogostemon*

FIG. 6. Adventitious roots in *Coleus*

arise spontaneously, or more commonly as a result of injury (e.g. when incised), or they may be induced to grow by the application of certain chemicals, called *hormones*, which are growth-promoting substances. Thus the *Pogostemon* leaf, when treated with a synthetic hormone, e.g., indole-butyric acid, is seen to produce a cluster of roots from the petiole. Such roots are not very common but can be induced to grow by the above treatment.

(3) **Adventitious roots** are also given off by many plants from their **nodes** and sometimes from the **internodes** as they creep on the ground, as in Indian pennywort (see FIG. III/55), wood-sorrel (see FIG. 32), etc. Such roots are also produced in many cases from branch-cuttings when these are put into the soil, as in rose, sugarcane, China rose, marigold, tapioca, etc., or kept partially immersed in water in a bottle, as in garden croton (*Codiaeum*), *Coleus* (FIG. 6), etc. Adventitious roots also

more or less spindle-shaped in appearance, it is said to be fusiform, e.g. radish. In radish it is really the hypocotyl and the base of the stem that swell; only the tapering end is the root proper.

(2) **Napiform Root** (FIG. 7B). When the root is considerably swollen at the upper part (usually the hypocotyl), becoming almost spherical, and sharply tapering at the lower part, it is said to be napiform, e.g. turnip and beet. In turnip it is the hypocotyl that swells and becomes spherical, while in beet the hypocotyl and the root together become swollen.

(3) **Conical Root** (FIG. 7C). When the root is broad at the base and gradually tapers towards the apex like a cone, it is said to be conical, e.g. carrot. In carrot it is the root proper that swells.

(4) **Tuberous** or **Tubercular Root.** When the root is thick and fleshy but does not take a definite shape, it is said to be tuberous or tubercular, as in

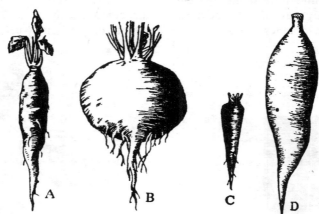

FIG. 7. Modified roots. *A*, fusiform root of radish; *B*, napiform root of turnip; *C*, conical root of carrot; *D*, tuberous root of *Mirabilis*

grow from foliar buds developing on leaves, as in sprout leaf plant (*Bryophyllum*; see FIG. 16A) and elephant ear plant (*Begonia*; see FIG. 16B).

MODIFIED ROOTS

A. TAP ROOT MODIFIED *For Storage of Food*

(1) **Fusiform Root** (FIG. 7A). When the root (hypocotyl) is swollen in the middle and gradually tapering towards the apex and the base, being

four o'clock plant (*Mirabilis*; FIG. 7D)

B. BRANCHED ROOT MODIFIED *For Respiration*

Pneumatophores. Many plants growing in marshy places and salt lakes, occasionally inundated by tides, as in the Sundarbans, develop special kinds of roots called respiratory roots or **pneumatophores** (FIG. 8), for the purpose of respiration. Such roots grow from the underground

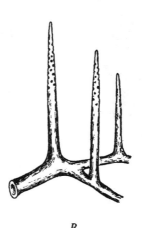

A   B

FIG. 8. Pneumatophores. *A*, two plants with pneumatophores; *B*, pneumatophores
growing vertically upwards from an underground root

roots of the plant but rise vertically upwards and come out of the water like so many conical spikes. They often occur in large numbers around the tree-trunk. Each such root is provided, towards the upper end, with numerous pores or respiratory spaces through which air is taken in for respiration. Such roots are seen in *Rhizophora* (B. KHAMO), *Heritiera* (B. SUNDRI), etc.

C. ADVENTITIOUS ROOTS MODIFIED

(a) For Storage of Food.

(1) **Tuberous** or **Tubercular Root** (FIG. 9A). This is a swollen root without any definite shape, as in sweet potato (*Ipomoe abatatas*). Tuberous roots, whether tap or adventitious, are produced singly and not in clusters. (2) **Fasciculated Roots** (FIG. 9B). When several tubercular roots occur in a cluster or fascicle at the base of the stem, they are said to be fasciculated, as in *Dahlia, Ruellia* and *Asparagus*. (3) **Nodulose Root** (FIG. 9C). When the slender root becomes suddenly swollen at the apex it is said to be nodulose, as in mango ginger (*Curcuma amada*), turmeric (*C. domestica*), *Asparagus sprengeri*, arrowroot (*Maranta*) and some species of *Calathea*. (4) **Moniliform** or **Beaded Root** (FIG. 10A). When there are some swellings in the root at frequent intervals, it is said

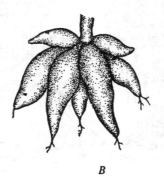
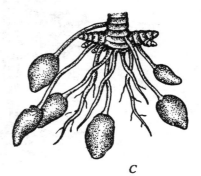

A   B   C

FIG. 9. Adventitious roots. *A*, tuberous roots of sweet potato; *B* fasciculated roots of *Dahlia*; *C*, nodulose roots of
mango ginger. growing vertically upwards from an underground root

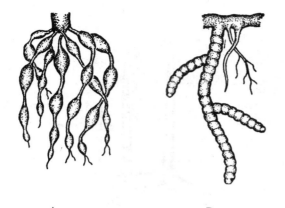

FIG. 10. Adventitious roots (contd.). *A*, moniliform roots of *Momordica*; *B*, annulated roots of ipecac

to be moniliform or beaded, as in *Portulaca*, Indian spinach (*Basella*), *Momordica*, wild vine (*Vitis trifolia*) and some grasses. (5) **Annulated Root** (FIG. 10B). When the root has a series of ring-like swellings on its body, it is said to be annulated, as in ipecac (*Psychotria*)— a medicinal plant.

(b) For Mechanical Support.

(6) **Prop or Stilt Roots** (FIG. 11). In plants like banyan, india-rubber plant, screwpine, *Rhizophora*, etc., a number of roots are produced from the main stem andoften from the branches. These roots grow vertically or obliquely down-

wards and penetrate into the soil. Gradually they get stouter and act as pillars supporting the main stem and the branches or the plant as a whole. Such roots are known as prop or stilt roots. The big banyan tree in the Indian Botanical Garden near Calcutta has produced over 900 such roots from its branches. Its age is over 200 years and the circumference of the crown is well over 360 metres. (7) **Climbing Roots** (FIG. 12A). Plants like betel (*Piper betle*), long pepper (*P. longum*), black pepper (*P. nigrum*) *Pothos*, Indian ivy (see FIG.17), etc., produce climbing roots from their nodes and often from the internodes to ensure a foothold on neighbouring objects. (8) **Buttress Roots.** In certain large forest trees, some of the stout roots around the base of the main trunk show prolific abnormal growth, particularly on their upper side. They at first grow obliquely downwards from the base of the trunk and then spread horizontally outwards at the ground level, sometimes to a considerable length. As they do so, they get stouter and plank-like in the vertical direction. A portion of the stem may also take part in their formation. They are meant to give support to the huge trunk and maintain it in an upright position. Trees like kapok (*Ceiba*), silk cotton tree (*Bombax*), *Terminalia catappa* and *T. belerica*, *Adina cordifolia*, *Heritiera marcrophylla* and *H. acuminata*, etc., bear such roots.

FIG. 11. Adventitious roots (contd.). *A*, prop or stilt roots of banyan (*Ficus bengalensis*); *B*, the same of screwpine (*Pandanus odoratissimus*)

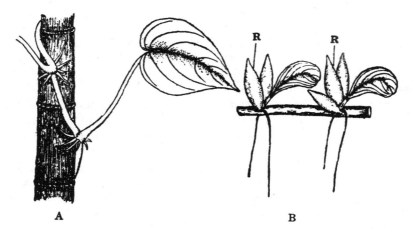

FIG. 12. Adventitious roots (contd.). *A*, climbing roots of betel (*Piper betle*);
B, respiratory roots (*R*) of *Jussiaea repens*

(c) For Vital Functions.

(9) Sucking Roots or **Haustoria** (see FIG. 22B). Parasites develop roots which penetrate into the tissue of the host plant and suck it. Such roots are known as sucking roots or haustoria (sing. haustorium). Parasites, particularly non-green ones, have to live by sucking the host plant, i.e. by absorbing food from it with the help of their sucking roots.

Loranthus, **(10) Respiratory Roots** (FIG.12B). In *Jussiaea* (B. KESSRA), an aquatic plant, the floating branches develop adventitious roots which are soft, light, spongy and colourless. They usually develop above the level of water and serve to store up air. Thus, they facilitate respiration. **(11) Epiphytic Roots** (FIG.13). There are certain plants, commonly orchids, which grow perched on branches of trees. Such plants are known as

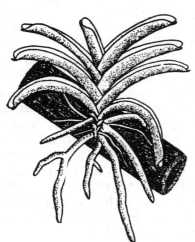

FIG. 13. Epiphytic roots of *Vanda*
(an orchid)

Common examples are dodder (*Cuscuta*, see FIG. 22A), *Cassytha*, broomrape (*Orobanche;* see FIG. 23A), mistletoe (*Viscum;* see FIG.24) and

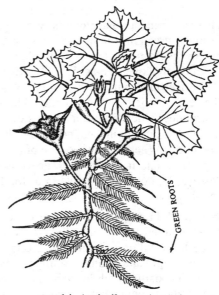

FIG. 14. Assimilatory (green)
roots of *Trapa natans*

epiphytes (*epi*, upon; *phyta*, plants). They never suck the supporting plants as do the parasites. So instead of sucking roots they develop a special kind of aerial roots which hang freely in the air. Each hanging root is surrounded by a spongy tissue, called **velamen** (see FIG.26). With the help of this velamen, the hanging root absorbs moisture from the surrounding air. *Vanda* (B. & H. RASNA), an epiphytic orchid, is a fairly common example. (12) **Assimilatory Roots.** Branches of *Tinospora* (B. GULUNCHA; H. GURCHA) climbing on neighbouring trees produce long, slender, hanging roots which develop chlorophyll and turn green in colour. These green roots are assimilatory roots. The submerged roots of water chestnut (*Trapa*

natans; FIG.14), usually formed in pairs from the nodes, are green in colour and perform carbon-assimilation. The hanging roots of epiphytic orchids also often turn green in colour and act as assimilatory roots.

Functions and Adaptations of the Root. The root performs manifold functions—*mechanical*, such as **fixation**, and *physiological*, such as **absorption, conduction** and **storage**. These are the normal functions of the root. Roots also perform specialized functions and they adapt themselves accordingly. All these functions and adaptations have been discussed in detail in connection with modified roots.

CHAPTER 2

THE STEM

CHARACTERISTICS OF THE STEM. The stem is the ascending portion of the axis of the plant, developing directly from the plumule, and bears leaves, branches and flowers. When young, it is normally green in colour. The growing apex is covered over and protected by a number of tiny leaves which arch over it (FIG. 15). The stem often bears multicellular hairs of different kinds. It branches exogenously and is provided with nodes and internodes which may not be distinct in all cases. Leaves and branches normally develop from the nodes. When the stem or the branch ends in a vegetative bud it continues to grow upwards or sideways. If, however, it ends in a floral bud, the growth ceases.

FORMS OF STEMS. There is a variety of stem structures adapted to perform diverse functions. They may be aerial or underground. Aerial stems may be erect, rigid and strong, holding themselves in an upright position, while there are some too weak to support themselves in such a position. They either trail on the ground or climb

neighbouring plants and other objects. Some stems remain permanently underground and from there periodically give off aerial shoots under favourable conditions. Such stems are meant for food storage and perennation (see pp. 16-19).

1. Erect or Strong Stems. The unbranched, erect, cylindrical and stout stem, marked with scars of fallen leaves, is called **caudex**, as in palms. The jointed stem with solid nodes and hollow internodes is called **culm**, as in bamboo. Some herbaceous plants, particularly monocotyledons, have no aerial stem. The underground stem in them produces an erect unbranched aerial shoot bearing either a single flower or a cluster of flowers; such a flowering shoot is called **scape**, as in tuberose, onion, aroids banana, etc.

2. Weak Stems. Weak-stemmed plants are commonly of three kinds : (1) trailers, (2) creepers and (3) climbers. **Trailers** are those plants whose thin and long or short branches trail on the ground, with or without rooting at the nodes. When such plants lie prostrate on the ground they are said to be (*a*) **prostrate** or **procumbent**, e.g. *Oralis* and *Evolvulus*. When the branches of such plants, after trailing for some distance, tend to rise at their apex they are said to be (*b*) **decumbent**, e.g. *Tridax* (see FIG.VII/43). When the plants are much branched and the branches spread out on the ground in all directions, they are said to be (*c*) **diffuse**, e.g. *Boerhaavia*. Weak-stemmed plants with their long or short branches creeping along the ground and rooting at the nodes are said to be **creepers;** a creeping stem may be a runner, stolon, offset or sucker according to its varied nature (see FIG.32-35). **Climbers** are those plants that attach themselves to any neighbouring object, often by means of some special devices, and climb it to a long or short distance, e.g. pea, passion-flower, gourd, vine, etc. (see pp. 11-13).

Nodes and **Internodes**. The place on the stem or branch where one or more leaves arise is known as the **node,** and the space between two successive nodes is called the **internode**. Sometimes nodes and internodes are very conspicuous, as in bamboos and grasses; in others they are not always distinct.

BUDS

A bud is a young undeveloped shoot consisting of a short stem and a number of tender leaves

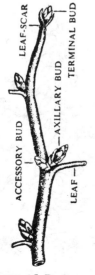

FIG. 15. Buds

arching over the growing apex. In the bud, the internodes have not yet developed and thus, the leaves remain crowded together, forming a compact structure. The lower leaves of the bud are older and larger than those higher up. A cabbage cut longitudinally gives a good idea of a bud—the development of the leaves in acropetal succession and the condensed shoot with the growing apex. The normal position of a bud is at the apex of the stem or the branch and in the axil of a leaf. The bud, in the former case, is known as the **terminal** or **apical bud**, and in the latter as the **axillary bud**. Sometimes some extra buds develop by the side of the axillary bud. These are known as **accessory buds**. Sometimes buds appear at various other parts of a plant such as the root (radical buds), as in sweet potato, or the leaf (foliar buds), as in sprout leaf plant (*Bryophylum*; (FIG. 16A), *Kalanchoe* (see FIGS. III/56, 57), *Crassula*, elephant ear plant (*Begonia*; FIG. 16B), *Scilla*, walking fern (*Adiantum*; see FIG. III/54), and sometimes water lily (*Nymphaea*), or at different positions of the stem and the branches (cauline buds). Such buds are called **adventitious** because of their abnormal position.

Protection of the Bud. Since buds have to give rise to flowers, leaves and branches, it is imperative that these should be protected against external injuries—sun, rain, fungi, insects, etc., and this protection is afforded in different ways. (1) The young leaves of the bud normally overlap each other and remain variously rolled or folded to protect themselves and the growing apex against sun and rain. (2) They may be covered by hairs, or in some cases they remain bathed in resinous or gummy secretions. (3) They may be enclosed by some dry and scaly outer leaves, called bud-scales, as in banyan, jack, *Magnolia*, iron-wood tree (*Mesua*; B. NAGESWAR; H. NAGKESAR), etc. (4) There may be a coating of wax or cutin on the leaf-surface to check evaporation of water and to prevent the leaves and the growing apex from getting wet.

Modification of the Bud. Vegetative buds may be modified into tendrils (see FIG. 20A), as in passion-flower and vine, or into thorns (see FIG. 38),

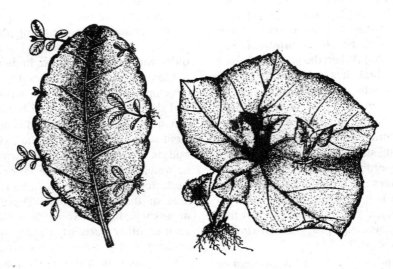

FIG. 16. *A*, foliar buds and adventitious roots of *Bryophyllum pinnatum*; *B*, the same of *Begonia*

as in *Duranta, Carissa*, wood-apple (*Aegle*), etc. Sometimes these may become modified into special reproductive bodies known as **bulbils** (see p. 23). Floral buds may likewise be modified into tendrils (See FIGS. 36 B & 37), as in Sandwich Island climber (*Corculum = Antigonon*) and balloon vine (*Cardiospermum*), or into bulbils (see p. 23) for the purpose of reproduction.

HABIT OF THE PLANT. The nature of the stem, the height the plants attain and the duration and mode of their life determine their habit.

　1. Herbs. These are small plants with soft stems. According to the duration of their life they may be classified as (1) **annuals**, (2) **biennials** and (3) **perennials**. **Annuals** are those plants that attain their full growth in one season, living for a few months or at most for one year producing flowers, fruits and seeds within this period, e.g. sunflower, mustard, rice, pea, bean, etc. **Biennials** are those plants that live for two years. They attain their full vegetative growth in the first year and produce flowers and seeds in the second year, after which they die off. Common examples are cabbage, radish, beet, carrot, turnip, etc. (In tropical climates they behave like annuals.) **Perennials** are those plants that persist for a number of years. The aerial parts of such plants may die down every

year at the end of the flowering season but next year new shoots develop again from the underground stem after a few showers, e.g. *Canna*, ginger (*Zingiber*), arrowroot (*Maranta*), etc.

　2. Shrubs. These are medium-sized plants with hard and woody stems which branch profusely from near the ground so that the plants often become bushy in habit without having a clear

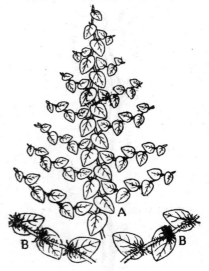

FIG. 17. Indian ivy (*Ficus pumila*)—
a rootlet climber. *A*, upper side; *B*, lower side

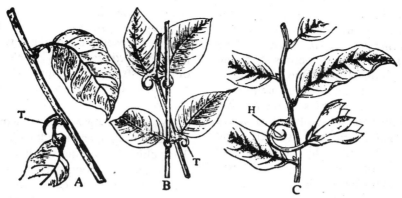

FIG. 18. Hook and Thorn Climbers. *A*, glory of the garden (*Bougainvillea*); *T*, thorn; *B*, *Uncaria*; *T*. hooked thorn; *C. Artabotrys*; *H*, hook

trunk. They are larger than herbs, but much smaller than trees, e.g. China rose, garden croton, night jasmine, *Duranta*, etc.

3. Trees. These are large plants with a single stout trunk and hard and woody branches profusely formed (except most palms), e.g. mango, jack, teak, *Casuarina* (B. & H. JHAU), country almond, etc. Some trees like *Eucalyptus*, redwood tree (*sequoia sempervirens*) and mammoth tree (*Sequoia gigantea*) attain a height of over 90 metres. It may also be noted that *Eucalyptus* lives for about 300 years, and the other two for 1,000-1500 years. Some conifers have a life-span of 2,500 years or even more.

4. Climbers. These have thin and long stems with diffuse branches. They climb by means of some special organs of attachment or by their twining stem.

(1) **Rootlet Climbers.** Such plants climb by means of small adventitious roots, which often form small adhesive discs or claws to act as holdfasts, or secrete a sticky juice, as in betel (*Piper betle*; see FIG. 12 A), long pepper (*Piper longum*), *Piper chaba*, ivy (*Hedera helix*), Indian ivy (*Ficus pumila*; FIG. 17), wax plant (*Hoya*), *Pothos*, etc.

(2) **Hook Climbers.** The flower-stalk of *Artabotrys* (B. & H. KANTALI-CHAMPA) produces a curved hook (FIG. 18 C), which facilitates to some

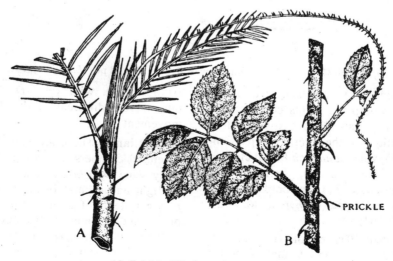

FIG. 19. Prickle Climbers. *A*, cane; *B*, rose

PRICKLE

extent the climbing of the branches. Often **prickles** and **thorns** are curved and hooked in certain plants. Thus, in cane (*Calamus*; FIG. 19 A) a long, slender axis beset with numerous sharp and curved hooks is produced from the leaf sheath. Climbing rose (FIG. 19 B) and *Pisonia* are provided with numerous curved prickles for the purpose of climbing (and also for self-defence). Glory of the garden (*Bougainvillea*; FIG. 18 A), and *Uncaria* (FIG. 18 B) climb by curved hooks (thorns). In cat's nail (*Bignonia unguis-cati*; see FIG. 65) the terminal leaflets become modified into very sharp and curved hooks.

(3) **Tendril Climbers.** These are plants which produce slender, leafless, spirally-coiled structures known as tendrils, and climb objects with the

any neighbouring object that helps the plant climb. In glory lily (*Gloriosa*; FIG. 21 B) the leaf-apex becomes closely coiled like a tendril. In pitcher plant (*Nepenthes*; FIG. 21 C) the stalk of the pitcher often twists round a support like a tendril and holds the pitcher in a vertical position (see also FIG. 69).

(5) **Stem Climbers or Twiners.** These are plants with long and slender stems and branches. They climb by twining bodily round trees, shrubs and hedges, e.g. country-bean (*Dolichos*), railway creeper (*Ipomoea*), *Clitoria*, Rangoon creeper (*Quis-qualis*), etc. They have no special organs of attachment like the climbers proper. Some of the climbers twine clockwise (dextrorse), e.g. white yam (*Dioscorea alata*) or anticlockwise (sin-

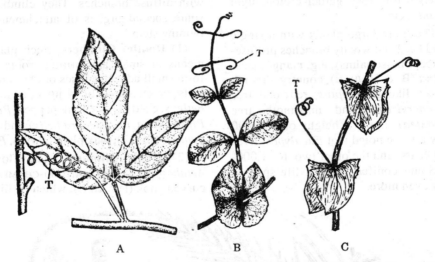

FIG. 20. Tendril Climbers. *A*, passion-flower; *B*, pea; *C*, wild pea (*Lathyrus*); *T*, tendril

help of these. Tendrils twine themselves round some support and help the plants concerned to support their weight and climb easily. Tendrils may be modifications of the stem, as in passion-flower (FIG. 20 A), vine, *Sandwich* Island climber (*Corculum*; see FIG. 36 B), balloon vine (*Cardiospermum*; see FIG. 37), etc., or of leaves, as in pea (FIG. 20 B), wild pea (*Lathyrus*; FIG. 20C), *Naravelia* (see FIG. 64), etc.

(4) **Leaf Climbers.** The petiole (i.e. the leaf-stalk) of *Clematis* (FIG. 21A) and that of garden nasturtium are sensitive to contact and coil round

istrorse), e.g. wild yam (*D. bulbifera*), while others are indifferent in the direction of their movement.

(6) **Lianes.** These are very thick and woody perennial climbers, commonly found in forests. They twine themselves round tall trees in search of sunlight and ultimately reach their tops. There, they get plenty of sunlight and produce a canopy of foliage. Common examples are woodrose (*Ipomoea tuberosa*), *Hiptage madablota* (B. MAD-HABILATA), camel's foot climber (*Bauhinia vahlii*; B. LATA-KANCHAN; H. CHAMBULI; see FIG. 183),

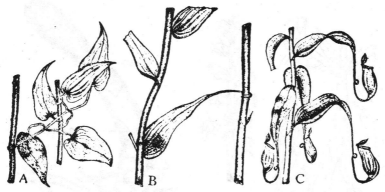

FIG. 21. Leaf climbers. *A*, *Clematis*; *B*, glory lily (*Gloriosa*);
C, pitcher plant (*Nepenthes*; see also FIG. 69)

nicker bean (*Entada gigas*; B. & H. GILA), etc.

SPECIAL TYPES OF PLANTS

Green plants normally prepare their own carbohydrate food and nourish themselves. Such plants are said to be **autophytes** or **autotrophic plants** (*autos*, self; *phyta*, plants; *trophe*, food) or self-nourishing. There are, however, many plants which draw their organic food from different sources; such plants are said to be **heterophytes** or **heterotrophic** plants (*heteros*, different). These are of various kinds.

1. PARASITES. These are plants that grow upon other living plants or on animals, and absorb organic food from the hosts by their sucking roots called **haustoria**. Common examples of different types of phanerogamic parasites are as follows:

(1) Total stem-parasites, eg. dodder (*Cuscuta*, FIG. 22A).

(2) Partial stem-parasites, e.g. mistletoe (*Viscum*; FIG. 24), *Loranthus*, *Cassytha*, and *Arceuthobium*.

(3) Total root-parasites, e.g. broomrape (*Orobanche indica*; B. BANIA-BAU; H SARSON-BANDA; FIG. 23A)—parasite on roots of potato, tomato, brinjal, mustard, tobacco, etc., often doing

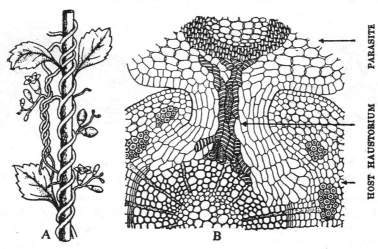

FIG. 22. *A*, dodder (*Cuscuta*)—a total stem-parasite; *B*, a section through dodder (and the host plant) showing the sucking root (haustorium)

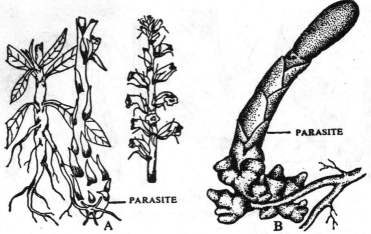

FIG. 23. A, broomrape (*Orobanche*)—a total root-parasite;
B, *Balanophora*—a total root-parasite

considerable damage to these crops—common in Bihar and Uttar Pradesh; *Aeginetia indica*—parasitic on roots of grasses and other plants in Khasi Hills; *Balanophora* (FIG. 23 B)—parasitic on roots of forest trees (*B. dioica* is common in Khasi Hills); *Sapria* (1 sp.)— parasitic on roots of various plants in Arunachal and Nagaland; and *Rafflesia* (6sp.)—parasitic on *Vitis* roots in Java and Sumatra.

(4) Partial root-parasites, e. g. sandalwood tree (*Santalum*) and *Striga*—both found abundantly in Karnataka, the latter also in Maharashtra.

like, twining, leafless parasite. It resembles *Cuscuta*, but is very slender, much branched and matted. It also has some minute scales but unlike *Cuscuta*, which is golden-yellow in colour, *Cassytha* is pale green to dark green in colour. The plant grows extensively on hedges on the Madras and Sundarbans coasts.

Striga lutea is a small, green plant, 25-30 cm. in height. It is parasitic on the roots of some of field crops, such as Sorghum, maize, etc., in south India. It produces abundant minute seeds and thus spreads rapidly. As it is weeded out every year while ploughing the fields, it seldom gets a chance to damage any crop. There are five species of *Striga*

FIG. 24. Mistletoe—
a partial stem-parasite

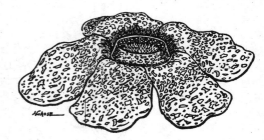

FIG. 25. *Rafflesia*—
a total root-parasite

Arceuthobium minutissimum is a minute, green, leafless parasite. Among dicotyledons this is known to be the minutest plant. It has been found to grow on *Pinus excelsa*, almost within its bark, in the Kumaon Himalayas at an altitude of 3,260 metres.

Cassytha filiformis, as the name implies, is a thread-

common in south India and Maharashtra, e.g. *S. orobanchoides, S. densiflora*, etc.

Rafflesia arnoldi (FIG. 25) is a very interesting plant inasmuch as it bears the most gigantic flower in the world, measuring 50 cm in diameter and weighing 8 kg. The plant was first discovered in 1818 by Sir Stamford

Raffles on a tour of the interior of Sumatra, and was named after him. Altogether, 12 species have been discovered in Sumatra, Java and the neighbouring islands. The flower is of a livid, fleshy colour and the smell is like that of putrid meat. Another point of interest is that its stem and root are reduced to a network of slender threads which penetrate into the root of the host plant, ramify through it and draw food from it. Here and there, the thread-like stem bears flower-buds within the host, which burst out and open into full-fledged flowers of this size. The flowers are unisexual.

Sapria himalayana, found only in the Aka and Dafla hills of Arunachal and in the Naga Hills of Nagaland, is identical with *Rafflesia arnoldi* in all respects and also belongs to the same family, i.e. *Rafflesiaceae*, but the flowers are smaller in size,

develop fibrous thickenings. There are also minute pits in the walls. The velamen acts as a sort of sponge and absorbs moisture from the surrounding air as well as water trickling down the root. Examples are found in many orchids, e.g. *Vanda* (B. & H. RASNA—see FIG. 13) and some ferns. Banyan, peepul, etc. are, in their earlier stages, often epiphytic on date-palm and other trees.

3. SAPROPHYTES (*sapros*, rotten; *phyta*, plants). These are plants that grow in places rich in decaying organic substances of vegetable or animal origin, and derive their nutriment from them. Fungi and bacteria are either parasites or saprophytes. Among the 'flowering' plants, Indian pipe (*Monotropa*; FIG. 27), *Burmannia* and some

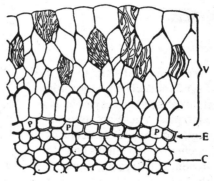

FIG. 26.
Vanda root
in transection
showing:
V, velamen;
E, exodermis;
P, passage cell;
C, cortex.

measuring 15-30 cm. in diameter. They are, however, the biggest in India.

2. EPIPHYTES (*epi*, upon; *phyta*, plants). These are plants that grow upon other plants (see FIG. 13), but do not suck them, i.e. do not absorb food from them, as do parasites. They usually develop three kinds of roots, viz, clinging roots, absorbing roots and hanging roots. The clinging roots grow into cracks and crevices in the bark of the supporting plant and fix the epiphyte in proper position on the branch. Besides, they act as reservoirs of humus which accumulates in the network formed by such roots. The absorbing roots developing from the clinging roots project into the humus and draw food from it. The hanging roots are provided with an outer covering of a special absorptive tissue, called velamen (FIG. 26), which usually consists of 4 or 5 layers of oblong-polygonal cells. The cells are dead, contain only air or water, and their walls

orchids, e.g. coral rot (*Corallorhiza*), bird's nest orchid (*Neottia*), chain orchid (*Pholidota*), etc., are good examples of saprophytes. *Monotropa uniflora* and a few species of *Burmannia*, e.g. *B. disticha, B. candida*, etc., grow in the Khasi Hills—*Monotropa* at an altitude of 1,800 metres and *Burmannia* 1,400 metres. Another interesting saprophyte is snowball (*Sarcodes*). It is allied to *Monotropa* and grows in the mountains around California in America. Total saprophytes are colour-less, while the partial ones are green in colour. Their roots become associated with a filamentous mass of a fungus which takes the place of and acts as root-hairs, absorbing food material from the decomposed organic substances present in the soil. The association of a fungus with the root of a higher plant is known as **mycorrhiza** (see p. 16).

4. SYMBIONTS (*syn*, together; *bios*, life). When two organisms live together, as if they are parts of

FIG. 27. *Monotropa*—a saprophyte

the same plant, and are of mutual help to each other, they are called symbionts. The relationship between the two is expressed as symbiosis. Lichens are typical examples. These are associations of algae and fungi and commonly occur as thin, round greenish patches on tree-trunks and old walls. The alga in a lichen, being green, prepares food and shares it with the fungus, while the latter absorbs water and mineral salts from the surrounding medium and also affords protection to the alga. Some mycorrhizas are also good examples of symbiosis.

Mycorrhiza. Mycorrhiza (fungus-root) is the association of a fungus with the root of a higher plant. This association was first discovered in 1885 by Frank, who found it to be a regular feature in many species of plants, particularly forest trees (beech, oak, etc.), many conifers (pine, etc.), saprophytic phanerogams, orchid seedlings, etc. The fungi concerned may belong to various classes. The infected root does not elongate but frequently branches profusely, and no root-hairs are formed. Two types of mycorrhiza are seen: (a) **endotrophic**, in which the fungus is internal, usually living within the cortical cells of the root, as in many orchids, and (b) **ectotrophic**, in which the fungus is external, growing attached to the surface of the root, as in conifers and most other plants. There are also certain types of mycorrhiza in which the fungus growing

outside gradually penetrates inside. The biological relationship between the fungus and the root is not very clear in all cases and divergent opinions have been given. The relationship may range from true parasitism to genuine symbiosis. In the latter case the fungus absorbs water, mineral salts and nitrogenous organic substances from the soil and in some cases, it even fixes free nitrogen of the air. The fungus also helps respiration of the root, as in pine. In return it receives food from the root. The mycorrhizal fungus particularly benefits certain plants. Thus, it is seen that orchid seeds often do not germinate if they are not infected by a particular fungus. Pine seedlings and orchid seedlings are slow in growth and become weak in the absence of a similar infection.

5. CARNIVOROUS PLANTS (See part III, chapter 7). Carnivorous plants are those that capture insects and small animals, and feed upon them, absorbing only the nitrogenous compounds from their bodies. Such plants are green in colour and prepare their own carbonaceous food, while they partially depend on insects and other animals for nitrogenous food. Some examples are sundew, butterwort, Venus fly-trap, *Aldrovanda*, pitcher plant, bladderwort, etc.

MODIFICATIONS OF STEMS

The main functions that modified stems perform are: (a) perennation, i.e. surviving from year to year through bad seasons by certain underground stems, (b) vegetative propagation by certain horizontal sub-aerial branches spreading out in different directions and (c) specialized functions by certain metamorphosed aerial organs.

1. UNDERGROUND MODIFICATIONS OF STEMS. For the purpose of perennation, stems develop underground and lodge there permanently, lying in a dormant, defoliated condition for some time and then giving off aerial shoots annually under favourable conditions. They are always thick and fleshy, containing a heavy deposit of reserve food material. Developing underground, they simulate roots in their general appearance, in being—non-green in colour and in lying buried in the soil—but are readily distinguished from the latter by the presence of (a) nodes and internodes,

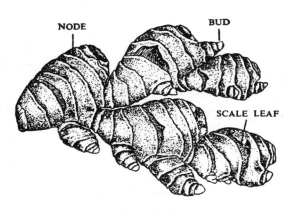

FIG. 28. Rhizome of ginger

(b) scale-leaves and (c) buds (axillary and terminal). The main function of this group of modified stems is, as already stated, (a) perennation, but they are also meant (b) to store up food material and (c) to propagate, i.e. to multiply plants vegetatively. The various types met with in this group are as follows:

(1) **Rhizome** (FIG. 28). Rhizome is a prostrate, thickened stem, creeping horizontally under the surface of the soil. It is provided with distinct nodes and long or short internodes. It bears some scaly leaves at the nodes, possesses a bud in the axil of the scaly leaf and ends in a terminal bud.

Some slender, adventitious roots are given off from its lower side. The rhizome may be unbranched or sometimes the axillary buds grow out into short, stout branches. It remains dormant underground and then with the approach of the vegetative season, the terminal bud and often some of the axillary buds as well grow into aerial shoots. Its direction is normally horizontal, but sometimes it grows vertically (**rootstock**), as in *Alocasia* (B. MANKACHU; H. MANKANDA). Examples of rhizome are seen in *Canna*, ginger, turmeric, arrowroot, water lily, lotus, ferns and many aroids.

(2) **Tuber** (FIG. 29). This is the swollen end of a special underground branch. (Tuber means a swelling.) The underground branch arises from the axil of a lower leaf, grows horizontally outwards and ultimately swells up at the apex. It has on its surface a number of 'eyes' or buds which grow into new plants. Adventitious roots, abundantly formed in other underground stems, are usually absent in tubers. A tuber is often very swollen owing to a heavy deposit of food material, becoming almost spherical, e.g. potato. Jerusalem artichoke (*Helianthus tuberosus*; B. & H. HATICHOKE) with edible tubers is another example.

(3) **Bulb** (FIG. 30). This is an underground modified shoot (rather a single, often large, terminal

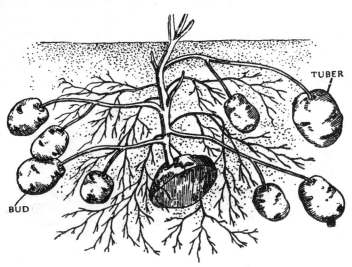

FIG. 29. Tubers of potato

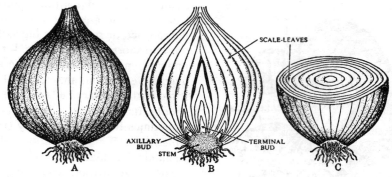

FIG. 30. Bulb of onion. *A*, an entire onion showing the lower part of the bulb with adventitious roots, and outer dry scale-leaves with distinct veins; *B*, an onion cut longitudinally; and *C*, an onion cut transversely

bud) consisting of a shortened, convex or slightly conical stem, a terminal bud and numerous scale-leaves (which are the swollen bases of foliage leaves). The scale-leaves, often simply called scales, grow from the upper surface of the stem or around it, while a cluster of adventitious (fibrous) roots are given off from its base. The inner scales are commonly fleshy, the outer ones dry. The scales may surround the stem in concentric rings, as in onion, leek, garlic, tuberose, most lilies, etc., or they may be narrow, partially overlap each other by their margins only, as in tulip and certain lilies. The former type of bulb is most common and is said to be *tunicated* or *coated*, while the latter is rather rare and is said to be *scaly*. The fleshy scales store food (sugar in onion and mostly starch in others), while the dry scales give protection. The bulb is vertical in direction and its terminal bud gives rise to the aerial shoot. Some

axillary buds may also be produced in the axils or fleshy scales. These may develop into aerial shoots and finally form daughter bulbs, or they may remain dormant. The daughter bulbs grow in the following season.

(4) **Corm** (FIG. 31). This is a condensed form of rhizome consisting of a stout, solid, fleshy, underground stem growing in the vertical direction. It is more or less round in shape or often somewhat flattened from top to bottom. It contains a heavy deposit of food material and often grows to a considerable size. It bears one or more buds in the axil of scale-leaves and some of these buds develop into daughter corms. Adventitious roots normally develop from the base but sometimes also from the sides. Corm is found *Amorphophallus* (B. OL; H. ZAMIKAND), *Gladiolus*, taro (*Colocasia*), saffron (*Crocus*) and meadow saffron (*Colchicum*).

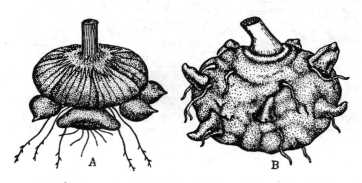

FIG. 31. *A*, corm of *Gladiolus*; *B*, corm of *Amorphophallus*

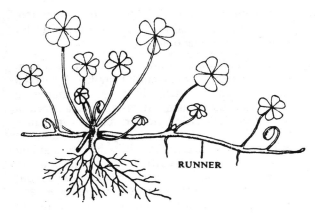

FIG. 32. Runner of wood-sorrel (*Oxalis*)

2. SUB-AERIAL MODIFICATIONS OF STEMS.

These are meant for vegetative propagation and are of the following kinds:

(1) **Runner** (FIG. 32). This is a slender, *prostrate* branch with long or short internodes, creeping on the ground and rooting at the nodes. The runner arises as an axillary bud and creeps some distance away from the mother plant, then strikes roots and grows into a new plant. Many such runners are often produced by the mother plant and they spread out on the ground on all sides. They may break off from the mother plant and grow as independent daughter plants. Examples are seen in wood sorrel (*Oxalis*), *Marsilea*, strawberry (*Fragaria*), Indian pennywort (*Centella* = *Hydrocotyle*), etc.

(2) **Stolon** (FIG. 33). Like the runner, this is also a slender, lateral branch originating from the base of the stem. But it first grows *obliquely* upwards to some extent and then bends to the ground, striking roots at the tip and producing a bud. The latter soon grows into a daughter plant. A stolon may grow further in the same way, producing roots and buds at successive stages. Many such stolons, each provided with long or short internodes, may grow out of the mother plant and spread out in different directions. Common examples are peppermint (*Mentha piperita*), wild strawberry (*Fragaria indica*), *Oenanthe stolonifera* etc.

(3) **Offset** (FIG. 34). Like the runner, this originates in the axil of a leaf as a short, more or less thickened, horizontal branch. It elongates only to a certain extent and produces at the apex, a tuft of leaves above and a cluster of small roots below. The offset often breaks away from the mother plant and then the daughter plant embarks on a separate career. Common examples are water lettuce (*Pistia*) and water hyacinth (*Eichhornia*). An offset is shorter and stouter than a runner, and is found only in the rosette type of plants.

(4) **Sucker** (FIG. 35). Like the stolon, the sucker is also a lateral branch developing from the underground part of the stem at its node. But it grows

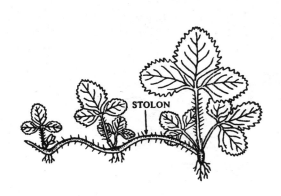

FIG. 33. Stolon of wild strawberry (*Fragaria indica*)

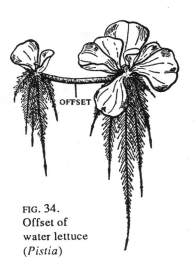

FIG. 34. Offset of water lettuce (*Pistia*)

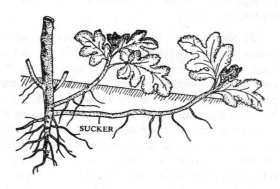

FIG. 35. Suckers of *Chrysanthemum*

obliquely upwards and directly gives rise to a leafy shoot or a new plant. Occasionally it grows horizontally outwards only to a certain extent, but soon it turns up, as in *Chrysanthemum*, or it may be shorter and stouter, as in banana. Examples of sucker are seen in *Chrysanthemum*, garden mint (*Mentha arvensis*), raspberry (*Rubus idaeus*) banana, pineapple, bamboo, etc.

3. AERIAL MODIFICATION: METAMORPHOSES.

Vegetative and floral buds, which would normally develop into branches and flowers, often undergo extreme degrees of modification (metamorphosis) in certain plants for definite purposes. Metamorphosed organs are stem-tendril for climbing, thorn for protection, phylloclade for food manufacture and bulbil for vegetative reproduction.

(1) **Stem-tendril** (FIGS. 36-37).This is a thin, wiry, leafless, spirally-curled branch, by which climbers attach themselves to neighbouring objects and climb them. Stem-tendrils are seen in vine (*Vitis*), passion-flower, etc. In passion-flower (FIG. 36 A), the axillary bud is modified into the tendril and in *Vitis*, it is the terminal bud that becomes so modified. Sometimes, as in Sandwich Island climber (*Corculum = Antigonon*; FIG. 36 B) and balloon vine *Cardiospermum*; FIG. 37), floral buds are modified into tendrils. In *Gouania* and *Serjania*, extensive woody climbers (lianes), some of the branches end in strong watch-spring like tendrils for the support of such plants.

(2) **Thorn** (FIG. 38). The thorn is a hard, often straight and pointed structure. It is regarded as a modified branch because it arises in the axil of a leaf or sometimes at the apex of a branch, which is the normal position of a bud. Thus in lemon, *Duranta*, pomegranate, *Vangueria* (B. & H. MOYNA), etc., the axillary bud is modified into a thorn, and in *Carissa* (B. KARANJA; H. KARONDA) the terminal bud is modified into a pair of thorns. The thorn sometimes bears leaves, flowers and fruits, as in *Duranta* and prune (*Prunus*), and

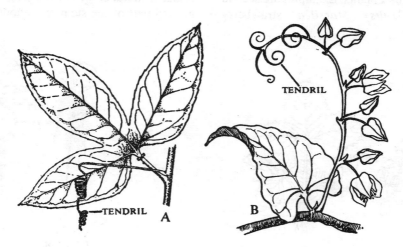

FIG. 36. Stem-tendrils. *A*, tendril of passion-flower (*Passiflora*); *B*, tendrils of Sandwich Island climber (*Corculum = Antigonon*)

FIG. 37. Tendrils of balloon vine
(*Cardiospermum*). *T*, a tendril

sometimes it becomes branched, as in *Flacourtia* (B. & H. PANIALA).

Differences between Thorns and Prickles. Both thorns and prickles are primarily defensive organs, being sharp and pointed. They also act as climbing organs. Their morphological differences are: a thorn is a modification of an axillary bud or sometimes of a terminal bud, **as in** *Carissa*, and may bear leaves, flowers or fruits, and may also be branched, whereas a prickle is a mere outgrowth, never bears leaves, flowers or fruits, and is unbranched. A thorn is axillary or terminal in position, whereas a prickle is irregular in distribution occurring in any part of the stem, branch or even leaf. Further, a thorn is deep-seated while a prickle

is superficial in origin. Thorns are found in *Carissa*, *Duranta*, etc., and prickles in rose, coral tree (*Erythrina*), etc.

(3) **Phylloclade** (FIGS. 39-40). This is a *green*, flattened or cylindrical stem or branch of *unlimited growth*, consisting of succession of nodes and internodes at long or short intervals. The phylloclade characteristically develops in many xerophytic plants where the leaves often grow out feebly, or fall off early, or are modified into spines, evidently reducing evaporating surfaces. The phylloclade then takes over all the functions of leaves, particularly photosynthesis. It also often functions as storage tissue, retaining plenty of water and mucilage. Further, because of strong development of cuticle, it can reduce transpiration to a considerable extent. Common examples are cacti, such as prickly pear (*Opuntia dillenii*; FIG. 39 A), night-blooming cacti (*Cereus* and *Phyllocactus*; FIG. 40 B), *Epiphyllum truncatum* (FIG. 39 C), etc., cocoloba (*Muehlenbeckia*; FIG. 39 B), *Casuarina* (B. & H. JHAU), several species of *Euphorbia*, e.g. *E. tirucalli* (phylloclades cylindrical FIG. 40 A), *E. antiquorum* (phylloclades flattened), etc. The phylloclade is otherwise called *cladophyll*.

(4) **Cladode** (FIG. 41). In some plants, one or more short, *green* cylindrical or sometimes flattened branches *of limited growth* develop from the node of the stem or branch in the axil of a scale-leaf. Such a branch is known as the cladode. *Asparagus* is a typical example (FIG. 41B). Here, the cladode is cylindrical and consists of one internode only. A very interesting example is

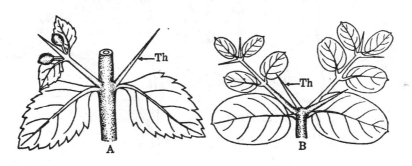

FIG. 38. Thorns. *A*, *Duranta*; *B*, *Carissa Th*, thorn

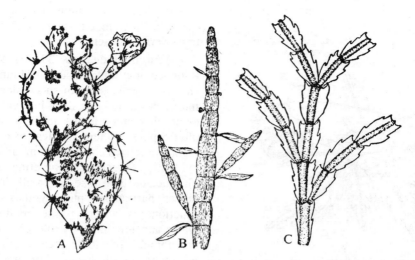

FIG. 39. Phylloclades. *A*, prickly pear (*Opuntia dillenii*); *B*, clcoloba
(*Muehlenbeckia platyclados*); *C*, Christmas cactus (*Epiphyllum truncatum*)

butcher's broom (*Ruscus aculeatus*; FIG. 41 A), a small shrub. In this plant the green, flat, leaf-like organs (branches), each arising in the axil of a scale-leaf, are the cladodes. The cladodes bear male or female flowers (*Ruscus* is dioecious) from a point (representing a node) half-way up on their surface in the axil of another scale-leaf. The female flower subsequently produces a large red berry. In *Phyllocladus* (a conifer) the green, flat, leaf-like 'short shoots', each developing in the axil of scale leaf on the 'long shoot', are the cladodes. The flat, green, floating blade (stem) of duckweed (*Lemma*; see FIG. 2 D) is also regarded by many as a cladode. Similarly the frond of *Wolffia*, a minute rootless, floating plant, is regarded as a cladode. *Wolffia*, it may be noted, is the smallest 'flowering plant', with its frond as small as a sand grain.

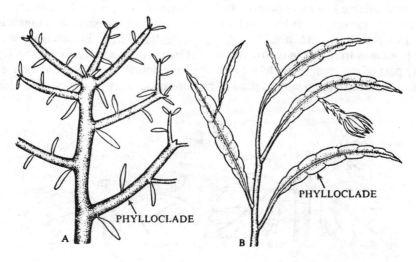

FIG. 40. *A*, Phylloclades of *Euphorbia tirucall*;
B, the same of *Phyllocactus latifrons*

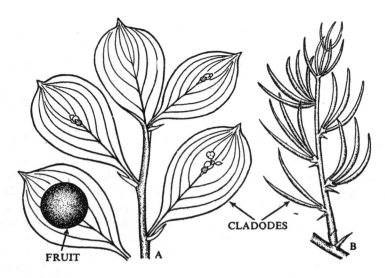

FIG. 41A, Cladodes of *Ruscus aculeatus*; B, the same of *Asparagus racemosus*.

(5) **Bulbil** (see FIGS. III/58-62). The bulbil is a special multicellular body, essentially meant for the reproduction of the plant. It may be the modification of a vevgetative bud or of a floral bud. In any case, it detaches itself from the mother plant and grows into a new independent one. Bulbils are seen in *Dioscorea bulbifera*, *Oxalis repens*, *Globba bulbifera*, *Agave americana*, onion (*Allium cepa*), *Lilium bulbiferum*, etc.

BRANCHING

The mode of arrangement of branches on a stem is known as **branching**. There are two principal types of branching, *viz.* **lateral** and **dichotomous**.

A. LATERAL BRANCHING

When the branches are produced laterrally, that is, from the sides of the main stem, the branching is called **lateral**. Lateral branching may be **racemose** or indefinite or monopodial (*monos, one; pod-, foot or axis*) and **cymose** or definite.

1. Racemose Type. Here the growth of the main stem is idenfinete, that is, it continues to grow indefinitely by the terminal bud and give off branchhes laterally in acropetal. succession, i.e, the lower branched are older and longer than the upper ones (FIG. 42A). Branching of this type is also called **monopodial** because there is a single continuous axis, as in *Casuarina*, mast tree

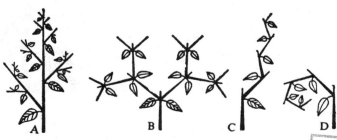

FIG. 42. Types of Branching. *A*, racemose type; *B*, true (biparous) cyme; *C*, scorpioid cyme; *D*, helicoid cyme

(*Polyalthia*), pine (*Pinus*), etc. As a result of this branching, the plant takes on a conical or pyramidal shape.

2. Cymose Type. Here, the growth of the main stem is definite, that is the terminal bud does not continue to grow, but lower down, the main stem produces one or more lateral branches which grow more vigorously than the terminal one. The process may be repeated over and over again. As a result of cymose branching, the plant spreads out above and becomes more or less dome-shaped. Cymose branching may be of the following kinds:

(1) **Uniparous Cyme.** If, in the cymose type, only one lateral branch is produced at a time, the branching is said to be uniparous or monochasial. The uniparous type of branching is otherwise called **sympodial** (*syn*, together or united; *pod-*, foot) because there is a sucession of daughter axes (false axes) fused together in the course of the plant's development (FIGS. 43-4). It has two distinct froms: (a) **helicoid** or one-sided cyme (FIG. 42D), when successive lateral branched devlop on the same side, forming a sort of helix, as

in *Saraca* (B, ASOK; H. SEETA ASHOK) and (b) **scorpioid** or alternate-sided cyme (FIG. 42C), when successive lateral branched develop on alternate sides, forming a zigzag, as in vine (*Vitis vinifera*), wild vine (*V. trifolia*), *Cissus quadrangularis* (B. & H. HARHJORA; FIG. 44), etc. In these, the apparent or false axis (**sympodium**) is a sucession of lateral axes and the tendrils are modified terminal vegetative buds (FIGS. 43-4).

(2) **Biparous Cyme.** If, in the cymose branching, two lateral axes develop at a time, it is called biparous or dichasial (FIG.42B). Examples are seen in mistletoe (*Viscum*; see FIG. 24), four o'clock plant (*Mirabilis*), temple or pagoda tree (*Plumeria*), *Ervatamia* (= *Tabernaemontana*), *Datura*, *Carissa* (see FIG. 38B), etc. Sometimes, it so happens that the terminal bud remains undevloped or soon dies off. The branching then looks like a dichotomy, often called *false dichotomy*.

(3) **Multiparous Cyme.** If more than two branches develop at a time, the branching is said to be multiparous or polychasial, as in *Croton sparsi-florus* and some species of *Euphorbia*.

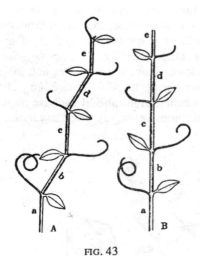

FIG. 43

FIG. 43. Sympodial Branching. *A*, scorpoid type showing terminal tendrils and lateral axes; *B*, the same straightened out after growth; *a-e* are respective axes of sympodium.

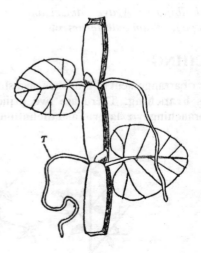

FIG. 44

FIG. 44. Sympodial branching of *Cissus quadrangularis* (B. & H. HARHJORA); *T*, a tendril

FIG. 45. Dichotomous branching in *Riccia*

B. DICHOTOMOUS BRANCHING

When the terminal bud bifurcates, that is divides into two, producing two branches in a forked manner, the branching is termed **dichotomous**. Dichotomous branching is common among the 'flowerless' plants, as in *Riccia* (FIG. 45), *Marchantia* (see FIG. V/118), *Lycopodium phlegmaria* (see FIG. V/151A) and *L. squarrosum* (see FIG. V/150). Among the 'flowering' plants, examples are afforded by *Hyphaene* (a kind of palm), screwpine (*Pandanus*), *Canscora* (a weed), etc.

Functions of the Stem. The main propose of the stem is to bear leaves and flowers and spread them out on all sides for proper functioning—for the leaves to get an adequate amount of sunlight for manufacture of food material and the flowers to attract insects from a distance for the purpose of pollination and reproduction. Other functions are support of the branches which push forward the leaves and flowers, conduction of water, mineral salts and perpared food through the plant body, storage of water and food in many cases and manufacture of food by the green shoot.

CHAPTER 3

THE LEAF

The leaf may be regarded as the flattened, lateral outgrowth of the stem or the branch, developing exogenously (i.e. from superficial tissues) from a node and having a bud in its axil. In this respect, the leaf is a partial stem or branch having a limited growth. It is normally green in clour and is regarded as the most important vegetative organ of the plant since food material is prepared in it. Leaves always follow an *acropetal* order of development and are *exogenous* in origin.

PARTS OF A LEAF (FIG. 46). a typical leaf consists of the following parts, each with its own function.

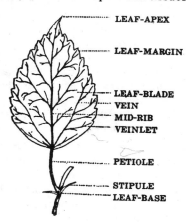

FIG. 46. Parts of a leaf

1. **Leaf-base** is the part attached to the stem. In monocotyledons, the leaf-base commonly expands into a sheath which partially or wholly clasps the stem, while in many dicotyledons, the leaf-base bears two lateral outgrowths known as the **stipules**. In *Leguminosae* and in many other plants, the leaf-base is swollen, and then it is

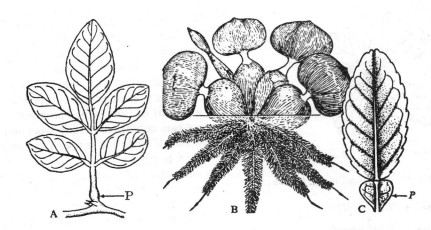

FIG. 47. *A, Clitoria* leaf showing pulvinus (P); *B*, water hyacinth (*Eichhornia*) leaf showing bulbous petiole; *C*, pummelo (*Citrus*) leaf showing winged petiole (*P*)

known as the **pulvinus**. (FIG. 47A).

2. **Petiole** is the stalk of the leaf. A long petiole pushes out the leaf-blade and thus helps it to secure more sunlight. When the petiole is absent, the leaf is said to be **sessile**, and when present, it is said to be **petiolate** or stalked. Commonly, the petiole is cylindrical, being terete or grooved, but in many cases the petiole shows certain peculiarities. Thus, in water hyacinth or lilac devil (FIG. 47B), it swells into a spongy bulb, often called pseudo-bulb containing innumerable air chambers for facility of floating, while in *Citrus* (e.g. orange, pummelo, etc.), it becomes winged (FIG. 47C). In Australian *Acacia* (see FIG. 67), the petiole together with the rachis of the leaf is modified into a flattened sickle-shaped lamina or blade, called phylode. In *Clematis* (see FIG. 21A) the petiole is tendrillar in nature. In sarsaparilla (*Smilax;* FIG. 48) two strong, closely coiled tendrils, one on each side, develop from the leaf-stalk. They are formed, as now known on the basis of anatomical work, by chorisis (splitting or branching) of the petiole.

3. **Leaf-blade** or **lamina** is the green, expanded portion. A strong vein, known as the **mid-rib**, runs centrally through the leaf-blade from its base to the apex. This produces thinner lateral **veins**, which in their turn, give rise to still thinner veins or **veinlets**. The lamina is the most important part of the leaf since this is the seat of food-manufacture for the entire plant. Its external and internal organization is well adapted for this purpose as well as for the other functions it has to perform.

When the lobes at the base of th leaf partially enclose the stem, the leaf is said to be **auriculate** (*auricle*, lobe), as in madar (*Calotropis*), Sonchus, etc.; when completely, it is called **amplexicaul** (*amplexus*, embrace; *caulis*, stem), as in grass, wheat and cauline leaves of *Emilia*; when incompletely, it is called **semi-amplexicaul**, as in buttercup, palms, etc. When the lobes meet across the stem and fuse together so that the latter seems to pass through the leaf-blade, the leaf is said to be **perfoliate** (*per*, through; *folium* a leaf), as in *Canscora perfoliata, Aloe perfoliata*, etc. When two sessile opposite leaves meet each other across the stem and fuse together, they are said to be **connate**, as in *Canscora diffusa* (B. DANKUNI) and wild honeysuckle (*Lonicera flava*). In some cases, as in Laggera pterodonta, *Laggera alata, Canscora decurrens, Crotalaria alata* and some of the thistles, the petiole and the leaf-base become winged, and is wing extends down the stem so that the latter also seems to be winged. A leaf of this nature is said to be **decurrent.**

TYPES OF LEAVES. 1. **Foliage leaves** are ordinary green, flat, lateral appendages of the stem or the branch borne at the node. 2. **Cotyledons** or **seed** leaves are attached to the axis of the embryo of the seed. As the seed germinates, they usually turn green and become leaf-like. 3. **Cataphylls** or **scale leaves** are reduced forms of leaves, stalkless and often brownish. They are

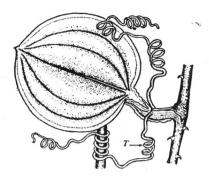

FIG. 48. Tendrils (*T*) of *Smilax*

the bud-scales, scales on the rhizome, and also on other parts of the plant body. 4.**Hypsophylls** or **bract leaves**

(otherwise called prophylls). 5. **Stipules** are the lateral appendages of the leaf borne at its base. Like the bracts, they are also of various kinds. 6. **Ligules** are minute, scaly less outgrowths borne at the upper end of the leaf-sheath, as in *Gramineae*. They are very rare in dicotyledons. 7. **Floral leaves** are members of a flower, forming into two acessory whorls (calyx and corolla), and two essential whorls (androecium and gynacium). 8. **Sporophylls** are the spore-bearing leaves concerned in asexual reproduction of plants. They may be ordinary vegetative leaves bearing spores, as in the common ferns, or metamorphosed leaves separating into a distinct reproductive region (called cone, spide or strobilus), as in *Lycopodium, Selaginella* and *Equisetum* and also gymnosperms, or into distinct flowers, as in angiosperms. In gymnosperms and angiosperms, the stamens and carples are the sporophylls.

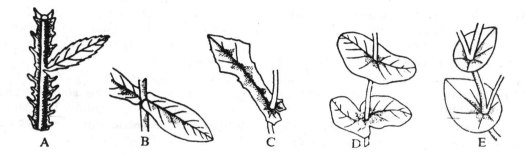

FIG. 49. Sessile Leaves. *A*, decurrent leaf of *Laggera pterodonta*.
B. auriculate leaves of madar (*Calotropis*); *C*, amplexicaul leaf of *Emiba sopla folia*; *D*, connate leaves of *Lonicera flava*; *E*, perfoliate leaves

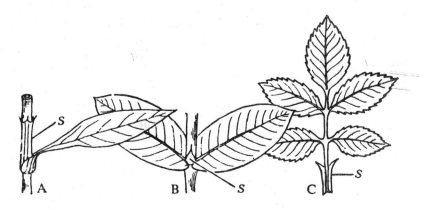

FIG. 50. Kinds of Stipules. *A*, Ochreate stipule (*S*) *of Polygonum*;
B, interpetiolar stipule (*S*) of *Ixora*; *C*, adnate stipule (*S*) of rose

STIPULES

Stipules are the lateral appendages of the leaf borne at its base. Their function is to protect the young leaves in the bud, and when green they manufacture food material in the same way as leaves. When stipules are present the leaf is said to be **stipulate**, and when absent **exstipulate**. Stipules are present in many families of dicotyledons, but they are absent or very rare in monocotyledons. A few cases of the latter class showing free lateral stipules are *Dioscorea*, *Hydrocharis* and *Potamogeton*. They appear as outgrowths of the leaf-sheath and are interpreted as stipules. Sometimes, as in butterfly pea (*Clitoria*; B. APARAJITA; H. APARAJIT), a small stipule is present at the base of each leaflet. Such a small stipule is otherwise known as a **stipel**.

KINDS OF STIPULES (FIG. 50). According to their shape, position, colour and size, the stipules are of the following kinds:

(1) **Free Lateral Stipules** (see FIG. 46). These are two free stipules, usually small and green in colour, borne on the two sides of the leaf-base, as in China rose, cotton, etc.

(2) **Scaly Stipules.** These are small dry scales, usually two in number, borne on the two sides of the leaf-base, as in *Desmodium*, e.g. Indian telegraph plant (*Desmodium gyrans*).

(3) **Adnate Stipules** (FIG. 50 C). These are two lateral stipules that grow along the petiole up to a certain height, adhering to it and making it somewhat winged in appearance, as in rose, groundnut or peanut, strawberry and lupin.

(4) **Interpetiolar Stipules** (FIG. 50 B). These are the two stipules that lie between the petioles of opposite or whorled leaves, thus alternating with the latter. They are seen in *Ixora* (B. RANGAN; H. GOTAGANDHAL), *Anthocephalus* (B. & H. KADAM), *Vangueria* (B. & H. MOYNA), etc. Sometimes, as in cape jasmine, (*Gardenia*; B. & H. GANDHARAJ), *Randia*, *Pavetta*, etc., the two stipules are axillary in position, each lying between the petiole and the stem. They are then known as the **intrapetiolar stipules.**

(5) **Ochreate Stipules** (FIG. 50 A). They form a

FIG. 51. Spinous stipules (*S*) Indian plum (*Zizyphus*)

hollow tube encircling the stem from the node up to a certain height of the internode in front of the petiole, as in *Polygonum*, sorrel (*Rumex*) and buckwheat (*Fagopyrum*).

(6) **Foliaceous Stipules** (see FIG. 63 A-B). These are two large green, leafy structures, as in pea (*Pisum*), wild pea (*Lathyrus*), some species of passion-flower (*Passiflora*) and *Cassia Auriculata*.

(7) **Bud-scales.** These are scaly stipules which enclose and protect the vegetative buds, and fall off as soon as the leaves unfold. They are seen in banyan, jack, *Magnolia*, iron-wood tree (*Mesua*; B. NAGESWAR; H. NAGESAR), etc.

(8) **Spinous Stipules** (FIG. 51). In some plants, as in gum tree (*Acacia*), Indian plum (*Zizyphus*), sensitive plant (*Mimosa*), caper (*Capparis*), wood-apple (*Aegle*), etc., the stipules become modified into two sharp pointed structures known as spines, one on each side of the leaf-base. Such spinous stipules give protection to the leaf against the attack of herbivorous animals. [Note that the last three kinds of stipules are regarded as modified ones.]

LEAF-BLADE

Apex of the leaf (FIG. 52). The apex of the leaf is said to be (1) **obtuse**, when it is rounded, as in banyan (*Ficus bengalensis*); (2) **acute**, when it is pointed in the form of an acute angle, but not stiff, as in China rose; (3) **acuminate** or **caudate**, when it is drawn out into a long slender tail, as in peepul (*ficus religiosa*) and lady's umbrella or Chinese hat (*Holmskioldia*); (4) **cuspidate**, when it ends in

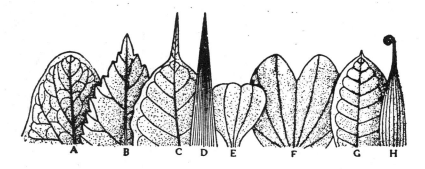

FIG. 52. Apex of the leaf. *A*, botuse; *B*, acute; *C*, acuminate;
D, cuspidate; *E*, retuse; *F*, emarginate; *G*, mucronate; and *H*, cirrhose

long rigid sharp (spiny) point, as in date-palm, screwpine and pineapple; (5) **truncate**, when it ends abruptly as if cut off in a straight line, as in Indian sago palm (*Caryota urens*) and *Bauhinia anguina* (a large climber); (6) **retuse**, when the obtuse or truncate apex is furnished with a shallow notch, as in water lettuce (*Pistis*); (7) **emarginate**, when the apex is provided with a deep notch, as in *Bauhinia* (B. KANCHAN; H. KACHNAR) and woodsorrel (*Oxalis*); (8) **mucronate**, when the rounded apex abruptly ends in a short point as in *Ixora* (B. RANGAN; H. GOTAGANDHAL); and (9) **cirrhose** (*cirrus*, a tendril or a curl), when it ends in a tendril, as in glory lily, or in a slender, curled thread-like appendage, as in banana.

Margin of the leaf. The margin of the leaf may be (1) **entire**, i.e. even and smooth, as in mango, jack, banyan, etc.; (2) **repand**, i.e. shallowly wavy or undulating, as in mango; (3) **sinuate**, i.e. deeply undulating, as in mast tree (*Polyalthia*; B. DEB-DARU; H. ASHOK) and some garden crotons; (4) **serrate**, i.e. cut like the teeth of a saw and the teeth directed upwards, as in China rose, and margosa (*Azadirachta*; B. & H. NIM OR NIMBA); (5) **biserrate**, i.e. doubly serrate (each tooth serrated again); (6) **serrulate**, i.e. minutely serrate (7) **dentate**, i.e. the teeth directed outwards at right angles to the margin of the leaf, as in melon and water lily; (8) **runcinate**, i.e. serrated with the teeth pointed backwards; (9) **crenate**, i.e. the teeth round, as in sprout leaf plant (*Bryophyllum*) and Indian pennywort (*Centella*); (10) **fimbriate**, i.e. fringed with fine segments; (11) **ciliate**, i.e. fringed with hairs and (12) **spinous**, i.e. provided with spines.

Surface of the Leaf. The leaf is said to be (1) **glabrous**, when its surface is smooth and free from hairs or outgrowths of any kind; (2) **rough**, when the surface is somewhat harsh to touch; (3) **glutinous**, when the surface is green and shining; (5) **spiny**, when it is provided with spines and (6) **hairy**, when it is covered, densely or sparsely, with hairs. A hairy surface may be (a) **pubescent**, when it is covered with short, soft, straight hairs; (b) **pilose**, i.e. thinly covered with long, soft hairs; (c) **villous**, i.e. thickly covered with long, soft hairs; (d) **tomentose**, i.e. densely covered with short, soft, more or less tangled hairs like cotton; (e) **floccose**, i.e. cottony with locks of hair easily detachable; (f) **hispid**, i.e. beset with rigid or bristly hairs; (g) **hirsute**, i.e. covered with long, coarse, stiff hairs.

Shape of the Leaf (FIG. 53). *A*, **Acicular**, when the leaf is long, narrow and cylindrical, i.e. needle-shaped, as in pine, onion, etc. *B*. **Linear**, when the leaf is long, narrow and flat, as in many grasses, tuberose, *Vallisneria*, etc. *C*. **Lanceolate**, when the shape is like that of a lance, as in bamboo (*Bambusa*), oleander (*Nerium*), mast tree (*Polyalthia*), etc. *D*. **Elliptical** or **oval**, when the leaf has more or less the shape of an ellipse, as in *Carissa* (B. KARANJA; H. KARONADA), periwinkle (*Vinca*), guava (*Psidium*), rose-apple (*Syzygium*), etc. *E*. **Ovate**, when the blade is egg-shapped, i.e. broader at the base than the apex, as in China rose, banyan etc. When the leaf is inversely egg-shaped

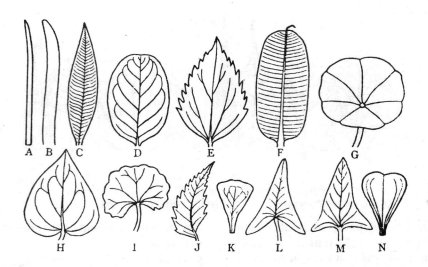

FIG. 53. Shape of the Leaf. *A*, acicular; *B*, linear; *C*, lanceolate; *D*, elliptical or oval; *E*, ovate; *F*, oblong; *G*, rotund or orbicular; *H*, cordate; *I*, reniform; *J*, oblique; *K*, spathulate; *L*, sagittate; *M*, hastate and *N*, cuneate

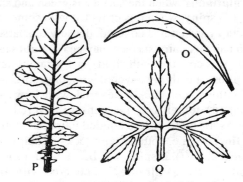

FIG. 53. (*Contd.*). *O*, falcate leaf of *Eucalyptus globulus; P*, lyrate leaf of radish; *Q*, pedate leaf of *Vitis pedata*

it is said to be **obovate**, as in country almond (*Terminalia*) and jack (*Artocarpus*). *F.* **Oblong**, when the blade is wide and long, with the two margins running straight up, as in banana. *G.* **Rotund** or **orbicular**, when the blade circular in outline, as in lotus, garden nasturtium, etc. *H.* **Cordate**, when the blade is heart-shaped, as in betel (*Piper betle*), *Peperomia*, etc. When the leaf is inversely heart-shaped it is said to be **obcordate**, as in wood-sorrel (*Oxalis*). *I.* **Reniform**, when the leaf is kidney-shaped, as in Indian pennywort. *J.* **Oblique**, when the two halves of a leaf are

unequal, as in *Begonia*. In margosa (*Azadirachta*; B. & H. NIM) and Indian cork tree (*Millingtonia*; B. & H. AKASNIM), Persian lilac (*Melia; B.* GHORA-NIM), etc., the leaflets are oblique. *K.* **Spathulate**, when the shape is like that of a spatula, i.e. broad and somewhat rounded at the top and narrower towards the base as in sundew (*Drosera*) and *Calendula. L.* **Sagittate**, when the blade is shaped like an arrow, as in arrowhead (*Sagittaria*) and some aroids. *M.* **Hastate**, when the two lobes of a sagittate leaf are directed outwards, as in water bindweed (*Ipomoea*) and *Typhonium. N.* **Cuneate**, when the leaf is wedge-shaped, as in water lettuce (*Pistia*). *O.* **Falcate**, when the leaf is sickle-shaped as in *Eucalyptus globulus* and *Arundinaria falcate* (a bamboo). In Australian *Acacia* the phyllode is falcate. *P.* **Lyrate**, when the shape is like that of a lyre, i.e. with a large terminal lobe and some smaller lateral lobes, as in radish, mustard, etc. *Q.* **Pedate**, when the leaf is like the claw of a bird, with the lobes spreading outwards, as in *Vitis pedata*.

VENATION

Veins are rigid, linear structures which arise from the petiole and the mid-rib and traverse the leaf-

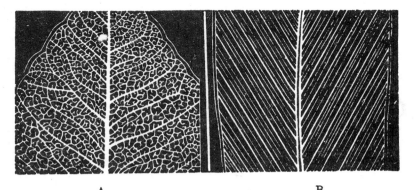

FIG. 54. Systems of Veins. *A*, reticulate venation in a dicotyledonous leaf;
B, parallel venation in a monocotyledonous leaf

lamina in different directions. They are really vascular ramifications made of conducting and mechanical tissues—the former serving to distribute the water and dissolved mineral salts through the lamina and to carry away the prepared

network, and **parallel**, when they run parallel to each other. The former is characteristic of dicotyledons and the latter of monocotyledons.

Exceptions. Among monocotyledons, yams (*Dioscorea*), *Smilax*, aroids, etc., show reticulate

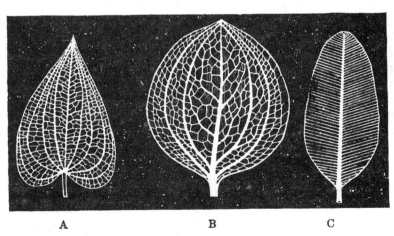

FIG. 55. *A*, leaf of *Dioscrea* (a monocotyledon) showing reticulate venation;
B, leaf of *Smilax* (a monocotyledon) showing reticulate venation; *C*, leaf of
Calophyllum (a dicotyledon) showing parallel venation

food from it, and the latter to give the necessary amount of strength and rigidity to the thin, flat leaf-lamina.

The arrangement of the veins and the veinlets in the leaf-blade is known as **venation**. There are two principal types of venation, viz. **reticulate**, when the veinlets are irregularly distributed, forming a

venation (FIG. 55 A-B), and among dicotyledons, *Calophyllum* (B. & H. SULTANA-CHAMPA; FIG. 55C) and a few others show parallel venation.

I. RETICULATE VENATION

1. Pinnate or **Unicostate Type** (*unus*, one; *costa*, a rib). In this type of venation, there is a strong

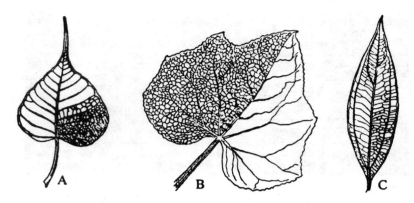

FIG. 56. Types of Reticulate Venation. *A*, pinnate type in peepul (*Ficus*) leaf; B, palmate (*divergent*) type in cucumber (*Cucumis*) leaf; *C*, palmate (convergent) type in bay leaf (*Cinnamomum*)

mid-rib or costa. This gives off lateral veins which proceed towards the margin or apex of the leaf, like plumes in a feather (FIG. 56 A). These are then connected by smaller veins which pass in all directions, forming a network, as in peepul (*Ficus*), mango (*Mangifera*), guava (*Psidium*), etc.

2. Palmate or **Multicostate Type** (*multi*, many). In this type, there are a number of more or less equally strong ribs which arise from the tip of the petiole and proceed outwards or upwards. There are two types: (a) **divergent** (FIG. 56 B), when the main veins diverge towards the margin of the leaf, as in papaw, gourd, castor, China rose, etc., and (b) **convergent** (FIG. 56 C) when the

veins converge to the apex of the leaf, as in Indian plum (*Zizyphus*), bay leaf (*Cinnamomum*), etc.

II. PARALLEL VENATION

1. Pinnate or **Unicostate Type** (FIG. 57 A). In this type of venation, the leaf has a prominent mid-rib and this gives off lateral veins which proceed parallel to each other towards the margin or apex of the leaf-blade, as in banana, ginger, *Canna*, turmeric, etc.

2. Palmate Type. There are two forms of palmate type: (a) the veins arise from the tip of the petiole and proceed (diverge) towards the margin of the leaf-blade in a more or less parallel manner

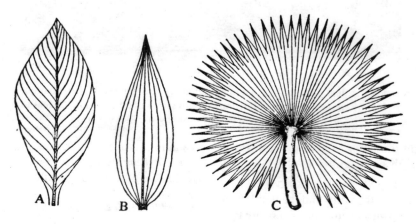

FIG. 57. Types of Parallel Venation. *A*, pinnate type in *Canna leaf; B*. palmate (convergent) type in bamboo leaf; *C*, Palmate (divergent type in pamyra-palm leaf

(**divergent type;** FIG. 57C), as in fan palms such as palmyra-palm; and (b) a number of more or less equally strong veins proceed from the base of the leaf-blade to its apex in a somewhat parallel direction (**convergent type;** FIG. 57 B), as in water hyacinth, grasses, rice, bamboo, etc.

FUNCTIONS OF VEINS. Veins are rigid structures and their mechanical functions are to give necessary strength to the leaf-blade so that it may not get torn or crumpled when a strong wind blows and, at the same time, to help the leaf-blade remain flat so that its surface may be evenly illuminated by sunlight. A very important physiological function of veins is to carry water and inorganic salts into the leaf-blade and finally, the prepared food material from the leaf into the main body of the plant, particularly the storage organs.

Incision of the Leaf-blade. In the pinnately-veined leaf, the incision or cutting of the leaf-blade proceeds

TARULATA; H. KAMALATA), *Cosmos,* etc., (4) **Pinnate compound,** when the incision of the margin reaches the mid-rib, thus dividing the leaf-blade into a number of segments or leaflets, as in pea, gram, gold mohur, *Cassia,* etc.

Second Series : Palmate Type. (1) **Palmatifid,** as in passion-flower, cotton, etc., (2) **Palmatipartite,** as in castor, papaw, etc., (3) **Palmatisect,** as in tapioca (*Manihot*), hemp (*Cannabis;* B. &. H. GANGA) and some aroids, e.g., snake plant (*Arisaema;* see FIG. 83), (4) **Palmate compound,** when the incision is carried down to the base of the leaf-blade, as in silk cotton trees (*Bombax*) and *Gynandropsis* (see FIG. 62 A-B).

COMPOUND LEAVES: PINNATE AND PALMATE

Simple Leaf and **Compound Leaf.** A leaf is said to be **simple** when it consists of a single blade which may be entire or incised (and, therefore, lobed) to any depth, but not down to the mid-rib or

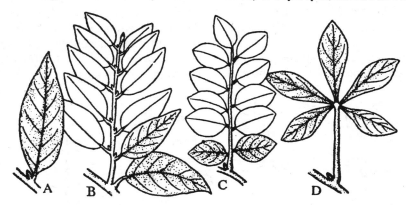

FIG. 58. *A,* simple leaf; *B,* a branch; *C,* a pinnately compound leaf with the leaflets articulated to the mid-rib; *D,* a palmately compound leaf with the leaflets articulated to the petiole. Note the position of the bud in each case

from the margin towards the mid-rib (**pinnate type**) and in the palmately-veined leaf, it passes towards the base of the leaf-blade (**palmate type**).

First Series : **Pinnate Type.** (1) **Pinnatifid,** when the incision of the margin is half-way or nearly half-way down to the mid-rib, as in poppy, (2) **Pinnatipartite,** when the incision is more than half-way down to the mid-rib, as in radish, mustard, etc., (3) **Pinnatisect,** when the incision is carried down to near the mid-rib, as in some ferns, e.g., *Quamocilt* (B. KUNJALATA or

the petiole. It is said to be **compound** when the incision of the leaf-blade goes down to the mid-rib (rachis) or to the petiole so that the leaf is broken up into a number of segments, called leaflets, these being free from one another, that is, not connected by any lamina, and more or less distinctly jointed (articulated) at their base. A bud (axillary bud) is present in the axil of a simple or a compound leaf, but it is never present in the axil of the leaflet of a compound leaf. There are two types of

FIG. 59. Bifoliate leaf of *Balanites*

compound leaves, viz. **Pinnate** and **Palmate**.

Compound Leaf and **Branch.** A compound leaf may be distinguished from a branch by the following facts: (1) A compound leaf never bears a terminal bud, whereas a branch always does so. (2) A compound leaf, like a simple one, always bears a bud (axillary bud) in its axil, but itself does not arise in the axil of another leaf, whereas a branch does not bear an axillary bud but itself occupies the axillary position of a leaf—simple or compound— developing directly from the said bud. (3) The leaflets of a compound leaf have no axil-

an opposite manner, as in tamarind, gram, gold mohur, rain tree, sensitive plant, gum tree (*Acacia*), *Cassia*, etc. It may be of the following types:

(1) **Unipinnate.** When the mid-rib of a pinnately compound leaf bears the leaflets directly, it is said to be unipinnate, as in rose, margosa (B. & H. NIM or NIMBA), etc. When the leaflets are even in number, the leaf is said to be **paripinnate** (FIG. 60A), as in tamarind, *Abrus, Sesbania, Saraca, Cassia*, etc. When the leaflets are odd in number, the leaf is said to be **imparipinnate** (FIG. 60B), as in rose, margosa (*Azadirachta*), Chinese box (*Murraya*), etc.

The pinnate leaf is said to be unfoliate when it consists of only one leaflet, as in *Desmodium gangeticum, Aphania canura* and *Bauhinia*; bifoliate or unijugate (one pair), when of two leaflets, as in *Balanites* (B. HINGON; H. HINGOL; FIG. 59) and sometimes in rose; trifoliate or ternate, when of three leaflets, as in bean, *Erythrina* and *Vitis trifolia*. It may similarly be quadrifoliate, pentafoliate or multifoliate, according as the leaflets are four, five or more in number. Leaflets may also vary in number on the same plant.

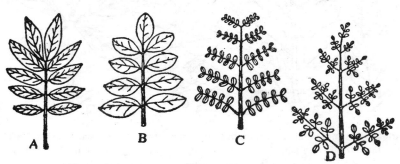

FIG. 60. Pinnate Leaves. *A*, unipinnate (paripinnate); *B*, unipinnate (imparipinnate); *C*, bipinnate; *D*, tripinnate

lary buds, whereas the leaves (simple) borne on a branch have a bud in their axil. (4) A branch is always provided with nodes and internodes, while the rachis of a compound leaf is free from them.

1. PINNATELY COMPOUND LEAF. A pinnately compound leaf is defined as one in which the mid-rib, known as the rachis, bears laterally a number of leaflets, arranged alternately or in

(2) **Bipinnate** (FIG. 60C). When the compound leaf is twice pinnate, i.e. the mid-rib produces secondary axes which bear the leaflets, it is said to be bipinnate, as in dwarf gold mohur (*Caesalpinia*), gum tree (*Acacia*), sensitive plant (*Mimosa*), etc.

(3) **Tripinnate** (FIG. 60 D). When the leaf is thrice pinnate, i.e. the secondary axes produce the tertiary axes which bear the leaflets, it is said to

FIG. 61. Decompound leaf of coriander

be tripinnate, as in drumstick (*Moringa;* B. SAJI-NA; H. SAINJNA) and *Oroxylum* (B. SONA; H. ARLU).

(4) **Decompound** (FIG. 61). When the leaf is more than thrice pinnate, it is said to be decompound, as in anise (*Foeniculum*), carrot (*Daucus*), coriander (*Coriandrum*), *Cosmos,* etc.

2. PALMATELY COMPOUND LEAF. A palmately compound leaf is defined as one in which the petiole bears *terminally,* articulated to it, a number of leaflets which seem to be radiating from a common point like fingers from the palm, as in silk cotton tree (*Bombax*), lupin (*Lupinus*), *Gynandropsis* and *Polanisia* (= *Cleome*), etc.

According to the number of leaflets, it may be **unifoliate**, when a single leaflet is articulated to the petiole (rare). In *Citrus* (shaddock or pummelo,

orange, lemon, etc.) the unifoliate leaf with a joint at the junction of the blade and the petiole is now regarded as a simple leaf—possibly derived from a compound leaf. It may be **bifoliate**, when there are two leaflets so articulated (rare); **trifoliate**, when three as in wood-apple (*Aegle*), *Crataeva* (B. BARUN; H. BARNA); and wood-sorrel (*Oxalis*); **quadrifoliate**, when four (rare); **multifoliate** or **digitate** (FIG. 62 A-B), when five or more leaflets are so jointed and spread like fingers from the palm, as in silk cotton tree (*Bombax*), lupin (*Lupinus*), *Gynandropsis*, *Polanisia* (= *Cleome*), etc.

Note: **Trifoliate Leaves.** A Trifoliate leaf of the pinnate type can be distinguished from a trifoliate leaf of the palmate type by the following: in the former, as seen in coral tree (*Erythina*) and country bean (*Dolichos lablab*), the petiole prolongs into a mid-rib (or rachis) and the terminal leaflet is articulated to its apex, while in the latter, all three leaflets are directly borne by (or articulated to) the apex of the petiole, as in wood-apple (*Aegle*).

Duration of the Leaf. The leaf varies in its duration. It may fall off soon after it appears, and then it is said to be (1) **caducous**. If it lasts one season, usually falling off in winter, it is (2) **deciduous** or **annual**. If it persists for more than one season, usually lasting a number of years, it is (3) **persistent** or **evergreen**.

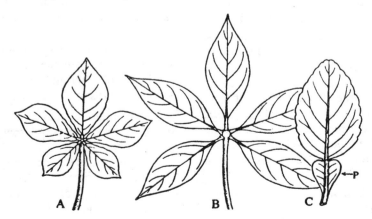

FIG. 62. Palmate Leaves. *A*, digitate leaf of *Gynandropsis*; *B*, the same of silk cotton tree (*Bombax*); *C*, unifoliate leaf of pummelo (*Citrus*); *P* winged petiole

Some Descriptive Terms. (1) **Peltate Leaf.** The leaf-blade and the petiole usually stand on one and the same plane. In some cases, however, as in lotus, water lily, garden nasturtium, etc., the petiole is attached to the centre of the blade at a right angle to it. Such a leaf is said to be peltate. (2) **Dorsiventral Leaf.** When the leaf is flat, with the blade placed horizontally, showing a distinct upper surface and a lower surface, as in most dicotyledons, it is said to be dorsiventral, (*dorsum*, back; *venter*, belly or front). A dorsiventral leaf is more strongly illuminated on the upper surface than on the lower and, therefore, this surface is deeper green in colour than the lower. In internal structure also, there is a good deal of difference between the two sides (see FIG. II/67). (3) **Isobilateral Leaf.** When the leaf is directed vertically upwards, as in many monocotyledons, it is said to be isobilateral (*isos*, equal; *bi*, two; *later-*, side). An isobilateral leaf is equally illuminated on both the surfaces and, therefore, the leaf is uniformly green and its internal structure is also uniform from one side to the other (see FIGS. II/68-9). (4) **Centric Leaf.** When the leaf is more or less cylindrical and directed upwards or downwards, as in pine, onion, etc., the leaf is said to be centric. A centric leaf is equally illuminated and, therefore, evenly green on all sides. (5) **Cauline Leaf.** Commonly, leaves are directly borne by the aerial parts of the stem and the branches. Such leaves are said to be cauline (*caulis*, a stem). (6). **Radical Leaf.** In some cases, as in pineapple (*Ananas*), Indian aloe (*Aloe;* B. GHRITAKUMARI; H. GHIKAVAR), American aloe (*Agave*), many lilies (*Lilium*), tuberose (*Polianthes*), etc., a cluster of leaves arises from the short underground stem as if from the root. Such leaves are said to be radical (*radis*, a root). Radical leaves are rather common among monocoty-ledons. Both radical and cauline leaves may be borne by the same plant, as seen in mustard, radish, etc.

Phyllode Theory. A majority of monocotyledonous leaves consist of either an expanded blade, which is nothing but the sheathing leaf base, or a distal limb (blade) with a sheathing leaf base, where the blade represents the modified expanded petiole. In the former case, both petiole and true lamina are absent or suppressed, while in the latter case, only the true lamina is absent.

When the petiole becomes modified, taking the shape of the leaf, or the leaf base assumes a lamina-like structure, it is called **phyllode**. A majority of monocotyledonous leaves are, therefore, phyllode in nature. Many dicotyledonous plants also have phyllode leaves. There is a lot of resemblance between monocot leaves (phyllode leaves) and phyllode leaves of dicotyledonous plants.

Arber (1920, 1925) advanced the 'Phyllode theory' on the basis of the fact that a majority of monocotyledonous families have phyllode leaves, i.e. the real leaf blade is absent in them. Phyllode theory explains the nature and origin of phyllode leaves in monocotyledons.

In many dicotyledonous plants either the leaf sheath is modified, forming a long, limb-like structure (leaf sheath phyllode), as in *Oreomyrrhis linearis*, or the petiole is modified into an expanded limb, (Petiolar phyllode) as in *Acacia auriculoformis* and others. Similarly, phyllodes of monocotyledonous plants either represent leaf sheath or petiole. In *Allium cepa*, the leaf is cylindrical, green in colour and contains a membranous leaf sheath. It is apparent that the cylindrical leaf is a prolonged petiole functioning as lamina. Hence, the leaf is a petiolar phyllode. In *Triglochin maritimum*, the leaf is composed of the basal sheath and an awl-shaped petiole. In the case of ribbon-shaped leaves seen in many monocotyledonous plants, the petiole flattens in a horizontal direction, whereas in the case of ensiform or equitant leaves of other monocotyledonous plants, the petiole expands in a vertical plane.

The isobilateral leaves of *Gladiolus* sp. and *Sisyrinchium* sp. are petiolar phyllodes, which can be compared with the phyllodes of *Acacia auriculoformis*, as they are similar in morphology. The petiolar morphology of these leaf blades is evident from their anatomical structures. In both *Gladiolus* sp. and *Acacia* sp., the internal structure reveals that two lateral bundles form pseudo midribs and are very prominent, while the two main median bundles are smaller and not very distinct.

The petiolar phyllode (ribbon-like) in many genera of *Potamogatonaceae* is generally transversed by a single series of bundles and even in these the petiole and leaf sheath may have similar anatomical structures.

Leaf sheath phyllodes are also seen in many monocotyledonous plants. In these plants, the leaf is reduced and represented by just a flattened base. In many genera of *Iridaceae* and *Liliaceae*, the petiole is absent, suppressed or reduced to such an extent that it is represented by a small apical portion. In these plants, the blade is merely the flattened base. A case of a typical leaf base phyllode is seen in *Hemerocallis* sp., where the true lamina and petiole are completely suppressed and the blade comprises only the leaf base.

MODIFICATIONS OF LEAVES

Leaves of many plants which have to perform specialized functions become modified or metamorphosed into distinct forms. These are as follows:

1. Leaf-tendrils (FIGS. 63-4). In some plants leaves are modified into slender, wiry, often closely coiled structures, know, as tendrils. Tendrils are always climbing organs and are sensitive to contact with a foreign body. Therefore, whenever they come in contact with a neighbouring object, they coil round it and help the plant to climb. The leaf may be partially or wholly modified. Thus, in pea (*Pisum*; FIG. 63A), *Lathyrus sativus* (B. & H. KHE-SARI), golden shower or Venus' flower (*Bignonia venusta*), etc., only the upper leaflets turn into tendrils. *Bignonia venusta*, it may be noted, is an ornamental climber bearing orange-coloured flowers in huge trusses. In traveller's joy (*Naravelia*; FIG. 64), it is only the terminal leaflet that is converted into a long coiling tendril. In lentil (*Lens culinaris*; B. & H. MASUR) the rachis of the leaf ends in a tendril. In glory lily (*Gloriosa*; FIG. 63C), the leaf-apex ends in a closely coiled tendril. In pitcher plant (*Nepenthes;* see FIG. 69), the petiole often acts as a tendril holding the pitcher in an upright position. In sarsaparilla (*Smilax*), the leaf-stalk is modified into two tendrils (see FIG. 48). The above are cases of partial modification. In wild pea (*Lathyrus aphaca*; FIG. 63 B), however, the whole leaf is transformed into a single tendril, while the two foliaceous stipules take over the functions of the leaf.

Hooks. In cat's nail (*Bignonia unguis-cati*; FIG. 65), an elegant climber, the terminal leaflets become modified into three, very sharp, stiff and curved hooks, very much like the nails of a cat. These hooks cling to the bark of a tree and act as organs of support for climbing. The plant, thus, easily climbs to the top of a lofty tree.

FIG. 63. Modified Leaves; Leaf-tendrils. *A*, leaf of pea (*Pisum*) with upper leaflets modified into tendrils; *B*, portion of wild pea (*Lathyrus*) stem; *T*, tendrils; *S*, stipules; *C*, portion of glory lily (*Gloriosa*) stem with the leaf-apex modified into a tendril

FIG. 64. Leaf of *Naravelia* with the
terminal leaflet modified into a tendril

2. Leaf-Spines (FIG. 66). Leaves of certain plants become modified for defensive purposes into sharp, pointed structures known as **spines**. That spines are modifacations of leaves is evident from the fact that they occupy the same position as the leaves and that they often bear a bud in their axil, as seen in the flowering shoot of barberry (*Berberis;* FIG. 66A). In prickly pear (*Opuntia;* see FIG. 39A), ordinary leaves are feebly developed and soon fall off, but the minute leaves of the axillary bud are modified into spines. In barberry (FIG. 66A), on the other hand, the leaf itself becomes modified into a spine, while the leaves of the axillary bud are normal. Spines may also

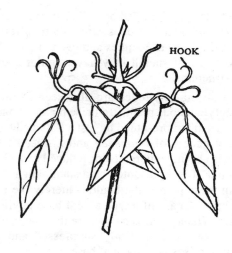

FIG. 65. Cat's nail (*Bignonia unguis-cati*)
with hooks

develop at the apex, as in date-palm, dagger plant (see FIG. 81), etc., or on the margin, as in prickly poppy (*Argemone;* FIG. 66B), or in the both the places, as in Indian aloe (*Aloe*) and American aloe or century plant (*Agave*).

3. Scale-leaves. Typically, these are thin, dry, stalkless, membranous structures, usually brownish in colour or sometimes colourless. Their

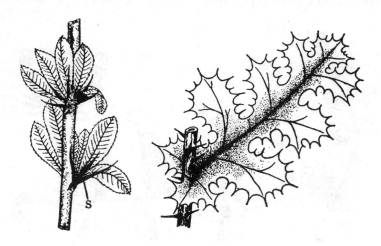

A   B

FIG. 66. *A*, barberry (*Berberis*) : primary leaves modified into
spines (*S*); *B*, leaf of prickly poppy (*Argemone*) showing spines

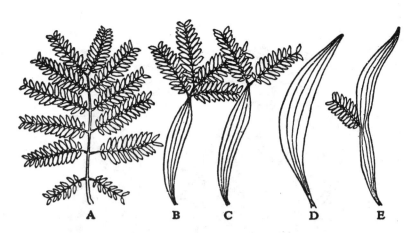

FIG. 67. Development of phyllode in Australian *Acacia. A,* pinnately compound
leaf; *B-C* petiole developing into phyllode; *D,* phyllode; and *E,* petiole and rachis
developing into phyllode

function is to protect the axillary bud that they
bear in their axil. Sometimes scale-leaves are
thick and fleshy, as in onion; then their function is
to store up water and food. Scale-leaves are common on underground stems, saprophytes, parasites, *Ficus,Casuarina* (B. & H. JHAU), *Tamarix*
(B. & H. BANJHAU), etc.

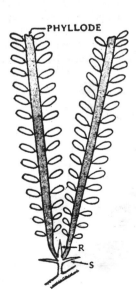

FIG. 68. Phyllodes of *Parkinsonia aculeata.*
R, spiny rachis; *S,* a pair of spiny stipules

4. Phyllode (FIGS. 67-8). In Australian *Acacia,* the
petiole or any part of the rachis becomes flattened
or winged, taking the shape of the leaf and turning
green in colour. This flattened or winged petiole
or rachis is known as **phyllode.** In some species,
as in *A. moniliformis,* the normal bipinnate leaf
develops in the seedling stage only, but soon falls
off. Later, only the phyllodes develop throughout
the life of the plant. In other species, as in *A.
melanoxylon,* the adult plant bears both bipinnate
leaves and phyllodes in all stages of development.
In all cases, the leaflets fall off soon and the phyllodes take over their functions, particularly photosynthesis. Further, the edge of the phyllode is
normally turned upwards, thus avoiding direct
sunlight. This mechanism reduces evaporation of
water. There are about 300 species of Australian
Acacia, all showing the phyllode. In Jerusalem
thorn (*Parkinsonia aculeata*), a small prickly tree,
the primary rachis of the bipinnate leaf ends in a
short spine, while each secondary rachis is a phyllode, green and often much flattened. The phyllode performs the functions of the leaflets, which
are very small and often fall off early. Some
species of *Oxalis* (e.g. *O. bilimbi*) also develop
phyllodes, particularly in their younger stage.

5. Pitcher (FIG. 69). In the pitcher plant (*Nepenthes*), the leaf becomes modified into a **pitcher.**
There is a sort of slender stalk which often coils

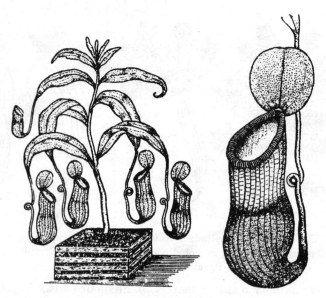

FIG. 69. *A*. Pitcher plant (*Nepenthes*); *B,* a pitcher

like a tendril, holding the pitcher vertical, and the basal portion is flattened like a leaf. The pitcher is provided with a lid which covers its mouth when the pitcher is young. The function of the pitcher is to capture and digest insects. The morphology of the leaf of a pitcher plant is that the pitcher itself is a modification of the leaf-blade, the inner side of the pitcher corresponding to the upper surface of the leaf. The lid arises as an outgrowth of the leaf-apex. The slender stalk, which coils like a tendril, stiffening as it does so, is the petiole. The laminated structure, which looks like and behaves as the leaf-blade, develops from the leaf-base.

Another peculiar modification of the leaf into a kind of pitcher is found in a climbing epiphyte, called *Dischidia rafflesiana* (FIG. 70), common in Assam. The pitcher usually varies in size from 5 to 8 cm. in length and 2 to 2.5 cm. in width. It is, however, not carnivo-

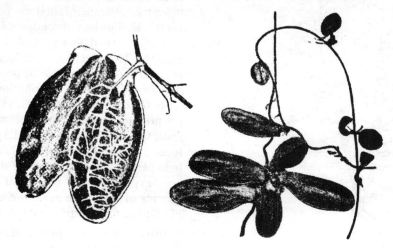

FIG. 70. *Dischidia rafflesiana*; *left,* a pitcher opened out

rous by nature. As in *Nepenthes,* it has an opening—a basal one, but nolid, and instead of this, there is a sort of tongue projecting inwards. A root enters the cavity of the picher and becomes much branched. After a shower of rain, water flows down into the pitcher. Prior to this, debris is collected there by ants. All this is then absorbed by the root.

6. Bladder (FIG. 71). In bladderwort (*Utricularia*), a rootless free-floating or slightly submerged weed common in many tanks, the leaf is very much segmented. Some of these segments are modified to form bladder-like structures, with

may be as follows :

(A) **Reclinate,** when the upper half of the leaf-blade is bent upon the lower half as in loquat (*Eriobotrya joponica*).

(B) **Conduplicate,** when the leaf is folded lengthwise along the mid-rib, as in guava, sweet potato and camel's foot tree (*Bauhinia;* B. KAN-CHAN; H. KACHNAR).

(C) **Plicate** or **Plaited,** when the leaf is repeatedly folded longitudinally along ribs in a *zig-zag* manner, as in fan- or palmyra-palm.

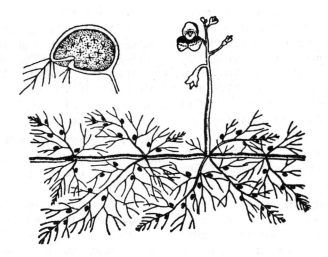

FIG. 71. Bladderwort (*Utricularia*) with many small bladders; *top,* a bladder in section (magnified)

a trap-door entrance which allows aquatic animalcules to pass in, but never to come out.

PREFOLIATION. The way in which leaves are arranged in the bud is known as **prefoliation.** This is considered from two standpoints, viz. *first,* the way in which each individual leaf is rolled or folded in the bud (**ptyxis**); *second,* the way in which the leaves are arranged in the bud with respect to each other (**vernation**). The arrangement of foliage leaves in the vegetative bud and that of the floral bud are nearly the same, and as such, the same terms are used to explain the identical types in both cases.

Ptyxis. Rolling or folding of individual leaves

(D) **Circinate,** when the leaf is rolled from the apex towards the base like the tail of a dog, as in ferns.

(E) **Convolute,** when the leaf is rolled from one margin to the other, as in banana, aroids and Indian pennywort (*Centelle=Hydrocotyle*).

(F) **Involute,** when the two margins are rolled on the upper surface of the leaf towards the mid-rid or the centre of the leaf, as in water lily, lotus. Sandwich Island climber (*Corculum = Antigonon*) and *Plumbag.* (B. CHITA; H. CHITRAK).

(G) **Revolute,** when the leaf is similarly rolled on its lower surface, as in oleander and country almond.

FIG. 72. Ptyxis. *A*, reclinate; *B*, conduplicate; *C*, plicate;
D, circinate; *E*, convolute; *F*, involute; *G*, revolute

(H) **Crumpled,** when the leaf is irregularly folded, as in cabbage.

PHYLLOTAXY

The term **phyllotaxy** (*phylla*, leaves; *taxis*, arrangement) means the various modes in which the leaves are arranged on a stem or branch. The object of this arrangement is to avoid shading one another so that the leaves may get the maximum amount of sunlight to perform their normal functions (see p. 44), particularly manufacture of food. Three principal types of phyllotaxy are noticed in plants.

(1) **Alternate** or **Spiral** (FIG. 73A), when a single leaf arises at each node, as in tobacco, China rose, mustard, sunflower, etc.

(2) **Opposite** (FIG. 73B), when two leaves arise at each node, standing opposite each other. In opposite phyllotaxy, one pair of leaves is most commonly seen to stand at a right angle to the next upper or lower pair. Such an arrangement of leaves is said to be **decussate**. This is seen in *Ixora*, sacred basil (*Ocimum*), madar (*Calotropis*),

guava (*Psidium*), etc. Sometimes, however, a pair of leaves is seen to stand directly over the lower pair on the same plane. Such an arrangement of leaves is said to be **superposed**, as in Rangoon creeper (*Quisqualis*).

(3) **Whorled** (FIG. 73C-D), when there are more than two leaves at each node and these are arranged in a circle or whorl, as in devil tree (*Alstonia*), oleander (*Nerium*), *Allamanda*, *Vangueria* (B. & H. MOYNA), etc. Sometimes, both opposite and whorled phyllotaxes may be seen in the same plant.

ALTERNATE PHYLLOTAXY. The leaves in this case are seen to be spirally arranged round the stem. Now, if an imaginary spiral line be drawn from the base of one particular leaf, and this line be passed round the stem through the bases of the successive leaves, it is seen that the spiral line finally reaches a leaf which stands vertically over the starting leaf. The imaginary spiral line, thus drawn, is known as the **genetic spiral**, and vertical line, i.e. the vertical row of leaves, known as the **orthostichy** (*orthos*, straight; *stichos*, line).

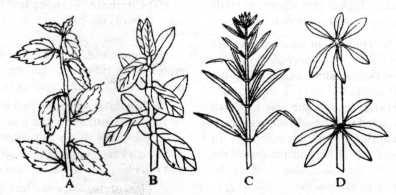

FIG. 73. Types of Phyllotaxy. *A*, alternate phyllotaxy of China rose; *B*, opposite phyllotaxy of madar (*Calotropis*); *C*, whorled phyllotaxy of oleander (*Nerium*); *D*, ditto of devil tree (*Alstonia*)

FIG. 74. Traveller's tree (*Ravenala*)
showing distichous phyllotaxy

(1) **Phyllotaxy $1/2$** or **2-ranked** or **distichous** (FIG. 75). In grasses, elephant grass (*Typha*), traveller's tree (*Ravenala;* FIG. 74), ginger, *Vanda* (see FIG. 13), *Belamcanda, Iris,* etc., the *third* leaf stands over the *first* and the genetic spiral makes *one* complete revolution to come to that leaf. It involves two leaves (leaving out of consideration the first or the third leaf). The fourth leaf stands over the second, the fifth over the first and the third, and so on. Thus, there are only two orthos-

tichies, i.e. leaves are arranged in two rows or ranks. Phyllotaxy is, therefore, 2-ranked or distichous (*di*, two; *stichos*, line). If now the position of the leaves is marked out on a circle or helix, these are seen to be placed at half the distance of the circle, the leaves being equidistant from each other. The phyllotaxy is said to be half and represented by the fraction 1/2, the numerator indicating the number of turns of the genetic spiral and the denominator the number of intervening leaves. The genetic spiral makes one complete turn in this case, subtending an angle of 360° in the centre of the circle, and it involves two leaves. So, the **angular divergence**, that is, the angular distance between any two consecutive leaves, is $1/2$ of 360°, i.e. 180°.

(2) **Phyllotaxy $1/3$** or **3-ranked** or **tristichous** (FIG. 76). In sedges (B. & H. MUTHA), the fourth leaf stands vertically over the first one, the genetic spiral makes one complete turn to reach that leaf and it involves three leaves. The fifth leaf stands over the second, the sixth over the third, and the seventh over the fourth and the first. Thus, there are three orthostichies, i.e. the leaves are arranged in three rows or ranks. If now their position be marked out on a circle or helix, they are seen to be placed at one-third the distance of the circle; so the phyllotaxy is 1/3 or 3-ranked or tristichous. The **angular divergence** is $1/3$ of 360°, i.e. 120°.

(3) **Phyllotaxy $2/5$** or **5-ranked** or **pentastichous** (FIG.77). In China rose, the sixth leaf stands

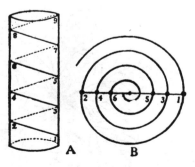

FIG. 75.

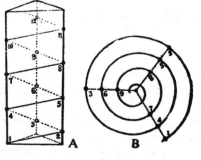

FIG. 76.

Phyllotaxy and Angular Divergence, FIG. 75. *A*, phyllotaxy, 1/2; *B*, angular divergence 180°, FIG. 76. *A* phyllotaxy 1/3; *B*, angular divergence 120°

over the first and the genetic spiral completes *two* circles to come to that particular leaf. The seventh leaf stands over the second, the eighth over the third, the ninth over the fourth, the tenth over the fifth, and the eleventh over the sixth and the first. Thus, there are five orthostichies, i.e. the leaves are arranged in five rows and because two turns of the genetic spiral involve five leaves, the latter are seen to be placed at two-fifths the distance of the circle. Phyllotaxy is, therefore, 2/5 or 5-ranked or pentastichous. This is the commonest type of alternate phyllotaxy. The **angular divergence** in this case is $2/5$ of 360°, i.e. 144°

being so, they tend to fit in with one another and adjust themselves in such a way that they may secure the maximum amount of sunlight with the minimum amount of overlapping. Thus, in climbers bearing a dense mass of leaves, as in ivy (*Hedera helix*), Indian ivy (*Ficus pumila;* see FIG. 17), railway creeper (*Ipomoea palmata*), etc., leaves are disposed in the pattern of a tile-roof. In plants with a rosette of radical leaves or with whorls of leaves, it is seen that the upper leaves alternate with the lower ones. In plants with crowded leaves, as in *Acalypha, Begonia,* garden nasturtium, etc. they are distributed like glass

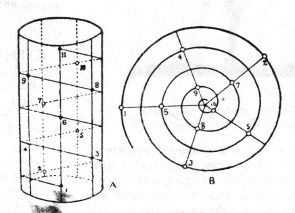

FIG. 77.
*A,*phyllotaxy 2/5
*B,*angular
    divergence
    144°

(The same fraction can also be arrived at by adding separately the numerators and the denominators of the two previous cases, e.g. $\frac{1+1}{2+3}=\frac{2}{5}$
The next case will, therefore, be $\frac{1+1}{2+3}=\frac{2}{5}$ and so on. Fractions higher than 3/8 are not commonly met with.)

Leaf Mosaic

In the floors, walls and ceilings of many temples and decorated buildings, we find setting of stones and glass pieces of variegated colours and sizes into a particular pattern. This pattern is known as mosaic. Similarly, in plants we find the setting or distribution of leaves in some definite patterns. Each such pattern of leaf-distribution is known as a **leaf mosaic.** Leaves are in special need of sunlight for manufacture of food material, and this

pieces fitting into a mosaic, with the smaller leaves fitting into the interspaces of the broader ones. Crowded leaves of prostrate plants like wood-sorrel, Indian pennywort, etc., also form a more or less perfect mosaic.

FIG. 78. Leaf mosaic of *Acalypha*

FUNCTIONS OF THE LEAF.

The normal functions of a green leaf are threefold: (1) **manufacture of food** by the chloroplasts in the presence of sunlight out of carbon dioxide and water obtained from the air and the soil, respectively; (2) **interchange of gases**—carbon dioxide and oxygen—between the atmosphere and the plant body, the former for manufacture of food by green cells only and the latter for respiration by all the living cells; (3) **evaporation of water**, mainly through the lower surface of the leaf. Besides, certain leaves have some subsidiary functions, e.g., storage of water

much dissected. Heterophylly in water plants is, thus, an adaptation to two different conditions of the environment. Among them water crowfoot (*Ranunculus aquatilis*), *Cardan-thera trifora* (FIG. 79A), etc., show heterophylly, with the submerged leaves much segmented and the floating (or aerial) leaves undivided or merely lobed. In water plantain (*Alisma plantago*) and arrowhead (*Sagittaria*; FIG. 80) the submerged leaves are sometimes narrow and ribbon-shaped, while the upper ones are entire or broadly lobed. All transitions of leaf forms are found in *Limnophila heterophylla*. Some land plants also exhibit this phenomenon without any apparent reason.

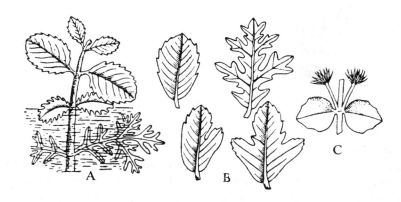

FIG. 79. Heterophylly. A, *Cardanthera triflora; B, Artocarpus chaplasha; C, Hemiphragma heterophyllum* with needle-like and broad leaves

and food by the fleshy leaves of Indian aloe, *Portulaca*, etc., fleshy scales of onion, lilies, *Amaryllis*, etc.; vegetative propagation by *Bryophyllum* (see FIG. 16A), *Begonia* (see FIG. 16B), *Kalanchoe* (see FIGS. III/56-7), walking ferns (see FIG. III/54), etc.

Heterophylly. Many plants bear different kinds of leaves on the same individual plant. This condition is known as heterophylly (*heteros*, different; *phylla*, leaves). Heterophylly is found in many aquatic plants, particularly in those growing in running water. Here, the floating or aerial leaves and the submerged leaves are of different kinds. The former are generally broad, often fully expanded, and undivided or merely lobed, while the latter are narrow, ribbon-shaped, linear or

Among them *Sterculia villosa*, Chaplash (*Artocarpus chaplasha*; FIG. 79B), jack (*A. heterophyllus*) in early stage, *Ficus heterophylla* (B. BHUI-DUMUR), etc., show leaves varying from entire to variously lobed structures, and *Hemiphragma heterophyllum* (FIG. 79C), a prostrate herb common in Darjeeling and Shillong, bears two kinds of leaves—those on the main stem are ovate and entire and those on the short axillary branches are needle-shaped.

Homology and Analogy. Homology is the morphological study of modified organs from the standpoint of their origin, and analogy is the study of organs from the standpoint of their identical structure and function. In other words, organs which resemble one another in their origin and

FIG. 80. Arrowhead (*Sagittaria*)
showing heterophylly

are, therefore, morphologically the same, whatever be their structure and function, are said to be homologous with one another, and organs which resemble one another in their structure and are adapted to the performance of identical functions, although their origin may be different, are said to be *analogous* with one another. Thus, all **tendrils**, whatever be their origin, are analogous with one another, being structurally the same and performing the same function. But tendrils of passion-flower (see FIG. 36A) are homologous with axillary buds, i.e., modifications of the latter, and tendrils of pea (see FIG. 63A) are homologous with leaflets. Likewise, **thorns** and **spines** are analogous structures, being defensive in function, but thorns are modifications of axillary or terminal buds and are, therefore, homologous with them, while spines are homologous with leaves, being modifications of them wholly or partly. It will further be noted that the thorn of *Duranta* and the tendril of passion-flower are homologous

structures. In addition, **modified stems** (e.g. rhizome and tuber) and **modified** roots (e.g. fusiform root and napiform root) are analogous structures, being adapted to the performance of an identical function, i.e. storage of food. But it must be noted that the former two (rhizome and tuber) are homologous with the stem, being modifications of it, while the latter (fusiform root and napiform root) are homologous with the root, being modifications of it. Again, we find that **phylloclades** (see FIGS. 39-40) are homologous with the stem, being modifications of it, but they are analogous with the leaves as they have adapted themselves to perform the functions of leaves. So far as the **flower** is concerned, we find that stamens and carpels are homologous with microsporophylls and megasporophylls of gymnosperms and *Selaginella* and with the sporophylls of ferns, and ultimately with vegetative leaves. Similarly, sepals and petals are modified vegetative leaves and are homologous with them.

CHAPTER 4

DEFENSIVE MECHANISMS IN PLANTS

The animal kingdom as a whole is directly or indirectly parasitic upon the plant kingdom, and this being so, plants must either fall victim to various classes of animals, particularly the herbivorous ones, which live exclusively on a vegetable diet, or they must be provided with special organs or arms of defence, or have other special devices to repulse or avoid the attack of their enemies. Being fixed to the ground they cannot, of course, manoeuvre when attacked by animals.

I. ARMATURE

1. Thorns, Spines, Prickles and Bristles.

These are all sharp, pointed, hard structures, specially developed to ward off herbivorous animals. Small spinous plants, commonly called thistles—globe thistle (*Echinops*), for example—are equipped with numerous spines and prickles all over their body so that no animal ever dares attack them.

(1) **Thorns** (see pp. 20-21) are modifications of branches and originate from deep-seated tissues of the plant body. They are straight and hard and can pierce the body of thick-skinned animals. Plants like *Vangueria* (B. & H. MOYNA), lemon (*citrus*), pomegranate (*Punica*), *Duranta, Carissa* and many others are well provided with thorns for self-defence.

(2) **Spines** (see p. 38) are modifications of leaves or parts of leaves, and serve the purpose of defence. These are seen in pineapple, date-palm, prickly poppy, American aloe (*Agave*), dagger plant or Adam's needle (*Yucca*), etc. In dagger plant (*Yucca*; FIG. 81), each leaf ends in a very sharp-pointed spine and is directed obliquely outwards. It acts as a sort of dagger or pointed spike, protecting the plant against grazing animals.

(3) **Prickles** (see p. 21) are also hard and pointed like thorns, but are usually curved and have a superficial origin. Further they are irregularly distributed on the stem, branch or leaf. They are found in rose, coral tree (*Erythrina*), silk cotton

tree (*Bombax*), *Prosopis* (B. & H. SHOMI), etc. Cane (*Calamus*) and *Pisonia* (B. BAGH-ANCHRHA), which are large climbing shurbs, are elaborately armed with numerous sharp prickles and spines for self-defence (as well as for climbing.)

FIG. 81. Dagger plant or Adam's needle (*Yucca*)

(4) **Bristles** are short, stiff and needle-like hairs, usually growing in clusters and not infrequently barbed. Their walls are often thickened with deposition of silica or calcium carbonate. Bristles are commonly met with in prickly pear (*Opuntia*; see FIG. 39A) and in many other cacti.

2. Stinging Hairs.

Nettles (B. BICHUTI; H. BARHANTA) develop stinging hairs on their leaves or fruits or all over their

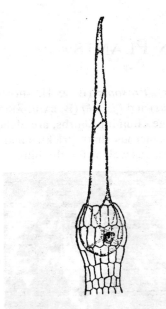

FIG. 82. A stinging hair

body. Each hair (FIG. 82) has a sharp siliceous apex which breaks off even when touched lightly. The sharp point penetrates into the body and inflicts a wound. The acid poison of the hair, contained in its bulbous base, is instantly injected into the skin of the victim's body. This evidently causes a sharp burning pain which is often attended with inflammation. The secretion of the poison is caused by the sudden pressure exerted on the swollen base of the hair. There are various kinds of nettles, e.g. *Laportea* (=*Fleurya*) *interrupta*, devil or fever nettle (*Laportea crenulata*), *Tragia involucrata*, *Girardinia zeylanica*, *Urtica dioica*, cowage (*Mucuna prurita*; B. ALKUSHI; H. KAWANCH), etc.

3. Glandular Hairs.

Many plants produce glandular hairs on their leaves, branches and fruits. These glandular hairs secrete a sticky substance which is a kind of gum. If any animal feeds upon such a plant, the glands stick to its mouth and the animal finds its difficult to brush them off. Plants bearing glandular hairs are thus never attacked by grazing animals. Glands of this nature are borne by plants like tobacco (*Nicotiana*), *Boerhaavia*, *Jatropha* and *Plumbago*.

4. Hairs.

A dense coating or the hairs of presence of stiff hairs on the body of a plant is always repulsive to animals as these hairs stick on to their throats and cause a choking sensation, e.g. cud-weed (*Gnaphalium*), *Aerua* and many gourd plants (*Cucurbita*).

II. OTHER DEVICES OF DEFENCE

5. Poisons.

Many plants secrete poisonous and irritating substances. Such plants are carefully avoided by animals who can intuitively distinguish between poisonous and non-poisonous plants.

(1) **Latex** is a milky juice secreted by certain plants. It always contains some waste products, and often irritating and poisonous substances so that it causes inflammation and even blisters when it comes in contact with the skin. Plants like madar (*Calotropis*), spurges (*Euphorbia*), oleander (*Nerium*), yellow oleander (*Thevetia*), periwinkle (*Vinca*), *Ficus* (e.g. banyan, fig, peepul), etc., contain latex in latex cells, while plants like papaw (*Carica papaya*), poppies, e.g. opium poppy (*Papaver somniferum*), garden poppy (*P. orientale*), prickly or Mexican poppy (*Argemone mexicana)*, and some plants of *Compositae*, e.g. *Sonchus*, contain latex in latex vessels.

(2) **Alkaloids** are in many cases extremely poisonous, and a very minute quantity is sufficient to kill a strong animal. There are various kinds of them found in plants, e.g. strychnine in nux-vomica (*Strychnos*), morphine in opium poppy (*Papaver*), nicotine in tobacco (*Nicotiana*), daturine in *Datura*, quinine in *Cinchona*, etc.

(3) **Irritating Substance**. Plants like many aroids, e.g. taro (*Colocasia*), *Amorphophallus*, etc., possess needle-like or otherwise sharp and pointed crystals of calcium oxalate, i.e. raphides. When such plants are fed upon, these crystals prick the tongue and throat, causing irritation. Therefore, such plants never fall victim to the attack of grazing animals.

6. Bitter Taste and Repulsive Smell.

These are also effective mechanisms to ward off

animals. *Paederia foetida* emits a bad smell so that no animal likes to go near it. Plants like sacred basil (*Ocimum*), mint (*Mentha*), *Blumea lacera, Gynandropsis*, etc., also emit a strong, disagreeable odour. The fetid smell of the inflorescence of *Amorphophallus* (see FIG. 137) is very offensive and nauseating. Margosa (*Azadirachta*), bitter gourd (*Momordica*), *Andrographis*, etc., have a bitter taste and are avoided by animals.

7. Waste Products.

Apart from latex, alkaloids, etc., as mentioned before, the presence of many other waste products, such as tanin, resin, essential oils and silica, also keeps plants free from the attack of animals.

8. Mimicry.

Certain plants also protect themselves against grazing animals by imitating the general appearance, colour, shape or particular feature of another plant or animal which has developed a special weapon of defence. For instance, there are certain aroids (e.g. varieties of *Caladium*),which resemble multicoloured and variously spotted snakes. Leaves are also variously spotted and striped in many species of bowstring hemp (*Sansevieria;* B.MURGA; H. MARUL) and other allied plants. Herbivorous animals, possibly mistaking them for snakes or some other deadly creatures, carefully avoid them. The inflorescences of devil's spittoon (*Amorphophallus bulbifer*; B. BAN-OL) look like the hoods of snakes, coming out of the ground, at least from a distance. In another aroid called

FIG. 83. Snake or cobra plant (*Arisaema*)

snake or cobra plant (*Arisaema*; FIG. 83), common in Shillong and Darjeeling during the rains, the spathe is greenish-purple in color and it expands over the spadix like the hood of a cobra. This act of imitating the appearance, colour or any particular feature of another plant or animal is called mimicry (*mimikos*, imitative).

Plants also have to protect themselves against the attack of many parasite fungi and gnawing insects, as well as against the scorching rays of the sun. This they do by developing a thick cuticle, cork and bark.

CHAPTER 5

THE INFLORESCENCE

The reproductive shoot bearing commonly a number of flowers, or sometimes only a single flower, is called the **inflorescence**. It may be terminal or axillary, and may be branched in various ways. Thus, depending on the mode of branching, different kinds of inflorescence have come into existence. These may primarily be classified into two distinct groups, viz., **racemose** or **indefinite** and **cymose** or **definite**.

Origin. It is not possible to trace the origin and phylogeny of inflorescence from the primitive to the recent type. This is particularly so because our knowledge regarding the phylogeny or angiosperms is still insufficient. The speculation in this regard is based on the following considerations, and three theories have been advanced to explain the origin of inflorescence. *1st Theory*: Nageli (1883) and Pilger (1922) were of the opinion that the primitive type of inflorescence was a panicle and other forms were derived from it. This view was also supported by Goebel in 1931. *2nd Theory*: Perkin (1914) believed that the primitive type was indicated by a solitary flower and other types with many flowers derived from it as a result of lateral growth of additional branches. It is, however, generally accepted that the solitary condition represents reduction and suppression. *3rd Theory*: Ricket (1944) considered the dichasium as the primitive type. According to him, a 3-flowered dichasium was the most primitive and a many-flowered dichasium was formed from it as a result of repeated branching. The relative primitiveness of the dichasium or panicle is, however, a disputed point. Analogy of angiosperms with pteridosperms suggests but does not prove that a paniculate type is more primitive. In any case, it is believed that one form, dichasium or panicle, has been derived from the other. Ricket suggested the following evolutionary stages from the primitive dichasium. According to him, the lines of development are: (a) the dichasium, on the one hand, gives rise to such types as verticillaster, cyme, helicoid cyme and scorpioid cyme by structural modifications and (b) the dichasium (or panicle), on the other hand, gives rise to such types as raceme, spike, etc., by reduction of individual dichasia. According to Ricket's view, the old classifications of inflorescences into racemose (indefinite) and cymose (definite) types is no longer valid. He cited the case of umbel, which is *indefinite* in some families, as in *Umbelliferae*, and *definite*, as in certain *Liliaceae* and *Amaryllidaceae*. In his scheme, a solitary flower is regarded as a product of reduction.

KINDS OF INFLORESCENCES

1. RACEMOSE INFLORESCENCES

Here, the main axis of inflorescence does not terminate in a flower, but continues to grow and give off flowers laterally in *acropetal* succession, i.e. the lower or outer flowers are older than the upper or inner ones, or, in other words, the order of opening of flowers is *centripetal*. The various forms of racemose inflorescence may be described under three heads: *first*, those in which the main axis is elongated; *second*, those in which the main axis is shortened and *third*, those in which the main axis becomes flattened, concave or convex.

A. WITH THE MAIN AXIS ELONGATED

(1) **Raceme** (FIG. 84A). The main axis in this

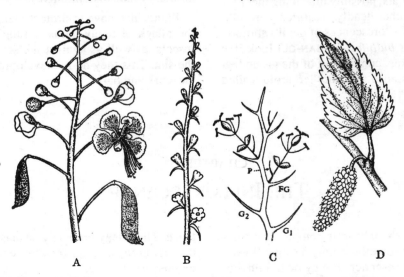

FIG. 84. Racemose Inflorescences. *A*, raceme of dwarf gold mohur; *B*, spike (diagrammatic); *C*, spikelet of a grass (*diagrammatic*); G_1, first empty glume; G_2, second empty glume; *FG*, flowering glume or lemma; and *P*, palea; *D*, female catkin of mulberry

case is elongated and it bears laterally a number of flowers which are all stalked, the lower or older flowers having longer stalks than the upper or younger ones, as in radish (*Raphanus*), mustard (*Brassica*), dwarf gold mohur (*Caesalpinia*), Indian laburnum (*Cassia*), etc. When the main axis of the raceme is branched and the lateral branches bear the flowers, the inflorescence is said to be a compound raceme or **panicle** (see FIG. 89), as in gold mohur (*Delonix*).

The main axis of the inflorescence together with the lateral axes, if present, is known as the **peduncle**. The stalk of the individual flower of the inflorescence is called the **pedicel** (see FIG. 94). In the case of the solitary flower, its stalk is regarded and termed as the peduncle. In some flowers such as China rose, gold mohur, etc., the peduncle and the pedicel may, however, be clearly marked out due to the presence of an articulation on the floral axis. When the peduncle of an inflorescence is short and dilated, forming a sort of convex platform, as in sunflower, or hollow and pear-shaped, as in fig (*Ficus*), it is often called a receptacle. The unbranched, often leafless, peduncle arising out of the underground stem in the midst of radical leaves and ending in a single flower, as in lotus, or in an inflorescence, as in onion, tuberose etc., is known as the **scape** (see also p. 8).

(2) **Spike** (FIG. 84 B). Here also, the main axis is elongated and the lower flowers are older, opening earlier than the upper ones, as in raceme, but the flowers are sessile, that is, without any stalk. Examples are seen in tuberose (*Polianthes*), *Adhatoda* (B. BASAK; H. ADALSA), amaranth (*Amaranthus*), chaff-flower (*Achyranthes*), etc.

(3) **Spikelets** (FIG. 84 C). These are very small spikes with one or a few flowers (florets). Spikelets are arranged in a spike, raceme or panicle, and may be sessile or stalked on the main inflorescence. Each spikelet bears at its base two minute scales or bracts called *empty glumes*. Slightly higher up, it bears a third bract called *flowering glume* or *lemma*, and opposite to the lemma, it bears a small 2-nerved bracteole called *palea*. Each flower of the spikelet remains enclosed by the lemma and the palea. Flowers and glumes are arranged on the spikelet in two opposite rows. Spikelets are characteristic of

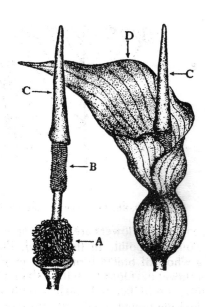

FIG. 85. Spadix of an aroid (*Typhonium*); *A*, female flowers; *B*, male flowers; *C*, appendix; and *D*, spathe

Gramineae, e.g. grasses, paddy, wheat, sugarcane, bamboo, etc.

(4) **Catkin** (FIG. 84 D). This is a spike with a long and pendulous axis which bears unisexual flowers only, e.g. mulberry (*Morus*), cat's tail (*Acalypha sanderiana*), birch (*Betula*) and oak (*Quercus*).

(5) **Spadix** (FIG. 85). This is also a spike with a fleshy axis, which is enclosed by one or more large, often brightly coloured bracts, called spathes, as in aroids (e.g. *Colocasia*, *Typhonium*, etc.), banana (*Musa*) and palms. The spadix is found in monocotyledons only.

B. WITH THE MAIN AXIS SHORTENED

(6) **Corymb** (FIG. 86A). Here, the main axis is comparatively short, and the lower flowers have much longer stalks or pedicels than the upper ones, so that all the flowers are brought more or less to the same level, as in candytuft (*Iberis*) and wallflower (*Cheiranthus*).

(7) **Umbel** (FIG. 86 B-C). Here, the primary axis is shortened and it bears at its tip a group of flowers which have pedicles of more or less equal

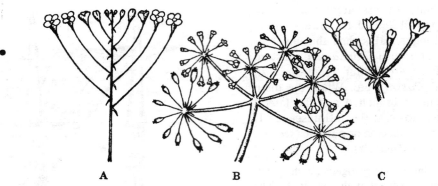

FIG. 86. *A*, corymb (diagrammatic); *B*, a compound umbel; *C* a simple umbel

lengths, so that the flowers are seen to spread out from a common point. In the umbel, there is always a whorl of bracts forming an involucre, and each flower develops from the axil of a bract. Commonly, the umbel is branched (**compound umbel**) and the branches bear the flowers, as in anise or fennel, coriander, cumin, carrot, etc. Sometimes, however, it is simple or unbranched (**simple umbel**), the main axis directly bearing the flowers, as in Indian pennywort (*Centella*) and wild coriander (*Eryngium*). Umbel is characteristic of the coriander family or *Umbelliferae*. Umbel is a near approach to capitulum.

C. WITH THE MAIN AXIS FLATTENED

(8) **Head** or **Capitulum** (FIG. 87). Here, the main axis or receptacle is suppressed, becoming almost flat, and the flowers (florets) are also without any stalk so that they become crowded together on the flat surface of the receptacle. In it, the outer flowers are older and open earlier than the inner ones. Although the whole inflorescence looks like a single flower, it really consists of a clustered mass of small sessile flowers (Florets), usually of two kinds—**ray florets** (marginal strap-shaped ones) and **disc florets** (central tubular ones). The head may also consist of only one kind of florets. The inflorescence is surrounded at the base by one or more whorls of often green bracts forming an *involucre* (see p. 59). A head or capitulum is characteristic of the sunflower family or *Compositae* (e.g. sunflower, marigold,

FIG. 87.

Head or capitulum of sunflower.

A, a head (a few ray florets removed to show the involucre);

B, a head in longitudinal section

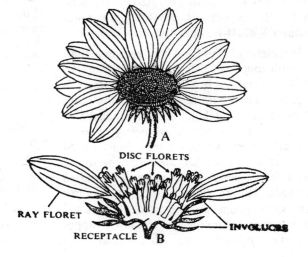

DISC FLORETS

RAY FLORET

RECEPTACLE   *B*

INVOLUCRE

safflower, *Zinnia, Cosmos, Tridax*, etc.). It is also found in gum tree (*Acacia*), sensitive plant (*Mimosa*), *Anthocephalus*(B. & H. KADAM), *Adina* (B. & H. KELI-KADAM), etc.

A capitulum is regarded as the most perfect type of inflorescence. Although the individual florets are often very small, their mass effect is not negligible at all. As a matter of fact, a head with often a few dozens of florets clustered together in it becomes quite conspicuous and attractive. The advantages of such an inflorescence are that there is a considerable saving of material in the construction of the corolla and other floral parts and that a single insect can easily pollinate innumerable florets within a very short time without having to fly from one flower to another. The ultimate advantage is that this mass pollination helps the setting of seeds in most heads for reproduction, multiplication in number and continuity of species.

2. CYMOSE INFLORESCENCES

Here, the growth of the main axis is soon checked by the development of a flower at its apex and the lateral axis, which develops below the terminal flower, also ends in a flower and, therefore, its growth is also checked. The flowers may be with or without stalks. In the cymose inflorescence, the flowers develop in *basipetal* succession, i.e. the terminal flower is the oldest and the lateral ones younger, or, in other words, the order of opening of the flowers is *centrifugal*. Cymose inflorescence may be **uniparous, biparous** or **multiparous**.

(1) **Uniparous** or **Monochasial Cyme** (*unus*, one; *parere*, to produce). In this type of inflorescence, the main axis ends in a flower and it produces only one lateral branch at a time, ending in a flower. The lateral and succeeding branches again produce only one branch at a time, like the primary one. Two forms of uniparous cyme may be seen—helicoid and scorpioid, (*A*)When the lateral axes develop successively on the same side, evidently forming a sort of helix, as in *Begonia, Hamelia*, sundew (*Drosera*), rush (*Juncus*), several species of *Solanum*, e.g. *S. sisymbrifolium*— a common prickly undershrub day lily (*Hemerocallis*), etc., the cymose inflorescence is said to a be a **helicoid** (or one-sided) **cyme** (FIG. 88C). (*B*) On the other hand, when the lateral branches develop on alternate sides, evidently forming a zig-zag, as in heliotrope (*Heliotropium*), forget-me-not (*Myosotis*), hound's tongue (*Cynoglossum*), *Geranium*, henbane (*Hyoscyamus*), *Crassula, Freesia*, bird of paradise (*Strelitzia*), etc., the cymose inflorescence is said to be a **scorpioid** (or alternate-sided) **cyme** (FIG. 88B). The scorpioid cyme is otherwise called **cincinnus**.

In *monochasial* cyme, successive axes may be at first zig-zag or curved, but subsequently become straightened out due to their rapid growth, thus forming the so-called central axis, otherwise known as *pseudo-axis*. This type of inflorescence is called a **sympodial cyme**. This may be distinguished from the racemose type by examining the position of a bract to a flower; in a sympodial cyme a bract appears opposite to a

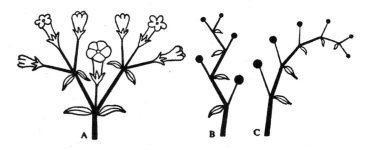

FIG. 88. Cymose Inflorescences. *A*, biparous cyme; *B*, scorpioid cyme; *C*, helicoid cyme

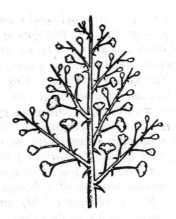

FIG. 89. A panicle

flower, while in a recemose type a bract appears at the base of a flower.

(2) **Biparous** or **Dichasial Cyme** (*bi*, two; *parere*, to produce). In this type of inflorescence, the main axis ends in a flower and at the same time, it produces two lateral younger flowers or two lateral branches. The lateral and succeeding branches, in their turn, behave in the same manner (FIG. 88A). This is **true cyme**. Examples are seen in pink, jasmine, teak, night jasmine, *Ixora, Bougainvillea*, etc.

opening of the middle flower first. This is seen in madar (*Calotropis*), blood-flower (*Asclepias*), etc.

Compound and Mixed Forms. When the main axis of the inflorescence is branched and the branches bear the flowers, the inflorescence is said to be compound. For example, when a raceme is branched, it is called a compound raceme or **panicle** (FIG. 89), as in gold mohur (*Delonix*), margosa (*Azadirachta*), dagger plant (see FIG. 81), etc. Similarly, other compound forms are also present, such as **compound spike**, as in wheat; **compound spadix**, as in palms; **compound corymb**, as in candytuft; **compound head**, as in globe thistle (*Echinops*). Frequently, mixed inflorescences can be found.

3. SPECIAL TYPES

The following types may be noted.

(1) **Cyathium** (FIG. 90). This is a special kind of inflorescence found in *Euphorbia*, e.g. poinsettia (B. & H. LALPATA) and spurges (B. & H. SIJ), and also in jew's slipper (*Pedilanthus*; B. RANGCHITA. H. NAGDAMAN). In cyathium, there is a cup-shaped involucre, often provided with nectar-

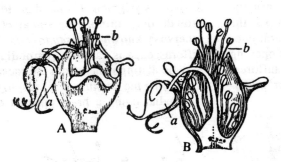

FIG. 90
Cyathium
of Poinsettia.
A, cyathium;
B, the same in
longitudinal
section;
(a) female flower;
(b) male flower.
Note the involucre

(3) **Multiparous** or **Polychasial Cyme**. In this kind of cymose inflorescence the main axis, as usual, ends in a flower and at the same time, it again produces a number of lateral flowers around. There being a number of lateral flowers developing more or less simultaneously, the whole inflorescence looks like an umbel, but is readily distinguished from the latter by the

secreting glands. The involucre encloses a single female flower (reduced to a pistil) in the centre, seated on a comparatively long stalk, and a number of male flowers (each reduced to a solitary stamen) around this, seated on short stalks. That each stamen is a single male flower is evident from the fact that it is articulated to a stalk and that it has a scaly bract at the base. The flowers follow the

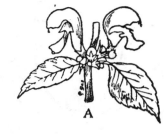

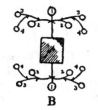

FIG. 91
Verticillaster
of *Coleus*.
A, verticillaster;
B, diagram of
verticillaster

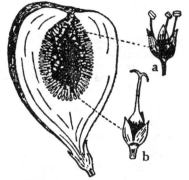

FIG. 92 Hypanthodium of fig (*Ficus*).
a, male flower; *b*, female flower

centrifugal (cymose) order of development. The female flower in the centre matures first, then the stamens (male flowers) just surrounding it and ultimately, the marginal ones.

(2) **Verticillaster** (FIG. 91). This is a condensed form of a cymose inflorescence with a cluster of sessile or almost sessile flowers in the axil of a leaf, forming a false whorl at the node. The first axis gives rise to two lateral branches and these branches and the succeeding ones bear only one branch each on alternate sides. This kind of inflorescence is characteristic of the basil family or *Labiatae*, e.g. *Coleus, Leonurus,* etc. In sacre basil (*Ocimum*; B. & H. TULSI), sage (*Salvia*) and a few others, the verticillaster is, however, reduced to a dichasial cyme, the succeeding branches remaining undeveloped.

(3) **Hypanthodium** (FIG. 92). When the fleshy receptacle forms a hollow cavity, more or less pear-shaped, with a narrow apical opening guarded by scales, and the flowers are borne on the inner wall of the cavity, the inflorescence is a hypanthodium, as in *Ficus* (e.g. banyan, fig, peepul, etc.). Here, the female flowers develop at the base of the cavity and the male flowers higher up towards its mouth.

CHAPTER 6

THE FLOWER

The **flower** is a specialized shoot of limited growth, bearing reproductive organs—**microsporophylls** (or **stamens**) and **megasporophylls** (or **carpels**) or only one, often with two accessory whorls—**calyx** and **corolla**, sometimes only one or even none at all. The flower serves as a means of sexual reproduction. A typical or complete flower consists of *four* whorls—two lower *acces-sory* whorls—**calyx** and **corolla**, and two upper *essential* or *reproductive* whorls—**androecium** and **gynoecium** or **pistil**. The individual units of a calyx are **sepals**, of a corolla, **petals**; of an androecium, **stamens** or microsporophylls, and of a gynoecium, **carpels** or megasporophylls. The term **perianth** is collectively used for undifferentiated calyx and corolla and its members are called

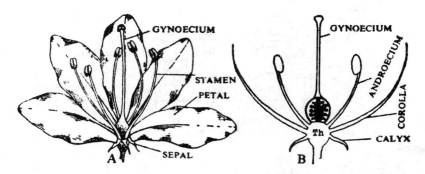

FIG. 93. *A*, parts of a flower; *B*, a flower in longitudinal section
showing the position of the whorls on the thalamus (*Th*)

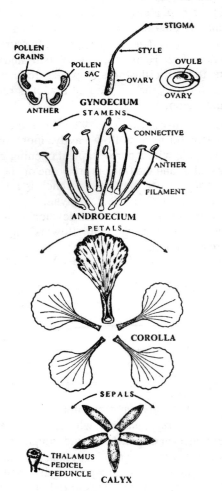

FIG. 94. Flower of gold mohur (*Delonix regia*)
dissected out.

tepals. The four whorls develop in an ascending order from the swollen, suppressed end (**thalamus**) of the floral axis or stalk (**pedicel**). The androecium is the male whorl and each of its stamen differentiated into a **filament. anther** and **connective.** Gynoecium or pistil is the female whorl differentiated into the **ovary, style** and **stigma.**

Flowers having both androeciums and gynoeciums are said to be **bisexual** or **hermaphrodite.** and those having only one of them **unisexual.** either **staminate** (male) or **pistillate** (female). A plant bearing both male and female flowers is said to be **monoecious.** e.g. gourd, and a plant bearing either male flowers or female flowers is said to be **dioecious.** e.g. mulberry, papaw, palmyra-palm, etc. A plant bearing bisexual, unisexual and even neuter flowers is said to be **polygamous.** e.g. *Polygonum,* mango and wild mangosteen (*Diospyros*; B. GAB; H. KENDU). Further, it may be noted that a flower without calyx and corolla is said to be naked or **achlamydeous.** as in betel. A flower with only one whorl is **monochlamydeous.** as in *Polygonum* and a flower with both whorls is **dichlamydeous.**

The flower is said to be **cyclic** when its sepals, petals, stamens and carpels are arranged in circles or whorls round the thalamus, as in most flowers, and **acyclic** when these are spirally arranged, as in water lily, *Magnolia* (B. & H. DULEE-CHAMPA), *Michelia* (B. CHAMPA; H. CHAMPAK), etc. The flower may be **hemicyclic** when some parts are cyclic and others acylic, as in rose.

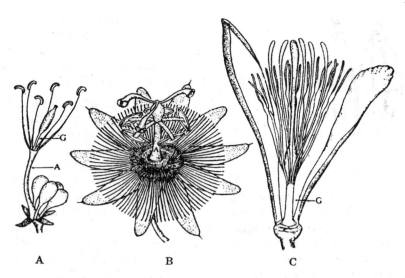

FIG. 95. Thalamus. *A*, flower of *Gynandropsis*; A, androphore; G, gynophore; *B*, passion-flower; A, androphore;
C, flower of *Pterospermum*; G, gynophore (with the staminal tube adnate to it)

THALAMUS

The thalamus (FIG. 93B), also called torus or receptacle, is the suppressed swollen end of the flower-axis on which are inserted the floral leaves, viz. the sepals, petals, stamens and carpels. In most flowers the thalamus is very short, but in a few cases it becomes elongated, and then it shows distinct nodes and internodes. Thus, the internode between the calyx and the corolla, when elongated, is known as the **anthophore** (*anthos*, a flower; *phore*, a stalk), as in *Silene*. In *Gynandropsis* (FIG. 95A) and passion-flower (FIG. 95B), the internode between the corolla and the androecium is consi-

derably elongated and is known as the **androphore** (*andros*, male) or gonophore. In *Capparis* (FIG. 96A), *Gynandropsis* (FIG. 95A), *Pterospermum* (B. MOOCHKANDA; H. KANAKCHAM-PA; FIG. 95C), drumstick (*Moringa*; B. SAJINA; H. SAINJNA), etc., the axis between the androecium and the gynoecium is elongated, and is known as the **gynophore** (*gyne*, female). When both androphore and gynophore develop, they are together known as the **androgynophore**. as in *Gynandropsis*. In *Magnolia* and *Michelia*, the thalamus is fleshy and elongated, and bears the floral leaves spirally round it. In rose (FIG. 96B) it is concave and pear-shaped. The thalamus of lotus

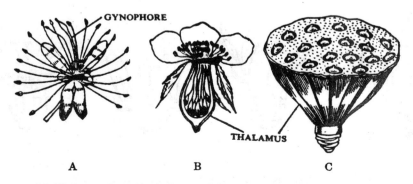

FIG. 96. Thalamus (contd.). *A*, flower of *Capparis*; *B*, rose (in section); *C*, lotus

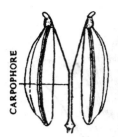

FIG. 97, Fruit of anise (*Foeniculum*)

(*Nelumbo*; FIG. 96C) is spongy and top-shaped. When the thalamus becomes prolonged upwards into a slender axis with the carpels remaining attached to it at first and separating from it on maturity, the axis is called **carpophore**. as in balsam (*Impatiens*), anise (*Foeniculum;* FIG. 97), coriander (*Coriandrum*), cumin (*Cuminum*), *Geranium*, etc.

Position of Floral Leaves on the Thalamus. Normally the calyx, corolla, androecium and gynoecium of a flower lie on the thalamus in their proper sequence. But in many flowers, the relative positions of the first three whorls in respect of the ovary become disturbed due to the unusual growth of the thalamus. The relative positions, as seen in the flowers of different plants, are of three kinds, viz. hypogyny, perigyny and epigyny (FIGS. 98-100).

(1) **Hypogyny.** In a hypogynous flower the thalamus is conical, convex, flat or slightly concave, and the ovary occupies the highest position on the thalamus, while the stamens, petals and sepals are separately and successively inserted below the ovary. The ovary is said to be *superior* and the rest of the floral members *inferior*. Examples are seen in mustard, brinjal, China rose, *Magnolia*, etc.

(2) **Perigyny.** In a perigynous flower the margin of the thalamus grows upward to form a cup-shaped structure, called the calyx-tube, enclosing the ovary but remaining free from it, and carrying with it the sepals, petals and stamens. The ovary is said to be *half-inferior*. In some perigynous flowers, the ovary may be partially sunken in the thalamus. Examples are seen in rose, primrose, *Prunus*, e.g. plum, peach, prune, etc., crepe flower (*Lagerstroemia*), and sometimes in *Leguminosae* (e.g. pea, bean, gold mohur, etc.)

(3) **Epigyny.** In an epigynous flower the margin of the thalamus grows further upward, completely enclosing the ovary and getting fused with it, and bears the sepals, petals and stamens above the ovary. The ovary in this case is said to be *inferior* and the rest of the floral members, *superior*. Examples are seen in sunflower, guava, gourd, cucumber, apple, pear, etc.

BRACTS

Bracts (FIG. 101) are special leaves from the axil of which one or more flowers arise. When a small leafy or scaly structure is present on any part of the flower-stalk (pedicel), it goes by the name of bracteole. Bracts vary in shape, size, colour and duration. They may be of the following kinds.

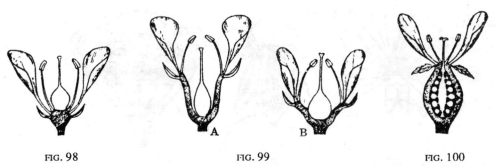

FIG. 98   FIG. 99   FIG. 100

Position of floral leaves on the thalamus.
FIG. 98. Hypogyny. FIG. 99. Perigyny (two types—A & B). FIG. 100. Epigyny

(1) **Foliaceous (or Leafy) Bracts**. These are green, flat and leaf-like in appearance, as in *Adhatoda, Acalypha, Gynandropsis*, etc.

(2) **Spathe** (*A-B*). This is a large, sometimes very large, and commonly boat-shaped bract enclosing a cluster of flowers or even an inflorescence (spadix), as in banana, aroids, palms, maize cob, etc.

(3) **Petaloid Bracts** (*C*). These are brightly coloured bracts looking somewhat like petals, as in glory of the garden (*Bougainvillea*). In poinsettia (*Poinsettia*) the petaloid bracts, red in colour, take the shape of leaves.

(4) **Involucre** (*D*). This is one or more whorls of bracts, normally green in colour, present around a cluster of flowers. The involucre is characteristic of *Compositae*, e.g. sunflower, marigold, *Cosmos*, etc. It is also present in *Umbelliferae*, e.g. coriander, anise, carrot, etc.

(5) **Epicalyx** (*E*). This is one or more whorls of bracteoles developing at the base of the calyx. The epicalyx is characteristic of *Malvaceae*, e.g. China rose, cotton, lady's finger, etc. It is also present in many plants of *Rosaceae*, e.g. strawberry (*Fragaria*).

(6) **Scaly Bracteole** (*G*). At the base of the individual florets of the head or capitulum of *Compositae*, there is often a thin, membranous, awl-shaped scaly bracteole.

(7) **Glumes** (*F*). These are special bracts—small, dry and scaly—found in the spikelet of *Gramineae*. The bracts take the form of two minute scales called *empty glumes* at the base, a flowering glume called *lemma*, and a bracteole called *palea* (see also p. 51).

Flower is a Modified Shoot

The following facts may be cited to prove that the thalamus is a modified branch, that *sepals, petals, stamens* and *carpels* are modified vegetative leaves; and the *flower* as a whole a modified vegetative bud.

(1) The thalamus represents the axis of the floral whorls with the inter-nodes between them normally remaining undeveloped or suppressed, but in some flowers the thalamus becomes elongated, showing distinct nodes and internodes (see FIGS. 95-7), as in *Gynandropsis,* passion flower, *Capparis, Pterospermum*, etc. The thalamus may, therefore, be regarded as a modified branch.

(2) The thalamus sometimes shows monstrous development, i.e. after bearing the floral members it prolongs upwards and bears ordinary foliage leaves. The thalamus thus behaves as a branch.

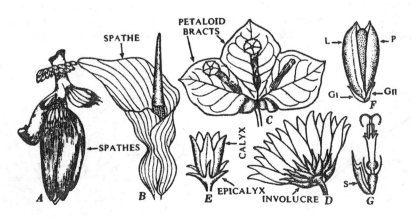

FIG. 101. Bracts and bracteoles. *A*, spathes of banana; *B*, spathe of an aroid (*Typhonium*);
C, petaloid bracts of *Bougainvillea; D*, involucre of sunflower; *E*, epicalyx (bracteole) of China rose;
F, glumes of paddy grain (Gᵢ, Gᵢᵢ, empty glumes; L, lemma or flowering glume; P, palea—a bracteole);
G, scaly bracteole (S) of a disc floret of sunflower

FIG. 102. Rose showing monstrous
development of the thalamus

Examples are sometimes seen in rose (*Rosa;* FIG.
102), larkspur (*Delphinium*), *Calendula*, pear
(*Pyrus*), etc.

(3) The foliar nature of sepals is evident from
their similarity to leaves as regards structure, form
and venation. In fact, in *Mussaenda* (FIG. 103) one
of the sepals becomes modified into a distinct
leafy structure, often coloured or sometimes white.
The origin of petals is controversial. Some are of
the opinion that petals are related to sepals, while

others consider petals to have been derived from
stamens. In green rose, the petals are leaf-like in
structure and green in colour. But the stamens and
carpels are unlike leaves in all respects. The
homology of stamens and carpels with leaves can
be made out from certain flowers. Thus, water lily
(FIGS. 104-5) shows a gradual transition from sepals to petals and from petals to stamens. The cultivated rose shows many petals, while in wild roses
(e.g. dog rose—*Rosa canina*), there are only five.
The explanation is that many stamens have gradually become modified into petals. Similarly, in
some species or varieties of *Hibiscus*, e.g. *Hibiscus
mutabilis* (B. STHALPAMDA; H. GULAJAIB), some or
many of the stamens have passed into petals.

(4) A floral bud, like a vegetative bud, is either
terminal or axillary in position. The arrangement
of sepals, petals, etc. on the thalamus is much the
same as that of the leaves on the stem or the
branch, being either whorled, alternate (spiral) or
opposite.

(5) The inflorescence axis normally bears flowers. But in *Globba bulbifera* (see FIG. III/58) and
American aloe (*Agave;* see FIG. III/60), some of the
floral buds become modified into vegatative buds,
called bulbils, for vegetative reproduction. In
pineapple also, the inflorescence axis bears one or
more vegetative buds or bulbils (see FIG. III/62)
for the same purpose. Such bulbils thus show a
reversion to ancestral forms, i.e., the forms from
which they have been derived.

FIG. 103. *Mussaenda* flower showing a modified
(petaloid and leaf-like) sepal (S)

FIG. 104. Water lily flower showing transition
of floral parts

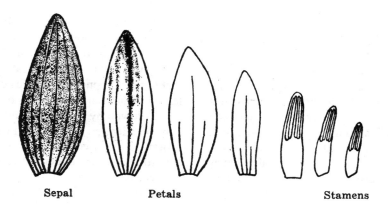

Sepal | Petals | Stamens

FIG. 105. Transition of floral parts in water lily flower

MORPHOLOGY OF THE STAMEN

A stamen is a reproductive metamorphosed leaf. It consists of an anther borne terminally on a slender filament, which may be long or short. The anther has two or more chambers which contain pollen grains. A median strip of sterile tissue, called connective, separates the pollen chambers. The number of stamens in a flower varies from one to many. All the stamens in a flower collectively constitute the male reproductive whorl, called androecium.

Basically, a stamen is a microsporophyll and it resembles a leaf in morphological and anatomical structures and also in ontogeny. The primitive stamen, present in *Magnoliales–Ranales*, is somewhat leaf-like in structure, without any clear distinction between the fertile and sterile regions. The anther lobes are in the middle of such stamens and the connective is broad and hardly distinguishable from the filament. It is assumed that the lamina of the primitive sporophyll underwent many modifications (specialization and progressive evolution) and, in due course, became slender, its proximal part representing the filament and the distal part the anther.

There are various theories regarding the morphology of the stamen.

(1) In 1790, Goethe advocated that a flower is a metamorphosed vegetative shoot and the floral members are equivalent to vegetative leaves. In 1827, de Candole elaborated this theory and stated that an individual stamen is a vegetative leaf, which has been modified into a reproductive structure. There are two schools of thought on the composition of a stamen. According to one school, a stamen consists of two fundamental parts, namely, filament and anther. The other school differentiates it into three parts, namely filament, anther and connective. The foliar nature of the stamen is exhibited in its formation by the inrolling of the margins of the lamina towards the mid-rib, where the filament represents the petiole of the leaf, anther the lamina and connective the mid-rib. Originally, the male reproductive bodies were borne by the margins of the lamina. Through various stages of evolution, the margins of the leaf blade rolled inwards, forming the pollen chambers, which encapsule the male reproductive bodies. This theory is known as the classical theory. Though there is no palaeo-botanical evidence in support of this theory, many botanists support it on the basis of anatomical studies (orientation of vascular strands, etc.).

(2) Wilson (1937, 1941, 1942) proposed another theory, called the 'Telome theory', regarding the morphology of the stamen. He explained that Goethe's theory could not be accepted because of the absence of any fossil record. He held that the body of an early land plant was a simple branched axis. The proximal part of the axis formed an absorbing organ and the distal part evolved a sterile and a terminal, fertile branched system. The

fertile branched system was dichotomously branched and the apex of each such dichotomous branch gave rise to a sporangium. The ultimate terminal portion of the dichotomously branched axis, bearing sporangia, is called a 'Telome'. According to this theory, a stamen or a microsporophyll has been derived from this primitive, dichotomously branched system, bearing terminal sporangia. Hence, this theory is called the Telome theory. Wilson explained that, in due course, the leaves arose from the distal sterile branch, or, in other words, sepals and petals were formed from the sterile branch, whereas the essential reproductive organs, such as stamens and carpels, were derived from the dichotomously branched, fertile system. The stamen, according to him, came into existence through extensive reduction and specialization of this branched system. The filament may represent the branches of such a system, which were extensively reduced and ultimately fused and the anther, the fused sporangia. The four-chambered anther is supposed to have evolved by the reduction of the ultimate and penultimate branch of such a system and the subsequent fusion of pairs of sporangia into an anther made of two synangia, each composed of two sporangia. According to Wilson's theory, the fusion of the short, basal parts of the axes of many distal branches led to the evolution of the fasciculated androecium.

However, this theory, that stamens have evolved from the dichotomously branched, fertile system of early land plants, lacks anatomical evidence.

(3) A 'Revolutionary theory' was put forward by Thomson, in 1937. According to this theory, the flower is essentially a heterosporous, sporogenous axis and the floral parts are local extensions of the torus. The base of the sporogenous axis is sterile and has given rise to structures, such as bracts, bracteoles and sepals. The portion of the sporogenous axis lying above the sterile base developed into microsporangia and then evolved into anthers with sterile bases (the filaments). The petals and the staminodes were formed from the sterile, lower portion of the microsporangia. Thus, according to this theory, stamens are local outgrowths of the torus and not distinct entities.

(4) Melville (1960) suggested that the primitive stamen was a modification of the epiphyllous branch and has, through various stages of evolution, given rise to the present-day stamen. He held that the development of leaves on the terminal or lateral dichotomous branches of early land plants was followed by condensation to the branch system and adnation of leaves to the terminal (micro) sporangia. This condition is termed epiphyllous condition and the condensed branch system, with the terminal sporangia adnated to the leaves, is called the epiphyllous branch. Then, somehow, such an epiphyllous branch developed into a male reproductive structure and formed what is known as the androphyll. The first androphyll, which evolved from the epiphyllous branch, is called the primary androphyll. Secondary androphylls, which developed from primary androphylls, later condensed into lamina-like structures, giving rise to reproductive organs on the surface of branches. According to Melville, this was the earliest phase in the evolution of the stamen and this condition still exists in some angiosperms.

MORPHOLOGY OF THE CARPEL

The carpel is the female reproductive organ of an angiospermic flower. The number of carpels varies from one to many. When many in number (compound), carpels may remain free (apocarpous) or be united (syncarpous). The carpel is differentiated into the ovary (the ovule-bearing chamber), the style (the sterile, cylindrical, short or long median stalk), and the stigma (the proximal pollen-receiving centre). Carpels constitute what is known as the gynoecium or pistil.

The carpel is a metamorphosed leaf. It is laminar in structure, anatomy and ontogeny. The foliar nature of the carpel may be made out from certain flowers which have a single carpel. For example, in the *Pisum* sp., *Colutea* sp., etc., the carpel folds along its mid-rib to form the ovary. When such a carpel is opened along the ventral suture, it looks like a leaf. In many cases, the ovary has a stalk, which can be compared to the petiole of a leaf.

The carpel is an ovule-bearing structure, evolved from what is generally accepted to have been a non-photosynthetic leaf-like appendage and, as such, a megasporophyll. It is believed that such an appendage was probably derived from a foliar leaf. This primitive carpel gradually differentiated into style and stigma and developed into the present-day carpel.

There are various views regarding the morphology of the carpel.

(1) The classical theory, based on anatomical studies, was proposed by Goethe in 1790. It was publicized by de Candole in 1827 and was developed further by Van Tieghem (1871), Eames (1931), Arber (1939) and others. According to this theory, the ancestor of the present-day carpel was a non-photosynthetic, palmately 3-veined, dorsiventral, foliar leaf-like structure. Functionally, it is believed to have been an open, flat megasporophyll, bearing ovules on its margins. This megasporophyll folded length-wise, bringing the ovules inside and ultimately its margins fused. The resultant structure was a unicarpel, represented by a one-loculed ovary, termed a simple ovary. In due course, the tip of the carpel elongated and gave rise to the style, the ultimate tip of which represented the stigma. The primitive carpel went through various lines of development in terms of the number of carpels, their arrangement, reduction, adnation, etc., to give rise to various forms of the gynoecium.

(2) The polymorphic view of the carpel was put forward by Saunders, (1923) who did not accept the foliar theory, which considers the carpel solely to be a modified leaf. According to her, the carpel is not simply a modified leaf but it is also the organ *sui generis*. She held the opinion that various organs of carpels are metamorphosed, producing many forms with different morphological stuctures. Hence, this theory is known as carpel polymorphism (*Poly* = many; *morph* = form).

Saunders held the view that the various forms of carpels developed in their own way during the course of evolution and not simply as a result of the marginal fusion of the leaf blade explained on the basis of monocarpellary and polycarpellary views.

From the study of different types of fruits in different genera of *Leguminosae, Crucifeae* and other taxa, she believed that there are three types of carpels in angiosperms, namely (a) valve or hollow type (b) pseudovalve or semi-solid type and (c) solid type.

The valve or hollow type of carpel shows leaf nature, its mid-rib extends into the style. This type develops as a protruberance from the receptacle and is considered to be primitive. During its development, the vascular strand forming the mid-rib grows upward and the lateral tissues lying on both sides of the mid-rib expand on the outer side and, finally, it is hollowed out, forming an ovary chamber. Saunders explained that when such carpels develop independently of one another on the same receptacle, they form an apocarpous gynoecium. The syncarpous gynoecium came into existence as a result of the development of lateral tissues and their fusion amongst the valve type of carpels growing very close to one another. In this way, a multilocular or many-chambered ovary was formed.

The pseudovalve or semi-solid type represents a consolidated, usually narrow, fertile carpel with lateral wings. This type possesses the characteristics of both the other types of carpels (valve and solid). Here, the vascular strands are prolonged into two mid-ribs (instead of one, as in valve or hollow type), from which the vascular connections go to the stalk of the ovule and the branches to the ovary. This type of carpel is found to be present either in the solid type or valve type.

The solid type of carpel developed from the valve type of carpel. Here, the radial surfaces of the carpels project like false partition walls which give the impression that many carpels are present in the gynoecium.

She held the view that though in *Leguminosae* there is apparently one carpel (gynoecium is monocarpellary), actually there are two carpels of two types (one solid and one valve) instead of one. Likewise, in *Cruciferae,* according to her, there are 4-8 or more carpels of two types or even 40-30 carpels of three types (solid, semi-solid and valve types), as in the genus *Rapistrum* and not only two carpels.

There are many such examples which suggest the polymorphic nature of the carpel.

The carpel polymorphism theory carries little weight at present because it was proposed without considering the basic vascular structure of the plant body.

(3) McLean and Thomson (1929) proposed another theory which considered the flower to be an essentially heterosporous, sporogenous axis. Its form was determined by the limitation of the growth of the carpel. They held that the various floral parts were local outgrowths of the torus. The sterile base of the sporogenous axis gave rise to bracts, bracteoles and sepals. The portion of the axis lying above this sterile region bore petals and staminodes. The higher portion of the axis was potentially microsporogenous and fertile stamens were the local outgrowths of this region. The upper limit of the sporogenous axis was potentially megasporogenous and the ovary (pistil) developed from this region. Thus, the inferior ovary resulted from the suppression of the apical growth of the floral axis at an early stage, accompanied by the more active growth of the torus along its margin. The sepals, petals and stamens are, thus, rays on the ring of the apical cup, according to this theory. The development of the superior ovary took place in the same way, except that in this case, the apical growth of the axis was continuous, while the marginal growth of the torus was suppressed. In the case of both inferior and superior ovaries, the nature, number and arrangement of the other floral organs on the torus depended on factors like space and nutrition.

(4) Wilson suggested the Telome theory to explain the morphology of the carpel. According to him, the carpel developed from a trilobed, palmately veined appendage. This appendage was derived from the 'telome', the fertile, dichotomously branched system of early land plants. According to him, further development of such an appendage took place in two directions, forming: (a) the carpel in which the stigma developed from the central and mid-lobe areas, supplied by a dorsal trace bundle (ovary with stigma), and (b) the carpel with the style made of all three lobes, each lobe retaining the bundles of the original appendage. In this case, the tip of the style represented the stigma (ovary with style).

SYMMETRY OF THE FLOWER

A flower is said to be symmetrical when it can be divided into two exactly equal halves by *any* vertical section passing through the centre. Such a flower is also said to be **regular** or **actinomorphic** or radially symmetrical. Examples are found in mustard, *Datura*, brinjal, chilli, etc. When a flower can be divided into two similar halves by *one* such vertical section only, it is said to be **zygomorphic**, **monosymmetrical** or bilaterally symmetrical, as in pea, bean, rattlewort (*Crotalaria;* B. ATASHI; H. JHUNJHUNIA), gold mohur (*Dolonis*), *Cassia,* etc. When it cannot be divided into two similar halves by any vertical plane whatsoever, it is said to be **asymmetrical** or **irregular.**

A flower is also said to be symmetrical when its whorls have an equal number of parts or when the number in one whorl is a multiple of that of another. Such a symmetrical flower is said to be **isomerous** (*isos,* equal; *meros,* a part). An isomerous flower may be *bimerous, trimerous, tetramerous* or *pentamerous,* according as the number of parts in each whorl is 2, 3, 4, or 5 or any multiple of these. Carpels, however, often do not fit into this symmetry and may, therefore, be ignored. **Trimerous** flowers are characteristic of monocotyledons, and **pentamerous** as well as **tetramerous** flowers, of dicotyledons. When the number in all the whorls is neither the same nor any multiple, the flower is said to be **heteromerous** (*heteros,* different).

CALYX

The **calyx** is usually green (*sepaloid*), and sometimes coloured (*petaloid*). In its symmetry, the calyx may be regular, zygomorphic or irregular. It may again be **polysepalous** (sepals free) or **gamosepalous** (sepals united). The calyx may be modified into **pappus,** as in *Compositae.* In *Mussaenda* (see FIG. 103), one of the sepals becomes distinctly leafy, large, often yellow or orange, sometimes scarlet or white.

Duration. If the calyx falls off as soon as the floral bud opens, it is said to be **caducous,** as in poppy. The calyx is said to be **deciduous** if it falls off when the flower withers. But sometimes, when it remains adherent to the fruit, it is known as

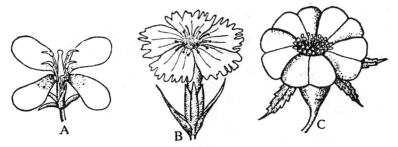

FIG. 106. Forms of Corollas. *A*, Cruciform; *B*, caryophyllaceous; *C*, rosaceous

persistent. A persistent calyx may assume a withered appearance, as in cotton, or it may continue to grow and form a sort of cup at the base of the fruit, as in brinjal, or it may be inflated enclosing the fruit, as in balloon vine (see FIG. 37), gooseberry and wild gooseberry, or it may be quite fleshy, as in *Dillenia* (B. & H. CHALTA), and rozelle (*Hibiscus sabdariffa*; B. MESTA; H. PATWA), or it may be fleshy and coloured forming the outer envelope of the fruit, as in *Duranta*.

COROLLA

The **corolla** may also be **regular** or radially symmetrical, **zygomorphic** or bilaterally symmetrical, or **irregular** (see above). Like the calyx again, the corolla may be **gamopetalous** or **polypetalous**, according as the petals are united or free. In the former case, the petals may be united partially or wholly.

FORMS OF COROLLAS

I. REGULAR AND POLYPETALOUS

(1) **Cruciform** (FIG. 106*A*). The cruciform corolla consists of four free petals, each differentiated into a claw and a limb, and these are arranged in the form of a cross, as in *Cruciferae*, e.g. mustard, radish, cabbage, cauliflower, candytuft, etc.

(2) **Caryophyllaceous** (FIG. 106*B*). This form of corolla consists of five petals with comparatively long claws, and the limbs of the petals are placed at right angles to the claws, as in pink (*Dianthus*).

(3) **Rosaceous** (FIG. 106*C*). This form consists of five petals, as in the previous case, but these have very short claws or none at all, and the limbs spread regularly outwards, as in rose, tea, prune, etc.

II. REGULAR AND GAMOPETALOUS

(1) **Campanulate** or **Bell-shaped** (FIG. 107 *A*). When the shape of the corolla resembles that of a bell, as in gooseberry (*Physalis*), bell flower (*Campanula*), wild mangosteen (*Diospyros*; B. GAB; H. KENDU), etc., it is said to be campanulate.

(2) **Tubular** (FIG. 107*B*). When the corolla is cylindrical or tube-like, that is, more or less equally expanded from base to apex, as in the central

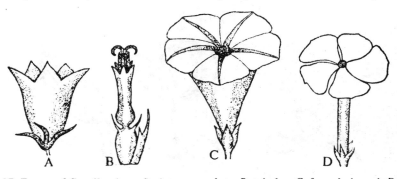

FIG. 107. Forms of Corollas (*contd*). *A*, campanulate; *B*, tubular; *C*, funnel-shaped; *D*, rotate

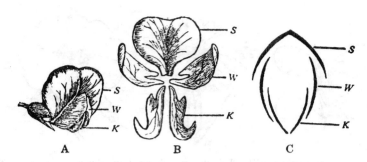

FIG. 108. *A*, papilionaceous flower of pea; *B*, petal of the same opened out;
C, vexillary aestivation of papilionaceous corolla; *S*, standard or vexillum; *W*, wing; *K*, keel

florets of sunflower, it is said to be tubular.

(3) **Infundibuliform** or **Funnel-shaped** (FIG. 107*C*). When the corolla is shaped like a funnel, that is, gradually spreading outwards from a narrow base, as in thorn-apple (*Datura*), *Ipomoea*, e.g., water bindweed (B. & H. KALMI-SAK), railway creeper, morning glory, etc., it is said to be infundibuliform.

(4) **Rotate** or **Wheel-shaped** (FIG. 107*D*). When the tube of the corolla is narrow and short and its limb is at a right angle to the tube, the corolla having more or less the appearance of a wheel, as in jasmine (*Jasminum*), night jasmine (*Nyctanthes*), brinjal, etc., it is said to be rotate.

(5) **Hypocrateriform** or **Salver shaped**. In a rotate type, the corolla-tube is often seen to be comparatively long, and the corolla as a whole more or less salver-shaped, as in periwinkle (*Vinca*), *Ixora*, *Iomoea quamoclit* (B. KUNJALATA; H. KAMLATA), etc. Such a corolla is said to be hypocrateriform or salver-shaped.

III. ZYGOMORPHIC AND POLYPETALOUS

Papilionaceous or **Butterfly-like** (FIG. 108*A*). The general appearance is like that of a butterfly. It is composed of five petals, the outermost of which is the largest and known as the **standard** or **vexillum**. The two lateral ones, partially covered by the former, are somewhat like the two wings of a butterfly and are known as the **wings** or **alae**. The two innermost ones, apparently united to form a boat-shaped cavity, are the smallest and are together known as the **keel** or **carina**. Examples are found in *Papilionaceae*, e.g. pea, bean, gram, butterfly pea (*Clitoria*), rattlewort (*Crotalaria*), etc.

IV. ZYGOMORPHIC AND GAMOPETALOUS

(1) **Bilabiate** or **Two-lipped** (FIG. 109*A*). In this form, the limb of the corolla is divided into two portions or lips—the upper and the lower—with the mouth gaping wide open. Examples are seen in basil (*Ocimum*; see FIG. VII/59), *Leonurus* (see FIG. VII/60), *Leucas*, *Asteracantha* (=*Hygrophila*), *Adhatoda*, etc.

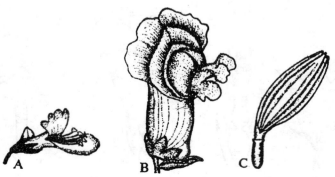

FIG. 109. Forms of Corollas (*contd.*). *A*, bilabiate; *B*, personate; *C*, ligulate

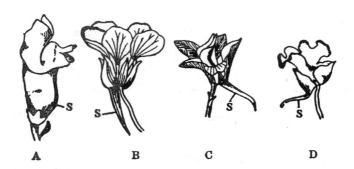

FIG. 110. Appendages of perianth. *A*, saccate corolla (*S*) of snapdragon; *B*, flower of garden nasturtium; *C*, flower of larkspur; *D*, flower of balsam; *S*, spur

(2) **Personate** or **Masked** (FIG. 109*B*). This is also two-lipped, like the previous one, but in this case the lips are placed so near each other as to close the mouth of the corolla. The projection of the lower lip closing the mouth of the corolla is known as the *palate*, as in snapdragon (*Antirrhinum*) and toad-flax (*Linaria*).

(3) **Ligulate** or **Strap-shaped** (FIG. 109*C*). When the corolla forms a short, narrow tube below, but is flattened above like a strap, as in the outer florets of sunflower, it is said to be ligulate.

Appendages of the Corolla. The corolla or the perianth is sometimes provided with outgrowths or appendages of various kinds. For instance, in snapdragon, the tube of the corolla is slightly diluted on one side like a pouch or sac. It is then said to be **saccate** or **gibbous** (FIG. 110*A*). In some cases, as in balsam (*Impatiens*), garden nasturtium (*Tropae-olum*), larkspur (*Delphinium*), orchids, etc., the perianth is prolonged into a tube known as the **spur** (FIG. 110 *B-D*), and it (the perianth) is then said to be spurred. The spur contains nectar. In many flowers of *Ranunculaceae, Compositae, Labiatae, Rubiaceae*, etc., a special gland known as the nectary develops, containing nectar (see also p. 82).

Sometimes, by a transverse splitting of the corolla, an additional whorl may be formed at its throat. This additional whorl may be made up of lobes, scales or hairs, free or united, and is known as the **corona** (*crown*). The corona may be well seen in passion flower (*Passiflora*; FIG. 111*A*), dodder (*Cuscuta*; FIG. 111*B*), and oleander (*Nerium*; FIG. 111*C*). A beautiful cup-shaped corona is seen in daffodil (*Narcissus*). The corona adds to the beauty of the flower and is thus an adaptation to attract insects for pollination.

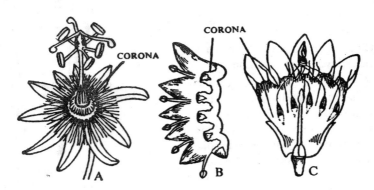

FIG. 111. Appendages of corolla: Corona. *A*, passion-flower; *B*, flower of dodder; *C*, flower of oleander

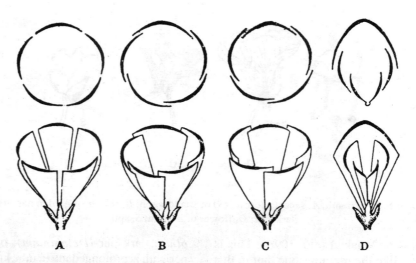

FIG. 112. Aestivation of Corolla. *A*, valvate; *B*, twisted; *C*, imbricate; *D*, vexillary

AESTIVATION

The mode of arrangement of the sepals or petals, more particularly the latter, in a floral bud with respect to the members of the same whorl (calyx or corolla) is known as **aestivation**. Aestivation is an important characteristic from the viewpoint of classification of plants, and may be of the following types:

(1) **Valvate** (FIG. 112*A*), when the members of a whorl make contact with each other by their margins, or when they lie close to each other without overlapping, as in custard-apple (*Annona*), madar (*Calotropis*), *Artabotrys*, etc.

(2) **Twisted** or **Contorted** (FIG. 112*B*), when one margin of the sepal or the petal overlaps that of the next one, and the other margin overlaps the third one, as in China rose, cotton, lady's finger, etc. Twisting of the petals may be clockwise or anticlockwise. In China rose, however, both types (clockwise and anticlockwise) are common.

(3) **Imbricate** (FIG 112*C*), when one of the sepals or petals is internal, overlapping on both margins, one of them is external and each of the remaining ones overlaps one margin and overlaps the next one on the other margin, e.g. *Cassia*, gold mohur (*Delonix*), dwarf gold mohur (*Caesalpinia*), etc.

(4) **Vexillary** (FIG. 112*D*), when there are five petals of which the posterior one is the largest and almost covers the two lateral petals, and the latter, in their turn, nearly overlaps the two anterior or smallest petals. Vexillary aestivation is universally found in all papilionaceous corollas (see also FIG. 108), as in the pea family or *Papilionaceae*, e.g. pea, bean, butterfly pea (*Clitoria*), rattlewort (*Crotalaria*), etc.

ANDROECIUM

The **androecium** (*andros*, male) is composed of a number of **stamens** or microsporophylls. Each sta-

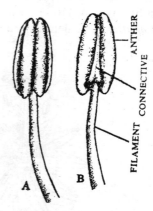

FIG. 113. Two stamens. *A*, face of the anther showing four pollen sacs; *B*, back of the anther showing the connective

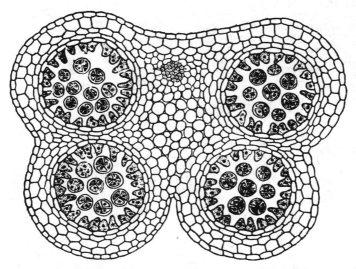

FIG. 114. An anther in transection showing four loculi and pollen grains
in tetrads. Each tetrad separates into four pollen grains

men consists of a **filament, anther** and **connective** (FIG. 113). Each of the two anther-lobes has two chambers or loculi, called the **pollen-sacs** or *microsporangia*. Thus, there are altogehter four loculi in each anther (FIG. 114). But in many cases there are only two, or even one. Each chamber of the anther is filled with pollen grains or *microspores*. The filament corresponds to the petiole of the leaf, the anther to the leaf-blade, and the connective to the mid-rib. The connective is attached to the *back* of the anther. Evidently, the other side of the anther is its face. The face often has a longitudinal groove running along the whole length of the anther. When the face is turned inwards, the anther is said to be **introrse,** and when outwards, the anther is **extrorse.** A sterile stamen (without pollen grains) is known as a **staminode,** as in pink (*Dianthus*), noon flower (*Pentapetes*), *Pterospermum* (see FIG. 95C) elengi (*Mimusops;* B BAKUL; H. MULSARI), etc.

The Pollen. *Pollen grains* are very minute in size, usually varying from 10 to 200 μ (microns) and are like particles of dust. Each pollen grain consists of a single microscopic cell and possesses two coats—the **exine** and the **intine.** The exine is a tough, cutinized layer, which is often provided with spinous outgrowths or reticulations of differ-

ent patterns, sometimes smooth. The intine is a thin, delicate, cellulose layer inside the exine. In pine, the pollen grain is provided with two distinct wings. At first, each pollen grain contains only one nucleus which lies in the vacuolated cytoplasm. The nucleus divides by mitosis to form two nuclei, the larger of which is known as the vegetative nucleus or tube nucleus, and the smaller, the generative nucleus.

Development of Pollen grains or Microsporogenesis (FIG. 115)

At an early stage of the anther, four vertical rows of cells—one at each lobe, with dense protoplasmic contents—become apparent (*A*). Each cell of the row divides into an inner larger cell—the **sporogenous cell** or **archesporium,** and an outer smaller cell— the **parietal cell** (*B*). The latter divides tangentially into 2 or 3 layers (*C*). These (parietal) cells divide repeatedly to extend radially around the sporogenous cell (*D*) which also begins to divide, forming a central group of cells (*E*). These (sporogenous) cells grow separate from one another and become the **pollen (spore) mother cells.** The innermost layer of parietal cells, directly abutting upon the sporogenous cells and later, the pollen mother cells, is called the

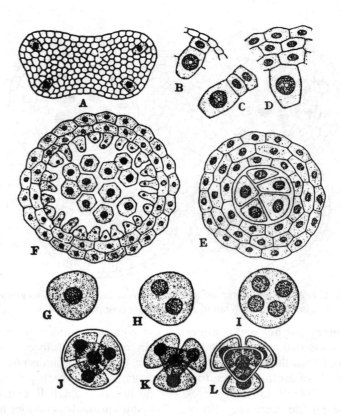

FIG. 115. *A-F*, development of pollen-sac; *G-L*, development of pollen grains. (Explanation in the text)

tapetum (F). The cells of the tapetum are more or less wedge-shaped and contain one or more nuclei. It is a nutritive tissue, supplying food to the pollen grains as they develop. Ultimately, the tapetum disintegrates.

The nucleus of each pollen mother cell (*G*) divides twice so that four nuclei are formed in it. Of the two successive divisions, the first one (*H*) is meiosis and the second one (*I*) is mitoisis so that each nucleus has half (n) the usual number (2n) of chromosomes. The four nuclei so formed are arranged in a tetrahedral manner, and cleavage of the cytoplasm occurs, separating the nuclei into four distinct segments—the pollen cells (*J*). The wall of the mother cell disappears (*K*) and each pollen cell secretes a thick outer wall —the **exine,** and a thin inner wall—the **intine** (*L*). The four mature cells separate from one another and form four pollen grains. In monocotyledons, however, the cleavage of the cytoplasm takes place along two planes at right angles to each other, and not in a tetrahedral manner, as in dicotyledons.

In elephant grass (*Typha*), rush (*Juncus*), sundew (*Drosera*) and in certain orchids, the four cells formed in a group (tetrad) do not separate, but remain more or less coherent. In Asclepiadaceae, e.g. madar (*Calotropis*), milkweed

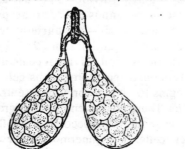

FIG. 116. Pollinia of madar (*Calotropis*)

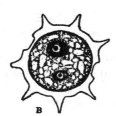

FIG. 117.

Pollen grains.
A, an entire grain;
B, a grain in
section showing
tube-nucleus
(bigger one) and
generative nucleus
(smaller one)

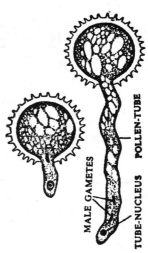

FIG. 118. Growth of the pollen-tube

(*Asclepias*), *Hoya,* etc., and in *Orchidaceae*, e.g. *Vanda* (see FIG. 13), *Dendrobium, Orchis*, etc., the pollen cells of each pollen-sac, instead of separating into loose pollen grains, are united into a mass known as the **pollinium** (FIG. 116). Pollen cells may also be in compound forms, i.e. united in small masses called pollen masses or pollinium, each consisting of 8-32 or more cells, as in *Mimosa and Acacia.*

Microgametogenesis or the Formation of Male Gametophyte

When the pollen grain (haploid or n) germinates, the intine grows into a tube (called the pollen tube) (FIG. 118) through some definite, thin and weak slits or pores, called germ pores, present in the exine (FIG. 117). Sometimes the pore is covered by a distinct lid, which is pushed open by the growth of the intine.

After pollination, that is, after the pollen grains reach the stigma of a gynoecium, the intine of each pollen grain grows into a pollen tube. Normally, one pollen tube grows out from each pollen grain, but there are cases where multiple tubes grow from each grain. When many tubes grow from a single pollen grain, only the one with the tube nucleus and the generative nucleus becomes functional. The pollen tube, as it grows, penetrates the stigma and pushes its way through the style and

the wall of the ovary or alongside it. It carries, at its apex, the tube nucleus and the generative nucleus, the former going ahead of the latter (FIG. 118). The generative nucleus soon divides into two nuclei, which form the two male reproductive units, known as the male gametes. The tube nucleus then disintegrates.

In angiosperms, the pollen tube nucleus and the generative nucleus (or the two male gametes) represent an extremely reduced male gametophyte. Further, the male gametes are non-ciliated, non-motile, rudimentary (represented only by two nuclei) reproductive units (each with haploid number of choromosomes). The process of the developmment of the male gametophyte from the pollen grain in angiosperms is known as microgametogenesis. This process occurs when the pollen grains have reached the stigma causing the formation of the male gametophyte from the pollen grain.

Pollinia

In certain plants, the pollen cells remain united and form a mass, known as pollinium. Two short or long stalks, called caudicles, grow out of the base of the anther. Each caudicle is attached to the posterior, sterile part of the stigma (called rostellum) at the base and to the mass of pollen grains (pollinium) at the apex. The tissue of the rostellum develops sticky glands, which fix the two caudicles to it.

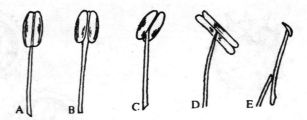

FIG. 119. *A*, basifixed or innate; *B*, adnate; *C*, dorsifixed; *D*, *versatile;* E, elongated connective of
sage (*Salvia*) separating the two anther-lobes (upper one fertile and lower one sterile)

Initially, the nucleus of each pollen mother cell divides twice to form four nuclei. Of the two successive divisions, the first one is meiosis and the second one mitosis.

This is followed by the cleavage of the cytoplasm, which results in the formation of four pollen cells. The wall of the mother cell disappears and each pollen cell secretes an outer wall (exine) and an inner wall (intine), forming a pollen grain.

In monocotyledons, the cleavage of the cytoplasm takes place along with two planes at right angles to each other and not in a tetrahedral manner as in dicotyledons.

In *Asclepiadaceae*, e.g., madar (*Calotropis*), milkweed (*Asclepias*), etc., and in *Orchidaceae*, e.g. Vanda, *Dendrobium*, etc., the pollen cells of each pollen sac instead of separating into loose pollen grains remain united in a viscid substance. This mass of pollen cells in a viscid substance is known as pollinium. (116)

Attachment of the Filament to the Anther (FIG. 119). There are four principal ways in which

the filament is attached to the anther. The anther is said to be (1) **basifixed** or **innate,** when the filament is attached to the base of the anther, as in mustard, radish, sedge, water lily, etc; (2) **adnate,** when the filament runs up the whole length of the anther from the base to the apex, as in *Michelia, Magnolia*, etc; (2) **dorsifixed,** when it is attached to the back of the anther, as in passion-flower; and (4) **versatile,** when it is attached to the back of the anther at one point only so that the latter can swing freely in the air, as in grasses, palms, spider lily (*Pancratium*), etc. In sage (*Salvia*; FIG. 119E), the filament is attached to the elongated connective separating the two anther-lobes, of which the upper one is fertile and the lower one sterile.

Cohesion and Adhesion. The terms 'adhesion', 'adnate', and 'adherent' used to designate the union of members of different whorls, e.g. petals with stamens, or stamens with carpels. 'Cohension', 'connate', and 'coherent' designate the union of members of the same whorl, e.g. stamens with each other and carpels with each other.

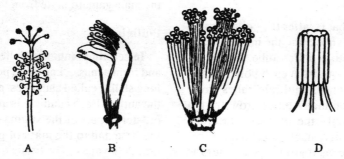

FIG. 120. Cohesion of Stamens. *A*, monadelphous; *B*, diadelphous; *C*, polydelphous; *D*, syngenesious

Cohesion of Stamens (FIG. 120). Stamens may either remain free or they may be united (coherent). There may be different degrees of cohesion of stamens, and these may be called (a) the adelphous condition, when the stamens are united by their filaments only, the anthers remaining free; (b) the syngenesious condition, when the stamens are united by their anthers only, the filaments remaining free; or (c) the synandrous condition, when the stamens are united by both the filaments and anthers. Accordingly, the following types are to be noted:

(1) **Monadelphous Stamens** (*monos*, single; *adelphos*, brother). When all the filaments are united together into a single bundle but the anthers are free, the stamens are said to be monadelphous (A). as in *Malvaceae*, *e.g.* China rose (*Hibiscus*), lady's finger (*Abelmoschus*), cotton (*Gossypium*), etc. In these, the filaments are united into a tubular structure, called the staminal tube, ending in free anthers.

(2) **Diadelphous Stamens** (*di*, two). When the filaments are united into two bundles, the anthers remaining free, the stamens are said to be diadelphous (B), as in *Papilionaceae*, e.g. pea, bean, gram, butterfly pea (*Clitoria*), rattlewort (*Crotalaria*), etc. In these there are altogether ten stamens of which nine are united into one bundle and the tenth is free.

(3) **Polyadelphous Stamens** (*polys*, many). When the filaments are united into a number of bundles—more than two—but the anthers are free, the stamens are said to be polyadelphous (C), as in silk cotton tree (*Bombax*), castor (*Ricinus*), lemon (*Citrus*), etc.

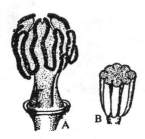

FIG. 121. Synandrous stamens. *A*, ash or ash gourd (*Denincasa*); *B*, taro (*Colocasia*)

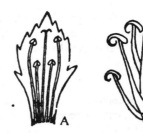

FIG. 122. Length of Stamens. *A*, didynamous; *B*, tetradynamous.

(4) **Syngenesious Stamens** (*syn*, together or united; *gen*, producing). When the anthers are united together into a bundle or tube, the filaments remaining free, the stamens are said to be syngenesious (D), as in *Compositae*, e.g. sunflower, marigold, etc.

(5) **Synandrous Stamens.** When the stamens are united throughout their whole length by both the filaments and the anthers, they are said to be synandrous (FIG. 121), as in *Cucurbitaceae*, e.g. ash or wax gourd (*Benincasa*), and in *Araceae*, e.g. taro (*Colocasia*), etc.

Adhesion of Stamens. Stamens are said to be (1) **epipetalous,** when they are attached to the corolla wholly or partially by their filaments, as in *Datura*, *Ixora*, potato, sunflower, etc., (2) **epiphyllous,** when attached to the perianth, as in *Liliaceae* and (3) **gynandrous,** when united with the carpels, either wholly or by their anthers only, as in *Calotropis*, *Asclepias*, orchids, etc.

Length of Stamens (FIG. 122) In *Labiatae*, e.g. *Ocimum*, *Leonurus*, *Leucas*, etc., there are four stamens, of which two are long and two short. Such stamens are said to be (1) **didynamous** (*di*, two; *dynamis*, strength). In *Cruciferae*, e.g. mustard, radish, turnip, rape, etc., there are six stamens, of which the inner four are long and the outer two short. Such stamens are said to be (2) **tetradynamous** (*tetra*, four). Sometimes different kinds of flowers, some with longer stamens and others with shorter stamens, are borne by the same plant (*dimorphic* stamens).

Dehiscence of the Anther. Dehiscence of the anther may be (1) **longitudinal,** as in China rose, cotton, *Datura*, etc.; (2) **transverse**,as in basil; (3) **porous** (by pores), as in *Solanum*, e.g. potato, brinjal etc.; and (4) **valvular** (by valves), as in *Cinnamomum*, e.g. cinnamon, camphor, bay leaf, etc.

Appendages of Stamens. Both filaments and anthers may have outgrowths or appendages in the form of hairs, scales, etc. Thus in, *Osbeckia, the* anthers are beaked, while in oleander (*Nerium*), they are provided with long, hairy appendages twisted together into a cone over the stigma (see FIG. 111C). Similarly, filaments may have appendages. When these are in the form of a regular whorl, they form the staminal corona. Thus, in madar (*Calotropis*), the filaments form a whorl of horn-like corona. In spiderwort (*Tradescantia*), there is a circle of hairs. In spider lily (*Pancratium*) and eucharis lily (*Eucharis*), the corona is formed as a membranous cup adherent to the filaments at their base.

GYNOECIUM OR PISTIL

The **gynoecium** (*gyne*, female) or **pistil** (*pistillum*, a pestle) is composed of one or more **carpels** or megasporophylls which bear female spores or megaspores (embryo-sacs). The pistil may be **simple** (made of one carpel) or **compound** (made of two or more carpels). In a compound pistil the carpels may be free, as in lotus (*Nelumbo*), *Michelia*, rose, stonecrop (*Sedum*—a pot herb), *Magnolia, Artabotrys, Unona* etc., when the pistil is said to be **apocarpous** (*apo*, off or free; *karpos*, fruit or ovary; FIG. 125). The carpels may be united together, as is more commonly found, when the pistil is said to be syncarpous (*syn*, together or united; FIG. 124). Each pistil consists of three parts—stigma, style and ovary (FIG. 124A). The ovary contains one or more little roundish or oval, egg-like bodies which are the rudiments of seeds and are known as the ovules (FIG. 124B-C). Each ovule encloses a large oval cell known as the embryo-sac (see FIG. 133). A sterile pistil is known as the pistillode. In position, the style may be terminal, lateral or gynobasic. The gynobasic style (see FIG. 126) rises from the depressed centre of the four-lobed ovary, as if from its base or directly from the thalamus, as seen in *Labiatae* and also in heliotrope (*Heliotropium*).

The Ovary. The carpel is a metamorphosed leaf. The foliar nature of the carpel may be made out from the flowers of pea, bean, gram, etc., where a single carpel is present. In such cases, the carpel or the pod may be compared to a leaf which has been folded along its mid-rib (FIG. 127). In a folded carpel, when the two margins meet and fuse together, a chamber is formed, the junction of the fused margins of the carpel being known as the *ventral suture* and the mid-rib along which the carpel is folded being known as the *dorsal suture*. Along the ventral suture a ridge of tissue, called the placenta, develops and bears the ovules. The closed chamber formed by the folding of the carpel, enclosing the ovules, is the ovary. In the apocarpous pistil, as in buttercup (*Ranunculus*),

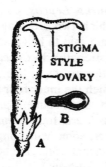

FIG. 123

FIG. 123. Pistil. *A*, simple pistil of pea; *B*, one-chambered ovary of the same

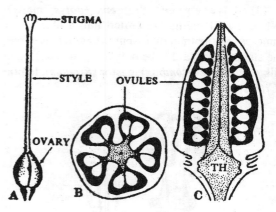

FIG. 124.

FIG. 124. *A*, syncarpous pistil; *B*, five-chambered ovary of the same (in transection); *C*, ovary of the same in longi-section. *TH*, thalamus

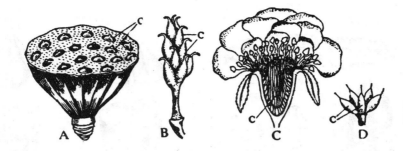

FIG. 125. Apocarpous Pistil. *A, lotus; B,* Michelia; *C,* rose: *D,* stonecrop (*Sedum*). c, carpels

the ovary is also formed in the above way (FIG. 128). In the syncarpous pistil, however, the carpels may be united by their margins only, forming a one-chambered ovary (FIG. 129), as in orchids, papaw, etc. Alternately, the carpels may be folded inwards, their margins meeting in the centre, thus resulting in a few-to many chambered ovary (usually as many as the carpels) with a central axis (FIG. 130), as in lily (*Lilium*), China rose (*Hibiscus*), etc. In gymnosperms, however, the carpels are not closed up to form the ovary and , therefore, there is no stigma, style or ovary. In these, the ovules are borne, freely exposed, along the margins of open carpels.

Carpels in Syncarpous Pistils. In a syncarpous pistil, it is often difficult to determine the number of carpels. To obviate this difficulty, the following points should be noted: (1) the number of stigmas or of stigmatic lobes; (2) the number of styles; (3) the number of lobes of the ovary; (4) the number of chambers (loculi) of the ovary; (5) the number of placentae in the ovary and (6) the number of groups of ovules in the ovary. It is seen that in most cases, the number of parts, as mentioned above, corresponds to the number of carpels making up the syncarpous pistil.

Cohesion of Carpels (Syncarpy). The carpels may be united either throughout their whole length, as in most syncarpous pistils, or they may be united in the region of the ovary alone, the styles and stigmas remaining free, as in pink (*Dianthus*), linseed (*Linum*) and *Plumbago* (B. CHITA; H. CHITRAK). They may also be united in the region of the ovary and the style, the stigmas remaining free, as in cotton and China rose, or in the region of the style and the stigma, only the ovaries remaining free, as in periwinkle (*Vinca*), oleander (*Nerium*), or in the region of the stigma (and the style partly), as in madar (*Calotropis*).

PLACENTATION

The **placenta** is a ridge of tissue—a parenchymatous outgrowth—in the inner wall of the ovary to which the ovule or ovules remain attached. The plancentae most frequently develop on the margins of carpels, either along their whole line of union, called the **suture**, or at their base or apex. The manner in which the placentae are distributed in the cavity of the ovary is known as **placentation**. As a rule, the origin of an ovule or a group of ovules determines the position of the placenta.

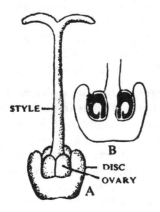

FIG. 126. *A*, gynobasic style of basil (*Ocimum*); *B*, the same in section

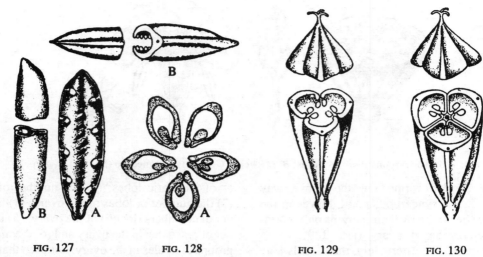

FIG. 127   FIG. 128   FIG. 129   FIG. 130

Development of the Ovary. FIG. 127., *A*, a single carpel opened out with the ovules on the margins; •
B, one-chambered ovary formed by the folding of the carpel with ovules at the ventral suture.
FIG. 128. *A*, one-chambered ovaries formed by five free carpels of an apocarpous pistil; *B*, -one of the five ovaries
(carpels). FIG. 129. One-chambered ovary formed by the union of margins of three carpels of a syncarpous pistil.
FIG.130.Three-chambered ovary formed by the infolding of three carpels and their margins meeting at the centre

Types of Plancentation (FIG. 132). In the simple ovary (of one carpel), there is one common type of placentation, known as **marginal**. and in the compound ovary (of two or more carpels united together), placentation may be **axile, parietal, central, free-central, basal,** or **superficial.**

(1) **Marginal.** In Marginal placentation (A), the ovary is one-chambered and the placenta develops along the junction of the two margins of the carpel, called the *ventral suture,* as in *Leguminosae* (e.g. pea, gram, bean, gold mohur, *Cassia, Mimosa,* etc.) The line, or suture, corresponding to the mid-rib of the carpel is known as the dorsal suture. No placenta develops here.

(2) **Axile.** In axile placentation (B), the ovary is two or many-chambered—usually as many as the number of carpels— and the placentae bearing the ovules develop from the central axis corresponding to the confluent margins of carpels, and hence the name axile (lying in the axis), as in lemon, orange, China rose, lady's finger, tomato, potato, etc.

(3) **Parietal** (*parietis,* wall). In parietal placen-

tation (C), the ovary is one-chambered and the placentae bearing the ovules develop on the inner wall of the ovary. Their position corresponds to the confluent margins of the carpels and their number corresponds to the number of carpels, as in papaw (*Carica*), poppy (*Papaver*), prickly poppy (*Argemone*), orchids, etc. In *Cruciferae*,e.g., mustard, radish, etc., the placentation is also partial although the ovary is two-chambered. In these, the ovary is at first unilocular but soon, a false partition wall develops across the ovary, dividing it into two chambers, while the seeds remain attached to a wiry framework called the *replum.*

(4) **Central.** In central placentation (D), the septa or partition walls in the young ovary soon break down so that the ovary becomes one-chambered and the placentae bearing the ovules develop from the central axis, as in *Caryophyllaceae,* e.g. pink (*Dianthus*), *Polycarpon* (B. GIMA-SAK), soapwort (*Saponaria*), etc. Remnants of partition walls may often be seen in the mature ovary.

(5) **Free-central.** In free-central placentation (E) the placenta arises from the base of the ovary,

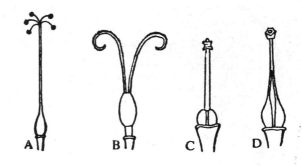

FIG. 131.
Cohesion of carpels.
A, pistil with free stigmas in China rose;
B, the same with free styles in pink;
C, the same with free ovaries in oleander;
D, the same with free ovaries and styles in madar

projects far into its cavity as a swollen central axis and bears the ovules all over its surface. Since the placenta lies free in the single chamber of the ovary, the placentation is said to be free-central. This is seen in primrose (*Primula*).

(6) **Basal.** In basal placentation (F), the ovary is unilocular and the placenta develops directly on the thalamus, bearing a single ovule at the base of the ovary, as in *Compositae*, e.g. sunflower, marigold, *Cosmos*, etc.

(7) **Superficial.** In superficial placentation (G), the ovary is multilocular, the carpels being numerous, as in axile placentation, but the placentae in this case develop all round the inner surface of the partition walls, as in water lily (*Nymphaea*).

THE OVULE

Structure of the Ovule. Each ovule (FIG. 133) is attached to the placenta by a slender stalk known as (1) the **funicle.** The point of attachment of the body of the ovule to its stalk or funicle is known as (2) the **hilum.** In the inverted ovule, as shown in FIG. 133, the funicle continues beyond the hilum alongside the body of the ovule, forming a sort of ridge. This ridge is called (3) the **raphe.** The upper end of the raphe, which is the junction of the integuments and the nucellus, is called (4) the **chalaza.** The main body of the

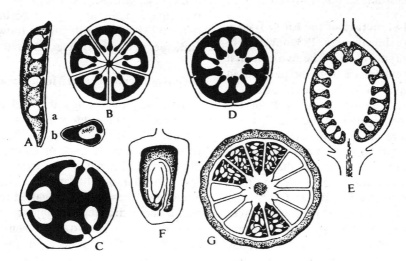

FIG. 132. Types of placentation. A, marginal—*a*, in longi-section;
b, in transection; B, axile; C, parietal; D, central; E, free-central; F, basal and G, superficial

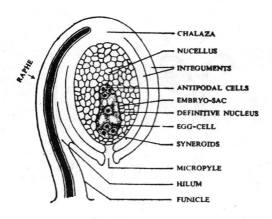

CHALAZA
NUCELLUS
INTEGUMENTS
ANTIPODAL CELLS
EMBRYO-SAC
DEFINITIVE NUCLEUS
EGG-CELL
SYNERGIDS
MICROPYLE
HILUM
FUNICLE
RAPHE

FIG. 133.
An anatropous ovule in longitudinal section.

ovule is called (5) the **nucellus**, and it is surrounded by *two* coats termed (6) the **integuments**. But
in many families with gamopetalous corrola, there
is only *one*. In parasites like sandalwood
(*Santalum*) and *Loranthus,* there is no integument.
A small opening is left at the apex of the integuments, called (7) the **micropyle**. Lastly, there is a
large, oval cell lying embedded in the nucellus
towards the micropylar end. This is (8) the
embryo-sac, that is, the sac that bears the embryo,
and is the most important part of the ovule.

Development and Structure of the Embroy-sac.
The embryo-sac, as shown in FIG. 133, develops in
the following way (FIG. 134.1). The ovule at first
arises as a tiny protuberance from the placenta in
the cavity of the ovary (A). In it, even at a very
early stage, a cell, i.e. the mother cell of the
embryo-sac, becomes evident in the nucellus (B).
This mother cell increases in size and *divides twice*
to form a row of four megaspores, known as the linear tetrad (C). It is to be noted that of the two successive divisions of the mother cell, only the first is
the reduction division (see FIG. II/22). Of the four
cells so formed, each with half (n) the usual number
($2n$) of chromosomes, the three upper ones degenerate and appear as dark caps, while the lowest one
functions (D). The nucleus of this cell divides and
the two daughter nuclei move to the two poles (E).
These divide again so that the number goes up to

four (F). Each of these nuclei divides again so that
altogether eight nuclei are formed in the embryo-
sac, four at each end (G). The embryo-sac increases in size. Then one nucleus from each end or pole
passes inwards, and the two polar nuclei fuse
together somewhere in the middle, forming the
definitive nucleus (H). The remaining three nuclei
at the micropylar end, each surrounded by a very
thin wall, form the egg-apparatus, and the other
three at the opposite or chalazal end, lying in a
group or sometimes in a row and often surrounded
by very thin walls, form the antipodal cells (I).

Of the three cells constituting (1) the **egg-apparatus,** one is the female gamete known as (a) the
egg-cell (or **ovum** or **oosphere**), and the other two
are known as (*b*) the **synergids.** Synergids are
more or less pear-shaped, and the egg-cell which is
enlarged lies below them. On fertilization, the egg-
cell gives rise to the embryo, while the synergids
are ephemeral structures, getting disorganized
soon after fertilization or sometimes even before or
during the process. The **antipodal cells** appear to
have no definite function, so, sooner or later, they
also get disorganized. They may, however, be
nutritive in function. They possibly represent vegetative cells of the extremely reduced female
gametophyte. (In angiosperms, the fully formed
embryo-sac with the eight nuclei in it is regarded as
the female gametophyte.) The **definitive nucleus**
(FIG. 133) on fertilization (now called the
endosperm nucleus) gives rise to the endosperm.

Megasporogenesis and Megagametogenesis

At a very early stage, the nucleus of an ovule
contains only a mother cell, called the megaspore
mother cell. This megaspore mother cell increases
in size and divides once or twice, or it may not
divide at all. When it divides twice, it gives rise to
four cells in a row (linear tetrad), each containing
a nucleus. These cells are called megaspores, of
which three disintegrate and the surviving one
gives rise to the embryo-sac. When the megaspore
mother cell divides once, it forms two cells
(megaspores), each containing a nucleus, of which
only one cell survives and gives rise to the
embryo-sac. When the megaspore mother cell

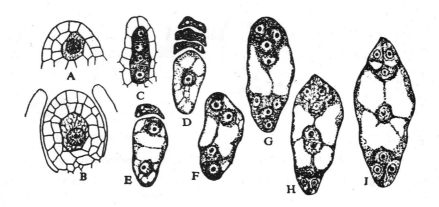

FIG. 134.1. Development of the embryo-sac. *A-H*, are
stages in its development; *I*, fully developed embryo-sac

does not divide, its nucleus undergoes two divisions. Four nuclei are formed inside the megaspore mother cell, which acts as a megaspore and gives rise to the embryo-sac.

The process by which a megaspore mother cell gives rise to a megaspore within the nucellus of an ovule is called megasporogenesis.

In angiosperms, the development of the female gametophyte (embryo-sac) takes place within the megaspore, i.e., it is endosporous. The processes by which a megaspore finally develops into an embryo-sac with the nucellus of an ovule is termed megagametogenesis.

The process as a whole, i.e,. the formation of the embryo-sac from the megaspore mother cell, shows a great deal of variation. When four megaspores are formed from the megaspore mother cell and only one of the four gives rise to the embryo-sac, the process is called monosporic embryo sac development, namely monosporic 8-nucleate polygonum type and monosporic 4-nucleate oenothera type. In the former case (FIG. 134.1), the upper three of the four megaspores (linear tetrad) degenerate, while the lowest one functions. The surviving megaspore does not divide any more. It enlarges and allows its nucleus to undergo division. The nuclear division continues until eight nuclei are formed inside the enlarged megaspore.

The eight nuclei arrange themselves in a set of four at each pole. One nucleus from each pole migrates to the centre and the two nuclei fuse to form the secondary or definitive nucleus. Each nucleus at the two poles surrounds itself with a wall. The three cells formed at the chalazal end, lying in a group or sometimes in a row, are called the antipodal cells. The other three nuclei lying at the micropylar end, constitute one egg cell (ovum or oosphere) and two synergids. The enlarged megaspore, with the antipodal cells, the definitive nucleus and the egg cell along with the synergids, represents a fully formed embryo-sac within the nucellus of the ovule.

In the monosporic 4-nucleate oenothera type, the development of the embryo-sac is monosporic, but the nucleus of the megaspore divides until four nuclei are formed. Here, the antipodal cells are absent.

There are two other kinds of embryo-sac development, namely, bisporic type and tetrasporic type. In the bisporic type, the megaspore mother cell divides once, to give rise to two haploid cells. One of these acts as a megaspore and forms the bisporic embryo-sac, while the other degenerates. This type of development is called the bisporic (as the nuclei of two megaspores are present in it) 8-nucleate allium type. In this case, too, the

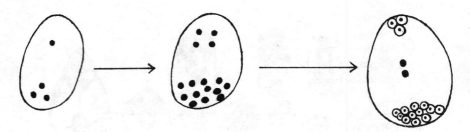

MEGASPORE   EMBRYO SAC

FIG. 134.2. 1.6–nucleate drusa type of embryo sac development

nucleus of the megaspore divides to form eight nuclei inside the embryo-sac, as in the monosporic 8-nucleate polygonum type.

In many cases, the megaspore mother cell does not divide. Therefore, no separate megaspores are formed. Its nucleus divides by meiosis and gives rise to four nuclei. The megaspore mother cell itself acts as a megaspore and develops into a tetrasporic (the nuclei of the four megaspores are within the same cell) embryo-sac. There is a great deal of variation in the tetrasporic type of embryo-sac development. The number of nuclei (4, 8, or 16) formed inside the embryo-sac, their arrangement within the sac and accordingly, the appearance of the embryo sac may vary greatly. Antipodal cells may be absent. When present, their number may vary. There may be one or more synergids. The definitive nucleus may be formed by only one nucleus, two nuclei, or more than two nuclei. The tetrasporic 16-nucleate drusa type of embryo-sac development is described below.

Here, within the 4-nucleate megaspore, three nuclei lie at one pole and the fourth at the other pole. Each nucleus divides and redivides, forming 16 nuclei in total. Of these, 12 nuclei lie at one pole and four at the other. One nucleus from each pole migrates to the centre. The nuclei at both poles surround themselves by cell walls. The three cells lying at one pole from the egg cell and the two synergids, while the 11 cells lying at the other pole are the antipodal cells. (See 134.2)

Forms of Ovules (FIG. 135). The ovule is said to be (1) **orthotropous** (*ortho*, straight; *topos*, a turn) or **straight,** when the ovule is erect or straight so that the funicle, chalaza and micropyle lie on one and the same vertical line, as in *Polygonaceae*, e.g. *Polygonum*, sorrel (*Rumex*), etc., *Piperaceae*, e.g. betel (*Piper betle*), long pepper (*Piper longum*), black pepper (*Piper nigrum*), and *Casuarinaceae*, e.g. beef-wood tree (*Casuarina*); (2) **anatropous** (*ana*, backwards or up) or **inverted,** when the ovule bends along the funicle so that the micropyle lies close to the hilum. The micropyle and the chalaza, but not the funicle, lie on the same straight line. This is the commonest form of ovule; (3) **amphitropous** (*amphi*, on both sides) or **transverse,** when the ovule is placed transversely at a right angle to its stalk or funicle, as in duckweed (*Lemna*) and (4) **campylotropous**

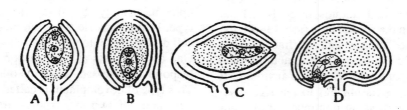

FIG. 135. Forms of Ovules. *A*, anatropous; *B*, orthotropous; *C*, amphitropous, *D*, campylotropous

(*kampylos*, curved) or **curved**, when the transverse ovule is bent round like a horse-shoe so that the micropyle and the chalaza do not lie on the same straight line, as in several members of the following families, viz *Capparidaceae*, e.g. caper (*Capparis*), *Cruciferae*, e.g. mustard (*Brassica*), *Caryophyllaceae*, e.g. *Polycarpon, Chemopodiaceae*, e.g., Beta, *Chenopodium*, and also some members of *Gramineae*.

Position of the Ovule Within the Ovary. An ovule may be (1) **ascending**, i.e. directed upwards, as in the sunflower family or *Compositae* and basil family or *Labiatae*; (2) **pendulous**, i.e. turned downwards from the apex, as in *Euphorbia, Anemone*, coriander, anise, rose, etc. ; (3) **suspended**, i.e. turned obliquely downwards from the side and (4) **horizontal**, i.e. turned horizontal, i.e. turned horizontally inwards from the side.

CHAPTER 7

POLLINATION

In 1694, Camerarius, as a result of his experimental work on mulberry, maize, castor, etc., carried out in Tubingen, established for the first time the fact that pollination is essential for the production of the seed, and thus proved the existence of sexuality in plants. He distinguished the stamen with the pollen grains as the male organ and the pistil with the style and the ovary as the female organ. But his work was not widely known, and no further advance was made for several years. From 1764 to 1806, Koelreuter pollinated as many as 310 flowers of many different species in Berlin, Leipzig and other places. He is regarded as the first scientific hybridizer. He realized the importance of insects and wind as pollinating agents. He also made some plant hybrids. The actual process (fertilization) leading to seed-production, however, remained unravelled. But he made a very interesting observation. By microscopic examination of the pollen grains on the stigma, he noticed that something—an oily substance—escaped from the grains and this, mixed with the oil secreted by the stigma, worked down into the style and entered the ovary, producing an embryo there. In 1793, Konrad Sprengel published an account of his observations on many common wild flowers and made it clear for the first time that various adaptations of flowers are meant to achieve cross-pollination by means of insects. He also concluded from his observations on dichogamy and dicliny that nature does not intend that flowers should be self-pollinated. Further elaborate experimental work on pollination should also be noted, such as Charles Darwin's *The Effect of Cross and Self Pollination in the Vegetable Kingdom*, Hermann Muller's *The Fertilization of Flowers*, Paul Knuth's *Handbook of Flower Pollination* and Anton Kerner's *The Natural History of Plants*.

Pollination is the transference of pollen grains from the anther of a flower to the stigma of the same flower or of another flower of the same or sometimes allied species, often through various agents such as wind, insects, etc. Pollination is of two kinds, viz. (1) **self-pollination** or **autogamy** (*autos*, self; *gamos*, marriage) and (2) **cross-pollination** or allogamy (*allos*, different). Pollination within a single flower (evidently bisexual) or between two flowers borne by the same parent plant is self-pollination; the latter method is otherwise called **geitonogamy** (*geiton*, neighbour), i.e. pollination between neighbouring flowers of the same plant. It will be noted that in self-pollination, only one parent plant the off-spring. On the other hand, pollination between two flowers (bisexual or unisexual) borne by two separate plants of the same or allied species is cross-pollination. This is otherwise called **xenogamy** (*xenos*, stranger). In cross-pollination, two parent plants are involved and, therefore, a mingling of two sets of parental characteristics takes place, resulting in healthier off spring (see p. 85). Both methods are, however, widespread in nature.

A. SELF-POLLINATION OR AUTOGAMY

The following adaptations are commonly met with in flowers to achieve self-pollination.

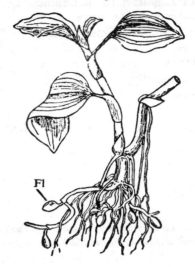

FIG. 136. *Commelina bengalensis*.
Fl, underground flower.

1. Homogamy (*homos*, the same). This is the condition in which the anthers and the stigmas of a bisexual flower mature at the same time. Under this condition, some of the pollen grains may reach the stigma of the same flower through the agency of insects or wind or by the sudden bursting of the anther, thus effecting self-pollination.

2. Cletsogamy (*kleistos*, closed). There are many bisexual flowers which never open. They are called cleistogamous or closed flowers, and self-pollination is the rule in them. Cleistogamy is seen in the underground flowers of *Commelina bengalensis* (FIG. 136), and also in some species of pansy (*Viola*), balsam (*Impatiens*), sundew (*Drosera*), wood-sorrel (*Oxalis*), sage (*Salvia*), *Juncus, Cardamine, Stellaria, Parochetus* (common in Darjeeling), etc.

B. CROSS-POLLINATION OR ALLOGAMY

Cross-pollination is brought about by external agents, such as insects (bees, flies, moths, etc.), animals (birds, snails, etc.), wind and water. Cross-pollination is the rule in unisexual flowers, while in bisexual flowers, it is of general occurrence. Nature favours cross-pollination and, therefore, adaptations in flowers to achieve it through external agents are many and varied.

1. ENTOMOPHILY (*entomon*, an insect; *philein*, to love). Pollination by insects is of very general occurrence among flowers. Entomophilous or insect-loving flowers have various adaptations by which they attract insects and use them as conveyors of pollen grains for the purpose of pollination. The principal adaptations are **colour, nectar** and **scent**.

Colour. One of the most important adaptations is the colour of the petals. In this respect, the brighter the colour and the more irregular the shape of the flower, the greater the attraction. Sometimes, when the flowers themselves are not conspicuous, other parts may become coloured and showy to attract insects. Thus, in *Mussaenda* (see FIG. 103) one of the sepals is modified into a large, white or coloured leafy structure which serves as an 'advertisement' flag to attract insects. In some cases, bracts become highly coloured and attractive, as in glory of the garden (*Bougainvillea*), poinsettia (*Poinsettia pulcherrima*), etc. Spathes are often brightly coloured, as in bananas and aroids.

Nectar. Another important adaptation is nectar. Nearly all flowers with gamopetalous corolla secrete **nectar**, which is a positive attraction to more clever insects like bees. Nectar is contained in a special gland, called nectary, and sometimes in a special structure, called the spur (see p. 67). The nectary occurs at the base of one of the floral whorls, and as the bees, which are very active pollinating agents, collect the nectar from the nectary or the spur, they incidentally bring about pollination.

Scent. The third adaptation is **scent**. Most nocturnal flowers are insect-loving and emit a sweet scent at night to attract insects from a distance. At night, when the colour is not visible, the scent is particularly useful in directing insects to the flowers. Thus, nocturnal flowers are mostly sweet-smelling. Common examples are night jasmine (*Nyctanthes*), queen of the night (*Cestrum*), jasmines, Rangoon creeper (*Quisqualis*), etc.

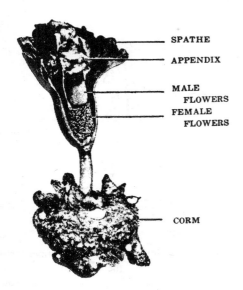

SPATHE

APPENDIX

MALE
FLOWERS
FEMALE
FLOWERS

CORM

FIG. 137. Spadix of *Amophophallus companu
latus* (B. OL; H. ZAMIKAND)

Sometimes, the smell that is offensive and nauseating to human beings is liked immensely by certain small insects. Thus, the appendix of the
mature inflorescence of *Amorphophallus* (B. OL.;
H. ZAMIKAND; FIG. 137) and *Arum* emit a stink that
is more offensive than that of putrid meat but it
always attracts swarm of carrion-flies, and pollination is achieved through them.

The pollen grains of entomophilous flowers are
either sticky or provided with spinous outgrowths.
The stigma is also sticky. Pollen grains and nectar
sometimes afford excellent food for certain
insects. Insects often visit the flowers in search of
shelter from the sun and rain, and incidentally
bring about pollination.

Pollination in Dagger Plant (*Yucca*). In *Yucca* (see
FIG. 81), the adaptation of the flower and its dependence on a special moth, *Pronuba*, to achieve cross-
pollination may be noted. The white, egg-shaped
flowers borne on a large panicle open fully at night and
become scented. The stigma protrudes far beyond the
anthers and thus, self-pollination is prevented. The
female moth becomes active at night. It visits a flower
and collects a load of pollen grains, pressing them into

a sort of ball. It then visits a second flower, carrying the
load on its body. With its long ovipositor, it bores a
number of holes in the wall of the ovary, each hole usually close to an ovule, and deposits eggs there, often
singly. At the end of oviposition, the moth goes to the
top of the stigma. Here, it deposits the ball of pollen
grains and presses it into the stigmatic depression with
its tongue. Thus, cross-pollination is effected. After
fertilization, the larvae and the seeds begin to develop
simultaneously, some of the ovules acting as food for
the larvae. As the larvae grow into insects, they bore
their way out through the wall of the fruit. A few seeds
drop through these holes but the majority of the seeds
are liberated only after the dehiscence of the fruit.

Special Adaptations. In sunflower, marigold,
Cosmos, Anthocephalus (B & H. KADAM), gum
tree (*Acacia*), etc., where the individual flowers
are small and inconspicuous, they are massed
together into a dense inflorescence which evidently becomes much more showy and attractive.
Dense inflorescence has another advantage. Being
close together, the flowers have every chance of
being pollinated (see p. 68).

In snapdragon (*Antirrhinum*; see FIG. 109B) and
toad-flax (*Linaria*), where the corolla is personate,
insects only of a particular size and weight can
open the mouth of the corolla. Conversely, only
long-tongued insects are useful in the case of the
flowers with long corolla-tubes.

In *Ficus* (e.g. banyan, peepul, fig, etc.), the
insects enter the hollowed out chamber of the
fleshy receptacle through its narrow apical opening and as they crawl over the unisexual flowers
inside the chamber, they bring about pollination
(FIG. 138). Female flowers lie at the base of the
cavity and open earlier, while male flowers lie
near the apical opening and open later, so that
pollen grains have to be brought over from another
inflorescence.

Pollination in *Compositae*. Although there is a vast
assemblage of forms in *Compositae*, the mechanism of
cross-pollination is more or less uniform in most cases.
Honey (nectar) is secreted around the base of the style
within a ring-shaped nectary, adequately protected by
the corolla-tube. The latter varies in length within wide
limits, allowing only the right type of insect to get to
the nectary, either bodily or by its proboscis. When the

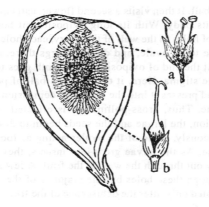

FIG. 138. Fig (*Ficus*) cut lengthwise. Note the apical pore guarded by scales. *a*, male flower; *b*, female flower

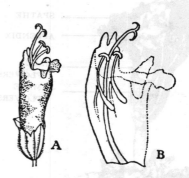

FIG. 139. Sage (*Salvia*). A, entire flower; B, showing elongated connective

flower is still young, the style with the two closed stigmas project just beyond the anther tube. Later, as the anthers mature they discharge their pollen grains into the anther tube. Now, as the hairy style elongates, it sweeps the pollen grains and pushes them upwards to the upper end of the anther tube and deposits them there. At this stage, the insect visitors get dusted with pollen grains all over their body. They fly or crawl over to other flowers with these pollen grains. The style elongates further and the two, often large, stigmas open and spread out over the flower, their upper receptive surfaces exposed. From this vantage position, the stigmas receive the pollen grains from the visiting insects. Thus, the flowers of a head become easily and quickly cross-pollinated. By default, the stigmas roll back and receive the pollen grains from the same or adjoining flowers. This ensures pollination, self- or cross-, and setting of seeds. Further, it should be noted that in *Centaurea*, e.g. sweet sultan (*C. moschata*), the stamens are irritable. When they come into contact with the pollinating insects (or any hard object), they contract and twist, forcing out the pollen grains to the top of the anther tube.

Pollination in Sage (*Salvia*). A very interesting case of cross-pollination by insects is seen in this plant (FIG.139). There are two stamens in the flower, with the two anther lobes of each widely separated by the elongated, curved connective which plays freely on the filament. The upper lobe is fertile and the lower one sterile. In the natural position the connective is upright. When the insect enters the tube of the corolla, it pushes the lower, sterile anther lobe of each stamen. The connec-

tive swings round with the result that the upper fertile lobe comes down and strikes the back of the insect and dusts it with pollen grains. The flower is protandrous, and later when the stigma matures, it bends down and touches the back of another insect-visitor coming with pollen grains from another flower. Thus, pollination is brought about. This is a special mechanism of cross-pollination.

2. ANEMOPHILY (*anemos*, wind). In some cases, pollination is brought about by wind. Anemophilous or wind-loving flowers are small and inconspicuous. They are never coloured or showy. They do not emit any smell, nor do they secrete any nectar. The anthers produce an immense quantity of pollen grains, wastage during transit from one flower to another being considerable. They are also light and dry. Sometimes, as in pine, they are provided with wings for facility of distribution by wind. The stigmas are comparatively large and protruding sometimes branched and often feathery. Examples are afforded by grasses, bamboos, cereals, millets, sugarcanes, sedges, pines and several palms. Anemophily is well illustrated by maize or Indian corn plant (*Zea mays*).

Pollination in Maize (FIG. 140). The plant bears a large number of male flowers (spikelets) in a terminal panicle, and lower down it bears 1 or 2 female spadices, with a tuft of fine, long and silky threads—the styles—hanging from them. When the anthers burst, a

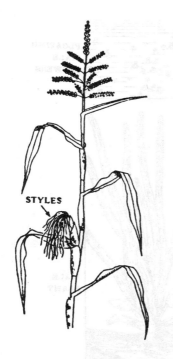

STYLES

FIG. 140. Anemophily in maize plant. Male flowers in a panicle (on the top) and female flowers in a spadix (at the bottom)

cloud of dust-like pollen grains is seen floating in the air around the plant. Some of them are caught by the protruding stigmas and thus, pollination is effected. By far, the greater majority of pollen grains are, however, blown away and wasted.

3. HYDROPHILY (hydro, water). Pollination may also be brought about in some aquatic plants, particularly the submerged ones, through the agency of water, e.g. Naias, Vallisneria, Hydrilla, Ceratophyllum, etc. Those aquatic plants that lift their flowers above the water level normally achieve pollination through insects or the wind. Hydrophilous flowers are, as a rule, small and inconspicuous.

Pollination in Vallisneria (FIG. 141). The mode of pollination in this plant is as follows. Vallisneria is dioecious and submerged. The male plant bears a large number of very minute male flowers in a small spadix surrounded by a spathe and borne on a short stalk, while the female plant bears solitary female flowers, each on a long slender stalk. The stalk quickly elongates and lifts the female flower to the surface of the water. The spathe bursts and the male flowers are released from the spadix, while still closed, and float on the surface of the water. The perianth expands, giving buoyancy to them. Some of the floating male flowers come in contact with the female flowers. The anthers dehisce and some of the sticky pollen grains adhere to the margins and surfaces of the trifid stigmas, which then close up. After pollination, the stalk of the female flower becomes spirally coiled and thus pulls the female flower down into the water. The fruit develops and matures under water, a little above the bottom.

4. ZOOPHILY (zoon, animal). Birds, squirrels, bats, snails, etc., also act as useful agents of pollination. For example, birds and sometimes squirrels bring about pollination in the coral tree (Erythrina), silk cotton tree (Bombax), rose-apple (Syzygium), Bignonia, etc. Bats do so in Anthocephalus (B. & H. KADAM) and snails in certain large verieties of aroids and snake plant (Arisaema— see FIG. 83). (Insects are also instrumental in bringing about pollination in them).

Advantages and Disadvantages of Self- and Cross Pollination. Self-pollination has the advantage that it is almost certain in a bisexual flower, provided that both its stamens and carpels have matured at the same time. Continued self-pollination, generation after generation has, however, the disadvantage that it results in weaker progeny. The advantages of cross-pollination are many, as first shown by Charles Darwin in 1876 : (a) it always results in much healthier offspring which are better adapted to the struggle for existence; (b) more abundant and viable seeds are produced by this method; (c) germinating capacity is much better; (d) new varieties may also be produced by the method of cross-pollination and (e) the adaptability of the plants to their environment is better by this method. The disadvantages of cross-pollination are that the plants have to depend on external agencies for the purpose and, this being so, the process is more or less precarious and also less economical as various devices have to be adopted to attract pollinating agents. There is also always a considerable waste of material (pollen) when wind is the pollinating agent.

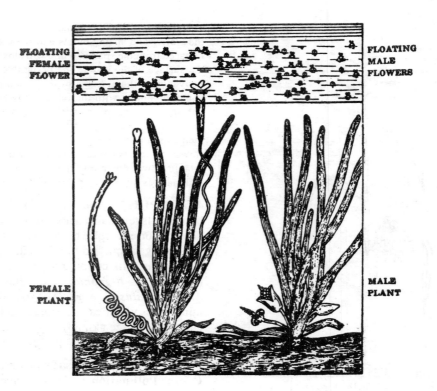

FIG. 141. Hydrophily in *Vallisneria*. Female plant with a floating flower, a submerged flower
(-bud) and a fruit (15 cm. long) maturing under water. Male plant with three spadices—young
(covered by spathe), mature (with the spathe bursting) and old (after the escape of the male flowers).
Male flowers are now seen floating on water

CONTRIVANCES FOR CROSS-POLLINATION.

The contrivances met with in flowers favouring cross-pollination, either wholly or sometimes partially preventing self-pollination, are many and varied. These are as follows:

(1) **Dicliny** or **Unisexuality**. Diclinous (*di*, two or asunder; *kline*, a bed) flowers are unisexual, i.e. their stamens and carpels lie in separate flowers—male and female—either borne by the same plant or by two separate plants. It is thus evident that there are two cases of dicliny: (a) when the male and the female flowers are borne by one and the same plant, it (the plant) is said to be monoecious (*monos*, single; *oikos*, a house), e.g. gourd, cucumber, castor, maize, jack, etc. and (b) when the male and the female flowers are borne by two

separate plants, they are said to be dioecious (*di*, two or asunder), e.g. palmyra palm, papaw, mulberry, etc. Cross-pollination is evident in them.

(2) **Self-sterility.** This is the condition in which the pollen of a flower has no fertilizing effect on the stigma of the same flower. As a matter of fact, it is seen, as in some orchids, that the pollen has an injurious effect on the stigma of the same flower. When the pollen is applied to it, the stigma dries up and falls off. Tea flowers, some species of passion flower (*Passiflora*) and mallow (*Malva*) are also self-sterile. Only pollen applied from another plant of the same or allied species is effective in such cases. Cross-pollination is thus the only method for the setting of seeds in such plants.

(3) **Dichogamy** (*dicha*, in two). In many bisexual flowers, the anther and stigma often mature at

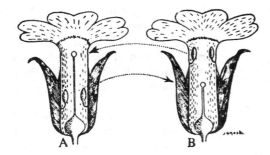

FIG. 142.
Dimorphic heterostyly in
primrose.
A, a flower with long style;
B, a flower with short style

different times. This condition is known as
dichogamy. As the anther and the stigma come to
maturity at different times, dichogamy is often a
barrier to self-pollination. There are two conditions of dichogamy: (a) **protogyny** (*protos*, first;
gyne, female) when the gynoecium matures earlier
than the anthers of the same flower. Here, the stigma receives the pollen grains brought from another flower. Common examples are *Ficus* (fig,
banyan, peepul, etc.), four o'clock plant
(*Mirabilis*), *Magnolia*, custard-apple (*Annona*),
some palms, etc. and (b) **protandry** (*protos*, first;
andros, male) when the anthers mature (burst and
discharge their pollen) earlier than the stigma of
the same flower. Here, the pollen grains are carried
over to the stigma of another flower. Common
examples are China rose, cotton, lady's finger,
sunflower, marigold, coriander, wood-sorrel

(*Oxalis*), rose, etc. Protandry is more commonly
found than protogyny.

(4) **Heterostyly** (*heteros*, different). There are
some plants which bear flowers of two different
forms (FIG. 142). One form bears long stamens and
a short style, while the other form bears short stamens and a long style. This is known as *dimorphic*
(*di*, two; *morphe*, form) *heterostyly*. Similarly,
there may be cases of *trimorphic heterostyly*, that
is, stamens and styles of three different lengths
borne by three different forms of flowers. In all
such cases, cross-pollination is effective only
when it takes place between stamens and styles
of the same length borne by different flowers
(*legitimate pollination*). Dimorphic heterostyly is
seen in primrose, buckwheat (*Fagopyrum*), wood-
sorrel (*Oxalis*), linseed (*Linum*) and *Woodfordia*

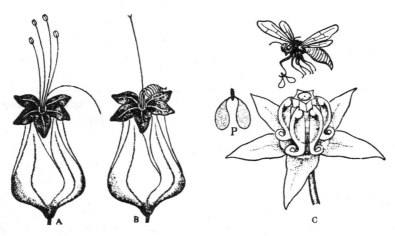

FIG. 143. Pollination in *Clerodendrum thomsonae*. *A*, stamens standing etect;
B, style standing etect later; *C*, pollination in madar (*Calotropis*);
an insect carrying a pair of pollinia from a flower; *P*, a pair of pollina

(B. DHAINPHUL). Trimorphic heterstyly is found in some species of *Oxalis* and *Linum*.

(5) **Herkogamy** (*herkos*, a fence or barrier). In many flowers, there are often certain adaptations of the floral parts which act as obstructions to self-pollination and thus favour cross-pollination by insects. The two organs may lie at some distance from each other, the anthers may be inserted within the corolla tube and the style far exserted, or the anthers far exserted and the style inserted, or the anthers may be facing outwards, or they may be sheltered or hooded by the petals or by the petaloid style, as in *Iris*.

The stamens and the style may also move away from each other so as to keep the anthers and the stigma suitably apart. Thus, in bleeding heart (*Clerodendrum thomsonae*; FIG. 143A-B)—a garden climber bearing flowers with white calyx and red corolla—the stamens stand erect and the style bends down on one side. After the anthers burst

and the pollen grains are removed by insects, the filaments roll up in close coils on one side of the flower. The style now stands erect and takes the original position of the stamens. In this position the bifid stigma directly receives the pollen grains from the body of the incoming insect.

The relative position of the anthers and stigma may be such as to prevent self-pollination. Thus, we find that the pollinia of orchids and madar (*Calotropis*) develop in a position whence they are not able to reach the stigma of the same flower by themselves. They also remain fixed in their position by adhesive discs and can only be carried away by insects, evidently to another flower. The peculiar arrangement of the stamens and pistil in sage (*Salvia*) to achieve cross-pollination has been discussed already (see p. 84). Heterostyly (FIG. 142) is also an effective mechanism to achieve the same end. In pansy (*Viola tricolor*), the stigma is guarded by a flap or lid.

CHAPTER 8

FERTILIZATION

Fertilization is the fusion of two dissimilar sexual reproductive units, called *gametes*. In 'flowering' plants, the process of fertilization (FIG.144), first discovered by Strasburger in 1884, is as follows. After pollination, that is, after the pollen grains reach the stigma, the intine of each grows out into a tube, called the **pollen tube** (see FIG.116), through some thin or weak spot or *germ pore* in the exine (see FIG. 115). Normally, one pollen tube is formed from each pollen grain but there are cases showing multiple tubes, as in *Malvaceae* and *Cucurbitaceae*. Of the many tubes, only the one with the generative nucleus and the tube-nucleus is functional. Although the growth of the pollen tube as far as the micropyle was first observed by Amici in *Yucca* in 1830, the details were worked

out much later by Strasburger. The tube, as it grows, penetrates the stigma and pushes its way through the style and the wall of the ovary or alongside it, carrying with it the tube-nucleus and the generative nucleus. The generative nucleus soon divides, forming two male gametes, while the tube-nucleus gets disorganized sooner or later. Sometimes, however, the generative nucleus divides even before pollination. As the tube elongates, the two male gametes move to the tip of the pollen tube and lie there in a mass of cytoplasm. The tube then turns towards the micropyle, passes inwards through it and, at length, reaches the embryo-sac close to the egg cell. This phenomenon is called **porogamy** and is the normal method. Sometimes, however, as in *Casuarina*

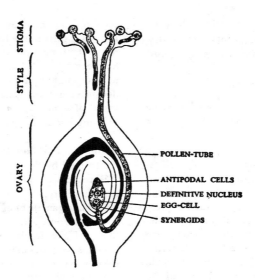

FIG. 144. Ovary in longitudinal section, showing the process of
fertilization. Note the two male gametes at the tip of the pollen tube

(B. & H. JHAU), walnut (*Juglans regia*) and birch
(*Betula*), the pollen tube enters the embryo-sac
through the base (chalaza) of the ovule, or even
pierces the integuments. This phenomenon is
called **chalazogamy** and was first discovered by
Treub in 1891. The growth of the pollen tube is no
doubt stimulated by proteins and sugars secreted
by the stigma and the style, but the factor controlling the direction of its movement towards the
embryo-sac is still unknown. It may be due to
some sort of chemotactic attraction by the egg
cell. After the pollen tube penetrates into the
embryo-sac, the tip of the tube dissolves and the
male gametes are set free. Of the two gametes, one
fuses with the **egg cell** (first observed by
Strasburger in 1884), while the other pushes farther into the embryo-sac and fuses with the two
polar nuclei or their fusion product, i.e. the **definitive nucleus** (first observed by Nawaschin in
1898). Thus, fertilization (actually double fertilization, which is the rule in angiosperms) is

completed. The fusion of a male gamete with the
two polar nuclei is often termed *triple fusion*.
Synergids are ephemeral structures, and do not
seem to be essential in the process of fertilization.
They get disorganized soon after fertilization, or
sometimes even before or during the process.
Antipodal cells have no positive function, so they
may disappear even before fertilization.[1] After fertilization, the egg cell clothes itself with a cell
wall and becomes known as the **oospore**. The
oospore gives rise to the embryo, the ovule to the
seed, and the ovary as a whole to the fruit, and the
definitive nucleus, now called the **endosperm
nucleus**, to the endosperm. If fertilization fails for
some reason or other, the ovary simply withers and
falls off. In certain cultivated varieties of banana,
papaw, orange, grape, apple, pineapple, etc., the
ovary may develop into the fruit without fertilization. The development of the fruit without fertilization is spoken of as **parthenocarpy**.
Parthenocarpic fruits rarely contain seeds. The

[1] Antipodal cells, synergids and two polar nuclei are generally regarded as vestiges of the female prothallus cells, the
egg apparatus or the group of four polar nuclei as the vestige of an archegonium (synergids representing its neck
cells), and the embryo-sac as a much reduced female prothallas (Straburger, 1879 and Porsch, 1907). The above
explanation is, however, still controversial.

time involved between pollination and fertilization varies a good deal in different plants. Generally, the time taken is from a few hours to a few days, but in some cases, from a few to several months, as in oak (*Quercus*) and birch (*Betula*).

Double Fertilization. It must have been noted from the foregoing description that in angiosperms, fertilization occurs twice : (a) one of the two male gametes of the pollen tube fuses with the ovum of the embryo-sac and (b) the other gamete fuses with the definitive nucleus. This process is called double fertilization. It was first discovered by Nawaschin in 1898 in *Lilium* and *Fritillaria*. This amazing discovery attracted great attention and many investigators soon established the fact that double fertilization is of universal occurrence among angiosperms. The significance of double fertilization is not clearly understood. The fusion of the male gametes with the ovum results in the formation of the embryo, while the fusion of the other male gamete with

the definitive nucleus (product of fusion of two polar nuclei) results in the formation of the endosperm, and not in the formation of a sister embryo, as expected. It has been suggested that the presence of a second polar nucleus might be a disturbing element, and as such, the definitive nucleus (endosperm nucleus) develops as a result of *triple fusion*, into the endosperm instead of growing into an embryo.

Reduction Division. Pollen grains and the embryo-sac are formed by the process of reduction division from their respective mother cells (see FIG. 117 and FIG. 134) and, therefore, the male gamete of the pollen tube and the female gamete or egg cell of the embryo sac contain *n* chromosomes, i.e. half as many chromosomes as those of the mother cells. Then, when these two gametes fuse together, the number of chromosomes in the oospore doubles (n + n = 2n). This is how a constant number of chromosomes is maintained from generation to generation.

CHAPTER 9

THE SEED

Development of the Seed. After fertilization, a series of changes takes place in the ovule, and as a result, the seed is formed. The fertilized egg cell or ovum grows and gives rise to the embryo, and the definitive nucleus to the endosperm. Other changes also take place in the ovule.

1. Development of the Embryo (Embryogeny). The early stages of embryo development in both dicotyledonous and monocotyledonous plants are alike. However, there are some differences between the two processes in the later stages.

After fertilization, the egg cell secretes a cellulose wall around itself and becomes the oospore, which finally gives rise to the embryo. In the initial stage, the oospore normally divides by a transverse wall into two cells. This two-celled stage is called the proembryo. Sometimes, the oospore may be divided by an obliquely placed vertical wall. The upper cell of the proembryo (lying away from the

micropyle), called the embryonal cell, develops into the embryo. The lower cell of the proembryo (lying towards the micropyle) forms the suspensor, which acts as a feeding organ for the developing embryo. In many cases, the basal cell also takes part in the formation of the embryo. Depending on whether (a) the oospore divides by a transverse wall or a vertical wall, (b) the basal cell contributes towards the development of the embryo or not and (c) the terminal cell further divides by a vertical wall or a transverse wall, the process of embryo development in angiosperms has been divided into six different types (Johansen, 1950).

(i) **Piperad type.** This type of embryo development occurs only in a few cases. For example, in *Peperomia, Balanophora*, etc., it has been observed that after fertilization the oospore divides by an obliquely placed vertical wall and gives rise to a two-celled proembryo.

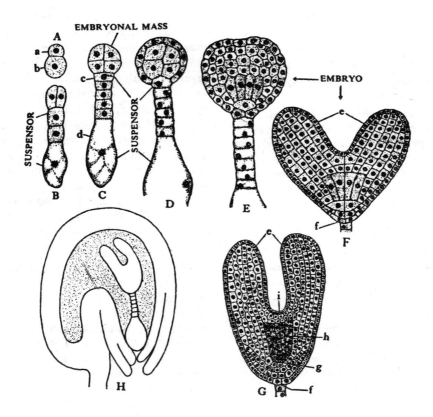

FIG. 145. *A-H*, development of dicotyledonous embryo. *a*, embroynal cell; *b*, suspensor cell; *c*, hypophysis cell; *d*, basal cell of the suspensor; *e*, cotyledons; *f*, root-cap; *g* , root tip; *h*, hypocotyl; *i*, stem-apex; *H*, embryo within the seed

(ii) **Crucifer type.** In this type, the oospore initially divides by a transverse wall, as in most cases, into a two-celled procmbryo. But the embryonal cell divides by a vertical wall and in due course, forms the embryo. Generally, the basal cell does not take part in the formation of the embryo. This type of embryo development is seen in *Cruciferae, Ranunculaceae, Liliaceae*, etc.

(iii) **Asterad type.** In this type of embryo development, as seen in *Compositae*, the oospore divides by a transverse wall into a two-celled proembryo. The embryonal cell then divides by a vertical wall and both the basal cell and the embryonal cell take part in the formation of the embryo.

(iv) **Caryophyllad type.** In the caryophyllad type, the oospore divides by a transverse wall to give rise to a two-celled proembryo. The embryonal cell then divides by a transverse wall. The basal cell merely enlarges and becomes a singled-celled suspensor. The embryo develops from the embryonal cell. This type of embryo development is seen in *Caryophyllaceae* etc.

(v) **Solanad type.** In this case, the oospore divides by a transverse wall to form a two-celled procmbryo. The embryonal cell also divides by a transverse wall. The basal cell may divide once to form a two-celled suspensor, or it may form a few more cells. The basal cell does not take part in the formation of the embryo, as in Solanaceae, Papavaraceae, etc.

(vi) **Chenopodiad type.** In *Chenopodiaceae*, etc., the oospore divides by a transverse wall and forms a two-celled proembryo. The embryonal cell divides by a transverse wall, but both the basal cell and the embryonal cell form the embryo.

Embryo development (embryogeny) in a dicotyledonous plant and a monocotyledonous plant are described below.

(a) *Dicotyledonous Embryo* (FIG.145). The oospore divides into two cells— an *upper* (away from the micropyle) and a *lower* (towards the micropyle) cell. The lower one lying towards the micropyle divides further in one direction into a row of cells, called the **suspensor**. The suspensor, as it elongates, pushes the developing embryo deep into the embryo-sac and also acts as a feeding organ for the embryo during the formation of the latter. For this purpose, the basal cell of the suspensor often enlarges and acts as an absorbing organ. The suspensor, however, becomes disorganized as the radicle is formed. The terminal cell of the suspensor lying next to the embryonal mass is called the **hypophysis cell** (*hypo*, below; *physis*, growth). It divides and gives rise to the apex of the radicle. The upper cell lying away from the micropyle is called the **embryonal cell**. It enlarges and divides by three walls at right angles into eight cells (octants or compartments), the four cells lying towards the suspensor forming the posterior octants and the other four cells lying away forming the anterior octants. Each octant then divides by a wall parallel to its curved surface. Thus, a surface (superficial) layer of cells and a central mass of cells, the latter being known as the **embryonal mass**, are formed. The surface layer divides in one direction by radial walls only and remains single-layered. Finally, it gives rise to the dermatogen, i.e. the outer layer of the stem-apex and the root-apex. The embryonal mass gives rise to the whole of the embryo except the root-tip. The cells of the embryonal mass divide repeatedly and the various parts of the embryo become differentiated. Thus, it is seen that the **plumule** and the **two cotyledons** are derived from the anterior octants, and main part of the radicle and the **hypocotyl** form the posterior octants. The apex of the radicle, as already stated, is derived form the hypophysis cell.

(b) *Monocotyledonous Embryo* (FIG. 146). Although the monocotyledonous embryo follows the same general trend of development as the dicotyledonous one, the former has only *one* cotyledon against the latter's *two*. Besides, in some monocotyledons the cotyledon is terminal and the stem-apex is lateral, although in others the reverse is the case, as in dicotyledons. There is also a considerable variation in the details of the development of monocotyledonous embryos. A typical case may be as follows. The oospore divides into two cells. The upper one (lying towards the micropyle) enlarges considerably and forms a massive suspensor. The terminal cell of these two, by repeated divisions on different planes, gives rise to

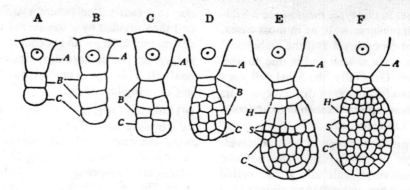

FIG. 146. A-F, development of monocotyledonous embryo. A, 3-celled proembryo; *A*, basal cell; *B*, middle cell; *C*, terminal cell; at successive stages (B-F), *A* gives rise to the suspensor, *B* to the stem-apex (*S*), hypocotyl (*H*) and root-tip with some accessory cells above (E-F), and *C* to cotyledon

the single cotyledon. The other cell also divides in the same way and gives rise to the stem-apex, the hypocotyl and the root-tip.

2. Development of the Endosperm. In all families of 'flowering' plants, with the exception of *Orchidaceae* and *Podostemaceae*, as, result of triple fusion (see p. 89) the definitive nucleus, now called the endosperm nucleus, tends to grow into a food storage tissue called the **endosperm**, usually triploid (*3n*), and sometimes tetraploid (*4n*). In due course, the endosperm may be a permanent feature of the seed (as in all endospermic seeds), or it may represent only a temporary phase, i.e. its development does not proceed far and whatever be the extent of development, it becomes completely absorbed by the growing embryo (as in all non-endospermic seeds). Usually, the endosperm nucleus begins its division and even a large portion of the endosperm may be formed before the oospore begins to divide. As a general rule, two polar nuclei fuse first to form the definitive nucleus. One of the male gametes of the pollen tube then fuses with the definitive nucleus to form the endosperm nucleus. But certain variations have been observed in some cases. Thus (a) in *Fritillaria, Tulipa, Nicotiana, Zea*, etc., the three nuclei (two polar nuclei and one male gamete) may unite simultaneously or (b) the micropylar polar nucleus may unite with the male gamete first, followed by the fusion of the antipodal polar nucleus, as in *Monotropa*, or, (c) the reverse may be the case, as in *Lilium, Adonis*, etc., i.e. the antipodal polar nucleus unites with the male gamete first or, (d) in extreme cases, as in *Limnocharis, Oenothera, Adoxa*, etc., where the antipodal polar nucleus is absent, the other polar nucleus directly fuses with the male gamete.

There are two main types of **endosperm development**, viz. the **nuclear type** and the **cellular type**. There is a third type also, called the **helobial type**, noticed in some cases.

(a) **Nuclear Type.** In this type the endosperm nucleus, immediately after double fertilization, divides repeatedly without corresponding wall formation. As a result, a number of free nuclei appear in the embryo-sac (free nuclear phase). In a large embryo-sac several hundreds of such free nuclei may be formed, while in a

small sac divisions are few. Soon a large central vacuole appears in the embryo-sac, and the cytoplasm together with the free nuclei is pushed to the periphery of the sac. Here, the nuclei become more or less evenly distributed with an aggregate mass at each pole. Now cell-wall formation starts, usually from the periphery, gradually proceeding inwards, i.e. centripetally (see FIG. II/24). Sometimes, however, the wall formation may be synchronous throughout the sac. In any case, a cellular mass of tissue laden with food material in formed. This is the food storage tissue of the seed, otherwise called **endosperm**. As the endosperm grows it fills up the nucellus. During wall formation, a few nuclei may often be included within a cell, or a single nucleus of a cell may divide, i.e. a multinucleate stage may appear at an early stage. Later, however, the enclosed nuclei fuse so that finally each cell is left with a single nucleus.

(b) **Cellular Type.** In this type, as the endosperm nucleus divides, there is corresponding formation of a cell wall around each nucleus. The free nuclear phase, which is characteristic of the previous type, is absent here. Within this type, however, there is some difference in the direction of formation of the first (primary) wall with respect to the embryo-sac. Thus, the first wall may be longitudinal, as in *Adoxa*, or it may be transverse, as in many species of *Annonaceae*, or it may be oblique, as in some species of *Boraginaceae*.

(c) **Helobial Type.** In this type, after the first division of the endosperm nucleus, a transverse wall is formed between the two newly formed nuclei, separating the embryo-sac into two unequal portions. The smaller portion lies towards the antipodal end, while the bigger portion occupies the major area of the sac. In the latter portion, by free nuclear divisions as in the nuclear type, a number of free nuclei appear. Formation of the cell wall then proceeds inwards, finally giving rise to the endosperm. In the smaller portion, the nucleus may not divide at all or it divides only a few times. If wall formation takes place here, a small mass of cells may be seen adhering to this end of the endosperm.

Endosperm Haustoria. In several plants, special sucking organs or haustoria have been found to develop from the micropylar or chalazal end of the endosperm, or sometimes even from both ends. *Micropylar haustoria* often appear as unicellular outgrowths from the upper end of the endosperm. They enlarge and grow throughout the micropyle, and finally branch and spread over the ovule. The endospermal nuclei migrating into them undergo repeated free nuclear divisions. This type is seen in certain members of *Labiatae*. A massive micropylar haustorium is seen in *Impatiens*. *Chalazal haustoria* develop from the lower end of the endosperm. This end elongates and assumes a tubular form. It penetrates into the nutritive tissue at the base (chalazal end) of the ovule and acts as a sucking organ or haustorium. This type is found in *Proteaceae*, e.g. *Grevillea* and *Macadamia*. In silver oak (*Grevillea*), the haustorium takes the form of a tubular, twisted and worm-like organ (called vermiform appendage). It invades the nutritive tissue at the chalazal end and acts as a very efficient sucking organ. In nut tree (*Macadamia*), the tubular haustorium is provided with several lobes for the same purpose. Endosperm haustoria formed from both ends of the endosperm are found in *Scrophulariaceae* and *Acanthaceae*.

3. **Other Changes in the Ovule.** The two integuments develop into two **seed-coats**, of which the outer one is called the *testa* and the inner one the *tegmen*. In some seeds, as in water lily (*Nymphaea*), nutmeg (*Myristica*), wild mangosteen (*Diospyros*; B. GAB; H. KENDU), etc., there

is usually found an outgrowth of the funicle, which grows up around the ovule and more of less completely envelops the seed. An outgrowth of this nature is called an **aril**. The bright red, deeply lobed and aromatic mace (B. JAITRI) of nutmeg (*Myristica fragrans*) is the aril, and so also is the flesh of litchi and *Baccaurea* (B. LATKAN; H. LUTKO). In *Pithecolobium* (B. & H. DEKANI-BABUL), too, the aril is fleshy and edible. A small outgrowth formed at the micropyle may also be seen in some seeds, as in castor, balloon vine (*Cardiospermum*), etc. This is known as the **caruncle** (see FIG. 150). In several cases, as in *Scitamineae*, e.g. banana (*Musa*), ginger (*Zingiber*), *Canna*, etc., in *Nyctaginaceae*, e.g. four o'clock plant (*Mirabilis*), etc., the nucellus of the ovule is not completely used up but it persists in the seed as a thick or thin nutritive tissue like the endosperm, with the embryo lying embedded in it. This nutritive tissue, which is in fact a remnant of the nucellus, is called the **perisperm**. In some cases, as in castor (see FIG. 150), in *Piperaceae*, e.g. pepper (*Piper nigrum*), in *Nymphaeaceae*, e.g. water lily (*Nymphaea*), etc., both the perisperm and the endosperm are present in the seed.

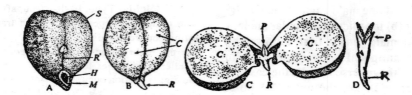

FIG. 147. Gram seed (*Cicer arietenum*). *A*, entire seed; *B*, embryo (after removal of the seed-coat); *C*, embryo with the cotyledons unfolded; and *D*, axis of embryo. *S*, seed-coat; *R*, raphe; *H*, hilum; *M*, micropyle; *C*, cotyledons; *R*, radicle; and *P*, plumula

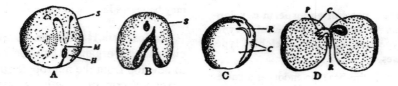

FIG. 148. Pea seed (*Pisum sativum*). *A*, entire seed; *B*, seed-coat with hilum and micropyle; *C*, embryo (after removal of the seed-coat); and *D*, embryo with the cotyledons unflolded. *S*, seed-coat—testa (it encloses a thin membranous tegmen); *M*, micropyle; *H*, hilum; *R*, radicle; *C*, cotyledons; *P*, plumule

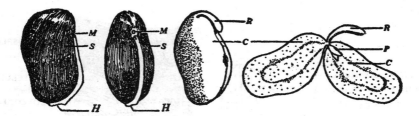

FIG. 149. Country bean seed (*Dolichos lablab*). *M*, Micropyle;
S, seed-coat; *H*, hilum; *R*, radicle; *C*, cotyledons; *P*, pulule

A. DICOTYLEDONOUS SEEDS

Parts of Exalbuminous Seeds (gram, pea, country bean, gourd, tamarind, mango, sunflower, etc.). **Seed coats** consist of two layers or integuments, united or free, the outer being called **testa** and the inner **tegmen**, and are provided with **hilum** (representing the point of attachment with the stalk), **micropyle** (a minute opening above the hilum) and **raphe** (a ridge formed by the funicle or stalk in many seeds). The embryo lying within consists of an axis and two fleshy **cotyledons** laden with food material. The pointed end of the axis is the **radicle** and the feathery or leafy end the **plumule**. As the seed germinates the radicle gives rise to the root and the plumule to the shoot.

Parts of Albuminous Seeds (castor, papaw, custard-apple, four o'clock plant, etc.). **Castor Seed. Seed-coat** or **testa** is the outer hard, blackish and mottled shell. The outgrowth formed at the micropyle is the **caruncle**. It absorbs moisture and helps germination. The **hilum** is almost hidden by the caruncle. The **raphe** is prominent. **Perisperm** is the thin, white, papery membrane surrounding the endosperm. This is a remnant of the nucellus, and is a nutritive tissue (see also above). The **endosperm** is the fleshy food storage tissue, rich

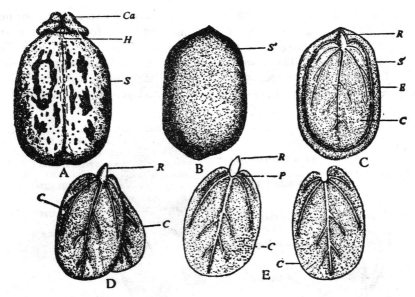

FIG. 150. Castor seed (*Ricinus communis*). *A*, an entire seed; *B*, the seed enclosed by the perisperm;
C, the same split edgewise showing the embryo lying embedded in the endosperm; *D*, embryo;
E, the same with the two cotyledons separated. *Ca*, caruncle; *H*, hilum; *S*, testa; *S'*, perisperm;
R, radicle; *E*, endosperm; *C*, cotyledon; *P*, plumule

FIG. 151.
Rice grain (*Oryza sativa*).
A, the grain enclosed in husk
 (consisting of glumes);
B, the grain in
 longitudinal
 section
 (a portion)

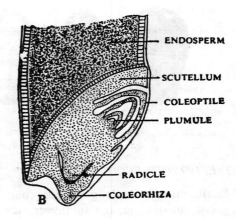

in oil, lying immediately within the perisperm. The **embryo** lies embedded in the endosperm and consists of an **axis** with a distinct **radicle** pointing outward, an undifferentiated **plumule** and two thin, flat **cotyledons** with distinct veins.

B. MONOCOTYLEDONOUS SEEDS

Parts of Albuminous Seeds (rice, maize, wheat, onion, palms, etc.).

Rice Grain and Maize Grain. The grain in each case is a small one-seeded fruit called caryopsis. Each grain remains enclosed by a brownish husk which consists of four parts, called *glumes*, arranged in two rows. The two minute ones at the base are *empty glumes*, while the two bigger ones

enclose a flower. Of these two, the outer and slightly bigger one is called the *flowering glume* or *lemma*, while the inner and slightly smaller one, partially enveloped by the former, is called the *palea*. Each grains consists of the following parts :

(1) The **seed-coat** is the brownish membranous layer adherent to the grain. This layer is made up of the seed-coat and the wall of the fruit fused together.

(2) The **endosperm** forms the main bulk of the grain and is the food storage tissue of it, being laden with reserve food material, particularly starch. In a longitudinal section of the grain, it is seen to be distinctly separated from the embryo by a definite layer known as the *epithelium*.

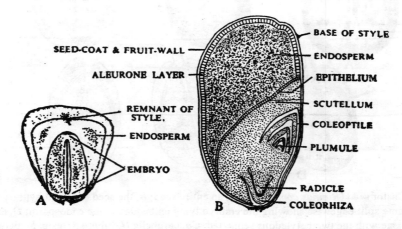

FIG. 152. Maize grain (*Zea mays*). A, the entire grain; B, the grain in longitudinal section

(3) The **embryo** is very small and lies in a groove at one end of the endosperm. It consists of only (a) *one* shield-shaped cotyledon known as the **scutellum** and (b) a short **axis** with (i) the **plumule** and (ii) the **radicle** protected by the **root-cap**. The plumule as a whole (growing point and foliage leaves) is surrounded by a protective sheath called the plumule-sheath or **coleoptile**. Similarly, the radicle (including the root-cap) is surrounded and protected by a root-sheath called the **coleorhiza**. The surface layer of the scutellum lying in contact with the endosperm is the **epithelium**. Its function is to digest and absorb food material stored in the endosperm.

In cereals (e.g. rice, wheat, maize, barley and oat), millets and other plants of the grass family, the cotyledon is known as the **scutellum**. It

mant embryo wakes up, grows out of the seed-coat and establishes itself as a seedling is called **germination**. The embryo grows by absorbing food material stored up in the cotyledons, or in the endosperm when it is present. Two kinds of germination will be noticed: epigeal and hypogeal.

1. Epigeal Germination (FIGS. 153-55). In some seeds such as tamarind, cucumber, cotton, gourd, castor, papaw, etc., the cotyledons are seen to be pushed upwards by the rapid elongation of the **hypocotyl** (*hypo*, below), i.e. the portion of the axis lying immediately below the cotyledons. Germination of this kind is called **epigeal** or **epigeous** (*epi*, upon; *ge*, earth). In most such cases, as the cotyledons come up above the ground they become flat, green and leaf-like in appearance, while in other such cases, particularly when the

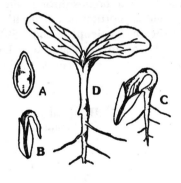

Epigeal Germination. FIG. 153.
Gourd seed (*Cucurbita pepo*)

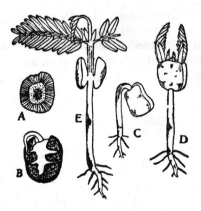

FIG. 154. Tamarind seed (*Tamarindus indica*)

supplies the growing embryo with food material absorbed from the endosperm with the help of the epithelium. Monocotyledonous seeds are mostly albuminous. A few exalbuminous ones are orchids, water plantain (*Alisma*), arrowhead (*Sagittaria*), *Naias*, etc.

GERMINATION

The embryo lies dormant in the seed, but when the latter is supplied with moisture, the embryo becomes active and tends to grow and develop into a small seedling. *The process by which the dor-*

cotyledons are very thick (as in tamarind, sword bean, etc.), they do not turn leafy but gradually shrivel up and fall off.

2. Hypogeal Germination (FIGS. 156-157). In other seeds such as gram, pea, mango, litchi, jack, broad bean (*Vicia*), groundnut, etc., the cotyledons are seen to remain in the soil or just on its surface. In such cases, the **epicotyl**, i.e. the portion of the axis lying immediately above the cotyledons, elongates and pushes the plumule upwards. The cotyledons do not turn green, but gradually dry up and fall off. Germination of this kind is called **hypogeal** or **hypogeous** (*hypo*, below; *ge*, earth).

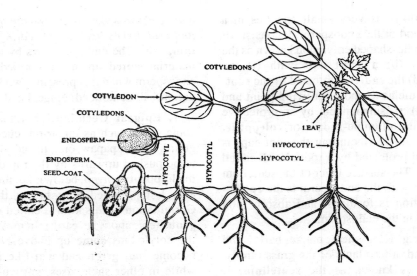

Epigeal Germination. FIG. 155. Castor seed (*Ricinus communis*).

Hypogeal Germination of Monocotyledonous Seeds (FIGS. 158-159). Monocotyledonous seeds are mostly albuminous and in their germination, the cotyledon and endosperm remain buried in the soil. Germination is, therefore, hypogeal (except

while the plumule breaks through the upper distinct cylindrical portion of the sheath, called the plumule-sheath or **coleoptile** (FIG. 159). The radicle grows downwards and, at first, it develops into the primary root. In most cases, the primary root

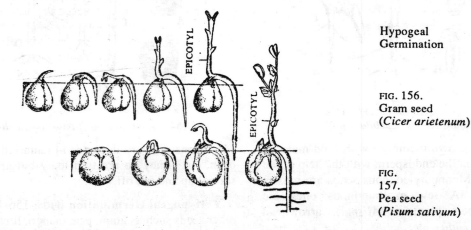

Hypogeal Germination

FIG. 156.
Gram seed
(*Cicer arietenum*)

FIG. 157.
Pea seed
(*Pisum sativum*)

in the case of onion; see FIG. 162). In the germination of monocotyledonous seeds like paddy (unhusked rice) and maize, the cotyledon (or scutellum) absorbs the food material stored up in the endosperm. On germination, the radicle makes its way through the lower short, collar-like end of the sheath called the root-sheath or **coleorhiza**,

soon perishes and a cluster of fibrous roots appears from the base. The plumule grows upwards. The first leaf soon emerges out of the plumule-sheath and others follow in succession. In the germination of many palms, e.g. date-palm and palmyra-palm (but not coconut-palm) a part of the cotyledon extends into a sheath, long or short,

Hypogeal
Germination.

FIG. 158
Paddy
(*Oryza sativa*)
A-E,   stages in
germina-
tion

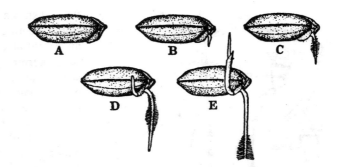

which encloses the axis of the embryo a little behind the tip and carries it down to some depth in the soil (see FIGS. 163-64).

Special Type of Germination.

Many plants growing in salt lakes and sea coasts show a special type of germination of seeds, known as **vivipary** (FIG. 160). The seed germinates inside the fruit while still attached to the parent tree and nourished by it. The radicle elongates, swells in the lower part and gets stouter. Ultimately, the seedling separates from the parent plant due to its increasing weight, and falling vertically, becomes embedded in the soft mud below. The radicle presses into the soil and lateral roots are quickly formed for proper anchorage. Examples are seen in *Rhizophora* (B. KHAMO), *Sonneratia* (B. KEORA), *Heritiera* (B. SUNDRI), etc.

Conditions Necessary for Germination.

Dry seeds retain their viability for many months and even years, depending on their nature, provided, of course, that the embryo is not damaged by insects or fungi. Then the following external conditions are necessary for their germination : (1) **water or moisture**, (2) **moderate temperature** and (3) **air or oxygen.**

(1) **Moisture.** For germination of a seed, its protoplasm must be saturated with water. In air-dried seeds the water content is usually 10-15 per cent. No vital activity is possible at this low water content. Water is, thus, necessary to bring about the vital activity of the dormant embryo—to dissolve various salts and to hydrolyse many organic substances stored in the cotyledons or in the endosperm, to facilitate necessary chemical

Hypogeal
Germination.
FIG. 159.

Maize-grain
(*Zea mays*).
Pl, plumule;
Cl, coleoptile;
Cr, coleorhiza

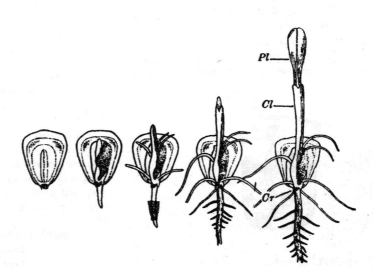

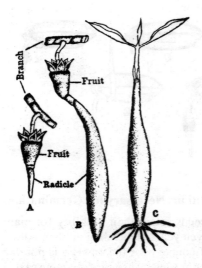

FIG. 160. Viviparous germination.
A-B, stages in germination; *C*, seedling.

changes and to help the embryo come out easily by softening the seed-coat.

(2) **Temperature.** A suitable temperature is necessary for the germination of a seed. The protoplasm functions normally within a certain range of temperature. Within limits, which vary according to the nature of the seed, the higher the temperature the more rapid the germination.

(3) **Air.** Oxygen is necessary for the respiration of a germinating seed. By this process, a considerable amount of energy stored in the food material is liberated and utilized by the protoplasm. Respiration in the germinating seed is very vigorous as the active protoplasm requires a constant supply of oxygen and hence, a seed sown deeply in

the soil shows very little or no sign of germination. It may be noted in this connection that **light** is not an essential condition for germination. In fact, seeds germinate more quickly in the dark. Some seeds – tomato, for example – will not germinate unless they are kept in the dark. For subsequent growth, however, light is indispensable. Seedlings grown continually in the dark elongate rapidly but become frail, develop no chlorophyll and bear only pale, undeveloped leaves. Such seedlings are said to be *etiolated* (see FIG. 111/43).

Three Bean Experiment (FIG. 161). That all the conditions mentioned above are essential for germination can be shown by a simple experiment, known as the three bean experiment. Three air-dried seeds are attached to a piece of wood, one at each end and one in the middle. This is then placed in a beaker and water and is poured into it until the middle seed is half immersed in it. The beaker is then left in a warm place for a few days. From time to time, water is added to maintain the original level. It is seen that the middle bean germinates normally because it has sufficient moisture, oxygen and heat. The bottom bean has sufficient moisture and heat, but no oxygen. It may be seen to put out only the radicle, but further development is checked for want of oxygen. The top bean, having only sufficient oxygen and heat but no moisture, does not show any sign of germination.

This experiment evidently shows that moisture and oxygen are indispensable for germination. The effect of temperature is only indirectly proved. It can, however, be directly proved in the following way. Other conditions remaining the same, if the temperature is considerably lowered or increased by placing the beaker with seeds in a freezing mixture or in a bath with a high, constant temperature, it will be seen that none of the beans will germinate. Thus, suitable temperature is also an essential condition for germination.

ADDITIONAL MONOCOTYLEDONOUS SEEDS

1. Onion Seed (FIG. 162). **Structure.** The seed is small, black, roughly semi-curcular in shape, flattened on one side and grooved at the narrow end. Its outer black covering is (a) **the seed-coat** or testa. Cut the seed lengthwise and observe (b) the **endosperm,** which is the whitish mass within the seed-coat and (c) the **embryo,** which is the slender, elongated, colourless, curved body lying embedded in the endosperm. The embryo consists of (i) a **single cotyledon** and (ii) a **radicle.** The bigger portion of the curved body looped at the end is the

FIG. 161. Three bean experiment.

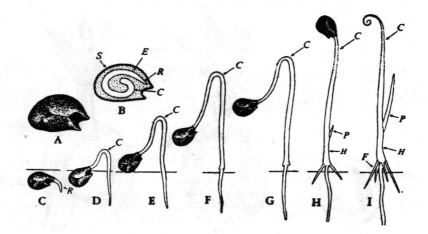

FIG. 162. Onion seed (*Allium cepa*). *A*, an entire seed; *B*, the seed in longitudinal section; *C-I*, stages in germination. *S*, seed-coat; *E*, endosperm; *R*, radicle; *C*, cotyledon; *P*, plumule; *H*, hypocotyl; *F*, fibrous roots.

cotyledon and the narrow end of it directed towards the pointed end of the seed is the radicle. The plumule which is very minute and undifferentiated, lies hidden laterally in the region of the very short hypocotyl and is clearly distinguishable only on the germination of the seed.

FIG.163.
Date-palm seed
(*Phoenix sylavestris*).
A,   seed in section;
B,   germinating seed
      in section;
C,   seedling;
S,   seed-coat and
      inner wall of the fruit;
E,   endosperm;
Em, embryo
      (undifferentiated);
C,   cotyledon;
Sh, sheath of cotyledon;
Cr, coleorhiza

FIG.164.
Palmyra-palm seedling
(*Borassus flabellifer*).
M,   mesocarp (fibrous);
E,   endocarp (stony) :
S,   endosperm with
      seed-coat;
C,   cotyledon (spongy);
Sh, sheath;
Cl, coleoptile;
Cr, coleorhiza

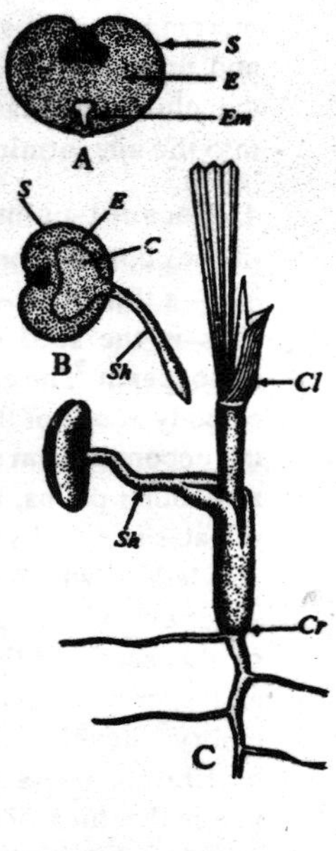

FIG.163.

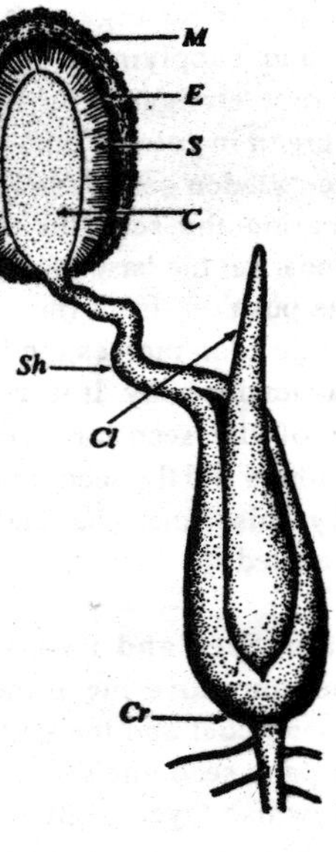

FIG.164.

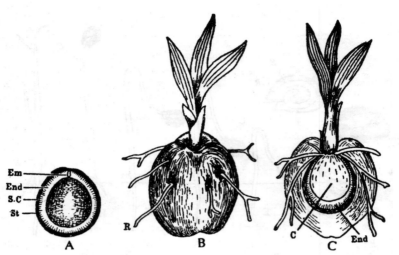

FIG. 165. Coconut-palm seed (*Cocos nucifera*). *A*, the seed cut lengthwise; *B*, germinating fruit; *C*, the same cut lengthwise. *Em.* embryo; *End*, endosperm; *S.C*, seed-coat; *St*, stone; *R*, root; *C*, cotyledon

Germination. As germination takes place, the radicle comes out through the pointed end of the seed and grows downward (C). The cotyledon elongates, emerges out of the seed, except for its looped end, and forms a distinct arch or loop (D). It turns green in colour and elongates further as a leaf-sheath, lifting the seed from the soil (E). The germination is epigeal. The end of the cotyledon still coils within the seed and functions as an absorbing organ, drawing food from the endosperm and supplying the same to the growing parts. The root elongates further and the cotyledon turns deep green in colour, functioning as the first leaf (F-G). The cotyledon grows further and almost straightens out, bearing the seed on the top. (H). A slight swelling appears at the base of the hypocotyl and a few fibrous roots push out from this region. A little higher up, the plumule soon pierces the leaf-sheath and grows upward as a slender body. It turns green and forms the second leaf of the seedling. The coiled end of the cotyledon withers and the seed-coat drops now or a little later (I). By this time, the endosperm has already become exhausted.

2-3 Date-palm Seed and Palmyra-palm Seed (FIGS. 163-64). The stony covering of the date-palm seed represents the seed-coat and the endocarp of the fruit. In the palmyra-palm seed, the shell is the endocarp, while the inner brownish layer is the seed-coat. In both, the seed-coat is adherent to the endosperm. Other parts in both are: a large **endosperm** filling up the cavity of the

seed and a small, undifferentiated **embryo** lying embedded in the endosperm on one side.

When germination begins, the single **cotyledon** enlarges and a portion of it breaks through the seed-coat in the form of a sheath, enclosing the **axis of the embryo**. The **sheath** of the cotyledon elongates and carries down with it the axis of the embryo. After it has gone into the soil, the radicle of the axis comes out, piercing the root-sheath or colerhiza, grows downwards and produces the root. Eventually, the plumule bursts the plumule-sheath or coleoptile and grows upwards into the air, forming the shoot.

4. Coconut-palm Seed (FIG. 165) On removing the fibrous coat and breaking open the shell, a black covering—a thin layer—adherent to the endosperm is seen. This is the seed-coat. The white, thick mass is the **endosperm.** The embryo lies as a small, undifferentiated body at one of the three 'eyes'. In the germination of the coconut-palm seed, a regular sheath is not formed, as in other palms, and the undifferentiated embryo germinates *in situ*. Its lower end extends and forms a single **cotyledon**, which gradually enlarges and swells into a spherical, white, spongy body and fills the whole cavity of the seed. With the growth of the cotyledon the endosperm is seen to thin out. The upper end of the embryo develops into a small **shoot** with a number of fibrous **roots** produced at its base. These roots pierce the thick fibrous coat of the fruit and come out in different directions.

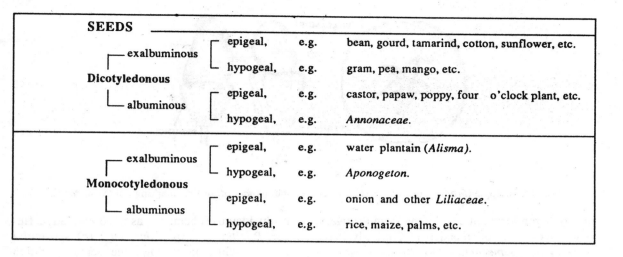

SEEDS				
Dicotyledonous	exalbuminous	epigeal,	e.g.	bean, gourd, tamarind, cotton, sunflower, etc.
		hypogeal,	e.g.	gram, pea, mango, etc.
	albuminous	epigeal,	e.g.	castor, papaw, poppy, four o'clock plant, etc.
		hypogeal,	e.g.	*Annonaceae.*
Monocotyledonous	exalbuminous	epigeal,	e.g.	water plantain (*Alisma*).
		hypogeal,	e.g.	*Aponogeton.*
	albuminous	epigeal,	e.g.	onion and other *Liliaceae*.
		hypogeal,	e.g.	rice, maize, palms, etc.

CHAPTER 10

THE FRUIT

DEVELOPMENT OF THE FRUIT.

Apart from the development of the seed, fertilization stimulates the growth of the ovary also.* As it grows and matures, it becomes converted into the fruit. The fruit may, therefore, be regarded as a mature or ripened ovary. A fruit consists of two portions, viz. the **pericarp** (*peri*, around; *karpos*, fruit), developed from the wall of the ovary, and the seeds, developed from the ovules. The pericarp may be thick or thin. When thick, it may consist of two or three parts. The outer, called the *epicarp*, forms the skin of the fruit. The middle, called the *mesocarp*, is pulpy in fruits like mango, peach, plum, etc., and the inner, called the *endocarp*, is often very thin and membranous, as in orange, or it may be hard and stony, as in many palms, mango,

etc. In many cases, however, the pericarp is not differentiated into these three regions.

When only the ovary of the flower grows into the fruit, it is commonly known as the **true fruit,** but often it is found that other floral parts, such as the thalamus, receptacle, or calyx, may also grow and form a part of the fruit. Such a fruit is known as the **false** or spurious fruit, or pseudocarp. Thus, in *Dillenia* (B. & H. CHALTA), the calyx is persistent and fleshy forming the prominent and the only edible part of the fruit . In apple (FIG. 166A) and pear, the thalamus grows round the inferior ovary and becomes fleshy in the fruit. In cashew-nut (*Anacardium;* FIG 166B), the peduncle and the thalamus grow and become swollen and fleshy, forming an edible fruit-like body which is a false fruit or pseudocarp, while the actual fruit, which is

* **Auxin Theory of Fruit Development.** It may be noted that auxin (a growth hormone) plays an important role in the development of the fruit from the ovary. It has been found that there is an increase in the auxin content of the ovary of immediately after pollination, growth of the pollen tube and fertilization. Lund (1956) actually found that an enzyme secreted by the pollen-tube can convert the amino-acid, *tryptophan*, into auxin.

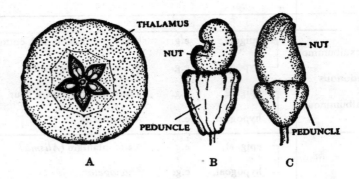

FIG. 166. *A*, apple (*Malus*) cut transversely; *B*, cashew-nut (*Anacardium*); *C*, marking nut (*Semecarpus*)

an edible reniform nut developing from the ovary, is seated on the swollen peduncle. Similarly, in the marking nut (*Semecarpus;* FIG. 166C), the peduncle becomes fleshy with the actual nut seated on its top. The nut is not edible but is used by washermen to mark cotton clothes.

Dehiscence of Fruits (FIG. 167).

There are many modes of dehiscence of fruits for the liberation of their seeds. It may be of the following types: (1) **transverse** (C), as in cock's comb (*Celosia*), purslane (*Portulaca*), etc; (2) **porus** (B), i.e. by pores, as in poppy (*Papaver*), bath sponge (*Luffa*), etc; (3) **valvular**, i.e. bursting partially or completely into pieces called valves. Dehiscence may be of the following kinds : (*a*) **sutural** (A), i.e. opening by one or both the sutures, as in periwinkle, pea bean, etc; (*b*) **loculicidal** (D), i.e.splitting through the back

of the loculus (chamber), as in cotton, lady's finger, *Ruellia, Andrographis,* etc.; (c) **septicidal** (E), i.e.dehiscing through the septa (partition walls), as in linseed (*Linum*), devil's cotton (*Abroma*), mustard (*Brassica*), etc. and (d) **septifragral** (F-G), i.e. dehiscing loculicidally or septicidally with the valves falling away, leaving the seeds attached to the central axis, as in thorn-apple (*Datura*), toon (*Cedrela*), *Pterospermum*, etc.

CLASSIFICATION OF FRUITS

Fruits, whether true or spurious, may be broadly classified into three groups, viz. **simple, aggregate** and **multiple** or composite.

A. Simple Fruits.

When only one fruit develops from the single ovary (either of simple pistil or of syncarpous

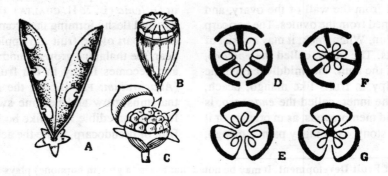

FIG. 167. Dehiscence of fruits. *A*, sutural (pea); *B*, porous (poppy);
C, transverse (cock's comb); *D*, loculicidal; *E,* septicidal *F-G,* septifragal

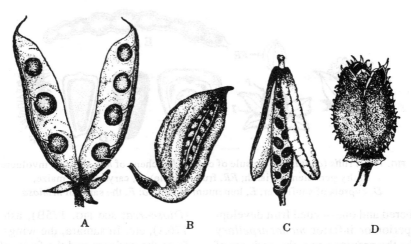

FIG. 168. Fruits. *A*, legume or pod of pea; *B*, follicle of madar (*Calotropis*);
C, siliqua of mustard; *D*, capsule of thorn-apple (*Datura*)

pistil) of a flower, with or without, accessory parts (true or spurious fruits as explained above), it is said to be a **simple fruit**. A simple fruit may be dry or fleshy. Dry fruits may again be dehiscent, indehiscent or schizocarpic (in which the carpel or carpels split into one-seeded parts).

I. DEHISCENT OR CAPSULAR FRUITS

(1) **Legume** or **Pod** (FIG. 168A). This is a dry *monocarpellary* fruit developing from a superior, one-chambered ovary and dehiscing by both the sutures, as in *Papilionaceae*, e.g. pea, bean, pulses, rattlewort (*Crotalaria*; B. ATASHI; H. JHUNJHUNIA), etc.

(2) **Follicle** (FIG. 168B). This also is a dry, *monocarpellary*, superior, one-chambered fruit like the previous one, but it dehisces by one suture only. Simple follicles are rare. They are sometimes seen in madar (*Calotropis*). Most commonly, however, follicles develop in an aggregate of two, three or many fruits (see pp. 108–9)

(3) **Siliqua** (FIG. 168C). This is a long, narrow, many-seeded fruit developing from a superior, *bicarpellary* ovary with two parietal placentae. It dehisces from below, upwards along the two ventral sutures into two valves, leaving a two-ribbed, wiry framework called the *replum* with seeds attached to it and a false septum across the replum.

It may be noted that the ovary is at first one-chambered but after the ovules appear, a thin papery longitudinal membrane grows inwards from the placenta at each suture. The two membranes thus formed meet and give rise to the false septum, dividing the ovary into two chambers, while the two suture ribs form the framework, i.e. the replum. Siliqua is commonly found in *Cruciferae*. A short, broad and flat siliqua is otherwise called a **silicula**. It is found in some members of *Cruciferae*, as in *Alyssum*, candytuft (*Iberis*), shepherd's purse (*Capsella*), *Senebiera*, etc.

(4) **Capsule** (FIGS. 168D and 169A) This is a many-seeded, uni- or multilocular fruit developing from a superior (or sometimes inferior), *bi*- or *polycarpellary* ovary, and dehiscing in various ways. All dihiscent fruits developing from a syncarpous ovary are commonly known as capsules, e.g. poppy (*Papaver*), cotton (*Gossypium*), lady's finger (*Abelmoschus*), *Datura*, etc.

II. INDEHISCENT OR ACHENIAL FRUITS

(1) **Caryopsis** (FIG. 169C). This is a small, dry, one-seeded fruit developing from a superior, *monocarpellary* ovary with the pericarp fused with the seed-coat. Examples are found in *Gramineae*, e.g. rice, wheat, maize, etc.

(2) **Achene** (FIG. 169B). An achene is a small

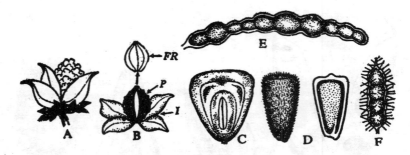

FIG. 169. Fruits (*contd.*). *A*, capsule of cotton; *B*, achene of *Mirabilis* (I, involucre;
P, dry persistent perianth; *FR*, fruit–achene); *C*, caryopsis of maize,
D, cypsela of sunflower; *E*, lomentum of *Acacia*; *F*, the same of *Mimosa*

dry, one-chambered and one-seeded fruit developing from a superior or inferior *monocarpellary* ovary but unlike the previous one, the pericarp of this fruit is free from the seed-coat. Simple achenes are found only in a few cases, as in four o'clock plant (*Mirabilis*),hogweed(*Boerhaavia*) and buckwheat (*Fagopyrum*). Most commonly, however, achenes develop in an aggregate (see p. 108).

(3) **Cypsela** (FIG. 169D). This is a dry, one-chambered and one-seeded fruit developing from an inferior, *bicarpellary* ovary with the pericarp and the seed-coat free, as in the sunflower family of *Compositae*, e.g. sunflower, marigold, *Cosmos*, etc.

(4) **Samara** (FIG. 170B). This is a dry, indehiscent, one- or two seeded fruit developing from a superior, *bi-* or *tri-carpellary* ovary, with one or more flattened, wing-like outgrowths, e.g *Hiptage* (B. MADHABILATA; H. MADHULATA; FIG. 170B), yam

(*Dioscorea*; see FIG. 175B), ash (*Fraxinus*; FIG. 176A), etc. In samara, the wings always develop from the pericarp and the fruit splits into its component parts, each enclosing a seed. In the sal tree, (*Shorea*; B. & H. SAL; FIG. 170E), *Hopea* (FIG. 170D) wood-oil tree (*Dipterocarpus*; B. & H. GARJAN; see FIG. 177A),etc., the fruit is also a winged one but here, the wings are the dry, persistent sepals. Winged fruits of this nature are known as **samaroids**.

(5) **Nut**. This is a dry, one-chambered and one-seeded fruit developing from a superior, *bi-* or *polycarpellary* ovary, *with the pericarp hard and woody*, eg. cashew-nut (*Anacardium*; see FIG. 166B), water chestnut (*Trapa*; see FIG. 14), chestnut (*Castanea*), oak (*Quercus*), beech (*Fagus*), etc.

Coconuts and palmyra-palms are drupes because in them it is the endorcarp that becomes hard and woody

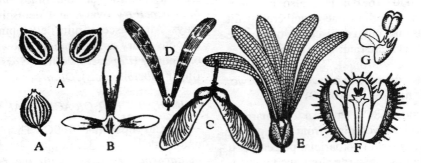

FIG. 170. Fruits (*contd.*). *A*, cremocarp of coriander; *A¹*, the same splitting away from the
axis (carpophore) into two mericarps; *B*, samara of *Hiptage*; *C*, double samara of
maple (*Acer*); *D*, samaroid of *Hopea*; *E*, the same of *Shorea*; *F*, regma of castor; *G*, carcerule of *Ocimum*

(and not the whole of the pericarp), and areca-nuts or betel-nuts and date-palms are (one seeded) berries because in them the pericarp is soft (fibrous in areca-nuts and pulpy in date-palms). It is the seed that is stony (and not the pericarp).

III. SPLITTING OR SCHIZOCARPIC FRUITS

(1) **Lomentum** (FIG. 169E-F). This is a type of dry, indehiscent legume constricted or partitioned between the seeds into a number of one-seeded compartments. The fruit splits transversely along the constrictions or partitions into one-seeded pieces, as in gum tree (*Acacia*), sensitive plant (*Mimosa*), Indian laburnum (*Cassia fistula*), nicker bean (*Entada gigas*; B. & H. GILA), *Desmodium*, e.g. Indian telegraph plant (*Desmo-dium gyrans*), etc.

(2) **Cremocarp** (FIG. 170A). This is a dry, indehiscent, two-chambered fruit developing from an inferior, bicarpellary ovary. When ripe, the fruit splits apart into indehiscent, one-seeded pieces, called *mericarps*. The mercarps remain attached to the prolonged end (*carpophore*) of the axis. Cremocarp is the characteristic fruit of *Umbelliferae*, e.g. coriander (*Coriandrum*), cumin (*Cuminum*), anise or fennel (*Foeniculum*), carrot (*Daucus*), etc.

(3) **Double Samara** (FIG. 176D). In maple (*Acer*), the fruit develops from a superior, bicarpellary ovary. When mature, it splits into two samaras, each with a wing and a seed. Such a fruit is called a double samara.

(4) **Regma** (FIG. 170F). This is a dry, indehiscent fruit developing from a syncarpous pistil. It splits away from the central axis into as many parts, called *cocci*, as there are carpels, each part containing one or two seeds. The seeds are liberated later, on the decay of the dry pericarp. Common examples are castor (*Ricinus*), *Euphorbia*, *Jatropha*, *Geranium*, etc.

(5) **Carcerule** (FIG. 170G). This is small, dry, indehiscent, four-chambered fruit developing from a superior, bicarpellary pistil. This is a fruit characteristic of *Labiatae*. The fruit remains enclosed

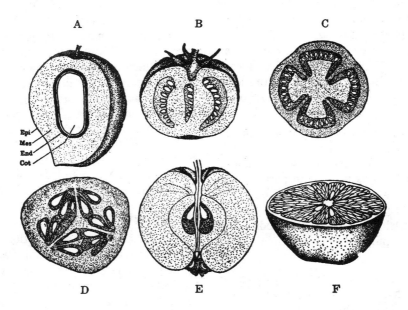

FIG. 171. Fruits (*contd.*). *A*, drupe of mango; *Epi*, epicarp; *Mes*, mesocarp; *End*, endocarp; *Cot*, cotyledon; *B-C*, berry of tomato in longitudinal and transverse sections; *D*, pepo of cucumber; *E*, pome of apple (see also FIG. 166A); *E*, hesperidium of orange

by the persistent calyx and later splits into four chambers, each enclosing a seed or nutlet.

IV. FLESHY FRUITS

(1) Drupe (FIG. 171A). This a fleshy, one- or more chambered and one- or more seeded fruit developing from a *monocarpellary* or *syncarpous* pistil. with the pericarp differentiated into the epicarp which forms the skin of the fruit, the mesocarp which is often fleshy, and the *endocarp which is hard and stony*. Hence, this fruit is also known as stone-fruit, e.g. mango (*Mangifera*), plum and peach (*Prunus*), coconut-palm (*Cocos*), palmyra-palm (*Borassus*), country almond (*Terminalia*), etc.

(2) Bacca or Berry (FIG. 171B-C). This is a superior (sometimes inferior), indehiscent, usually many-seeded, fleshy or pulpy fruit developing from a *single carpel* or more commonly, from a *syncarpous* pistil, with axile or parietal placentation, e.g. tomato, gooseberry, grapes, brinjal, banana, guava, papaw, etc. In berry, the seeds at first remain attached to placentae, but they separate from them (placentae) later and lie free in the pulp. Sometimes, a one-seeded berry may be found, e.g. date-palm. In *Artabotrys* (B. & H. KAN-TALI-CHAMPA), one-seeded berries develop in an aggregate (see FIG. 172E). The epicarp, mesocarp and endocarp may also be distinguished in such a berry, but it differs from the drupe in having no stony endocarp.

(3) Pepo (FIG. 171D). This is also a fleshy or pulpy, many-seeded fruit like the berry but it develops from an inferior, one-celled or spuriously three-celled, *syncarpous* pistil with parietal placentation. This type is seen most often in *Cucurbitaceae*, e.g. gourd, cucumber, melon, water melon, squash, etc. In pepo, the seeds, lying embedded in the pulp, remain attached to the placentae.

(4) Pome (FIG. 171E). This is an inferior, two- or more celled, fleshy, *syncarpous* fruit surrounded by the thalamus. The fleshy, edible part is composed of the thalamus, while the actual fruit lies within. Examples are found in apple and pear.

(5) Hesperidium (FIG. 171F). This is a superior,

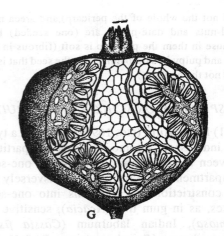

FIG. 171G. Balausta of pomegranate
(*Punica granatum*)

many-celled, fleshy fruit developing from a *syncarpous* pistil with axile placentation. Here, the endocarp projects inwards, forming distinct chambers, and the epicarp and mesocarp, fused together, form the loose or tight skin (rind) of the fruit as in *Citrus*, e.g. orange, lemon, etc.

(6) Balausta (FIG. 171G). This is a special type of inferior, many-chambered and many-seeded fruit developing from a *syncarpous* pistil with usually two whorls of basal carpels lying within the receptacle. But during the development of the ovary, the outer carpels become tilted up and superposed. The result is that two layers of chambers are formed, with the outer or upper ones occupying a parietal position. The pericarp of the fruit is tough and leathery and the chambers are made of thin walls of carpels. The testa of the seed is filled with an acid juice while the tegmen is horny. Pomegranate is a fruit characteristic of the balansta type.

B. Aggregate Fruits (FIG. 172).

An aggregate fruit is a collection of simple fruits (or fruitlets) developing from the apocarpous pistil (free carpels) of a flower. An aggregate of simple fruits borne by a single flower is otherwise known as an 'etaerio' and the common forms of etaerios are: (1) an **etaerio of follicles**, as in madar (*Calotropis*), *Daemia extensa*, and periwinkle (*Vinca*) with two follicles, in larkspur (*Delphinium*) and aconite (*Aconitum*) with three follicles

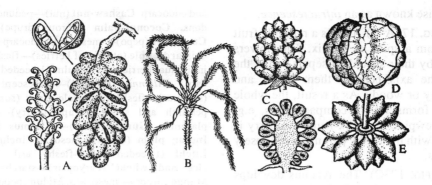

FIG. 172. Aggregate fruits. *A*, an etaerio of follicles in *Michelia*; *B*, an etaerio of achenes in *Naravelia*; *C*, an etaerio of drupes in *Rubus*; *D*, an etaerio of berries in custard-apple (*Annona*); *E*, the same in *Artabotrys*s

and in *Michelia* with numerous follicles; (2) an **etaerio of achenes**, as in *Clematis, Naravelia, Ranunculus*, strawberry, rose and lotus; (3) an **etaerio of drupes**, as in raspberry (*Rubus*), with small drupes or drupels (also called drupelets) remaining aggregated together on a fleshy thalamus; (4) an **etaerio of berries**, as in custard-apple (*Annona squamosa*) and bullock's heart (*A. reticulata*), where the berries lie embedded in the fleshy

thalamus, while in *Artabotrys* (B. & H. KANTALI-CHAMPA) and *Polyatlhia* (B. DEBDARU; H. DEVADARU or ASHOKA), the berries are distinct and separate.

C. Multiple or Composite Fruits (FIG. 173).

A multiple or composite fruit is that which develops from a number of flowers juxtaposed together, or in other words, from an inflorescence. Such a

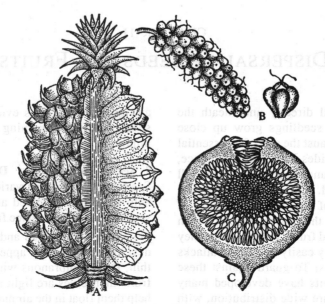

FIG. 173. Multiple fruits. *A*, sorosis of pineapple (*Ananas*); *B*, the same of mulberry (*Morus*); *C*, syconus of fig (*Ficus*)

fruit is otherwise known as an *infructescence*.

(1) **Sorosis** (FIG. 173A-B). This is a multiple fruit developing from a spike or spadix. The flowers fuse together by their succulent sepals and at the same time, the axis bearing them grows and becomes fleshy or woody. As a result, the whole inflorescence forms into a compact mass, e.g. pineapple, screwpine and jack-fruit. Mulberry is also a sorosis, with the fleshy part made of loosely attached sepals.

(2) **Syconus** (FIG. 173C). The syconus develops from a hollow, pear-shaped, fleshy receptacle which encloses a number of minute male and female flowers. The receptacle grows, becomes fleshy and forms the so-called fruit. It really encloses a number of true fruits or achenes, which develop from the female flowers lying within the receptacle at its base, as in *Ficus*, e.g. fig, banyan, peepul, etc.

Some Common Fruits and their Edible Parts. Apple (pome)—fleshy thalamus. **Banana** (berry)—mesocarp and endocarp. **Cashew-nut** (nut)—peduncle and cotyledons. **Coconut-palm** (fibrous drupe)—endosperm. **Cucumber** (pepo)— mesocarp, endocarp and placentae. **Custard-apple** (etaerio of berries)—fleshy pericarp of individual berries. **Date-palm** (1-seeded berry)—pericarp. *Dillennia* (special)—accrescent calyx. **Fig** (syconus)—fleshy receptacle. **Jack** (sorosis)—bracts, perianth and seeds. **Grape** (berry)—pericarp and placentae. **Guava** (berry)—thalamus and pericarp. **Indian plum** (drupe)—mesocarp including epicarp. **Litchi** (1-seeded nut)—fleshy aril. **Maize, oak, rice and wheat** (caryopsis)—starchy endosperm. **Mango** (drupe)—mesocarp. **Melon** (pepo)—mesocarp. **Orange** (hesperidium) —juicy placental hairs. **Palmyra-palm** (fibrous drupe)—mesocarp. **Papaw** (berry)—mesocarp. **Pea** (legume)—cotyledons. **Pear** (pome)—fleshy thalamus. **Pineapple** (sorosis) —outer portion of receptacle, bracts and perianth. **Pomegranate** (special)—juicy outer coat of the seed. **Pummelo or shaddock** (hesperidium)—juicy placental hairs. **Strawberry** (etaerio of achemes)—succulent thalamus. **Tomato** (berry)—pericarp and placentae. **Wood-apple** (a special type called amphisarca) —inner endocarp and placentae.

CHAPTER 11

Dispersal of Seeds and Fruits

If seeds and fruits fall directly underneath the mother plant and the seedlings grow up close together, they soon exhaust the soil of its essential food constituents. Besides, the available space, light and air (oxygen) under such a condition fall far short of the demand. A struggle for existence thus ensues for want of an adequate quantity of essential requirements, the consequence of which may be fatal to seeds and fruits. Further, when they grow together, they may easily be prey to attacks by herbivorous animals. To guard against these dangers, seeds and fruits have developed many special devices to ensure wide distribution, with the result that at least some of them are likely to meet with favourable conditions for germination and growth. It is thus evident that the risk of a species of plant becoming extinct is reduced to a minimum.

1. Seeds and Fruits Dispersed by Wind. Seeds and fruits have various adaptations which help them to be carried away by the wind to a shorter or longer distance from the parent plant.

(1) **Wings.** The seeds and fruits of many plants develop one or more appendages in the form of thin, flat, membranous wings, and the seeds and fruits thenselves are light and dry. These devices help them float in the air and facilitate their dispersion by wind. Thus, we find that the seeds of *Oroxylum* (FIG. 174A), *Cinchona* (FIG. 174B),

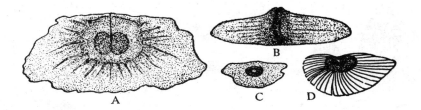

FIG. 174. Winged Seeds. *A, Oroxylum; B, Cinchona; C, Stereospermum; D, Lagerstroemia*

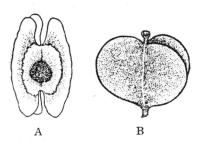

FIG. 175. *A*, winged seed of drumstick
(*Moringa*): *B*, winged fruit of yam (*Dioscorea*)

Stereospermum (FIG. 174C), *Lagerstroemia* (B. &.
H. JARUL; FIG. 174D) drumstick (*Moringa*; B. SAJI-
NA; H. SAINJNA; FIG. 175A), and *Tecoma* are pro-
vided with wings. Similarly, many fruits are also
provided with one or more wings for the same pur-
pose, e.g. yam (*Dioscorea*; FIG. 175B), ash
(*Fraxinus*; FIG. 176B), *Terminalia myriocarpa* (B.
HOLOK; FIG. 176B) *Hopea* (FIG. 176C), maple

(*Acer*; FIG. 176D), wood-oil tree (*Dipterocarpus*;
B. & H. GARJAN; FIG. 177A), *Hiptage* (B. MADHA-
BILATA; H. MADHULATA; FIG. 177B), *Dodonaea* (a
hedge plant), and sal tree (*Shorea*; B. & H. SAL;
FIG. 177C).

(2) **Parachute Mechanism.** In many plants of
Compositae, the calyx is modified into hair-like
structures known as **pappus** (FIG.179A). The pappus is persistent in the fruit and opens out in an
umbrella-like fashion. As the fruit gets detached
from the parent plant, the pappus acts like a
parachute and helps it float in the air. The fruit is
often seen being carried by the wind to a great
distance.

(3) **Censer Mechanism.** The seeds of certain
plants can be scattered by the wind only after the
dehiscence of the fruit. In such cases, the seeds are
often not discharged from the fruit unless the latter is
shaken by the wind. Thus, in poppy (*Papaver*),

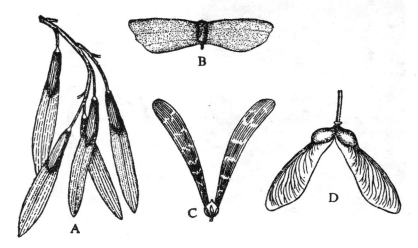

FIG. 176. Winged fruits. *A*, ash (*Fraxinus*): *B, Terminalia myriocarpa; C, Hopea; D*, maple (*Acer*)

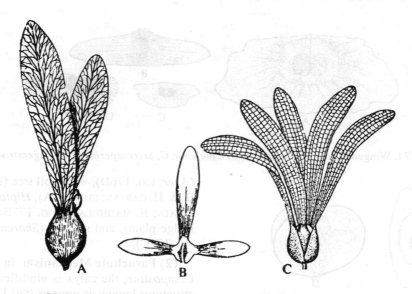

FIG. 177. Winged Fruits (*contd.*). *A, Dipterocarpus; B, Hiptage; C, Shorea*

prickly poppy (*Argemone*), bath sponge or loofah (*Luffa*), pelican flower (*Aristolochia gigas*; B. HANSALATA; FIG.178A), etc., the fruit dehisces and then, when it is disturbed by the wind, the seeds are thrown out.

(4) Hairs. The seeds of madar (*Calotropis*; FIG.179B), milkweed (*Asclepias*), *Holarrhena* (B.

KURCHI; H. KARCHI), devil tree (*Alstonia*; FIG. 179C) and cotton (FIG. 179D) are provided with hairs either in 1 or 2 tufts, or all over the body. These hairs aid the distribution of seeds by the wind.

(5) Persistent Styles. In *Clematis* (FIG. 180A) and *Naravelia* (FIG. 180B), the styles are persistent

FIG. 178. *A*, pelican flower (*Aristolochia gigas*) with duck-shaped flowers; *B*, a fruit of the same like a hanging basket

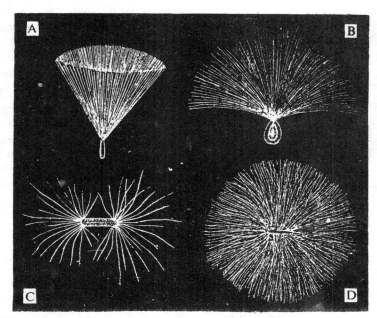

FIG. 179. Pappus and Hairy Seeds. *A*, pappus of a *Compositae* fruit; *B*, hairy seed of madar (*Calotropis*); *C*, hairy seed of devil tree (*Alstonia*); *D*, hairy seed of cotton

and very feathery. The fruits are, thus, easily carried away by the wind.

(6) **Light Seeds and Fruits.** Some seeds and fruits are so light and minute in size that they may easily be carried away by the gentlest breeze. Orchids bear the smallest seeds in the vegetable kingdom. In them, millions of dust-like seeds are produced in a capsule. The seeds (fruits) of some grasses are also very small and light. The seeds of *Cinchona* (the quinine-yielding plant) are also very small, thin and extremely light, and also provided with a membranous wing (see FIG. 174B). There are about 2,500 seeds to a gram. In *Bucklandia*, a handsome tree of the Khasi Hills, about 250 seeds, mostly winged, weigh a gram. In *Terminalia myriocarpa* (HOLOK), a timber tree of Assam, about 180 seeds weigh a gram.

2. Seeds and Fruits Dispersed by Water. Seeds and fruits to be dispersed by water usually develop floating devices in the form of spongy or fibrous outer coats. The fibrous fruit of coconut is capable of floating long distances in the sea without suffering any injury. Hence, coconut is commonly seen on sea coasts and marine islands. The

same is the case with double coconut or *coco de mer* (*Lodoicea maldivica*; FIG.181), a native of the Seychelles Islands. The plants are dioecious and begin to flower after 30 years of growth. The female plant bears the largest, two-lobed seed and fruit weighing 18 kg., or sometimes even more, and measuring often about a metre in length. The fruit takes 6-10 years to ripen. The fruits were seen floating in the Indian Ocean long before the tree was discovered. In lotus (see FIG. 96C), the spongy thalamus, bearing the fruits on its hemispheric top, floats about in water and drifts along the currents of

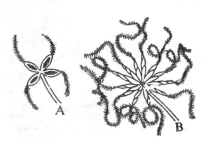

FIG. 180. Persistent sytles. *A*, fruits of *Clematis*; *B*, fruits of *Naravelia*

FIG. 181. Double coconut seed (*Lodoicea*)

the water or wind. Sometimes the seeds are small and light and can float on water, e.g. seeds of water lily. They are also provided with an *aril* which encloses air. The seeds and fruits of river-side plants are regularly carried downstream by currents.

3. Seeds Dispersed by Explosive Fruits. Many fruits burst with a sudden jerk, with the result that the seeds are scattered a few yards away from the parent plant. Common examples of explosive fruits are afforded by balsam (*Impatiens*), wood-sorrel (*Oxalis*), night jasmine (*Nyctanthes*), castor (*Ricinus*), etc. The ripe fruits of balsam burst

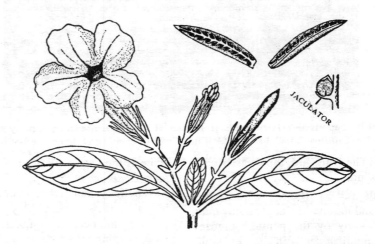

FIG. 182. *Ruellia tuberosa*; note the explosive fruit

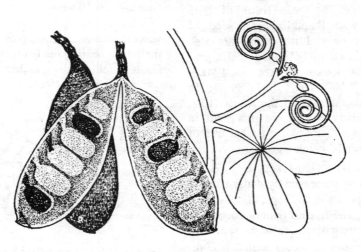

FIG. 183. *Bauhinia vahlii*; note the explosive fruit

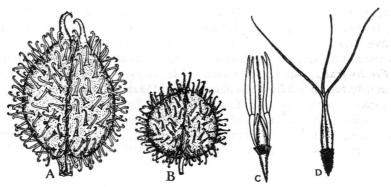

FIG. 184. *A*, fruit *Xanthium* with curved hooks; *B*, fruit of *Urena* with curved hooks;
C, spikelet of love thorn (*Chrysopogon*) with stiff hairs; *D*, seed (fruit) of spear grass (*Aristida*) with stiff hairs

suddenly when touched. The valves roll up inwards and the seeds are ejected with great force and scattered in all directions. Many plants of *Acanthaceae* bear explosive fruits which, under wet or dry conditions, dehisce suddenly from the apex to the base and throw out the seeds with considerable force. In many such cases, the seeds are also provided with jaculators (curved hooks) which straighten out suddenly and help in their ejection. Thus, when the dry fruits of *Ruellia tuberosa* (FIG. 182) come in contact with water, usually after a shower of rain, they suddenly burst with a noise into two valves and the seeds are scattered on all sides. Similarly, the mature fruits of *Andrographis, Barleria, Acanthus,* etc. burst suddenly when the air is dry, and the seeds are ejected. The cracking sound of the bursting fruits of *Phlox* and *Barleria* is distinctly audible on a bright sunny day.

A very interesting example of bursting fruits is found in camel's foot climber (*Bauhinia vahlii*; B. CHEHUR or LATAKANCHAN; H. CHAMBULI; FIG. 183). Its long pods, sometimes more than 30 cm. in length, explode violently with a loud noise, scattering the seeds in all directions.

4. Seeds and Fruits Dispersed by Animals. Many seeds and fruits are dispersed through the agency of animals, including human beings, and have, thus, evolved certain adaptations for the purpose. (a) *Hooked fruits:* Many fruits are provided with hooks, barbs, spines, bristles, stiff hairs, etc., on their bodies, by means of which they adhere to

the bodies of woolly animals as well as to the clothing of mankind, and are often unwittingly carried by them to distant places. Thus, the fruits of *Xanthium* and *Urena* (FIG. 184A-B) are covered with numerous curved hooks. The spikelets of love thorn (*Chrysopogon*; FIG. 184C) and the seeds (fruits) of spear grass (*Aristida;* FIG. 184D) are provided with a cluster of minute, stiff hairs pointing upwards. The flower clusters of *Pupalia* (FIG. 185B) bear stellate hooked bristles spreading outwards. Tiger's nail *(Martynia annua = M. diandra;* B. BAGHANKHI; H. SHERNUI; FIG. 185C) is a very interesting case. Its seed is provided with two, very sharply pointed, stiff and bent hooks for effective dispersion by woolly animals. In *Tribulus* (B. GOKHRI-KANTA; H. GOKHRU), there are sharp,

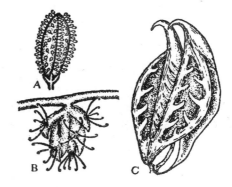

FIG. 185. *A*, fruit of *Boerhaavia* with sticky glands (see also FIG. II/41B); *B*, flowers of *Pupalia* with hooked bristles; *C*, seed of tiger's nail (*Martynia*) with a pair of sharp, curved hooks

rigid spines on the fruit. (b) *Sticky fruits*: For the same purpose, the fruits of *Boerhaavia* (FIG. 185A) and *Plumbago* have sticky glands on their body. The seeds of mistletoe (*Viscum*; see FIG. 24) are very sticky. (c) *Fleshy fruits*: Many such fruits, coloured conspicuously, are carried from one place to another for the sake of their beauty. (d) *Edible fruits*: Human beings and birds are active and useful agents in distributing such fruits. Commonly, birds feed upon the pulpy portion of fruits like guava, grape, fig, etc., and pass out the undigested seeds with the faeces. The seeds then germinate and grow up into new plants. The seeds of many pulpy fruits are also distributed by birds over wide areas. Jackals feed upon dates, plums, etc., and the seeds germinate after passing through their alimentary canal. Bats and squirrels are also useful in dispersing seeds and fruits. Seeds and fruits are widely distributed, even from one country to another, also through the agency of mankind.

2   HISTOLOGY

THE CELL

A Short History. The study of histology dates from the year 1665 when plant cells were discovered for the first time. It was **Robert Hooke** (1635-1703), an Englishman, who first studied the internal structure of a thin slice of bottle cork with the help of a microscope improved by himself. He discovered, for the first time, a porous structure in it very much like a honey-comb, and to each individual cavity of such a structure he applied the term **cell.** It was only the cell-wall that was noticed, this being the prominent part of the cell. **Jansen,** a spectacle maker of Middleburg, in Holland, invented the compound microscope in 1590. **Leeuwenhoek** (1653-1723), a clerk in cloth warehouse of Delft, in Holland, at the age of 21, in the year 1653 developed a mania for grinding lenses. He pursued this work with zeal and assidity and within 20 years (1653-73) achieved marvellous fineness, accuracy and perfection in his lenses. He made about 400 compound microscopes and gave a demonstration of these before the Royal Society in 1667. He was the first to discover bacteria, protozoa and other minute forms of life—'the wretched beasties' as he called them—under his own microscope.

The prominent workers of that time, who studied plant tissues under the microscope, were **Grew** and **Malpighi.** Grew (1628-1711), an English physician and botanist, published his first paper on plant tissues in 1671 and the second one in 1682. Malpighi (1628-94), an Italian physician, studied the various tissues of vascular plants, and published his first paper in 1675. Grew and Malpighi discovered parenchymata, fibres and vessels. Malpighi further discovered stomata.

In 1838-39, **Schleiden** (1804-81), a German botanist, and **Schwann** (1810-82), a German zoologist, proved definitely that both plants and animals are cellular in character and founded the **cell theory. Von Mohl** (1805-72) and **Nageli** (1817-91), working independently, distinguished in 1844 the two main parts of a cell : the cell-wall and the contents. To the granular semi-fluid contents filling up the cavity of the plant cell the name **protoplasm** was given by Von Mohl in 1846. **Cohn** in 1850 established the fact that plant protoplasm and animal protoplasm are identical. **De Bary** (1831-88), investigating plant cells, and Max Schultze, investigating animal cells, established the **protoplasm theory** about the year 1861. This states that the cells or units of plants and animals are tiny masses of protoplasm, each mass containing a **nucleus.** The cell-wall of a plant cell, though prominent under the microscope, is of secondary importance, being formed later by the protoplasm for its own advantage.

In 1831, the nucleus of the cell was discovered by **Robert Brown** (1773-1858). In 1846, **Nageli** (1817-91) first showed that new cells arose by division of the pre-existing cells. In 1880, the first satisfactory account of the structure of the nucleus and its mode of division was, however, given by **Strasburger** (1844-1912) although the division was roughly observed by **Hofmeister** in 1849. The early discovery by Strasburger of the constant number of chromosomes in species was finally confirmed by **Boveri** in 1900. In 1884, it was recognised by Strasburger, Weismann (1834-1914) and others that the nucleus is concerned in the problem of inheritance of characters. Between 1880 and 1892, **Flemming** gave a detailed account of the longitudinal splitting of the chromosomes and their equal distribution among the daughter cells. In 1888, Strasburger discovered reduction division in angiosperms and in 1891, he observed the same phenomenon in mosses and ferns. In 1905, the term meiosis was applied to reduction division by **Farmer** and **Moore.** Polyploidy and aneuploidy were discovered between 1912 and 1927—triploidy ($3n$) by **Miss Lutz** in 1912, tetraploidy ($4n$) by **Digby** in the same year, pentaploidy ($5n$) by **Nawaschin** in 1925 and 1927, aneuploidy ($2n-1, 2n+1, 4n+1$) by **Tackholm** in 1992, and by **Blakeslee** in 1924.

Further important early work on plant anatomy may

only be mentioned. **Sanio's** work on the activity of the cambium and the formation of the secondary tissues (1863), **De Bary's** work on comparative anatomy (1877) and on tissue systems (1884), **Jeffrey's** theory of stellar structure (1868), **Nageli's** theory of single-celled apical meristem (1858), **Hanstein's** histogen theory of apical meristem (1868), **Schmidt's** tunica—corpus theory (1924), **Haberlandt's** work on physiological plant anatomy (1884), etc., cannot be dealt with here.

The **electron microscope**, the latest in the series of microscopes, magnifying objects more than 2,00,000 X, was invented by two German scientists, Knoll and Ruska, in 1932. Exciting pictures of cells began to be revealed by this instrument, much improved in the meantime, since early 1950. Many of the solid grains and rods of the cytoplasm, as seen under a compound microscope, have now proved to be complex structures under an electron microscope. In view of such revelations, biologists are now forming a new concept of cell organization.

CELL STRUCTURE

Cells are the fundamental structural and functional units that the plant body or the animal body is composed of. A plant **cell** may be defined as a unit or independent, tiny or microscopic mass of **protoplasm** enclosing in it a denser spherical or oval body, called the **nucleus**. It is bounded by a distinct wall called the **cell-wall**. The protoplasm and nucleus are living, while the cell-wall is non-living, the latter having been formed by the protoplasm, primarily for its own protection. The living parts of a cell (protoplasm, nucleus and other living bodies) together constitute the **protoplast** of the cell—a collective and convenient term introduced by Hanstein in 1880. A plant cell thus consists of a protoplast (representing the living parts) and a cell-wall (forming a nonliving framework round the protoplast to maintain its shape and firmness and to afford protection required). The cell-wall also has to regulate the flow of materials into and out of the cell.

Cells vary widely in shape and size. In shape they may commonly be spherical, oval, polygonal, rectangular or considerably elongated. When young, they are often spherical or of like nature. Usually they are very minute in size and invisible to the naked eye. The average size of fully developed rounded or polygonal cells varies between 1/10 and 1/100 of a millimetre. Sometimes, as in fleshy fruits and pith, they may be as big as 1 mm. or even bigger, or as small as 1/200 mm. or even smaller. Among the known cells bacteria are the smallest, usually ranging between 1/100 and 1/1,000 mm. Still smaller in size are the viruses, which defy microscopic observation. Fibrous cells are considerably elongated. Their length usually varies from 1 to 3 mm., but in woody stems they may often be a big as 6 mm. or even 8 mm. In some fibre-yielding plants such as flax, hemp and rhea, the fibrous cells may grow to a length of 20 to 550 mm. Larger still are the latex cells.

THE PROTOPLAST

The protoplast is the living unit—actually the physiological unit—of a cell, while the **protoplasm** is the essential living material that comprises the different parts of it (the protoplast). Protoplasm is the only substance that is endowed with life and, therefore, plants and animals containing this substance in their body are regarded as living. As the protoplasm dies, the cell ceases to perform any function for the plant or the animal, which then becomes inert and dead as a whole. Protoplasm is, thus, fittingly described as the *physical basis of life*. As the protoplast as a whole has to perform manifold functions of a cell, such as manufacture of food, nutrition, growth, respiration, reproduction, etc., it is differentiated into distinct living (protoplasmic) bodies: (1) cytoplasm, (2) nucleus, and in special cells (3) plastids. These are only masses of protoplasm differentiated into distinct bodies (FIG. 1C) to perform specialized functions. It must, however, be noted that these living bodies are never newly formed in the cells but always develop from pre-existing ones and that one kind of living body cannot give rise to another kind.

1. CYTOPLASM.

The protoplasmic mass of a cell leaving out the nucleus and the plastids is otherwise called cell-protoplasm or **cytoplasm**. When the cell is young, the cytoplasm fills in the space between the cell-

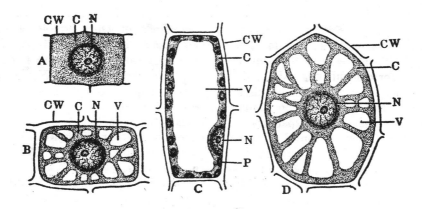

FIG. 1. Plant Cells. *A*, a very young cell; *B*, a growing cell with many small vacuoles; *C*, a mature cell with a large vacuole; *D*, a mature cell with many vacuoles. *CW*, cell-wall; *C*, cytoplasm; *N*, nucleus; *V*, vacuole; *P*, plastid (chloroplast)

wall and the nucleus. The surface of the cytoplasm forms into an extremely thin and delicate membrane known as the **plasma membrane** or **ectoplasm**. This plasma membrane is also hyaline but non-granular and somewhat firmer in consistency than the rest of the cytoplasm. It lies adpressed against the cell-wall and is a very important layer, controlling the entrance and exit of substances into and out of the cell. The inner granular mass of the cytoplasm is often called **endoplasm**. Besides, the cytoplasm encloses numerous granules whose nature is obscure. These are known as the *microsomes*. They may represent pieces of the endoplasmic reticulum (see FIG. 6B). The fluid portion or matrix of the cytoplasm is known as the **hyaloplasm**. When the cell is very young (FIG. 1A) it remains completely filled with the cytoplasm, but as it grows a large number of small, non-protoplasmic but fluid-filled cavities of varying sizes, apparently like little bubbles, appear in the cytoplasm. These are called **vacuoles** (*vacuus*, empty). As the cell enlarges (FIG. 1B), these small vacuoles begin to fuse together and finally, in the mature cell, they form one large central vacuole which occupies the major part of the cell-cavity. The cytoplasm under this condition is pushed outwards as a thin layer alongside the cell-wall, with the nucleus and the plastids lying embedded in this layer (FIG. 1C). Sometimes, instead of one, a number of comparatively small vacuoles persist in

a mature cell, and then the cytoplasm occurs as delicate strands around those vacuoles and also as a very thin layer lining up with the cell-wall. These strands are seen to radiate from around the nucleus, often suspending it in the cavity of the cell (FIG. 1D). The vacuole is filled with a fluid called **cell-sap**. Dissolved in the cell-sap, or lying in a state of suspension in it, there occur various chemical compounds. The vacoule is, thus, regarded as a storehouse of water, various salts, certain organic substances (mainly soluble food materials), anthocyanins, etc. It also maintains the requisite turgidity of the cell and of the tissue as a whole. The layer of cytoplasm in contact with the vacuole and surrounding it as a membrane is known as the **vacuole membrane** or **tonoplasm**. Like the ectoplasm, this membrane is also differentially permeable.

Physical Nature of Protoplasm. Protoplasm is a transparent, foamy or granular, slimy, semi-fluid substance, somewhat like the white of an egg. It is never homogeneous but contains granules of varying shapes and sizes, suspended in solution. Therefore, it looks finely granular under the microscope. There are, of course, many dissolved materials in it. Although often semi-fluid, it may be fluid, or viscous. It completely fills up the cavity of the young cell, but in a mature cell it may ocur as a thin layer against the cell-wall (FIG. 1C) or it may occur as delicate strands around the vacuoles (FIG. 1D), as already described. In its *active* state, the protoplasm remains saturated with water, which makes up 75-90 per cent of the content. With decreasing water content, its vital activity diminishes and gradually comes to a standstill, as in dry seeds. Protoplasm coagulates on heating and when killed, it loses its transparency. It responds to the action of external stimuli, such as a needle or pin-pricks, electric shocks, application of particular chemicals, sudden variations of temperature or of light, etc. On stimulation, the protoplasm contracts but expands again when the

a highly complex mixture of a variety of organic compounds, of which proteins are predominant, and these are of various kinds. A complex type of protein called **nucleoprotein** is constant in the cytoplasm and the nucleus. Nucleoprotein (see p. 123) is composed of nucleic acids and certain proteins. There are two important types of nucleic acids — DNA (deoxyribonucleic acid) and RNA (ribonucleic acid). While RNA is constant in the cytoplasm and nucleolus, DNA is constant in the chromosomes.

The exact chemical composition of the living protoplasm, however, cannot be determined

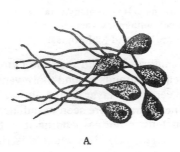 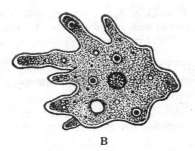

A   B

FIG. 2. Movements of Protoplasm. *A*, ciliary movement; *B*, amoeboid movement

stimulating agent is removed. This 'contractility', involving both contraction and expansion, first demonstrated by Kuhne in 1864 in the staminal hair of spiderwort (*Tradescantia*), is an inherent power of protoplasm.

Protoplasm is semi-permeable in nature, i.e. it allows only certain substances and not all to enter its body. This property is, however, lost when the protoplasm is killed.

Under normal conditions, the protoplasm of a living cell is in a state of slow but constant motion. In many cases, however, it shows distinct movements of different kinds (see pp. 121-22).

Chemical Nature of Protoplasm. The principal component of protoplasm is water. Otherwise, it is

because any attempt to analyse it kills it outright, causing some unknown changes in it. Besides, it undergoes continual change and, therefore, its composition is not constant. Further, protoplasm always encloses in its body many foreign substances in varying quantities, so it is not possible to get it in a pure state. The analysis of dead protoplasm reveals a long list of elements present in it. Of these the most conspicuous are oxygen (O)—about 65%, carbon (C)—about 18.3%, hydrogen (H)—about 11%, and nitrogen (N)—about 2.5%. Other elements making up the remaining 3% evidently occur in very small quantities. These are chlorine (Cl), sulphur (S), phosphorus (P), silicon (Si), calcium (Ca), magnesium (Mg), potassium (K), iron (Fe) and sodium (Na).

Structure. Protoplasm, as it works in the cell, undergoes dynamic physical changes and, therefore, its ultimate structure cannot be known with any amount of certainty. So from time to time, its structure has been variously expressed as *(a)* **fibrillar**—consisting of interlacing, fine fibres or fibrils (Flemming, 1882), *(b)* **alveolar** or **foamy**—consisting of a froth of minute bubbles (Butschli, 1878) and *(c)* **granular**—consisting of fine grains or granules more or less uniformly dispersed throughout the protoplasm (Hanstein, about 1886).

Traces of the following are also present : zinc (Zn), manganese (Mn), aluminium (Al), copper (Cu), boron (B) and molybdenum (Mo) and often a few others. Active protoplasm contains a high percentage of water—usually 75-90%. and remains saturated with it. The solid matter of the protoplasm contains the following : proteins—40-60%, fatty substances (true fats and lipids, particularlylecithin)—12-14%,carbohydrates—12-14%, and inorganic salts—5-7%.

Colloidal State of Protoplasm. The constituents protoplasm, mainly proteins, form a colloidal system (see part III, Chapter 1). In a colloidal state a matter is divided into very fine particles—aggregations of molecules, and no individual molucules as in a solution, which are dispersed through a continuous medium, mostly a liquid or a semi-solid. In the case of protpplasm the dispersion medium is water with dissolved salts and other substances in it, and the colloidal particles of proteins are dispersed through the medium. A colloid exists as a mixture and not as a compound but the colloidal particles are mostly not filterable through a fine parchment membrane. In many colloids the particles are stable, while in others they are unstable, settling down under slight chemical or physical change. A colloidal mixture may be fluid or viscous. A fluid colloid is cassed a sol and a viscous colloid, a gel. Protoplasm mostly exists in the state of a sol but may change to a gel under certain conditions, the changes being reversible (sol ↔ gel). But when it dies, it cannot change from one state to the other. The colloidal system of protoplasm is believed to be responsible for its various life-processes.

Tests. (a) Iodine solution stains protoplasm brownish yellow. (b) dilute caustic potash dissolves it. (c) Milton's reagent (nitrate of mercury) stains it brick-red; the reaction is hastened by heating.

Movement of Protoplasm. Protoplasm shows movement of different kinds. Naked masses of protoplasm, not enclosed by the cell-wall, show two kinds of movement—**ciliary** and **amoeboid.** A streaming movement, known as *cyclosis*, can be seen within protoplasm enclosed by the cell-wall. Cyclosis is of two kinds—**rotation and circulation.**

(1) **Ciliary Movement** (FIG. 2A) is the *swimming* movement of free, minute, protoplasmic bodies, such as the zoospores of many algae and fungi, bacteria, antherozoids of mosses and ferns, etc., provided with one or more special organs of motion in the form of whip-like structures, called cilia or flagella. The vibration of these cilia enable such ciliary bodies to move or swim freely and rapidly in water.

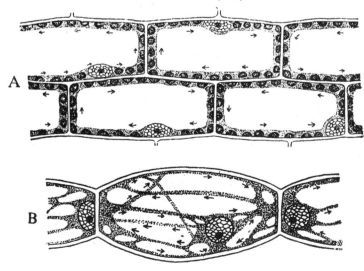

FIG. 3. Movements of Protoplasm (*contd.*), *A*, rotation in the leaf of *Vallisneria;*
B, circulation in the staminal hair of *Commelina obliqua*

(2) **Amoeboid Movement** (FIG. 2A) is the creeping movement of a naked mass of protoplasm. This protoplasmic mass moves or creeps by the protrusion of one or more parts of its body in the form of false feet or pseudopodia (*pseudos*, false; *podes*, foot) and their withdrawal at the next moment, very much like the animalcule *Amoeba*. In the absence of a cell-wall, the protoplasmic mass has no definite shape and is capable of engulfing solid particles of food. Amoeboid movement is exhibited by many slime fungi and large solitary zoospores and gametes of certain algae and fungi.

(3) **Rotation** (FIG. 3A). When the protoplasm moves or streams within a cell alongside the cell-wall, clockwise or anti-clockwise, round a large central vacuole, the movement is expressed as rotation. The direction of movement is constant so

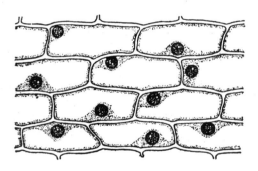

FIG. 4A. Cellular structure and nuclei in onion scale

far as a particular cell is concerned. As the protoplasm rotates, it carries in its current the nucleus and the plastids. Rotation is distinctly seen in *Vallisneria, Hydrilla, Chara* and *Nitella,* and also in many other aquatic plants.

(4) **Circulation** (FIG. 3B). When the protoplasm moves or *streams* in different directions within a cell round a number of small vacuoles, the movement is called circulation. In this process, the protoplasmic mass around the nucleus radiates in different directions in the form of delicate strands. Each strand then moves round one or more vacuoles and finally comes back to the nucleus. Circulation is very distinctly seen in the purplish

staminal hairs of *Commelina obliqua* (B. JATA-KANSHIRA; H. KANJURA). It is also seen in the staminal hairs of spiderwort (*Tradescantia*) and *Rhoeo discolor,* and in the young shoot-hairs of gourd, elephant ear plant (*Begonia*) and in many other land plants.

2. NUCLEUS.

Embedded in the cytoplasm, is a specialized protoplasmic body, usually spherical or oval and much denser than the cytoplasm itself. This is the **nucleus**. Its shape depends to some extent on the nature of the cell in which it occurs. In the young cell it occupies a median position and is almost always spherical or oval, but in the long cell it may become correspondingly elongated. In the mature cell, due to the formation of vacuoles, it lies in the lining layer of the cytoplasm and may become flattened against the cell-wall. Nuclei are universally present in all living cells. In the higher plants, only a single nucleus is present in each cell (FIG. 4A). In the latex tissue (see FIG. 40) and in many algae and fungi, numerous nuclei are often seen in a single cell. In the lower organisms like bacteria and blue-green algae, however, true nuclei are absent, but there is corresponding nuclear material. Nuclei may vary widely in size from 1μ to 500μ (microns). Their usual size, however, is $5\text{-}25\mu$ (microns). A nucleus can never be newly formed, but multiplies in number by the division of the pre-existing one.

Structure. Each nucleus (FIG. 4B) is surrounded by a thin, transparent membrane known as (1) the **nuclear membrane** which separates the nucleus from the surrounding cytoplasm. The electron microscope reveals that the membrane is of a double nature and that it is provided with numerous

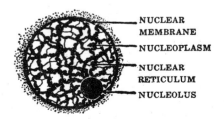

NUCLEAR MEMBRANE
NUCLEOPLASM
NUCLEAR RETICULUM
NUCLEOLUS

FIG. 4B. Nuclear structure

pores through which transport of materials takes place between the nucleus and the cytoplasm (see FIG. 6B). The shape of the nucleus depends partly on its membrane and partly on the shape of the cell in which it occurs. Within the membrane, completely filling up the space, there is a dense but clear mass of protoplasm known as (2) the **nuclear sap** or **nucleoplasm** or **karyolymph**. Suspended in the nucleoplasm are numerous, fine, crooked threads, loosely connected here and there, forming a sort of network, called (3) the **nuclear reticulum** or **chromatin network**. The modern idea is that the chromatin threads, otherwise called **chromosomes**, occur as separate and independent structures in the nucleus and that they are made of nucleoprotein (see below). Besides, one or more highly refractive, relatively large and usually spherical bodies without any membrane, but much denser than the nucleoplasm, also occur in the nucleus. There are known as (4) the **nucleoli**. They remain attached to certain chromosomes in their particular regions and are regarded as parts of those chromosomes.

Chemical Composition. Chemically, the nucleus is more or less similar to the cytoplasm. The nucleus, however, is predominantly composed of nucleoproteins, which are phosphorus-containing nucleic acids (see below and p. 124), and certain proteins. Nucleic acids occur in the nucleus to the extent of 15-30% of its dry weight. Besides, the nucleus also contains some amount of lipids, particularly phospholipid. Inorganic salts, such as those of Ca, Mg, Fe and Zn, are also present in the nucleus in small quantities and play an important role in several biochemical processes.

Functions. The nucleus and the protoplasm are together responsible for the life of the cell. Experiments and observations have proved that the nucleus is the controlling centre of all the vital activities of the cell, particularly assimilation and respiration. If the nucleus is removed from a cell, the protoplasm ceases to function and soon dies. The electron microscope has further revealed that it is the DNA of the chromosomes that is primarily responsible for the functioning of the nucleus. The DNA sends a code or message to the cytoplasm, particularly to the ribosomes, through nucleotides and RNA and induces the cytoplasm to take up specific work. The principal functions performed by the nucleus are, however, as follows: (1) The nucleus takes a direct part in reproduction, asexual or sexual. (2) The nucleus takes the initiative in cell division, i.e., it is the nucleus and the chromosomes that divide first and this is followed by the division of the cell. (3) The nucleus, more particularly the chromosomes, are the *bearers* of hereditary material, i.e. DNA. It is, in fact, the DNA of the chromosomes that is the sole hereditary material and the characteristics of the parent plants are transmitted to the offspring through the medium of this DNA. (See also Chemistry of Chromosomes, p.146).

Nucleic Acids[1]. Nucleic acids are wonderful discoveries of modern times. They are universally present in the nucleus and in the cytoplasm of all living cells, and are now definitely known to form the chemical basis of life. They are very complex organic compounds made of phosphate, pentose sugar (ribose, as in RNA or deoxyribose, as in DNA) and nitrogen bases (purine and pyrimidine; see p. 124). Nucleic acid molecules are very large, even larger than protein molecules, and consist of infinite numbers of *repeating* nucleotide units linked in any sequence into a long chain. They are, thus, high polymers of nucleotides and have very high molecular weights. Depending on the sequence of nucleotide units in the chain, the nucleic acids may be of an infinite variety of

---

[1] Much has been known about the importance of nucleic acids through the brilliant researches carried out by several investigators extending over a period of 30 years. In 1868, Miescher, a German chemist, first isolated from human pus cells a peculiar phosphorus-containing compound which he called nuclein (later renamed nucleic acid). Its importance was not, however, recognized for many years. In 1944, Avery, MacLeod and McCarthy, who were working on bacteria and virus at the Rockefeller Institute in New York, showed for the first time that DNA is the sole genetic material (confirmed by others within the next few years). In 1953, Wilkins, a bio-physicist of King's College, London, worked out the molecular structure of nucleic acids. In the same year (i.e. 1953), Watson and Crick

structures. **A nucleotide** is a molecular unit (monomer) of a nucleic acid molecule (macro-), and consists of three sub-units; a phosphate, a pentose sugar (ribose or deoxyribose) and a nitrogen base (purine or pyrimidine). Phosphate and sugar alternate as links (or subchains) in the chain, while the nitrogen base projects inward from the sugar link. There are a few types of nucleotides, each with a specific nitrogen base. They may also occur free in the cytoplasm as ATP, DPN, TPN, CoA (coenzyme A), etc. A nucleotide is formed when a phosphate group is added to a nucleoside. **A nucleoside** is a compound consisting of two sub-units : a pentose sugar and a nitrogen base. It is the precursor of a nucleotide. There are two kinds of nucleic acids, viz. **DNA** (deoxyribonuleic acid) and **RNA** (ribonucleic acid). The latter occurs in three forms : messenger RNA (mRNA), transfer RNA or soluble RNA (tRNA or sRNA) and ribosomal RNA (rRNA), as detailed on p. 265. A summary of nucleic acid formation may be given thus: pentose sugar + nitrogen base → nucleoside; nucleoside + phosphate group → nucleotide; nucleotide + nucleotide + → nucleic acid.

DNA and RNA. *Occurrence.* DNA occurs almost exclusively in the chromosome, and to a small extent only, as is now known, in chloroplasts and mitochondria. RNA occurs mostly in the cytoplasm (about 90% of a cell's RNA occurs here), nucleolus and ribosomes, and to some extent in the chromosomes, of course, in three different forms, as already mentioned. A big portion of the RNA formed in the nucleolus, possibly under the control of DNA, moves to the surrounding cytoplasm.

DNA or RNA, with a certain protein in each case, is the predominant constituent of most virus particles (see FIG. V/64). This is also true of many bacterial cells. *Chemistry.* DNA and RNA are close chemical relatives. The principal difference between the two lies in the kind of pentose sugar present in their molecules. RNA contains a 5-carbon atom (pentose) sugar, 'ribose', whereas DNA contains 'deoxyribose', also a 5-carbon (pentose) sugar, but it has one less oxygen atom in its molecule than the one in RNA. *Structure.* Both occur as macromolecules but RNA molecules are single stranded, while DNA molecules (FIG. 5) are double stranded (with but few exceptions in each case). The DNA and RNA bases are the same except that RNA has uracil, while DNA has thymine. *Functions.* DNA is the sole genetic material (analogous to genes) migrating intact from generation to generation through the reproductive units or gametes, and is responsible for the development of specific characteristics in successive generations. DNA is the controlling centre of all the vital activities of a living cell and is responsible for all biosynthetic processes, including protein synthesis. Biologists now believe that all secrets of life are confined to and controlled by the DNA of a living cell. RNA, under the instructions of DNA, is directly connected with the synthesis of proteins (see DNA and Protein Synthesis, part III, chapter 6).

DNA Molecule (FIG. 5). The DNA molecule of a single chromosome is very long and complex (macromolecule), forming the backbone of each chromosome. While investigating nucleic acids in 1953, Watson and Crick (see footnote on p.123)

(co-winners of the 1962 Nobel Prize along with Wilkins) of the Cambridge University worked out the famous *double helix* model of DNA, and the role played by DNA and RNA in the synthesis of proteins. Kornberg, in 1956, isolated from *Escherichia coli* (an intestinal bacterium) an enzyme, *DNA-polymerase,* which could duplicate DNA *in vitro.* For this wonderful discovery, Kornberg was awarded the Nobel Prize in 1956. This enzyme is now found to be present in living cells. Later, Hargobind Khorana, Marshall Nirenberg and Robert Holley (Nobel Prize winners in 1968), investigating nucleic acids independently at the Massachusetts Institute of Technology, U.S.A., worked out suitable methods for synthesis of nucleic acids in the laboratory, leading to the understanding of genetic codes. Their work may possibly lead to the manufacture of synthetic proteins not in the very distant future. Subsequently, after nine years' research, Khorana has actually succeeded in artificially creating an exact copy of a bacterial gene and successfully transplanting the same for normal behaviour. There may thus be a possibility of curing certain hereditary diseases carried through defective genes. Fritz, another geneticist of the same institute, however, asserts that the creation of a mammalian gene, being much more complicated, is a remote possibility.

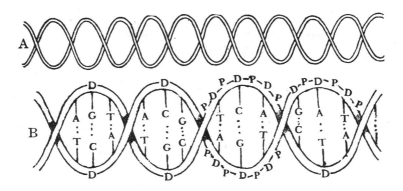

FIG. 5. *A*, Watson-Crick model of DNA molecule. The two strands are twisted about each other; *B*, a portion of the same magnified. Note the distribution of deoxyribose sugar (*D*), phosphate (*P*) and cross-links— thymine-adenine (*T-A*) and guanine-cytosine (*G-C*)

proposed a *double helix* model of the DNA molecule (Watson-Crick model), universally accepted since then. According to them, DNA ocurs as a double-stranded molecule, with the two strands profusely coiled and entwined about each other throughout their whole length. The structure is like a ladder twisted in a helical fashion. Each spiral strand is made of groups (micromolecules) of deoxyribose sugar (a 5-carbon or pentose sugar), alternating with groups of phosphate, and an infinite number of cross-links connecting the two strands (like the rungs of a ladder). Each pair of cross-links is made of two distinct types of nitrogenous bases—**purines** and **pyrimidines**— each attached to a sugar. Each pair of bases is loosely linked by hydrogen bonds. Altogether, there are two purines (adenine and guanine) and two pyrimidines (thymine and cytosine). It is the rule that a specific purine always pairs with a specific pyrimidine as alleles, (i.e. complementary pairs), e.g. adenine with thymine (A-T) and guanine with cytosine (G-C). It may be noted that each base is a part of a nucleoside (see p. 123). It is important to note that the pairs of nitrogenous bases occur in infinite sequences in a DNA molecule, enabling the latter to coin an infinite number of chemical codes (messages or information) and transmitting the appropriate codes through its working partner, RNA, to the surrounding cytoplasm for its manifold activities. In summary, a DNA strand (FIG. 6B) is made of four types of nucleotides—PDT, PDA, PDG and PDC, evidently including four types of nucleosides— DT, DA, DG and DC, and also four kinds of nitrogenous bases—T, A, G and C. Although such bases combine in only four specific pairs—T-A, A-T, G-C and C-G, they may occur in infinite sequences in a DNA molecule.

3. PLASTIDS.

Besides the nucleus, the cytoplasm of a cell encloses many small specialized protoplasmic bodies, usually discoidal or spherical. These are called **plastids** (see FIG. 3A). Their average size is 4μ to 6μ. Each plastid is bounded by a double membrane. The ground substance or matrix of the plastid, first investigated by Pringsheim in 1874, is called the **stroma**, which is a proteinaceous material. Lying embedded in the stroma is a large number of granules called **grana**. Each granum consists of a varying number of discs (see FIG. 6C). The stroma is colourless, whereas the granules contain the pigment or colouring matter. Plastids are living and multiply by division of the pre-existing ones (Sanio, 1864). Although plastids were known from the time of Von Mohl (about the middle of the nineteenth century), their origin could not be traced for many years. According to Guilliermond and his students (1920-24), the mitochondria (see p. 127) present in the embryo cells of phanerogams become partly differentiated into plastids and partly remain as they are. This view has since been discarded. According to recent studies, plastids arise from pre-existing bodies, called **proplastids**, present in the embryonic cells. As the cells grow, the plastids also grow, multiply by division and assume their characteristic forms. Plastids occur in cells which have to perform specialized functions, and are always absent in blue-green algae, fungi and bacteria. Plastids are of three types, viz. **leucoplasts**, **chloroplasts** and **chromoplasts**. One form of plastids can change into another. For example, leucoplasts change into chloroplasts when exposed to light for a prolonged period. Similarly, chloroplasts change into leucoplasts in the continued absence of light. Similar changes may take place in chromoplasts. In the young tomato fruit, the leucoplasts gradually change into chloroplasts and the latter into chromoplasts as the fruit ripens.

(1) **Leucoplasts** (*leucos*, white). These are colourless plastids. Leucoplasts occur most commonly in the storage cells of roots and underground stems. They are also found in other parts not exposed to light. They vary in shape, often being spherical, discoidal or rod-like. Leucoplasts convert sugar into starch in the form of minute grains for the purpose of storage. Larger leucoplasts, specially acting as starch-storing bodies, are known as **amyloplasts**. There is another type of colourless plastids called elaioplasts. They are concerned with the formation and storage of fats, as is the cytoplasm. Elaioplast are also capable of forming starch. They are common in liverworts and are also found in many monocotyledons and certain dicotyledons.

(2) **Chloroplasts** (*chloros*, green). These are green plastids, which owe their colour to the presence of a pigment named **chlorophyll** by Caventou in the year 1818. The green colour, which is present in green leaves and in green parts of the shoot, may sometimes be marked by other colours. Chloroplasts are mostly spherical or discoidal, but in some bryophytes and algae, they may assume peculiar forms. *Functions.* They work *only in the presence of sunlight* and perform some very important functions with the help of their chlorophyll. They absorb carbon dioxide from the air; manufacture sugar and starch from this carbon dioxide and the water absorbed from the soil, and liberate oxygen (by splitting the water) into the surrounding air.

Willstatter and Stoll discovered in 1906 that **chlorophyll** is a mixture of four different pigments, viz. chlorophyll *a* (blue-black), chlorophyll *b* (green-black), carotene (orange-red) and xanthophyll (yellow). Chlorophyll *a* and chlorophyll *b* are associated with each other in the chloroplast, but carotene and xanthophyll may also occur without chloroplast in any part of the plant. Chlorophyll as a whole can be easily extracted with alcohol, benzene, acetone, ether, or chloroform, and the leaves then become colourless. The chlorophyll solution appears deep green in transmitted light, but blood-red in reflected light. This physical property of chlorophyll is called *fluorescence*. A mixture of the two pigments—carotene and xanthophyll—which are always associated with chlorophyll, can be easily separated from the chlorophyll solution by shaking it with a small quantity of benzene and allowing the solution to settle for a few minutes. The benzene floats to the top (green solution), carrying chlorophyll, while the alcohol settles at the bottom (yellow solution), retaining carotene and xanthophyll. Ether or olive-oil may be used instead of benzene. Chlorophyll is not soluble in water, even under prolonged boiling. Chlorophyll forms about 8% of the dry weight of the chloroplast, while carotene and xanthophyll form about 2%. *Functions.* It is definitely known that chlorophyll absorbs light energy from sunlight and initiates the process of photosynthesis. It does not, however, undergo any chemical change in the process but acts as a catalyst. *Origin.* Chlorophyll has its origin in a colourless substance called *leucophyll*. The latter is first converted into proto-chlorophyll (or chlorophyllogen), which is finally transformed into chlorophyll in the presence of light.

Chemical Composition of Chlorophyll

Chlorophyll *a*	—$C_{55}H_{72}O_5N_4Mg$
Chlorophyll *b*	—$C_{55}H_{70}O_6N_4Mg$
Carotene	—$C_{40}H_{56}$
Xanthophyll	—$C_{40}H_{56}O_2$

(3) **Chromoplasts** (*chroma*, colour). These are variously coloured plastids—yellow, orange and red. They are mostly present in the petals of flowers and in fruits, and the colouring matters (pigments) associated with them are **xanthophyll** (yellow) and **carotene** (orange-red). Various other colours are formed as a result of combinations of red, yellow and green. The function of pigments occurring in flowers is to attract insects for cross-pollination (see p. 82).

Carotenoids. A number of pigments—yellow, orange and sometimes red—are found in plants. These are collectively called carotenoids. They may be divided into two main groups—**carotenes** and **xanthophylls**. They are always associated with chlorophyll, but may also occur independently in any part of the plant body. They are not connected with photosynthesis. All carotenoids are insoluble in water but dissolve readily in ethyl ether. They are not easily destroyed by heat or light. A carotene is a hydrocarbon, i.e. it consists of carbon and hydrogen, its formula being $C_{40}H_{56}$. It is readily soluble in petroleum ether. A xanthophyll, on the other hand, is an oxidation product of carotene, i.e. it has oxygen too, its formula being $C_{40}H_{56}O_2$. It is readily soluble in ethyl alcohol but not in petroleum ether.

Anthocyanins. Most violet, purple and blue flowers, and also many red and brown ones, owe their colour to pigments—**anthocyanins,**—*dissolved in the cell-sap.* Anthocyanins occur in flowers, coloured roots, e.g. beet-root, and coloured stems, e.g. balsam stem. They also occur in the variegated leaves of garden crotons and amaranth, and in the young red leaves of many plants, e.g. mango, country almond, etc., and frequently mask the chlorophyll. They possibly serve as a screen for the chloroplasts, protoplasm, etc. protecting them against strong sunlight. When they occur in flowers, they naturally serve to attract insects for pollination. They are soluble in water and alcohol. When a coloured leaf is boiled in water, anthocyanins are extracted and the leaf then appears greenish due to the presence of chlorophyll. Anthocyanins are capable of changing their colour which depends upon the reaction of the sap of the cells in which they occur. The colour is red when the sap is acid, and blue when it is alkaline in reaction. Various other pigments are also found in the plant body.

Other Cytoplasmic Bodies (FIG. 6).

(1) **Centro-somes** are minute bodies occurring close to the nuclei of animal cells and the cells of lower plants (many algae and fungi). They are not found in seed plants. The centrosome usually has two central granules called **centrioles**, which are deeply stainable. During nuclear division, the centrioles pass on to two opposite ends of the cell and organize the nuclear spindle. They are also associated with the formation of cilia in motile ciliate gametes.

(2) **Mitochondria** are very small bodies, usually $0.2\text{-}2\mu \times 3\text{-}5\mu$, often present in very large numbers in the cytoplasm of both plant and animal cells. They occur in the form of rods or filaments, or as somewhat spherical or sausage-shaped bodies. They are mostly distributed throughout the cytoplasm, but in certain cells, they cluster round the nuclear membrane or beneath the plasma membrane. They are, however, absent in bacteria and blue-green algae. The electron microscope reveals the following structural details of a mitochondrion: (*a*) an outer membrane, (*b*) an inner membrane which is thrown in folds (called *cristae*) into the cavity of the mitochondrion, and (*c*) a granular matrix filling up the cavity. Mitochondria are largely composed of protein and phospholipid (a phosphorus-containing fatty substance). They have certain characteristic staining properties, and can be observed only after special treatment. They are easily destroyed by acid-containing fixatives. They multiply by division, and are carried down to the next generation through the reproductive cells. Mitochondria are now regarded as very important constituents of plant and animal cells, inasmuch as they provide *energy* for the vital activities of living cells, being closely associated with respiration and photosynthesis. They contain most of the oxidative enzymes of the respiratory cycle, particularly of the Krebs cycle. Several oxidative enzymes, concerned with the breakdown of glucose and other food materials during respiration, are also located in them. ATP (adenosine triphosphate), an energy-rich phosphate compound commonly used to phosphorylate glucose to 'active' glucose-phosphate, is formed in the mitochondria. Since

mitochondria are abundant in the young metabolic tissue, they may also be connected with other physiological activities. They are, in fact, the powerhouses of a cell, releasing the energy required for vital work. According to some investigators, mitochondria are the precursors of different types of plastids. However, according to recent studies, this view is no longer valid.

(3) **Golgi bodies** occur as a packet of tiny, elongated, flattened sacs in the cytoplasm of certain types of cells. They can be observed only after the

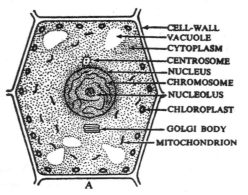

cells have been treated by a special method. They appear as net-like bodies under the compound microscope. Under the electron microscope, the Golgi body is seen to consist of (a) a stack of parallel, flattened sacs, each with two membranes, (b) some conspicuous vacuoles between the two membranes, and (c) clusters of very small vesicles which are the pinched off ends of the sacs. This whole structure is also known as the *Golgi complex*. The Golgi body was first noted in animal cells (nerve cells of cat and owl) by Golgi, an Italian physician, in 1898. Although more common in animal cells, Golgi bodies are also found in several plant cells. In the gland cells of animals, Golgi bodies are associated with secretions (certain enzymes, hormones, etc.), and also with the storage of proteins. Their role in plant cells is still obscure. Golgi bodies are composed of almost equal quantities of protein and phospholipid.

(4) **The endoplasmic reticulum** is an intricate network of tube-like structures distributed extensively throughout the cytoplasm. This can be observed only under the electron microscope. It was first described elaborately by Porter, an American scientist, in 1960-61. Some of the tubes

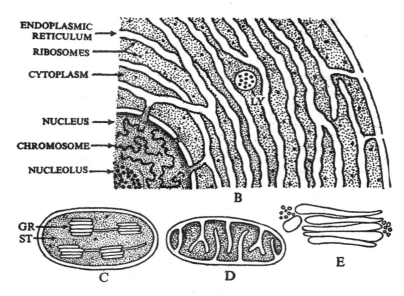

FIG. 6. Parts of a cell. *A*, as seen under a compound microscope; *B-E*, as seen under an electron microscope; *B*, a portion of the cell (*LY*, lysosome); *X*, a chloroplast (*GR*, granum; *ST*, stroma); *D*, mitochondrion; *E*, Golgi body

of the reticulum touch the nuclear nembrane and after extending through the cytoplasm, open on the cell-membrane. The tubes increase the surface area of the cytoplasm to facilitate the metabolic activities of the cell. They also appear to be associated with enzyme formation, protein synthesis, storage and transport of metabolic products. In nuclear division, they contribute to the formation of the cell-plate and the new nuclear membrane around each daughter nucleus.

(5) **Ribosomes.** Associated with the membrane of the endoplasmic reticulum, and also occurring free in the hyaloplasm, are extremely minute particles called ribosomes. Ribosomes occur in abundance and are composed of nucleoprotein, particularly RNA (ribonucleic acid), and protein. Ribosomes are the main seats of protein systhesis.

(6) **Lysosomes.** The electron microscope also reveals other tiny, usually spherical, cytoplasmic particles. Each particle has an outer membrane and dense contents. Those particles are called lysosomes. They have been found in many animal cells and in the meristematic cells of a few plants. They are associated with intracellular digestion. Several enzymes, particularly acid hydrolases (but not oxidative enzymes), are seen to remain confined to them.

THE CELL-WALL

Formation and Structure of the Cell-wall. The cell-wall is a constant feature of all plant cells. Each cell is bounded by a non-living wall, thick or thin, according to the nature of the cell, forming an elastic or semi-rigid framework around it. This framework is called the **cell-wall**. It maintains the form of the cell and provide requisite protection to the protoplast. Besides, cell-walls form the skeleton of the plant body and are responsible for its strength, rigidity and flexibility. The cell-wall is a laminated structure, i.e. it consists of layers laid down one against another by the protoplasm. In a young cell, a thin cell-plate (see FIG. 20 I) is formed across the cell's centre (equator). Cellplate extends to the lateral walls in the form of a complete layer or septum, thus dividing the cell into two daughter cells. This original thin layer,

which later stands as the middle layer of the cell-wall, is called the **middle lamella**. It is composed of calcium pectate (calcium salt of pectic acid), and acts as a cementing material, holding the contiguous cells together firmly. As the cells enlarge, a thin wall is deposited on either surface of the middle lamella by the protoplasm of each cell. This wall is called the **primary wall** and is composed of varying proportions of cellulose, hemicellulose and pectose. The primary wall is very thin and elastic so that it can keep pace with the growth of the cell. Several types of cells continue to have primary walls even when they mature. This is the case with most parenchyma, collenchyma, cambium, mesophyll, etc. But in certain other cells, the cell-wall may thicken as the cell matures. The protoplasm lays down new layers on each surface of the primary wall, thus thickening the cell-wall. The thickened wall is called the **secondary wall**, and is composed exclusively of pure cellulose. It is tough and has high tensile strength. The cell-wall, as a whole, connecting two adjoining cells, now comprises a middle lamella, two primary walls and two secondary walls in their sequence of development. In special cases, as in woody tissues, e.g. tracheids, vessels, wood fibres, bast fibres, stone cells, etc., each side of the secondary wall thickens further due to the deposition of lignin. This thickening may follow special patterns (see FIG. 8). With the development of the lignified secondary wall, the cell often loses its protoplasmic contents and becomes dead. The whole wall, including the primary wall and the middle lamella, may often be strongly lignified. It is further seen that the cytoplasm of one cell is connected with that of the adjoining cell by fine cytoplasmic strands, which extend through extremely minute pits that develop in the cell-wall during its formation. These cytoplasmic strands are called **plasmodesmata** (sing. plasmodesma; FIG. 7). They were first discovered by Tangl in 1879 and later, more elaborately studied by Strasburger in 1901. According to Pfeffer (1896) and Sharp (1926), the strands are concerned with the transmission of stimuli from cell to cell, and also translocation of nutritive materials, particularly in the storage tissues.

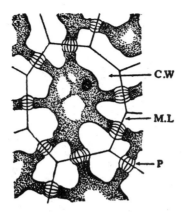

FIG. 7. Cells from the endosperm of date seed.
C.W, cell-wall (hemicellulose, see pp. 132-33);
M.L, middle lamella; *P*, plasmodesma

The electron microscope reveals that the cell wall has a complex structure. The wall is seen to be made of a network of extremely fine, interwoven strands. These strands are the chain molecules of cellulose and occur in the cell-wall in bundles of 100-170 (up to 200) to form the smallest structural unit called the *micelle*. Approximately 20 micelles may be associated together to form a larger structural unit called the *microfibril*. Micelles and microfibrils are detectable only in an electron micrograph. A *fibril*, considered to be an aggregation of 25 microfibrils, is the smallest unit visible under a light microscope. The wall develops in successive layers, and each layer consists of a fine network of cellulose strands. The primary wall consists of one layer, in which the micelles extend transversely or somewhat obliquely with reference to the long axis of the cell, forming a loose network. Its meshes are filled with pectic compounds. This arrangement helps the cell-wall elongate as the cell grows. The secondary wall, when formed, commonly consists of three layers, sometimes more, on each side of the primary wall. The microfibrils are laid down in different directions in the successive layers, forming a compact network in each case, evidently adding to the strength of the cell-wall. At this stage, nine layers may be counted in the cell-wall as a whole. Cellulose, no doubt, is the chief constituent of the cell-wall but as the wall grows in thickness, various new substances (see p. 132) are freshly deposited in the meshes of the network.

Plasma Membrane. This is an extremely thin, hyaline, living membrane that covers the cytoplasm like a surface layer. It is mainly made of fat and protein. In plant cells, it lies adpressed against the cell-wall and is hardly distinguishable from it, except under special treatment, but in animal cells (cell-wall being absent), this membrane forms the boundary of each cell. The plasma membrane plays a very important role in the physiology of the cell. It has a selective power unlike the dead cell-wall, allowing only certain materials to pass through it into the cell and out of it. Large molecules of proteins, fats and carbohydrates cannot pass through it. Such a membrane having a selective transmitting power is said to be semipermeable or differentially permeable. The electron microscope reveals some pores in the membrane. These pores may help in the diffusion of materials that have to enter the cell or leave it. This outer plasma membrane is otherwise called ectoplasm, while a similar plasma membrane surrounding the vacuole is called tonoplasm (see p. 119). This membrane is also semipermeable, like the outer one.

Secondary Thickening of the Cell-wall (FIG. 8). Secondary thickening of the cell-wall may be more or less uniform all round the cell and almost always has a stratified appearance. But in those cells which have to ultimately grow into vessels (see FIG. 37) and tracheids (see FIGS. 34-6), it may be localized to particular portions of the wall, forming in special patterns. In these cases, it is due to the deposit of a chemically complex and hard substance, called *lignin*, in the meshes of the cellulose network. Such thickening takes place only after the aforesaid elements have grown and attained their full dimensions. The thickening being localized, a portion of the wall may remain unthickened. The patterns of thickening may be as follows :

(1) **Annular or ring-like** (A)—when the deposit of lignin is in the form of rings, which are placed one a little above the other in the interior of the original cell-wall, the remaining portion of the wall being unthickened.

(2) **Spiral** (B)—when the thickening takes the form of a spiral band.

(3) **Scalariform or ladder-like** (C)—when the thickening matter or lignin is deposited transversely in the form of rods or the rungs of ladder, hence,

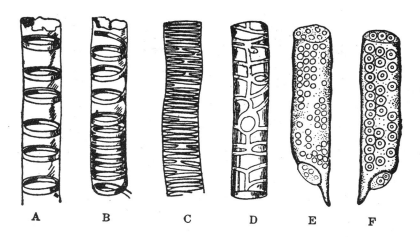

FIG. 8. Thickening of the cell-wall. *A*, annular; *B*, spiral; *C*, scalariform; *D*, reticulate; *E*, pitted (with simple pits); *F*, pitted (with bordered pits)

the term scalariform or ladder-like. The unthickened portions of the wall appear as transverse pits, while the thickened spaces between them give a ladder-like appearance to the wall.

(4) **Reticulate or netted** (D)—when the thickening takes the form of a network, evidently leaving a number of irregular, unthickened spaces in the wall.

(5) **Pitted** (E-F)—when the whole inner surface of the cell-wall is more or less uniformly thickened, leaving some small, unthickened areas or cavities here and there. These unthickened areas are called pits, and are of two kinds, viz. (a) **simple pits** and (b) **bordered pits**. Pits are formed in pairs and they lie against each other on opposite sides of the wall. The portion of the original wall separating the two opposing pits is called the *closing membrane*. The closing membrane in the bordered pits shows a slight swelling or thickening in the middle, called **torus** (FIG. 11 B-C). When the area of a pit is uniform throughout its whole depth, it forms a simple pit (FIGS. 9-10). When the area is unequal, broader towards the original wall and narrower towards the cavity of the cell, more or less like a funnel without a stem, it forms a bordered pit (FIG. 11). In a bordered pit, the adjoining thickening matter of the wall grows inwards and arches over the pit from all sides, forming an overhanging border, and hence the name 'bordered' pit. Viewed from the surface the simple pit may be

circular, oval, polygonal, elongated or somewhat irregular, while the bordered pit is often circular or oval. Pits are areas through which the diffusion of liquids takes place more easily. In bordered pits, this diffusion is regulated to a great extent by the torus, which, when pushed from one side, blocks the pit (FIG. 11C). The diffusion of protoplasm, too, takes place through simple pits, which are found in living cells. Bordered pits are abundantly found in the tracheids of conifers (e.g. pine; FIGS. 12, 34 & 36) and in the vessels of angiosperms. Simple pits are also found in these, but they occur more frequently in some of the living cells, and

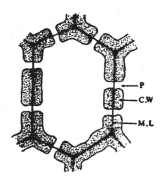

FIG. 9. Simple Pits. A cell in section showing simple pits in its wall; *P*, pit; *C.W.*, cell-wall; *M.L.* middle lamella.

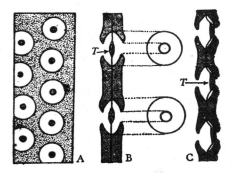

FIG 11. Bordered Pits. *A*, cell-wall with bordered pits (surface view); *B*, the same (sectional view); *C*, the same showing the torus (t) pushed against the pit and blocking it

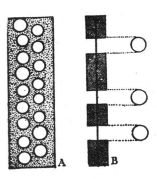

FIG. 10. Simple Pits. *A*, cell-wall with simple pits (surface view); *B*, the same (sectional view).

occur largely in the wood parenchyma, medullary rays, phloem parenchyma, companion cells, etc. Fibres are often provided with simple, oblique pits and sometimes with bordered pits as well, and stone cells with simple, branched pits.

Chemical Nature of the Cell-wall. The chemical substances of which the cell-wall is composed are mainly pectin, cellulose, lignin, cutin, suberin and mucilage. Many mineral matters may also be introduced into the cell-wall.

Cellulose. Cellulose, an insoluble carbohydrate, is universally present in the cell-walls of all plant

cells with the exception of fungi. In fact, cellulose is the chief constituent of the cell-wall. Associated with it are other compounds deposited at different stages of wall formation (see p. 129). In the primary wall, as already mentioned, cellulose is associated with hemicellulose and pectose, making the wall soft and elastic. Almost pure cellulose occurs in the secondary wall formed later, making the wall stiff but flexible. Later still, cellulose may be associated with lignin, cutin, suberin, etc in special cases. Cellulose is a soft, elastic and transparent substance, and is readily permeable to water but insoluble in it. Seed fibres like cotton and

FIG. 12. Tracheids with bordered pits of pine stem (diagrammatic)

kapok are made of pure cellulose, while bast fibres and woody tissues are made predominantly of cellulose impregnated with lignin (lignocellulose). Chemically, cellulose is a polysaccharide represented by the formula $(C_6H_{10}O_5)n$. Cellulose molecules are mostly long, straight chains of D-glucose units. *Origin*. Going by his X-ray studies of 1929, Sponsler strongly believes that cellulose is directly transformed from glucose in the presence of protoplasm. *Uses*. Cellulose is a very important substance in many respects. Many micro-organisms utilize cellulose as food. They secrete an enzyme, *cellulase,* to hydrolyse it. It forms a major part of the food of herbivorous animals. However, they have to depend for its digestion on the enzyme secreted by such bacteria which dwell in their digestive canal. Cellulose, however, cannot be digested by human beings. Articles like paper, cellophane, gun-cotton, celluloid, rayon (artificial silk), lacquer, etc., are prepared from cellulose for commercial use all over the world.

Hemicellulose is a mixture of different organic compounds (and not chemically allied to cellulose). It occurs in cell-walls which may sometimes be heavily thickened. There is a thick deposit of hemicellulose in the cell-walls of the endosperm of date seed (see FIG. 7) and certain other palm seeds. It is stored there as reserve food for the use of the embryo, and is often called **reserve cellulose**. When the seed germinates, it becomes converted into glucose and other compounds by the action of the enzyme, *cytase*. In the vegetable ivory palm (*Phytelephas*), the reserve cellulose is very hard and is called vegetable ivory. Billiard balls, buttons, handles of sticks and umbrellas, etc., are made from it. It is also abundant in many stony seeds and fruits and in woody tissues of certain trees, e.g. apple tree. **Pectic compounds** occur in plants in three forms: insoluble pectose (protopectin), soluble pectin and insoluble pectic acid. They occur in the cell-walls, and one form may change into the other in the plant body. In water, pectin swells into mucilage, as the gelatinous sheath of many algae. It is present in many fruits and vegetables, and is responsible for the setting of jellies made from certain fruits. Protopectin present in the primary cell-walls acts as a binding or cementing material, holding together the cells of the plant body. Protopectin and hemicellulose associated with cellulose, as deposited in the corners of collenchymatous cells, make the cells elastic.

Lignin. Lignin is deposited in the meshes of the network formed by cellulose microfibrils in the cell-wall (see p. 132), and is responsible for considerable thickening and strengthening of the secondary cell-wall, as in xylem elements. It may, however, be present in the middle lamella, primary wall and secondary wall, as in woody tissues, i.e. the whole wall may be lignified. Lignin is a hard and chemically complex substance. Its exact chemical composition is not known. Possibly, it is a mixture of several organic compounds and occurs in different forms in hard and woody tissues. Lignified cells are usually thick-walled and always dead. Although hard, lignin is permeable to water. Sclerenchyma, sclereids, bast fibres, tracheids, wood vessels and wood fibres are common lignified structures. The function of lignified tissues is mechanical, i.e. they contribute to the rigidity of the plant body.

Cutin. Cutin is a mixture of some pectic compounds. It forms a definite layer, sometimes of considerable thickness, called the **cuticle**, on the skin (outer surface of the epidermal layer) of the stem, leaf and fruit. Cutin makes the cell-wall impermeable or very slightly permeable to water. Its function, therefore, is to prevent or check evaporation of water from the exposed surfaces of the plant body.

Suberin. The cell-walls of certain tissues may be charged with another waxy substance, called suberin. Like cutin, it is a mixture of some waxy substances and is, therefore, allied to cutin. The constituent fatty acids are, however, different in the two cases. Suberin occurs in the walls of cork cells, and also in the endodermis and exodermis of the roots of several plants. Being waxy in nature, it makes the cell-wall almost impervious to water and, therefore, like cutin, it prevents or checks evaporation of water. The bark of cork oak (*Quercus suber*) on the Mediterranean coasts is the source of bottle cork used for this purpose.

Mucilage. Mucilage is a slimy substance widely distributed in various parts of plants. Chemically, it is a complex carbohydrate. Its physical property is that it absorbs water greedily, retains it tenaciously and forms a viscous mass.

Micro-chemical Tests of the Cell-wall

	Reagents	Cellulose Suberin	Lignin	Cutin and	Mucilage
1	Iodine solution	pale yellow	deep yellow	deep yellow	—
2	Chlor-zinc-iodine	blue or violet	yellow	yellowish brown	—
3	Iodine solution + sulphuric acid or zinc chloride	blue	brownish	deep brown	violet
4	Aliline sulphate	—	bright yellow	—	—
5	Phloroglucin (acid)	—	violet red	—	—
6	Caustic potash solution (concentrated)	—	—	yellow and brown	—
7	Potash + chlor-zinc-iodine	—	—	violet	—
8	Chlorophyll solution	—	—	green	—
9	Sudan IV	—	—	red	—
10	Methylene blue	—	—	—	deep blue

But when dry, it is very hard and horny. It is insoluble in alcohol. Mucilage is abundantly found in the fleshy leaves of Indian aloe (*Aloe*; B. GHRI-TAKUMARI; H. GHIKAVAR). It is also abundant in the flowers of China rose, in the fruits of lady's finger, in the branches and leaves of Indian spinach (*Basella*; B. PUIN; H. POI), and in the seeds of linseed (*Linum*), flea seed (*Plantago*; B. ISOBGUL; H. ISOBGOL), *Lallimantia* (B. & H. TOPMARI), etc. Such seeds, when wetted, swell up and become mucilaginous. Mucilage also occurs in the fleshy leaves of desert plants.

In the majority of fungi and also in certain algae (but not in higher plants), the cell-wall is made of *chitin*—a substance somewhat allied to cellulose. Chitin, however, is peculiar to animals.

Besides, various mineral crystals such as silica, calcium oxalate and calcium carbonate may be introduced into the cell-walls, but not as integral parts of them. In several plants, certain organic compounds like tannin, resin, gum, lipids or fatty substances, organic acids, etc., may also enter the cell-walls.

CELL INCLUSIONS (non-living)

Various chemical substances appear in the plant body as products of metabolism or as by-products. These are called **ergastic substances** and include a number of compounds of varied nature. They may occur in vacuoles (particularly the soluble ones), or in cytoplasm (particularly insoluble ones), or even in the cell-wall (particularly some of the waste products). Carbohydrates, proteins, fats and oils are such substances. They constitute the *food* of plants and animals, supplemented by vitamins and essential minerals. A number of other compounds, whose utility is not wholly known, are also formed in several plants as by-products, commonly called *waste products*. They are tannins, essential oils, resins, gums, etc. (see pp. 140-43)

1. CARBOHYDRATES

These are substances containing carbon, hydrogen and oxygen. Of these, hydrogen and oxygen occur in the same proportion as they do in water. The general chemical formula is $Cx(H_2O)y$. When these substances are heated, they become charred, forming a black mass. This black mass is carbon. The water escapes and the carbon is left behind. From the economic point of view, carbohydrates are very important. Many of them are widely consumed as food, many are extensively employed in various industries, as in the manufacture of fabrics and paper, and many are used in the production of alcohol.

Classification of Carbohydrates

(a) **Monosaccharides** (sugars) are the simplest carbohydrates, i.e. they cannot be hydrolysed further into simpler ones. They may be (i) *pentoses* with five carbon atoms—($C_5H_{10}O_5$), of which the ones commonly found in plants are **arabinose** (occurring as a constituent of glycosides) and **ribose** (occurring as a constituent of nucleic acids), and (ii) *hexoses* with six carbon atoms—$C_6H_{12}O_6$, of which glucose and fructose are the ones commonly found in plants.

(b) **Disaccharides** (sugars) are represented by the formula $C_{12}H_{22}O_{11}$. These are most abundant in the higher green plants. **Sucrose** and **maltose** are examples of disaccharides.

(c) **Polysaccharides** (non-sugars) are represented by the formula $C_6H_{10}O_5$. These are condensation products of simple sugars, e.g. **inulin**, **starch, dextrin** and **glycogen**. (Cellulose and hemicellulose also belong to this group.)

(d) **Compound carbohydrates** (non-sugars) are complex carbohydrate-molecules, e.g. **gums, mucilages, tannins** and **glycosides**.

Hydrolysis of Carbohydrates

The more complex forms of carbohydrates may be readily hydrolysed by acids or by hydrolytic enzymes into simpler forms, soluble and easily diffusible. Thus, starch, on boiling with sulphuric acid, is converted into glucose through certain intermediate stages, described below. Starch (blue with iodine) + $H_2O\rightarrow$ less diffusible dextrin (red with iodine) + $H_2O\rightarrow$ more diffusible dextrin (no colour with iodine) + $H_2O\rightarrow$ maltose + $H_2O\rightarrow$ glucose. In germinating seeds and elsewhere, starch undergoes similar hydrolysis under the action of certain hydrolytic enzymes, such as *diastase (amylase)* and *maltase*, as follows:

$$2n\ (C_6H_{10}O_5) + nH_2O + diastase \rightarrow nC_{12}H_{22}O_{11}$$
$$\text{(maltose)};$$

$$C_{12}H_{22}O_{11} + H_2O + maltase \rightarrow 2C_6H_{12}O_6 \text{ (glucose)}$$

(1) **Sugars.** Sugars are sweet, crystalline, white and soluble substances and are of various kinds, such as grape-sugar or **glucose** (a reducing sugar, chiefly found in grapes and fruit-sugar or fructose (a reducing sugar found in many fruits associated with glucose). Fructose may be readily formed from glucose or by hydrolysis of **sucrose.** Others sugars are cane-sugar or **sucrose** (a non-reducing sugar chiefly found in sugarcanes and beet-roots) and malt-sugar or **maltose** (a reducing sugar formed by the action of *diastase*, an enzyme on starch and, therefore, commonly present in germinating seeds, particularly cereals). Grape-sugar is the simplest of all carbohydrates and is formed in the leaves by chloroplasts *in the presence of sunlight.* Other forms of carbohydrates are derived from it under the action of specific enzymes. Glucose travels in the plant body until it reaches the storage tissues, where it is mostly converted into starch, an insoluble carbohydrate, and deposited for short or long periods. This starch may again be converted into sugar. The chemical formula of grape-sugar is $C_6H_{12}O_6$, and that of cane-sugar $C_{12}H_{22}O_{11}$. Grapes have a glucose content of 12-15% or more, apples 7-10%, and plums 3-5%. Sugarcane has a sucrose content of 10-15% and beet-roots, 10-20%.

Test for Glucose. Add Fehling's solution or an alkaline solution of **copper sulphate** to it, and boil. A yellowish-red precipitate of cuprous oxide is formed. **Test for Sucrose.** Boil sucrose solution with 1 or 2 drops of **sulphuric acid,** and then apply the test for glucose.

(2) **Inulin** (FIG. 13). Inulin is a soluble carbohydrate and occurs in solution in the cell-sap. Like starch, it is easily converted into a form of sugar. Inulin is present in the tuberous roots of *Dahlia* are some other plants of *Compositae.* When pieces of *Dahlia* roots are steeped in alcohol or glycerine

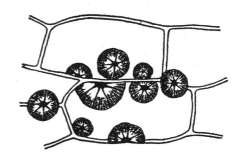

FIG. 13. Inulin crystals in the tuberous root of Dahlia

for 6 or 7 days, preferably more, inulin is precipitated in the form of spherical, crystalline masses. A section is then prepared from one of the pieces and examined under the microscope. Inulin may also be precipitated by cutting rather thick sections from fresh material and keeping them in strong alcohol for about an hour. Under the microscope, fully-formed inulin crystals are seen to be star or wheel-shaped, and half-formed ones are more or less fan-shaped. These crystals are deposited mostly across the cell-walls, and occasionally, only in the cell-cavity. Sometimes, they are so large that they extend through many cells. Inulin has the same chemical composition as starch, viz. $(C_6H_{10}O_5)n$. When precipitated, inulin is easily recognized by its peculiar form.

(3) **Starch** (FIGS. 14-15). This is an insoluble carbohydrate occurring as a reserve food in the form of minute grains. Starch grains are of universal occurrence in plants, with the exception of fungi. They occur in almost all parts of a plant, but are specially abundant in storage tissues. Cereals and millets, which constitute the staple food of mankind, are specially rich in starch. When required for nutrition, it is converted into glucose. Starch grains are of various forms. They may be *rounded* and *flat*, as in wheat, *polygonal*, as in maize, nearly *spherical*, as in pea and bean, or more usually *oval*, as in potato. They are rarely *rod* or *dumb-bell shaped*, as in the latex cells (see FIG. 40A). They also vary very much in size, the largest known being about 100μ or (1/10 mm.) in length, as in the rhizome of *Canna*, and the smallest about 5μ (or 1/200 mm.) in length, as in rice.

In potato, they are of varying sizes. Starch may be synthesized in green cells by chloroplasts (*assimilation starch*) or in non-green cells by leucoplasts (amyloplasts, *storage starch*). In any case, it is always formed from glucose. Large and well-formed starch grains are always found in the storage organ. Starch is made of two components: amylose and amylopectin. Amylose is more soluble in water than amylopectin. The former turns deep blue with iodine solution, while the latter turns light blue with iodine solution. Waxy starch consists almost wholly of amylopectin, which becomes viscous in solution. Mealy starch contains a high percentage of amylose. Both amylose and amylopectin are derived from glucose.

In the starch grain, a definite roundish or elongated scar, called the **hilum**, may be observed. It represents the grain's centre of origin. Around the hilum, a variable number of layers or striations of different densities are deposited alternately. Each starch grain has, thus, a *stratified* appearance. When the layers are laid down on one side of the hilum, as in potato, the grain is said to be **eccentric**, and when they are deposited concentrically round the hilum, as in wheat, maize, pea, bean and many pulses, the grain is said to be **concentric**. The former is more commonly met with than the latter. Starch grains are said to be **simple** when they occur singly with one hilum. Sometimes, however, two or more grains occur together in a solid group with the same number of hila and grains. This group is said to form a **compound** grain. It is seen that the leucoplast simultaneously begins to secrete two or more grains very close to

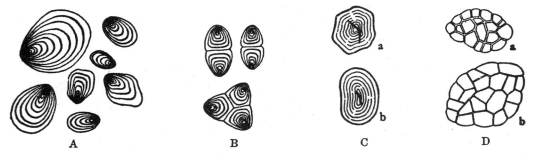

FIG. 14. Starch Grains. *A*, simple eccentric grains in potato; *B*, compound grains in the same; *C*, *a*, simple concentric grain in maize, and *b*, ditto in pea; *D*, *a*, compound grain in rice, and *b*, ditto in oat

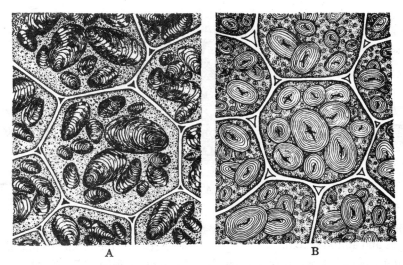

FIG. 15. Starch Grains (contd.). *A*, section through a potato tuber showing a
few cells with eccentric grains; *B*, section through a cotyledon of pea showing
a few cells with concentric grains (and small granules of protein)

one another and subsequently, as fresh layers are added to the grains, they become pressed together into a mass. This mass is the compound grain. Often the whole mass remains enveloped by a few common outer layers secreted by the leucoplast. Compound grains are found in the endosperm of rice and oat (FIG. 14D). A few compound grains are also often found in potato (FIG. 14B) and sweet potato. Starch has the same chemical composition as cellulose and inulin, viz. $(C_6H_{10}O_5)n$. It is insoluble in water and alcohol. Rice contains 70-80% starch, wheat about 70%, maize about 68%, barley 65-66%, arrowroot 20-30%, and potato 20%.

Test for Starch. Starch turns **blue** to **black** when treated with **iodine solution**, the density of the colour depending on the strength of the reagent.

Uses of Starch. Apart from its use as food for both plants and animals, including human beings, starch has a variety of industrial uses. When boiled in water, it forms a thin solution or paste which is extensively used in laundry, textile industry, paper industry, China clay industry, etc., as a sizing and cementing material. Starch is also widely used in the preparation of toilet powders, commercial glucose (by hydrolysis) and industrial alcohol (by fermentation) on a large scale. The sources of commercial starch are mainly potato, maize, tapioca, rice, wheat, sago-palm and arrowroot.

(4) **Dextrin.** This is formed as an intermediate product in the hydrolysis of starch and also in the synthesis of the latter. It does not, however, accumulate in the plant body as such, but occurs only as a transitory product. When starch is gently boiled or hydrolysed with a dilute mineral acid, it becomes converted into a whitish or yellowish, amorphous power (dextrin), which dissolves in water and forms an adhesive paste (called British gum). It is used as a substitute for natural gums.

(5) **Glycogen.** This is a common form of carbohydrate occurring in fungi. In yeast, a unicellular fungus, it occurs to the extent of about 30% of the dry weight of the plant. It is not found in higher plants but is the major carbohydrate reserve in animals, occurring mainly in the liver and the muscles, and is, therefore, sometimes called 'animal starch'. It occurs in the form of granules in the cytoplasm of the cell. Glycogen is a white amorphous powder and dissolves in hot water. It turns **reddish brown** on addition of **iodine solution**. The colour disappears on heating and reappears on cooling. Its chemical formula is $(C_6H_{10}O_5)n$.

2. NITROGENOUS MATERIALS

The nitrogenous reserve materials occurring in

FIG. 16.
Aleurone grains.
A, grains in the endosperm cells of castor seed

B, a few grains (magnified). Note the crystalloid and the globoid

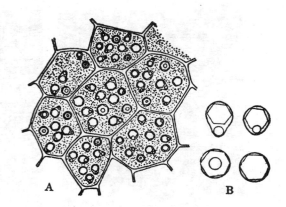

A   B

plants are various kinds of proteins and amino-compounds (amines and amino-acids).

(1) Proteins. Proteins[1] are very complex, nitrogenous, organic compounds, essentially containing carbon (C), hydrogen (H), oxygen (O), and nitrogen (N). All plant proteins also contain sulphur (S), and many complex ones contain phosphorus (P), too. Of all the organic compounds, with the exception of protoplasm and nucleus, proteins have the most complex chemical composition, and various kinds are found in the plant body. In plants, some proteins occur in solution and some as solids (either crystalline or amorphous), while most of them occur in a colloidal state. Some proteins are soluble in dilute salt solution, while all are soluble in weak acid or alkaline solution. Proteins are found in plenty in storage tissue, less so in active (growing) tissue, and they are practically absent from mature, inactive tissue. A common form of insoluble or sparingly soluble protein abundantly found in the endosperm of the castor seed is the **aleurone grain** (FIG. 16). Each aleurone grain is a solid, ovate or rounded body, which encloses a crystal-like body known as the **crystalloid,** and a rounded mineral body called the **globoid.** The crystalloid occupies the wider part of the grain and is protein in nature, while the globoid occupies a narrower part and is a double phosphate of calcium and magnesium. The occurrence of the crystalloid and globoid is not always

constant in the aleurone grain. There may be one or more of them, or sometimes none at all. Aleurone grains vary in size. When they occur with starch, they are very small, as in pea, but they are very much larger in oily seeds, as in castor.

Fatty seeds usually contain a higher percentage of protein than starchy seeds, e.g. rice contains only 7% protein, wheat 12%, while sunflower seeds have a protein content as high as 30%. The starchy seeds of leguminous plants, however, contain as high a percentage of proteins as fatty seeds. For example, the average protein content of pulses is about 25%, of soya-bean (*Glycine max = Glycine soja*), 35% or more, and of groundnuts, 31% (easily assimilable proteins).

Uses of Proteins. Proteins materially contribute to the building up of the plant and animal bodies. Half the dry weight of the protoplasm is made of proteins. The nucleus is predominantly made of nucleoprotein. All enzymes are proteins. Proteins are also a source of energy. In fact, proteins are indispensable for sustaining life. It has been estimated that of the total protein consumed by man, plants account for 65% and animals 35%. An intake of about 75 gms of protein per day may be considered adequate for human beings. However, the amino-acids of animal proteins (milk, meat, fish and egg) rather than those of plant proteins make for a more balanced human diet.

Tests for Proteins. (1) Proteins turn yellowish-brown with strong **iodine solution** (see No. 5). (2) Some of them, e.g. albumins and globulins, coagulate on heating. (3) **Xanthoproteic reaction**—a white precipitate is

[1] Average percentage composition may be given thus: carbon—50-54%; hydrogen—about 7%; oxygen—20-25%; nitrogen—16-18%; sulphur—0.4%; and phosphorus—0.4%.

formed with the addition of some strong nitric acid. It turns yellow on boiling. After cooling, add a little strong ammonia and the yellow colour changes to orange. (4) **Millon's reaction**—add Millon's reagent (nitrate of mercury) and a white precipitate is formed; on boiling it turns brick-red. (5) **Biuret reaction**—an excess of caustic soda followed by a few drops of copper sulphate produces a violet colour, which deepens on heating. (6) Treat a thin section of castor endosperm with 90% alcohol for 3-4 minutes and then with strong iodine solution. Mount it in thick glycerine and note under the microscope that the aleurone grains and the crystalloids turn deep brown, while the globoids remain colourless. Add 1% or 2% caustic soda solution to a fresh section and note that the aleurone grains get dissolved, while the globoids remain unaffected. Treat another section with dilute acetic acid and observe that only the globoids get dissolved.

Classification of Proteins. A precise classification of proteins has not been devised yet because of our imperfect knowledge of them, their infinite numbers, the similarity in their general composition, and identical chemical reactions. However, a general classification based on their solubility and hydrolytic products is as follows:

(a) Simple Proteins. On hydrolysis, they yield only amino-acids. Some are soluble in pure water or in dilute salt water, while others are insoluble in it. The soluble ones are (1) albumins found in barley and in egg white, (2) histones and (3) protamines. The last two are found in nuclei, and are probably associated with nucleic acids. The insoluble ones are (4) globulins, mainly occurring as storage proteins in seeds and in egg white, (5) glutelins, found in cereal grains, and also in wheat and rice (stickiness of flour is due to them), and (6) prolamines, found in many plant seeds, e.g. zein of maize, hordein of barley, and gliadin of wheat.

(b) Conjugated Proteins. These are composed of a simple protein and another compound (a prosthetic group) associated with it. On hydrolysis, they yield amino-acids and the component prosthetic group. They are (1) nucleoproteins (proteins + nucleic acids), occurring in DNA, RNA and viruses, (2) glycoproteins (proteins + carbohydrates), occurring in cell membranes, (3) lipoproteins (proteins + lipids, e.g. lecithin), found in cell membrane, nuclear membrane, vacuolar membrane, and egg yolk, (4) chromoproteins (proteins + a coloured pigment), (5) metalloproteins (proteins + a metal), found in many enzymes, and (6) phosphoproteins (proteins + phosphoric acid), e.g. casein of milk.

Hydrolysis of Proteins. When proteins are subjected to hydrolysis, i.e. when treated with a mineral acid or acted on by enzymes such as trypsin, they are finally resolved into amino-acids (out of which they have been built up) after passing through intermediate stages. The stages are as follows: proteins → metaproteins → proteoses → peptones → polypeptides → amino-acids.

(2) Amino-compounds. Amino-acids and amines are the simplest forms of all nitrogenous food materials, and occur in solution in the cell-sap. They are abundantly found in the growing regions of plants and less frequently in storage tissues. When translocation is necessary, proteins become converted into amines and amino-acids. The amines and amino-acids travel to the growing regions, where the protoplasm is very active, and they are directly assimilated by it. They are also the initial stages in the formation of proteins. They contain carbon, hydrogen, oxygen and nitrogen, and in the amino-acids, cystine, cysteine and methionine sulphur is also present. Some of the other amino-acids are glycine, alanine, glutamic acid, aspartic acid, leucine, lysine, tyrosine, etc.

3. FATS AND OILS

Fats and oils occur to a greater or lesser extent in all plants. They occur in the form of minute globules in the protoplasm of the living cells in which they are formed, and cannot travel from cell to cell. In 'flowering' plants, special deposits of them are often found in seeds and fruits. But in starchy seeds and fruits, there is very little fat. Fats and oils are composed of carbon, hydrogen and oxygen, but the last two do not occur in the same proportion as they do in water, the proportion of oxygen always being much less than in carbohydrates. They contain no nitrogen. They are insoluble in water, but very readily soluble in ether, petroleum and chloroform. Comparatively few of them are soluble in alcohol, e.g. castor oil. Fats are synthesized in living bodies from fatty acids (mainly oleic, palmitic and stearic acids) and glycerine under the action of the enzyme, *lipase*. Both these products, viz, fattty acids and glycerine, are derived from carbohydrates (sugar and starch) during respiration. They form an important reserve food with a considerable amount of *energy* stored in them. Their energy value is more than double that of carbohydrates. When fats are decomposed, the energy stored in them is liberated and utilized by the protoplasm for its manifold activities. Digestion of fats into fatty acids and glycerine is also brought about by the enzyme, *lipase*. Fats that are liquid at ordinary temperature are known as oils. In plants, fats are usually present in the form of oils. Oils are of two kinds, viz. *fixed* or *non-volatile*, as described above, and *essential* or *volatile* (see p. 140).

A large number of them are used for food, manufacture of soap, toilet products and oil paints, illumination, lubrication, etc., and are, therefore, of considerable economic importance. Among these are coconut oil, olive oil, sesame or gingelly oil, castor oil, groundnut oil, linseed oil, mustard oil, cotton seed oil, etc.

Tests for Fats and Oils. (1) Osmic acid (1% aqueous solution) stains them black. (2) Alcoholic solution of **Sudan III, Sudan IV** or **Sudan Red** stains them red. (3) Alcoholic solution of **alkanet** (or alkannin) stains them red, but the stain develops only after an hour or so. (4) They leave a permanent greasy mark on it when pressed against paper.

Other Cell Products

It must also be noted that some other cell products like vitamins, hormones and enzymes play an important role in the physiology of the cell. These are described in detail later. Besides, a number of by-products, commonly known as water products, also appear in different plants or in different parts of the same plant, either in isolated cells or in groups of cells. The role they play in the physiology of a cell is not, however, clear. Some of the common ones are as follows.

1. Tannins. These are a heterogeneous group of complex compounds widely distributed in plants. They commonly occur dissolved in the cell-sap, either in single, isolated cells or in small groups of cells in almost all parts of the plant body. They are also found in the cell-walls, often abundantly in certain dead tissues, as in the bark and the heart-wood. Tannins are abundant in young and old leaves and in many unripe fruits. As the fruits ripen, the tannins disappear and are converted into glucose and other substances. They are abundant in the fruits of myrobalans, e.g. emblic myrobalan (*Emblica officinalis;* B. AMLAKI; H. AMLA), chebulic myrobalan (*Terminalia chebula*; B. HARITAKI; H. HARARA), and beleric myrobalan (*Terminalia belerica*; B. BAHERA; H. BHAIRAH). Tea leaves contain about 18% tannin. Catechu, a kind of tannin, is obtained from the heart-wood of *Acacia catechu*, and is also present in betel or areca-nut. Tannin is a bitter substance, and that is why 'very strong' tea and fruits of myrobalans taste bitter. It is aseptic, i.e. free from the attack of parasitic fungi and insects. The presence of tannin makes the wood hard and durable. Tannins have a variety of uses. Mixed with iron salts, they are used in the manufacture of ink. They are extensively used in tanning, i.e. converting hide into leather. They are also used for various medicinal purposes. They turn **blue-black** with an **iron-salt**, such as ferric chloride.

2. Essential Oils. These are volatile oils and occur mostly in glands, (known as *oil-glands*—see FIG. 41A). The transparent spots on the leaves of sacred basil, pummelo or shaddock, lemon, lemon grass (*Cymbopogon*), *Eucalyptus*, etc., and those in the rind of fruits like orange, lemon, shaddock, etc., are all oil-glands. They are also present in the petals of the flowers of many plants, as in rose, jasmine, etc. The fragrant odour of such flowers is due to the presence of essential oils formed in them. They differ from fatty oils in their chemical composition, as well as in being volatile. They are sufficiently soluble in water to impart to it their taste and odour. Being volatile, essential oils are obtained by mere pressure. Like fatty oils, they are readily soluble in ether, petroleum, etc., and respond to the same tests (see above). They are soluble in alcohol, but fixed oils are not. They commonly occur in mere traces. In some cases, however, they may occur to the extent of 1.2%. There are some 200 essential oils of commercial value. Some of the common ones are lemon grass oil, eucalyptus oil, clove oil, lavender oil, sandalwood oil, thyme oil, etc.

3. Resins. These are mostly found in the stems of conifers, and occur in abundance in special canals or ducts, known as *resin-ducts* (see FIG. 27). They are yellowish solids, insoluble in water but soluble in alcohol, turpentine and spirit. When present in wood, resins add to its strength and durability. They occur associated with a small quantity of turpentine which is removed by distillation, and the residue is pure resin.

4. Gums. Gums are formed in various kinds of plants as a result of the breakdown of the cell-walls and cell-contents (gummosis). They are insoluble in alcohol but soluble in water, readily swell up in it, and form a viscous mass. They are found in many phanerogamic plants, and are of various kinds. *Acacia senegal* yields the best gum-arabic of commerce. Gums also occur in mixtures with resins.

5. Mineral Crystals. The common forms of crystals consist of silica, calciuum carbonate and calcium oxalate. They occur either in the cell-cavity or in the cell-wall. Of the above, crystals of calcium oxalate are the most common, and are very widely

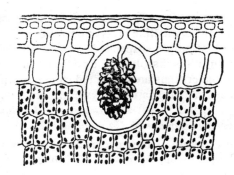

FIG. 17. Mineral Crystals. Cystolith in the leaf of india-rubber plant

distributed among various plants.

(1) **Silica** occurs as an incrustation on the cell-wall, or it lies embedded in it. It is abundantly found in the leaves and stems of horsetail (*Equisetum*), several grasses, e.g. lemon grass, rice straw, wheat straw, etc., and in several algae with silicified structures, e.g. diatoms. Wheat straw contains about 72% silica, rye straw about 50% and *Equisetum* about 71%.

(2) **Calcium carbonate** occurs in the form of a crystalline mass, often pear-shaped in appearance, in the leaf of *Ficus* (e.g. india-rubber plant, banyan, etc.). This crystalline mass is called cystolith (FIG. 17), and it remains enclosed in a large cell. In its formation, the inner cellulose wall of the upper (multiple) epidermis extends inwards into the cell in the form of a stalk, and calcium

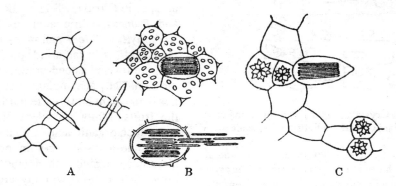

FIG. 18. Mineral Crystals (*contd.*). *A*, solitary raphides (two) in the petiole of water hyacinth; *B*, a bundle of raphides in the same; *bottom*, needles (raphides) shooting out; *C*, sphaero-crystals (four) and a bundle of raphides in taro (*Colocasia*)

carbonate is deposited on it as small crystals. Finally, the crystalline mass or cystolith looks like a bunch of grapes suspended from a stalk. When the cystolith is dissolved, the cellulose matrix on which the crystals are deposited shows stratifications and radial striations. Cystoliths are found in many plants of *Acanthaceae, Moraceae, Urticaceae, Ulmaceae, Cannabinaceae,* etc.

(3) **Calcium oxalate** occurs as crystals of various forms, including (*a*) raphides, (*b*) conglomerate or sphaero-crystals, and (*c*) octahedral and other forms. (*a*) **Raphides** (FIG. 18) are needle-like crystals occurring singly or in bundles. These are found in many plants in small or large quantities, but are specially common in water hyacinth (*Eichhornia*), balsam (*Impatiens*), water lettuce (*Pistia*) and aroids, such as *Colocasia, Alocasia, Amorphophallus,* etc. They are frequently shut off by a cell-wall and prevented from coming in contact with the protoplasm. (*b*) **Conglomerate crystals** or **sphaero-crystals** (FIG. 18C) are clusters of crystals which radiate from a common centre, and hence, have a more or less star-shaped appearance. They are found in water lettuce (*Pistia*), taro (*Colocasia*), etc. (c) **Octahedral, cubical, prismatic** and **rod-like crystals** (FIG. 19) of calcium oxalate are also common in plants. They can be readily seen in the dry scales of onion.

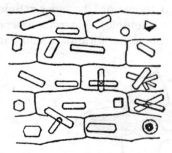

FIG. 19. Mineral Crystals (*contd.*) Various forms of calcium oxalate crystals in th dry onion scale

Tests. (a) 50% nitric acid solution (or any other mineral acid) dissloves both calcium carbonate and oxalate crystals, but bubbles of CO_2 gas are evolved only in the case of carbonate crystals. (b) 30% acetic acid solution readily dissolves calcium carbonate crystals only, but not the oxalate crystals.

6. Latex. This is a milky juice found in latex cells and latex vessels (see FIG. 40). Latex occurs as an emulsion consisting of a variety of chemical substances. Among the nutritive materials, sugars, starch grains (rod or dumbbell shaped), proteins and oils are often found, and among the waste products, gum, resin, tannin, alkaloids, rubber, etc., are common. Latex also contains some salts, enzymes, and often some poisonous substances, as in yellow oleander (*Thevetia*). The function of latex is not clear. Perhaps in some way, it is associated with nutrition, healing of wounds and protection against parasites and animals. The latex of *Hevea* is the source of rubber, and that of papaw (*Carica papaya*) contains a digestive enzyme called *papain*. Latex is commonly milky, as in *Ficus, Euphorbia,* etc., sometimes coloured (yellow, orange or red), as in opium poppy (*Papaver*), prickly poppy (*Argemone*), etc., or even watery, as in banana (*Musa*).

7. Organic Acids. Living cells give an acid reaction. The sour taste of many fruits, particularly of unripe ones, is due to the presence of some such acid in them. Several organic acids are formed in plants and they contain a carboxyl group (-COOH). They are formed as a result of respiration in both the anaerobic and aerobic phases. Oxalacetic acid, citric acid, aconitic acid, etc., are formed during the aerobic phase (see FIG. III/34), but they do not acccumulate in the plant body in appreciable quantities (with the exception of citric acid, as in *Citrus*), while oxalic acid (as in *Oxalis* and *Rumex*), malic acid (as in the leaves of *Bryophyllum, Cicer* and many unripe fruits), tartaric acid (as in tamarind, pineapple and grape), etc., are formed as end-products of anaerobic respiration. They accumulate in considerable quantities in the plant body, particularly in the leaves and the fruits. Many succulent plants also contain some such organic acid in abundance. Fatty acids and amino-acids are very important organic acids directly concerned with metabolism. For example, fatty acids combine with glycerol to form fats and oils, and different amino-acids combine to form proteins. All these organic acids are mostly the result of glucose breakdown during respiration, and the reactions are reversible in many cases.

8. Alkaloids. These are complex nitrogenous substances, and occur in combination with some organic acid, mostly in the seeds and roots of some plants. They may be by-products of nitrogen metabolism in plants. They have an intensely bitter taste and many are extremely poisonous. A few of them are liquids. The majority of them are, however, crystalline solids which are insoluble or sparingly soluble in water, but readily so in alcohol. Alkaloids are generally, but not universally, formed in the roots and translocated from there to certain organs of a plant. There are over 200 known alkaloids found in plants. A few examples are quinine and cinchonine in the root and stem of *Cinchona*, strychnine in the ripe seeds of nux-vomica (*Strychnos*), morphine in the unripe fruits of opium poppy (*Papaver*), atropine in the leaves and roots of deadly nightshade (*Atropa belladonna*), nicotine in the leaves of tobacco (*Nicotiana*), daturine in the leaves and seeds of *Datura*, caffeine in the seeds of coffee and tea, solanine in the stem and ripe fruits of bitter-sweet (*Solanum dulcamara*), etc. The role played by alkaloids in the physiology of plant cells is not known.

Contents of the Vacuole. The vacuolar sap may contain as much as 98% water, and dissolved in it are some of the reserve materials, secretory products and waste products. Although the cell-sap is specially rich in soluble substances, it often contains some solid bodies in amorphous or crystalline conditions. (1) **Inorganic salts**, such as chlorides, sulphates, nitrates and phosphates, are always present in the cell-sap. (2) **Organic acids**, such as oxalic, malic, citric, tataric, etc., and their various salts are fairly common in the cell-sap. (3) **Soluble carbohydrates** are specially common in the cell-sap, e.g. grape-sugar in grapes, cane-sugar in sugarcane, inulin in *Dahlia*, etc. (4) Of the nitrogenous materials, **soluble proteins, amines and amino-acids** occur dissolved in the cell-sap, particularly in the cells of the growing regions, and to some extent only in the storage cell. (5) **Anthocyanins** frequently occur in the petals of flowers and also in the young leaves of some plants. (6) Some **enzymes** are also found in the cell-sap. (7) In some plants, **mucilage** may be found in the cell-sap. (8) Some waste products are also common in particular cells. These are **tannins, latex, alkaloids** and **glucosides**. Glocosides are substances which, on decomposition, give rise to a kind of sugar together with other products—that are chiefly aromatic. Common glucosides are saponin of soap-nut, indican of the indigo-dye, amygdalin of bitter almond, etc. It is not known what role they play in the metabolism of cells. In many cases, however, glucosides are distinctly poisonous.

FORMATION OF NEW CELLS

However big and complicated the body of a plant may ultimately grow to be, it begins its existence as a single cell—the embryonic or egg-cell. But plants have to grow from the initial stage to their normal size and form. Growth is initiated by the formation of new cells and their enlargement, and two processes are closely associated with this : first, division of the nucleus (mitosis) and second, division of the cell (cytokinesis). The division of the egg-cell often begins immediately after fertilization, sometimes after a resting period, and continues throughout the life of the plant. But later, with the formation of tissues and organs, cell-formation becomes restricted mostly to the meristematic regions, such as the root-tip and the stem-tip. Different methods of cell-formation are found in different parts of the plant body or in different plants. The methods are as follows :

1. SOMATIC CELL DIVISION. Cell division leading to the development of the vegetative body (soma) of the plant is known as somatic cell division. It includes the division of the nucleus, called **mitosis** (*mitos*, thread), or **karyokinesis** (*karyon*, nut or nucleus) or **indirect nuclear division**, and the division of the cytoplasm, called **cytokinesis**.

Mitosis (FIG. 20) In mitosis (first worked out by Strasburger, a German botanist, in 1875, and later more elaborately by Flemming, a German biologist, during 1879-82), the behaviour of chromosomes is the most important feature. In this process, the metabolic nucleus (A) passes through a complicated system of changes, of which the most important are the longitudinal doubling of chromosomes and the even distribution of the longitudinal halves among the two daughter nuclei. This can be studied in properly fixed and stained preparations of the root-tip or the stem-tip. The

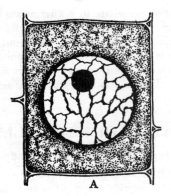

FIG. 20. Mitosis. Metabolic nucleus

changes comprise four stages : prophase, metaphase, anaphase and telophase.

Prophase. This is the longest mitotic stage. The metabolic nucleus contains in its karyolymph numerous crooked, often coiled, delicate threads called **chromonemata**, not recognizable as distinct entities. The first sign of the prophase is the appearance of a certain number of distinct, slender threads called **chromosomes** (B). The term chromosome was first introduced by Waldeyer in 1888. The chromosomes, particularly the longer ones, are more or less spirally coiled. Close scrutiny shows that the individual chromosomes are always longitudinally double, with the two threads remaining closely coiled about each other throughout their length, and each longitudinal half

of the chromosome is called a **chromatid**. Chromosomes are composed of nucleoproteins, and are the vehicles of genes or hereditary factors. As prophase proceeds, the chromosomes relax their coils and thicken somewhat (C). Their double nature becomes more apparent. The outlines of the chromatids present a slightly irregular, hairy appearance. Soon, however, they lose their hairiness and become thicker and smoother. It is also seen that each chromatid divides longitudinally into two. Thus, a chromosome at this stage consists of four threads (chromonemata), two belonging to a chromatid. Further, a chromosomal substance accumulates in a sheath or **matrix** round each chromatid and the two threads become closely coiled in it (D). In well-fixed chromosomes, some unstained gaps or constrictions are seen. These are the attachment regions, called **centromeres**. The matrix soon becomes more apparent, and the nucleoli lose their staining power, decrease in size, and finally disappear at the end of the prophase. The nucleus then rapidly passes into the next stage—the metaphase.

Metaphase. The nuclear membrane disappears and a spindle-like body, known as the **nuclear spindle** (usually bipolar, in some cases multipolar or even monopolar), consisting of very delicate fibres or fibrils, makes its appearance (E). The mode of origin of the spindle varies considerably. It may be formed out of the nuclear sap or

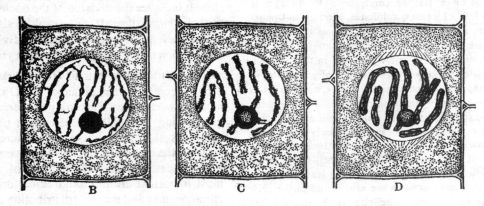

FIG. 20 *B-D*. Mitosis (*contd.*). Prophase

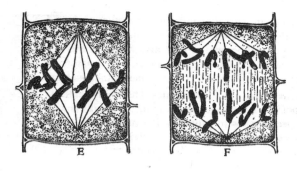

FIG. 20 *E-F*. Mitosis (contd.). *E*, metaphase; *F*, anaphase

karyolymph (nuclear origin), or more frequently out of the cytoplasm (cytoplasmic origin). Usually, in root-tips, it appears as two opposite polar caps outside the nuclear membrane (as in D). The membrane then disappears and the spindle extends into the nuclear area. The chromosomes move to the equatorial plane of the spindle and stand there clearly apart from one another. A feature of mitotic metaphase is that the centromeres of the chromosomes are lined up along the equator, while the arms of the chromosomes extend outwards into the cytoplasm (*cf.* meiotic metaphase, p. 146). In the mitotic cycle, the chromosomes are most sharply defined and best observed at this stage. The chromatids are now seen to come even more close together. The centromere of each chromosome divides so that each chromatid has its own centromere. The centromeres of each pair of chromatids become attached to the spindle fibres, called *tractile fibres,*

passing to the opposite poles (E). The number of chromosomes is normally constant for a particular species of plants. This number is also usually even, expressed as $2n$ (or $2x$) or **diploid**. Chromosome numbers cover a wide range, but 24 seems to be a common figure. It may also be noted that in plants, the chromosomes range in length from 0.1μ to 30μ. In a few cases, they are slightly bigger.

Anaphase. At the end of the metaphase, the centromeres of each pair of chromatids appear to repel each other. They diverge and move ahead towards the two opposite poles along the course of the tractile fibres (F). The movement of the chromatids is autonomous. The causes of this movement are, however, not clearly understood. The chromatids soon separate from each other. The spindle may also undergo elongation and, thus, help the complete separation of the two sets of chromatids. It is apparent from the above that the two longitudinal halves (chromatids) of a chromosome go to the two opposite poles of the spindle. Anaphase covers the shortest period in mitosis.

Telophase. At each pole, the chromatids (now regarded as chromosomes) form a close group (G). The polar caps of the spindle disappear and a nuclear membrane is formed round each group of chromosomes (H). Nucleoli reappear at definite points of certain chromosomes. The spindle body disappears and so does the matrix. The chromosomes reorganise as two nuclei. The nuclear sap reappears and each nucleus increases in size (1). It passes into the metabolic stage or prepares for the next division. The duration of mitosis varies

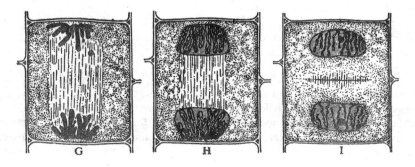

FIG. 20 *G – I*. Mitosis (contd.). Telophase

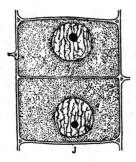

FIG. 20 *J* Mitosis (*contd.*) Cytokinesis

considerably in different plants and also in the same plant under different conditions. In this respect, temperature is an important factor. Generally, the time taken for complete division is from 1/2 to 2 or 3 hours. Regarding temperature effect, Sharp gives the following figures in connexion with mitosis in the staminal hair of *Tradescantia*—about 30 minutes at 45°C., 75 minutes at 25°C., and 135 minutes at 10°C.

Cytokinesis or the *division of the cytoplasm and the formation of the cell-wall.* Cytokinesis has recently been the subject of considerable investigation. The division of cytoplasm appears to take place in one of two ways: by the formation of a new cell-wall in the equatorial region or by furrowing (i.e. by cleavage of the cytoplasm). The former process, known as the cell-plate method, is the usual one in a vegetative cell. It usually begins in the telophase, when new cellulose particles are gradually deposited in the equatorial zone, and soon these particles fuse together to form a delicate membrane, dividing the cytoplasm into two new cells (J). In the latter process, as in the formation of pollen grains in the anther (see FIG. I/117J), constrictions or furrows appear in the ectoplast and these gradually proceed within, dividing the cytoplasm into two parts.

Importance. The importance of mitosis lies in the fact that by this complicated process of nuclear division, the DNA, which is the chief component of chromosomes, is distributed equally among the two daughter nuclei formed. Thus, the daughter nuclei becomes qualitatively

and quantitatively similar to the mother nucleus. DNA is the sole genetic (hereditary) material of the chromosomes and because of even distribution of this material among the two daughter nuclei, they possess all the characteristics and qualities of the mother nucleus.

Chemistry of Chromosomes. The main chemical components of chromosomes are nucleic acids and certain special types of proteins. The nucleic acids occur in chromosomes in the form of DNA and to some extent, as RNA (see p. 124). The nature and quantity of the DNA present in diploid cells are constant for a particular species of plants or animals, and in haploid cells, just half this quantity occurs. The DNA of the chromosomes is the sole genetic material (see p 124). Although DNA is chemically the same in all living organisms, each species of plants or animals is characterized by its own specific type of DNA. This is why a species cannot normally go out of bounds, or in other words, a particular species always gives rise to the same species. The diversity in species may, however, be due to an infinite number of combinations of nitrogenous bases (purines and pyrimidines) in the DNA molecules (see Genes, Part VIII, Chapter 2).

Structure of the Chromosome (FIG. 21). The structure of the chromosome may best be studied in its metaphase or anaphase stage, preferably in the latter. It must be noted that chromosomes always appear in their

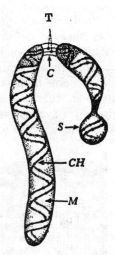

FIG. 21 Structure of a chromosome at anaphase stage. *T*, tractile fibres; *C*, centromere; *S*, satellite; *CH*, chromonema; *M*, matrix

Fig. 21 redrawn after Fig. 57 in *Fundamentals of Cytology* by L. W. Sharp by permission of McGraw-Hill Book Company

characteristic shapes and sizes, apart from their constant number, in the succeeding divisions of the nucleus so far as a particular species of plants is concerned. Most commonly, the anaphasic chromosomes of somatic cells lie within limits of 1-20μ in length. Long chromosomes, of course, give a better idea of their constitution. As previously stated, a chromosome consists of two parts : usually two spiral threads, called **chromonemata**, twisted about each other, and a chromosomal **matrix**, often very clear at certain stages of mitosis. The two chromonemata are sometimes so closely associated that their double nature cannot be clearly made out. This has led to a controversy as to their true nature—single or double, or more according to some. The evidence is, however, in favour of two chromonemata. Along the whole length of each chromonema, there is a series of granules called **chromomeres**, which look like beads in a chain. These are, however, more clear in meiosis than in mitosis. The attachment region or **centromere** (also called kinetochore or primary constriction) is a very important part of the chromosome. Tractile fibre extends from it to the pole. The position of the centromere is always constant in a given chromosome, as seen in successive divisions. It is a clear achromatic zone. The chromonemata are continuous through this zone, and each of them may contain a minute granule or spherule (also called kinocome). The portions of the chromosome lying on the sides of the centromere are called **arms**. These may be equal or unequal depending on the position of the centromere. Usually, one of the chromosomes of a nucleus has in one of its arms, sometimes in both, a seecondary constriction which is connected with the organization of the nucleolus. The small distal segment of the chromosome, thus formed, is called the **satellite**. Its position is also fixed in the chromosome so that it (the chromosome) may be recognized in the succeeding divisions of the nucleus. Abundant matrices, particularly after staining, often obscure this feature. Besides, it is seen that some parts of the chromosome, often close to the centromere, are much denser and more strongly stainable (chromatic) than other parts. The significance of this difference is not clearly understood. It is, however, suggested that the denser parts are connected with the formation of nucleic acid.

2. MEIOSIS or REDUCTION DIVISION (FIG. 22).

Meiosis (*meiosis*, reduction) was first worked out by Strasburger in 1888, and later more elaborately by Farmer and Moore in 1905. Meiosis is a complicated process of nuclear division, whereby the chromosome number is reduced to half (n) in the four nuclei so formed by this method. Supposing then, that the mother nucleus bears 12 chromosomes ($2n$), each of the daughter nuclei will have only 6. Reduction division takes place in all sexually reproducing organisms at some point in their life-cycle. Sexual reproduction means the fusion of a male gamete with a female one, resulting in the formation of a zygote from which the offspring develops in due course. If gametes contained the same number of chromosomes as their parents, the offspring would have an everincreasing number of chromosomes from generation to generation, apart from the peculiar composition of the latter. As a consequence, the offspring would develop into new, peculiar and distinct types since chromosomes are the bearers of hereditary characteristics and meiosis is the mechanism for transmission of these characteristics. Thus, in all sexually reproducing plants and animals, the gametes are **haploid** (n) to compensate for the chromosome doubling ($n + n = 2n$) in the zygote as a result of fertilization. The DNA (see p. 146) of the chromosomes, which is the sole hereditary material, is also distributed in equal halves among the gametes. In higher plants showing an alternation of generations, meiosis occurs as soon as a plant enters into the gametophytic phase in its life-cycle and, therefore, during the formation of spores from the spore mother cell. In lower plants, on the other hand, meiosis occurs immediately after fertilization or on the germination of the zygote.

Process. Meiosis comprises two successive divisions of the mother nucleus (meiocyte), of which *division I* is reduction division, whereby the chromosome number ($2n$) is reduced to half or (n), and *division II* is mitotic in nature. This being so, the four nuclei that are formed by this process have the same reduced number (n) of chromosomes.

Fig. 22 A-B redrawn after Fig. 76 in *Fundamentals of Cytology* by L. W. Sharp by permission of McGraw-Hill Book Company.

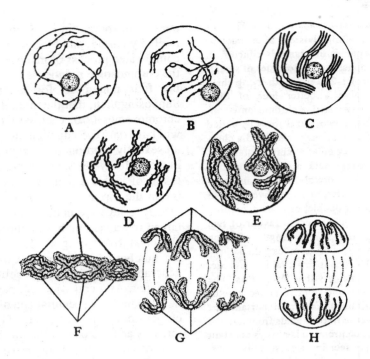

FIG. 22A Meiosis. Division I Prophase—*A*, Leptotene; *B*, zygotene; *C*, pachytene;
D, diplotene; *E*, Diakinesis; *F*, metaphase; *G*, anaphase; *H*, telophase

Division I (FIG. 22A). In this division, too, the nucleus passes through the same phases as in mitosis, but there are certain special features of meiosis distinct from mitosis.

Prophase I. This phase of meiosis is a prolonged and complicated one, and can be subdivided into the following five stages. **Leptotene (A):** At the early prophase, the nucleus increases in volume, and the chromosomes appear as long, slender and single threads (not double, as in mitosis) in diploid number. It will, however, be noted that the threads are present in exactly identical pairs, one being paternal and the other maternal. They now begin to coil. In each thread, there appear a number of small beadlike granules known as the **chromomeres**, which represent the tightest coils of the chromosome. **Zygotene (B):** It is seen that the identical chromosomes develop a strong attraction for each other, and they soon come together in pairs, part by part, throughout their whole length, except in very long chromosomes. This pairing, called **synapsis**, is only in the nature of close asso-

ciation (bivalent condition) and not their actual fusion. The pairing chromosomes are *homologous*, being derived from the same parent chromosome. They now begin to shorten and thicken. **Pachytene (C):** The pairing chromosomes become shorter and thicker still due to their increased coiling. Each chromosome splits longitudinally, and thus, four chromatids (two from each homologue) are produced. The homologous chromosomes, each with two chromatids, can be clearly identified at this stage. Pachytene is a long process. **Diplotene(D):** At this stage, a sort of repulsive force (or loss of attraction) develops between the homologous chromosomes, and they begin to separate from each other. They, however, remain connected in one point (usually in shorter ones) or more points (usually in longer ones). These points are known as **chiasmata**, and they are quite conspicuous. At each chiasma, a physical exchange of genetic material ('genes') takes place by *crossing over*— a special feature of meiosis. The chromosomes coil further in a thick sheath or matrix and become shorter still. **Diakinesis** (E): At this stage, the chromosome bivalents move to the periphery of the nucleus and become almost separated from each other, except at the chiasmata. The nucleolus soon disappears and the nuclear membrane also breaks down. The chromosomes are, thus, released into the cytoplasm. At about this time, the nuclear spindle begins to be formed.

Metaphase I (F): The chromosomes (each with two chromatids) move to the equatorial region of the spindle. But this phase is distinct from the mitotic metaphase. Here, the centromeres of the chromosome pairs become attached to spindle fibres near the equator, clearly apart from each other and facing opposite poles, while their arms lie towards the equator, i.e. the chromosomes are not lined up along the equator, as in mitosis (see p. 144).

Anaphase I (G). The two centromeres of the homologous chromosomes repel each other and move towards the opposite poles of the spindle along the course of the tractile fibres, each carry-ing a chromosome (paternal or maternal, but not both) with it to one pole. This finally results in the reduction of the chromosome number from diploid to haploid. This is the essential feature of meiosis.

Telophase I (H). As in mitosis, the chromosomes (each with a pair of chromatids) form a compact group at each pole. The nucleolus reappears and a nuclear membrane is formed around each polar group of chromosomes. The two daughter nuclei thus formed evidently contain haploid or (n) chromosomes, each with a pair of chromatids. A cell-membrane may or may not be formed at this stage, separating the two nuclei. Almost immediately or a little later, each nucleus passes on to division II.

Division II (FIG. 22 B). The phases are almost the same as found in mitosis. In **prophase II** (I) of meiosis, the two chromatids of a chromosome remain distinctly separate and loose except at the centromeres. The chromosomes, however, are long and coiled. Soon, they become shorter and thicker by further coiling. This phase ends with the

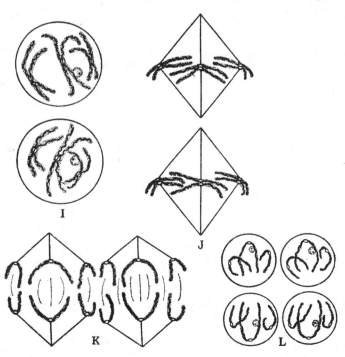

FIG. 22B Meiosis (*contd.*). Division II. *I*, prophase. *J* metaphase; *K,* anaphase; and *L*, telophase

disappearance of the nucleolus and the nuclear membrane, and the appearance of the spindle fibres. In **metaphase II** (J), the chromosomes take up an equatorial position in the newly-formed spindle. This phase is short. Further, the chromosome pair separates, each having its own centromere. In **anaphase II** (K), the two sister chromosomes of each pair begin to move towards the opposite poles, being drawn by their centromeres. In **telophase II**(L), a nuclear membrane is formed around each polar group of chromosomes, and the nucleolus reappears. Finally, by cytokinesis, *four* cells are formed, each nucleus having haploid or (*n*) chromosomes. It will be noted that the first division of meiosis is *reductional,* while the second division is *equational.*

Differences between Mitosis and Meiosis

1. Mitosis occurs in somatic (meristematic) cells, while meiosis occurs in reproductive cells, resulting in the formation of spores of gametes.

2. In mitosis, the chromosome number remains constant (diploid or 2*n*) with full quantity of DNA, while in meiosis (or reduction division), the chromosome number is reduced to half (haploid or *n*) with half the quantity of DNA, i.e. mitosis is *equational,* while meiosis is *reductional.* This is the essential difference between the two processes. Meiosis is really a mechanism to keep the chromosome number constant from generation to generation.

3. In the prophase of both, the chromosomes appear in specific numbers but in mitosis, they appear in double threads, while in meiosis they appear in single threads but in identical pairs.

4. Pairing (synapsis) of identical (homologous) chromosomes (one paternal and one maternal) occurs in meiosis (each pair subsequently acting as a unit), but no pairing occurs in mitosis. In mitosis, on the other hand, each chromosome splits longitudinally into two.

5. The prophase of mitosis is short, while it is a prolonged one in meiosis and, therefore, divided into substages.

6. The meiotic metaphase is different from the mitotic metaphase. In the former, the centromeres of the homologous chromosomes lie towards the two opposite poles of the spindle near the equator and their arms extend towards the equator, while in the latter, the centromeres are lined up in the equatorial plane and the arms extend into the cytoplasm.

7. Mitosis continues one after the other with the diploid number of chromosomes, whereas meiosis is completed in two divisions (the first only being the reduction division), resulting in four cells (each with haploid or *n* chromosomes) in a group (tetrad).

8. The haploid (*n*) gametes (of opposite sexes) formed by meiosis normally fuse in pairs in sexual reproduction, and their fusion product, i.e. the zygote, becomes diploid (2*n*). Normally, no such fusion of diploid cells (nuclei) takes place.

9. In mitosis, the centromere divides at metaphase and the sister chromatids move to the opposite poles; in meiosis, the centromere does not divide and the homologous chromosomes, each with its own centromere, move to the opposite poles. In both processes the centromere moves first and draws the chromosome.

10. Chromomeres are more prominent in the meiotic chromosome than in the mitotic one.

11. Chiasma and crossing over (exchange of genes) are normal and exclusive features of meiosis.

12. In mitosis, the chromosomes are equally apportioned to the daughter nuclei, i.e. the latter are qualitatively and quantitatively the same as the mother nucleus, while in meiosis the four threads of a chromosome go to the four cells (and their assortment is also a matter of chance, i.e. it is not known which thread will go to which cell). Thus, meiosis results in four new types of cells.

Polyploidy. Normally, plants and animals have in their somatic cells two sets of chromosomes (paternal and maternal), expressed as diploid or 2*n*, while in their reproductive cells they have one set of chromosomes, expressed as haploid or *n*. An increase in the number of chromosomes in certain tissues or entire organisms in multiples of the basic or haploid number is expressed as polyploidy. This is of wide occurrence in nature, particularly in plants (wild or cultivated) and rarely in animals. There are, however, organisms with more than two sets or less than two sets of chromosomes in their somatic cells. The term *heteroploidy* is sometimes used to include all types of variations found in chromosome numbers. All such variations may be discussed under the following heads: euploidy and aneuploidy.

Euploidy (*eu,* true or even; *ploid,* unit). This represents cases where the somatic chromosome complements[1] are exact multiples of the haploid number, characteristic of a particular species. Among euploid, a *monoploid* organism has but a single genome[2] per nucleus instead of a double set. This, however, is not common and is found more often in animals. Among plants it has been found in *Sorghum, Triticum, Hordeum, Datura,* etc. Such individuals are small, weak and generally sterile. They have very irregular meiosis because of the absence of homologues. More commonly, however, the individuals are *triploid,* having 3 sets of chromosomes, *tetraploid* (with 4 sets), *hexaploid* (with 6 sets), and *octoploid* (with 8 sets). Other multiples are also found. Organisms having 3 or more sets of chromosomes are, however, commonly known as polyploids.

Polyploidy. As stated above, individuals, cells or tissues having 3 or more sets of chromosomes are called polyploids. Among them, *triploidy* ($2n + n = 3n$) was first discovered by Miss Lutz (1912) in *Oenothera.* Since then, triploidy has been found in many cultivated plants, e.g. hyacinths, chilli, tomato, rice, maize, *Datura,* etc. Such plants show certain variations and are distinct from the normal types. *Tetraploidy* ($2n + 2n = 4n$) was first discovered by Digby (1912) in *Primula.* This has since been found to be widespread, and is perhaps the most important polyploid type. Gigantism and great vigour (heterosis) are frequently associated with this condition, e.g. giant *Chrysanthemum,* marigold, rose, etc. Similarly, *hexaploidy* ($6n$), *octoploidy* ($8n$) and other multiples have been found. It may be noted that different varieties of cultivated wheat show tetraploidy ($4n$), pentaploidy ($5n$) and hexaploidy ($6n$). Nawaschin (1925 & 1926) found $3n$, $4n$ and $5n$ in *Crepis.* Polyploidy is often differentiated into two major types on the basis of the source of chromosomes: autopolyploidy and allopolyploidy. **Autopolyploids** are organisms in which the multiple genomes are identical. The increase in chromosome number is due to doubling of the chromosomes of a single homozygous diploid. On the other hand, a**llopoly-**

ploids are organisms in which the multiple genomes are different, coming together from different sources through crossing or hybridization. They are, therefore, found in hybrids only. The increase in chromosome number may be due to crossing between two diploid gametes, or multiplication of chromosomes in the hybrids. There are several cases on record. A classical example is *Raphanobrassica* (a tetraploid with 36 chromosomes), which is a hybrid produced by Karpechenko (1927) in Russia as a result of a cross between radish (*Raphanus*) and cabbage (*Brassica*), each with 9 chromosomes. Other examples of allopolyploidy are the several hybrids of *Rosa, Primula, Papaver, Iris,* etc.

Aneupolyploidy (*aueu,* uneven). This represents cases where the somatic chromosome complements are not exact multiple of the basic number. There is addition or loss of usually 1 or 2 chromosomes. Thus, when the number is less, it is expessed as *hypoploidy,* and when more, it is *hyperploidy.* These conditions are due to unequal distribution of chromosomes during anaphase. One daughter cell may get an additional chromosome, while the other has to lose one. An organism (individual) lacking one chromosome of a diploid number is called *monosomic* ($2n - 1$). A *trisomic* individual has two sets of chromosomes plus one extra chromosome ($2n+1$). A *tetrasomic* one has two sets plus two extra chromosomes ($2n + 2$), and a *double tetrasomic* one has ($2n + 2 + 2$).

Effect of Polyploidy. Polyploid plants are usually healthier, stronger and larger than their diploid counterparts. This may be due to increase in size and chromatin contents of the polyploid cells. Working on *Nicotiana,* Smith found in a series consisting of haploids, diploids, triploids and tetraploids that with an increase in each additional set of chromosomes, there was a corresponding increase in the width of the corolla tube, size of leaves, thickness of parts of plants including pollen grains, guard cells, and the cells of the root-tip. In octoploids, however, he observed a

---

[1] A chromosome **complement** is a group of chromosomes making up a nucleus, irrespective of their number and kind.
[2] A complement is said to be a **genome** when it consists of a set of chromosomes inherited as a unit from one parent, whatever be their number, form and function.

reduction in the size of certain organs. Blakeslee and Warmke (1938) found that many tetraploid plants possess larger seeds, larger pollen grains, wider and thicker leaves, larger inflorescences, larger floral parts and stouter fruits. In polyploidy, some differences are also detected in certain physiological properties. For example, the vitamin content of fruits (e.g. vitamin C in tomato, and vitamin A in maize) and vegetables increases. In sugar beet (*Beta vulgaris*), the sugar content increases, and in tobacco, the percentage of nicotine is seen to be higher (see below).

Origin of Polyploidy. All biologists agree that the diploid condition is primitive, and that polyploids are derived from diploids and are more advanced. The question, however, arises: 'How does polyploidy originate'? Polyploidy can originate in the following ways: (1) *Doubling of chromosome number in the somatic tissue.* This may be due to some irregularities affecting normal mitosis in certain somatic cells. For example, (*a*) the cell-wall may not be formed after the division of the chromosmes during mitosis. The result is a tetraploid nucleus ($2n + 2n = 4n$). The gamete mother cell formed this way may give rise to diploid ($2n$) gametes; (*b*) the spindle may not develop properly, and a single nuclear membrane may surround the two diploid nuclei. The restitution nucleus may thus have four sets of chromosomes (tetraploid or $4n$); (*c*) two diploid gametes may also fuse, resulting in a tetraploid somatic cell. (2) *Doubling of chromosome number in the formation of reproductive cells (gametes).* The irregularities leading to an increase in chromosome number in such cells may take the following forms: (*a*) Failure of meiotic division (one or both) may lead to the formation of diploid gametes. (*b*) The cell-wall may not be formed after division of the chromosomes during meiosis. Thus, no reduction in the chromosome number takes place. (*c*) Production of a gamete mother cell with two nuclei— their homotypic spindles may fuse together, producing diploid gametes. (*d*) The tetraploid nucleus of the gamete mother cell may give rise to diploid gametes by meiosis. The above conditions may arise spontaneously in nature, and can also be induced artificially. If a tetraploid condition arises in a bud primordium, a $4n$ branch will result. A triploid ($3n$) somatic cell may be produced by the union of a diploid ($2n$) gamete with a normal haploid (n) gamete. A triploid plant is usually sterile and has lower vitality. Other multiples may arise as a result of through repeated duplication of chromosomes or through intercrossing among polyploids.

Induced Polyploidy. Polyploidy can be artifically induced by drastic changes in the environment with the use of different agents. (1) Sudden change in temperature, extreme heat or cold brings about polyploidy. (2) Wounding the plant leads to the formation of callous. It is seen that in many cells of the callous, the walls are not formed after mitosis, and as a result, doubling of chromosomes takes place. The buds formed from them develop into polyploid shoots (Winkler, 1916). (3) Application of the alkaloid *colchicine* (Blakeslee, 1937 and Nebel, 1938) and other chemicals like veratrine sulphate (Whitus and Derger, 1944), benzene, acenaphthane, sulfanilamide, chloral hydrate, heteroauxin, etc. (4) Infection by bacteria, insects and other infective agents. (5) Changes in osmotic pressure. (6) Irradiation by X-ray.

Importance of Polyploidy. Polyploidy is now considered very important from the standpoint of evolution, plant breeding and geographical distribution. Its economic and ornamental value in many cases is no less important. Among cultivated plants, polyploidy has led to a great number of varieties or species, e.g. rice, wheat, maize, tobacco, cotton, mustard, sugarcane, etc. Polyploid plants have many advantages over diploid ones. This is particularly true of tetraploidy. With additional chromosomes, an increased number of genes and certain new physiological properties (see above), polyploid forms tend to be far better than diploid forms in many respects. Such plants are more liable to variation and mutation, and may ultimately lead to the evolution of new species. It is seen that in many polyploids, the cell size increases while the growth rate decreases. Polyploidy may lead annuals to become biennials or perennials (Muntzing, 1936). In 1934, Sharp reported that a certain polyploid variety of maize is perennial, while the diploid variety is annual.

Polyploidy, thus, may be one of the methods by which new species are evolved. *Raphanobrassica* (see p. 151), which has 4*n* chromosomes formed by allopolyploidy, breeds true and is regarded as a new species. Similarly, Muntzing crossed two species of *Galeopsis* and produced a hybrid with 4*n* chromosomes, which is as good as a new species. It is believed that in nature, several new species have arisen by allopolyploidy. Besides, many of them become large and show hybrid vigour (heterosis), and have certain other favourable properties (see p. 151). Their commercial value is being gradually exploited. Another advantage is that polyploidy can be artificially induced, and many polyploid plants are seen to be very fertile. In many cases, they are also disease resistant. As such, plant breeders are specially interested in this line of research work. A special feature of polyploidy is giganticism (gigantism). This means that polyploid plants normally show more vigorous growth, often resulting in much larger size. Such plants also develop larger vegetative and reproductive parts (see pp. 192-93). Thus, the tetraploid variety of jute (*Corchorus*) with 4*n* chromosomes may be twice as tall as the diploid variety. Sometimes, giganticism is associated with an increase in the size of the chromosomes. A gigas polyploid form reproducing vegetatively, e.g. sugarcane, is a decided advantage. Polyploidy is also common in many garden plants, e.g.

Hibiscus, Chrysanthemum, marigold, rose, snapdragon, etc. Besides, the sturdier nature of many polyploids helps them extend over wide areas against adverse conditions. *Saccharum spontaneum* is known to have invaded new extensive areas as a result of a gradual increase in the chromosome number.

3. AMITOSIS or DIRECT NUCLEAR DIVISION (FIG. 23). In this case, the nucleus elongates to some extent and then undergoes constriction, i.e. it becomes narrower and narrower in the middle or at one end, and finally splits into two. The nuclei so formed are often of unequal sizes. Amitosis may or may not be followed by the division of the cell. Amitosis is of frequent occurrence in lower organisms like algae and fungi. In the higher plants, it is seen to occur in old cells and in those showing distinct signs of degeneration.

4. FREE CELL FORMATION (FIG. 24). This is a modification of indirect nuclear division. It differs from the latter in that the cell-wall is not formed immediately after the division of the nucleus. In this process, a large number of nuclei are formed within the mother cell through repeated mitotic divisions. When the divisions of the nuclei cease, the cytoplasm aggregates round them, and a cell-wall is formed round each nucleus. The formation of the cell-wall gradually proceeds from one side to the other, resulting in a regular tissue (combination

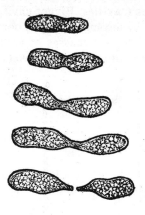

FIG. 23. Amitosis

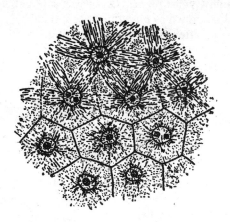

FIG. 24. Free cell formation in the development of endosperm

of cells). The endosperm, i.e. the food storage tissue of the seed, is formed by this method.

In some cases, mitosis may be immediately followed by the formation of the cell-wall, resulting in free cells, e.g. ascospores, or the nuclei may remain free (without wall-formation), e.g. zoospores, or repeated nuclear divisions may result in a large number of free nuclei within the mother cell, which quickly elongates and often becomes branched, e.g. latex cell. Such a structure is called a **coenocyte**. *Vaucheria* is another good example of a coenocyte.

5. BUDDING (FIG. 25). This is seen in yeast—a unicellular fungus. In this plant, the cell forms one

FIG. 25. Building in yeast

or more tiny outgrowths on its body. The nucleus undergoes direct division (amitosis) and splits into two. One of them passes on to one outgrowth. The outgrowth increases in size and is ultimately cut off from the mother yeast as a new independent cell (a new yeast plant). This process of cell-formation is known as *budding*. Often, budding continues one after the other so that chains and even sub-chains of cells are formed. Ultimately, all the cells separate from one another.

VESSELS, INTERCELLULAR SPACES AND CAVITIES

Vessels. Sometimes it is only the cross-walls of a cylindrical row of cells that get dissolved, and consequently, a large continuous opening is formed, the side or longitudinal walls remaining intact. The constituent cells together thus give rise to a tube or pipe-like structure. This pipe-like structure without partition walls is known as the **vessel** (FIG. 26). The ends of the constituent cells, or vessel segments, are mostly narrow with oblique perforation (see FIG. 37 E-F). Vessels are of different kinds. They are thick-walled, lignified and dead. Lignin is deposited as a thickening material on the inner surface of the side-walls in various patterns, and according to the mode of thickening (see p. 129), vessels may be of the following types—**annular**, **spiral**, **scalariform**, **reticulate**, and **pitted** (see, FIG. 37). Vessels are carriers of water and raw food materials, i.e., they conduct these substances from the root to the leaf. Being thick-walled and lignified, they also serve to give strength to the plant body.

Intercellular Spaces. When the cells are young, they remain closely packed without any empty space or cavity between them. As they grow, their walls split at certain points, giving rise to small cavities or empty spaces. These are intercellular spaces. They remain filled with air or water.

Schizogenous Cavities. Bigger cavities are also often formed by the splitting up of common walls and the separation of masses of cells from one another. These are schizogenous (*schizein*, to

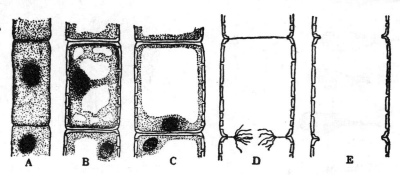

FIG. 26. Development of a vessel. *A-E* are stages in its development

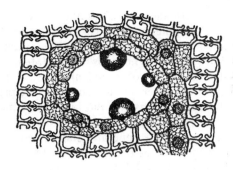

FIG. 27. Resin-duct of pine stem with resins

split) cavities. Intercellular spaces and these cavities form an intercommunicating system so that gases and liquids can easily diffuse from one part of the plant body to the other. Most resin-ducts in plants are schizogenous cavities (FIG. 27).

Lysigenous Cavities. Sometimes, during the development of a mass of cells, their walls break down and dissolve and as a consequence, large irregular cavities appear. These are known as **lysigenous** *(lysis,* loosening) cavities. They are meant for storing water, gases, essential oils, etc., and thus, act as glands (see FIG. 41A).

CHAPTER 2

THE TISSUE

Cells grow and assume distinct shapes to perform definite functions. Cells of the same shape grow together and combine into a group for the discharge of a common function. Each group of such cells gives rise to a tissue. *A tissue is,thus, a group of cells of the same type or of mixed type, having a common origin and performing an identical function.* Tissues may primarily be classified into two groups : **meristematic** and **permanent.**

MERISTEMATIC TISSUES (*meristos,* divided).

These are composed of cells that are in a state of division or retain the power of dividing. These cells are essentially alike and isodiametric. They may be spherical, oval or polygonal and their walls thin and homogeneous; the protoplasm in them abundant and active with large nuclei, and the vacuoles small or absent.

Classification of Meristems. Meristems are classified in different ways on the basis of certain factors. Thus, according to their origin and development, they may be classified as *promeristem* or *primordial meristem, primary meristem* and *secondary meristem.* According to their position in the plant body, they may be classified as *apicl, intercalary,* and *lateral.* According to their functions they may be classified as *protoderm, procambium,* and *ground* or *fundamental meristem.*

The **promeristem** consists of a group of meristematic cells representing the earliest or youngest stage of a growing organ. It is, in fact the stage from which differentiation of later meristems and finally, of permanent tissue, takes place. It occupies a small area at the tip of the stem and the root. The promeristem gives rise to the primary meristem by cell division and is, therefore, the earliest stage or originator of the latter.

The **primary meristem** is derived from the promeristem, and still fully retains its meristematic activity. As a matter of fact, its cells divide rapidly and become differentiated into distinct tissues—the *primary permanent tissues* which make up the fundamental structure of the plant body. It is primarily the growing apical region of the root and the stem. It should also be noted that the cambium of the stem is also a primary meristem although it gives rise to the *secondary permanent tissues*. Another fact to be noted in this connexion is that the cambial cells divide mainly in one plane (tangential), while those of the primary meristem divide in 3 or more planes.

The **secondary meristem**, on the other hand, appears later, at a certain stage of the development of an organ of a plant. It is always lateral, lying along the side of the stem and the root. It is seen that some of the primary permanent tissues become meristematic, i.e. they acquire the power of division, and constitute the secondary meristem, e.g. the cambium of the root, the inter fascicular cambium of the stem, and the cork-cambium of both. All lateral meristems (primary and secondary) give rise to the *secondary permanent tissues*, and are responsible for growth in the thickness of the plant body.

As stated before, on the basis of their position, the meristems may be apical, intercalary and lateral. (*a*) An **apical meristem** lies at the apex of the stem and the root, representing their *growing regions*, and is of varying lengths, usually ranging from a few millimetres to a few centimetres. It includes the promeristem and the primary meristem, gives rise to the *primary permanent tissues*, and is responsible for growth in the length of the plant body. It should be noted that the promeristem consists of a group of meristematic cells in phanerogams (mostly), while in pteridophytes (mostly), it is represented by a single cell. (*b*) The **intercalary meristem**, when present, lies between

masses of permanent tissues, either at the base of the leaf, as in pine, or at the base of the internode, as in some grasses and horsetail (*Equisetum*), or sometimes below the node, as in mint (*Mentha*). It is a detached portion of the apical meristem, separated from the latter due to growth of the organ. Like the apical meristem, the intercalary meristem, when present, gives rise to the primary permanent tissues. It is generally short-lived, either disappearing soon or becoming transformed into permanent tissues. (*c*) The **lateral meristem**, e.g. cambium of the stem, lies laterally in strips of elongated cells, extending from the apical meristem, as in the stems of dicotyledons and gymnosperms. It divides mainly in the tangential direction, giving rise to the *secondary permanent tissues* to the inside and outside of it, and is responsible for growth in the thickness of the plant body.

Theories regarding Apical Meristem. (a) Apical cell theory. Nageli (1858) first coined the term 'meristem' and said that the apical meristem consists of a single apical cell in all plants, and that the sequence of cell divisions is responsible for the formation of different members of the plant body. Nageli's 'single cell' theory is no doubt true of the thallophytes and vascular cryptogams, but his assumption that this is applicable to all cryptogams and phanerogams has proved to be wrong. His 'single cell' theory was supported by Hofmiester, but he expressed doubts regarding its applicability in all cases, particularly phanerogams. (b) **Histogen theory.** In 1870, Hanstein formulated his 'histogen' theory. According to this theory, the apical meristem of

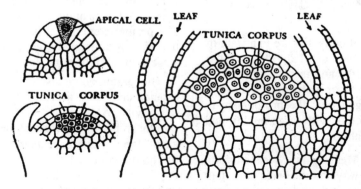

FIG. 28. Apical meristem. *Top,* apical cell in a pteridophyte; *bottom,* tunica and corpus in an angiosperm

angiosperms is divisible into three zones, each consisting of a variable number of layers, and these zones he called dermatogen (outer), periblem (middle) and plerome (inner). These zones give rise to the epidermis, cortex and stele, respectively. Further, he put forth the idea that even in the embryo of the phanerogams, there was a clear differentiation into outer layer (dermatogen) and an inner core. Sachs accepted this view, but on a physiological basis, he proposed three systems derived from the above, viz. epidermal, fascicular (vascular) and fundamental. Sachs, however, recognized an apical single cell in most cryptogams and zonal layers in phanerogams. (c) **Tunica-corpus theory.** In 1924, Schmidt proposed the 'tunica-corpus' theory. According to this theory, there are two zones in the apical meristem. Tunica is the outer zone consisting of one or more peripheral layers of small uniform cells normally showing anticlinal divisions, and corpus is the undifferentiated mass of larger cells enclosed by the tunica. Its cells vary in number from a few to many, divide in many planes and, therefore, they are more or less irregular in shape and arrangement. The epidermis arises from the outer layer of the tunica, while the remaining tissues arise from the corpus (or partly from the tunica). This view is now generally accepted.

Haberlandt (1914) introduced another system, on a physiological basis, to explain the differentiation of the apical meristem. According to him the promeristem differentiates into the **protoderm**, which gives rise to the epidermal tissue system, **procambium**, which gives rise to the vascular tissue system, and **ground or fundamental meristem**, which gives rise to the ground tissue system.

APICAL MERISTEMS OF STEM AND ROOT

1. STEM APEX (FIG. 29A). A median longitudinal section through the microscope shows that the apical meristem or growing region is composed of a small mass of usually rounded or polygonal cells, which are all essentially alike and are in a state of division. These meristematic cells constitute the **promeristem** (or primordial meristem). The cells of the promeristem soon differentiate into three regions, viz. dermatogen, periblem and plorome. The cells of these three regions grow and give rise to primary permanent tissues in the mature portion of the stem. The section further shows a number of outgrowths on either side. The outgrowths arch over the growing apex. These are the young leaves of the bud, which cover and protect the tender, growing apex of the stem.

(1) **Dermatogen** (*derma*, skin; *gen*, producing). This is the single, outermost layer of cells. It passes right over the apex and continues downwards as a single layer. The cells divide by *radial* walls only, i.e. at right angles to the surface

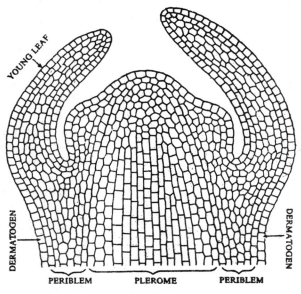

FIG. 29A. Stem apex in median longitudinal section

of the stem, and increase in circumference, thus keeping pace with the increasing growth in the volume of the underlying tissues. The dermatogen gives rise to the skin layer or epidermis of the stem.

(2) **Periblem** (*peri*, around; *blema*, clothing or covering). This lies internal to the dermatogen, and is the middle region of the apical meristem. At the apex it is single-layered but lower down, it becomes multi-layered. It forms the cortex of the stem which is often (particularly in dicotyledons) differentiated into the hypodermis, general cortex and endoderms.

(3) **Plerome** (*pleres*, full). This lies internal to the periblem, and is the central region of the stem apex. At a little distance behind the apex certain groups or strands of cells show a tendency to elongate. These groups or strands of elongated

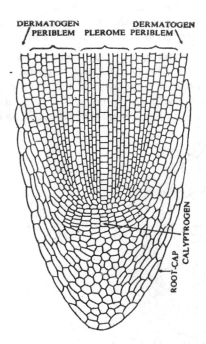

DERMATOGEN   DERMATOGEN
/ PERIBLEM   PLEROME   PERIBLEM \

ROOT-CAP CALYPTROGEN

FIG. 29B. Root apex in median longitudinal section

cells are said to form the **procambium**. The procambial strands ultimately become differentiated into bundles of vessels and sieve-tubes, i.e. into vascular bundles. A portion, however, remains

undifferentiated and forms the fascicular cambium, i.e. the cambium of the vascular bundle. The plerome is differentiated into the pericycle, medullary rays, pith and vascular bundles (derived from the procambial strands), and forms the central cylinder or *stele* of the stem.

2. ROOT APEX (FIG. 29B). A median longitudinal section through the apex of the root shows that it is covered over and protected by a many-layered tissue which constitutes the root-cap. The apical meristem or growing region lies behind the root-cap (see FIG. I/3). The promeristem, as in the stem, soon differentiates into three regions, viz. dermatogen, periblem, and plerome. In many roots, however, these three regions are not clearly marked.

(1) **Dermatogen**. As in the stem, this is also single-layered, but it merges into the periblem at the apex. Just outside this, the dermatogen cuts off many new cells, thus forming a small-celled tissue known as the **calyptrogen** (*calyptra*, cap; *gen*, producing). The calyptrogen is also meristematic, and by repeated divisions of its cells, gives rise to the **root-cap**. As the root passes through the hard soil, the root-cap often wears away, but is then renewed by the underlying calyptrogen. In some plants, the dermatogen directly gives rise to the root-cap without the intervention of the calyptrogen. The walls of the outer cells of the root-cap may be modified into mucilage, which helps the root to push forward into the soil more easily. The root-cap is absent from aquatic plants, although an analogous structure, called *root-pocket*, is conspicuous in many of them (see p. 3). Sometimes, as in dicotyledons generally, the dermatogen continues upwards as a single, outermost layer (epiblema) of the root. However, in monocotyledons generally, the dermatogen is exhausted in the formation of the root-cap so that the outermost layer of the root is derived from the outermost layer of the periblem. At a little distance from the root-tip, the outermost layer bears a large number of *unicellular root-hairs*. Root-hairs are mostly absent from aquatic plants.

(2) **Periblem**. As in the stem, this is also single-layered at the apex and many-layered higher up. In monocotyledons generally, the outermost

layer of the periblem forms the outermost layer of the root. The periblem forms the middle region or cortex of the root.

(3) **Plerome.** The plerome's structure and function are practically the same as those of the stem. But here, some procambial strands give rise to bundles of vessels (xylem) and others to bundles or sieve-tubes (phloem) in an alternating manner (see FIG.49)

PERMANENT TISSUES.

These are composed of cells that have lost the power of dividing, having attained their definite form and size. They may be living or dead and thin-walled or thick-walled. Permanent tissues are formed by differentiation of the cells of the meristems, and may be **primary** or **secondary**. The primary permanent tissues are derived from the apical meristems of the stem and the root, and the secondary permanent tissues from the lateral meristems, i.e. cambial layers. In dicotyledons and gymnosperms, the cambium is present, and due to activity, secondary growth takes place in these cases, while *in monocotyledons, there is no cambium* and hence no secondary growth.

Classification of Permanent Tissues. In their earlier stages, cells are more or less similar in structure, but as the division of labour increases, they gradually assume various forms and give rise to **permanent tissues**. These may be classified as *simple* and *complex*. A simple tissue is made up of one type of cells that form a homogeneous or uniform mass, and a complex tissue is made up of more than one type of cells that work together as a unit. To these may be added another kind of tissue—the secretory tissue.

A. SIMPLE TISSUES

1. PARENCHYMA (FIG. 30A). The parenchyma consists of a collection of cells which are more or less isodiametric, that is, equally expanded on all sides. Typical parenchymatous cells are oval, spherical or polygonal. Their walls are thin and made of cellulose. They are usually living. Parenchymatous tissue is of universal occurrence in all the soft parts of plants. Its main function is storage of food material. When parenchymatous tissue contains chloroplasts, it is called

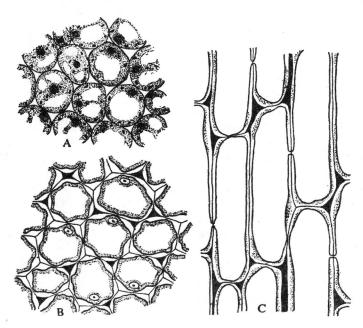

FIG. 30. *A.* paraenchyma; *B*, collenchyma in transection; *C*, collenchyma in longitudinal section

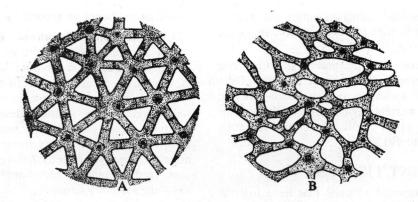

FIG. 31. *A*, aerenchyma in the petiole of banana; *B*, the same in the petiole of *Canna*

chlorenchyma. Its function is to manufacture food material. A special type of parenchyma develops in many aquatic plants and in the petiole of *Canna* and banana. The wall of each such cell grows out in several places, like rays radiating from a star and is, therefore, stellate or star-like in general appearance. These cells leave a lot of air cavities between them, where air is stored up. Such a tissue is often called *aerenchyma* (FIG. 31).

2. COLLENCHYMA (FIG. 30 B-C). This tissue consists of somewhat elongated, parenchymatous cells with oblique, slightly rounded or tapering ends. The cells are much thickened at the corners against the intercellular spaces. They look circular, oval or polygonal in a transverse section of the stem. The thickening is due to a deposit of cellulose, hemicellulose and protopectin. Although thickened, the cells are never lignified. Simple pits can be found here and there in their walls. Their thickened walls have a high refractive index and, therefore, this tissue in section is very conspicuous under the microscope. Collenchyma is found under the skin (epidermis) of herbaceous dicotyledons, e.g. sunflower, gourd, etc., occurring there in a few layers with special development at the ridges, as in gourd stem. It is absent from the root and the monocotyledon, except in special cases. The cells are living and often contain a few chloroplasts. Being flexible in nature, collenchyma gives tensile strength to the growing organs, and being extensible, it readily adapts itself to rapid elongation of the stem. Since it contains chloroplasts, it also manufactures sugar and starch. Its functions are, therefore, both mechanical and vital.

3. SCLERENCHYMA (FIG. 32). Sclerenchyma (*scleros*, hard) consists of very long, narrow, thick and lignified cells, usually pointed at both ends. They are fibre-like in appearance and hence, they are also called sclerenchymatous fibres, or simply **fibres**. Their walls often become so greatly thickened that the cell cavity is nearly obliterated. They have simple, often oblique, pits in their walls. The

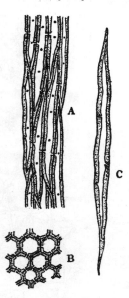

FIG. 32. Sclerenchyma. *A*, fibres as seen in longitudinal section; *B*, the same as seen in tran-section; and *C*, a single fibre

middle lamella is conspicuous in sclerenchyma. Sclerenchymatous cells are abundantly found in plants, and occur in patches or definite layers, which are seen to dovetail into each other in the longitudinal direction. Sometimes, they also occur singly among other cells. They are dead cells and serve a purely mechanical function, that is, they give the requisite strength, rigidity, flexibility and elasticity to the plant body and thus enable it to withstand various strains. Their average length is 1 to 3 mm. in angiosperms, and 2 to 8 mm. in gymnosperms. In special cases, as in hemp (*Cannabis*; B. & H. GANJA), rhea (*Boehmeria nivea*), flax (*Linum*), etc., the fibres are of excessive lengths, ranging from 20 mm. to 550 mm. Such long, thick-walled cells make excellent textile fibres for commercial use. Other common plants yielding long fibres are jute, coconut, Indian or sunn hemp (*Crotalaria juncea*; B. SHONE; H. SAN), Madras or Deccan hemp (*Hibiscus cannabinus*), sisal hemp (*Agave sisalana*), bowstring hemp (*Sansevieria*; B. MURGA; H. MARUL), rozelle (*Hibiscus sabdariffa*; B. MESTA; H. PATWA), etc.

Sclereids (FIG. 33). Sometimes, special types of sclerenchyma develop in various parts of the plant body to meet local mechanical needs. They are known as **sclereids** or **sclerotic cells**. They may occur in the cortex, pith, phloem, hard seeds, nuts, stony fruits, and in the leaves and stems of many dicotyledons and also gymnosperms. The flesh of pear, and sometimes of guava, is gritty because of the presence of such cells (also called *grit cells*). The cells, though very thick-walled, hard and strongly lignified (sometimes cutinized or suberized), are not long and pointed like sclerenchyma, but are mostly isodiametric, polyhedral, short-cylindrical, slightly elongated, or irregular in shape. Usually, they have no definite shape. They are dead cells (seldom living), and have very narrow cell-cavities which may be almost obliterated, owing to excessive thickness of the cell-wall. Their walls are provided with many simple pits, which may be branched or unbranched. Further, their thickened walls often show distinct lamellation. They may be somewhat loosely arranged or closely packed. They may also occur singly. They

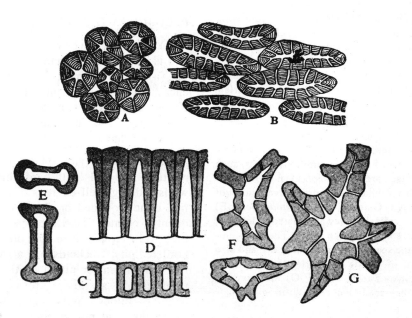

FIG. 33. Sclereids. *A*, brachysclereids (grit cells) in the flesh of pear; *B*, the same in coconut shell (endocarp); *C*, macrosclereids in the epiderms of onion scale; *D*, the same in the seed coat of *Phaseolus*; *E*, osteosclereids (two) in the seed coat of pea; *F*, astrosclereids (two) in tea leaf; *G*, the same in *Tsuga* (a conifer)

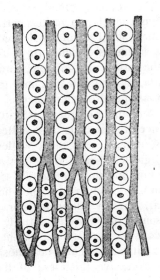

FIG. 34. Tracheids of pine stem (in radial section) with bordered pits.

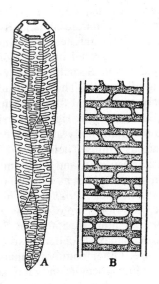

FIG. 35. A, a scalariform tracheid of fern; B, a portion of the wall of the same magnified

contribute to the firmness and hardness of the part concerned.

Types of Sclereids (FIG. 33) The following four common types may be noted. (1)**Brachysclereids** (*brachys*, short; A-B) or stone cells are more or less isodiametric in nature, and are commonly found among masses of parenchyma in different parts of the plant body, as in the pith, cortex, bark, phloem, fleshy pericarp of certain fruits (e.g. pear), coconut shell, etc.

2. Macrosclereids (*makros*, long; C-D) are rod-like or columnar cells, with truncated ends, forming a solid, palisade-like epidermal layer. They are common in the bark and seed-coats of many leguminous plants, such as pea (*Pisum*), black gram (*Phaseolus*) and other pulses. They are also found in the protective scales of onion, garlic, etc. (3) **Osteosclereids** (*ostoon*, bone; E) are also columnar cells, but they are dilated or lobed at one or both ends, somewhat like bones. They are commonly found in the seed-coats and fruit walls, and also in the leaves, of some dicotyledonous plants. (4) **Astrosclereids** (*astron*, star; F-G) are irregular stone cells, i.e. they are branched in an irregular way, with radiating arms of varying lengths, giving a stellate or star-like appearance. Evidently, they assume various forms depending on the nature of branching. They are found in the leaves of certain dicotyledons, as in tea leaf, and also in *Tsuga* (a conifer) and *Gnetum*. They

are also found in the bark of certain conifers, as in *Abies* and *Larix*.

B. COMPLEX TISSUES

1. XYLEM. Xylem or wood is a conducting tissue and is composed of elements of different kinds, viz. (a) tracheids, (b) vessels or tracheae (sin., trachea), (c) wood fibres, and (d) wood parenchyma. Xylem, as a whole, is meant to conduct water and mineral salts upwards from the root to the leaf, and to give mechanical strength to the plant body.

(a) **Tracheids** (FIGS. 34-6). These are elongated, tube-like cells with hard, thick and lignified walls and large cell-cavities. Their ends are tapering, either rounded or chisel-like, and less frequently, pointed. They are dead, empty cells and their walls are provided with one or more rows of bordered pits. Tracheids may also be annular, spiral, scalariform or pitted (with simple pits). In transverse section, they are mostly angular—either polygonal or rectangular. Tracheids (and not vessels) occur alone in the wood of ferns and gymnosperms, whereas in the wood of angiosperms, they are associated with the vessels. Their walls being lignified and hard, their

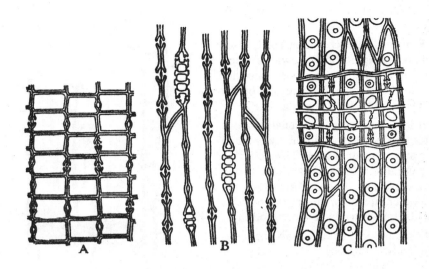

FIG. 36. Tracheids with bordered pits. *A*, pine stem in transection; *B*, the same in tangential (logitudinal) section; *C*, the same in radial (longitudinal) section

function is conduction of water from the root to the leaf.

(b) **Vessels or Tracheae** (FIG. 37). Vessels are cylindrical, tube-like structures. They are formed from a row of cells placed end to end, from which the transverse partition walls break down (see pp. 154-55). A vessel or trachea is, thus, a tube-like series of cells, very much like a series of water pipes forming a pipe-line. Their walls are thick-ened in various ways, and vessels can be **annular, spiral, scalariform, reticulate,** or **pitted,** according to the mode of thickening. Associated with the vessels are often some tracheids. Vessels and tracheids form the main elements of the wood or xylem of the vascular bundle (see FIG. 48). They serve to conduct water and mineral salts from the roots to the leaves. They are dead, thick-walled and lignified, and as such, they also serve the

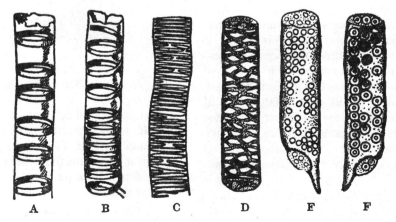

FIG. 37. Kinds of Vessels. *A*, annular; *B*, spiral; *C*, scalariform; *D*, reticulate; *E*, a vessel with simple pits; *F*, a vessel with bordered pits

mechanical function of strengthening the plant body.

(c) Wood Fibres. Sclerenchymatous cells associated with wood or xylem are known as wood fibres. They occur abundantly in woody dicotyledons and add to the mechanical strength of the xylem and of the plant body as a whole.

(d) **Wood Parenchyma.** Parenchymatous cells are of frequent occurrence in the xylem, and are known as wood parenchyma. The cells are alive and generally thin-walled. The wood parenchyma assists, directly or indirectly, in the conduction of water, upwards, through the vessels and the tracheids. It also serves to store food.

2. PHLOEM. The phloem or bast is another conducting tissue, and is composed of the following elements: (*a*) **sieve-tubes,** (*b*) **companion cells,** (*c*) **phloem parenchyma,** and (*d*) **bast fibres** (rarely). Phloem, as a whole, is meant to conduct prepared food materials from the leaf to the storage organs and growing regions.

(a) **Sieve-tubes** (FIGS. 38-9). Sieve-tubes are slender, tube-like structures, composed of elongated cells which are placed end to end. Their walls are thin and made of cellulose. The transverse partition walls are, however, perforated by a number of pores. The transverse wall then looks very much like a sieve, and is called the **sieve-plate.** The sieve-plate may sometimes be formed in the side (longitudinal) wall. In some cases, the sieve-plate is not transverse (horizontal), but inclined obliquely, and then different areas of it become perforated. A sieve-plate of this nature is called *a compound plate.* At the close of the growing season, the sieve-plate is covered by a deposit of colourless, shining substance in the form of a pad, called the **callus** or **callus pad.** This consists of carbohydrate, called *callose.* In winter, the callus completely clogs the pores, but in spring, when the active season begins, it gets dissolved. In old sieve-tubes, the callus forms a permanent deposit. The sieve-tube contains no nucleus, but has a lining layer of cytoplasm, which is continuous through the pores. Sieve-tubes are used for the longitudinal transmission of prepared food materials — proteins and carbohydrates — downward

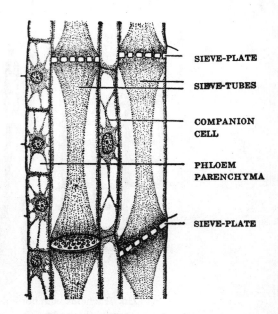

FIG. 38. Sieve-tissue in longitudinal section

from the leaves to the storage organs, and later upward from the storage organs to the growing regions. A heavy deposit of food material is found on either side of the sieve-plate with a narrow median portion.

(b) **Companion Cells.** Associated with each sieve-tube and connected with it by pores is a thin-

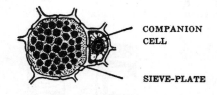

FIG. 39. Sieve-tube in transection

walled, elongated cell known as the **companion cell.** It is living and contains protoplasm and an elongated nucleus. The companion cell is present only in angiosperms (both dicotyledons and monocotyledons). It assists the sieve-tube in the conduction of food.

(c) **Phloem Parenchyma.** There are always some parenchymatous cells forming a part of the phloem in all dicotyledons, gymnosperms and

ferns. The cells are living, and often cylindrical. They store up food material and help conduct it. Phloem parenchyma is, however, absent in most monocotyledons.

(d) **Bast Fibres.** Sclerenchymatous cells occurring in the phloem or bast are known as bast fibres. These are generally absent in the primary phloem, but occur frequently in the secondary phloem.

Position of Phloem. In angiospermic stems, the phloem normally lies external to the xylem. But in several families of dicotyledons, such as *Acanthaceae, Apocynaceae, Asclepiadaceae* (e.g. *Leptadenia*; see FIG. 85), *Combretaceae, Convolvulaceae, Cucurbitaceae, Myrtaceae, Solanaceae, Compositae,* etc., a part of the *primary phloem*, called **intraxylary phloem** or **internal phloem**, is seen to occur, often in small groups or strands, internal to the primary xylem around the pith, either in association with this xylem or detached from it. The internal phloem is similar to the normal external phloem in origin, structure, and compostion, but its elements are fewer in number and do not increase as a result of cambial activity. Sometimes, small groups of *secondary phloem* formed by the cambium are seen embedded in the secondary xylem. This is called **interxylary phloem** or **included phloem**. Among dicotyledons, this is found in *Acanthaceae, Asclepiadaceae* (e.g. *Leptadenia*; see FIG. 85), *Salvadoraceae* (e.g. *Salvadora;* see FIG. 84), *Combretaceae, Cucurbitaceae, Nyctaginaceae,* (e.g. *Mirabilis;* see FIG. 82), *Loganiaceae* (e.g. *Strychnos*),

etc. Among monocotyledons it is found in some arborescent types showing secondary growth, e.g. *Dracaena* (see FIG. 89), *Yucca* (see FIG. 1/81), *Agave, Aloe,* etc. It will be noted that some dicotyledonous families have both types of phloem.

C SECRETORY TISSUES

1. LATICIFEROUS TISSUE. This consists of thin-walled, greatly elongated and greatly branched ducts (FIG. 40), and contains a milky juice known as latex (see p. 142). Laticiferous ducts are of two kinds: *latex* vessels and latex cells. They contain numerous nuclei which lie embedded in the thin layer of protoplasm lining the cell-wall, which is usually thin and made of cellulose. They are irregularly distributed in the mass of parenchymatous cells, and their function is not clearly understood. They may act as food storage organs or as reservoirs of waste products. They may also act as translocatory tissues.

Latex vessels (FIG. 40B) are a result of the fusion of many cells. They are formed from rows of elongated, meristematic cells, the partition walls of which soon dissolve, as in wood vessels. They grow more or less as parallel ducts, and in the mature portion of the plant, they anastomose with one another *by the fusion of their branches, forming a network.* Latex vessels are found in poppy (*Papaver*), e.g. opium poppy, garden poppy

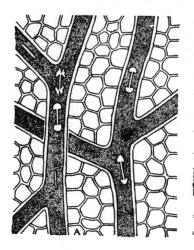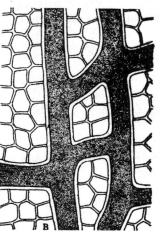

FIG. 40. Laticiferous tissue. *A*, latex cells; *B*, latex vessels

and prickly poppy, and also in some species of the sunflower family or *Compositae*, e.g. *Sonchus*.

Latex cells (FIG. 40A), on the other hand, although much branched like the latex vessels, are really single or independent units. They originate as minute structures and then, with the growth of the plant, elongate and branch, ramifying in all directions through the tissues of the plant, but *without fusing together to form a network*. They are coenocytic in nature (see p. 154). Latex cells are found in madar (*Calotropis*), spurges (*Euphorbia*), oleander (*Nerium*), yellow oleander (*Thevetia*), periwinkle (*Vinca*), *Ficus* (e.g. banyan fig, peepul), etc.

Latex cells may be isolated and studied in the following way. Slice off a big portion of the pith from a piece of *Euphorbia neriifolia* stem. Break transversely the cortical portion of the stem with a light incision on its surface, and then pull it apart. Some slender threads will come out. Mount them carefully in the usual way and examine under the microscope. A number of elongated, tubular, branched cells will be clearly seen. These are the latex cells. On irrigating with iodine solution, rod and dumb-shaped starch grains may be distinctly seen in the latex cells. A longitudinal section through the stem will, however, show that the latex cells lie embedded in parenchyma, as shown in FIG. 40A.

2. GLANDULAR TISSUE. This tissue is made of glands, which are special structures containing some secretory or excretory products. Glands may consist of single, isolated cells or small groups of cells, with or without a central cavity. They are of various kinds and may occur as *external glands* on the epidermis, or as *internal glands* lying embedded in other tissues in the interior of the plant body. They are parenchymatous in nature, have large nuclei and contain abundant protoplasm. They contain different substances and have manifold functions.

Internal glands are (1) oil-glands (FIG. 41A) secreting essential oils, as in the fruits and leaves of orange, lemon, pummelo, etc., (2) mucilage-secreting glands, as in the betel leaf, (3) glands secreting gum, resin, tannin, etc. (see FIG. 27), (4) digestive glands secreting enzymes, and (5) water-secreting glands known as **hydathodes.**

Hydathodes (FIG. 42) are special structures through which exudation of water takes place in liquid form. They are found mainly in aquatic plants and in some herbaceous plants growing in moist places. They occur at the apices of the veins at the tips of leaves or on their margins. Hydathodes are made of a group of living cells with numerous intercellular spaces filled with water, but few or no chloroplasts. They represent modified bundle-ends. These cells, called *epithem cells*, open out into one or more sub-epidermal chambers. These, in turn, communicate with the exterior through an open **water stoma** or **water pore**. The water stoma structurally resembles an ordinary stoma (see FIG. 44A), but is usually larger and has lost the power of movement. Hydathodes are commonly seen in water lettuce (*Pistia*), water hyacinth (*Eichhornia*), garden nasturtium (*Tropaeolum*), rose (*Rosa*), balsam (*Impatiens*), aroids, many grasses, etc.

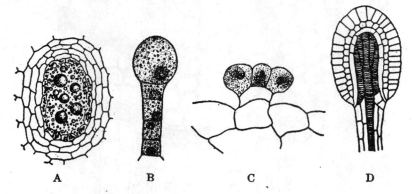

A   B   C   D

FIG. 41. Glands. *A*, an oil-gland of orange rind; *B*, a glandular hair of *Boerhaavia* fruit; *C*, a digestive gland of butterwort (*Pinguicula*); *D*, digestive gland of sundew (*Drosera*)

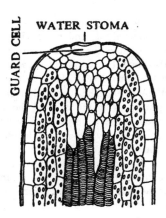

FIG. 42. Hydathode of water lettuce (*Pistia*)

External glands occur as outgrowths and are in the nature of short hairs tipped by glands, known as glandular hairs. External glands are: (1) water-secreting hairs or glands, also called hydathodes, (2) glandular hairs (FIG. 41B) secreting gummy substances, as in tobacco (*Nicotiana*), *Plumbago* (B. CHITA; H. CHITRAK), and *Boerhaavia* (B. PUNARNAVA; H. THIKRI); (3) glandular hairs secreting irritating, poisonous substances, as in nettles (see FIG. I/82), (4) nectar-secreting glands or nectaries, as in many flowers, and (5) enzyme-secreting glands (FIG. 41 C-D), as in carnivorous plants.

THE MECHANICAL SYSTEM. For the existence and stability of a plant, the development of mechanical or strengthening tissues is a necessity. They help the plant to not only maintain a particular shape but also to withstand the various kinds of mechanical strain and stress that they are often subjected to under the prevailing or changing environmental conditions. The stem has to bear the weight of the aerial parts, often extensive and heavy, and the branches have to withstand transverse stresses caused by the load of leaves and periodically, flowers and fruits. The leaves have to bear shearing stress against high winds. The root system has to stand longitudinal compression caused by the aerial parts, a pulling force from the swaying stem and branches, and also applied lateral pressure by the surrounding soil. It is, thus, evident that the distribution of mechanical tissues should be such as to help the plant body withstand

various strains to the maximum degree. If this were not so, the plant body would collapse.

Kinds of Mechanical Tissues.

(1) **Sclerenchyma** is the most important and efficient mechanical tissue. It is widely distributed in plants for the specific purpose of mechanical strength. It includes (*a*) **bast fibres**, sometimes of excessive lengths, and (*b*) **wood fibres**, associated with wood or xylem. (2) **Collenchyma** is mostly another such tissue. It is mostly associated with young, growing parts, finally forming a permanent structure of those organs. Collenchyma, though not as efficient as sclerenchyma, has many advantages of its own. It has the power of growth, offers no resistance to the growing organs, and is flexible. Further, it does not interfere with secondary growth but sometimes helps it. Both the sclerenchyma and collenchyma are remarkable for their tensile strength. (3) **Vessels and tracheids** also give mechanical strength to the plant body. (4) **Sclereids** often meet local strain (see p. 161-2).

Principles Governing the Distribution of Mechanical Tissues. The principle governing the construction of mechanical tissues and their distribution in the plant body is 'maximum strength with minimum expenditure of material', as in the case of a building or a bridge. Therefore, the mechanical strength of the tissues is correlated with their economical distribution, according to certain principles, to yield maximum efficiency. The main principles involved are: (1) inflexibility, (2) inextensibility, and (3) incompressibility.

(1) *Inflexibility*. To achieve this, the ideal arrangement is to have the mechanical tissues in the form of girders, as in the case of the engineer's architecture. A simple girder is one in which there is no flange and it is like an "I" in cross section. A compound girder is one in which there may be one flange like a 'T' or sometimes two flanges. Where much strength is not needed, simple girders may do, but in some cases, many of them may be required to maintain the strength needed. More efficient are, of course, the compound girders. This principle of distribution of mechanical tissues applies to stems, which evidently have to bear the enormous weight of the branches, leaves, flowers and fruits. Stems are also swayed back and forth (bending stress) by the wind, often very strong. They are, thus, subjected to alternate stretching and compressing on all their sides. In them, therefore, the best position for the

strengthening tissues is close to the periphery, in the form of separate girders. In dicotyledons, it is also of the utmost importance that the mechanical tissues do not obstruct secondary growth in thickness.

Stems, as said above, are subjected to bending stress in any direction, and the collenchyma and sclerenchyma appear in suitable places to meet this stress. The distribution of collenchyma has already been mentioned (see p. 160). The distribution of sclerenchyma is, however, more diversified. A few cases may be mentioned. (i) Long strands of vascular bundles are associated with and strengthened by fibrous tissue, in most cases. (ii) Patches of sclerenchyma lie in association with phloem and form a *hard bast,* as in sunflower stem. (iii) Pericyclic sclerenchyma forms a hollow cylinder, as in *Cucurbitaceae.* In monocotyledons, there is no secondary growth so the sclerenchyma occurs in various forms. (iv) A sclerenchymatous sheath, complete and encircling a vascular bundle, is a common feature. (v) Patches of sclerenchyma of varying sizes associate with the vascular bundles, as in *Colocasia.* (vi) Subepidermal patches, as in *Cyperus.* (vii) Isolated patches, in the cortical region, as in bamboo. (viii) Tangentially connected patches as in many palms. (ix) Simple hollow cylinder, broken or unbroken, in the cortical region, as mostly in *Liliaceae,* e.g. *Asparagus* (see FIG. 59).

2. *Incompressibility.* Roots are subjected to longitudinal compression caused by the load they carry overhead, and to the lateral pressure exerted by the surrounding soil. Roots meet these forces by developing solid wood cylinders in or around the centre. At an early stage, the lignified wood vessels make the root, as whole, sufficiently incompressible. With the progress of secondary growth later the new thick-walled elements—new wood vessels and wood fibres—form a solid central column which lends more mechanical strength to the root. Hard bast is present in some dicotyledons, as in broad bean (*Vicia faba*). Roots are wanting in collenchyma. The scattered arrangement of mechanical tissues, as in the case of the stem, may prove fatal to the root since individual strands are liable to break under very heavy pressure. In monocotyledonous roots, the vascular bundles provide the strength required. There are cases, however, as in *Pandanus,* where each bundle is surrounded by a strong sclerenchymatous sheath, and in addition, it contains strands of sclerenchyma. In aroids, the pith is often lignified and thickened, and in orchids, the conjunctive tissue is often so (see FIG. 64).

3. *Inextensibility.* Roots are also subjected to the pulling force exerted by the swaying stem. As in the previous case, the centralization of vascular bundles and the associated mechanical tissues forming a solid central column seems to be very effective in withstanding the longitudinal tension caused by the bending of the stem. Sometimes, however, as in the maize root, an additional fibrous cylinder develops in the peripheral region.

It may also be noted that the leaves are subjected to shearing stress, and to guard against it, the sclerenchyma is distributed in various ways, depending on the requirement. Usually, there are patches of sclerenchyma flanking the upper and lower epidermis, as well as in the mesophyll. Vascular bundles may also be strengthened by sclerenchymatous sheath, complete or incomplete.

CHAPTER 3

THE TISSUE SYSTEM

On the principle of division of labour, tissues are arranged in three systems, each playing a definite role in the life of the plant. Each system may consist of only one tissue or a combination of tissues which may structurally be of similar or different nature, but perform a common function and have the same origin. The three systems are: (I) the **epidermal tissue system.** (II) the **ground or fundamental tissue system,** and (III) the **vascular tissue system.**

1. THE EPIDERMAL TISSUE SYSTEM

EPIDERMIS. The epidermal tissue system is derived from the dermatogen of the apical meristem and forms the **epidermis** (*epi*, upon; *derma*, skin) or outermost skin layer, which extends over the entire surface of the plant body. It is continuous, except for certain openings (stomata and lenticels). Viewed from the surface, the cells of the epidermis are somewhat irregular in outline (see FIG.43),varying in shape and size, but closely fitted together without intercellular spaces. However, they appear more or less rectangular in cross-section. The epidermis is mostly single-layered, but sometimes, as in the leaves of the india-rubber plant, banyan, oleander, etc., it has many layers. This is called a *multiple epidermis*. Epidermal cells are parenchymatous in nature and a comparatively small amount of cytoplasm lines the cell-wall. They have large vacuoles filled with colourless cell-sap. In some plants, the cells may contain anthocyanins or chromoplasts, but not chloroplasts, except in guard cells, ferns, submerged plants and a few others. However, in the leaves and young green shoots, the epidermis possesses numerous **stomata** through which an interchange of place between the plant and the atmosphere take place. Epidermal cells soon die off and become filled with various substances, such as tannin, silica particles, gum, mucilage, crystals, etc. The inner and radial walls of epidermal cells are thin, while the outer walls are thick and usually impregnated with cutin or suberin. Cutinization or suberization sometimes extends to the radial walls as well. The cutinized layer, called the **cuticle**, acts as a hard varnish-like coating and protects the inner cells against loss of water, mechanical injury and potential parasites (see below). Excretion of wax in the form of rods, scales, grains, etc., prevents further loss of water. In many plants, the epidermal cells often bear outgrowths, known as **hairs** or **trichomes**. These may be unicellular or multicellular, simple or branched, soft or sharp and stiff. Besides, the epidermis may also bear stinging hairs (see FIG. I/82), as in nettles, glandular hairs (see FIG. 41B), as in *Boerhaavia* (B. PUNARNAVA, H. THIKRI), tobacco,

Plumbago (B. CHITA; H. CHITRAK), etc. A dense coating of hairs, as in *Gnaphalium* and *Aerua*, is another feature of the epidermis.

The outermost layer of the root is called the **epiblema** or **piliferous layer**. It is concerned mainly with the absorption of water and mineral salts from the soil. Thus, to increase the absorbing surface, which has been estimated to be 5 to 20 times greater, the outer walls of most of its cells extend outwards and form tubular, unicellular prolongations called **root-hairs**. The epiblema is neither cutinized nor provided with stomata.

Functions. (1) The primary function of the epidermis is protection of the internal tissues against mechanical injury, excessive heat or cold, fluctuations of temperature, attacks of parasitic fungi and bacteria, and against the leaching effect of rain. This is possible due to the presence of cuticle, hairs, tannin, gum, etc. (2) Prevention of excessive evaporation of water from the internal tissues by the development of thick cuticles, wax and other deposition, cutinized hairs, scales, multiple epidermis, etc., is another important function of the epidermis. (3) Strong cuticles and cutinized hairs, particularly a dense coating of hairs, protect the plant against intense illumination (i.e. strong sunlight) and excessive radiation of heat. (4) The epidermis also has to protect the plant against attacks by herbivorous animals. This is done with the help of sharp and stiff hairs (as in some cucurbits), a dense coating of hairs (as in *Gnaphalium,*) stinging hairs (as in nettles—see FIG. I/82), glandular hairs as in *Boerhaavia* (see FIG. 41B), silica particles (as in many grasses, e.g. lemon grass, *Equisetum,* etc.), and raphides (as in many aroids; FIG. 18). (5) The epidermis also acts as a storehouse of water, as in desert plants. (6) The epidermis sometimes has some minor functions like photosynthesis, secretion, etc.

STOMATA. *Structure and Behaviour.* Stomata (*stoma*, a mouth) are very minute openings (FIG. 43) formed in the epidermal layer in the green aerial of the plant, particularly the leaves. The roots and non-green parts of the stem are free from them. Each stoma is surrounded by two semi-lunar cells, known as the *guard cells*. The term 'stoma'

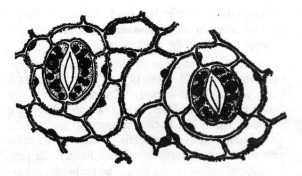

FIG. 43. Stomata (surface view) in epidermal layer

is often applied to the stomatal opening plus the guard cells. The guard cells are living and always contain chloroplasts. Their inner walls are thicker and outer walls thinner. They guard the stoma or the passage, i.e. they regulate the opening and closing of the stoma-like lips. Sometimes, the guard cells are surrounded by two or more cells which are distinct from the epidermal cells. Such cells are called *accessory cells*. In dicotyledonous leaves the stomata remain scattered, while in monocotyledonous leaves, they occur in parallel rows. Under normal conditions, the stomata remain closed at night, i.e. in the absence of light. They remain open during the daytime, i.e. in the presence of light. In most plants they open fully only in bright light, but in certain plants the stomata do so in diffuse light. Usually they open fully in the morning and close towards the evening. They may close at daytime, when very active tran-

spiration (evaporation of water) takes place from the surface of the leaf under certain conditions, such as dryness of air, blowing of dry wind and deficient supply of water in the soil. The intensity of light markedly affects the degree of stomatal opening. The guard cells' movement regulates opening and closing of the stomata. When the guard cells become turgid, i.e. full of water, expanding and bulging outward, the stoma opens. When the guard cells become flaccid by losing water, the stoma closes.

The turgidity or flaccidity of the guard cells is due to the presence of sugar or starch in them. In light, the sugar manufactured by the chlorplasts of the guard cells accumulates in them and, being soluble, increases the concentration of the cell-sap. Under this condition, the guard cells absorb water from the neighbouring cells and become turgid, opening the stoma. In darkness, on the other hand, the sugar present in the guard cells becomes converted into starch—an insoluble compound. The concentration of the cell-sap is, therefore, lower than that of the neighbouring cells. Under this condition, the guard cells lose water and shrink the closing stoma. The transformation of sugar into starch at night and vice versa at daytime is due to the acidity and alkalinity of the cell-sap of the guard cells. In the absence of photosynthesis at night, carbon dioxide accumulates in the guard cells and the cell's contents become weakly acid. Under this condition, sugar is converted into starch. During the daytime, carbon dioxide is utilized in photosynthesis, and thus the cell contents become slightly alkaline. Under this condition, starch is converted into sugar.

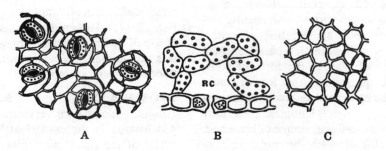

FIG. 44. Stomata in betel leaf. *A*, lower epidermis with numerous stomata (surface view); *B*, section of leaf (a portion of the lower side): *RC*, respiratory cavity internal to a stoma; *C*, upper epidermis with no stoma (surface view)

FIG. 45. Sunken stoma in the leaf of
American aloe (*Agave*)

FIG. 46. Sunken stomata in the leaf
of oleander (*Nerium*)

There is another hypothesis, called the **colloidal hypothesis**, put forward to explain the movement of the guard cells. According to it, the cell contents become alkaline as a result of the effect of sunlight on the guard cells and this causes the colloids present in them to swell, apart from the fact that it results in the transformation of starch into sugar. The swelling of the colloids, according to this theory, causes the guard cells to bulge out and the stoma to open. At night, the acidity of the guard cells increases and causes the colloids to shrink again, thus closing the stoma, apart from the fact that the increased acidity brings about the conversion of sugar into starch.

Functions and Distribution. Stomata are used for interchange of gases between the plant and the atmosphere—oxygen for respiration and carbon dioxide for manufacture of carbohydrates. To facilitate diffusion of these gases, each stoma opens internally into a small cavity, known as the respiratory cavity (FIG. 44B), which in its turn communicates with the system of interceullular spaces and air-cavities. Stomata are also the organs through which evaporation of water normally takes place, and the plant thus gets rid of the excess quantity. Stomata are most abundant in the lower epidermis (FIG. 44A) of the dorsiventral leaf (see p. 36). None (or sometimes comparatively few) are present in the upper (FIG. 44C), e.g. in sunflower leaf, the average numbers in the lower and upper surfaces are 325 and 175, in pea leaf, 216 and 101, in gourd leaf, 269 and 28, etc. In iso-bilateral and centric leaves (see p. 36), the stomata are more or less evenly distributed on all sides (see

FIGS. 68-9). In floating leaves, as in those of the water lily, the stomata remain confined to the upper epidermis. In the submerged leaves, no stoma is present. In desert plants and in those showing xerophytic adaptations, e.g. American aloe or century plant (*Agave*; FIG. 45), oleander (*Nerium*; FIG. 46), pine (*Pinus*; see FIG. VI/10), etc., one or more stomata are situated in grooves or pits in the leaf. This is a special adaptation to reduce excessive evaporation, as stomata sunken in pits are protected from gusts of wind. The number of stomata per unit area varies within wide limits. In ordinary land plants, there are an average of about 100 to 300 stomata per square millimetre, sometimes much less or many more. In the floating leaves of aquatic plants, stomata may be as many as 400 per square millimetre, while in submerged leaves, there are none. In desert plants on the other hand, there may be only 10 to 15 stomata per square millimetre, while there are cases with about 1,300 stomata in the same space.

2. THE GROUND OR FUNDAMENTAL TISSUE SYSTEM

This system forms the main bulk of the plant's body and extends from below the epidermis to the centre (excluding the vascular bundles). It is partly derived fromt the periblem and partly from the plerome. Its primary functions are manufacture and storage of food material. It also has a mechanical function. This system consists of various kinds of tissues of which parenchyma is most abundant. The other tissues are the sclerenchyma and collenchyma, and sometimes, laticiferous tissue and glandular tissue. It is differentiated into the following zones and sub-zones.

1. CORTEX. The cortex is the zone that lies between the epidermis and the pericycle, varying in thickness from a few to many layers. In dicotyledonous stems (see FIG. 53), it is usually differentiated into the following sub-zones, (*a*) **hypodermis**— a few layers of collenchyma or sometimes, sclerenchyma; (*b*) **general cortex** or cortical parenchyma—a few layers of thin-walled parenchymatous cells with or without chloroplasts, but often with intercellular spaces, and (*c*) **endodermis**—a single wavy layer, not often very conspicuous. This is also called the *starch sheath* as it often has numerous starch grains. In monocotyledonous stems (see FIG. 57), owing to the scattered arrangement of vascular bundles, the cortex is not marked out into the cortex proper and the endodermis. However, sclerenchyma is often present as the hypodermis. In roots (see FIG. 61), the cortex consists of (*a*) many layers of thin-walled parenchymatous cells (general cortex), often with conspicuous starch grains in them, and with many intercellular spaces between them (*b*) a distinct circular layer of endodermis and (*c*) sometimes a hypodermis —a few external layers of fairly big, often radially elongated, parenchymatous cells.

Functions. The cortex primarily functions as a protective tissue in stems. Its secondary functions are storage, photosynthesis, etc. In roots, the cortex is essentially a storage tissue. It is also the pumping station of the root where the individual cells act as microscopic pumps by their alternate expansion and contraction, forcing the water absorbed by the root-hairs into the xylem vessels.

Endodermis: This is the inner limiting layer of the cortex and is formed of vertically elongated cells. In cross-section, it appears as a single layer of barrel-shaped cells without intercellular spaces. The layer is wavy in stems and often not readily distinguishable, or even altogether wanting, while it is circular and well-defined in roots. The cells

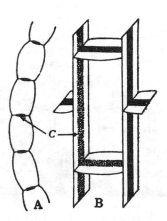

FIG. 47. Casparian strip (*C*) in endodermis; *A*, endodermis in transection; *B*, diagram of an endodermal cell (longitudinal view)

are living and contain abundant protoplasm, large nuclei and often starch grains—hence, this layer is also called the **starch sheath**. Some cells of the endodermis may contain mucilage, tannin, gum, etc. The outer wall of endodermal cells are thin, while the radial and inner walls are often thickened, being suberized, cutinized and sometimes even lignified, particularly in roots. The thickened walls are provided with numerous simple pits. The thickening often takes the form of a band or strip surrounding each cell. This band, first recognized by Caspary in 1985, is called the **Casparian strip**. It may be made of lignin or suberin. Among the thick-walled cells of the endodermis, as in many roots, there often occur some small thin walled cells opposite to protoxylem vessels. These are called **passage cells** (see FIG. 62). The sap absorbed by the root hairs enters the xylem vessel through these. The endodermis is well developed in the roots of all plants, in the stems of pteridophytes and herbaceous dicotyledons, and in the leaves of gymnosperms. However, it is absent or indistinct in the stems of woody plants and in the leaves of angiosperms.

Functions. The functions of the endodermis are somewhat obscure. Some regard it as a water-tight jacket between the xylem and the surrounding tissues. It may act as an air-dam, preventing diffusion of air into the vessels and thus clogging them.

It may be a 'diffusion layer', preventing loss of water, mineral salts and food from the vascular bundles. It may be a storage tissue containing starch grains, as in dicotyledons. It may be connected with the osmotic pressure that develops in the root-cortex. It may serve as a passage for water from the cortex of the root to the protoxylem.

2. PERICYCLE. This forms a multi-layered zone between the endodermis and the vascular bundles and occurs as a cylinder encircling the vascular bundles and the pith, as in dicotyledonous stems. In may consist wholly of sclerenchyma forming a continuous zone, as in the gourd (*Cucurbita*) stem, but more commonly, it is made of both parenchyma and sclerenchyma, the latter forming isolated strands in it (the pericycle). Each such strand associated with the phloem or bast of the vascular bundle in the form of a cap is known as the **hard bast**, as in sunflower stem. In the roots and stems of some aquatic plants, the pericycle is absent. It is not distinguishable in the monocotyledonous stems. In the stems of pteridophytes, the pericycle is single-layered, while in those of gymnosperms, it is multi-layered. In the roots of angiosperms and pteridophytes the pericycle is a single layer of very small, thin-walled and somewhat barrel-shaped cells. In some monocotyledonous roots, however, the pericycle may be a few layers thick and even lignified. In gynmosperms, it is multiseriate and thin-walled.

Functions. In all roots, the pericycle is the seat of origin of lateral roots (see FIG. 66). In dicotyledonous, it also further gives rise to secondary meristems —a portion of the cambium (see FIG. 75) and later, the whole of the cork-cambium (see FIG. 77). In all stems, the pericycle is the seat of origin of adventitious roots. Otherwise, its functions are mechanical, secretion, storage, etc.

3. PITH and PITH RAYS. The pith or **medulla** forms the central core of the stem and the root and is usually made of large-celled parenchyma with abundant intercellular spaces. In the dicotyledonous stem, the pith is often large and well developed, while in the monocotyledonous stem, it is not distinguishable, owing to the scattered distribution of vascular bundles. In the dicotyledonous root, the pith is either small or absent, the bigger vessels having met in the centre, while in the monocotyledonous root, a distinct pith is present. It is often parenchymatous, but sometimes sclerenchymatous. In the dicotyledonous stem, the pith extends outwards to the pericycle between the vascular bundles. Each extension which is a strip of parenchyma is called the **pith ray** or **medullary ray**. It is not present as such in the root. The cells of the pith and the pith ray are usually larger than those of the cortex and enclose numerous intercellular spaces.

Functions. They serve to store food material. The function of the scle-renchymatous pith is, of course, mechanical. The medullary ray also transmits water and food material outwards to the peripheral tissues, and is the seat of origin of a strip of cambium (i.e. the interfascicular cambium; see FIG. 72B) prior to secondary growth.

3. THE VASCULAR TISSUE SYSTEM

This system consists of a number of vascular bundles which are distributed in the **stele**. The stele is the central cylinder of the stem and the root (and the pine leaf, surrounded by the endodermis. It consists of vascular bundles, pericycle, pith and medullary rays. Each bundle is made up of **xylem** and **phloem**, with a cambium in dicotyledonous stems, or without a cambium in monocotyledonous stems, or of only one kind of tissue— xylem or phloem, as in roots. The function of this system is to conduct water and raw food material from the roots to the leaves, and prepared food material from leaves to the storage organs and the growing regions. The elements of a vascular bundle are derived from the procambial strands of the plerome, which show a tendency to elongate even at an early stage. The vascular bundles may be regularly arranged in a ring, as in the stems of dicotyledons, gymnosperms and in all roots, or they may be scattered in the ground tissue, as in the stems of monocotyledons.

ELEMENTS OF A VASCULAR BUNDLE (FIG. 48). The vascular bundle of a dicotyledonous stem, when fully formed, consists of three well-defined tissues: (1) xylem or wood, (2) phloem or

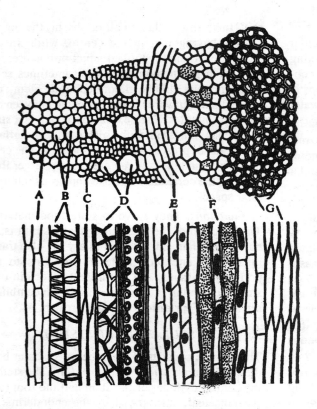

bast, and (3) cambium. They have different kinds of tissue-elements.

(1) **Xylem or Wood.** This lies towards the centre and is composed of the following elements: (1) tracheae or vessels, (2) some tracheids, (3) a number of wood fibres, and (4) a small patch of wood parenchyma. Vessels are of various kinds (see FIG. 37) such as *spiral, annular, scalariform, reticulate* and *pitted* (with simple or bordered pits). Some tracheids also lie associated with the vessels. Wood fibres and wood parenchyma are ordinary sclerenchymatous and parenchymatous cells lying associated with the wood or xylem. Their walls are provided with simple pits. In the secondary xylem the wood parenchyma sometimes becomes thick-walled and lignified. Xylem vessels and tracheids

are used for the conduction of water and mineral salts from the roots to the leaves and other parts of the plant. The Xylem parenchyma assists them in their task and also serves for food storage, and wood fibres give proper rigidity to the xylem. Except for wood parenchyma, all the other elements of xylem are dead and lignified, and hence, their secondary function is to give mechanical strength to the plant.

The first-formed xylem or **protoxylem** consists of *annular, spiral* and *scalariform* vessels; it lies towards the centre of the stem and its vessels have smaller cavities. The later-formed xylem or **metaxylem** consists of *reticulate* and *pitted* vessels and some *tracheids*; it lies away from the centre and its vessels have much bigger cavities. Of

Note. The wood of gymnosperms and ferns consists exclusively of tracheid. No vessels are present there. The primary wood in them consists of annular and spiral tracheids, and the secondary wood (in gymnosperms only) consists of pitted tracheids (with bordered pits). Also, no companion cells are formed in these two divisions of plants. In mono-cotyledons, there is seldom any phloem parenchyma. Cambium is also absent from them. In all roots, xylem forms one bundle and phloem another.

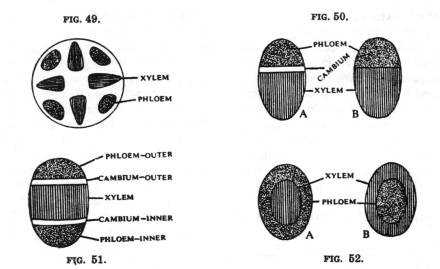

FIG. 49.

FIG. 50.

FIG. 51.

FIG. 52.

Types of Vascular Bundles. FIG. 49. Radial. FIG. 50. Collateral—*A*, open; *B*, closed. FIG. 51. Bicollateral. FIG. 52. Concentric—*A*, xylem central (amphicribral); *B*, phloem central (amphivasal)

course all transitional stages are noticed between protoxylem and metaxylem. The development of xylem is *centrifugal* in the stem, or, in other words, it is said to be *endarch* (meaning inner origin).

(2) **Phloem or Bast.** This lies towards the circumference and consists of (1) sieve-tubes, (2) companion cells, and (3) phloem parenchyma. The companion cells and phloem parenchyma are provided with simple pits, particularly in the walls lying against the sieve-tubes. Phloem, as a whole, is used for downward translocation of prepared food materials (soluble proteins, amines and amino-acids, and soluble carbohydrates) from the leaves to the storage organs, and later, from there to the different growing regions in the upward direction. Sieve-tubes, constant in all higher plants, are the main channels through which this translocation takes place. Companion cells and phloem parenchyma, when present, assist the sieve-tubes in this task. They also transmit many of the soluble food materials sideways to the surrounding tissues. All the elements of phloem are made of cellulose and are living. Primary phloem hardly ever contains bast fibres, but it may be capped by a patch of sclerenchyma, called the **hard bast**, as seen in the sunflower stem (see FIG. 53).

The outer portion of phloem, consisting of narrow sieve-tubes, constitutes the **protophloem**. The inner portion, consisting of bigger sieve-tubes, constitutes the **metaphloem**.

(3) **Cambium.** This is a thin strip of primary meristem lying between the xylem and phloem. It consists of one or a few layers of thin-walled and roughly rectangular cells. Although cambial cells look rectangular in transverse section, they are very elongated, often with oblique ends. They become flattened tangentially, i.e. at right angles to the radius of the stem.

TYPES OF VASCULAR BUNDLES.

According to the arrangement of xylem and phloem, the vascular bundles are of the following types:

(1) **Radial**, when the xylem and phloem form separate bundles which lie on different radii, alternating with each other, as in roots (FIG. 49). The radial-bundle is the most primitive type of vascular bundles.

(2) **Conjoint**, when the xylem and phloem combine into one bundle. There are different types of conjoint bundle.

(*a*) *Collateral*, when the xylem and phloem lie together on the same raidus the xylem being internal and the phloem external. When cambium is present in a collateral as in all dicotyledonous stems, the bundle is said to be *open* (FIG. 50A), and when the cambium is absent, it is said to be *closed* (FIG. 50B), as in monocotyledonous stems.

(*b*) *Bicollateral* (FIG. 51), when the both phloem and combium occur twice in a collateral bundle—once on the outer side of the xylem and again on the inner side of it. The sequence is outer phloem, outer cambium, xylem, inner cambium and inner phloem. Bicollateral bundles are characteristic of *Cucurbitaceae*. They are also often found in *Solanaceae, Apocynaceae, Convolvulaceae, Myrtaceae*, etc. A bicollateral bundle is always open.

(*c*) *Concentric*, when one kind of vascular tissue (xylem or phloem) is surrounded by the other. Evidently, there are two types, according to whether one is central or the other one is so. When the phloem lies in the centre and is surrounded by xylem (FIG. 52B),. as in some monocotyledons, e.g. dragon plant (*Dracaena*; see FIG. 89), dagger plant (*Yucca*; see FIG. I/81),*Cordyline*, sweet flag (*Acorus*; B. & H. BOCH), etc., the concentric bundle is said to be **amphivasal**.[1] When, on the other hand, the xylem lies in the centre and is surrounded by phloem (FIG. 52A), as in many ferns, *Lycopodium, Selaginella* and some aquatic angiosperms, the concentric bundle is said to be **amphicribral**. A concentric bundle is always closed.

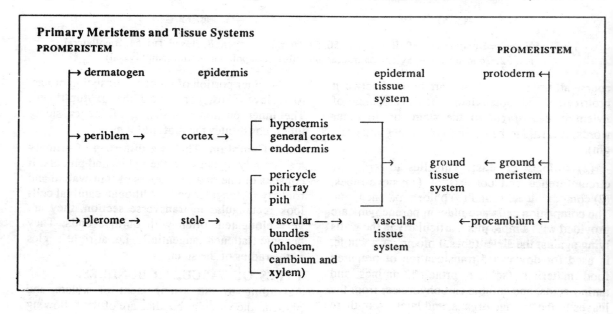

Primary Meristems and Tissue Systems

PROMERISTEM					PROMERISTEM
→ dermatogen	epidermis		epidermal tissue system	protoderm ←	
→ periblem →	cortex →	hyposermis general cortex endodermis			
			→	ground tissue system	← ground ← meristem
		pericycle pith ray pith			
→ plerome →	stele →	vascular → bundles (phloem, cambium and xylem)	vascular tissue system	←procambium ←	

---

[1] Haberlandt used the term *hadrome* for xylem, and the term *leptome* for phloem. Accordingly, an amphivasal bundle is said to be **leptocentric**, and an amphicribral bundle, **hadrocentric**.

CHAPTER 4

ANATOMY OF STEMS

Double Staining and Permanent Preparation of Microscopic Sections. For free-hand sections of ordinary material such as stem, root and leaf, the following procedure may be adopted by a beginner. Of the various combinations of stains, the following are recommended for a start. It must be noted that only thin and uniform sections can be properly stained.

A. Safranin and Haematoxylin. Aqueous solution of safranin (0.5–1%) or alcoholic solution of it (1% in 50% alcohol) and Delafield's haematoxylin (prepared according to the standard formula) may be used. Avoid overstaining with the latter; if necessary, dilute it with water in a watch glass before use. Safranin stains lignified elements deep red, while haematoxylin stains cellulose elements purplish. The schedule given below may be followed.

1. Safranin—5–10 minutes. 2. Washing in water (or 50% alcohol followed by water)—5 minutes (to remove most of the stain from cellulose elements). 3. Haematoxylin (better diluted)—1–2 minutes; the stain deepens in water at the next stage. 4. Washing in water—a few minutes. 5. Dehydration (by passing through grades of alcohol)—1/2–1 minute in each, with another change in 100% for 1/2–1 minute for complete dehydration. Note that incomplete dehydration will result in fogginess at next stage. 6. Clove oil—2–5 minutes or more. Clove oil is a clearing reagent. 7. Canada balsam (dissolved in xylol)—mount a section in it on a clean slide (after removing excess clove oil from the section with a piece of blotting paper). 8. Cover the section with a cover-glass by gently sliding it down with the help of forceps or needle. 9. Label and keep the slide flat for drying up, away from dust.

B. Safranin and Light Green. Safranin stains lignified elements dep red, while light green stains cellulose elements bright green. This is a good combination of stains and easy to manipulate. Chances of overstaining are minimized. Follow the schedule given below.

1. Safranin, as above. 2. Washing in water. 3. Dehydration, as above. 4. Light Green (in clove oil)—2–5 minutes (0.2 gm. of light green powder dissolved in 50 c.c. of absolute alcohol and 50 c.c. of clove oil). 5. Clove oil or xylol—1–2 minutes.   6. Canada balsam and the rest, as above.

Maceration. By this method, the tissues may be separated into individual cells. The principle lies in dissolving the middle lamella (made of pectic compounds) and then teasing out the cells. The procedure is as follows (Schultze's method). Cut the material into small pieces to the thickness of match-sticks and put them into a test-tube. Pour strong nitric acid, just enough to cover the pieces, then add a few crystals of potassium chlorate. Heat gently (in an open space to avoid disagreeable fumes) for 4 or 5 minutes until the fumes have ceased. Pour out the contents into water in a dish or beaker and wash the pieces thoroughly in water. For examination, a piece may be placed on a slide, crushed under cover-glass and then teased with needles. Stain and mount glycerine. Cover and examine the isolated elements. The washed pieces may be preserved in 3–4% formalin for future use.

DICOTYLEDONOUS STEMS

A . *YOUNG SUNFLOWER STEM* (FIG. 53)

At first, note the distribution of different zones and sub-zones, the arrange-ment of vascular bundles more or less in a ring close to the periphery, and a very large pith occupying the major part of the stem. Then study the tissues in detail.

1. Epidermis. This forms the outermost layer and consists of a single row of cells, flattened tangentially and fitting closely along their radial walls, with a well-defined cuticle extending over it. Here and there, it bears some multicellular hairs and a few stomata, but no chloroplasts. The guard cells of the stomata, however, contain chloroplasts.

2. Cortex. This lies below the epidermis and consists of the external collenchyma, central parenchyma and internal endodermis or starch sheath. (*a*) Hypodermis (collenchyma): This lies immediately below the epidermis and consists of some 4 or 5 layers of collenchymatous cells. These cells are specially thickened at the corners, against the intercellular spaces. The thickening is due to a deposit of cellulose impregnated with pectin. The cells are living and contain a number of chloroplasts. (*b*) **General cortex or cortical**

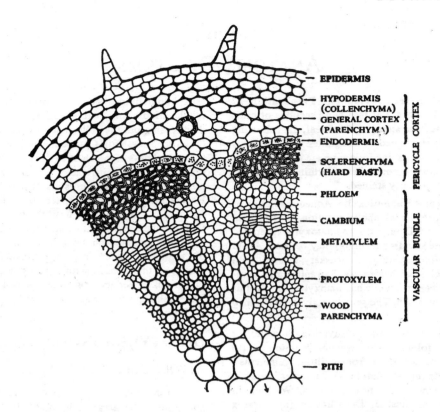

EPIDERMIS

HYPODERMIS
(COLLENCHYMA)
GENERAL CORTEX
(PARENCHYMA)
ENDODERMIS

PERICYCLE CORTEX

SCLERENCHYMA
(HARD BAST)

PHLOEM

CAMBIUM

METAXYLEM

PROTOXYLEM

WOOD
PARENCHYMA

VASCULAR BUNDLE

PITH

FIG. 53. Young sunflower stem (a sector) in transection. Note the resin-duct in the cortex, and the medullary ray in between the two vascular bundles

parenchyma: This lies internal to the hypodermis and consists of a few layers of thin-walled, large, rounded or oval, parenchymatous cells. It may be reduced to 1 or 2 layers outside the vascular bundle. There are conspicuous intercellular spaces in it. Some isolated resin-ducts, each surrounded by a layer of small thin-walled living cells, can also be seen. (*c*) **Endodermis**: This is the innermost layer of the cortex and demarcates it from the stele. The cells are more or less barrel-shaped and fit closely without intercellular spaces. The endodermis is conspicuous outside the patch of sclerenchyma, but loses its identity on either side. It almost invariably contains numerous starch grains and is also known as the *starch sheath*.

3. Pericycle. This is the region lying between the endodermis and the vascular bundles, and is represented by semi-lunar patches of sclerenchyma and intervening masses of parenchyma. Each patch lying associated with phloem of the vascular bundle is called the **hard bast**. The middle lamella is very prominent in this tissue.

4. Medullary Rays. A few layers of fairly big, polygonal or radially elongated cells lying between two vascular bundles constitute the medullary rays.

5. Pith. This is very elaborate in the sunflower stem and occupies the major portion of it. It extends from below the vascular bundles to the centre and is composed of rounded or polygonal, thin-walled, living cells with conspicuous intercellular spaces between them.

6. Vascular Bundles. These are collateral and open, and are arranged in a ring. Each bundle is composed of (1) **phloem** or **bast**, (2) **cambium**, and (3) **xylem** or **wood**.

(1) **Phloem.** This lies externally and is composed of only thin and cellulose-walled elements. It consists of: (*a*) **Sieve-tubes,** which appear as slightly larger cavities than the rest of the phloem. On the whole, the sieve-tubes of the sunflower stem are very narrow. Associated with each sieve-tube may be seen a smaller cell. This is (*b*) the **companion cell.** The rest of the phloem is packed with small-celled parenchyma known as (*c*) the **phloem parenchyma.** All the phloem elements are living, and contain various kinds of food material.

(2) **Cambium.** Passing inwards, a band of thin-walled tissue is seen, whose cells are regularly arranged in radial rows and are roughly rectangular very small and thin-walled. (If the section be cut through a comparatively old portion of the stem, the cambium is seen to be continuous from one vascular bundle to another, and the division of its cells noted both inside and outside. This indicates the beginning of secondary growth.)

(3) **Xylem or Wood.** This lies internally and consists of the following elements: (*a*) **Wood Vessels:** Some large, thick-walled elements, arranged in a few radial rows, can be easily recognized in the wood. These are the wood vessels. The development of xylem is *centrifugal,* or in other words, it is said to be *endarch* (meaning inner origin). The smaller vessels constituting the *protoxylem* lie towards the centre, and the bigger ones constituting the *metaxylem* lie away from the centre. The protoxylem consists of annular, spiral and scalariform vessels, and the metaxylem of reticulate and pitted vessels. Their walls are always thick and lignified. (*b*) **Tracheids:** Surrounding the *metaxylem* vessels and lying in between them, some small, thick-walled cells can be seen. These are the tracheids. In transverse section of the stem, they are hardly distinguishable from the wood fibres which lie mixed up with them. (*c*) **Wood fibres:** These appear somewhat irregular and polygonal in section. They are thick-walled and lignified, and stained like the wood vessels. Except for the vessels, nearly the whole of the wood is packed with these elements. (*d*) **Wood Parenchyma:** A patch of thin-walled cells seen on the inner side of the bundle surrounding the protoxylem is the wood parenchyma. The cells of the wood parenchyma retain their protoplasm.

B. YOUNG RANUNCULUS STEM (FIG. 54)

Note the zones, sub-zones and nature of tissues as labelled in the diagram. Also note that a number of

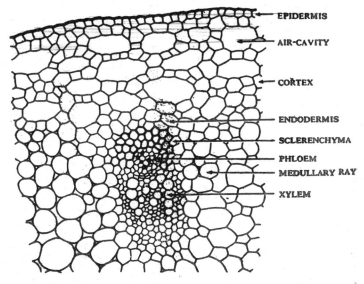

FIG. 54. Young *Ranunculus* (*R. sceleratus*) stem (a sector) in transection.
Note that the cambium is absent or very feebly developed

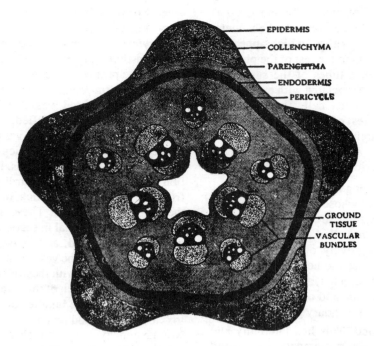

EPIDERMIS
COLLENCHYMA
PARENCHYMA
ENDODERMIS
PERICYCLE
GROUND TISSUE
VASCULAR BUNDLES

FIG. 55. Young *Cucurbita* stem in transection, as seen under a pocket lens

air-cavities develop in the cortex (the plant being sub-aquatic in habit), and that the cambium is absent. Some feebly-developed cambium-like cells represent the remnant of the procambium. Study the tissues in detail with reference FIG. 54.

C. YOUNG CUCURBITA STEM (FIGS. 55-6)

Note that it is hollow and usually has five ridges and five furrows. The vascular bundles are usually ten in number and arranged in two rows, those of the outer row corresponding to the ridges and those of the inner to the furrows (FIG. 55). Then study the tissues in detail (FIG. 56).

1. Epidermis. This is the single, outermost layer passing over the ridges and furrows. It often bears many long and narrow multicellular hairs.

2. Cortex. In the cortex, the hypodermis lies externally, the general cortex or cortical parenchyma lies in the middle, and the endodermis lies internally.(a) **hypodermis (collenchyma)** lies immediately below the epidermis. It consists of six or seven (sometimes more) layers of collenchymatous cells in the ridges, only two or three layers,

(sometimes none). The collenchyma contains some chloroplasts. (b) The **general cortex** or **cortical parenchyma** forms a narrow zone in the middle, two or three layers thick. In the furrows, it passes outwards, right up to the epidermis through the collenchyma. Chloroplasts are abundant in it. (c) The **endodermis** is the innermost layer of the cortex, lying immediately outside the pericyclic sclerenchyma. This layer is wavy in outline and contains starch grains.

3. Pericycle. Below the endodermis is a zone of sclerenchyma, which represents the pericycle. This zone consists of four or five layers of thick-walled, lignified cells, which are polygonal.

4. Ground Tissue. This is the continuous mass of thin-walled, parenchymatous cells extending from below the sclerenchyma to the pith cavity. The vascular bundles lie embedded in this tissue.

5. Vascular Bundles. These are bicollateral, usually ten in number and arranged in two rows. Each bundle consists of (1) **xylem**, (2) **two strips of cambium**, and (3) **two patches of phloem**.

(1) **Xylem** occupies the centre of the bundle. It

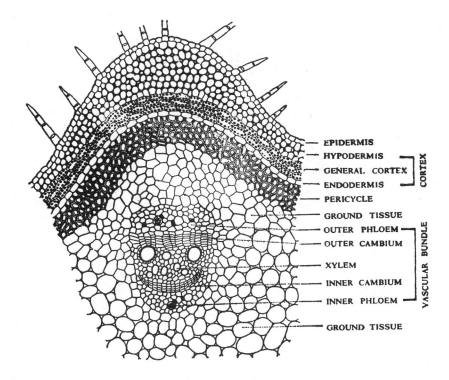

FIG. 56. Young *Cucurbita* stem (a sector) in transection

consists of *protoxylem* (smaller vessels on the inner side) and *metaxylem* (slightly bigger vessels a little higher up) The larger vessels still higher up represent the beginning of secondary xylem. There may be some tracheids and wood fibres, but wood parenchyma is abundant. The vessels are not arranged in radial rows, as in the sunflower stem.

(2) **Cambium.** This tissue occurs in two strips—the outer and the inner, one on each side of the xylem. It forms a narrow strip between the phloem and the xylem to the inside, and between the xylem and the phloem to the outside. Its cells are thin-walled and rectangular, and are arranged in radial rows. The outer cambium is many-layered and is more or less flat, while the inner cambium is few-layered and curved (crescent-shaped).

(3) **Phloem** occurs in two patches—the outer and the inner. Note that the outer phloem is plano-convex and the inner one is semilunar. Each patch of phloem consists of sieve-tubes, companion cells and phloem parenchyma. Sieve-tubes are very

conspicuous in the phloem of the *Cucurbita* stem. Sieve-plates with perforations may be seen distinctly in some places (SEE FIGS. 38-9). The rest of the phloem is made up of small, thin-walled cells, which constitute the phloem parenchyma.

D. YOUNG CASUARINA STEM (FIG. 57)

The stem is wavy in outline. It has distinct ridges and furrows, which vary in number (commonly 7-12). Assimilatory tissue develops in the ridges, while a large number of stomata remain confined to the lateral walls in the furrows. Hairs grow out from the base of the furrow. They are of two kinds—simple and branched—with usually two short basal cells and a long terminal cell. The different tissues are as follows. The **epidermis** is the single, outermost layer of cells. It has a thick cuticle with warty protuberances on the ridge but is devoid of stomata, while the furrow is interspersed with numerous stomata. The **hypodermis** develops in the ridge and consists of one to a few layers

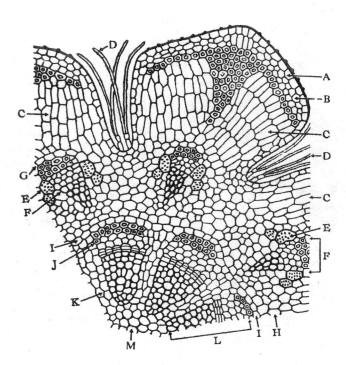

FIG. 57. Young *Casuarina* stem (a sector) in transection. *A*, epidermis; *B*, hypodermis with T-shaped
sclerenchyma; *C*, palisade tissue (assimilatory tissue); stomata remain confined to the epidermal
layer of the furrow; *D*, hair; *E*, tranfusion tracheid; *F*, leaf trace bundle (note xylem and phloem,
capped by sclerenchyma); *G*, endodermis (outer); *H*, ground tissue; *I*, endodermis (inner); *J*, hard bast;
K, medullary ray; *L*, cauline bundle (note xylem, cambium and phloem, capped by hard bast); and *M*, pith

of parenchyma, followed internally by a T-shaped
group of sclerenchyma. The stem of the T extends
deep in towards a leaf trace bundle, thus dividing
the assimilatory tissue into two groups, more or
less symmetrical. **Assimilatory tissue**
(chlorenchyma) occurs on each side of the T and
consists of a few rows of radially elongated palisade cells. **Leaf trace bundles** occur in a ring,
each opposite to a ridge, lying embedded in a mass
of thin-walled parenchyma (ground tissue). Each
bundle is feebly developed with xylem on the
inside and phloem on the outside, capped by a
small patch of sclerenchyma. A wavy layer of
endodermis (outer) passes over the bundle.
Transfusion tracheids occur on either side of the
bundle and are conspicuous. **Cauline bundles**
occur in a ring in the central cylinder, alternating
with the leaf trace bundles. While still young, they
are separated by distinct, rather broad, medullary

rays. The bundles, however, soon become compact
with the progress of secondary growth. They are
collateral and open, consist of xylem, cambium
and phloem, and are capped by a sheath of sclerenchyma (hard bast). A wavy layer of **endodermis** (inner) passes over the bundles. The **pith**
contains a mass of parenchyma at the centre.

MONOCOTYLEDONOUS STEMS

A. MAIZE OR INDIAN CORN

1. Epidermis. This is a single, outermost layer
with a thick cuticle on the outer surface. A few
stomata may be seen at some places in the epidermis.

2. Hypodermis (Sclerenchyma). This forms a
narrow zone of sclerenchymatous cells, usually
two or three layers thick, lying below the epidermis.

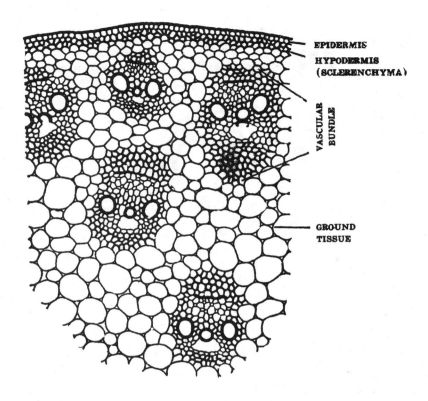

FIG. 58. Maize or Indian corn stem (a sector) in transection

3. Ground Tissue. This is the continuous mass of thin-walled, parenchymatous cells, extending from below the sclerenchyma to the centre. It is not differentiated into cortex, endodermis, pericycle, etc., as in a dicotyledonous stem. The cells of the ground tissue enclose numerous intercellular spaces between them.

4. Vascular Bundles (FIG. 59). These are collateral and closed, and lie scattered in the ground tissue. They are numerous, and lie closer together near the periphery than at the centre. The peripheral ones are also seen to be smaller than the central ones. Each vascular bundle is somewhat oval and is more or less completely surrounded by a **sheath** of sclerenchyma, which is specially developed on the two sides—upper and lower. The bundle consists of two parts, viz. xylem and phloem.

(1) The **xylem** consists mainly of four distinct vessels arranged in the form of a Y, and a small number of tracheids arranged irregularly. The two smaller vessels (annular and spiral) lying radially towards the centre constitute the *protoxylem*, and the two bigger vessels (pitted) lying laterally together with the small pitted tracheids between them constitute the *metaxylem*. Besides, the protoxylem has a thin-walled, wood (or xylem) parenchyma that almost surrounds a conspicuous water-containing cavity. A few wood fibres also occur, associated with the tracheids, in between the two big pitted vessels. This water-containing cavity has been formed lysigenously, i.e. by the breaking down of the inner protoxylem vessel and contiguous parenchyma during the rapid growth of the stem.

(2) The **phloem** consists exclusively of sieve-tubes and companion cells. Phloem parenchyma is

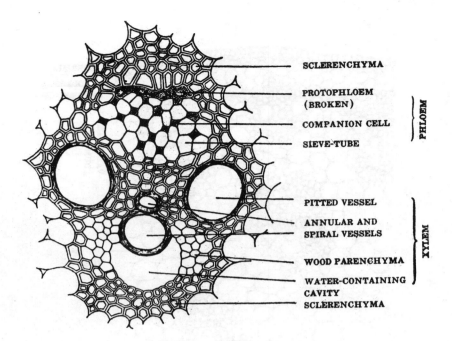

FIG. 59. A vascular bundle of maize stem (magnified)

Differences between Dicotyledonous and Monocotyledonous Stems

		Dicotyledonous stem (e.g. sunflower)	Monocotyledonous stem (e.g. maize)
1.	Hypodermis	collenchymatous	scle renchymatous
2.	General Cortex	a few layers of parenchyma	a continuous mass of parenchyma up to the
3.	Endodermis	a wavy layer	centre (ground tissue)
4.	Pericycle	a zone of parenchyma and sclerenchyma	without differentiation into distinct tissues
5.	Medullary Ray	a strip of parenchyma in between vascular bundles	not marked out
6.	Pith	the central cylinder	not marked out
7.	Vascular Bundles	(a) collateral and open	collateral and closed
		(b) arranged in a ring	scattered
		(c) of uniform size	larger towards the centre
		(d) phloem parenchyma present	it is absent
		(e) usually wedge-shaped	usually oval
		(f) bundle sheath absent	strongly developed

not present in the monocotyledonous stem. The outermost portion of the phloem, which is a broken mass, is the *protophloem* and the inner portion is the *metaphloem*. The former soon gets disorganized, and the latter shows distinct sieve-tubes and companion cells.

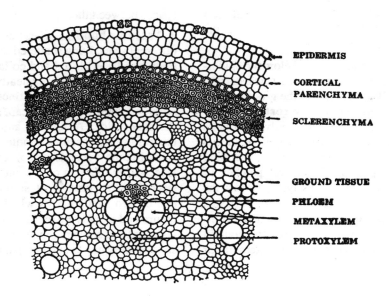

FIG. 60. *Asparagus* stem (a sector) in transection

B. ASPARAGUS STEM (FIG. 60)

In a transverse section of the stem, note the tissues as labelled the sketch, and study them in detail.

C. FLOWERING STEM (SCAPE) OF CANNA (FIG. 61)

1. Epidermis. This is the outermost layer consist-

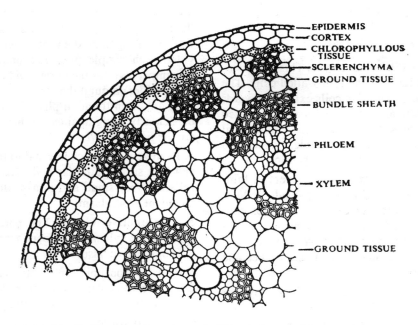

FIG. 61. Flowering stem (scope) of *Canna* (a sector) in transection

ing of a single row of very small, polygonal cells flattened tangentially. The outer walls of the epidermis are cutinized.

2. Ground Tissue System. From below the epidermis to the centre the whole mass of tissues, barring the vascular bundles, constitutes the ground tissue system. It is differentiated into (a) **cortex**, consisting of two layers of fairly large polygonal cells (b) chlorophyllous tissue, consisting of one or two layers of chloroplast-bearing cells, intruding inwards at some places, (c) several patches of sclerenchyma of different sizes lying against the chlorophyllous tissue, and (d) ground tissue, consisting of a continuous mass of large, thin-walled, parenchymatous cells, which contain starch grains and enclose numerous intercellular spaces between them.

3. Vascular bundles. These are numerous and of different sizes, lying scattered in the ground tissue. Each bundle is closed and collateral. It is incompletely surrounded by a sheath of sclerenchyma (**bundle sheath**), with a distinct patch of it on the outer side in the form of a cap, and a thin strip on the inner side. A regular and complete sheath encircling the vascular bundle is seldom formed. Each bundle consists of (a) xylem on the inner side, and (b) pholem on the outer. The **xylem** consists of a large, prominent, spiral vessel, often with one or two smaller ones which are also spiral in nature and usually lie on its outer side. The xylem also contains some parenchyma. The **phloem** consists of sieve-tubes and companion cells.

CHAPTER 5

ANATOMY OF ROOTS

DICOTYLEDONOUS ROOTS

A. YOUNG GRAM ROOT (FIG. 62)

1. Epiblema or Piliferous Layer. This is the single, outermost layer of the thin-walled cells. The outer walls of most of these cells extend outwards and form unicellular root-hairs. This layer is used for absorption of water and solutes from the soil and, therefore, it has no cuticle. Root-hairs increase the absorbing surface of the root.

2. Cortex. This consists of many layers of thin-walled rounded cells, with numerous intercellular spaces between them. The cells of the cortex contain leucoplasts and store starch grains. The epiblema is, in some cases, only short-lived. As it dies off, a few outer layers of the cortex become cutinized and form the *exodermis* of the root.

3. Endodermis. This is a single, ring-like layer of barrel-shaped cells which are closely packed without intercellular spaces. The radial walls of this

layer are often thickened and sometimes, this thickening extends to the inner walls also. The walls abutting upon the protoxylem are often provided with simple pits. The endodermis is the innermost layer of the cortex and occurs as a ring (or cylinder) around the stele. Small, thin-walled cells are often found at places in the endodermis particularly lying against the protoxylem. These are the *passage cells*.

4. Pericycle. This lies internal to the endodermis, and is a single, circular layer like the latter. Its cells are very small and thin-walled, but contain abundant protoplasm.

5. Conjunctive Tissue. The parenchyma lying between the xylem and phloem bundles constitutes the conjunctive tissue.

6. Pith. This occupies only a small area in the centre of the root. But soon, the pith is obliterated owing to the wood vessels meeting in the centre.

7. Vascular Bundles. These are arranged in a ring,

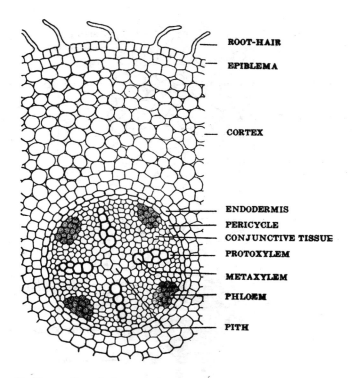

ROOT-HAIR
EPIBLEMA
CORTEX
ENDODERMIS
PERICYCLE
CONJUNCTIVE TISSUE
PROTOXYLEM
METAXYLEM
PHLOEM
PITH

FIG. 62. Young dicotyledonous root (gram seedling) in transection

as in the dicotyledonous stem, but here the xylem and phloem form an equal number of separate bundles, the arrangement of which is *radial* (see p. 226). The protoxylem lies away from the centre so that the development of wood is *centripetal,* or in other words, the xylem is said to be *exarch* (meaning outer origin). The number of xylem (or phloem) bundles varies from two to six (di-, tri-, tetr-, pent-, or hex-arch), very seldom more. The cambium makes its appearance only later as a secondary meristem. The **phloem bundle** consists of sieve-tubes, companion cells and phloem parenchyma. The **xylem bundle** consists of protoxylem which lies towards the circumference abutting on the pericycle, and metaxylem towards the centre, i.e. the xylem is exarch. The protoxylem is composed of small vessels (annular and spiral), and the metaxylem of bigger vessels (reticulate and pitted). The metaxylem groups often meet in the centre, and then the pith is obliterated (it gets disorganized).

B. YOUNG RANUNCULUS ROOT (FIG. 63)

1. Epiblema—the single, outermost layer.

2. Exodermis—a few layers internal to the epiblema, representing the outer zone of the cortex (corresponding to the hypodermis of the stem).

3. Cortex—several layers of rounded or oval cells, with a lot of intercellular spaces between them.

4. Endodermis—the innermost layer of the cortex. The layer is distinct and cylindrical, with thick-walled cells except the *passage cells* lying against the protoxylem.

5. Pericycle—a single, ring-like layer internal to the endodermis. The cells are small and thin-walled.

6. Conjunctive tissue—the parenchyma in between the xylem and phloem.

7. Vascular bundles— radial, with 4 or 5 xylem bundles and as many phloem bundles. The xylem

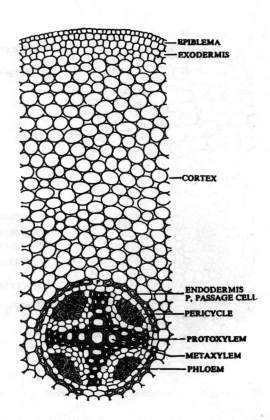

FIG. 63. Young dicotyledonous root (*Ranunculus sceleratus*) in transection

is exarch and the metaxylem vessels meet in the centre. The pith is absent.

MONOCOTYLEDONOUS ROOTS

A. AMARYLLIS ROOT (FIG. 64)

1. Epiblema or Piliferous Layer. This is the single, outermost layer with a number of unicellular root-hairs.

2. Cortex. This is a many layered zone of rounded or oval cells with intercellular spaces between them. As the epiblema dies off, a few outer layers of the cortex become cutinized and form the *exodermis*.

3. Endodermis. This is the innermost layer of the cortex and forms a definite ring around the stele. The radial walls, and often the inner walls, of the endodermis are considerably thickened. The cells of the endodermis are barrel-shaped. *Passage cells* are often present in this layer, lying against the protoxylem.

4. Pericycle. This is the ring-like layer lying internal to the endodermis. Its cells are very small and thin-walled.

5. Conjunctive Tissue. The parenchyma in between the xylem and pholem bundles is known as the *conjunctive tissue*.

6. Pith. The mass of parenchymatous cells in and around the centre is the pith. It is well-developed in most monocotyledonous roots. In some cases, the pith becomes thick-walled and lignified.

7. Vascular Bundles. The xylem and phloem form an equal number of separate bundles, and they are arranged in a ring. The arrangement is *radial* (see

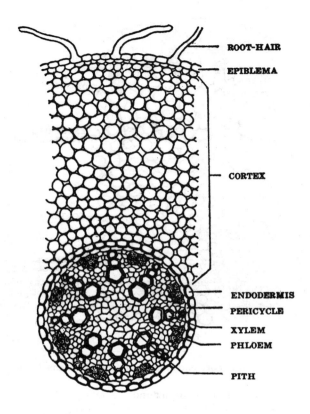

FIG. 64. Monocotyledonous root (*Amaryllis*) in transection

p. 226). There are many bundles (polyarch). Rarely, as in onion, is there a limited number of bundles. The development of wood is *centripetal*, in other words, the xylem is *exarch*. The **phloem bundle** consists of sieve-tubes, companion cells and phloem parenchyma. The **xylem bundle** consists of protoxylem, which abuts on the pericycle, and the metaxylem lies towards the centre, i.e. the xylem is *exarch*. The protoxylem consists of annular and spiral vessels, and the metaxylem of reticulate and pitted vessels. A few isolated, big vessels may often be seen in the pith.

B. VANDA (ORCHID) ROOT (FIG. 65)

1. Velamen—a few layers of outer absorbtive tissue, spongy in nature (see p. 20). It is derived from the dermatogen of the root, and its outermost layer is sometimes called the *limiting layer.*

2. Exodermis—a single layer of thick-walled cells, with unthickened *passage cells* at places.

3. Cortex—several layers of rounded or oval parenchymatous cells. A few outer layers contain chloroplasts.

4. Endodermis—a single layer of somewhat barrel-shaped cells. Inner walls, and also the radial walls to some extent, are specially thickened and suberized. Unthickened *passage cells* are present, lying against the protoxylem.

5. Pericycle—a single layer of cells, lying internal to the endodermis.

6. Conjunctive tissue—thick walled and lignified, lying between the xylem and phloem.

7. Vascular bundles—numerous and radial, with exarch xylem and small patches of phloem alternating with the xylem.

8. Pith—well-developed and parenchymatous in nature, sometimes becoming sclerified.

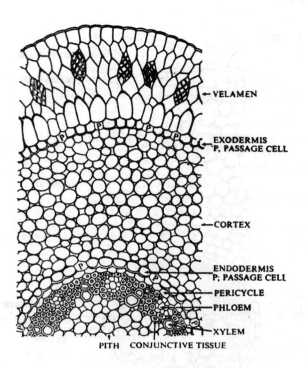

← VELAMEN

← EXODERMIS
P, PASSAGE CELL

← CORTEX

ENDODERMIS
P; PASSAGE CELL
PERICYCLE
PHLOEM
XYLEM

PITH   CONJUNCTIVE TISSUE

FIG. 65. Monocotyledonous root (*Vanda*) in transection

Differences between Dicotyledonous and Monocotyledonous Roots

		Dicotyledonous root	*Monocotyledonous root*
1.	Xylem bundles	vary from 2 to 6 (dito-hexarch), rarely more	numerous (polyarch), rarely a limited number.
2.	Pith	small or absent	large and well-developed.
3.	Pericycle	gives rise to lateral roots, cambium and cork-cambium	gives rise to lateral roots only.
4.	Cambium	appears later as a secondary meristem	altogether absent.

Transition from the Root to the Stem (FIG. 66). Vascular bundles are continuous from the root to the stem, but different arrangements are found in the two cases. In the stem, they are collateral with endarch xylem, while in the root, they are radial with exarch xylem. How and where has this transition taken place? The transition involves splitting, twisting and reorientation of the xylem or phloem, or both. It takes place in the region of the hypocotyl, sometimes a little lower or a little higher up. This region is known as the **transition region**. Usually, four types of transition are noted, as follows.

Type 1. Each of the xylem and phloem bundles divides radially into two. As they pass upwards, they move laterally. As the xylem bundles move, they twist round by 180°, and each comes to lie on the inner side of the adjacent phloem bundle, evidently in an inverted position, i.e. the centripetal (exarch) xylem in the root now becomes centrifugal (endarch) in the stem. In other words, the radial bundles become collateral. The number of collateral bundles in the stem is just double that of the phloem bundles in the root. This type is rather common and is characteristically found in *Phaseolus, Cucurbita, Tropaeolum*, etc.

Type II. In this type, each xylem bundle divides radially into two, while each phloem bundle remains more or less in its own position, without any division. The two strands of xylem bundles then move laterally by 180° and come to lie on the inner side of the two adjacent phloem bundles. It is thus evident that each phloem bundle receives two xylem strands which soon fuse. The number of collateral bundles formed in the stem corresponds with that of the phloem bundles, as seen in the root. This type is found in *Mirabilis, Fumaria, Dipsacus*, etc.

Type III. In this type, the phloem bundles divide radially and change their position laterally, while the xylem bundles neither divide nor shift. They, however, twist round by 180°, as in the previous cases, so that the exarch xylem now becomes endarch. The halves of the phloem bundles move laterally in the opposite direction and come to lie on the outer side of the xylem bundles and fuse. The number of collateral bundles in the stem thus remains the same as that of the phloem bundles in the root. This type is found in *Lathyrus, Medicago, Phoenix*, etc.

Type IV. In this type, half the number of xylem bundles divide, while the other half remain undivided. The divided strands move laterally, twisting round as they do so by 180°, and join the undivided strand, which, in the meantime, has already become inverted. The phloem bundles do not divide but unite in pairs on the outer side of the three xylem strands. The collateral bundle is now made of three xylem strands and two phloem strands. The number of bundles in the stem is half that of the phloem bundles in the root. This is a rare type found only in certain monocotyledons.

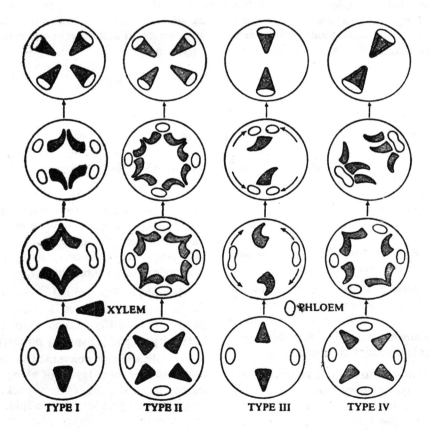

XYLEM　　PHLOEM

TYPE I　　TYPE II　　TYPE III　　TYPE IV

FIG. 66. Transitional stages from the root (bottom) to the stem (top)—four types (diagrammatic)

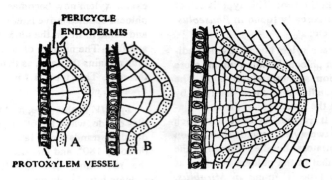

PERICYCLE
ENDODERMIS

PROTOXYLEM VESSEL

FIG. 67. Origin of a lateral root. *A, B* and *C* are stages in its formation from the pericycle

Origin of Lateral Roots (FIG. 67). Lateral roots originate from an inner layer, so they are said to be *endogenous*. The inner layer is the pericycle. The cells of the pericycle lying against the protoxylem begin to divide tangentially, and a few layers are, thus, cut off. They push the endodermis outwards and tend to grow through the cortex. At this stage,

the three regions of the root apex, viz. dermatogen (or calyptrogen), periblem and plerome, become well marked out. The endodermis and some of the cells of the cortex form a part of the root-cap, but as the root passes through the soil, this portion soon wears off and the root-cap is renewed by the calyptrogen.

CHAPTER 6

ANATOMY OF LEAVES

A. DORSIVENTRAL LEAVES (FIG. 68)

A section cut through the blade of such a leaf (see p. 47) at a right angle to one of the veins reveals the following internal strructure.

1. Upper Epidermis. A single layer of cells with a thick cuticle which checks excessive evaporation of water from the surface. It also protects the internal tissues from mechanical injury. It usually contains no chloroplasts, except in special cases.

2. Lower Epidermis. Also a single layer but with a thin cuticle. It is, however, interspersed with numerous stomata, the two guard cells of which contain some chloroplasts. None are present in the epidermal cells. A large cavity, known as the *respiratory cavity*, may be seen internal to each

stoma. The lower epidermis of the leaf is meant for the exchange of gases (oxygen and carbon dioxide) between the atmosphere and the plant body. Any excess water in the plant body also evaporates mainly through the lower epidermis.

3. Mesophyll. The ground tissue lying between the two epidermal layers is known as the mesophyll. It is differentiated into (1) **palisade parenchyma** and (2) **spongy parenchyma**.

(1) **Palisade parenchyma**: Consists of usually one to two or three layers of elongated, more or less cylindrical cells, closely packed with their long axes at right angles to the epidermis, leaving only narrow intercellular spaces here and there. They contain numerous chloroplasts, which are arranged alongside the cell-walls. The function of

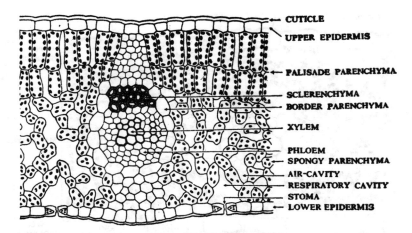

CUTICLE
UPPER EPIDERMIS
PALISADE PARENCHYMA
SCLERENCHYMA
BORDER PARENCHYMA
XYLEM
PHLOEM
SPONGY PARENCHYMA
AIR-CAVITY
RESPIRATORY CAVITY
STOMA
LOWER EPIDERMIS

FIG. 68. A dorsiventral leaf in section

palisade parenchyma, as a whole, is to manufacture sugar and starch in the presence of sunlight, i.e. during the day.

(2) **Spongy parenchyma:** Consists of oval, rounded, or more commonly irregular cells, loosely arranged towards the lower epidermis, enclosing numerous large intercellular spaces and air-cavities. They, however, fit closely around the vein or the vascular bundle. The cells contain a few chloroplasts, and manufacture sugar and starch only to some extent. The spongy cells help diffusion of gases through the empty spaces left between them.

4. Vascular Bundles. Vascular bundles (or veins) ramify through the leaf-blade to facilitate distribution of water and mineral salts among the green cells, and collection of prepared food material from these cells. As they pass from the base of the leaf-blade towards its apex or margin their size decreases the number of their elements. Each vascular bundle (vein) consists of xylem, which always lies towards the upper epidermis. The phloem always lies towards the lower epidermis. The **xylem** consists of various kinds of vessels (particularly annular and spiral), tracheids, wood fibres and wood parenchyma. Towards the apex of the vein, the xylem is represented by only a few narrow annular and spiral tracheids, or even by a single spiral tracheid. The other elements disappear. The xylem conducts and distributes water

and the raw food material to different parts of the leaf-blade. The **phloem** consists of some narrow sieve-tubes, companion cells and phloem parenchyma. A few undeveloped sieve-tubes with companion cells may be seen towards the apex. The phloem carries prepared food material from the leaf-blade to the growing and storage regions.

Surrounding each vascular bundle is a compact layer of thin-walled parenchymatous cells, containing a few to many chloroplasts or none at all. This layer is known as the **border parenchyma** or **bundle sheath.** The cells of this layer are elongated and run parallel wih the course of the vascular bundle, extending right up to the end of it. The bundle sheath may also extend radially towards the upper or the lower epidermis, or towards both, as bundle sheath extensions. The border parenchyma takes part in conduction between the vein and the mesophyll. It often photosynthesizes actively and may act as a starch sheath.

The distribution of **sclerenchyma** is rather irregular in leaves. Sometimes it forms patches at places in the mesophyll. At other times, it forms a continuous zone connecting two or more vascular bundles, or it occurs as a patch flanking a vascular bundle, or it extends from the epidermis, upper or lower, to one or more bundles. However, it frequently occurs as one or two patches lying associated with the xylem or phloem or both (FIGS. 69-71). Sometimes, the sclerenchyma occurs as a

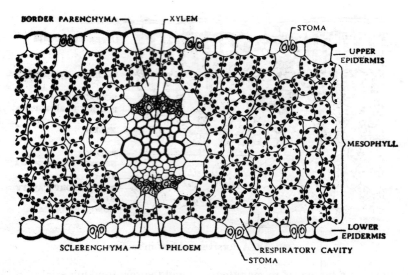

FIG. 69. An isobilateral leaf (a lily leaf) in section

complete or incomplete sheath (**sclerenchyma-tous sheath**) surrounding a vascular bundle (vein). In any case, the sclerenchyma gradually disappears towards the end of the vein.

B. ISOBILATERAL LEAVES (FIGS. 69-70)

A section cut at a right angle to one or more veins of any of such leaves (see p. 47) reveals the following internal structure.

The structure is more or less uniform from one surface to the other. The epidermis contains more or less an equal number of stomata on either side, and is also somewhat uniformly thickened and cutinized. The mesophyll is not normally differentiated into palisade and spongy parenchyma, but mostly consists of only spongy cells, in which the chloroplasts are evenly distributed. The mesophyll may consist of only palisade cells instead of spongy cells, as in many shade plants. In some cases, the mesophyll is seen to be differentiated into spongy parenchyma in the centre and palisade parenchyma on either side. The vascular bundle, border parenchyma and sclerenchymatous sheath are much the same as in a dorsiventral leaf.

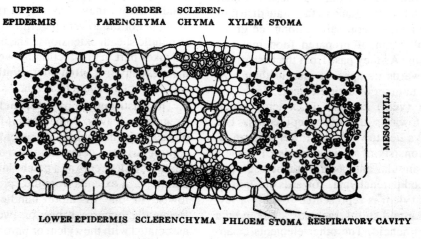

FIG. 70. An isobilateral leaf (maize leaf) in section

CHAPTER 7

SECONDARY GROWTH IN THICKNESS

I. DICOTYLEDONOUS STEM

In perennial dicotyledons (shrubs and trees), after the primary tissues are fully formed, the **cambium** becomes active and begins to cut off new (secondary) tissues in the stelar region. Sooner or later, another strip of meristem, the **cork-cambium**, makes its appearance in the peripheral region and begins to form other secondary tissues, viz. cork, etc., in that region. All these secondary tissues are added on to the primary ones, and as a result, the stem increases in thickness. *This increase in thickness, due to the addition of secondary tissues cut off by the cambium and the cork-cambium in the stelar and extra-stelar regions, respectively, is spoken of as* **secondary growth.**

A. ACTIVITY OF THE CAMBIUM

Cambium Ring. It is seen that some of the medullary ray cells, mostly in a line with the **fascicular cambium** (i.e. the cambium of the vascular bundle), become meristematic and form a strip of **interfascicular cambium** (i.e. the cambium in between two vascular bundles). This joins on to the fascicular cambium on either side and forms a complete ring known as the **cambium ring.**

Secondary Tissues. The cambium ring as a whole becomes actively meristematic and gives off new cells, both externally and internally. Those cut off on the outer side are gradually modified into the elements of phloem. These constitute the **secondary phloem**. The secondary phloem consists of sieve-tubes, companion cells and phloem parenchyma, and often some bands or patches of bast fibres too. Many of the textile fibres of commercial value, such as jute, hemp, flax, rhea (or ramie), etc., are the bast fibres of secondary phloem.

The new cells cut off by the cambium on its inner side are gradually modified into the various elements of xylem. These constitute the **secondary xylem**. The secondary xylem consists of scalariform and pitted vessels, tracheids, numerous wood fibres arranged mostly in radial rows, and some wood parenchyma. The cambium is always more active on the inner side than on the outer. Consequently, the xylem increases more rapidly in bulk than the phloem, and soon forms a compact mass. As a matter of fact, the secondary

FIG. 71. Cut surface of stem showing annual rings

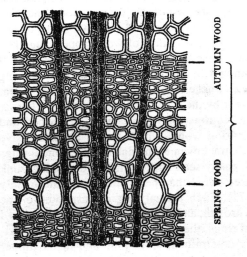

FIG. 72. An annual ring in section (magnified)

AUTUMN WOOD

SPRING WOOD

xylem forms the main bulk of the plant body after secondary growth. Because of the continued formation of secondary xylem and the pressure exerted by it, the cambium, phloem and surrounding tissues are gradually pushed outwards. For the same reason, some of the primary tissues also get crushed. The primary xylem, however, remains more or less intact in or around the centre.

At places, the cambium forms some narrow bands of parenchyma, radially elongated and passing through the secondary xylem and the secondary phloem. These are the secondary **medullary rays**. They are one, two or a few layers in thickness, and one to many layers in height.

Annual Rings (FIGS. 71-2). In regions with distinct climatic variations, the activity of the cambium is not uniform throughout the year. The need to transport sap is acute in spring or during the active vegetative seasons, considering the increase in the production and activity of foliage leaves. Hence, at this time of the year, the cambium is more active and forms a greater number of vessels with wider cavities (large, pitted vessels). In winter or during the inactive period, however, when there is less demand for transporting sap, the cambium is less active and forms elements of narrower dimensions (narrow, pitted vessels, tracheids and wood fibres). The wood thus formed during spring is called **spring wood** or early wood, and that formed in winter is called **autumn wood** or late wood. These two kinds of wood appear together, in a transverse section of the stem, as a concentric-ring known as the **annual ring** or **growth ring** (FIG. 72). Successive annual rings are formed year after year by the activity of the cambium. There is a sharp contrast between late autumn wood and early spring wood, which makes the successive rings distinct even to the naked eye. Annual rings can be easily seen with the naked eye in the trunk of a tree which has been cut down transversely (FIG. 71). Each annual ring corresponds to one year's growth, and by counting the total number of annual rings, the age of the plant can be approximately determined, as in pine and many timber trees. The number of annual rings may, however, vary in many plants. In some trees, large spring

vessels are arranged more or less in a ring. The wood is then said to be **ring-porous**. In others, the vessels have equal diameters and are uniformly distributed throughout the whole wood. The wood is then said to be **diffuse-porous**. The annual rings of successive years may vary greatly in width. Wide rings are formed under favourable conditions of growth, and narrow ones are formed when conditions are unfavourable.

Heart-Wood and Sap-wood. In old trees, the central region of the secondary wood is filled up with tannin and other substances which make it hard and durable. This region is known as the **heart-wood** or **duramen**. It looks black, owing to the presence of tannins, oils, gums, resins, etc., in it. The vessels often become plugged with *tyloses* (see FIG. 90), which are balloon-like ingrowths, developing from the adjoining parenchyma, through the pits. The function of heart-wood is no longer conduction of water, but simply to give mechanical support to the stem. The outer region of the secondary wood, which is of lighter colour, is known as the **sap-wood** or **alburnum**. This alone is used for conduction of water and salt solutions from the root to the leaf.

Reaction Wood. Reaction wood (Dadswell, 1958; Sinnot, 1952) is a kind of wood which contains rounded tracheids and fibres with intercellular spaces. It is found in dicotyledons and conifers, but the exact nature of the stimulus which causes the development of reaction wood is still unknown. In conifers, reaction wood, called compression wood, is produced on the lower sides of branches and crooked stems. The tracheids are well lignified. The middle layer of the walls of the tracheids has many radial discontinuities. The outer layer is wider than the middle layer and the inner layer is absent.

In dicotyledons, reaction wood, called tension wood, contains fibres with gelatinou layers, which are rich in cellulose and not lignified. This kind of wood has fewer vessels. Reaction wood occurs on the upper sides of the branches and crooked stems of dicotyledons.

B. ORIGIN AND ACTIVITY OF THE CORK-CAMBIUM

The formation of new tissues by the cambium exerts considerable pressure on the peripheral tissues of the stem. The epidermis becomes considerably stretched and gets ruptured in places, often breaking down altogether. The sclerenchyma and collenchyma become much flattened tangentially. The cortex is also similarly affected but it persists for a long time because of the elastic nature of the cell-walls and the power of accommodation of its cells. To replace or to reinforce the peripheral protective tissues, particularly the epidermis, a strip of secondary meristem, called the **cork-cambium** or **phellogen** (*phellos*, cork: *gen*, producing), arises in that region to give rise to new (secondary) tissues for better protection of the stem at the secondary stage. The cork-cambium commonly originates in the outer layer of the collenchyma. It may also arise in the epidermis itself, or in the deeper layers of the cortex. In the formation of the cork-cambium, the outer layer of collenchyma becomes meristematic. It divides and forms a thin strip of cork-cambium consisting of a few rows of narrow, thin-walled and roughly rectangular cells. These cells are living and active. The cork-cambium takes on meristematic activity and begins to divide and give off new cells on both sides, forming the **secondary cortex** on the inner side and the **cork** on the outer side.

Secondary Cortex. The cells that are cut off on the inner side are parenchymatous in nature. These constitute the **secondary cortex** or **phelloderm**. The cells of the secondary cortex generally contain chloroplasts and carry on photosynthesis. Sometimes, they are thick-walled, but are made up

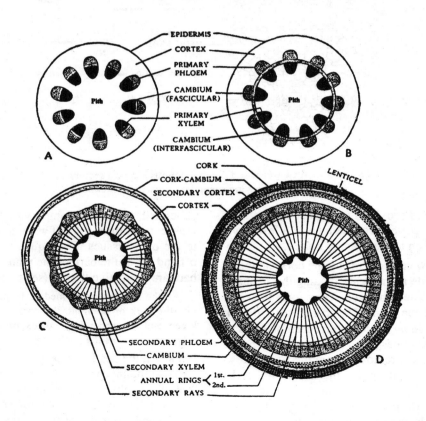

FIG. 73. Diagrams showing stages in the secondary growth of a dicotyledonous stem up to two years

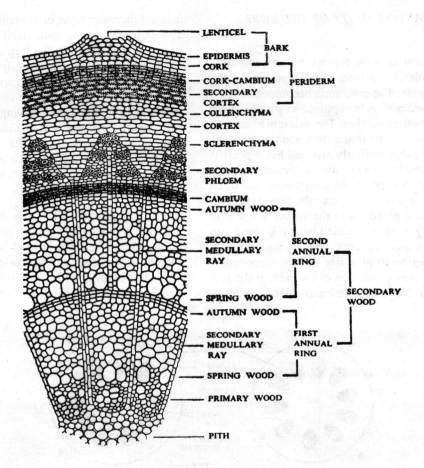

LENTICEL
EPIDERMIS   BARK
CORK
CORK-CAMBIUM   PERIDERM
SECONDARY
CORTEX
COLLENCHYMA
CORTEX
SCLERENCHYMA
SECONDARY
PHLOEM
CAMBIUM
AUTUMN WOOD
SECONDARY
MEDULLARY   SECOND
RAY   ANNUAL
                 RING
SPRING WOOD   SECONDARY
AUTUMN WOOD   WOOD
SECONDARY   FIRST
MEDULLARY   ANNUAL
RAY   RING
SPRING WOOD
PRIMARY WOOD
PITH

FIG. 74. A two-year-old dicotyledonous stem (a sector)
in transection, showing secondary growth in thickness

of cellulose and provided with pits. The cells of the secondary cortex are arranged in a few rows, and are added on to the primary cortex.

Cork. The new cells cut off by the cork-cambium on its outer side are roughly rectangular in shape and soon become suberized. They form the **cork or phellem** of the plant. The cork tissue of cork oak (*Quercus suber*), a Mediterranean plant, is of considerable thickness, and is the source of bottle cork. When this is removed from the tree, a fresh strip of cork is produced by the underlying cork-cambium. Cork cells are dead, suberized and thick-walled. They are arranged in a few radial rows, without leaving intercellular spaces between them, and are usually brownish in colour. Being

suberized, the cork is impervious to water, and thus, cuts off the supply of water and food material to the outer tissues. Consequently, they soon die off and act as the bark of the plant. Both cork and bark are protective tissues (see p. 202).

All the new tissues formed at the peripheral region, viz. the cork or phellem, the cork-cambium or phellogen and the secondary cortex or phelloderm, are together known as the **periderm**.

Bark. All the dead tissues lying outside the active cork-cambium constitute the bark of the plant. Therefore, the bark includes the epidermis, lenticels and cork, and sometimes also the hypodermis and a portion of the cortex, depending on the position of the cork-cambium. The deeper the origin of the cork-cambium, the thicker the bark.

When the cork-cambium appears in the form of a complete ring, the bark that is formed comes away in a sheet. Such bark is known as the **ring-bark**, as in *Betula* (B. BHURJJA-PATRA). When it appears in strips, the resulting bark comes away in the form of scales. Such bark is, therefore, known as **scale-bark**, as in guava. The function of the bark is protection (see p. 202).

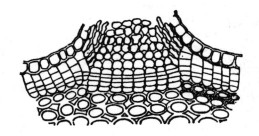

FIG. 75. A lenticel, as seen in transection

Lenticels (FIG. 74). These are aerating pores formed in the bark, through which exchange of gases takes place. Externally, they appear as scars or small protrusions on the surface of the stem. A section through one of the scars shows that the lenticel consists of a loose mass of small, thin-walled cells (**complementary cells**). At each lenticel the cork-cambium, instead of producing compact rows of cork cells, usually forms oval, spherical or irregular cells which are very loosely arranged, leaving a lot of intercellular spaces. The lenticel commonly develops below a stoma, and as its cells increase in number and size, the epidermis gets ruptured. Communication is thus established between the atmosphere and the internal tissues of the plant. The gases can then easily diffuse in and out through the lenticel. To facilitate the diffusion of gases empty spaces are left between the different rows, upper and lower, of the cork and the cork-cambium. The lenticel may be closed in winter by the formation of cork. This, however, gets ruptured as the new active season begins.

C. SECONDARY GROWTH IN VITIS STEM (FIG. 76)

Grape vine (*vitis vinifera*) is a liane type of plant, and it shows the internal structure of a typical dicotyledon. **Epidermis**—a single, outermost layer with thick cuticle. **Hypodermis**—a few layers of collenchyma. **Cortex**— several layers of parenchyma. **Pericycle**—many-layered, containing isolated strands of sclerenchyma. **Vascular bundles**—numerous but distinct and arranged in a ring. Each bundle is collateral and open with

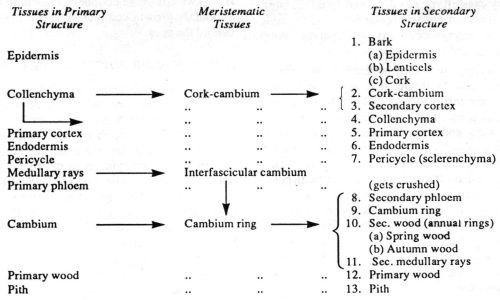

Tissues in Primary Structure	Meristematic Tissues	Tissues in Secondary Structure
Epidermis		1. Bark (a) Epidermis (b) Lenticels (c) Cork
Collenchyma	Cork-cambium	2. Cork-cambium
	.. .. ..	3. Secondary cortex
	.. .. ..	4. Collenchyma
Primary cortex	.. .. ..	5. Primary cortex
Endodermis	.. .. ..	6. Endodermis
Pericycle	.. .. ..	7. Pericycle (sclerenchyma)
Medullary rays	Interfascicular cambium	
Primary phloem	.. .. ..	(gets crushed)
		8. Secondary phloem
		9. Cambium ring
Cambium	Cambium ring	10. Sec. wood (annual rings) (a) Spring wood (b) Autumn wood
		11. Sec. medullary rays
Primary wood	.. .. ..	12. Primary wood
Pith	.. .. ..	13. Pith

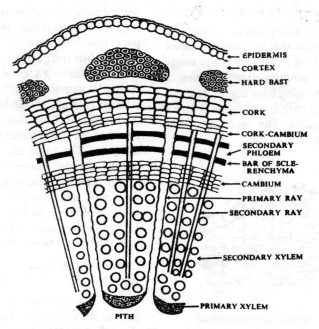

FIG. 76. Secondary growth in *Vitis vinifera* stem

Labels on figure:
← EPIDERMIS
← CORTEX
← HARD BAST
← CORK
← CORK-CAMBIUM
← SECONDARY PHLOEM
← BAR OF SCLE-RENCHYMA
← CAMBIUM
← PRIMARY RAY
← SECONDARY RAY
← SECONDARY XYLEM
← PRIMARY XYLEM
PITH

xylem, cambium and phloem from inside to out-side. The vessels are characterized by a wide diameter. Tyloses often present. The phloem has distinct sieve-tubes and associated cells, and is capped by a patch of sclerenchyma (hard bast). **Primary medullary rays**—broad (multiseriate), clearly separating the vascular bundles. Crystals occur in many cells as transparent dots. Pith—large and parenchymatous.

Secondary growth soon begins with the activity of the vascular cambium. It produces secondary xylem on the inside and secondary phloem on the outside, as usual. The xylem consists of series of wide vessels and some amount of parenchyma. Secondary medullary rays are distinct and extend up to the secondary phloem. The secondary phloem consists of bands of sieve-tubes with com-panion cells and parenchyma, altenating with tan-gential bars of sclerenchyma, a few layers thick. Soon, cork-cambium arises in the primary phloem and begins to cut off layers of cork on the outside. As a consequence, all the tissues outside the cork-cambium die out and collapse, forming the perid-erm of the stem.

II. DICOTYLEDONOUS ROOT

As in a stem, secondary growth in the thickness of a root is due to the addition of new tissues cut off by the cambium and the cork-cambium in the inte-rior as well as in the peripheral region. In the root, secondary growth commences a few centimetres behind the apex.

A. ORIGIN AND ACTIVITY OF THE CAMBIUM

The conjunctive tissue just flanking the phloem on its inner side becomes meristematic and by divid-ing, gives rise to a strip of cambium. It is evident that the number of cambium strips is the same as the number of phloem bundles. The cells of the conjunctive tissue lying between the xylem and phloem bundles also become meristematic, so that the strips of cambium are seen to extend outwards between the phloem and xylem. Then the portion of the pericycle abutting on the protoxylem becomes meristematic. It divides and forms a strip of cambium there, joining with the cambium strips formed earlier on either side of the xylem. Thus, a continuous, wavy band of cambium is formed,

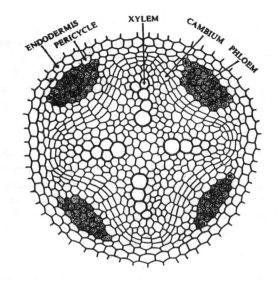

FIG. 77. Secondary growth of dicotyledonous root (early stage)

the cambium adjoining the inner phloem becomes active first. It begins to cut off new cells on both sides, but more profusely on the inside causing the cambium and the phloem to be gradually pushed outwards. The wavy band of cambium soon becomes circular or ring-like and, thus, a cambium ring is formed (FIG. 78). The whole of the cambium ring then becomes actively meristematic and behaves in the same way as in the stem, giving rise to secondary xylem on the inside and secondary phloem on the outside.

Secondary Xylem. The new cells cut off by the cambium on the inner side gradually become differentiated into the elements of xylem and all these new elements together constitute the secondary xylem. The cambium is always more active on the inner side than on the outer, and consequently, secondary wood increases more rapidly in bulk than secondary phloem. In fact, the secondary wood forms the main bulk of the plant body after secondary growth. It is made of numerous large vessels with comparatively thin walls, an abundance of wood parenchyma, but few wood fibres.

extending over the xylem and down the phloem (FIG. 77). Secondary growth then commences with the activity of this cambium band. The portion of

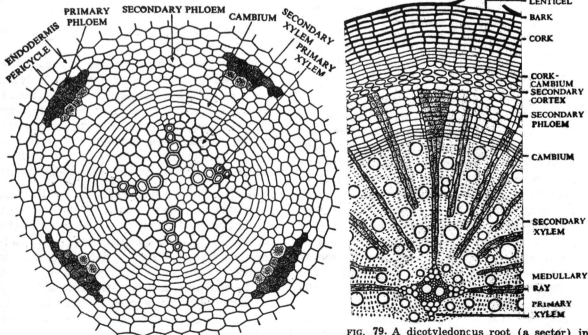

FIG. 78. Secondary growth of dicotyledonous root (later stage)

FIG. 79. A dicotyledoncus root (a sector) in transection showing secondary growth in thickness.

As more wood is added, the cambium and phloem are gradually pushed farther out. As the root lies underground, it is not subjected to variations of aerial conditions. Consequently, annual rings, which are so characteristic of woody stems, are rarely formed in the root. Even when the root has increased considerably in thickness the primary xylem bundles remain intact and can be recognized under the microscope in several cases. Against the protoxylem, the cambium forms distinct and widening radial bands of parenchyma, which constitute the **primary medullary rays**. These extend up to the secondary phloem. Other smaller and thinner medullary rays are also formed later by the cambium. Medullary rays are larger and more prominent in the root than in the stem.

Secondary Phloem. The new elements cut off by the cambium on the outer side become gradually modified into the elements of phloem. All these together constitute the secondary phloem. It consists of sieve-tubes with companion cells and abundant parenchyma, but fewer bast fibres (except in special cases). The secondary phloem is much thinner than the secondary xylem. The primary phloem soon gets crushed.

B. ORIGIN AND ACTIVITY OF THE CORK-CAMBIUM

When secondary growth has advanced to some extent, the single-layered pericycle as a whole becomes meristematic and divides into a few rows of thin-walled, roughly rectangular cells. These constitute the **cork-cambium** or **phellogen**. The cork-cambium may also arise, in some cases, in the phloem. As in the stem, it produces a few brownish layers of **cork** or **phellem** on the outside, and the **secondary cortex** or **phelloderm** on the inside. The secondary cortex of the root does not contain chloroplasts. The bark of the root is not extensive and forms only a thin covering. The cortex, being thin-walled, is very much compressed. It ultimately gets disorganized and sloughs off. The fate of the endodermis is similar. The epiblema dies out earlier. **Lenticels** may form

in places, as in the stem.

Functions of Cork and Bark. Cork and bark are the protective tissues of plants. They are meant to check evaporation of water, to guard the plant body against variations of external temperature and to protect it against attacks of parasitic fungi and insects.

(1) **Cork.** The epidermis in shrubs and trees is sooner or later reinforced or sometimes replaced by the cork, which then takes on the functions of the former, being essentially a protective tissue. The cork is always much thicker than the epidermis, and, as such, it can provide greater protection than the epidermis. The renewal of the cork by the underlying cork-cambium is a decided advantage in this respect. All the cork cells are suberized and, thus, the cork acts as a waterproof covering to the stem. Loss of water by evaporation is, therefore, prevented or greatly minimized. The cork tissue also protects the plant against attacks by parasitic fungi and insects. Cork cells, being dead and empty and containing only air, are bad conductors of heat. This being so, sudden variations in outside temperature do not affect the internal tissues of the plant. Cork is also utilized by the plant for the healing of wounds.

(2) **Bark.** Since bark is a mass of dead tissues lying in the peripheral region of the plant body as a hard, dry covering, its function is protection. It protects the inner tissues against attacks by fungi and insects, against loss of water by evaporation, and against variation, external temperature. In many plants the bark sloughs off, and all these functions are then performed by the cork part only.

Protective Tissues. It is to be noted that there are three tissues in plants, namely (1) the epidermis, (2) the cork, and (3) the bark, which develop for the specific purpose of protection. At an early stage, the epidermis alone provides the protection required by the plant (see pp. 217-18), but in shrubs and trees at a later stage the epidermis becomes reinforced or even replaced at a later stage by the cork and the bark for the same purpose.

CHAPTER 8

ANOMALOUS SECONDARY GROWTH IN THICKNESS

I. DICOTYLEDONOUS STEMS

A large number of dicotyledonous plants of varying habits, including many lianes, show anomalies in the growth of thickness, sometimes resulting in peculiar structures, particularly in respect of the xylem and phloem. Since cambium is responsible for growth in thickness, the anomalous structure may be directly correlated with the irregular behaviour of the cambium and, also, often its abnormal position. The anomalous growth varies considerably in different plants. (1) In some plants, as in *Bignonia, Bauhinia, Thunbergia, Aristolochia*, etc., the cambium is normal in position but its behaviour is irregular, giving rise to secondary xylem and secondary phloem in incompatible proportions and arrangements. (2) In other plants, as in *Amaranthus, Boerhaavia, Mirabilis, Tinospora*, etc., (and also in *Gnetum*), the fascicular cambium of the primary bundles does not function or is least active. One or more accessory cambia arise in the peripheral region outside the primary bundles and give rise to secondary xylem and secondary phloem in an irregular manner. (3) In others still, as in *Piperaceae*, e.g. *Piper betle, P. nigrum*, etc., the anomalous structure is attributable to the development of distinct medullary bundles around the pith and cortical bundles towards the periphery.

1. Anomalous Growth in *Amaranthus* Stem (FIG. 80). In the young stem, the primary (medullary) vascular bundles remain scattered in the ground tissue. They are numerous and collateral. The cambium in them is either feebly developed and functionless, or absent. The region of the pericycle just outside the outer primary bundles soon becomes meristematic and forms into a few-layered cambium. The cambium soon becomes active and begins to cut off secondary xylem and secondary phloem in the form of collateral bundles,

only towards the inside. In addition, the cambium also cuts off several layers of parenchyma (conjunctive tissue) towards the inside, which soon becomes thick-walled and lignified. All the bundles of secondary origin lie embedded in this tissue. On the outer side, the cambium produces a little parenchyma, sometimes none at all. The endodermis soon gets distorted. As the secondary bundles increase in number, they, together with the conjunctive tissue, form a compact secondary structure. The compact structure so formed by the

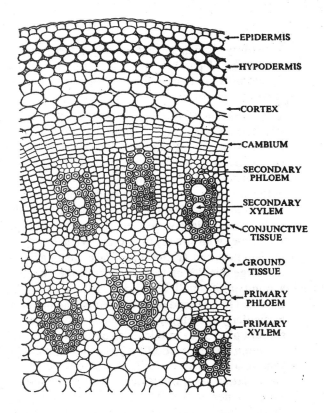

FIG. 80. Anomalous growth in *Amaranthus* stem

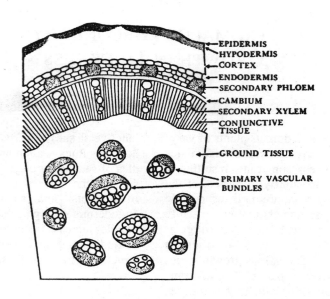

FIG. 81. Anomalous growth in *Boerhaavia* stem

secondary tissues is occasionally interrupted by thin strips of parenchyma. The formation of the periderm is either minimal or altogether absent in *Amaranthus*.

2. Anomalous Growth in *Boerhaavia* Stem (FIG. 81). The primary structure consists of (*a*) the epidermis with a thick cuticle and some stomata the (*b*) hypodermis (collenchyma) below the epidermis, interrupted by the underlying cortex, usually below a stoma, (*c*) the cortex (chlorenchyma) in several layers with abundant chloroplasts, (*d*) the endodermis, clearly defined, (*e*) the pericycle, sometimes with strands of sclerenchyma, (*f*) vascular bundles, and (*g*) the pith. Vascular bundles – two large bundles on the two sides of the pith, and a number of small bundles (6-14) just outside, arranged in a second or middle ring. The bundles, particularly the bigger ones, show only a limited amount of growth in thickness by their fascicular cambium. Soon secondary growth begins. The cambium arises secondarily from the pericycle or from certain layers outside the primary bundles, and becomes active. It cuts off a peripheral ring (third or outer ring) of several collateral bundles (secondary), each consisting of xylem on the inner

side and phloem on the outer, with the fascicular cambium lying in between. Soon, the interfascicular cambium becomes active and begins to produce rows of cells internally. These soon become thick-walled and lignified and are called the conjunctive tissue. The former also produces some amount of parenchyma externally. A little later, cork and lenticel develop outside the hypodermis.

3. Anomalous Growth in *Mirabilis* Stem (FIG. 82). In the primary structure a large number of primary (medullary) vascular bundles of varying sizes, each collateral with cambium either feebly developed or absent, occur scattered in and around the pith. Secondary cambium soon arises from the pericycle or from layers outside the primary bundles. It becomes active and begins to produce secondary bundles – xylem on the inner side and a little phloem on the outer. Depending, however, on the irregular activity of the cambium, small strands of secondary phloem may be formed centripetally at places evidently lying embedded in the secondary xylem. This embedded phloem is called **interxylary phloem** or **included phloem**. Besides, the cambium also forms rows of cells on the inside, which soon become thick-walled and

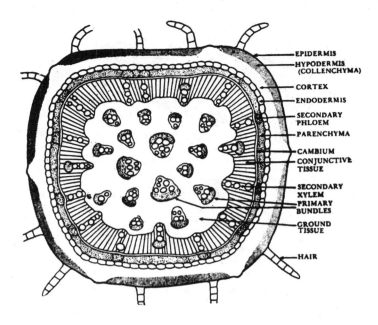

FIG. 82. Anomalous growth in *Mirabilis* stem

lignified, (the conjunctive tissue). It appears as a distinct band connecting the groups of secondary xylem.

4. Anomalous Growth in *Piper* Stem (FIG. 83). The anomalous structure is due to the presence of distinct medullary (pith) bundles and cortical

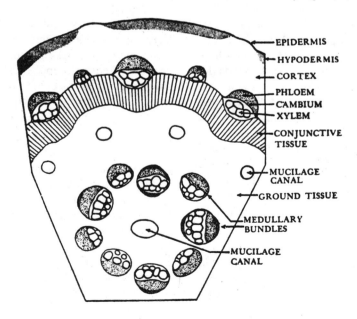

FIG. 83. Anomalous growth in *Piper* stem

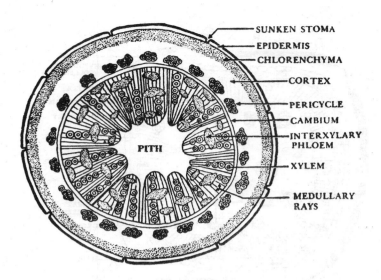

FIG. 84. Anomalous growth in *Salvadora* stem

(peripheral) bundles. The former occur around the pith in a somewhat irregular ring (as in *Piper betle*) or a regular ring (as in *Piper nigrum*). These bundles are collateral and contain little or no cambium. The xylem or phloem, or both, may have a thin strip of sclerenchyma on the outer or inner margin, or on both. There are some distinct mucilage canals (up to 12) in the ground tissue, and a large one in the pith, as well. Cortical bundles of different sizes occur in large numbers (many of them are leaf-trace bundles) towards the periphery in a somewhat irregular ring. Each bundle is collateral, consist of xylem and phloem, and has little or no cambium. The phloem may have a thin cap of sclerenchyma on the outer margin. The cortical bundles are bounded internally by a broad wavy band of thick-walled and lignified cells, called the conjunctive tissue. Towards the periphery occurs the cortex (made of parenchyma) hypodermis and (made of collenchyma) interrupted by the underlying parenchyma, and the epidermis (on the outside).

5. Anomalous Growth in *Salvadora* Stem (FIG. 84).

Vascular bundles occur in a circle, separated by broad medullary rays, which become lignified in the region of the xylem. The vessels are of different sizes and occur in irregular clusters, mixed with parenchyma and tracheids. The most interesting feature is the presence of strands of phloem, called **interxylary** or **included phloem**, arising centripetally in the xylem due to the irregular activity of the cambium. These strands, however, get disorganized as the stem begins to mature. Externally, the pericycle is multiseriate and includes several strands of fibrous cells, particularly opposite the bundles. The cortex forms a narrow zone of parenchyma and contains numerous crystals. The chlorenchyma contains abundant chloroplasts and the epidermis has a thick cuticle. Soon, cork arises in the periphery. Centrally, there is a broad parenchymatous pith.

6. Anomalous Growth in *Leptadenia* Stem (FIG. 85).

Leptadenia, a much branched, often leafless, shrub of *Asclepiadaceae*, shows anomalous secondary growth. The primary structure consists of (a) the **epidermis** with a thick cuticle, (b) the **hypodermis** (collenchyma) in 1 or 2 layers below the epidermis (c) **cortex** (chlorenchyma) in a few layers of thin-walled cells, containing chloroplasts, (d), **endodermis** in a single conspicuous layer of somewhat barrel-shaped cells, representing the innermost layer of the cortex (e) the **pericycle**, composed of a few layers of thin-walled parenchyma with patches of sclerenchyma in it, (f) the

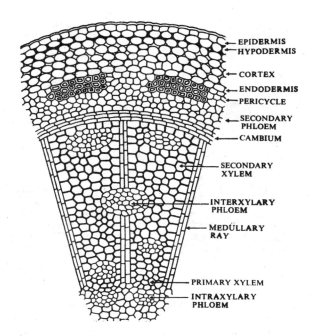

EPIDERMIS
HYPODERMIS

CORTEX
ENDODERMIS
PERICYCLE
SECONDARY
PHLOEM
CAMBIUM

SECONDARY
XYLEM

INTERXYLARY
PHLOEM

MEDULLARY
RAY

PRIMARY XYLEM
INTRAXYLARY
PHLOEM

FIG. 85. Anomalous growth in *Leptadenia* stem

primary vascular bundles in a ring, bicollateral in nature, and (g) **pith** in the centre. Secondary growth begins with the formation of a complete ring of cambium and its activity, cutting off a profuse amount of secondary xylem towards the inside and a thin band of secondary phloem towards the outside. The cambium, however, is irregular in behaviour, giving rise to an anomalous secondary structure. It so happens that at places, certain cells of the cambium ring, instead of forming secondary xylem elements, begin to produce elements of secondary phloem on the inner side contrary to their normal behaviour. Soon, however, these cambial cells revert to normal activity, their producing secondary xylem inwards. The result is the appearance of a number of secondary phloem islands in the compact mass of secondary xylem. Each such phloem patch lying embedded in the secondary xylem is called **interxylary** or **included phloem** (see p. 211). The primary phloem soon gets crushed, while the primary xylem is pushed inwards. The inner primary phloem of the bicollateral bundle remains associated with the primary xylem on the inner side, and is known as the **intraxylary or internal phloem** (see p.). The secondary xylem consists of rows of vessels and tracheids and some amount of parenchyma, with narrow but distinct medullary rays; while the secondary phloem consists of sieve-tubes with companion cells and phloem parenchyma (but no phloem fibres). There is a small pith in the centre, consisting of parenchymatous cells.

7. Anomalous Growth in Bignonia **Stems** (FIGS. 86-7). Several species of *Bignonia* are liane types of plants, and they show different kinds of anomalous secondary growth. Two types are described below. In the young stem, the orimary structure is normal and similar to other typical dicotyledons. In most cases, the stem has a wavy outline. **Epidermis** – single-layed with a thick cuticle. **Hypodermis** – 2 or 3 layers of collenchyma. **Cortex** (chlorenchyma) – a few layers of parenchyma with chloroplasts, often with isolated strands of sclerenchyma. **Pericycle**— contain patches of sclerenchyma. **Primary vascular bundles**—arranged in a ring around the central pith.

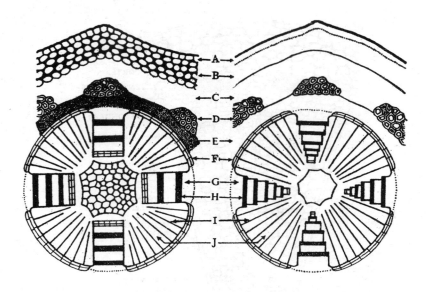

FIGS. 86-7. Anomalous Growth in *Bignoia* Stems. FIG. 86. Bignonia venusta.
FIG. 87.*B. unguis-cati*. *A*, epidermis; *B*, hypodermis (collenchyma); *C*, cortex; *D*, hard bast;
E, **secondary phloem**; *F*, cambium (outer strip); *G*, wedge of secondary pholem; *H*, sclerenchyma bar;
I, cambium (inner strip); *J*, secondary xylem; *K*, medullary ray; and *L*, pith

They, however, get obliterated with the progress of secondary growth. The cambium is also normal in position but its behaviour is abnormal, soon giving rise to anomalous secondary structure, mainly furrowed xylem and wedge-shaped phloem. With the activity of the cambium, the secondary growth of the stem starts at an early stage. Initially, the secondary growth is normal for a while, forming secondary xylem towards the inside and secondary phloem towards the outside. Soon, however, the cambium begins to show abnormal behaviour, producing uneven secondary xylem and secondary phloem. Secondary xylem increases rapidly, and consists of wide vessels and distinct medullary rays. As secondary growth proceeds, it is seen in several species that four longitudinal furrows appear in a crosswise manner in the secondary xylem and extend to a considerable depth. Soon, secondary phloem is wedged into the furrows of xylem. In some species, as in *Bignonia venusta* (FIG. 86), the wedges of phloem may be of uniform width throughout their whole length, with a strip of cambium (inner) on the inside of each furrow; while in some other species, as in Bignonia

unguis-cati (FIG. 87), the wedges may widen from inside to outside in a step-like manner. In the same way, additional wedges of smaller depths may be formed later. Each wedge is strengthened by bars of sclerenchyma. It will thus be noted that the cambium ring splits into four strips – four bigger ones in their normal position outside the secondary xylem, and four smaller strips, each at the base of a furrow. Each strip of cambium in the furrow produces a wedge of secondary phloem, while each outer strip of cambium produces a thin ring of secondary phloem.

II. DICOTYLEDONOUS ROOT

Anomalous Growth in Beet Root (*Beta vulgaris*, FIG. 88). Morphologically the beet root consists of three parts: root, hypocotyl and swollen portion of the stem. A section through the upper part of the root reveals the following anomalous structure. The main feature of the root is a succession of growth rings or vascular bundles formed by separate cambia arising from the proliferation (i.e. repeated multiplication) of the pericycle. The

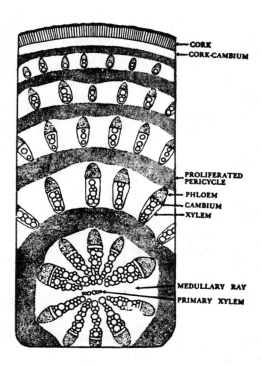

FIG. 88. Anomalous growth in beet root (*Beta vulgaris*)

cambia, apparently appearing as circular bands, form separate vascular bundles and the intervening parenchyma (*conjunctive parenchyma*) in between the bundles. The first cambium forms the first growth ring of campact vascular bundles around the diarch primary xylem lying the centre. Against each protoxylem, there is also a wide band of medullary ray. A second cambium (arising similarly by proliferation of the pericycle) forms almost immediately a second ring of separate vascular bundles in the same way. Successive cambial layers appear and function likewise. In the meantime, the pericycle also proliferates and produces, each time, a wide band of parenchyma, which acts as a storage tissue together with a major part of the phloem parenchyma. It is thus seen that rings of vascular bundles alternate with the bands of storage parenchyma (proliferated pericycle). Several such growth rings are formed one after the other in quick succession. It will be noted that all the cambia are normal in behaviour producing xylem and phloem in the usual way, and

are simultaneously active. But the outer cambia are progressively less active than the inner cambia. Consequently, smaller bundles and thinner rings appear in the outward direction. Each bundle consists of abundant parenchyma, a few lignified xylem elements and a patch of phloem (with plenty of phloem parenchyma in it) on the outer side. The simultaneous proliferation of the cambia, pericycle and parenchyma of the bundle leads to a rapid increase in the root's diameter. Soon, cork-cambium and cork appear in the periphery. A broken mass of cells forms the external dark covering. It may be noted that spinach (*Spinacia oleracea*) and carrot (*Daucus carota*) also show an almost similar type of anomalous growth.

III. MONOCOTYLEDONOUS STEM

Secondary growth in monocotyledons is rather rare. It is commonly seen in woody monocotyledons such as *Dracaena, Yucca, Aloe, Agave*, etc. An exceptionally large amount of secondary growth in thickness is seen in most species of *Dracaena*. One plant of *Dracaena draco* in the Canary Isles measured 14 metres in girth at the base and was 6,000 years old when it was destroyed by a storm in 1868. It may be noted that the stout stems of palms are not the result of secondary growth, but of protracted primary growth by a primary thickening meristem occurring beneath the apical meristem. Although they are often very stout, no cambium is formed in them and, therefore, there is no secondary growth in such plants.

Secondary Growth in *Dracaena* Stem (FIG. 89). The primary structure is a typically monocotyledonous one with many closed and collateral or concentric (amphivasal type; see p. 176) vascular bundles lying scattered in the ground tissue. Secondary growth begins with the formation of a secondary meristematic tissue—the cambium—in the parenchyma outside the primary bundles. This parenchyma divides tangentially and forms a band of cambium, a few layers in thickness. The cambium thus formed is more active on the inner side. It begins to cut off new cells towards the inside,

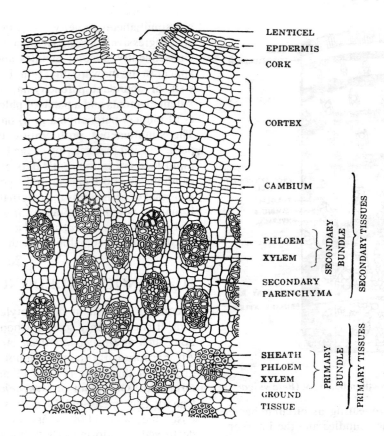

FIG. 89. Secondary growth in monocotyledonous stem (*Dracaena*)

which soon become differentiated into distinct vascular bundles (secondary) and thick-walled, often lignified parenchyma (secondary). On the outer side, the cambium produces only some amount of thin-walled parenchyma which may contain some crystals. While the primary bundles remain scattered, the secondary ones are somewhat radially scriated as is the surrounding secondary parenchyma. The vascular bundles are oval in transection, and concentric with phloem in the centre surrounded by xylem (amphivasal). In some species of *Dracaena*, the vascular bundles are, however, collateral. The phloem consists of short sieve-tubes, companion cells and phloem parenchyma, while the xylem consists of long tracheids with a small amount of thick-walled (lignified) wood parenchyma. After the secondary growth has proceeded to some extent, the peripheral parenchyma becomes meristematic and begins to divide tangentially, as do the cells derived from them until a few linear layers are formed. The cells then become suberized and differentiated into cork. Some deeper lying parenchyma begins again to divide and the new layers formed again give rise to a strip of cork in the same way. Thus, the cork in *Dracaena* appears in scriated bands without the formation of cork-cambium (phellogen) and is known as **storied cork**.

CHAPTER 9

HEALING OF WOUNDS AND FALL OF LEAVES

HEALING OF WOUNDS. In cases of simpler wounds, the wounded cells die and dry up, while the outer walls or cells of the underlying, uninjured layers become impregnated with protective substances.

In the case of larger wounds, the outermost, uninjured layer of living parenchymatous tissue forms a meristem (phellogen) which produces one or more layers of cork—the **wound cork.** The cork then protects the wounded surface.

In woody plants, the uninjured cells adjoining the wound do not directly produce the cork tissue, but give rise to a succulent mass of parenchymatous cells, called the **callus.** This callus fills up and covers the wound and, not infrequently, overgrows it. This explains the origin of knots in some trees. If the cambium is injured, the cells of the callus often form a fresh strip of cambium which becomes connected with the original cambium.

Sometimes, instead of the formation of a fresh layer, the tracheae or wood vessels develop tracheal plugs, called **tyloses** (FIG. 90), which are balloon-like ingrowths developing from the adjoining parenchyma through pits. Tyloses plug the lumen of the vessels, while other elements simply dry up. Latex, if present, coagulates. In this way, loss of water is prevented from the exposed surface.

Fall of Leaves. In deciduous trees and shrubs, leaves fall in the dry season, when the absorption of water by the roots is minimized and the evaporation of water from the surfaces of the leaves is enhanced. Both these conditions prevail in winter or in a prolonged, dry summer and, therefore, leaves are seen to fall at that time. The immediate structural cause of the falling of leaves is the formation of a layer of cork across the base of the petiole and the development of a well-defined *separation layer*, called the **abscission layer,** just external to the cork. The living, parenchymatous

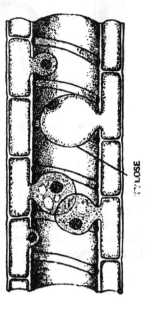

FIG. 90. Vessels with tyloses

cells lying across the bass of the petiole, and also those of the vascular bundles, become meristematic and form a layer of cork. Alternatively, these living cells become suberized directly, forming the cork layer without any division. In either case, the cork is later reinforced by a fresh strip of cork formed by the underlying cork-cambium. In some cases, the cork-cambium directly produces a few layers of cork at the base of the petiole. The cork being suberized and the vessels getting constricted owing to the lateral pressure of the cork, the

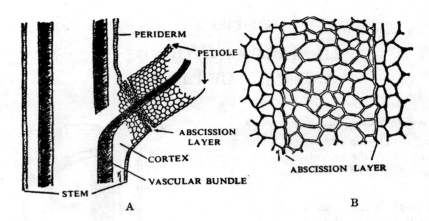

FIG. 91. *A*, formation of abscission layer at the base of the leaf; *B* a portion of the abscission layer in surface view some time before leaf-fall

supply of water to the leaf is cut off. The leaf then dries up and dies. The separation layer (or the abscission layer) lying just external to the cork turns yellowish and gets disorganized. The cellulose of this layer becomes converted into pectin, which dissolves. Thus, the cells get separated from one another. The leaf is then supported by only the vessels only, and it breaks off mechanically at the abscission layer, either under its own weight or when disturbed by the wind. The vessels are clogged with gum and tyloses, and the exposed surface is covered with cork. This prevents the exudation of sap. When the leaf falls, a scar is left on the stem. This is called the **leaf-scar**.

3 PHYSIOLOGY

GENERAL CONSIDERATIONS

A Short History. Experimental physiology actually began from the time of **Stephens Hales** (1677-1761), curate of Teddington in Middlesex. He was the first to devise experimental methods with his knowledge of physics and statistics to trace the movement of sap through the plant body, rate of transpiration current, suction due to transpiration, loss of weight due to transpiration, root pressure and capillarity as factors in the ascent of sap. Hales was the first to show that leaves make use of air to form a part of body substance. He also showed that the apical regions are the most active regions of growth. These and several other experiments were the first contributions to our knowledge of plant physiology. His *Vegetable Staticks*, published in 1727, is a famous work.

For half a century there was no further incentive for work in this new branch of study. **Priestley** (1733-1804), a chemist at Warrington (England) investigating the composition of different kinds of air, found in 1771 that green plants grown in an atmosphere rich in carbon dioxide (bad air) produced in the course of several days a large quantity of oxygen (pure air), as tested by a burning candle. His mouse and twig' experiment was very interesting in this respect. A mouse kept in a jar containing 'bad' air (by burning a candle in it, evidently releasing carbon dioxide) soon died. But a mouse kept under the same condition with a twig of mint enclosed in survived, and the twig also remained healthy. Priestley, however, could not recognize the conditions that led to the gas exchanges between the twig and the mouse. It was very unfortunate that Priestley could not pursue his work. He met with strong opposition, his house was mobbed, and he barely escaped with his life and fled to America. **Ingenhousz** (1730-99), a physician educated in Holland, who later migrated to London in 1765, was interested from the medical point of view in the composition of air. Priestley's work attracted his notice. He reported in 1779 that *green plants exposed to light* for a few hours absorb carbon dioxide (bad air)

unfit for respiration and exhale oxygen and thus, purify the air. He further proved that at night plants vitiate the air by their respiration, as do animals.

Photosynthesis. Early work on photosynthesis, by **De Saussure** (1804), **Boussingault** (1864), **Sachs** (1862 & 1864), **Timiriazeff** (1875), **Engelmann** (1881), **Pfeffer** (1881 & 1896), **Kny** (1897) and others, established the following initial stages in the process: carbon dioxide is absorbed and oxygen is liberated (De Saussure, 1804; Sachs, 1882); the two volumes are equal (Boussingault, 1864); sunlight is essential for the process; chlorophyll absorbs light, which induces chemical changes in carbon dioxide (Timiriazeff, 1872); plastids cannot photosynthesize without chlorophyll; water is also fixed in the process; starch is the first visible product (Sachs, 1862 & 1864); CO_2 is the source of all organic compounds in plants. In 1870, **Baeyer** formulated the 'formaldehyde theory' for the production of carbohydrates in photosynthesis (later discarded). **Willstatter and Stoll** modified Bayer's view in 1918 and suggested that sugar is formed in several stages (at least six). Working on *Chlorella* in 1919, **Warburg** agreed with Willstatter and Stoll but introduced 'light reaction' and 'dark reaction' (which he called Blackman reaction) in the intermediate processes of photosynthesis. Since then, much spadework has been done and only recently have the main facts regarding photosynthesis been elucidated (see text).

Nitrogen Assimilation. In 1840, **Liebig**, an agricultural chemist, put forward the idea that plants obtain their nitrogen from the air and that ammonia is the source. **Boussingault** (1802-87) carried out a long series of experiments from 1837 to 1852 (and later) and came to the conclusion that plants do not utilize free nitrogen of the air and that nitrate of the soil is the principal source. In 1838, however, he reported that certain plants like lupin, *Trifolium*, etc., grown in calcined soil to which only distilled water was added, showed a gain in weight in nitrogen, while wheat grown under the same condition showed no such gain. Boussingault's views were corroborated by **Lawes** and **Gilbert** in 1861 and later by **Hellriegel, Russell** and others. The importance of nitrogen in plant growth was determined by **Sachs** and **Knop** in 1860 and 1865 by their water culture experiments. In 1887, **Hellriegel** and **Wilfarth** first discovered the fixation of nitrogen by symbiotic bacteria in the root-nodules of leguminous plants. The formation of ammonia from plant proteins in the soil by the action of certain soil organisms (especially *Bacillus mycoides* and also several fungi) was made known by the work of **Marchal** in 1893 and later, by others. **Winogradsky's** (1856-1934) elucidation of nitrification in 1890-91 was most valuable. He established the fact that one type of oval bacteria, which he named *Nitrosomonas*, is responsible for the oxidation of ammonia to nitrite, and a second type of rod-shaped bacteria, which he named *Nitrobacter*, for further oxidation of nitrite to nitrate. **Jensen** showed in 1898 that denitrification is due to the action of a group of putrifying bacteria called *Pseudomonas*.

The Colloidal System

Protoplasm exists in a colloidal condition (see p. 121) and various physiological processes are attributable to the colloidal nature of the cell contents. Most soils also contain materials in colloidal state. As a matter of fact, colloids play an important part in the physiology of plants and animals.

In the course of his investigations on *diffusion* in solution, Thomas Graham (1861) found that soluble substances (inorganic or organic) could be divided into two classes–crystalloids and colloids—according to the rates at which their solutions passed through a parchment membrane (dialyser). Substances like salts, sugar, urea, etc., which diffuse readily, were termed *crystalloids* because of the fact that they generally exist in crystalline form. On the other hand, substances like gelatine, albumen, gum, silicic acid, starch, etc., which diffuse at a very slow rate, were termed *colloids* (meaning glue-like). This distinction, as was later realized by Graham and others, is not rigid since many crystalline substances can be obtained in colloidal solution, e.g. sodium chloride in benzene. Further X-ray studies have shown that particles in colloidal systems are often truly crystalline

in character. Consequently, instead of the term colloid or colloidal substance, it is the practice to refer to the colloidal state or to a colloidal system.

General Properties of the Colloidal System. In a colloidal solution, the particles are either very large molecules or aggregates of a large number (even thousands) of molecules, still not visible under the microscope. If, however, the colloidal particles grow further in size, they become visible under the microscope. A colloidal solution is essentially a two-phase system: a disperse phase or discontinuous phase consisting of the discrete particles, and a dispersion medium or continuous phase consisting of the medium (solid, liquid or gaseous) in which the particles are distributed. When the dispersion medium is water, the colloidal solution is commonly called *hydrosol*. In a true solution, however, the particles are of molecular size and there is no true surface of separation between the disperse phase and the dispersion medium. Colloidal solutions consisting of large insoluble particles lying in a state of suspension in the dispersion medium are called *suspensoids*. Suspensoids do not play any significant role in plant physiology. Suspensoids are, however, common in soils. Two immiscible liquids–water and oil, for example–may form an emulsion. Particles in both the suspensoid and the emulsoid slowly separate out of the dispersion medium under the influence of gravity. Emulsions can be stabilized by adding a third substance called *emulsifier*, e.g. casein in milk stabilizes fat globules. When a colloidal solution resembles a solid or jelly-like substance, it is called a gel. Gelatine, agar agar, pectin, silicic acid, etc., easily form gels. Common fruit jelly is a familiar example of gel. When the colloidal solution looks like a liquid, it is called a sol. A gel and a sol may be reversible, and protoplasm is a reversible colloid (see p. 121). Colloidal solutions in water are termed *hydrosols*. Similarly, there may be alcosols, benzosols, etc.

Colloidal solutions with a liquid as the dispersion medium fall into two classes: *lyophobic* (liquid-hating) and *lyophilic* (liquid-loving). When water is the dispersion medium the corresponding terms used are *hydrophobic* and *hydrophilic*.

Gelatine, agar agar, gum, silicic acid, various albumens, starch, soap and many dyes, etc., which directly pass into colloidal solutions when brought in contact with water, are examples of hydrophilic colloids. They are also called reversible colloids. On the other hand, insoluble substances like metals, metal sulphides, metal hydroxides and other substances which do not readily yield colloidal solutions, when brought in contact with water, are examples of hydrophobic colloids. They are also called irreversible colloids.

The characteristic property of the disperse system is attributable to the enormous surface area of the disperse phase. A solid block reduced to colloidal particles enormously increases the exposed surface area. One of the most important results of large surface area is the adsorption of ions and other materials by the particles. This adsorption may lead to the formation of electric charges on the particles, which prevents them from collecting into larger aggregates. The surface of the colloidal particles is the seat of chemical energy and various chemical reactions take place here. The adsorption is somewhat selective, and is an important factor in plant physiology, particularly with reference to the cytoplasmic membrane (ectoplasm).

Optical Properties. The presence of colloidal particles, although not detectable under a microscope, can be demonstrated made evident by optical means. Thus, if an intense beam of light be passed through a colloidal solution, its particles scatter the light and the beam is rendered visible, indicating the presence of particles which are larger than molecules but too small to be separated by filtration. The phenomenon of the particles scattering the light, named after its discoverer, is known as the Tyndall effect. The Tyndall effect has been better demonstrated by the ultramicroscope invented by Siedentopf and Zsigmondy. Under this instrument, individual particles can be seen as flashes of scattered light. It does not, however, reveal the shape, colour, or relative size of the particles.

Brownian Movement. Careful ultramicroscopic examination of a colloidal solution reveals that the particles of the disperse phase are in constant,

rapid, zigzag motion called the Brownian movement) named after its discoverer, Sir Robert Brown). Particles within the range of microscopic visibility also show this phenomenon. Brownian movement counteracts the force of gravity acting on the colloidal particles and is, thus, responsible to a certain extent for the stability of the colloidal solution. Brown first noted this movement while examining pollen grains suspended in water. Brownian movement is caused by molecular impacts, i.e. bombardment by the molecules of the dispersion medium on the colloidal particles on any one side of them at any given moment.

Electric Properties. An important property of colloidal solutions is that their particles carry an electric charge, either positive or negative, and therefore, move towards one or the other electrode when a solution is placed in an electric field. This migration of colloidal particles under the influence of an electric field is called *cataphoresis.*

Flocculation. Flocculation of many colloidal systems, e.g. white of egg, is the change into an irreversible gel condition brought about by various means such as increased frequency of collision of particles resulting in the formation of larger particles or masses, or by the application of heat or cold, or by the addition of a dehydrating agent like alcohol. Flocculation is most commonly initiated by the introduction of electrolytes. An important property of many colloidal systems is their sensitivity to small quantities of electrolytes. The presence of a small quantity of ionizable substances causes the particles of many colloidal systems to coagulate so that a visible precipitate is readily formed. The term flocculation, or coagulation or precipitation, is used to describe such a condition. It may be noted that very small quantities of an electrolyte may cause flocculation of a large volume of the solution.

Diffusion. This is the movement of molecules or ions of a solute or a solvent, be it a liquid or a gas, from the region of its higher concentration to that of its lower concentration. Diffusion continues until an equilibrium is reached. The molecules or ions are in continuous motion, following straight paths at different speeds (according to their specific nature and the surrounding conditions). They are deflected, however, only by collision. Molecules or ions enter plant cells and move from one to the other by following the simple law of diffusion from the region of higher concentration to that of lower concentration. So far as the diffusion of soil solution into the root-hairs is concerned, the process is not considered to be of primary importance. Diffusion is, however, the basic phenomenon of osmosis and imbibition.

Imbibition. Imbibition is the phenomenon whereby certain materials, particularly in dry or semi-dry conditions, soak up water. Fibres, pieces of wood, some proteins, sponges, etc., are some such materials. The cell-wall and the protoplasm are also able to absorb water by imbibition, which plays an important role in the physiology of plant life. Imbibition can occur only when there is an affinity between the two. Thus, cotton fibres imbibe water, while rubber does not. In this process, the constituent particles of a particular substance take up water by *surface attraction* and increase in volume. For this reason, seeds soaked in water are seen to swell up. The amount of attraction of dry cell-walls and of protoplasm for water is often very great and a considerable imbibition force may be developed within the plant body. As a result of imbibitional pressure, the seed-coat of a germinating seed bursts. Germinating seeds kept in a closed vessel often burst it with tremendous pressure. Imbibition is believed to be an important force involved in the ascent of sap. It also plays an important part (together with osmosis) in the intake of soil-water by the root-hairs. In an imbibing system, it is the rule that the water always moves with some force from a saturated region to a drier region.

Osmosis. It has been observed that there are certain membranes which, when used to separate a solvent (e.g. water, which is the only important solvent in plants) and a solute (salt or sugar in water), allow the solvent on the one side to pass through them freely but at the same time, resist the solute on the other side so that only a minute quantity of the latter can pass through. On account of this property of selective transmission, such membranes are said to be semi-permeable or differentially permeable. Parchment paper, fish or animal bladder and egg-membranes are some such membranes. So far as the plant cells are concerned, the ectoplasm (and not the cell-wall) acts as the differentially permeable membrane. When weak and strong solutions are separated by such a membrane, there is a net transfer of the solvent from the weaker solution to the stronger one. *This process of selective transmission of a liquid in preference to another or a solvent in preference to the solute through a semi-permeable membrane is termed* **osmosis.** By the process of osmosis, one liquid passes on to the side of the other liquid, or the solvent passes from the side of the weaker to that of the stronger solution and goes on accumulating there. The process continues until the *hydrostatic* pressure (turgor pressure; see p. 218) due to the accumulated flow of the liquid or solvent has attained a value sufficient to stop further flow. This excess pressure, which is just sufficient to stop the flow through the membrane, is called the **osmotic pressure** of the stronger solution. It has been found that this pressure is proportional to the concentration (or density) of the solution, or, in other words, the greater the concentration (or density) of a solution the greater would be its (the solution's), osmotic pressure as first shown by Pfeffer in 1877. The magnitude of osmotic pressure varies considerably in different cells, and even in the same cell under different conditions. Usually, it is 10-20 atmospheres, seldom lower than 3.5 atmospheres. In cells containing sugar, the osmotic pressure may be as high as 40 atmospheres. In cells containing a high percentage of sodium chloride, as in halophytic plants, the osmotic pressure may be over 100 atmospheres. It may be noted that living protoplasm has the ability to adjust, within certain limits, the osmotic condition of a cell in response to changing environmental conditions. The protoplasm achieves this by changing, according to its need, the salt and sugar contents of the cell-sap. The following are two familiar examples of osmosis. Raisins immersed in water are seen to swell up as a result of endosmosis, and at the same time, a small quantity of the high percentage of sugar contained in them is

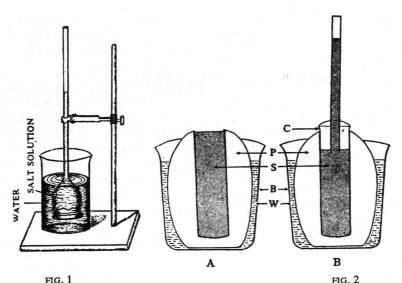

FIG. 1   FIG. 2

Experiments on Osmosis FIG. 1. Physical process of osmosis. FIG. 2. Physiological process of osmosis.
A, experiment with potato tuber; B, the same with potato osmometer. C, cork;
P, potato tuber; S, sugar solution; B, beaker; W, water

found in the water outside as a result of exosmosis. Similarly, grapes immersed in strong solution of sugar or salt (say, 25% or 30%) are seen to shrink.

Suction Pressure. Substances take up water vigorously or slowly. Evidently, there is some force which exerts pressure (suction) on the water to drive it into the absorbing material. Such a pressure is called suction pressure. It varies in degree according to the nature of the absorbing material and also on other conditions. Suction pressure is a measure of the water-absorbing power of a cell. It is specially important in the case of root-hairs (and also other contiguous cells of the plant body) where the suction pressure of the cell-sap often exceeds that of the soil water, and as a consequence, exerts a pull causing the entry of water from the soil particles. Suction pressure also brings about movement of water from cell to cell, as from the root–hairs to the cortical cells and finally to the vessels.The causes of suction pressure are to be sought in osmotic pressure and turgor pressure. The magnitude of suction pressure (also called diffusion-pressure deficit) is the difference between the osmotic pressure and the turgor pressure (Stiles, 1922): O.P.–T.P.=S.P. When the turgor pressure is equal to the osmotic pressure, no further movement of water takes place, i.e. the suction pressure becomes nil. As the turgor pressure of a cell decreases, its suction pressure increases.

Experiment 1. Physical process of osmosis (FIG. 1). Take a wide thistle-funnel with a narrow, long stem and close its mouth with parchment paper of fish-bladder. Fill it with strong salt solution till a little above its neck and introduce it, stem upwards, into a beaker containing water. Mark the level of the solution in the stem of the funnel. After a few hours, note that the level of the solution in the stem has gone up. This rise is due to the accumulation of water in the funnel as a result of more rapid flow of water into it by osmosis (endosmosis) through the membrane. This rise is seen to continue until the level has gone sufficiently high to exert a hydrostatic pressure on the membrane, which then stops further net transfer of water by osmosis. The value of the hydrostatic pressure is equal to the osmotic pressure of the solution. At the same time, a small quantity of salt also passes out through the membrane.

Experiment 2. Physiological process of osmosis (FIG. 2A) (*a*) Take a large potato tuber and shape it into a bowl in the following way. Remove its skin and slice off the bottom to make it flat. Scoop out the central flesh with a knife scalpel or borer into a deep hollow cavity with the wall comparatively thin. Place the potato-bowl in a small beaker and pour some strong salt or sugar solution into it so as to cover more or less three-fourths of the cavity. Then pour water into the beaker almost to its brim. The water may be coloured with a few drops of eosin. Within a short time, the solution in the cavity increases in volume turns reddish and overflows soon after, as a result of endosmosis. The presence of a small quantity of salt or sugar may also be detected in the water in the beaker as a result of exosmosis.

(b) The experiment may be carried out in a modified form with a potato osmometer (FIG. 2B). After skinning the sides and slicing off the *bottom* of the potato tuber, scoop out its insides to form a deep hollow cylindrical cavity, and salt or sugar solution into it. A soft cork of appropriate size with a glass tube fitted in it may then be gently but tightly pressed in. Place the potato tuber in a beaker and fill it (the beaker) with water. Within a short time, the salt or sugar solution rises in the glass tube and soon overflows. The actual rise is one to a few metres, depending on a number of factors.

Importance of Osmosis in Plant Life. (1) Root-hairs absorb water from the soil by the process of osmosis; at least the entry of water is controlled by osmosis. (2) From the root-hairs, cell-to-cell osmosis takes place until the cortical cells of the root become saturated with water. Similar cell-to-cell osmosis takes place throughout the body of the plant. It is, however, now asserted that suction pressure (and not osmotic pressure) is fundamentally responsible for the movement of water from cell to cell. (3) The osmotic pressure generated in the root-cortex is responsible for forcing the water into the xylem vessels, and possibly upwards through them at least to some height. (4) The living cells surrounding the xylem draw water from it by this process, and so do the mesophyll cells of the leaf at the upper end of the xylem, prior to transpiration. (5) Osmosis makes the cells turgid. This turgid condition gives a certain amount of rigidity to the young, soft parts of the plant body, and is also an essential condition of growth. The enlargement of meristematic cells at the root-apex and stem-apex is due initially to osmosis. (6) Various movements, particularly turgor movements, such as those exhibited by the leaflets of Indian telegraph plant (*Desmodium gyrans*; see FIG. 47), sensitive plant (*Mimosa pudica*; see FIG. 53), sensitive wood-sorrel (*Biophytum sensitivum*; see FIG. 52), sleep movements of most species of *Leguminosae*, opening and closing of stomata, bursting of many fruits and sporangia, etc., are largely due to osmotic phenomena. (7) By plasmolysis, which is an osmotic phenomenon, it is possible to determine the osmotic pressure of a cell (see experiment 3).

Turgidity. As a cell absorbs more and more water, which accumulates in the vacuole, a certain pressure is exerted on the surrounding protoplasm and the cell-wall. As a consequence, the protoplasm is forced outward against the cell-wall and the latter also gets considerably stretched. Being elastic, the stretched cellulose wall tends to return to its original shape and thus, in its turn, exerts a pressure upon the fluid contents of the cell. *A cell thus charged with water with its wall in a state of tension is said to be turgid; this condition is described as* **turgidity** *or* **turgor**. It will be noted that in a fully turgid cell two pressures are involved; outward and inward. The outward pressure exerted on the cell-wall by the fluid contents of the cell is called the **turgor pressure**, and the inward pressure exerted on the cell contents by the stretched cell-wall is called the **wall pressure**. Normally, these two pressures counterbalance each other and a state of equilibrium is maintained between them. Three factors influence the turgidity of a living cell, viz.(1) formation of osmotically active substances inside the cell, (2) an adequate supply of water, and (3) a semi-permeable membrane.

Importance. A turgid condition is necessary for the transit of nutrient solutions from cell to cell. This is so because of the difference in the concentration of the cell-sap between one cell and the other. Turgidity is also necessary for growth. In fact, it is always the initial stage of growth. Rapid growth of certain organs of a plant is principally due to turgidity, i.e. full expansion of the cells of those organs, and not to their rapid multiplication. Turgidity is also responsible for various movements of a plant's different organs. Thus, the movements of the guard cells of the stomata are due to changes in the turgidity of these cells and similarly, the rising and falling of the leaves and leaflets of sensitive plant (see FIG. 53), Indian telegraph plant (see FIG. 47), etc., are brought about by alterations in the turgidity of the cells of the pulvinus. Turgidity of the cells of the root-cortex is responsible for forcing the water into the xylem vessels. Turgidity also gives a certain amount of rigidity to the plant, particularly to the growing regions and the soft leaves which easily wilt in strong sunlight, and also to other soft parts composed of only thin-walled parenchyma without any mechanical tissue.

Plasmolysis (FIG. 3). If a section of a plant organ, a *Hydrilla* leaf, a coloured petal or a *Spirogyra* filament be immersed in a hypertonic solution[1] (say 5-10% sucrose solution) and observed under the microscope after a few minutes it will be seen that the cell as a whole contracts and more obviously, the protoplasm, together with the nucleus and the plastids, gradually shrinks away from the cell-wall and forms a rounded or irregular mass in the centre. The space between the cell-wall and the protoplasmic mass becomes filled with the sugar solution. It will be noted that while the cell-wall is freely permeable to the solution, the protoplasmic membrane is selectively or differentially permeable to it. The reason for such shrinkage of the protoplasm is that since the sugar solution has greater osmotic value than the cell-sap, the cell loses water by outward osmosis. As the water moves out of the cell, the protoplasm and the cell-wall are no longer in a state of tension. Further loss of water evidently results in the shrinkage of the protoplasm. *This shrinkage of the protoplasm from the cell-wall under the action of some strong solution–stronger than that of the cell-sap—is known as* **plasmolysis**. In one type of cells, the protoplasm commonly follows the same pattern of shrinkage on plasmolysis. If the sugar solution be replaced by pure water soon after plasmolysis, the protoplasm is seen to return to its normal position and the vacuole reappears (deplasmolysis). Potassium nitrate solution (10%) is a very good reagent for bringing about plasmolysis and is, therefore, useful for general class-work.

Plasmolysis is a vital phenomenon. It explains on the one hand the phenomenon of osmosis, and on the other, it shows the permeability of the cell-wall and semi-permeability of the outer layer of the

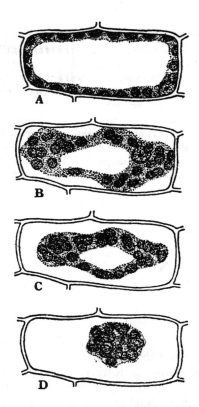

FIG. 3. Plasmolysis in a cell of *Vallisneria* leaf under the action of 10% potassium nitrate solution; A, a normal cell; B-D, stages in plasmolysis

protoplasm—the ectoplasm—to the entrance of certain substances. Plasmolysis also shows that the protoplasm can retain the osmotically active substances of the sap. This is evident from the fact that the plasmolysed protoplasm returns to its original position when the sugar solution is replaced by pure water. The phenomenon of plasmolysis also indicates whether the cells are living or dead. When a tissue is killed by boiling in water or by dipping into absolute alcohol or a strong formalin solution for a few seconds, the cells shows no plasmolysis. From plasmolysis it is also possible to determine the osmotic pressure of cells (see experiment 3).

Experiment 3. Determination of osmotic pressure of plant cells by plasmolytic method (De Vries' method,

---

[1]A solution is said to be hypertonic, isotonic or hypotonic when its osmotic pressure is greater than, equal to, or less than that of the cell being examined.

1888): Sucrose solutions are most commonly used for this purpose because the osmotic pressures of different molar concentrations[1] of sucrose have been worked out with a considerable amount of accuracy. First, a series of sucrose solutions of different molar concentrations are prepared. Then sections of plant tissues or entire material in particular cases (e.g. *Hydrilla* leaf or *Spirogyra* filament) are immersed in the graded solutions—0.1 M to 1.0 M—for 10 to 15 minutes and observed under a microscope. It will be found that in one particular solution, about 50% of the cells have just plasmolysed. This *incipient* plasmolysis indicates that the solution has the same osmotic pressure as that of the cell-sap, and is said to be *isotonic* with it. The isotonic solution having been found, it is now possible to determine the osmotic pressure of the cells. It is known that one molar solution[1] of sucrose (according to Morse, 1914) is equivalent to 26.64 atmospheres of pressure at 20°C. If the isotonic solution in the above experiment be 0.5 M at 20°C, then the osmotic pressures of the cells immersed in that solution would be equal to 13.32 atm. It must be noted that the osmotic pressure of different groups of cells or those of the same group under different conditions vary considerably. Most of the values, are, however, commonly within the range of 10-20 atm.

CHAPTER 2
SOILS

Since water and the mineral salts utilized by the plants are, almost exclusively obtained from the soil a knowledge of soil science in its different aspects is an essential prerequisite for the study of plant physiology.

Soil Formation. Soils are formed by the disintegration and decomposition of rocks due to weathering (action of rain-water, running streams, glaciers, wind, alternate high and low temperatures, atmospheric gases, etc.) and the action of soil organisms, such as several bacteria, fungi, protozoa, earthworms, etc. They are also formed through interactions of various chemical substances present in the soil. Although soils are normally formed from the underlying rocks in a particular region, they may be transported to long distances by rivers, glaciers, strong winds, etc.

Physical Nature. Physically, soil is a mixture of mineral particles of varying sizes—coarse and fine—of different degrees, some angular and others rounded, with a certain amount of decaying organic matter in it. Soil has been graded into the following types, according to the size of its particles :

Coarse particles	:	2-2 mm form coarse sand
Smaller particles	:	.2-.02 mm form sand
Finer particles	:	.02-.002 mm form silt
Very fine particles	:	less than .002 mm form clay

Types of Soils

The properties of a particular type of soil (both physical and chemical) depend largely on the size of the particles it is composed of, and are determined mainly by the proportion of clay present in it. On this basis, soils may be classified into the following types : (1) **sandy soil**, containing more or less 10% each of clay and silt with a large proportion of sand, (2) **clay soil**, containing 40% or more of clay, and (3) **loam**, containing 30-50% of silt, a small amount of clay (5-25%), the rest being

---

[1]A molar solution is prepared by dissolving one mol, i.e. one gram molecular weight of a substance in 1 litre (1,000 c.c.) of distilled water at 20°C. The molecular weight of sucrose ($C_{12}H_{22}O_{11}$) is 12 x 12 + 22 x 1 + 11 x 16 = 342. Thus 342 gms. of sucrose dissolved in 1 litre of water will give a normal molar solution or 1 M solution. This may be diluted to solutions of 0.1M, 0.2 M, 0.3 M, etc. Molar solutions are commonly used in experiments on osmosis.

sand. The physical properties of soils are: porosity (30:50% of the pore space of the soil volume required for water and air is suitable for most crops), capillary action, hygroscopicity, weight, colour, temperature, quantity of humus present (see p. 284), etc. The important physical properties of the above types of soils are as follows:

(1) **Sandy soil** is well aerated, being porous. However, as it allows easy percolation of water through large pore spaces between its particles, it dries up quickly and often remains dry. Capillarity decreases in this soil; such a soil can retain only 25-31 parts of water by weight. It is always light. (2) **Clay soil,** on the other hand, is badly aerated and it easily becomes water logged. However, it has a great capacity for retaining water (40 parts by weight), the particles being very fine. Drainage in this soil is difficult, while capillarity increases considerably. It is heavy, easily becomes compact, and cracks when dried up. Clay particles are mainly made of oxides of aluminium and are bound up with certain important minerals, such as K, Ca and Mg. A considerable amount of plant food is, however, available in this soil. (3) **Loam** is the best soil for vigorous plant growth and is most suitable for agricultural crops because all the important physical conditions—porosity for better aeration and for percolation (downward movement) of excess water, and capillarity for upward movement of sub-soil water It can retain 50 parts of water by weight. At the same time, it is rich in organic food. The proportions of the above constituents of the soil can be determined approximately by stirring a small lump of soil in a beaker to which an excess of water has been added, and then pouring the contents into a measuring cylinder. When allowed to settle, it is seen that sand particles collect at the bottom, silt higher up and clay on the top, in distinct layers. The fine portion of the clay, however, remains suspended in water. Their proportions are then determined and percentages calculated. Humus (see p. 223) mostly floats on water.

There are other kinds of soils too. Some of the common ones are: (a) *Calcareous soil, which* contains over 20% of calcium carbonate . The latter is useful in neutralizing organic acids formed from humus. It is whitish and the presence of calcium

carbonate may be detected by adding strong hydrochloric acid to a small sample of soil. Effervescence can be noticed either with the naked eye or under a pocket lens. (b) *Laterite soil,* contains a high percentage of iron and aluminium oxides. It is reddish, brownish or yellowish. *Peat soil*, which contains a high percentage (even up to 80% or 90%) of humus. It is dark, porous and light. The floating garden of Kashmir is made of peat soil and it can absorb water to the extent of several times its own weight.

Physical Properties of Soils.

The physical properties of soils depend largely on the size of the particles that they are composed of. As for size, the extremes are gravel and coarse sand at one end and clay at the other. Loam (see above) satisfies most of the physical conditions favourable for plant growth. Besides, it contains a good amount of organic matter. The physical properties are :

Porosity. Porosity is a very important factor. Irregularity in the size of the soil particles and their arrangement always leave some space, called *pore space,* between them however compact the soil may be. Porosity of the soil is essential because it makes room for water and air. It helps percolation of water, normally through bigger pores, and capillary retention of water, normally through smaller pores. Loam, which has a more or less even distribution of finer and coarser particles, is regarded as the best. In a good soil, 30-50% of the soil volume should be pore space.

Soil Water. Ordinarily, two-thirds of the pore space being occupied by water and one-third by air are found to be suitable for normal growth of most crop plants. An excess of water in the soil chokes its pore space and is, therefore, harmful to plants. Conversely, a very low percentage of water in the soil causes wilting of plants. The excess water is commonly removed by gravitational pull, drainage and evaporation. The water, which is held loosely by the small soil particles by capillary force and has mineral salts dissolved in it, is the water absorbed by the root-hairs (see pp. 234-35). So the *water-holding capacity* of the soil is of primary importance and depends mainly on the fineness of the soil particles. Ordinary agricultural soil takes up about 50 parts of water and this is good enough for normal plant growth.

Soil Air. Free space must be available for diffusion of gases—carbon dioxide and oxygen—through soils. The former escapes into the atmosphere above and the latter comes in close contact with all parts of roots, protozoa, earthworms etc., in order that they may respire and remain alive and active. Soil air is usually richer than atmospheric air in CO_2 and poorer in O_2. But in poorly aerated soil, the concentration of CO_2 may be as high as 10% and that of O_2 as low as 10%, as against 0.03% and 20%, respectively, in atmospheric air. The growth of most plants is retarded under this condition. Proper aeration of the soil is, therefore, a necessity for normal growth of plants.

Capillarity. The capillary power of soils to draw water from below depends on their texture. The maximum rise is exhibited by medium-sized grains like silt, and not by finer grained or coarser-grained soils. It has been estimated that over a period of 18 days, the capillary rise is 63 cm. in the case of sand, 84 cm. in the case of clay and 252 cm. in the case of silt (loam). The soils were air-dried in all cases. Initially, however, for a period of one hour sand shows more rapid capillary movement.

Experiment 4. Water content of the soil. To find out the water content of the soil, the following procedure may be adopted. Dig in the earth and collect from a depth of 0.3 to 1 metre a small sample of soil. Keep it in a stoppered jar. Take out a small lump from it and weight it. Heat it at 110°C. for a while, stirring the mass occasionally. All the water will be driven out by then. After cooling, take the weight of the soil again. To make sure that all the water has been driven out, heat the soil again. A constant weight will indicate the loss of all the water from the soil. The difference in weight will indicate the quantity of water originally present in the soil. Then calculate the water content on a percentage basis.

Experiment 5. Water holding capacity of the soil by capillarity. Crush a lump of air-dry soil to break up the clay aggregates, but do not grind it. Take a circular brass box ($5\frac{1}{2}$ cm. in diameter by $1\frac{1}{2}$ in height) which is perforated at the bottom. Place a filter paper at the

bottom of the box, and transfer the soil in small quantities at a time, gently pressing it after each addition until the box is nearly full. Place it in a petri dish and add water to the dish to a depth of 1 cm. After a time add water again, if necessary, to restore the above depth and maintain it. After a period of 12-24 hours, weigh the box after wiping the outside of it and deducting the weight of the filter paper. Then heat the box at 110°C. to drive off the water. Cool in a desiccator and weigh it again, deducting the weight of the filter paper. The weight of the box may be determined before or after the experiment. The weight of the soil after saturation with water minus that taken after heating will indicate the moisture content of the soil, i.e. the amount of water held by the soil particles. Then calculate the moisture content on a percentage basis.

Chemical Nature.

Chemically, soil water contains a variety of **inorganic salts** that are dissolved in it. These include nitrates, sulphates, phosphates, chlorides, carbonates, etc., of potassium (K), calcium (Ca), magnesium (Mg), sodium (Na) and iron (Fe), and of the 'trace' elements like boron (B), manganese (Mn), copper (Cu), zinc (Zn), aluminium (Al), molybdenum (Mo), etc. These salts, when analysed, are generally calculated in terms of oxides, and they often occur in the soil in very low percentages—less than 1. 'Trace' elements occur mostly within the range of .002-.0011%. Further, many of these remain in the soil in a variety of complex chemical forms and are not available to plants. In nature, however, the nutrient salts are very widely distributed. In the absence of any of the required compounds, the plant suffers. A certain quantity of **organic compounds**, chiefly proteins and their decomposition products, derived from the waste products of animals and dead bacteria and fungi, is present in the soil. **Humus** contains a certain amount of organic food (see p. 223). **Acidity and alkalinity** of the soil are also of considerable importance for normal plant growth (see below).

Acidity and Alkalinity of the soil are no less important for growth and distribution of plants than the availability of plant food in the soil and its physical condition. Soils containing a certain amount of lime (calcium carbonate) are alkaline, while soils containing a certain amount of humus, as in marshes and forests, are acid. These conditions may, however, be altered by the addition of one or the other, as the case may be. Some plants grow well in a neutral soil, but others require a more or less acid or alkaline condition. There are some species, e.g. *Acacia nilotica*, which are indifferent to this condition. Most field crops, such as maize, barley, tomato, potato, etc., prefer a slightly acid soil, while *Musa, Rhododendron, Erica, Rumex*, etc., require distinctly acid soils for normal growth. Leguminous crops, however, always prefer a slightly alkaline soil. Some plants, such as beet, lucerne, *Asparagus*, etc., grow well in neutral soil. Saline soil is required by certain plants, e.g. seablite (*Suaeda maritima* and *S. fruticosa*), *Salicornia brachiata*, saltwort (*Salsola foetida*), *Acanthus ilicifolius*, etc.

The acidity or alkalinity of the soil may be expressed in terms of pH. The soil's pH value may be determined by a simple and easy method—the chemical indicator method. This method is based on the colour reaction shown by a soil sample when treated by certain chemical indicators. The color observed varies according to the pH range of the soil sample. For plant growth and field experiments, the most useful range of the pH value of the soil is between 4 and 9. The colour reactions vary from red (pH 4) to deep blue (pH 9) through yellow and green, according to acidity or alkalinity. The neutral value is 7. Paddy grows on silty soils between pH 5.5 and 75. Potato grows on more sandy soils and can tolerate a more acid condition of pH 4.8, while *Luffa acutangula* can tolerate and even stronger acid soil of pH 4.5. Thus, the pH is of special importance from an agricultural standpoint. This gives the agriculturist an indication as to whether he should add lime to the soil or more organic acidic garbage, acidic phosphate, etc.

Soil Organisms. Various kinds of bacteria and fungi are present in the soil. The former sometimes occur to the extent of a few million individuals per gram of soil, particularly in the region of organic matter, and many are useful agents of soil fertility. Thus, nitrifying bacteria convert proteins of dead plants and animals into nitrates, and it is a fact that but for the activity of such bacteria, the proteins would have ever remained locked up in the soil as such without being used. Then there are nitrogen-fixing bacteria, ammonifying bacteria, sulphur

bacteria and a host of other types. Fungi are also abundant in the soil, particularly in acid soil, often replacing bacteria. Like bacteria, they are also useful agents in decomposing proteins. Many higher plants, particularly in forests, utilize mycorrhizal fungi (see p. 16) to absorb water and mineral salts from soil rich in humus. Many algae are also present in soil. It is now definitely known that many of the blue-green algae fix atmospheric nitrogen in soil. Among animals, soil-dwellers like many protozoa, earthworms, rats, etc., are useful agents in altering the soil. Burrowing animals loosen the soil for better aeration and percolation of water.

Humus. Humus is a dark substance present in many soils. It consists of organic (vegetable) matter, mainly cellulose and lignin combined with proteins, in various stages of decomposition in the soil. It is derived from dead roots, trunks, branches and leaves, under the action of various types of soil bacteria and fungi. Humus usually forms a surface layer, sometimes of some depth, as in forests and swamps. It is of considerable importance to plants, both chemically and physically. The nitrogenous organic compounds of humus are acted on by various bacteria and fungi and finally converted into nitrates, which are absorbed by plants. Humus, therefore, is a source of plant food. Physically, however, it is more important since it gives the soil a loose texture, ensuring better aeration. Being colloidal in nature, like clay particles, it also has a great capacity for imbibing and retaining water (to the extent of 190 parts of its own weight). Thus, added to sandy soil, it increases its water-holding capacity. Added to clay soil it loosens its compactness and increases porosity for better aeration. Soil containing 5-15% humus is suitable for agricultural crops. It is the seat of most bacterial processes in soil.

Experiment 6. Humus content of the soil. To find the humus content of a soil, proceed as follows (**ignition method**). After heating a lump of soil at 110°C. to drive off the water, cool it in a desiccator and then take its weight. Next, burn dehydrated soil in a platinum crucible at a high temperature for about an hour, occasionally stirring the mass. During ignition, fumes are seen to escape. (Organic matter becomes converted into ammonia, oxides of nitrogen or free nitrogen, sulphur dioxide and carbon dioxide and escapes as such). After complete combustion, cool it in a desiccator and then weigh it again. The loss in weight approximately represents the quantity of humus originally present in the soil sample. Then calculate the humus content of the soil on a percentage basis. The residue left after combustion is the incombustible or inorganic matter present in the soil.

Fertility of soil. A soil may be regarded as fertile when all the conditions—physical, chemical and biotic—are satisfied. The absence of any one of them acts as a limiting factor and affects the normal growth of a plant, and the crop as a whole suffers. A soil with the following composition (given in terms of volume) may be considered good: mineral particles—50-70%, pore space (containing water and air)—30-50%, and organic matter (humus)—5-15%. The following essential elements should occur in the following proportions: N—0.1-0.5%, P—0.08-0.5%, K—1.5-3.0%, Ca—0.1-2.0%, Mg 0.3-1.0%, S—0.01-0.14% and Fe—a trace. Oxygen and carbon (the latter as CO_2) are, of course, obtained from the air.

Fertilizers. Ordinarily, soil contains the salts required by plants. However, the soil is sometimes deficient in one or more of them, particularly in nitrogen, phosphorous, potassium and calcium, mainly due to the gravitational pull of the soil water, heavy drainage and intake by roots. Fertilizers or manures must be used to make up for such deficiencies. Fertilizers are certain chemical substances which, when added properly to the soil, make it fertile, i.e. enable it to produce more abundantly. Production may be doubled or even trebled through proper use of chemical fertilizers. Manuring of fields for better crop production may be done by any of the following three methods. (1) Artificial manuring is done by introducing into the soil particular compounds or their mixtures in suitable proportions, according to the existing deficiencies. Commonly, ammonium sulphate, urea superphosphate, leaf-compost, bonemeal, oil-cakes, etc., are used as chemical fertilizers. (2) Farmyard manuring is done by adding decomposed cow dung and organic refuses to the soil. (3) Green (natural) manuring is done by growing one or more types of leafy vegetables, preferably mixed with certain nodule-bearing, leguminous plants (see FIG. 5A), and finally ploughing the whole lot into the field.

Sulphate of ammonia is now extensively used as a chemical fertilizer for many field crops, like rice, barley, potato, sugarcane, tea, orange, cabbage, cauliflower, turnip, mustard, etc. This chemical becomes quickly nitrified in the soil in the course of a few days and converted to calcium nitrate. It, however, makes the soil acid and, therefore, is unsuitable for many crops. The remedy, however, lies in adding lime to the soil. Ammonium sulphate is not washed out of the soil even by torrential rain. Nitrate of soda is another source of nitrogen for various field crops.

Urea, $CO(NH_2)_2$, is a good source of nitrogen for normal, even vigorous, growth of many higher plants, as well as a large number of soil bacteria and fungi. Urea is present in small quantities in some seed plants, but is fairly abundant in some fungi. It may originate in the tissues from the amino-acid, *arginine* (formed from ornithine). In soil, urea is rapidly hydrolysed to ammonia and carbon dioxide by the action of the enzyme, *urease.* Some plants may, however, directly absorb urea in small quantities and utilize it to form some amino-acids and, finally, protein in their tissues. The radioactive C^{14} or N^{15} used in urea has been traced in certain amino-acids and proteins. Urea is, therefore, a valuable fertilizer, containing 46% nitrogen. Foliar application of urea, as shown by Webster (1955), is also effective in many cases.

The Fertilizer Corporation of India has set up a number of fertilizer units in the country to produce large quantities of chemical fertilizers, such as urea, ammonium sulphate, ammonium nitrate and phosphates in order to secure maximum agricultural production to feed the growing population. The production of fertilizers has rapidly increased. This meets most of India's domestic needs. The main operating units are (1) the Sindri unit (1951) in Bihar, (2) the Nangal unit (1961) in Punjab, (3) The Trombay unit (1965) in Maharashtra, (4) the Gorakhpur Unit (1969) in Uttar Pradesh, (5) the Namrup unit (1969) in Assam, (6) the Durgapur unit (1974) in West Bengal, the Korba unit in Madhya Pradesh, (7) the Panki unit in Uttar Pradesh, (8) the Talcher unit in Orissa, (9) the Ramagundam unit in Andhra, (10) the Barauni Unit in Bihar and (11) the Haldia unit in West Bengal.

CHAPTER 3

CHEMICAL COMPOSITION OF THE PLANT

The various elements that a plant is composed of may be determined by *chemical analyses*, and those essentially required by a plant, by *water culture experiments*.

1. CHEMICAL ANALYSES. analyzing a plant chemically, we can find out which elements it is composed of. For this purpose, a sample representative of the plant, (i.e. a sample representing all parts of the plant body), is taken and dried at 110°C. or so. All the water that the plant contains is thus driven off. Then, by careful weighing, the proportion of water to the total weight of the plant is determined. Plants, in general, are found to contain a high percentage of water—in woody parts about 50% cent, in soft parts about 75%, in succulent parts from about 85 to 95% and in water plants 95 to 98%. When a plant is charred, we get charcoal. The main bulk of this charocoal is carbon; in fact, almost half the dry weight of the plant is carbon. The dried plant is then carefully burnt over a flame at a temperature of about 600°C. The organic compounds like proteins, carbohydrates, fats and oils, etc., (which constitute often over 90% of the dry matter of plants), being combustible, are converted into carbon dioxide, water vapour, sulphur dioxide and ammonia or free nitrogen, and escape as such. These gases may be collected by proper methods and their composition studied. *Proteins*, when analysed, are seen to contain **carbon (C), hydrogen (H), oxygen (O), nitrogen (N), and often, sulphur (S) and phosphorus (P)** *Carbohydrates* and *fats and oils* contain only the first three elements. The residue left after the above treatment consists of only **inorganic compounds**, which are incombustible, and is known as **ash.** The percentage of ash varies greatly in different plants and also in different parts of the same plant, usually lying within the range of 1%-15%. Analyses of the ash show that of the 92 well-known chemical elements occurring in nature,

about 40, possibly more, are present in it. Most of these elements occur in very minute quantities and their presence is not very constant. The following, however, are constantly found in the ash of a plant, occurring of course in varying proportions in different plants: potassium (K), calcium (Ca), magnesium (Mg), iron (Fe) and sodium (Na) among the metals, and sulphur (S), phosphorus (P), chlorine (Cl) and silicon (Si) among the non-metals. In addition, certain other elements found in ash only in traces are: boron (B), manganese (Mn), zinc (Zn), copper (Cu) molybdenum (Mo), aluminium (Al), etc. These are known as 'trace' elements (see pp. 232-233).

Chemical analyses of the plant body (including the combustible material and the ash) show that, of the various elements present in it in easily detectable and measurable quantities, the following 13 elements are constant in all plants: potassium, calcium, magnesium, iron and sodium among the metals, and carbon, hydrogen, oxygen, nitrogen, sulphur, phosphorus, chlorine and silicon among the non-metals. Besides, some of the 'trace' elements which are now known to be constant in green plants are: boron, manganese, zinc, copper and molybdenum. Aluminium, though not constant, is also very commonly found in plants. The averge chemical composition of the plant body may be given thus: carbon—45.0%, oxygen—42.0%, hydrogen—6.5%, nitrogen—1.5% and ash—5.0% (after Maximov).

2. WATER CULTURE EXPERIMENTS. Water culture experiments are carried out to ascertain which elements are essentially required by plants for their normal growth, and which are absorbed only incidentally. These experiments help us to understand further the forms (chemical compounds) in which they are best taken up, the particular concentration of the solute and the source of supply (soil or air) of these elements. Water culture experiments consist of growing some seedlings in water containing some known salts in particular proportions, known as **normal culture solution**, and studying the effect produced on their (seedling's) growth and development. Normal culture solutions of various compositions are used (Sachs 1860, Knop 1865, Pfeffer 1887). The following composition has been worked out by Knop as forming the normal water culture solution, that is, the solution required by the seedling for normal growth.

Knop's normal culture solution

Potassium nitrate (KNO_3)	1 gm.
Acid potassium phosphate (KH_2PO_4)	1 gm.
Magnesium sulphate ($MgSO_4$)	1 gm.
Calcium nitrate ($Ca(NO_3)_2$)	4 gms.
Ferric chloride solution ($FeCl_3$)	a few drops
Water	1,000 c.c.

This is a stock solution of 0.7% strength. To make a 0.1% solution, which is suitable for water culture experiments, add 6,000 c.c. of water to the stock solution.

Experiment 7. Water culture experiments. A series of bottles or jars of the same size and shape are fitted with a split cork each. A number of seedlings of the same kind and more or less of the same size are taken. The bottles, marked A, B, C, D, etc., are filled with culture solutions of known composition. Through the split cork, a seedling is introduced into each bottle. The bottles are wrapped with black paper and exposed to light. Arrangements should be made for proper aeration of the roots. It is desirable that the culture solution should be renewed fortnightly. The following table shows the nature of the solutions used and the effect produced on the seedlings.

Inference. Water culture experiments prove conclusively that a plant can grow satisfactorily only when it is supplied with K, Ca, Mg, Fe and H, O, N, S, P. These experiments thus help to understand that these elements (together with C) are essential, while the others are not-essential, being only incidentally absorbed. They also show that these elements are absorbed in soluble compounds, in suitable proportions and in very dilute solutions, occurring in the soil; that free oxygen and carbon dioxide are obtained from the air (and not from the soil)—oxygen for the respiration of the living cells and carbon dioxide for the manufacture of food by the green cells; that the free nitrogen of the air is of no use to the plant and that the plant must be exposed to light. Chemical analyses give us no clue to any of the above-mentioned facts.

Sand or Charcoal Culture Experiments. To obviate many difficulties in water culture experiments, sand or charcoal culture have become a growing practice with physiologists. Charcoal is thoroughly washed and powdered. In the case of sand, it is washed, dried, then ignited to remove organic impurities. Normal culture solution is added to any of the two media and the growth of the seedling studied. The effect produced on the

	Solutions used	Observations
A	with normal culture solution	Growth of the seedling is normal.
B	the same minus potassium salts	Growth is checked, leaves lose their colour, seedling withers and carbohydrate formation is slow.
C	the same minus calcium salts	Root system does not develop properly, leaves become yellowish, spotted and deformed, and seedling becomes short, weak and is easily liable to disease.
D	the same minus magnesium	Chlorophyll is not formed, seedling becomes stunted in growth and carbohydrate formation is slow.
E	the same minus iron salts	Seedling becomes chlorotic.
F	the same minus phosphorus compounds	Growth is slow and seedling begins to weaken.
G	the same minus sulphur compounds	Leaves yellowish and stem slender.
H	the same minus nitrogen compounds	Seedling is weak and straggling, and leaves yellowish.

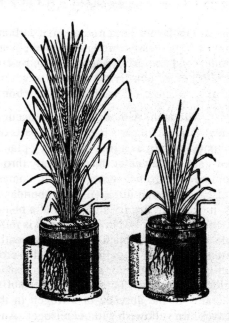

FIG. 4. Water culture experiments; *left,* in normal solution; *right,* in the same minus one of the essential elements

seedling in the absence of a particular element is studied in the same way as in water culture experiments.

Essential and Non-essential Elements. Chemical analyses of the plant reveal the presence of a long list of elements, while water culture experiments prove that *ten* elements (including carbon, which is obtained from the air) are essential for normal growth of all plants. Of the trace elements, boron, manganese, zinc, copper and molybdenum are also now regarded as essential (see pp. 232) Thus, the total number of elements now considered essential are 15 (see list below). Other elements present in the plant body are non-essential. It should, however, be noted that certain plants require one or more elements other than the established 15 essential elements. for normal growth.

Classification of Elements

Essential: metals—K, Ca, Mg and Fe.
non-metals—C, H, O, N, S and P.
Non-essential: metal—Na
non-metals—Cl and Si.
Trace (essential): metals—Mn, Zn, Cu and Mo.
non-metal—B

Role played by the Elements in the Plant Body.

(1) **Potassium** is abundantly present in the growing regions. It is essentially a constituent of the protoplasm and is closely connected with its vital activity. However, it is not present in the nucleus and plastids. Potassium is known to act as a catalytic agent in the synthesis of carbohydrates and proteins. Starch grains are not formed in its absence. It helps the plant grow and enables it to produce healthy flowers, seeds and fruits. A plant's growth suffers without potassium,—its stem becomes slender and its leaves lose their colour and gradually wither. Potassium nitrate and potassium chloride are the usual forms in which potassium is absorbed by plants. Water lettuce (*Pistia*), when burnt, yields about 12% potash, and is used as a valuable manure.

(2) **Magnesium** helps in the synthesis of phosphorus-containing lipid substances (phospholipids), which are important constituents of protoplasm. It is present in chlorophyll to the extent of about 5.6% by weight and, therefore, chlorophyll in its absence is not formed, and the plant's growth gets stunted. It is present to a considerable extent in the seeds of cereals and leguminous plants.

(3) **Calcium** is always present in green plants. It occurs in the cell-wall, particularly in the middle lamella, as calcium pectate. It is useful in neutralizing acids which would otherwise have a toxic effect on plants. It helps maintain the semi-permeability of the protoplasm. It is also anti-toxic to various poisonous substances and promotes the growth of roots as well. Plants like lemon, orange, shaddock, etc., grow well in a soil rich in calcium (lime). Fruits in general, and stone-fruits in particular, require plenty of calcium (lime) for normal development. The stone of the stone-fruit very often fails to form in the absence of lime in the soil. In general, its absence stunts growth in plants. Many plants, however, cannot stand a high amount of calcium in the soil, and they become chlorotic as a consequence.

(4) **Iron** is essential for the formation of chlorophyll although it is not present as a constituent. It may be associated with the plastids. Iron is always

present in the protoplasm and in the chromatin of the nucleus.

(5-6) **Sulphur** and **Phosphorus.** Sulphur is a constituent of an amino-acid, cystine, which is among the compounds that form plant protein. It is an important constituent of mustard oil. It is contained in the living substance, viz. the protoplasm. Leaves become chlorotic and the stem slender in its absence. Phosphorus is always present in the nucleoprotein, a constituent of the nucleus, and in lecithin, a constituent of protoplasm. It promotes nuclear and cell divisions, and is involved in carbohydrate breakdown in respiration. Phosphorus aids nutrition and hastens maturity and ripening of fruits, particularly of grains. It promotes the development of the root system. Underground organs like radish, beet and potato require phosphorus for normal development. Sulphur is absorbed as sulphates of some metals and phosphorus as phosphate of calcium or potassium.

(7) **Carbon** forms the main bulk—45% or even more—of the dry weight of the plant. It is the predominant constituent of all organic compounds which are, in fact, known as compounds of carbon. Carbon is absorbed from the atmosphere as carbon dioxide. Although carbon dioxide occurs in the air to the extent of only 0.03%, air is still the plant's only source of carbon as proved by water culture experiments. It is to be noted that there is a regular circulation of carbon dioxide and oxygen between the plant and the atmosphere, and two processes are connected with it: photosynthesis and respiration. In photosynthesis, *green* plants take in carbon dioxide from the atmosphere *during the daytime* and give off oxygen. (The oxygen that is given off in the process is, however, released from water). The atmosphere, thus, tends to become poorer in carbon dioxide and richer in oxygen. In the reverse process, i.e. in respiration, *all* plants and animals take in oxygen from the atmosphere at *all times* and give off carbon dioxide. In the combustion of coal and wood, too, carbon dioxide is given out to the atmosphere. Thus, the atmosphere tends to become richer in carbon dioxide and poorer in oxygen. It is evident, therefore, that by these two processes total volumes of these gases are kept constant in the air. The circulation of carbon by the above two processes through the green plants (and animals and non-green plants, as also by chemical combustion of non-living material, e.g. coal) and the atmosphere is referred to as the **carbon-cycle.**

(8) **Nitrogen.** Although nitrogen occurs to the extent of about 78 parts in every 100 parts of air by volume, it is not as a rule utilized by plants in its free state. It may enter the plant body through the stomata with other gases, but it comes back unused. Although nitrogen is so abundant in the air, it occurs in the dry substance of a plant to the extent of 1-3% only. Nevertheless, it is indispensable to the life of a plant, as it is an essential constituent of proteins, chlorophyll and protoplasm. Nitrogen is essential for growth, more particularly of the leaves. Leafy herbs like lettuce suffer considerably in the absence of nitrogen in the soil. Leaves turn yellowish without nitrogen. An excess of nitrogen causes vigorous growth of the vegetative parts, specially the leaves, but delays reproductive activity. Plants become easily susceptible to attacks by fungi and insects when nitrogen is in excess.

Nitrogen of the Soil. The amount of nitrogen in the soil varies from 0.096 to 0.21% (average Indian soil contains about 0.05% nitrogen). Soil is still the main source of nitrogen for the plant. It exists as both inorganic and organic compounds in the soil. The chief forms of *inorganic compounds* are the nitrates and nitrites of potassium and calcium, and also ammonia and ammonium salts, e.g. ammonium carbonate— $(NH_4)_2CO_3$. The *organic compounds* are mainly the decomposition products of proteins and also urea. A portion of the ammonia gas formed in the soil as a result of putrefaction of the above compounds may diffuse into the air, but most of it combines with other substances and forms ammonium salts, e.g. ammonium carbonate. Ammonia or ammonium salt is normally made available for the use of green plants after conversion into nitrate by the action of certain micro-organisms—the nitrifying bacteria—which live in the soil. This process of conversion is called **nitrification,** and it represents a very important phase in the nitrogen cycle (FIG. 6). In this process, as shown by Winogradsky in 1889, the ammonia or ammonium salt in the soil is oxidized into nitrate in two stages: (a) ammonia or any of its salts is first acted on by the nitrate-bacteria (*Nitrosomonas*) and oxidized into nitrite (NO_2), e.g. KNO_2 or $Ca(NO_2)_2$; (b) the nitrite thus formed is then acted on by the nitrate bacteria (*Nitrobacter*) and further oxidized into nitrate (-NO_3), e.g. KNO_3 or $Ca (NO_3)_2$. The nitrate thus produced is readily absorbed by green plants. In acid soils, however, ammonia is the chief form in which nitrogen is readily absorbed by many higher plants. Most bacteria and some fungi and algae readily assimilate ammonia. It should also be noted that a portion of the nitrates (and also nitrites) may be acted on by certain anaerobic bacteria—the denitrifying bacteria (*Bacterium denitrificans*, for example)—and reduced to free nitrogen (N_2), which then escapes into the air. The process is called **denitrification**. The denitrifying bacteria being anaerobic, their activity is less frequently evidenced in well-aerated soils, than in well-ploughed fields.

The chief forms of the organic compounds of nitrogen are amino-acids, amines and urea (see p. 224). The dead bodies of animals and plants, containing various proteins, are decomposed by several groups of putrefying (ammonifying) bacteria and certain fungi present in the soil. In the first stage, *in the absence of oxygen*, the proteins are reduced to amino-acids and then to ammonia (**ammonification**) by the putrefying bacteria in fungi. In the second stage, *in the presence of oxygen*, the ammonia undergoes nitrification, as stated before. The nitrate thus produced is readily absorbed by green plants.

Test for Nitrates. The presence of nitrates in plant tissue or soil is easily detected with diphenylamine. A 0.5% solution of it in strong sulphuric acid turns nitrates blue.

Ammonia of the Air. It has been suggested that ammonia of the air may be an important source of nitrogen for the soil. It is absorbed by some constituents of the soil, nitrified there and made available to plants in the form of nitrate. It is a known fact that acid soils always absorb ammonia from the air. Sea water releases ammonia during evaporation. This ammonia soon condenses on the surface of the soil, particularly cultivated soil. Ammonia of the air may, therefore, be regarded as one of the sources of nitrogen for the soil, particularly in the neighbourhood of the sea.

Fixation of Atmospheric Nitrogen. Under certain circumstances the gaseous nitrogen of the air may combine with other elements and is ultimately made available to the plants as compounds of nitrogen in the soil. The methods by which nitrogen may be fixed are as follows: *physico-chemical*—(1) discharge of electricity in the atmosphere (Boussingault 1837); *bio-chemical*—(2) activity of certain saprophytic bacteria (Winogradsky 1893, Beijerinck 1901); (3) activity of symbiotic bacteria (Hellreigel and Wilfarth 1887); (4) activity of blue-green algae (P. K. De 1944).

1. **Nitrogen Fixation by Electric Discharge.** To some some extent the free nitrogen of the air becomes available to green plants by the discharge of electricity, the (lightning) during a thunderstorm. Under the influence of electricity, nitrogen of the air combines with the oxygen to form nitric oxide—$N_2 + O_2 = 2NO$ (nitric oxide). This nitric oxide at once unites with oxygen of the air and forms nitrogen peroxide—$2NO + O_2 = 2NO_2$ (nitrogen peroxide). The nitrogen peroxide thus produced is then dissolved by the rain, forming nitrous acid (HNO_2) and nitric acid (HNO_3)—$2NO_2 + H_2O = HNO_2 + HNO_3$—and washed down into the soil. Here, they combine with some metal, like potassium or calcium, and form, respectively, nitrite and nitrate of potassium or calcium. Nitrate is directly absorbed by plants; while nitrite is oxidized into nitrate by nitrate-bacteria. On an average, rain-water brings down to the soil about 4 kilograms of nitrogen per year per hectare.

2. **Nitrogen Fixation by Saprophytic Bacteria of the Soil.** Various types of nitrogen-fixing bacteria present in the soil have the power of fixing the free nitrogen of the soil-air in their own bodies in the form of amino-acids and finally, building up proteins from them. After the death of these

bacteria, the proteins are released into the soil. In due course these are acted on by the nitrifying bacteria and finally transformed into nitrates, which are then made use of by the green plants. But it must be noted that the amount of free nitrogen fixed by saprophytic bacteria is much less than that fixed by symbiotic bacteria. There are two distinct groups of saprophytic bacteria—aerobic and anaerobic. Several species of *Clostridium* (anaerobic), first discovered and named by Winogradsky (1893), and *Azotobacter* (aerobic), first discovered and named by Beijerinck (1901), are typical of these two groups. These bacteria are widely distributed in soils. The efficiency of nitrogen fixation by these bacteria depends on the oxidation of carbohydrates (particularly sugars) in the soil as a source of energy. The chemistry of nitrogen fixation at different intermediate stages is not, however, definitely known. But it is certain that molecular nitrogen is reduced to ammonia (NH_3). Ammonia is toxic to plants and, therefore, occurs in a very dilute solution and is rapidly synthesized into some form of amino-acid (e.g. glutamic acid).

3. Nitrogen Fixation by Symbiotic Bacteria: Nodule Bacteria of *Leguminosae*. Agriculturists have noted for a long time that leguminous plants, such as pulses, grown in a soil make it fertile and lead to an increase in the yield of cereals. On an experimental basis, Boussingault first proved in 1851-52 that leguminous plants use the free nitrogen (N_2) of the air for normal growth. It was later discovered by Hellriegel and Wilfarth in 1887 that the roots of these plants possess some swellings, called **nodules** or **tubercles**, which are infected with some types of nitrogen-fixing bacteria, particularly the different species of *Rhizobium*. These bacteria have the power of fixing the free nitrogen of the soil air in their nodules. It is to be specially noted that neither the leguminous plants, nor the bacteria can fix nitrogen by themselves. It is now known that such bacteria are present in the nodules of most plants (but not all) of *Leguminosae*, particularly of *Papilionaceae*, and in the roots of a few other plants. The way in which these bacteria infect the roots and the mode of nodule formation is as follows. The bacteria enter through the tip of

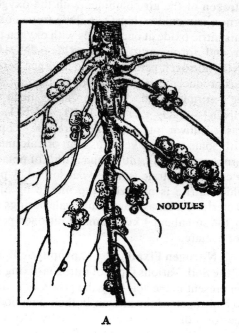

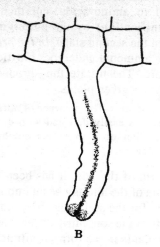

A   B

FIG. 5. *A*, nodules of a leguminous plant; *B*, a root-hair infected with bacteria. Note the bacterial thread

the root-hair. After penetrating it, they form into a sort of thread, consisting of innumerable bacteria cells held together by mucilage. This thread passes down the hair and reaches the cortex of the root, perforating the cell-walls. The bacteria then multiply and colonize the cortex. The cortical cells are stimulated to grow, perhaps due to the secretion of some stimulant by these bacteria. They thus give rise to small swellings or nodules of varying size and fix in them the nitrogen of the air in the form of some amino-compounds. The molecular nitrogen is first reduced to ammonia, which then rapidly changes to certain amino-acids (e.g. glutamic acid). A portion of the amino-compounds thus formed is absorbed into the plant body, another portion is excreted out of the nodules and the remaining portion remains locked up in the nodules. Thus, the soil becomes richer in nitrogen, more particularly so if the nodule-bearing leguminous plants are ploughed into the soil. The leguminous plants supply the bacteria with carbohydrates and the bacteria supply the former with nitrogenous food. So, this is a case of **symbiosis** (see p. 15). It is, however, to be noted that the intermediate chemical changes leading to the formation of amino-compounds in the nodules are not clearly understood.

4. Nitrogen Fixation by Blue-green Algae. It is now definitely known that certain members of Myxophyceae, particularly several species of *Nostoc* and *Anabaena*, which are common in many soils, apart from their aquatic habitat, have the power of fixing the free nitrogen of the air. A part of the nitrogenous compounds fixed in their body is excreted into the surrounding soil, while the remaining part is released to the soil after their death. In tropical agricultural soils, as in waterlogged rice-fields, these algae are particularly common and contribute to the soil's fertility.

Nitrogen Cycle (FIG. 6). Although plants are continually absorbing compounds of nitrogen from the soil, it should not be supposed that the nitrogen contents of the soil would sooner or later become exhausted. Under natural conditions, the soil soon becomes replenished of this element. This is so because of the fact that there is a regular circulation with nitrogen through the air, soil, plants and animals. Nitrogen in the soil is, therefore, inexhaustible. We have already seen how the free nitrogen of the air is brought down into the soil as ultimate products of nitrite and nitrate of some metals. Nitrates

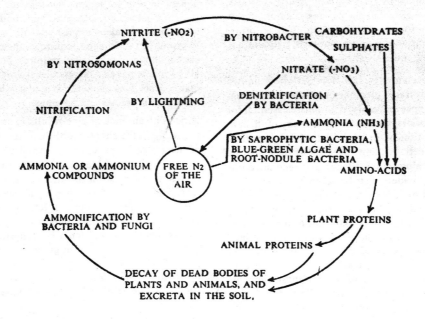

FIG. 6. Nitrogen cycle

are absorbed by plants and reduced to ammonia and then to amino-acids. Finally, proteins are made out of them. Plant proteins are taken up by animals. After the death and decay of the animals and plants, the proteins as well as the other nitrogenous organic compounds contained in their body are again converted into nitrates in several stages (ammonification and nitrification) and absorbed as such by plants again. At the same time, a portion of the nitrates and also nitrites present in the soil is disintegrated by denitrifying bacteria into free nitrogen or oxides of nitrogen which then escape into the surrounding air. This free nitrogen is again brought down into the soil from the air. It will be noted that ammonia holds a key position in protein metabolism, i.e. in the synthesis of proteins as well as in their breakdown. Ammonia is, however, toxic to plants and, therefore, it becomes quickly metabolized.

Rotation of Crops. The fixation of atmospheric nitrogen in the soil is of very great agricultural importance. Most crops absorb nitrogenous compounds from the soil and impoverish it. Leguminous plants, on the other hand, enrich it in nitrogen when their nodule-bearing roots are left in the soil. Thus, leguminous crops such as pulses, *Sesbania cannabina* (B. DHAINCHA), cow pea (*Vigna sinensis*) etc., are cultivated in rotation with non-leguminous crops such as cereals (rice, wheat, maize, barley, oats, etc.) and millets. For the same reason, certain leguminous plants—*Tephrosia* and *Derris*, for example—are grown in tea gardens as natural fertilizers (and also for shade). Root crops like turnip, radish, beet, etc., take plenty of potash, calcium and nitrogen from the soil.

Trace or Micro-elements. It is now definitely known that at least five 'trace' elements, such as boron, manganese, zinc, copper and molybdenum, are essential for normal growth of plants. The absence of any of them in the culture solution or in the soil leads to abnormal growth and to certain plant diseases. It may also be mentioned that aluminium, though not recognized as essential, is very widely distributed among plants. The normal culture solution, however, does not include any of the 'trace' elements, but the plant still grows. What is the explanation? It is likely that some of the so-called pure chemicals used by the early workers contained traces of these elements. Distilled water, commonly used in water culture experiments, might have contained traces of them. Traces of some of these elements might have dissolved out of the glass bottles and other vessels containing the chemicals and solutions. Besides, seeds themselves are likely to contain these

elements in their cotyledons or endosperm. Thus, the sources of contamination of the water culture solution being many, such elements crept into the solution undetected. In recent times, by using extra-pure chemicals, re-distilled water and special glass bottles, it has been proved beyond doubt that the five elements mentioned above are indispensable and essential for all green plants.

Boron. This is possibly required by all plants. The beneficial effect of boron has been proved in a number of cases, e.g. maize, tomato, potato, tobacco, lemon, beet, turnip, mustard, cotton, etc. Cauliflower, in particular, needs boron, while cereals have a very low requirement of it. Boron helps the formation of rootnodules in leguminous plants and improves the yield of sugar in beet. In its absence, beet suffers from 'heart rot', tobacco from 'top rot' and potato from 'leaf roll'. Fruits like apple and pear also suffer in its absence. In general, deficiency of boron results in retarded growth and spotted leaves. Its deficiency or absence particularly affects the storage organs of plants (not so much the green tissues), and also the apical meristems, i.e. the root-tip and the stem-tip, which become brittle and die off.

Manganese. Absence or deficiency of this element results in drying up of leaves, weak plant growth, poor bloom, chlorosis and certain diseased conditions of leaves. There is always an appreciable amount of manganese in orange, lemon and tomato. There is a relationship between manganese and oxidation enzymes. Manganese is also connected with the synthesis of chlorophyll. Cabbages require manganese, while, as stated above, cauliflower requires boron. Pines and allied plants haves a comparatively high percentage of manganese. This element particularly benefits leguminous plants, cereals and potatoes.

Zinc. The absence of zinc results in stunted growth of the leaf and the shoot, mottling of leaves, drying back of the growing tips and also various physiological diseases. The cells of leaves also do not utilize carbohydrates in respiration in the absence of zinc. The beneficial effect of zinc has been already proved in a number of cases, e.g. cereals, lettuce, pea, bean, lupin, beet, potato, kohl-rabi, tomato and many fruit trees. *Citrus* fruits are particularly benefited by it. Zinc occurs more abundantly in green tissues than in other parts and helps the formation of chloroplasts, as proved by Reed in 1935. Zinc also helps synthesis of auxin (indole-acetic acid) and several enzymes.

Copper. Plants deficient in copper lack in chlorophyll-formation. Barley, wheat and oat grains do not form in the absence of this element in the root medium. The beneficial effect of copper has also been already proved in flax, carrot, pea, bean, tomato, etc. Deposit of copper after spraying helps the formation of starch in the underlying tissues. Copper is a constituent of certain enzymes. Except very dilute solutions, copper salts are highly toxic.

Molybdenum. Molybdenum is known to be essential for plant growth. The first sign of the deficiency of this element is the formation of chlorotic or necrotic areas in the leaf. It has been claimed that cells need molybdenum to reduce nitrate to ammonia for protein synthesis. On this basis, it is considered to enter into the composi-tion of enzymes. There is also evidence that this element is required for nitrogen fixation by *Azotobacter* and *Rhizobium*.

Aluminium. Aluminium has been found in the ash of many plants in very small percentages, specially in wheat, maize, rye, bean, lentil, carrot, cabbage, turnip, lettuce, sunflower, etc. It is, however, found in large quantities in the ash of *Lycopodium*. Aluminium is found in almost all parts of the plant body, more so in the root and leaf. It occurs mainly in the protoplasm and nucleus. Aluminium in very low concentration stimulates growth, while in higher concentration, it is toxic. It influences the colour of the flower.

CHAPTER 4

ABSORPTION OF WATER AND MINERAL SALTS

Roots and leaves are the main absorbing organs of plants. Roots absorb water and dissolved mineral salts from the soil, and leaves take in oxygen and carbon dioxide from the atmosphere.

WATER AND INORGANIC SALTS. Green plants absorb water and inorganic salts from the soil by their unicellular root-hairs, which pass irregularly through the interestices of the soil particles and come in close contact with them. Absorption is also actively carried on by the tender growing region of the root. The maximum absorption of soil water takes place through the root-hairs and also the zone of cell enlargement, while the maximum absorption of inorganic salts takes place through the zone of cell division (see FIG. I/3). Water is absorbed in large quantities, always in excess of the plant's requirements. Small quantities of various soluble inorganic salts such as nitrates, chlorides, sulphates, phosphates, etc., dissolved in the soil water are absorbed in a state of *very dilute solution*. It must, however, be noted that the absorption of water and that of salts are independent of each other. While a large volume of water is absorbed by most plants, the intake of salts may be comparatively small. The absorption of water is not correlated to the accumulation of salts in the cells. The absorbing surfaces of the cells must be such as to allow ready passage of water and dissolved salts. In this context the membranes of an absorbing cell may be recalled to mind: the membranes are the cell-wall, plasma membrane (ectoplasm) and tonoplasm. The cellwall is easily permeable to water and is also minutely perforated, while the other two membranes, although very thin and delicate and possibly made of phospholipids, possess the property of selective permeability.

The substances absorbed from the soil may be classified into two goups: the first group consists of water (and also sugars, so far as other absorbing cells of the plant body are concerned) which undergo no or little ionization and may enter the cells by following the simple laws of diffusion and other physical processes, while the second group consists of mineral salts which undergo extensive ionization. The ionized particles of such salts are taken up by the cells, where they accumulate, sometimes in heavy concentration. The ions may travel as such, or they combine into suitable compounds.

Availability of Soil Water. A portion of the soil water moves downward in response to the force of gravity, rapidly through sandy soil and slowly through loam or clay soil, and carries down or sometimes even washes out a considerable quantity of essential food elements. This moving water percolates through the interspaces of large soil particles and is not of any use to the plant as the root-hairs cannot absorb it. Then again each soil particle holds some water on its surface as an extremely thin film by the force of imbibition (see p. 216). This water is known as *hygroscopic water*. It is held so tenaciously by the soil particle that the root-hair cannot dissociate it from the particle. Hygroscopic water also is not of any use to the plant. Surrounding each soil particle is a thin or sometimes thick film of water, loosely held to it by capillary force. This is known as *capillary water*. It also occurs in the spaces between the soil particles. Capillary water together with the various nutrient salts dissolved in it can be absorbed by the root-hairs and is, therefore, regarded as the plant's principal source of water supply. Capillary water may move from particle to particle in any direction. If the capillary water diminishes in quantity, the plant suffers and may even wilt and die. However, it must be noted that capillarity cannot raise water for more than 1 or 2 metres from the deeper water level of the soil, except near tanks, lakes and rivers. Capillarity still remains useful in the case of deep-rooted plants.

Soil and Root. The repeated branching of the root, its ramifications in all directions and penetration downward, coupled with the production of root-hairs in enormous numbers, help the plant absorb a huge quantity of water, etc., from the soil. It has been estimated that the total length of the root system of a plant may extend up to several kilometres and in some cases, a few hundred kilometres. Many millions of root-hairs, each coming in intimate contact with many soil particles, may be formed by a single plant, enormously increasing the absorbing area of the root. The plant has, thus, developed an elaborate system for the intake of water and mineral salts from the soil. It is the root-hairs and the tender-growing regions of the root that are utilized by plants for the purpose of absorption. The older parts of the roots, being impervious to water, are of no use in this respect. Root-hairs vary in length from a few millimetres to a few centimetres and are composed of cellulose and pectic compounds. Soil particles strongly adhere to the root-hairs because of the presence of pectic compounds in their walls.

Absorption of Water. Water adheres to the soil particles with some force (see above), particularly so when there is scarcity of water in the soil. Clay and humus retain water very tenaciously. There must, then, be some stronger force for the dissociation of this water from the soil particles and its uptake into the root-hairs. The forces concerned

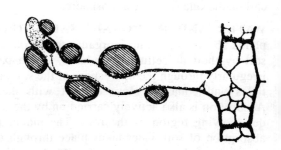

FIG. 7. A root-hair with soil particles adhering to it. Each particle is surrounded by a film of capillary water

Gases. Of the various gases present in the air, only the oxygen and carbon dioxide diffuse into the plant body and are finally utilized by the plant. Other gases may similarly diffuse into the plant body, but they are returned unused. Oxygen is utilized by all the living cells of a plant for respiration at all times, but carbon dioxide is utilized by only the green cells for the manufacture of carbohydrates, only during the daytime.

Composition of the Air. Of 100 parts of air by volume, nitrogen occupies 78%, oxygen 21%, carbon dioxide 0.03%, and other gases such as hydrogen, ammonia, ozone, aqueous vapour, etc., occur in traces only.

are diffusion (see pp. 215-16), imbibition (see p. 216), suction pressure (see p. 217) and osmosis (see p. 216). Of these, suction pressure and osmosis are particularly important. **Parts played by root-hairs** (FIG. 7). In the case of root-hairs, which contain some sugars and salts in solution, the cell-sap is stronger than the surrounding soil water. The two fluids (cell-sap and water) are separated by the cell-membrane (cellulose cell-wall + plasma membrane). As a consequence osmosis occurs. A flow of water takes place from the soil into the root-hairs through the intervening cell-membrane (endosmosis). Osmosis, however, is not a purely physical process in this case. Although the cell-wall is permeable to both the water and the solutes, the plasma membrane is but differentially and selectively permeable, allowing the water to flow in while stopping the sugars and salts of the cell-sap from flowing out. This selective permeability is characteristic of the plasma membrane. However, the permeability of the same membrane varies under different conditions.

ABSORPTION OF MINERAL SALTS (Ionic Theory or Electrolytic Dissociation Theory).

Several workers carrying out experiments on the physiological process of absorption of salts over a prolonged period (1917-44) have shown that inorganic salts are absorbed in the form of ions[1], although certain compounds, as experimentally proved by Osterhout and others, may as such enter the plant cell through the plasma membrane by the physical process of diffusion from the region of higher concentration of the soil solution to that of lower concentration of the cell-sap. However, it has been seen in many cases that the concentration of the cell-sap is higher than that of the soil solution. This being so, the process of absorption cannot be explained on the basis of simple diffusion (Stiles, 1924). As a matter of fact, many mineral salts which may undergo extensive ionization do not follow simple laws of diffusion. in 1936 Hoagland definitely proved that it is the ions (and not the undissociated molecules of salts in the soil solution) that make their entrance into the cell, independent of the rate of absorption of water, from the region of lower concentration (soil solution) to that of higher concentration (cell-sap). The physico-chemical nature of the plant cell is very complex, changing continually in response to its environment, and at the same time, the soil itself is a heterogeneous medium. So the forces concerned must be of varied nature. As already proved by many workers on the basis of experiments conducted by them, absorption of salts takes place in the form of ions (+ and −) produced by electrolytic dissociation (or ionization) of the molecules of different salts. Further, the component ions of the salts are taken up individually and independently of one another. The special feature of living cells is that they can accumulate individual ions (and not salts) to a concentration that far exceeds that of the surrounding medium. Several workers (notably Hoagland, 1944) have actually proved this by experimental work on *Nitella* and other plants.

Passive and Active Absorption. In modern research, passive absorption of salts and active absorption are distinguished from each other according to their dependence on non-metabolic energy and metabolic energy, respectively. One speaks of passive or non-metabolic absorption when the forces driving the salts through the membrane originate in the environment of the cell, i.e. these forces are physical and non-metabolic. One speaks of active metabolic absorption when it is dependent on metabolic energy which originates in the cell as a result of metabolic activity (particularly respiration) within it. Active uptake, as explained below, is known to be the principal

---

[1] Ions are atoms or groups of atoms which carry either a positive or negative charge of electricity. When an ionizable material in water is subjected to electrolysis, its molecules break up into two or more ions of different kinds—those charged with positive electricity are said to be electropositive ions, such as K^+, Na^+, Ca^{++}, Mg^{++} and also H^+, and those charged with negative electricity are said to be electro-negative ions, such as Cl^-, Br^-, No_3^-, $H_2PO_4^-$, OH^-, and SO_4^-. The process is reversible as the following examples will show: $NaCl \rightleftharpoons Na^+ + Cl^-$; $HCL \rightleftharpoons H^+ + Cl^-$. The breaking up of molecules may not always be complete.

method of salt absorption although some salts are absorbed, sometimes rapidly for a time, by the passive method. The interaction between the cell and its environment is essential to maintain a certain concentration within the cell in order to sustain life. By passive transport, an exchange of ions takes place between the external solution (soil colloids readily yield ions on electrolysis) and the cell. It is known that the cell membrane, possibly in all cases, maintains differences in electric potential between the inner side and the outer side, evidently acting as a driving force. This influences passive uptake of ions through the membrane into the peripheral or outer plasm (see below). The ions in this phase may move freely and even out of the cell. It may be noted that ions move by diffusion through the cellwall and the cytoplasm in their water phase, and that the plasma membrane has the ability to select and permit the entrance of certain ions and greatly restrict others. However, by passive uptake, soon an equilibrium is reached between the outer plasm and the external medium. Ions may move upwards through the transpiration current along with the mass flow of water. This being so, transpiration may help in the absorption of ions. By active transport, which is slow but steady, ions are brought into the inner or central plasm, i.e. from the region of lower concentration to that of higher concentration. There is supposed to be a dividing line or membrane in the cytoplasm, though not clearly demarcated, between the outer plasm and the inner plasm. This membrane is regarded as impermeable to the exchange of free ions between the two sides. This leads to the conception of a 'specific carrier' which can pick up ions from the outer plasm and release them to the inner plasm through the so-called membrane. Since this 'carrier' moves only in one direction (from the outer to the inner), ions once released into the inner plasm cannot reach out of the cell and, thus, cannot be exchanged for those in the external solution. Evidently, the ions may accumulate there for any length of time. The 'carrier' concept has received support from many investigators. It has been suggested that *lecithin*, a phospholipid, may act as such a 'carrier'. Active transport is closely connected with metabolic energy in the form of ATP (an energy-rich phosphate compound) formed in the living cell. The chemical energy required for active transport of ions is believed to be supplied by ATP. ATP, in its turn, receives this energy from glucose as a result of oxidation of the latter in root respiration. It is known that young roots respire vigorously. Synthesis of lecithin also depends on the availability of ATP. Thus, the absence of ATP in a cell interferes with active transport. Specific enzymes may also help the passage of certain ions through the cell membrane. The concentration of ions in the cells is not even in all cases, the maximum accumulation being K^+ ions and also some other cations (see footnote, p. 235). Ions of both the electric charges must be taken up by the cell in order to maintain an electric balance both on its inside and outside. For example, a negative ion released by the ectoplasm establishes a difference of potential between the two media. Thus, to equalize the charge, the soil solution yields a positive ion to the ectoplasm. In fact, an interchange of ions takes place between the cell and the surrounding solution.

Conditions. Absorption of salts depends on a number of conditions, viz. aerobic root respiration, amount of light, rate of transpiration, permeability of the plasma membrane, metabolic activity of the cell, influence of temperature, hydrogen-ion concentration, etc.

Experiment 8. Absorption of water. (*a*) An interesting experiment may be carried out in the following way. Dip the end of a white-flowered lupin branch into a coloured solution (preferably water coloured with eosin) and watch. Within a very short time, it will be seen that the white flowers turn pinkish—the colour of eosin—as a result of absorption of coloured water by the roots or by the cut end of the branch. *Peperomia* plant may also be similarly used, and streaks of red will be noticed through the stem.

(*b*) To demonstrate the **rate of absorption**, proceed in the following way. Arrange the experiment, as shown in FIG. 15, and mark the level of water in the graduated tube. Note the gradual fall of the water level every few hours. At the end, calculate the rate of absorption per unit of time. The experiment may be repeated under different conditions of light and temperature and the rates of absorption compared.

Drought resistance. The ability of a plant to withstand drought is called drought resistance. Drought, a condition of the soil or atmosphere or both, does not allow the plant to get sufficient water to carry out various functions. The main causes of drought are (a) non-availability of water in the soil (b) inability of the plant to absorb water from the soil. The second condition is known as physiological drought. It occurs in plants which grow in marshes and bogs and frequently have difficulty in obtaining sufficient water.

Plants which possess certain morphological and physiological characteristics, such as small leaf surface, exceptional development of the root system, short growing season, and certain other xeromorphic characteristics, have the ability to resist drought. To assist such plants in withstanding drought, the soil must be kept free of weeds and the plants must be well-spaced.

CHAPTER 5

CONDUCTION OF WATER AND MINERAL SALTS

ROOT PRESSURE

The water that is absorbed from the soil by the root-hairs, whether by osmosis or imbibition, gradually accumulates in the tissue of the cortex. As a result of this, the cortex cells become fully *turgid*. Under this condition, their walls, which are composed of cellulose, exert pressure on the fluid contents and force out a quantity of them towards the xylem vessels, and the cortical cells become *flaccid*. They absorb water again and become turgid, and this process of alternate expansion and contraction continues. Thus, an intermittent pumping action goes on in the cortex of the root. This pumping action naturally gives rise to a considerable pressure. As a result of this pressure, the water is forced into the xylem vessels through the passage cells and the unthickened areas and pits that the endodermis and the vessels are provided with. Besides, the lignified walls of the vessels are also permeable to water. **Root pressure** *is thus explained as the pressure exerted by the cortical cells of the root upon their liquid contents under a fully turgid condition, forcing a quantity of them into the xylem vessels and through them upwards into the stem.*

Experiment 9. Root pressure (FIG. 9). Cut across the stem of a healthy plant (preferably a pot plant) a few cm. above the ground in the morning, and fix to it, by means of a rubber tubbing, a T-tube. Pour some water into the tube and freely water the soil. Fill a **manometer** (i.e. the U-tube with a long arm and a bulb) partially with mercury, as shown in the figure. Connect the manometer to the T-tube through a rubber cork. Insert a cork fitted with a narrow glass tube to the upper end of the T-tube. Make all the connetions air-tight by applying melted paraffin-wax. Seal the bore of the narrow tube and note the level of mercury in the long arm of the manometer. *Observation.* After a few hours, note the rise of the mercury-level in the long arm. Also note the rise of the water level in the T-tube. *Inference.* The rise of mercury is certainly due to accumulation of water in the T-tube and the pressure exerted by it. This phenomenon is evidently due to exudation of water from the cut surface of the stem. This experiment shows that the water is *forced up* through the stem by root pressure.

Experiment 10. Quantity of exudate in root pressure. Arrange the apparatus as shown in FIG.10. The T-tube, fitted with a bent side-tube and a stopcock at the upper end, is fixed to the cut end of a stem through a rubber tube and tied or otherwise properly bandaged. The tubes are filled with water. Water the soil freely and keep the apparatus in a shady place.

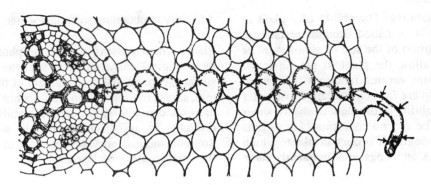

FIG. 8. A root in transection, showing the course of water from the root-hairs to the xylem

Leave it undisturbed till the next day or the day after. Note the quantity of water that has accumulated in the measuring cylinder, say, within 24 or 48 hours, as a result of root pressure.

Root pressure is continually forcing up the water through the xylem (or wood), but it is difficult to determine the process when active transpiration is in progress. The water accumulates in the vessels only when transpiration is in abeyance. Sometimes, it so happens that certain plants when cut, pruned, tapped or otherwise wounded, show a flow of sap from the cut ends or surfaces, quite often with considerable force. This phenomenon is commonly known as *bleeding*, and is often seen in many land plants in spring, particularly grape vine, some palms, sugar maple, etc. Although the flow of sap is ordinarily slow, a considerable quantity of it exudes within a period of 24 hours in certain plants. Thus a sap flow of 10-15 litres per day may occur in some palms when tapped. The sap in such plants contains sugar in addition to organic and inorganic salts.

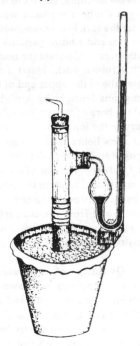

FIG. 9. Experiment on root pressure (qualitative)

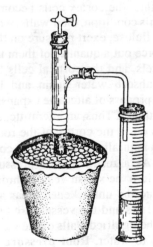

FIG. 10. Quantity of exudate in root pressure

Conditions Affecting Root Pressure.

(1) **Temperature**. The temperature of the air and soil affects root pressure. The warmer the air and

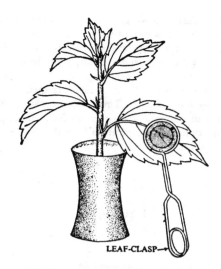

LEAF-CLASP→

FIG. 11. Unequal transpiration from the two surfaces of a leaf

he soil, the greater the activity of the root. (2) **Oxygen**. The roots must receive an adequate supply of oxygen from the soil for respiration. Otherwise, their activity diminishes and may soon come to a standstill. (3) **Moisture in the soil**. The soil must contain a certain amount of moisture. Within certain limits, the more the better. (4) **Salt in the soil**. Preponderance of salts, making the soil saline, greatly interferes with the absorption of water.

TRANSPIRATION

Plants absorb a large quantity of water from the soil by their root-hairs. Only a very small part (1–2%) of this water is retained in the plant body for the building-up processes, while the greater part (98–99%) of it is lost in the form of water vapour. **Transpiration** *is the giving off of water vapour from the internal tissues of living plants through the aerial parts, such as the leaves, green shoot, etc., under the influence of sunlight.* It is not a simple process of evaporation since it is influenced by the vital activity of the protoplasm and some structural peculiarities of the transpiring organs (see pp. 242-3). A detached leaf is seen to lose water much more rapidly than a leaf still attached to the plant, and this loss has been found to be 5 or 6 times greater. The total quantity of water that evaporates from a single plant is considerable. It has been estimated that the loss of water from a single sunflower plant during a period of 144 days is 27,000 c.c. This means there is a daily average loss of 187.5 c.c.

Mechanism of Transpiration. Water evaporates at all temperatures, and since the paranchymatous cells are charged with water, it continues to evaporate from these cells and collect in the intercellular spaces so long as these are not saturated with water vapour. From there, the water vapour escapes into the atmosphere, either through the stomata or through the thin cuticle. The former is called stomatal transpiration and the latter, cuticular transpiration. Stomatal transpiration is the rule, amounting to 80–90%, and is many times (approximately about ten times) in excess of cuticular transpiration under ordinary conditions of light, temperature and humidity. At night, the stomata remain closed and transpiration is checked. Since water vapour is given off in transpiration, the process markedly affects the humidity of the surrounding air. For this reason, the air under big leafy trees is moist and cool. In dorsiventral leaves, the lower surface always has a much larger number of stomata, while often none or sometimes comparatively few are present in the upper. Consequently, the lower surface transpires water more vigorously than the upper. In isobilateral leaves, however, the stomata are more or less evenly distributed on both the surfaces. The guard cells no doubt regulate transpiration to a considerable extent by partially or fully opening the stomata, or by closing it altogether, according to circumstances. But it cannot be said that transpiration always takes place at the maximum rate through fully-open stomata. As a matter of fact half-open stomata are as efficient as fully-open ones in some plants. Recent investigations have shown that the degree of stomatal opening cannot always be directly correlated with the rate of transpiration. Even when the stomata are fully open, transpiration is greatly influenced by the water vapour in the respiratory cavities and the intercellular spaces. In woody plants and in many fruits transpiration takes place through the lenticels (see FIG. II/74). These organs help transpiration as they always remain open, and the water vapour escapes through the loose mass of cells (i.e., the complementary cells) of each lenticel (**lenticular transpiration**).

Experiment 11. Transpiration: bell-jar experiment. Transpiration can be easily demonstrated in the following way. A pot plant with its soil-surface covered properly with a sheet of oil-paper is enclosed in a bell-jar and maintained at room temperature for some time. It is then seen that the inner wall of the bell-jar becomes bedewed with moisture.

Experiment 12. Unequal transpiration from the two surfaces of a dorsiventral leaf (FIG. 11). Soak small pieces of filter paper or thin blotting paper in 5% solution of cobalt chloride (or cobalt nitrate) and dry them over a flame. The property of cobalt papers is that they are deep blue when dried, but in contact with moisture they turn pink. Place two dried cobalt papers, one on the upper and the other on the lower surface of a thick, healthy leaf, and cover them completely with glass slides (or with a **leaf-clasp**, as shown in figure), and clamp them properly to the leaf. Then quickly seal the sides with vaseline. It will be seen that the cobalt paper on the lower surface of the leaf turns pink sooner than the one on the upper surface. This change in coloration takes place within a few minutes. This evidently shows that the leaf transpires water more vigorously from the lower surface than from the upper. This is due to the occurrence of a large number of stomata on the lower surface, none or few being present on the upper.

Experiment 13. Quantitative estimation of unequal transpiration from the two surfaces of a dorsiventral leaf. (a) Fit up the apparatus (Garreau's potometer), as shown in FIG. 12. The two small test-tubes containing dehydrated calcium chloride are weighed before introducing them into the small bell-jars. The leaf is placed in between the two jars and the sides smeared with vaseline. The other connections are also made air-tight. The two bent tubes at the two ends are partially filled with oil. The experiment is carried-out in bright light. After exposure for a few hours, the test-tubes are re-weighed. The difference between the initial and final weights in each case will indicate the quantity of water absorbed by calcium chloride, evidently lost by transpiration from a unit area of the leaf within a specified time. It will be noted that the loss of water from the lower surface is much greater than that from the upper surface.

(b) Two long-stalked leaves of *Begonia* or garden nasturtium are taken and weighed separately. The upper surface of one leaf is coated with vaseline, while the lower surface of the other is similarly coated. The two leaves are then exposed to sunlight for an hour or so. They are then separately re-weighed. The difference in weight will indicate in each case the quantity of water lost by transpiration. Thus, a comparative idea may be had of cuticular transpiration from the upper surface and stomatal transpiration from the lower surface of the leaves.

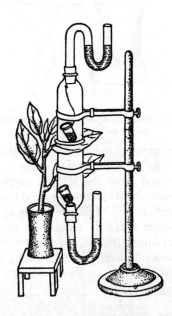

FIG. 12. Quantitative estimation of unequal transpiration with Garreau's potometer

Experiment 14. Rate of transpiration under varying external conditions. Cut three healthy leafy twigs and immediately put each in a light-weight bottle or conical flask half-filled with water. Pour a few drops of olive oil to prevent evaporation of water. Take the weight of each and expose one to direct sunlight, another to subdued light and keep the third one in a dark room, each for a specified period (say, two hours). Then weigh each again. The one exposed to sunlight will show the maximum rate, the second one much less and the third, very little or no transpiration.

Experiment 15. Transpiration in relation to stomatal aperture. Proceed as in Experiment 14 and then take a leaf from each. Peel off or slice off the epidermis and put it immediately into absolute alcohol to fix the

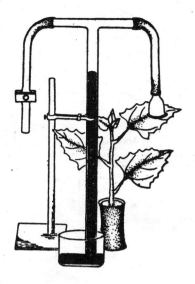

FIG. 13. Darwin's porometer (see Experiment 16)

stomatal aperture. Then, after washing and mounting in the usual way, take micrometric measurements of at least ten stomata in each case, and find the average width. Correlate the width with the rate of transpiration.

Experiment 16. To find out the degree of stomatal opening with Darwin's porometer (FIG. 13). The porometer is an ingenious and interesting device which gives a comparative idea of the degree of stomatal opening under different external conditions. The small jar of the apparatus at the end of the rubber tube is glued to the leaf-surface (a thick, smooth, isobilateral leaf of *Crinum* or *Amaryllis* will serve the purpose well), and the long arm of the T-tube dipped into mercury. With a suction pump fixed to the distal end of the other rubber tube, the mercury is lifted to a desired height in the long arm of the T-tube, and the rubber-tube is clipped. The experiment may be carried out in the morning, noon and evening (and also on a bright, sunny day or a cloudy day). The rate of fall of the mercury-column within a specified time in each case indicates the degree of stomatal opening. Evidently when the stomata are fully open, the mercury-column falls quickly. When only partially open, the rate is slower and when closed, the column remains almost stationary.

Experiment 17. Measurement of the rate of transpiration current (FIG. 14). This experiment is best carried out with the help of **Ganong's potometer**, as depicted in the figure. The apparatus is filled with water and a branch cut under water is inserted into the upper, wide end of the apparatus through a cork. The connections are made air-tight by applying paraffin-wax. The distal end of the apparatus is dipped into water contained in a beaker. The water of the beaker may be coloured with eosin. As transpiration proceeds, the coloured water is seen to enter the tube. Then remove the end of the tube from the beaker for a while and allow air to enter it. Dip it into water again. An air bubble is seen to form at the distal end of the tube. It rises and slowly travels through the horizontal arm of the potometer as a result of suction due to transpiration. Note the time that the bubble takes to cover the journey from one end of the graduation to the other. The volume of the graduated tube being known (or separately worked out), the rate of transpiration current is easily determined. By opening the stopcock, which is connected with the water reservoir on the top, the bubble may be pushed back and the experiment re-started.

Experiment 18. Relation between transpiration and absorption (FIG. 15). A wide-mouthed bottle with a graduated side-tube and a split india-rubber cork are required for this experiment. A small rooted plant is introduced through the split cork into the bottle, which is filled with water. The level of water is noted in the side-tube, and 1 or 2 drops of oil poured into it to prevent evaporation of water from the exposed surface. The conections are, of course, made air-tight. The whole apparatus is weighed on a compression (or pan) balance (FIG. 16) and the weight noted. It is seen after a time that the water-level in the side-tube has fallen, indicating the volume of water that has already been absorbed by the plant. The apparatus is then re-weighed. The difference in weight evidently shows the amount of water that has transpired from the leaf surfaces. If the experiment be continued for a period of 24 hours, it will be seen that the volume of water (in c.c.) absorbed is almost equal to the amount of water (in grams) lost by transpiration (1 c.c. of water = 1 gm.). In this way, the relation between transpiration and absorption can be worked out for the various hours of the day and under diverse external conditions. It will be noted that the experiment also shows separately the 'rate of absorption' and the 'rate of transpiration'.

Experiment 19. Suction due to transpiration (FIG. 17). Take a Darwin's potometer (i.e. the tube with a side arm, as shown in the figure) and fix to its lower end a long narrow glass tube. Fill the tubes completely with water and insert a leafy shoot, with the cut end kept under water, into one of the arms of the potometer through a rubber cork. Close the other end with a cork.

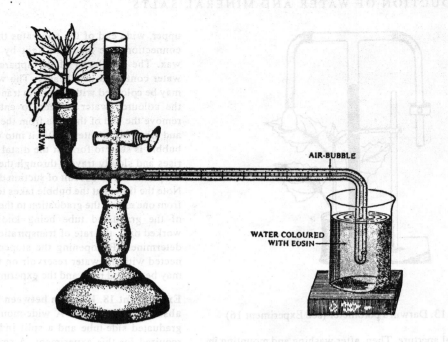

WATER

AIR-BUBBLE

WATER COLOURED
WITH EOSIN

FIG. 14. Ganong's potometer to demonstrate the rate of transpiration current

Make all the connections air-tight by applying melted paraffin-wax. Dip the lower end of the tube into mercury in a beaker. As transpiration proceeds water is absorbed and within a few hours the mercury is seen to rise to some height in the tube. The rise of mercury indicates the suction exerted by transpiration. The physiological processes connected with this phenomenon are : (a) osmosis in the mesophyll cells by which water is withdrawn from the tracheids in the veinlets (b) evaporation of water from the mesophyll cells through the leaf-surface, bringing about concentration of their cell-sap, and (c) transpiration pull exerted on the column of water in the long tube, resulting in its absorption into the resultant branch and the rise of mercury.

Transpiration Ratio. The term transpiration ratio (sometimes called *transpiration coefficient*) is widely used to express the ratio between the total amount of water that transpires from the plant body during the growing season and the total amount of dry matter that accumulates in it during this period. Since the difference between the amount of water transpiring from a plant and that absorbed by it is not great, the term *water require-*

ment is also often used to express the ratio between the total amount of water absorbed by the plant and the total amount of dry matter formed in it at the end of the growing season. Thus, the transpiration ratio or the water requirement represents the number of grams (or kilograms) of water that transpires (or is absorbed) to produce one gram (or kilogram) of dry matter. The ratio varies from plant to plant and also in the same plant under different conditions. The ratio has already been worked out for a number of crop plants and weeds. The values obtained for some of the common field crops are: 368 for maize, 513 for wheat, 636 for potato, 646 for cotton, 683 for sunflower, 831 for lucerne (or alfalfa), etc., meaning that to produce one gram of dry matter, the above quantity of water (in gm. or c.c.) has transpired (or has been absorbed) in each case.

Importance of Transpiration. Transpiration is of vital importance to plant in many ways. (1) In the first place, we find that roots are continually absorbing water from the soil and this water is several times in excess of the immediate requirement

FIG. 15

FIG. 15
Relation
between
transpiration
and absorption

FIG. 16.
Compression
(or pan) balance

FIG. 16

of the plant. The excess is got rid of by transpiration. (2) The rate of absorption of water is greatly influenced by the rate of transpiration. The greater the transpiration, the greater the rate of absorption of water from the soil. (3) Absorption of water helps the intake of raw food materials (inorganic salts) from the soil. It is, however, not a fact that the greater the transpiration the greater is the rate of absorption of inorganic salts from the soil. As a matter of fact, the intake of salts is independent of the quantity of water absorbed. (4) Transpiration secures concentration of the cell-sap and thereby helps osmosis. (5) As a result of transpiration from the leaf-surface, a suction force (see Experiment 19) is generated and this helps the ascent of water to the top of lofty trees. (6) Transpiration also helps the distribution of water throughout the plant body. (7) As a result of transpiration, plants become cool as a considerable amount of latent heat is lost in converting water from liquid to gaseous state. (8) Lastly, transpiration has some ecological significance in some plants. Hygroscopic salts are left on the surface of the leaf as the water evaporates. These salts absorb moisture from the atmosphere and do not allow the leaf or the plant as a whole to dry up. In the face of all these advantages the fact remains that excessive transpiration is a real danger to plant life. Many plants are often seen to dry up and die when excessive transpiration takes place for a prolonged period without adequate supply of water to the root medium.

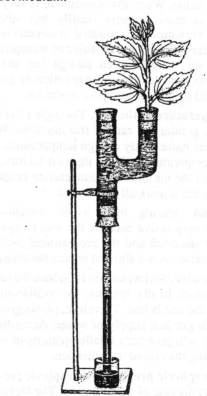

FIG. 17. Suction due to transpiration with Darwin's potometer

FACTORS WHICH AFFECT TRANSPIRATION

(1) **Light.** Light is the most important factor. Transpiration normally takes place in light and, therefore, during the daytime. This is due to the fact that in the presence of light the stomata remain fully open and evaporation of water takes place normally through them. At night, the stomata remain closed and consequently, transpiration (except for a little cuticular transpiration) is markedly checked. Variations in the intensity of light, as on a bright day and a cloudy day, bring about different degrees of stomatal opening and so have a marked effect on transpiration. During the daytime, the heat-rays of the sun fall directly on the leaves and to a great extent enhance the rate of transpiration.

(2) **Humidity of the Air.** The rate of transpiration increases or decreases according to whether the air is dry or moist. When the atmosphere is very dry, it receives moisture very readily, but when it becomes very moist or saturated, it can receive no more water vapour. Loss of water by transpiration is then very slight. Even though the stomata remain open at daytime, transpiration is greatly influenced by the water vapour in the air.

(3) **Temperature of the Air.** The higher the temperature, greater the rate of transpiration. Water evaporates more freely at high temperatures than at low temperatures. When the two factors, viz. dryness of the air and high temperature combine, transpiration is markedly enhanced.

(4) **Wind.** During high winds transpiration becomes very active because the water vapour is instantly removed and the area around the transpiring surface is not allowed to become saturated.

(5) **Soil water.** Soil water can influence the rate of transpiration. In dry regions, the availability of water in the soil is less. Therefore, plants growing there will get less supply of water. Accordingly, the plants will give out a smaller quantity of water, minimizing the rate of transpiration.

(6) **Atmospheric pressure.** Atmospheric pressure can affect the rate of transpiration. The higher the altitude, the lower the atmospheric pressure and the lower the atmospheric pressure, the greater the rate of transpiration. Therefore, plants growing in hills or at higher altitudes show different rates of transpiration from plants growing in plains.

Beside these external factors, some internal conditions can also affect the rate of transpiration. These are:

   (i) Width of the stomatal door.
   (ii) Water retaining capacity of the cells.
   (iii) Permeability of the cell wall.

Adaptations to Reduce Excessive Transpiration.

Anatomical. A thick cuticle and sometimes a multiple epidermis develop to check excessive evaporation of water. The loss of water from an apple with the cuticle removed is far greater than that from an apple with the cuticle intact. The presence of cutinized hairs, scales, rods, etc., minimize transpiration to a greater extent. A dense coating of hairs, or of wax or 'bloom', on the surface is very efficient in this respect. Latex also checks transpiration. The stomata may be closed temporarily even in the daytime when excessive transpiration is taking place from the leaf surface. In desert plants, the stomata are fewer in number and they remain sunken in pits (see FIGS. II/45-6). Cork is formed after a time in shrubs and trees to act as a waterproof covering. Being suberized, it is impervious to water and, therefore, loss of water by transpiration is prevented. A peeled potato transpires more quickly than an unpeeled one. Later still in the life of these plants, bark is formed as hard, dry covering to carry on similar functions.

Morphological. The leaf-area is often very much reduced. In extreme cases, the leaves are modified into spines. The size of the plant is also often reduced. The leaves may be rolled up or variously folded, exposing the minimum surface area for transpiration. They may also assume a drooping or vertical position to avoid strong sunlight. It is further seen that deciduous trees shed their leaves in winter as protection against excessive transpiration, while the leaves of evergreen trees have their leaves well covered with cuticle.

Exudation of Water

Many herbaceous plants get rid of the excess of water by a process commonly called *exudation* of *guttation.* Thus, in balsam, rose, water lettuce, grape vine, many aroids (e.g. taro), garden nasturtium, sunflower, *Chrysanthemum, Canna,* many grasses, etc., it is seen that drops of water accumulate at the apex or margin of the leaf early in the morning. The water has escaped through the water stomata (or water pores) and hydathodes that have developed in that region (see p.166). That the water is not dew-drops is evident from the fact that the drops are regularly arranged at the ends of veins, and that chemical analysis shows the presence of organic and inorganic salts. Exudation normally takes place during a warm and damp night. Some plants exude a considerable quantity of water every night. The cause of exudation is to be sought in the wall pressure (see p.218) that develops in the fully turgid parenchymatous cells that lie in the adjoining parts. Conditions necessary for the process are : abundant supply of water, suitable temperature, activity of the living cells of the root, and also other conditions which check transpiration. Practically no exudation takes place at very low temperatures.

Experiment 20. Escape of water in liquid form from the leaf : guttation. Fix the branch of a plant (e.g. balsam) to the short arm of a J-tube and apply paraffin-wax to the connection to make it air-tight. Fill the J-tube partially with water, leaving no air gap between the water-column and the connexion. Then pour mercury in the long arm of the J-tube, almost filling it. The excess water will flow out. The mercury column will compress the water column in the short arm and as a result, it will be seen within a short time that drops of water have accumulated on the leaf margin at the ends of the veins.

Transpiration and Exudation

(1) In transpiration, water escapes in the form of vapour, while in exudation, water escapes in liquid form.

(2) The water that escapes in transpiration is pure, while the water that escapes in exudation contains minerals in solution.

(3) In transpiration, water escapes through the stomata and, to some extent, through the cuticle. In exudation, water escapes through the hydathodes (see FIG. II/42) and water stomata (or water pores). Ordinarily, the stomata are distributed all over the surface (commonly lower) of the leaf, while the hydathodes and water stomata develop at the margin or apex of the leaf at the end of a vein.

(4) Transpiration is regulated by the movement of the guard cells, partially or wholly opening or closing the stomatal aperture. Exudation cannot be so regulated, the guard cells of the water stomata having lost the power of movement.

(5) Transpiration normally takes place in the presence of sunlight and, therefore, during the day-time. Exudation takes place in the absence of transpiration and, therefore, at night.

(6) Transpiration secures concentration of sap and also keeps the plant cool by dissipating the excess heat absorbed from sunlight. Exudation has no such effect.

Wilting Co-efficient. This term was first coined by Briggs and Shantz (1912). The wilting co-efficient is defined as the moisture content of the soil at the time when plants growing therein have undergone permanent wilting. It is expressed as percentage of dry weight.

The condition of plants whose cells lose their turgidity and whose leaves, young stems, etc., droop is termed wilting. It is caused by of excessive loss of water. Permanent wilting is the condition in which a plant that has undergone wilting cannot recover its normal turgidity, even when placed in a saturated atmosphere, without supplying water to the soil. The two major factors which influence wilting co-efficient are the type of soil and the kind of plant in question.

The type of soil determines the amount of water that remains in the soil at the time of permanent wilting. Investigations carried out on different types of soil show that the finer the soil particles, the greater the amount of water in the soil at the time of permanent wilting. Further, the water absorbing capacity of plants differs. Hence, the moisture content of the soil at the time of wilting is determined by the kind of plant in question.

The wilting co-efficient can be determined directly by growing plants in sealed containers and determining the percentage of moisture in the soil at the time of permanent wilting. This is the direct method of determining the wilting co-efficient.

ASCENT OF SAP

The water absorbed from the soil by the root-hairs is conducted upwards to the leaves and the growing regions of the stem and the branches. When a cut branch of lupin bearing white flowers is dipped into eosin solution its flowers undergo a gradual change in coloration from white to pink within a few minutes. In herbaceous plants, the height this water has to reach is small. However, in some trees, such as *Eucalyptus*, some conifers, etc., which may attain a height of 90 m. or even more, the distance to be traversed by this column of water is considerable and the water has to resist a considerable pressure to reach that height. The rate at which the transpiration current flows upwards through the vessels varies a good deal from plant to plant, and at different times in the same plant. Generally speaking, the rate is about 1 to 2 metres per hour in healthy trees. Two questions naturally arise in this connection: what is the path of movement of the sap and what are the factors responsible for its ascent?

Path of Movement of Sap. The path of movement of the sap may be determined in one of the following two ways: (*a*) a small herbaceous plant (e.g. *Peperomia*) or the small branch of a plant (e.g. lupin) may be stood in eosin solution. After a short time, sections—cross and longitudinal—are prepared from it at different heights and examined under the microscope. The sections will show the presence of coloured solution only in the vessels and tracheids. Therefore, these are the elements through which movement of the sap, or **transpiration current** as it is called, takes place, (*b*) All the peripheral tissues right up to the phloem and cambium may be removed in the form of a ring (girdling) from a branch, leaving the xylem intact. In a cut branch treated similarly, the pith may also be crushed. It is seen that wilting of leaves does not take place. As it is only the xylem that remains intact, we may conclude that the ascent of the sap takes place through it. This is known as the 'ringing' experiment.

FACTORS RESPONSIBLE FOR THE ASCENT OF SAP. Various theories have been advanced from time to time to explain the ascent of the sap, but none has proved satisfactory yet. It is believed that root pressure forces up the water to a certain height, and that transpiration exerts a suction force on this column of water from above. In short, it may be said that root pressure gives a 'push' from below and transpiration a 'pull' from above. In this respect, transpiration is a more powerful factor. Probable theories regarding the ascent of the sap are dealt with in the following section.

A. PHYSICAL THEORIES

(1) **Root Pressure.** Root pressure is regarded as one of the forces responsible for the ascent of sap. Many plants are seen to eject water with great force (bleeding) when the stem is cut above the ground. This phenomenon has been said to be due to the osmotic pressure which operates in the root-cortex to produce the root pressure. Root pressure may be adequate to force up water in herbs, shrubs and low trees, and that too in the absence of transpiration. The process can hardly generate 2 atmospheres of pressure and the maximum height to which a column of water may be raised by this pressure is only about 10 m. Since a pressure of 10-20 atmospheres is required to send the sap to the top of high trees, sometimes 90 m. or even more in height, root pressure cannot be the explanation. The process is also slow and cannot keep pace with the water lost by transpiration. Further, root pressure is lowest when transpiration is highest. In fact, during active transpiration, the water in the vessels is under a negative pressure. In many plants, root pressure is absent or feeble at certain times of the year. Besides, water still rises through the stem if the roots are decapitated and the cut end of the stem dipped into water.

The role of root pressure in the ascent of sap has, however, been emphasized by White (1938). He has experimentally shown that excised tomato roots exude water with a pressure amounting to 6 atmospheres or even more. This pressure is sufficient to raise a column of water to a height of 54 m. or even more.

(2) **Transpiration Pull and Force of Cohesion.** The **Cohesion Theory** (1895) of Dixon and Joly, Irish plant physiologists, considerably enhanced the understanding of the ascent of sap. The theory concerns the tensile strength of the water column in the vessels, caused by a strong force of attraction (cohesion) between the water molecules, osmosis in the mesophyll cells of the leaf, and transpiration pull due to evaporation of water from the leaf-surface. According to the 'cohesion' theory, the water molecules cohere together and form into a long continuous column in the vessels, extending from the root to the leaf, without any air bubbles. The water molecules cohere so strongly to one another that the column does not break or form bubbles anywhere in its entire length even under a state of very high tension due to transpiration pull, as further proved by Bode in 1923 by his microscopic observations of *Cucurbita, Impatiens, Tradescantia*, etc. This was again supported by Preston in 1958. Even if the water column breaks, its continuity is maintained by the vapour phase. The cohesive power of water, as has been experimentally proved by them, may maintain a very long column of water under tension greater than 100 atmospheres of pressure. Apparently, the water column behaves as a solid column. It is to be noted that a tension of only 10 atmospheres, possibly 20 atmospheres considering the frictional resistance of the walls, is required for the sap to ascend to a height of 104 m. The next operative factor is osmosis. It has been estimated that osmotically active mesophyll cells can draw up water from the ends of the vessels against a pressure of 10-20 atmospheres. Finally, transpiration plays an important part. A strong suction force, as already proved by Askenasy in 1880, is generated as a result of transpiration from the leaves. Evidently, a pull is exerted on the end of the water column and the whole column is bodily pulled up like an iron rod which can be lifted by one hand. The Cohesion Theory has been strongly supported by Dixon in 1914 and 1924, Fisher in 1948 and Briggs in 1950.

(3) **Capillarity.** The level of water inside a capillary tube is always higher than the level outside. The smaller the bore of the tube, the higher will be the rise of water in it. Xylem vessels may be regarded as so many capillary tubes extending from the root to the leaf, but it is obvious from the known diameter of the vessels that the rise of water can hardly exceed a metre or so. Further, the conducting elements in gymnosperms are so many tracheids with numerous transverse septa (and not vessels). Capillarity again implies free surface, but this is not found in plants as the vessels end in parenchymatous cells, and the water in the vessels is not in direct communication with the soil-water.

(4) **Imbibition Theory.** Sachs (1874) suggested that water moves along the walls of the xylem vessels (and not through their cavities) due to the imbibition force (see p. 216), and this is responsible for the ascent of sap in plants. But when the cavities of the vessels are artificially blocked with oil, air or gelatin, the branches are seen to wilt showing thereby that the amount of water absorbed by the process cannot at all keep pace with the amount of water lost by transpiration. The force of imbibition is no doubt great, but the movement of water by this process is slow.

B. VITAL THEORIES

(1) **Vital Force.** The activity of the living cells, e.g. wood parenchyma and medullary ray cells surrounding the xylem, has been held by Godlewski (1884) to be responsible for the rise of sap through the plant body. The role played by the living cells is like that of relay pumps. The living cells take water from the vessels at a particular level and then force it again into the vessels at a higher level, and the sap thus rises. Strasburger (1891), however, refuted the idea of vital force by killing the living cells with the application of heat as well as poisonous chemicals. He was certain that the forces concerned are physical rather than physiological. The vessels of the root no doubt withdraw water from the adjoining living cells.

(2) **Pulsation Theory.** According to the late Sir J. C. Bose (1923), the ascent of the sap is due to active *pulsation* of the internal layer of the cortex abutting on the endodermis. He proved this with the help of a fine electric probe, which was thrust

into the stem layer by layer. The probe was connected with a galvanometer. When it reached that particular layer the pulsation activity was suddenly exhibited; on either side of this layer, the activity suddenly disappeared. His conclusion was that due to the pulsating activity of the living cells of this layer a sort of pumping action is set up, and this is responsible for the *physiological* propulsion of the sap upwards through the stem. Conduction of water takes place through this layer even in the absence of root pressure and transpiration. The xylem vessels being dead and inactive, do not exhibit pulsation, and they were regarded by Bose as mere reservoirs of water. According to him, mechanical transport of water is possible to some extent through them only. The cortex injects water into them and withdraws it according to the circumstances. All the living cells exhibit pulsation to a greater or lesser extent, but the activity of the internal cortex is exceptionally great. Anatomical and experimental evidence, however, does not support this view.

CHAPTER 6

MANUFACTURE OF FOOD

1. CARBOHYDRATES

PHOTOSYNTHESIS. This name was first proposed by Barnes in 1898. *Photosynthesis (photo, light; synthesis, building up) consists in the building up of simple carbohydrates, such as sugars, in the green leaf by the chloroplasts in the presence of sunlight (as a source of energy) from carbon dioxide and water absorbed from the air and the soil, respectively.* The general consensus is that glucose is formed first and all other carbohydrates are derived from it. The process is accompanied by a liberation of oxygen (see Experiment 21). The volume of oxygen liberated has been found to be equal to the volume of carbon dioxide absorbed. But it is to be noted that all the oxygen liberated in the process is released exclusively from water (H_2O) and not from carbon dioxide (CO_2). Oxygen escapes from the plant body through the stomata. The formation of carbohydrates, commonly called **carbon-assimilation**, is the monopoly of green plants, chlorophyll being indispensable to the process. By this process, not only are simple carbohydrates formed, but a considerable amount of *energy* (initially obtained from sunlight as radiant energy) is also transformed by the green cells into chemical energy and stored up as such in the organic substances formed. It must be noted that photosynthesis takes place only in the green cells and, therefore, mainly in the leaf and to some extent in the green shoot. Under favourable conditions of light intensity and temperature, the rate of photosynthesis increases enormously and a tremendous amount of CO_2 is absorbed from the air for the process, so much so that on a windless day the CO_2 content of the air over a field crop may drop to 0.01% from the normal 0.03%.

Mechanism of Photosynthesis. Photosynthesis is the biological process by which some energy-rich, carbon-containing compounds are produced from carbon dioxide and water by the *illuminated* green cells, liberating oxygen as a by-product. It is essentially an oxidation-reduction process by which hydrogen is transferred from water to carbon dioxide through a 'carrier' substance. In the process, the volume of CO_2 absorbed is almost equal to that of O_2 liberated in most green plants (Boussingault, 1864). The overall reaction may be represented thus – $6CO_2 + 12H_2O \rightarrow C_6H_{12}O_6 + 6H_2O + 6O_2$.

Photosynthesis involves two distinct phases, the first phase of light reactions and the second of dark reactions. Plenty of evidence, such as the temperature co-efficient obtained (Q_{10}) in experiments with intermittent light, the induction phase and the fact that oxygen liberation and carbon dioxide reduction are two completely separate processes, clearly indicate the existence of two phases in photosynthesis.

The first phase of light reactions comprises the conversion of radiant energy into chemical energy (located in phosphate bonds, i.e., formation of ATP), photolysis (ionization) of water, formation of a reducing agent ($NADP.H_2$) and evolution of molecular oxygen (from water), which escapes to the atmosphere. The second phase of dark reactions comprises the reduction of carbon dioxide by $NADP.H_2$ and the participation of ATP, a series of enzymes, and ribulose-di-phosphate (carbon dioxide acceptor) to give rise to hexose sugar and regenerate ribulose-di-phosphate (RuDP).

The cycle of reactions through which the reduction of carbon dioxide (or carbon dioxide fixation) normally takes place in the dark during photosynthesis is called the C_3 cycle or Benson and Calvin cycle. However, there is an alternative cycle of reactions for carbon dioxide fixation in the dark during photosynthesis, known as the Hatch-Slack cycle, or C_4 cycle, which occurs in sugar-cane, maize, grasses, etc. Light reactions take place in the lamellar region and dark reactions in the stroma region of chloroplasts (Park and Pou, 1961).

Light reactions. These reactions take place in the green cells of plants in the presence of light. Chlorophyll absorbs light energy, which is then converted into chemical energy and temporarily stored in two compounds, namely, adenosine-tri-phosphate (ATP) and reduced nicotinamide adenine dinucleotide phosphate ($NADP.H_2$). There are two ways in which ATP is formed, but $NADP.H_2$ is formed only in one way.

The photolysis (ionization) of water also takes place in this phase. Water supplies hydrogen ions for the reduction of oxidized NADP into $NADP.H_2$ and is the source of oxygen which is evolved during photosynthesis.

When light falls upon a chlorophyll molecule, it becomes excited. This means when a photon (a quantum of light, which is a discrete packet of light energy) strikes the chlorophyll molecule, an electron is lifted into a new orbit, or a higher energy level, helping the chlorophyll molecule to gain an amount of energy equivalent to that of a photon.

It is now known that the main light-absorbing pigment is chlorophylla. The minimum number of chlorophyll-a molecules and accessory pigments required to absorb and convert a photon or quantum of light constitute a unit, called photosynthetic unit. Though many chlorophyll-a molecules are grouped together in such unit, it is only one chlorophyll-a molecule that acts as the reaction centre or trapping centre and can donate an electron. This chlorophyll-a molecule is termed P_{700}. The light absorbed by the remaining chlorophyll-a molecules passes from one molecule to another, and finally transferred to P_{700} chlorophyll-a molecule. These energy transferring chlorophyll-a molecules are called **antenna chlorophyll molecules.**

The electron (brought to a higher energy level) expelled by P_{700} is picked up by an electron carrier called **ferredoxin** (an iron-containing co-enzyme present in the chloroplast; the iron gets oxidized by donating an electron). From ferredoxin, the

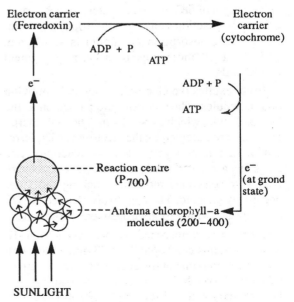

FIG. 18A. Cyclic Photophosphorylation

electron passes through a series of other electron carriers, such as cytochrome, quinones (plasto-quinone and vitamin K), etc. During the transfer of the electron from one carrier to another, the high energy of the electron is utilized for the addition of phosphate radical to ADP by the phosphate bond to form ATP (two or more ATP molecules are formed in this cycle). Finally, the excited electron gets back to its ground state and is returned to the chlorophyll. The chlorophyll, therefore, gets back the same electron. This is a closed circuit flow of electrons and is known as **cyclic photophospho-rylation** (FIG. 18A).

The second way that ATP is formed during pho-tosynthesis is called **noncyclic photophosphory-lation** (FIG. 18B), which also includes the photolysis of water, formation of $NADP.H_2$, and evolution of oxygen (from water). This process involves two photochemical systems (photo acts I and II or photosystem I and II or PS I and II). Light energy is absorbed separately by two different pig-ment systems. In photosystem I, light is absorbed by pigment system I. This system contains 200 to 400 chlorophyll-a molecules (chlorophyll-a 683) whose absorption maxima are at the long red wave-length of 683 nm (nanometer), one P_{700} mol-ecule (the reaction centre or chlorophyll-a mole-cule) whose absorption maximum is at 700 nm, and about 50 molecules of accessory pigment carotenoids.

Light excites the electrons of the chlorophyll-a 683 molecules. The electrons are passed on to the P_{700} molecule, which expels them. The high energy electrons are accepted by the electron carrier, ferre-doxin. In this noncyclic chain of reactions, two electrons are transferred from ferredoxin to every NADP (co-enzyme) molecule, making the latter negatively charged. The negatively charged NADP develops an affinity for hydrogen ions (from water).

Light is also absorbed by pigment system II, which contains chlorophyll-a 673 molecules with absorption maxima at the short red wave length of 673 nm, chlorophyll-b molecules (whose function is not clear) and a chlorophyll-a P700 molecule, which expels high energy electrons. The high energy electrons are picked up by electron carriers

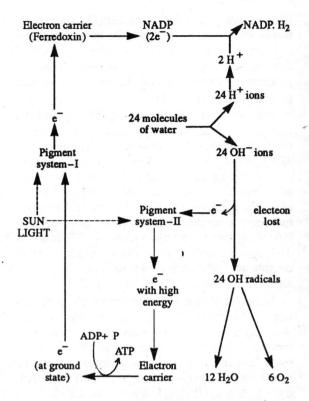

FIG. 18B. Non-cyclic Photophosphorylation

(probably cytochrome and others), which utilize their energy for the formation of ATP molecules (12 molecules of ATP). Finally, the electron carri-ers transfer the electrons (by that time returned to ground state) to the chlorophyll molecules of pig-ment system I. Thus, the chlorophyll of pigment system I does not get back the electrons it had expelled and it is not a closed circuit flow of elec-trons. Light energy is absorbed at one point by chlorophyll-a 683 molecules (PS I) and at another point by chlorophyll-a 673 molecules (PS II).

In PS I, the NADP molecules continue to receive electrons and develop an affinity for hydrogen ions from water, and more water gets ionized into hydrogen ions (H^+) and hydroxyl ions (OH^-). Two of these hydrogen ions join a molecule of negatively charged NADP, which then becomes electrically neutral and forms $NADP.H_2$. In this process, 24 molecules of water undergo ionization for the production of 12 molecules of

$NADP.H_2^-$. Each of the 24 OH^- ions formed loses an electron to become an OH radical. The 24 OH radicals combine to give rise to 12 molecules of water and 6 molecules of oxygen. The oxygen escapes to the outer atmosphere and the water molecules are left behind. The electrons lost by the hydroxyl ions replace the electrons expelled by pigment system II.

Samuel Ruben and Martin Kamen (1941) proved, with the help of the radioactive isotope O^{18}, that the oxygen evolved during photosynthesis comes from water molecules. Earlier, Hill (1937-1939) had shown that suspensions of chloroplasts in water evolved oxygen when illuminated, even in the absence of carbon dioxide, provided that a suitable hydrogen acceptor was available. This is known as the Hill Reaction.

Dark Reactions. These reactions, which constitute the second phase of photosynthesis, are not dependent on light and chlorophyll. This process utilizes the potential chemical energy stored in green cells during light reactions. The first step of dark reactions is carbon dioxide fixation, in which RuDP functions as carbon dioxide acceptor. Carbon dioxide is then reduced by $NADP.H_2$. Working on the unicellular alga *chlorella*, Benson and Calvin (1950), showed with the help of radioactive carbon C^{14}, that phosphoglyceric acid is formed as an intermediate product during the process. Phosphoglyceric acid gets converted to phosphoglyceraldehyde. For every six molecules of carbon dioxide absorbed and reduced, 12 molecules of phosphoglyceraldehyde are formed, two of which are utilized to give rise to one molecule of sugar, and 10 to regenerate RuDP molecules. This process is called the C_3 Cycle or Calvin Cycle. It is also known that the reactions leading to the formation of glucose are essentially a reversal of the glycolytic phase of cellular respiration and that they take place under the action of specific enzymes.

In recent years, the use of radioactive isotopes and chromatography have helped the study of dark reactions. It has been suggested that 5-carbon ribulose phosphate is activated by ATP to form ribulose diphosphate (also a 5-carbon compound). The latter combines with CO_2 and is carboxylated to an unknown 6-carbon compound. This unknown compound, along with water molecules, splits into two parts — one part forms 3-carbon phosphoglyceric acid and the other part may enter the mitochondria and follow the path of cellular respiration.

The two molecules of phosphoglyceric acid, formed per molecule of CO_2, are reduced to two molecules of 3-phosphoglyceraldehyde by the reducing agent $NADP.H_2$, in the presence of ATP, both formed during light reactions. 3-phosphoglyceraldehyde plays a key role in further transformations.

Some molecules of 3-phosphoglyceraldehyde isomerise to form dihydroxyacetone phosphate. Then some dihydroxyacetone phosphate molecules combine with some 3-phosphoglyceraldehyde molecules to form fructose 1-6-diphosphate molecules. These lose one phosphate each and convert to fructose-6-phosphate molecules. Some fructose-6 molecules lose another phosphate and convert into fructose molecules. Fructose molecules undergo reorganization to become glucose (sugar).

Some fructose-6-phosphate molecules follow another course of reactions. A molecule of fructose-6-phosphate combines with a molecule of 3-phosphoglyceraldehyde and forms erythrose phosphate and xylulose phosphate.

One molecule of erythrose phosphate combines with one molecule of dihydroxyacetone-phosphate to give one molecule of sedoheptulose diphosphate, which loses one phosphate molecule to become sedoheptulose phosphate. The latter combines with one molecule of 3-phosphoglyceraldehyde and breaks up into xylulose phosphate and ribulose phosphate. Ribulose and xylulose phosphate isomerise to form 5-carbon ribulose phosphate.

Various enzymes of the carboxydimutase system are involved at different stages of this cycle of reactions.

Alternative Path of CO_2 Fixation in Photosynthesis. Working on photosynthesis in sugar-cane with the help of the radioactive isotope

C^{14}, Kortschak, Hartt and Burr (1965) discovered, to their surprise, that the labelled carbon (about 80%) appeared in 4-carbon dicarboxylic acids, such as oxaloacetic acid, malic acid and aspartic acid, instead of phosphoglyceric acid in the C_3 cycle. In 1967, M. D. Hatch and C. R. Slack also found that malic acid appeared earlier than phosphoglyceric acid in sugar-cane leaves. Hence they concluded that malic acid, and not phosphoglyceric acid, was the intermediate product in this type of CO_2 fixation.

They put forward an alternative path of CO_2 fixation in photosynthesis, which is seen in sugarcane, maize, certain grasses, etc. This alternative path is known as the Hatch-Slack cycle or C_4 cycle. According to them, in the initial stage, phosphoenol pyruvic acid (and not RuDP) acts as a CO_2 acceptor and it is carboxylated under the action of the enzyme, phosphoenol pyruvate carboxylase, to an unstable compound, oxaloacetic acid. One molecule of water is also involved in the reaction.

Oxaloacetic acid is soon reduced by $NADP.H_2$, under the action of the enzyme, malic dehydrogenase, to malic acid, which undergoes enzymecatalysed oxidative decarboxylation to form pyruvic acid and free CO_2. Pyruvic acid reacts with ATP in the presence of phosphopyruvic dikinase to form phosphoenol pyruvic acid. The process is, thus, renewed.

All these reactions take place in the mesophyll cells of leaves. The free CO_2 evolved does not escape into the atmosphere. It is now accepted by RuDP, and the C_3 cycle reactions take place, but in the bundle sheath cells and not in the mesopyll cells.

Characteristics of C_4 Plants. Plants in which the C_4 cycle takes place have certain similar characteristics:

1. They have characteristic leaf anatomy (Kranz type). The vascular bundles are surrounded by a bundle sheath of compactly arranged, distinct parenchyma cells, which are rich in chloroplasts, mitochondria, etc. (Bundle sheaths are normally absent in C_3 plants. If

present, they do not have chloroplasts).

2. The chloroplasts of the mesophyll cells contain the enzyme phosphopyruvic dikinase (which catalyses the reaction between pyruvic acid and ATP) and not RuDP carboxylase, which is present in the mesophyll chloroplasts of C_3 plants (RuDP is present in the bundle sheath chloroplasts of C_4 plants).

3. Both C_4 and C_3 mechanisms are used for carbon assimilation. See Appendix I for C_4 and C_3 mechanisms.

4. C_4 plants can use higher light intensities and can adjust to high carbon dioxide concentration.

5. The rate of photosynthesis is much higher in C_4 plants.

Role Played by Light and Chlorophyll. Light is an essential condition for initiating the process of photosynthesis. The part played by it in any photochemical reaction is not, however, completely understood, and consequently, a clear and complete explanation of the action of light in photosynthesis cannot be given. Suffice to say that the light energy absorbed by chlorophyll is effective in splitting water molecules at the initial stage of photosynthesis (see photolysis of water p. 253) and in this process, it becomes transformed into chemical energy for further action, i.e. reduction and fixation of CO_2 in dark reactions. It has been estimated that an average green leaf absorbs about 80-85% light. In photosynthesis, however, only about 1% light is utilized. A portion of light may be reflected from the leaf-surface and from the chloroplasts, a portion is lost in heat and another portion is used in transpiration. Experiments have proved that only certain rays (not all) of light are used for photosynthesis (see p. 260).

Chlorophyll is indispensable for photosynthesis. However, its exact role in the process is not known except that (a) it absorbs light energy from sunlight and becomes 'activated' or 'excited', i.e. its energy level increases above normal to initiate the process of photosynthesis, (b) the extra energy stored in chlorophyll now goes to break up water molecules at the initial stage of photosynthesis,

(c) a part of this energy goes to form a reducing agent, TPN in all probability, which accepts hydrogen from water for reduction of CO_2, (d) another part of this energy goes to synthesize ATP, and (e) chlorphyll acts as a catalytic agent. The amount of chlorophyll or the constituent pigments remain unaltered through even a prolonged period of photosynthesis.

Photolysis of Water. The initial and essential part of photosynthesis lies in photolysis, i.e. splitting of a water molecule into its two components. This is essentially a *light reaction* taking place in the body of the chloroplast. In fact, all photosynthetic reactions, as shown by Arnon and his colleagues in 1954, occur in the grana of the chloroplast. In this respect, the chloroplast may be regarded as a complete unit. Under the influence of light energy and the catalytic action of chlorophyll, water, a substance of low energy value, is split up into oxygen (O_2) and hydrogen ($2H$). Oxygen escapes to the atmosphere, while hydrogen atoms (or their electrons) combine with a reducing agent, most likely NADP formed in the chloroplast. NADP becomes reduced to $TPNH_2$, a substance of high energy value. This further results in the synthesis of ATP from ADP. It is possibly during these reactions that light energy is converted to chemical energy which is needed for further reactions that immediately follow. It should be specially noted that all the oxygen evolved in photosynthesis is released from water (see Hill Reaction, below). Further, the volume of the oxygen released in photosynthesis has been found to be equal to the volume of the carbon dioxide absorbed. This may be represented by the following equation:

$$6CO_2 + 12H_2O \xrightarrow[\text{chlorophyll}]{\text{light energy}} C_6H_{12}O_6 + 6H_2O + 6O_2$$

Hill Reaction. Robin Hill, an English biochemist, conducted experiments with isolated chloroplasts suspended in water. He showed in 1937 and 1939 that such chloroplasts, or even their fragments, evolve oxygen when illuminated, even in the absence of CO_2, provided that a suitable hydrogen-acceptor is available. Hill used ferric oxalate for this purpose. Other compounds like ferricyanides, chromates and quinones (e.g. benzoquinone) have been used with similar results. However, it was not possible to make any further advance in the process of photosynthesis with isolated choloroplast. It became further evident from the Hill reaction that the source of O_2 released in photolysis is H_2O (and not CO_2) as previously believed). The Hill reaction is essentially the photolytic splitting of water with the release of O_2 and possibly, also the formation of a reducing agent to act as the hydrogen-acceptor. That all the oxygen evolved in photosynthesis is derived from H_2O (and not CO_2) has been definitely proved by Ruben and Kamen, American chemists, in 1941 and 1943, by using radioactive oxygen, O^{18}, in water, H_2O^{18}. When a CO_2 molecule was tagged with the radioactive O^{18}, no trace of it was found in the O_2 evolved.

Transfer of Hydrogen. It has been mentioned already that in photosynthesis, water is the specific hydrogen-donor and TPN (as evidence goes now) is the hydrogen-acceptor. Hydrogen (or electrons), now available from H_2O, is transferred to CO_2 through some intermediate 'carriers' for reduction of the latter (CO_2) in dark reactions. Experiments carried out so far have shown that a number of complex enzymes of the oxidation-reduction group take part in the whole series of reactions. It is now known that some of them (e.g. hydrogenase, dehydrogenase, cytochrome, DPN, thioctic acid, vitamin K, etc.) act as intermediate 'carriers' of hydrogen. They have been found in green cells although not in the chloroplasts in all cases, and in some cases, enzyme reactions have been proved *in vitro*.

Isotopes. Different kinds of atoms of a particular element, with different atomic weights but identical chemical properties, are called **isotopes**. For example, there are different kinds of carbon atoms with atomic weights of 10, 11, 12, 13 and 14, respectively. All isotopes are not radioactive. Some of the heavy elements like uranium and radium are naturally radioactive, while the stable isotopes of many elements can be artificially made radioactive. Thus, the atomic weight of stable carbon is 12, while that of artificially made radioactive carbon may be C^{10}, C^{12}, C^{13} or C^{14}. All radioactive elements disintegrate by the loss of charged particles and by radiation. The life of such an element is, therefore unstable, varying in duration from a second or even less to thousands of years. From the biological standpoint, radioactive elements have proved to be of immense value in elucidating certain intricate problems of plant life and animal life because it has been possible to trace such 'marked' elements through successive stages in the plant or animal's body. Thus, radioactive carbon can be traced in the intermediate and final products formed in the process of photosynthesis. This evidently helps to ascertain the nature of the products that appear during the process. The atomic weights of some radioactive elements used in plant research are C^{11}, C^{14}, O^{18}, S^{35}, P^{32}, K^{42} and Ca^{45}, their corresponding stable forms being C_{12}, O_{16}, S_{32}, P_{31}, K_{39} and Ca_{40}.

Production of Oxygen and Starch in Photosynthesis. Oxygen and starch are two important factors for testing photosynthesis. This is why they are commonly used for experimental purposes. As already stated, oxygen is derived from water, H_2O as a by—product in the initial stage of photosynthesis (Hill, 1937 & 1939), while starch is derived from sugar (glucose) as the final product in the process (Sachs, 1862 & 1864). Oxygen escapes from the leaf (see Experiment 21) but starch accumulates in its mesophyll cells (see Experiment 23). Starch may be detected in the following way. Collect one or more leaves in the evening and bleach them with methylated spirit. Then dip them in iodine solution. They are seen to turn bluish-black, indicating the presence of starch grains. It is better to treat the leaves further with

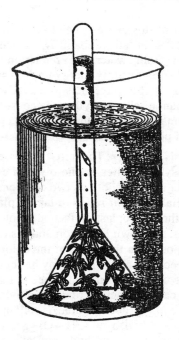

FIG. 19A. Evolution of oxygen bubbles in photo synthesis of submerged water plants (*Hydrilla*)

benzol for a few minutes. The brownish colour of the leaves, which is due to the action of iodine solution on protoplasm and cellulose, disappears and the bluish-black colour of the starch grains stands out clearly. Starch is insoluble in water. At night, it is converted to sugar by the action of the enzyme, *diastase*, and translocated to the storage organs (Sachs, 1864). In the storage tissues, sugar is reconverted into starch by the leucoplasts.

ATP — adenosine triphosphate. ADP — adenosine diphosphate. TPN — triphosphopyridine nucleotide = NADP — nicotinamide adenine dinucleotide phosphate. NAD — nicotinamide adenine dinucleotide = DPN — diphosphopyridine nucleotide.

ATP. ATP is an active, energy-rich phosphate compound consisting of adenine, ribose sugar and three phosphate bonds, two of them being high-energy bonds. It is now definitely known that ATP provides most of the chemical energy for the living cell's activities. For many biochemical reactions, particularly in respiration, photosynthesis, synthesis of proteins, fats, nucleic acids, etc., ATP is the source of chemical energy. These reactions are activated by the transfer of an energy-rich phosphate bond of ATP (as first stressed by Lipmann, a Nobel Prize winner, in 1941) when ATP becomes ADP. Again, with the addition of a phosphate bond + energy, ADP becomes ATP. This interconversion goes on continually in the living cell. The chemical energy needed for the conversion of ADP to ATP comes from oxidation of glucose (a substance much richer in chemical energy than ATP) during respiration and stored in the mitochondria. It may be noted that 1 molecule of glucose yields on complete oxidation 38 molecules of ATP. The light energy absorbed by chlorophyll also brings about synthesis of ATP in the chloroplast. In this process, light energy becomes converted to chemical energy.

Starch may be converted into sugar again when the need arises. This interconversion is independent of light and chlorophyll and may, therefore, take place anywhere in the plant body.

Experiment 21. Photosynthesis: to show that oxygen is given off during photosynthesis (FIG. 19A). Place some green submerged water plants (e.g. *Hydrilla*) in a large beaker filled with water. Add a small quantity of soda water or a pinch of sodium bicarbonate as a source of carbon dioxide. Cover the plants under water with a glass funnel, and invert over the funnel (under water) a test-tube filled with water. It is better to cut the stems and tie up the shoots into a bundle. The cut ends should be projected upwards into the funnel. *Observation.* When exposed to bright light, a stream of small gas bubbles is seen to rise upwards through the cut ends of the stems.The bubbles collect at the upper end of the test-tube, displacing the water. *Inference.* That the gas is oxygen can be proved in the following way. Close the test-tube with the thumb under water, and invert it over a dish containing a quantiy of pyrogallate of potash (5% pyrogallic acid to which an excess of caustic potash has been added). Then, with the help of a bent tube, introduce a quantity of this solution into the test tube. The pyrogallate solution coming in contact with the gas will absorb it and will, therefore, rise and fill up the test-tube completely. The pyrogallate solution absorbs oxygen. The gas in the tube is, therefore, oxygen.

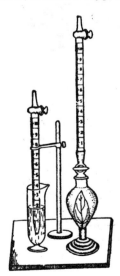

FIG. 19B. Ganong's photosynthometer
(see Experiment 22)

Experiment 22. Analysis of gases with Ganong's photosynthometer. This instrument is very useful in analyzing the gases — CO_2 and O_2 — and finding out their quotient. First fill up the graduated tube with water and then introduce into it a known volume of CO_2 from a generator by displacing water. Enclose a green leaf in the bulb of the photosynthometer, arrange the whole apparatus as shown in the (FIG.19B) and expose it to bright sunlight for a few hours. Remove the graduated tube to a cylinder containing KOH solution. Note the rise of the solution in the tube, indicating the volume of CO_2 still not used up by the leaf. The total volume of CO_2 being known, the actual volume of CO_2 absorbed by the leaf within a specified time can be easily calculated. Then transfer the graduated tube to pyrogallate of potash and note the further rise of the solution in it. This will indicate the volume of O_2 given out by the leaf in the same period. It will be noted that the two volumes — $CO_2 : O_2$ — almost maintain a quotient of unity.

Experiment 23. Photosynthesis: to demonstrate that starch is formed in photosynthesis (FIGS.20-22). Select a healthy, green leaf of a plant *in situ* and cover a portion of it on both sides with two uniform pieces of black paper, fixed in position with two paper clips or soft wooden clips. This should be done either in the morning before the sun rises or the previous evening, so that the experiment is performed with a starch-free leaf. Or keep a healthy, green pot plant in a dark room for 1 or 2 days so that its leaves become starch-free, and then cover a portion of a leaf of this plant as described above. To make sure that there is no starch, collect a few neighbouring leaves in the morning, decolorize them with alcohol and dip them into iodine solution. It will be seen that they do not turn black. Evidently, all the leaves are starch-free. Now expose the plant to bright light for some time, preferably till the evening. Then collect the leaf, decolorize it with alcohol and test it with iodine solution for starch grains. It will be seen that only the exposed portions turn blue or black.

A very interesting experiment known as the **starch print** (FIG. 21) may be carried out in the following way. A stencil (which may be a blackened, thin tin plate or a black paper) with the letters S T A R C H punched or cut in it is used for this purpose. The procedure is the same as that described under Experiment 23. Later, when the leaf is decolorized and treated with iodine solution, the printed S T A R C H will stand out boldly in black on the bleached leaf owing to the formation of starch grains with the access of light and their turning black in contact with the iodine solution.

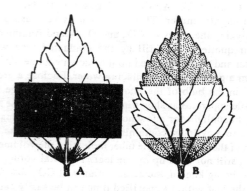

FIG. 20. Formation of starch grains in photosynthesis of land plants. *A*, leaf partially covered with black paper; *B*, covered portion without starch grains, and uncovered portions with plenty of them

Instead of loose black paper or stencil, a **light-screen** (FIG. 22) may be used to cover a portion of the leaf. The advantage of the light-screen is that it allows free ventilation and, at the same time, cuts off all light.

leaves with black paper or black cloth the previous day to make them starch-free. Cut out half of each leaf, very close to the mid-rib, and place the cut-out halves on a graph paper to determine their area as correctly as possible. Then expose the plant with the remaining halves to bright sunlight for some hours. Cut out those halves again very close to the mid-rib. Kill and dry both sets of half-leaves to get rid of all water, and weigh them separately. The difference in weight will indicate the quantity of photosynthetic products formed in the given area of leaves within a specified period.

(*b*) **Ganong's leaf-area cutter** (FIG. 23). With this instrument, cut out an equal number of circular discs (say, 20, each equivalent to 1 sq. cm.)—one set of discs from a plant kept in darkness and another set from the same plant exposed to sunlight for a few hours. Kill and dry them separately and find out the weight in each case. The increased weight in the latter set will indicate the quantity of photosynthate formed in a given area within a specified period.

Experiment 25. To show that plants cannot photo-

FIG. 21. Starch print in photosynthesis

Experiment 24. To find out the quantity of photosynthate in the given area of a leaf. (Sachs' half-leaf method.) (*a*) Cover a selected number of symmetrical

synthesize unless carbon dioxide is available: Moll's experiment (FIG. 24). (*a*) Arrange, as shown in FIG. 24, with some KOH solution in the bottle. The leaf should

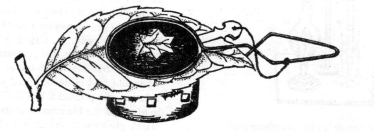

FIG. 22. A light-screen

FIG. 23. Ganong's leaf-area cutter

room for 1 or 2 days to free the leaves of starch grains. Then mark the green portions in 1 or 2 leaves, and expose the branch to bright sunlight for a whole day. In the evening, collect the marked leaves, decolorize them with methylated spirit and dip them into iodine solution for a few minutes. Note that only the green portions of the leaf turn black, indicating the presence of starch grains while the non-green portions turn yellowish. It is, therefore, evident that photosynthesis cannot take place without chlorophyll.

be starch-free (see Experiment 23). After exposure to sunlight for some hours, the leaf is decolorized and tested for starch grains with iodine solution. The portion of the leaf outside the bottle exposed to atmospheric CO_2 is the only part that turns black. A branch or a pot plant freed of starch may be used instead of a single leaf.

(*b*) Cover a healthy green pot plant, starch-freed, with a bell-jar stood on a large flat dish containing mercury (or distilled water), as shown in FIG. 25. Place a small pot with a little caustic potash solution inside the bell-jar to absorb all the enclosed carbon dioxide and fill the U-tube with sodalime. Expose the apparatus to direct sunlight for some hours. Afterwards, test the leaves for starch grains in the usual way. In the absence of CO_2, these are not formed.

(*c*) Replace the pot plant with *water plants* in a beaker, as in FIG. 19A. No evolution of gas (oxygen) bubbles is noticed.

Experiment 26. To show that chlorophyll is essential for photosynthesis. Select a variegated garden croton, tapioca, or *Coleus*. Cut out a small branch from it and dip the cut end into water in a bottle. Keep it in a dark

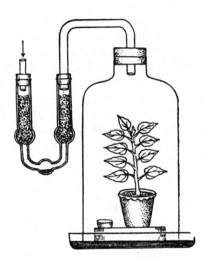

FIG. 25. Green plants cannot photosynthesize without carbon dioxide

FACTORS AFFECTING PHOTOSYNTHESIS. Light intensity, temperature carbon dioxide concentration and water supply are the chief *external conditions* for photosynthesis and its rate. The chief *internal factors* are chlorophyll content, accumulation of photosynthetic products and protoplasmic factor.

(1) **Light.** This is the most important factor in photosynthesis. The formation of carbohydrates cannot take place unless light is admitted to the chloroplasts. The process is naturally in abeyance during the night. If a leaf or any part of it be covered with black paper, starch grains are not formed there (see Experiment 23). The rate of photosynthesis also varies according to the intensity of light. In very weak light, no starch grains are formed except in shade-loving plants. Exclusively

FIG. 24. Moll's experiment on photosynthesis. (The bottle contains some KOH solution)

intense light also has the same effect. It is, however, a fact that a very small part of solar energy is used by green plants for photosynthesis.

(2) **Carbon dioxide**. The carbon dioxide of the air is the source of all carbon for the various organic products formed in the plant body, such as sugar, starch, etc., and, therefore, the process is in abeyance when carbon dioxide is not available to the plant (see Experiment 25). Carbohydrate formation increases greatly under favourable light and temperature conditions if the carbon dioxide concentration in the air rises from 0.03% to 0.1% or even more (say 2.5 to 5%, with a corresponding increase in light intensity). A higher concentration of CO_2 is harmful to the plant.

(3) **Temperature**. Photosynthesis takes place within a wide range of temperatures. It proceeds even when the temperature is below the freezing point of water, but the maximum temperature lies somewhere near 45°C. The optimum temperature, i.e. the most favourable temperature for photosynthesis, may be stated to be 35°C. Both maximum and optimum temperatures, however, vary in different species of plants and in those growing under different climatic conditions. Many cacti can, however, function at a temperature of 50°C.

(4) **Water**. Water is indispensable for photosynthesis because the process starts with the splitting of water into oxygen and hydrogen under the action of light and chlorophyll. Dryness of the soil and of the leaf thus retards photosynthesis. Water makes the photosynthetic cells turgid and active. It is, however, a fact that less than 1% of the water absorbed by the roots is utilized in photosynthesis.

(5) **Chlorophyll**. This is essential for photosynthesis. The plastids are powerless without chlorophyll. For the same reason, the non-green parts of plants cannot photosynthesize (see Experiment 26). Fungi, and saprophytic and parasitic phanerogams have altogether lost this power, being devoid of chlorophyll.

(6) **Accumulation of Photosynthetic Products**. A heavy accumulation of these products, whether sugar or starch, in the assimilating cells causes the process of photosynthesis to slow down and even come to a standstill.

(7) **Protoplasmic Factor**. An internal factor other than chlorophyll plays a part in photosynthesis. This is the called the protoplasmic factor (Briggs, 1920). But how it acts is not clearly understood. It is likely that this factor is enzymic in nature.

Two other factors may be considered in this connection. One is **oxygen** and the other is **potassium**. In the complete absence of oxygen, photosynthesis cannot take place. But a variation in the percentage of oxygen seems to have no effect on the rate of photosynthesis. The rate is not appreciably altered even if the oxygen contents are reduced to 2% or increased to 50%. But in the complete absence of oxygen, the process comes to a standstill. Potassium helps synthesis of carbohydrates and, therefore, starch grains are not formed in its absence. Potassium does not enter into the composition of carbohydrates but acts as a catalyst, helping in their synthesis.

Limiting Factors in Photosynthesis. The principle of limiting factors was enunciated by Blackman, a British plant physiologist, in 1905. He showed that **light intensity, carbon dioxide concentration** and **temperature** are the limiting factors in photosynthesis, i.e. the ultimate rate of photosynthesis is determined by each of these factors. Just as the strength of a chain is determined by its weakest link, so the rate of photosynthesis is controlled and limited by the least favourable factor, i.e. the weakest factor becomes the most important factor. Earlier workers tried to determine out the maximum rate of photosynthesis under the action of any one factor at a time. But Blackman for the first time considered all the factors simultaneously while examining the effect of any one factor on the rate of photosynthesis. Under the normal condition of 0.03% concentration of CO_2 in the air and within a certain range of temperature, photosynthesis may start with low intensity of light. Supposing then that the concentration of carbon dioxide remains constant, it is seen that with increasing intensity of light, the rate increases steadily until a particular maximum is reached. Without a further increase in the CO_2 concentration, the rate of photosynthesis does not increases, even if the light intensity is increased. It is evident then that at this point, carbon dioxide acts as a limiting factor. If the light intensity remains constant, it is seen that with increasing concentration of CO_2, say, from 0.03% to 0.5-1% or even more, the rate of photosynthesis will rise again up to a certain point. A further increase in the CO_2 concentration under the same light intensity will have no influence on the rate. At this point, light acts as a limiting factor. Different concentrations of CO_2 are correlated with different intensities of light, i.e. more intense light is required to utilize more concentrated carbon dioxide. These two factors balance each other, and photosynthesis progresses rapidly. But there is a limit beyond which each factor inhibits the rate .and may even check the process altogether. Within a certain range, the effect of temperature on the rate of photosynthesis shows very little variation. But it has been noted that with low intensity of light, even if the concentration of CO_2 be high, the rate of photosynthesis does not increase appreciably with increase in temperature. With high light intensity, however, even if the CO_2 concentration be low, the rate of photosynthesis increases with increasing temperature up to a maximum of 35°C, for most plants. With high light intensity and high CO_2 concentration, the rise in temperature may even double the rate of photosynthesis. Blackman's theory of limiting factors has been supported by Wilmott (1921) who worked on *Elodea* by his own bubble-counting technique, Warburg (1919), who worked on *Chlorella*, Harder (1921 and 1923),who worked on a number of aquatic plants, and many others.

The effect of the above factors may be determined easily by simple experiments, as first shown by Harder in 1921. A cut branch of *Hydrilla*, with its cut end projected upwards, is taken in a test-tube in water. It is then exposed to different intensities of light and the number of bubbles, counted for each illumination per unit of time. With the addition of sodium bicarbonate in different concentrations the experiments are repeated, and the bubbles counted again for each concentration. The experiments may be repeated by gradually increasing the temperature. The data obtained gives a good idea of the rate of photosynthesis under the action of individual factors and combinations of factors.

Conditions Necessary for the Formation of Chlorophyll. A number of factors, both internal and external, are responsible for the formation of chlorophyll. Chlorophyll synthesis is checked in the absence of any of them.

(1) **Light**. Normally, chlorophyll does not develop in most plants in the absence of light. Continued absence of light decomposes it into protochlorophyll (see p 155). But in many algae, mosses, ferns and in the seedlings of many conifers and certain angiosperms, chlorophyll may develop in the dark plants become pale green. These light, however, more chlorophyll develops in them and they become a deeper green. In most cases, a low intensity of light is quite effective in inducing chlorophyll formation. It may also be noted that very strong light decomposes chlorophyll, particularly in shade loving plants.

(2) **Temperature**. Chlorophyll develops within a wide range of temperature, the maximum usually varying from 26–30°C. Very high temperature, (45–48°C.) decomposes chlorophyll.

(3) **Iron and Magnesium**. Cholorophyll is not formed the absence of the salts of these metals and seedlings assume a sickly yellow appearance. In this condition, they are said to be *chlorotic*. Although both iron and magnesium are required for the formation of chlorophyll, it is only magnesium that enters into its composition.

(4) **Manganese**. It is believed that manganese is necessary, even essential, for the formation of chlorophyll.

(5) **Nitrogen**. Nitrogen enters into the composition of chlorophyll and, therefore, chlorophyll fails to develop.

(6) **Water**. When drying up in the absence of water, leaves are seen to lose their green colour. Desiccation, thus, brings about decomposition of chlorophyll. The leaves of many plants, particularly of grasses, turn brownish during prolonged drought.

(7) **Oxygen**. Oxygen is also essential in chlorophyll formation. Seedlings fail to develop

chlorophyll in its absence, even when they are exposed to sunlight. Chlorophyll formation is, therefore, an oxidation process.

(8) **Carbohydrates.** Cane-sugar, grape-sugar, etc., are also necessary for the formation of chlorophyll. Etiolated leaves that do not contain soluble carbohydrates develop chlorophyll and turn green when floated on sugar solution.

(9) **Heredity.** This is a powerful factor and determines the formation of chlorophyll in the off-spring. Familiar examples are garden crotons, aloes, aroids (e.g. *Caladium*), amaranth etc.

Chemistry of Chlorophyll. Chlorophyll, as it exists in the chloroplasts, is a mixture of four different pigments, as given below.

Finally, the four pigments are separated through the separating funnel and collected in four test-tubes. The nature of each pigment may be verified by spectrum analysis.

Effect of Rays of Light on Photosynthesis. It is a known fact that white light is composed of seven colours arranged in the following order: red, orange, yellow, green, blue, indigo and violet. Although photosynthesis normally takes place in white light, it is only a few of the above rays that are required for this function. Experiments carried out by Sachs (1864), Timiriazeff (1875), Engelmann (1881) and others have shown that chlorophyll normally utilizes a large portion of the red ray and also the blue-violet rays, and only to some extent the orange ray. The other rays are not

---

1. Chlorophyll *a*, $C_{55}H_{72}O_5N_4Mg$—a blue-black micro-crystalline solid
2. Chlorophyll *b*, $C_{55}H_{70}O_6N_4Mg$—a green-black micro-crystalline solid
3. Carotene, $C_{40}H_{56}$—an orange-red crystalline solid
4. Xanthophyll, $C_{40}H_{56}O_2$—a yellow crystalline solid.

Extraction of Chlorophyll and Separation of Pigments. Pieces of green leaves (preferably grass leaves) are bruised in a mortar with sand particles and transferred to a flask with about 100 c.c. of 80% acetone. The flask is shaken for a few minutes and then allowed to stand. The acetone takes up all the colour (deep green), which is then filtered off through a filter-funnel. The solution shows fluorescence (see p. 126). It is poured into a separating funnel, and petroleum ether and methyl alcohol added to it. The solution is stirred with a glass rod and allowed to settle. Within 2 or 3 minutes, the solution separates out into two distinct layers. The upper (call it *A*) deep green (containing chlorophyll *a* and carotene—both soluble in petroleum ether), and the lower (call it *B*), light-greenish yellow (containing chlorophyll *b* and xanthophyll—both soluble in methyl alcohol). From the separating funnel, the liquid *B* is collected in a test-tube, leaving the liquid *A* intact in the funnel. KOH solution and methyl alcohol are added separately to both the liquids (*A* and *B*), which are then shaken for a few minutes. The two liquids are then allowed to settle. Almost immediately, each liquid separates out into two layers. In *A,* the upper layer is deep green, containing chlorophyll *a,* and the lower layer is yellowish-brown containing carotene. In *B,* the upper layer is greenish, containing chlorophyll *b,* and the lower is light yellow, containing xanthophyll.

utilized to any extent (see Experiments 27 *a-c*).

Experiment 27. To find out the rays of light utilized in photosynthesis.

(a) Cover a green, starch-free pot plant with a double-walled bell-jar which is filled at a time with a red solution (aniline red), orange-yellow solution (potassium dichromate), blue solution (copper sulphate and ammonia; this transmits blue and violet rays), or green solution (ammoniacal copper sulphate and potassium dichromate). Expose it to bright sunlight for a few hours, then the leaves may be tested for starch grains. The intensity of the black colour, which is the effect of iodine treatment, gives a comparative idea of the quantity of starch formed in different rays. In the case of water plants, the effect of rays of light may be studied from the rate of evolution of oxygen bubbles.

(b) **Canong's light-screen** (large form). The proper use of this instrument gives a good idea of the rays of light utilized in photosynthesis. Of the five vials in it, four are filled each with red, orange, green and blue solution, and the fifth vial with water. A starch-free, broad, green leaf of a plant is inserted through the hole of the light-screen and laid flat underneath the five vials. Evidently, different rays of light will fall on the leaf in strips. After exposure to sunlight for some hours, the leaf is bleached and treated with iodine solution.

The intensity of coloration will indicate which rays have been utilized for photosynthesis.

(c) **Spectrum analysis of chlorophyll solution.** A direct-vision spectroscope may be used for this purpose. The spectrum analysis will show a broad, dark band in the region of red, another in blue-violet, but only a small one in orange. Therefore, these are the rays mainly utilized by chlorophyll for photosynthesis.

Crassulacean Acid Metabolism (CAM). In many plants that grow in deserts and dry conditions, the leaves become thick and fleshy, e.g., plants belonging to families like *Orchidaceae, Liliaceae, Crassulaceae*, etc. In others, the leaves are reduced, minimizing the exposed surface area of the blades, or they fall off early and the stem becomes thick, fleshy and green, e.g., cacti, euphorbias, etc. These plants have sunken stomata, stem and leaves with thick cuticle, and cells with large vacuoles. These characteristics help such plants to retain water and overcome longer periods of drought. The sunken stomata of these plants, also called CAM plants, remain open at night and closed during the day (when the air is hot and dry and the temperature high), thereby checking excessive transpiration.

A diurnal organic acid metabolism (CAM) occurs in such plants. At night, carbon dioxide diffuses through the stomata and reacts with phosphoenol pyruvic acid (CO_2 acceptor). The latter is carboxylated, leading to the formation of oxaloacetic acid and then malic acid. Malic acid is stored in the cell sap contained in the vacuoles. During the day, malic acid comes out of the cell sap and accumulates in the cytoplasm, where it is dehydrogenated (by NADP) and decarboxylated, leading to the evolution of CO_2 and the formation of pyruvic acid. Pyruvic acid reacts with ATP and gives rise to phosphoenol pyruvic acid.

The reactions from CO_2 fixation to the formation of phosphoenol pyruvic acid are the same as those of the C_4 cycle. But the CAM mechanism differs from the C_4 mechanism in the following respects:

1. In this case, phosphoenol pyruvic acid does not act as a CO_2 acceptor. Instead, it follows a different course of reactions (reverse pathway of glycolysis) to form hexose phosphate, sugar and, finally, starch. Phosphoenol pyruvic acid is then regenerated from starch. The phosphoenol pyruvic acid formed from starch acts as the CO_2 acceptor and the cycle is renewed, whereas in the C_4 cycle, the phosphoenol pyruvic acid formed from pyruvic acid acts as the CO_2 acceptor.

2. The released CO_2 is accepted by RuDP and the C_3 cycle occurs. In this case, both the C_4 and the C_3 cycles take place in the mesophyll cells, while in C_4 plants, the C_3 cycle takes place in the bundle sheath cells.

3. The vascular sheath is absent in CAM plants.

4. CAM plants are better adapted to extreme, hot and dry habitats than C_4 plants.

For CAM mechanism diagram see Appendix II.

Photosynthesis by Autotrophic Bacteria. Autotrophic bacteria may be photosynthetic or chemosynthetic. Photosynthetic bacteria develop a pigment closely related to chlorophyll. They are purple sulphur bacteria and green sulphur bacteria. Both are anaerobic. **Purple sulphur bacteria** develop a purple pigment (*bacteriochlorophyll*) which may be a substitute for chlorophyll. According to Van Niel (1941), an American microbiologist, they utilize light as a source of energy to decompose hydrogen sulphide (H_2S)—a poisonous gas (and not water as in normal photosynthesis) —into hydrogen and sulphur. The hydrogen thus released is used to reduce CO_2 to carbohydrate in a series of dark reactions, as in green plants. Sulphur (and not oxygen) is liberated in the process. In this case, H_2S oxidation and CO_2 reduction are closely interrelated according to the following overall equation—$6CO_2 + 12H_2S \rightarrow C_6H_{12}O_6 + 6H_2O + 12S$. Similarly, **green sulphur bacteria** containing the pigment *bacterioviridin* use light-energy for the oxidation of H_2S with the liberation of hydrogen, which is then used for the reduction of CO_2 to carbohydrate in a stepwise manner. This may suggest a primitive process of photosynthesis, from which the higher forms of plants have developed the use of water (H_2O) as the 'donor' of hydrogen in the normal photosynthetic process.

Chemosynthesis. Colourless, autotrophic bacteria are able to synthesize carbohydrate without chlorophyll and, therefore, without light as a source of energy. These bacteria are aerobic, and the energy required for the metabolic processes is derived from the oxidation of certain inorganic compounds present in their environment. The energy released by this oxidative process is used to convert CO_2, through several intermediate reactions, to carbohydrate and other organic compounds. Chemosynthesis, thus, involves the transformation of one kind of chemical energy (and not light-energy) to another. Chemosynthetic bacteria do not use water (H_2O) either as the 'donor' of hydrogen to reduce CO_2, as in normal photosynthesis and, therefore, no oxygen is liberated in this process. This may be evidence that the oxygen released in normal photosynthesis comes from water (H_2O) and not carbon dioxide (CO_2). Common chemosynthetic bacteria are sulphur bacteria, iron bacteria and nitrifying bacteria. (a) **Sulphur bacteria** grow in sulphur springs and in stagnant water containing hydrogen sulphide. They are filamentous cells. They obtain their energy for the synthetic processes, as first shown by Winogradsky (1887), by the oxidation of sulphur compounds present in water. Thus, they oxidize hydrogen sulphide (H_2S) and use the energy released to reduce CO_2 to carbohydrate and other organic compounds. Sulphur is deposited in the bacterial cells. This deposit is used again when the need arises. The reaction may be expressed by the following equation —$2H_2S + O_2 \rightarrow 2S + 2H_2O + 32.5$ cal. During the process, some of the sulphur deposit is further oxidized into sulphuric acid (H_2SO_4). (b) **Iron bacteria** are filamentous types. They grow in lakes and marshes, and in water containing ferrous iron. They obtain their energy for synthesis of organic compounds by the oxidation of ferrous hydroxide to ferric hydroxide. Such water is often reddish. Bog iron ore and deposits of iron oxides in lakes and marshes are due to their activity. (c) **Nitrifying bacteria** live in the soil and are of two types. As already discussed (see p. 229), they transform ammonia (NH_3), formed during the process of protein decay in the soil, first into nitrites by mobile, spherical nitrite bacteria (*Nitrosomonas*)—$2NH_3 + 3O_2 \rightarrow 2HNO_2 + 2H_2O + 79$ cal., and then into nitrates by non-mobile, rod-shaped nitrate bacteria (*Nitrobacter*)—$2HNO_2 + O_2 \rightarrow 2HNO_3 + 21.6$ cal. The energy liberated by the oxidation of ammonia is used to make metabolic products, together with CO_2 absorbed from the air.

2. PROTEINS

NATURE OF PROTEINS. These are very complex, organic, nitrogenous compounds found in plants and animals (see also p. 137). Analyses of plant proteins show that carbon, hydrogen, oxygen, nitrogen, sulphur and sometimes phosphorus enter into their composition, but we know little about their molecular structure. Protein molecules are often very large and extremely complex, consisting of thousands of atoms. They are composed of several chains of amino-acid molecules arranged in a definite order. Proteins are of high molecular weights, ranging from several thousands to several millions. (The examples of glucose and sucrose, which have molecular weights of 180 and 342, respectively, may be cited as a comparison). Proteins are also very complex in their chemical composition. As a matter of fact, the structural formulae of only a few proteins have been determined so far. The first formula of a protein was established by Dr Frederick Sanger of Cambridge University in 1954 after ten years' hard work. The protein is *insulin*, and its molecular formula has been determined to be $C_{254}H_{377}N_{65}O_{75}S_6$. Its molecule is, however, small compared to most proteins but is made of a sequence of 51 amino-acids, with many of them evidently repeated. Some of the other formulae known are of *zein* of maize—$C_{736}H_{1161}N_{184}O_{208}S_3$, and of *gliadin* of wheat— $C_{685}H_{1068}N_{196}O_{211}S_5$. Besides the elements mentioned above, small quantities of sodium, potassium, magnesium and iron are also present. Various kinds of proteins are found in plants (see pp. 138-39). Amino-acids are the initial stages in the formation of proteins, and they are also the degradation products of the latter. Proteins are the main constituents of living materials, and occur to the extent of nearly half the total dry weight of them. They are linked with the metabolism of the cell and its vital activities. A high rate of protein synthesis leads to a correspondingly high rate of respiration. Proteins are essential for growth and repair of the body (see also p. 138).

SYNTHESIS OF PROTEINS. Proteins are normally formed from nitrates absorbed from the soil. But the chemical reactions leading to the formation of these complex compounds are known only imperfectly. It has been already mentioned that phosphoglyceric acid holds a central position, from which chains of reactions start—one leading to the formation of carbohydrates and the other to that of various organic acids, fats and proteins through phosphopyruvic acid, as revealed by radioactive carbon. It is likely that the synthesis of the various products mentioned above proceeds simultaneously in different directions. Protein synthesis takes place mostly in the meristematic and storage tissues. Some proteins are also formed in all active cells of the plant body. The whole process of protein synthesis takes place in three different stages :

(A) **Reduction of Nitrates.** Nitrogen is an essential constituent of all proteins. We know that the nitrate of the soil is the main source of nitrogen supply to the higher plants. After the nitrate is absorbed into the plant body, it is first reduced to nitrite by the enzyme *nitrate reductase*. The nitrite is then reduced to ammonia (NH_3) by *nitrite reductase* through some unknown intermediate compounds, as follows: $NO_3 \rightarrow NO_2 \rightarrow NH_3$. The detailed chemical stages in the reduction series are, however, not yet known. Meyer and Schultze in 1894 first suggested that the reductive stages might be as follows: nitrate→ nitrite→ hyponitrite→ hydroxylamine → ammonia. Hydroxylamine has been actually detected in plant cells in small quantities though hyponitrite has not. The reduction of nitrate to ammonia usually takes place in the root and in the leaf. At the next step, ammonia is directly incorporated into

∝–ketoglutaric acid (see below). This is now known to be the main channel of entry of inorganic nitrogen into the system of nitrogen assimilation. Ammonia, thus, holds a key position in the process of protein synthesis. This is supported by the fact that a stable isotope, N_{15}, used in an inorganic nutrient solution can be traced in ammonia ($N^{15}H^3$) and later in ∝-ketoglutaric acid.

(B) **Synthesis of Amino-acids.** As stated before, amino-acids are the initial stages leading finally to the synthesis of proteins. About 20 amino-acids are known to be constituents of plant proteins. An amino-acid contains an acidic or carboxyl group (–COOH) and a basic or amino group (–NH_2) attached to a central C with a side chain or R group. The general structure of an amino-acid is shown on p. 264. The group R, it may be noted, is different in different amino-acids. As already mentioned, ammonia enters into ∝–ketoglutaric acid and reacts with it. The keto acid, chemically almost similar to an amino-acid, is an important intermediate product formed during the aerobic phase of respiration (see Krebs Cycle, FIG. 34). Ammonia combines with the keto acid and under the action of the enzyme, *glutamic hydrogenase*, which is widespread in plants, the first amino-acid makes its appearance in the form of *glutamic acid*, as demonstrated by Vickery in 1940 by the use of radioactive ammonia, i.e. $N^{15}H^3$. The glutamic acid thus formed holds a central position from which several other amino-acids are formed by a process called transamination (see below). In 1954, Wilson detected as many as 17 amino-acids formed by this process. Some amino-acids may also be formed otherwise. For example, NH_3 may directly combine with oxalacetic acid (and also fumaric acid) to produce *aspartic acid*, and with pyruvic acid to produce *alanine*. Amino-acids are synthesized mainly in the green leaf and root. There is experimental proof that the reduction of nitrate to ammonia and synthesis of amino-acids usually take place in the green leaf in the presence of light. Evidently, the synthetic process is correlated with photosynthesis, which supplies the required carbon, hydrogen and oxygen (80-85% of amino-acids are non-nitrogenous). It is, however, not known how exactly this takes place. Synthesis of amino-acids in the root appears to be connected with root respiration, which supplies the energy needed.

Transamination. As stated before, glutamic acid holds a central position from which several other amino-acids may be formed. Transamination involves the transfer of an amino group ($-NH_2$) of the glutamic acid to the carboxyl group ($-COOH$) of any of the keto acids. This takes place under the action of specific enzymes, called *transaminases*, with the formation of corresponding new amino-acids, as first demonstrated by Engel in 1934 and later by several others. Some amino-acids may also be formed by the transfer of an amino group of the glutamic acid or of the keto acid to oxalacetic acid to produce *aspartic acid*, and also to pyruvic acid to produce *alanine*. It will be noted that different transaminases work to produce different amino-acids. Twenty different amino-acids take part in the synthesis of proteins. The simplest amino-acid is *glycine*, represented by the formula NH_2-CH_2-$COOH$. Other important but complex ones are *alanine, leucine, aspartic acid, glutamic acid, cystine, tyrosine*, etc. *Cystine*, which is formed in all plants, also contains sulphur. It may be noted that animals do not normally utilize ammonia to produce an amino-acid.

$$R-CH-COOH$$
$$|$$
$$NH_2$$
(general formula)

e.g.

$$H-CH-COOH \qquad CH_3-CH-COOH$$
$$| \qquad\qquad\qquad |$$
$$NH_2 \qquad\qquad\qquad NH_2$$
(glycine)   (alanine)

(C) Synthesis of Proteins. Amino-acids are the precursors of all proteins and, therefore, they must be available to the living cells for final elaboration into proteins. Protein molecules are very large and complex, and hundreds of them may occur in a single cell. A protein molecule may finally be formed by linkage of hundreds or thousands of amino-acid molecules, which may be arranged in an infinite variety of chains. Linkage of different amino-acids in several long chains under the action of specific enzymes results in the synthesis of an infinite variety of proteins (see p. 138-39), each species having its own characteristic types. The arrangement of particular amino-acids in specific sequences in the chain, with one or more of them often repeated, is a pre-determining factor responsible for making a particular kind of protein. It follows, therefore, that the omission of a single amino-acid required in the chain directly affects protein synthesis. Apart from enzymes, the reactions in protein synthesis are activated by ATP. It may be noted that, the compound formed as a result of the combination of two or a few amino-acids in short chains is called a *peptide*. It is rather rare in plant or animal cells. When many amino-acids combine the resulting compound is called a *polypeptide*. Thus, by linkage of several amino-acid molecules, proteins are formed in the following order: amino acid→polypeptides→peptones→proteoses→proteins. Emil Fischer first suggested (1899-1906) that proteins are formed by condensation of numerous amino-acids. He mentioned 18 such amino-acids. It may be noted that protein synthesis and protein breakdown, the latter under the action of proteolytic enzymes or by a reversal of the synthetic process, go on simultaneously in plant cells. The amino-acids, formed by the breakdown, may again combine into proteins. Complex proteins contain sulphur and more complex ones, like nucleoprotein, contain phosphorus as well. Sulphur and phosphorus are obtained from the soil as sulphates and phosphates. As stated before, amino-acids are formed mainly in the root and leaf. They travel from there to distant tissue. Protein synthesis occurs mostly in the meristematic (root-tip and stem-tip) and storage tissues, and to some extent in most living cells. Proteins, however, do not travel as such. It may also be noted that protein synthesis is mostly localized in the ribosomes occurring in plenty in the cytoplasm (see p. 128). Some proteins may also be formed in the nucleus.

DNA and Protein Synthesis. Researches on nucleic

acids (DNA and RNA) by a number of investigators (see p. 123) have established the fact that the DNA of a chromosome is the sole genetic material controlling all the biosynthetic processes of the cell, including protein synthesis. To understand how DNA works in this respect, a preliminary acquaintance with the structure of the DNA molecule, with its purine and pyrimidine bases (see FIG II/5), is essential. The DNA prepares a master plan for the specific kinds of proteins and their quantities to be built up in particular cells of a plant. It must be noted that the synthesis of proteins in a cell is due to the co-ordinated action of DNA, RNA and ribosomes—the last two occurring abundantly in the cytoplasm of a cell (see FIG. II/6). RNA occurs in three forms: 'messenger' RNA or mRNA, 'transfer' or 'soluble' RNA or tRNA or sRNA, and 'ribosomal' RNA or rRNA (as follows). As stated before, protein molecules are made of long chains of amino-acid molecules, and one kind of protein is distinguished from another by the number and kinds of amino-acids and the sequence of their arrangement in each protein molecule. It is important to note that the purine and pyrimidine bases of the DNA and RNA molecules occur in infinite sequences. The specific order or sequence of these bases in the double-stranded DNA molecule determines the specific order of the amino-acid molecules that will finally be linked to synthesize a particular kind of protein (Hoagland, 1955). The information required to guide the synthesis of a protein is known to reside in coded form in the particular sequence of bases. DNA, however, does not play a direct role in protein synthesis and RNA acts as its working partner in the process. DNA remains in the chromosome permanently within the safe environs of the nucleus, and as said before, organizes a master plan for the whole process of protein synthesis, working through codes (or chemical messages). DNA coins a particular code and transmits it to 'messenger' RNA (mRNA), which is now used as a messenger, carrying the code from the DNA to the cytoplasm and finally to a ribosome in it or to a small group of ribosomes called polysome. It should be noted that mRNA is formed by transcription of one of the two strands of a DNA molecule, which serves as a template for the synthesis of the single-stranded mRNA molecule. The second type of RNA—'transfer' or 'soluble' RNA (tRNA or sRNA)—occurs as comparatively small molecules that are abundant in the cytoplasm in a free state. It possibly originates in the nucleolus under the control of DNA and then moves out to the surrounding cytoplasm. sRNA receives necessary information from

mRNA (through pairing of their bases), and accordingly selects a particular amino-acid, possibly by chemical attraction, out of a heterogenous mixture of compounds present in the cell. This, of course, is done with the aid of a highly specific enzyme. sRNA then carries the amino-acid to the ribosome. It is also known that the amino-acid molecule is attached to a specific location on the sRNA, and that there is a separate such RNA for each amino-acid (Hoagland and his colleagues, 1959). Obviously, there are 20 kinds of sRNA for the known 20 amino-acids. The third type of RNA—'ribosomal' RNA or rRNA—occurs in the ribosome. Ribosomes are distributed in the cytoplasm as very tiny particles in large numbers (see p. 127). They are the seats of protein synthesis. A ribosome consists of nucleoprotein, i.e. a nucleic acid (RNA in this case) and a protein in almost equal quantities. The process of protein synthesis is now as follows. DNA coins a particular code (or message) for the purpose of synthesizing a specific protein in a cell, and transmits this code to mRNA, which then moves out of the nucleus to a ribosome in the cytoplasm. Several amino-acids, each carried by a sRNA, are brought to the ribosome. It is now for the rRNA to do the rest of the work. It brings about the association of mRNA and sRNA, and receives the code and the amino-acids, respectively, from them. rRNA now deciphers the code, i.e. translates it into the language of physiology, and accordingly brings about linkage of specific amino-acid molecules in definite sequences into long chains. The result is the synthesis of a specific protein molecule, with the amino-acid molecules arranged in a definite order in it. Of course, a specific enzyme is indispensable to catalyze each reaction, and the energy required for the whole process is furnished by ATP, an energy-rich phosphate compound. Protein molecules become very lage and complex, depending on the number and frequency of amino-acid molecules entering into their composition, forming long chains. Further, on the basis of the infinite sequences of the two bases (purine and pyrimidine; see FIG II/5) in the long and complex DNA molecule it may be safely assumed that DNA may coin an infinite number of codes through them (the bases) and thus produce an endless variety of proteins. Although DNA is the same in all plants, it produces only specific kinds of proteins for each species of plants. It may further be noted that, after release from a ribosome, mRNA may move to several other ribosomes (particularly in higher plants). It has also been suggested that mRNA may be associated with several ribosomes by its long strand. In any case it soon becomes disorganized. rRNA moves back to the cytoplasm and repeats the process.

Investigations carried out in the later half of this century have established above facts and several investigators were awarded the Nobel Prize for their discoveries in different years. This is, however, just a part of the whole story. The mechanism of protein degradation still remains to be solved. Not much work has been done in this direction. One area that needs to be researched is a method by which the output of protein can be increased and its breakdown decreased, particularly in crops vital for the fulfilment of man's need for proteins. Intensive research is progressing in this direction.

3. FATS AND OILS

Fats and oils are lipid (fatty) substances formed in the living cells of both plants and animals. There is only a physical difference between the two—at ordinary temperature fats are solids, as mostly in animals, and oils are liquids, as mostly in plants. Fatty oils often occur in abundance in seeds and fruits. All fats and oils are composed of carbon, hydrogen and oxygen, the last one occurring in a low percentage. When fats and oils are hydrolysed by acids or alkalis, or by the action of lipase extract, glycerol (glycerine), one or more fatty acids are the products formed, indicating the compounds out of which the former are built up.

Although the different stages in the synthesis of fats and oils are only imperfectly known, they are no doubt the final condensation products of glycerol and fatty acids under the reverse action of lipase. Fats and oils are insoluble in water and cannot, therefore, diffuse out of the cells in which they are formed. It is known that both glycerol and fatty acids appear in living cells as a result of carbohydrate breakdown (particularly glucose and fructose) under the action of some enzymes (aldolase, etc.) during the anaerobic phase of respiration, passing through several complicated reactions. The reactions are reversible—from carbohydrate to fats and vice versa. Several fatty acids are formed in plants, e.g. palmitic, stearic, oleic, lauric, linoleic, linolenic, etc. Glycerol and fatty acids do not accumulate in cells but are immediately utilized in fat synthesis. Finally, it may be stated that the molecules of glycerol and one or more fatty acids (degraded products of carbohydrates) condense into fat molecules under the action of lipase. It should be noted that carbohydrates diminish in quantity with the increase of fatty oils in seeds. This supports the view that fats and oils are formed from carbohydrates. Three stages are known to be involved in the whole process, viz. (a) synthesis of fatty acids, (b) synthesis of glycerol and, finally, (c) synthesis of fats and oils by condensation of the first two.

CHAPTER 7

SPECIAL MODES OF NUTRITION

Green plants are **autotrophic** (*autos*, self; *trophe*, food) or self-nourishing, that is, they are able to manufacture carbohydrates from raw or inorganic materials and nourish themselves. Non-green plants, on the other hand, are **heterotrophic** (*heteros*, different). Such plants cannot prepare carbohydrates and nourish themselves. They get their supply of carbohydrate food from various sources. They can, however, prepare other kinds of food.

Heterotrophic plants are **parasites** when they depend on other living plants or animals, and **saprophytes** when they depend on the organic material present in the soil or in the dead bodies of plants and animals.

1. PARASITES (see pp. 13-15). Total parasites such as dodder (*Cuscuta*), broomrape (*Orobanche*), etc., are never green and consequently they cannot prepare their own food. They draw all their nourishment from the host plant on which they are parasitic. Partial parasites like mistletoe (*Viscum*), *Loranthus, Cassytha*, etc., on the other hand, are green and, therefore, not entirely dependent on the host plant. Parasitic phanerogams develop haustoria or sucking roots which go into the vascular bundles of the host plant and absorb its prepared food material and water. Fungi and bacteria are either total parasites or saprophytes. Parasitic fungi send their mycelia into the tissue of the host plant. The mycelia ramify in all directions and absorb the necessary food materials. Parasitic bacteria infect living plants and animals and absorb food from their bodies.

2. SAPROPHYTES (see p. 15).
Saprophytic phanerogams, such as Indian pipe (*Monotropa*; see FIG. I/27), some orchids, saprophytic fungi and saprophytic bacteria, grow on decaying animal or vegetable matter, and absorb the organic food from it.

3. SYMBIONTS (see p. 15-16).
Two organisms that live in close association and are of mutual benefit to each other are called symbionts. This condition is known as symbiosis. Lichen, mycorrhiza, etc., are examples.

4. CARNIVOROUS PLANTS.
These plants are known to capture lower animals of various kinds, particularly insects. They digest the prey and absorb the nitrogenous products (proteins) from its body. Being green, they can manufacture their own carbohydrate food. Till now, altogether over 450 species of carnivorous plants representing 15 genera belonging to 5 or 6 families have been discovered. Of these over 30 species occur in India.

Classified according to their systematic position

(a) *Droseraceae* (105 sp.), e.g. *Drosera* (100 sp.)—cosmopolitan, *Dionaea* (1 sp.)—the United States, *Drosophyllum* (1 sp.)—Morocco, Spain and Portugal, and *Aldrovanda* (1 sp.)—Europe, Asia and Australia.

(b) *Sarraceniaceae* (17 sp.), e.g. *Sarracenia* (10 sp.)—Atlantic North America, *Darlingtonia* (1 sp.)—California, and *Heliamphora* (4 sp.)— Guiana.

(c) *Nepenthaceae* (68 sp.), e.g. *Nepenthes* (67 sp.)—Malaysia, Australia, India and Malagasy.

(d) *Cephalotaceae* (1 sp.), e.g. *Cephalotus* (1 sp)—Australia.

(e) *Lentibulariaceae* (170 sp.), e.g. *Utricularia* (120 sp.)—cosmopolitan, and *Pinguicula* (35 sp.)—north temperate regions and temperate Himalayas.

Classified according to the mode of catching prey

(a) Plants with sensitive glandular hairs secreting a sweet, viscid, glistening substance, e.g. sundew (*Drosera*), butterwort (*Pinguicula*) and *Drosophyllum*.

(b) Plants with special sensitive hairs—trigger hairs—on the leaf-surface, e.g. Venus' fly-trap (*Dionaea*) and *Aldrovanda. Aldrovanda* is an aquatic plant.

(c) Plants with leaves modified into pitchers, e.g. pitcher plant (*Nepenthes*)—leaf partly modified into pitcher. Other pitcher plants (*Sarracenia, Darlingtonia, Heliamphora* and *Cephalotus*)—entire leaf modified into pitcher.

(d) Plants with leaf-segments modified into bladders, e.g. bladderwort (*Utricularia*). Bladderworts are mostly aquatic. A few tropical ones are terrestrial.

(1) **Sundew** (*Drosera*; FIG. 26)—100 sp. Only 3 species, viz. *D. peltata, D. burmanni* and *D. indica*, have been found in India. They are small herbs.

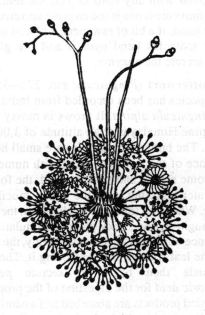

FIG. 26. Sundew (*Drosera*)

Each leaf is covered on the upper surface with numerous glandular hairs known as **tentacles**. Each gland, which is reddish, secretes a kind of fluid which glitters in the sun like dewdrops and hence the name 'sundew'. The gland is sensitive and reacts to only chemical stimuli. This means that the movement of the tentacles is initiated by the presence of nitrogenous substances. Contact with any foreign object does not prompt movement. When an insect mistaking the glistening substance for honey alights on the leaf, it gets entangled in the sticky fluid. The tentacles, stimulated by the digestible compounds present in the body of the insect, bend over it from all sides and cover it. When it is suffocated to death the process of digestion begins. The tentacles remain bent over the insect until all the nitrogenous compounds contained in its body have been absorbed. Digestion is extracellular in all carnivorous plants. The glands secrete an enzyme, called *pepsin hydrochloric acid*, which acts on the insect and changes the proteins of its body into soluble and simple forms. The products of digestion are then absorbed by the leaf. The carbonaceous materials are rejected in the form of waste products.

When poked with any hard object, the tentacles show no movement nor is the enzyme secreted. On the other hand, if a bit of raw meat is placed on the leaf, the tentacles bend over it and the glands begin to secrete the enzyme.

(2) **Butterwort** (*Pinguicula*; FIG. 27)—35 sp. Only 1 species has been recorded from India, and that is *Pinguicula alpina*. It grows in mossy beds in the alpine Himalayas at an altitude of 3,000 to 4,000 m. The butterwort species are small herbs. The surface of the leaf is covered with numerous glands, some sessile and some stalked, the former being water-secreting and the latter mucilage-secreting. When any small insect alights on the leaf, it gets caught by the sticky glands. Stimulated by the presence of proteins in the insect body, the margins of the leaf roll inwards, enclosing it. The sessile glands then begin to secrete *pepsin hydrochloric acid* for the digestion of the proteins. The digested products are absorbed and assimilated by the plant, after which the leaf unrolls again.

FIG. 27. Butterwort (*Pinguicula*)

Carnivory in butterwort was studied by Darwin, who found that meat, egg-white, cartilage, small seeds, pollen grains and other substances containing nitrogen caused secretion of the enzyme when placed on a leaf, while those containing no nitrogen caused none.

(3) **Venus' Fly-trap** (*Dionaea muscipula*; FIG. 28)—1 sp. The plant is a native of the U.S.A. It is herbaceous and grows in damp, mossy places. Each half of the leaf-blade is provided with three long, pointed hairs—trigger hairs—placed triangularly on the leaf-surface. The hairs are extremely sensitive from base to apex. If any of these hairs is touched even lightly, the leaf-blade is liable to close suddenly, the mid-rib acting as the hinge. The upper surface of the leaf is thickly covered with reddish digestive glands. When an insect is caught, or any nitrogenous material like meat, fish, etc., placed on the leaf, it closes suddenly and the glands begin to secrete *pepsin hydrochloric acid* for digestion of the proteins. The acid is stronger in this case than in most other carnivorous plants.

(4) **Water fly-trap** (*Aldrovanda vesiculosa*; FIGS. 29-30)—1 sp. This plant is very widely distributed over the earth. It has been found in abundance in the salt-lakes of the Sundarbans, the salt marshes south of Calcutta, the fresh-water 'jheels' of Bangladesh and in several tanks in Manipur. *Aldrovanda* may be regarded as a miniature *Dionaea* in some respects. It is a rootless, free-

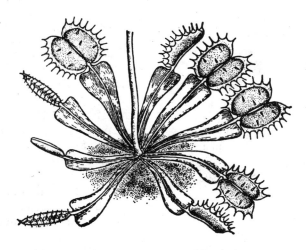

FIG. 28. Venus' fly-trap (*Dionaea*)

floating plant with whorls of leaves. The mechanism for catching the prey is practically the same as that of *Dionaea*, but instead of only six sensitive hairs, there are several hairs on either side of the mid-rib, and the leaf is protected by some bristles. The leaf's upper surface has numerous digestive glands, and the margins have minute teeth that point inwards.

(5) **Pitcher Plant** (*Nepenthes*; FIG. 31 and I/69)—67 sp. Only one species (*Nepenthes khasiana*) has been found in north-east India (in the Garo Hills and Khasi-Jaintia Hills of Meghalaya). Pitcher plants are climbing herbs or undershrubs which often climb by means of the tendrillar stalk of the pitcher. The pitcher itself is a modification of the leaf-blade. The tendrillar stalk supporting the pitcher is a modification of the petiole and the laminated structure is the modified leaf-base. The height of a pitcher varies from 10 to 20 cm., or even more. The mouth of a young pitcher remains closed by a lid, which later opens and stands more or less erect. Below the mouth, the inside of the pitcher is covered with many smooth and sharp hairs, all pointing downwards. Lower down, the inner surface is studded with several large digestive glands, each with a hood hanging down over it. Animals, as they enter, slip down the smooth surface and lose their footing, getting drowned in the fluid that partially fills the cavity of the pitcher. After they are dead, the process of digestion commences. The digestive power of the pitcher of *Nepenthes* was first discovered by Hooker in 1874. The digestive agent, secreted by the glands, is in the nature of a *trypsin*, as was first shown by Vines in 1877. It not only digests the proteins into peptones, but also converts the latter into amines. Amines are readily absorbed by the

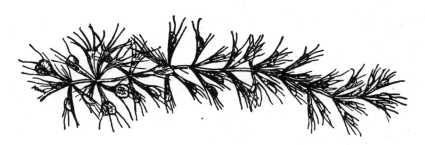

FIG. 29. Water fly-trap (*Aldrovanda*)

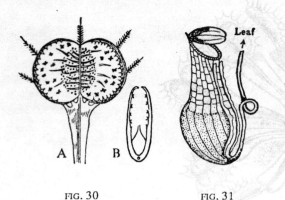

FIG. 30   FIG. 31

FIG. 30. *Aldrovanda*; *A*, an entire leaf open;
B, section of a closed leaf. FIG. 31. A pitcher of
pitcher plant. See also FIG. I/69

pitcher. Bits of egg-white, meat, etc., dropped into
the pitcher, as first found by Hooker, are seen to be
dissolved and ultimately absorbed in the form of
amines. Carbohydrates and other materials remain
undigested in the pitcher as waste products.

(6) **Bladderwort** (*Utricularia*; FIG. 32)—120
sp. Over 20 species have been found in India, *U.
flexuosa* being a very common one. They are
mostly floating or slighty submerged, rootless,
aquatic herbs. There are a few terrestrial species
also, e.g. *U. wallichiana*, which grows in moist
hill slopes of Shillong. The leaves are greatly segmented and simulate roots, except that they are
green. Some of these segments become transformed into *bladders*. Each bladder is about 3-
5 mm. in diameter and is provided with a trap-door
entrance. The trap-door acts as a sort of valve
which can be pushed open from outside, but never
from inside. Very small aquatic animals enter by
bending the free end of the valve, which gives way
easily. The valve then shuts automatically, trapping the animal inside. The inner surface of the
bladder is dotted all over with numerous digestive
glands which vary somewhat in shape. There function is to secrete the digestive enzyme and absorb
the digested products. A bit of raw meat, pushed
inside the bladder, is found to disappear within a
few days.

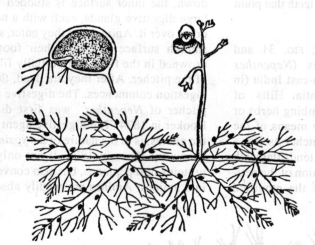

FIG. 32.
Bladderwort
(*Utricularia*)
with many
small bladders;
top, a bladder
in section
(magnified)

CHAPTER 8

TRANSLOCATION AND
STORAGE OF FOOD

TRANSLOCATION

Food material is mostly prepared in the leaves. From there, it is translocated to the storage organs and the growing regions, which are often considerably far from the leaves. There are definite and distinct channels extending through the whole length of the plant body for the translocation of raw food material or inorganic salts and prepared or organic food material. As already discussed (see p. 246), inorganic salts move upward through the xylem. As for downward transmission, the food material prepared in the leaves is first rendered soluble and diffusible by enzymic action—carbohydrates are converted into sugars, and proteins into amino-acids and amines. Once in the storage organs, the sugars are mostly reconverted into insoluble starch, and amino-acids and amines into different kinds of insoluble proteins. Two questions naturally arise in this connection: what is the pathway of translocation and what is the mechanism involved in the process? Extensive research was done in this area by Hartig (1858), Hanstein (1860) and Sachs (1874), and later, by Dixon (1923), Mason and his associates(1929), Curtis (1935), and several others. Despite all the research, the position is still far from clear in many respects. As a matter of fact, a mass of conflicting views has been expressed by modern scientists, which evidently indicates that much remains to be done yet.

PATHWAY OF TRANSLOCATION. That the phloem is the conduction channel was proved conclusively by scientists on the basis of 'ringing' experiments, first introduced by Malpighi in the late 17th century, and later by Hartig (1858), Hanstein (1860) and Sachs (1874). 'Ringing' experiments, it may be noted, also proved to be a useful tool for modern scientists. With improved techniques, chemical analyses and the use of radioactive elements, they have made many new discoveries. (a) Chemical analyses of the contents of the phloem have revealed the presence of many food substances, such as sugars (predominantly cane-sugar in many cases) among the carbohydrates, mostly amino-acids and amines, and also some soluble proteins among the nitrogenous materials. This fact itself is no proof of conduction but it leads to this view. It should also be noted that sugar is present in the bodies of certain insects and aphids that suck the phloem of the tender shoot and leaf-stalk. (b) Several scientists have shown through 'ringing' or 'girdling' experiments that the food material mainly moves through the phloem (sieve-tubes and companion cells). If a ring of bark completely encircling a branch is removed down to the wood (evidently including phloem), swellings and later buds appear just above the ring or girdle due to the accumulation of food which cannot move further down, the phloem having been removed. If such a girdle is made at the base of a flowering shoot; large flowers and fruits may be produced for the same reason. Similarly, if a ring of bark is removed from the lower end of a cut leafy branch (say, of garden croton) and the cut end dipped into water, roots are seen to develop only above the girdle where food has accumulated, the phloem portion being removed with the ring. The 'ringing' experiments prove that it is the phloem that is primarily responsible for transporting the food downward.

From the above and other experiments, the following facts become apparent. Phloem is definitely the principal conduction channel for food. Carbohydrates and proteins travel in the form of sugars (predominantly cane-sugar) and amines and amino-acids, respectively. Translocation is through the sieve-tubes, and to some extent, through the companion cells and phloem parenchyma. It will be noted that all the elements of phloem are living. Food material can easily pass through the perforated sieve-plates. It mostly moves downwards from the leaf and, later, upwards from the root (see below). The protoplasmic threads may facilitate the movement through the pores of the sieve-plates. Phloem elements are also permeable, and many minute pits develop in their walls. Food also moves through them laterally to other tissues (xylem parenchyma, medullary rays, etc.). Food substances formed in the mesophyll of the leaf and rendered soluble there move towards the vascular bundles. They pass through the border parenchyma and enter the phloem. The phloem extends in long strands from one end of the plant body to the others so that any soluble compound can be transported from the leaves to the other organs, particularly the storage ones and the growing regions. In the storage organs, the food accumulates in the form of insoluble, complex proteins and starch. During the period of active growth later, as in the spring, when new buds, flowers and fruits are in the offing, the various forms of stored food are rendered soluble and, therefore, can travel easily. Now an upward movement of the soluble food material takes place through the phloem at linear rates of up to 100 cm. per hour and finally, they are brought to the growing organs (Curtis, 1935). During the period of active growth, a part of the food also moves upwards through the xylem (Fischer, 1915; Atkins, 1916; Dixon, 1923). The movement of the solutes in the phloem is bidirectional, i.e. downward and upward, either at the same time or at different times. That this is so was proved in 1944 by Biddulph and his colleague, who grew a plant in an atmosphere containing radioactive carbon dioxide, $C^{13}O_2$. It was seen that the carbohydrate formed in the leaf, descending down the petiole, moved simultaneously in both directions—upward and downward—through the stem. This view was shared by researchers later, as well. There is also a diurnal variation in the rate of movement of the solutes in different plants.

A Short Historical Account. There was a time lag after the work of Hanstein (1860) and Sachs (1874). Sachs held the view that there is a mass movement of the solutes (dissolved organic substances) and the solvent (water) through the phloem from the higher concentration region (leaf) to the lower concentration region (root), aided by turgor and tension of the sieve tubes and the associated cells. Dixon, while working on the ascent of sap in 1923, held the view that the anatomical structure of the phloem does not warrant the movement of organic solutes through it and that the flow of such substances must take place through the transpiration current in the xylem under certain tensil forces. This view has been rejected by well-known researchers like Curtis (1935), Mason and Maskell (1928-29), Czapek (1905 onwards) and others, who have strongly defended the view that the food is conducted through the phloem, as was proved by the early scientists. Mason and Maskell stated clearly in 192? that the inorganic salts absorbed by the roots move upward in the transpiration current through the xylem and that the food elaborated in the leaf and converted into sugars (mainly cane-sugar), amino-acids, etc., is transported through the phloem. Convincing proof of this fact was offered by Hoagland and Stout in 1939 when they used radioactive K, Na, etc., in inorganic salts. In 1935, however, Curtis experimentally proved that certain inorganic salts like nitrates and phosphate also move upwards through the phloem. This view was supported by Gustafson in 1937.

MECHANISM OF TRANSLOCATION. The transport of solutes through the phloem seems to be a vital process rather than a purely physical one. With a segment of the twig chilled, or with the oxygen supply cut off, the rate of the translocatory process is very much affected. Further, if segments of the phloem tissue are killed with hot wax or steam above and below a node, translocation is seen to come to a standstill. The mechanism of solute movement in the phloem could be as follows:

1. **Cytoplasmic Streaming.** In 1923 Curtis held that food materials in solution is transported through the living cells of the phloem. As the cytoplasmic strands in the sieve-tubes move, although hardly noticeably in most cases, they carry the organic solutes with them to at least some distance, upward or downward. In his view, the transport of food depends greatly on the activity of the living cells. The streaming of the protoplasm accelerates the diffusion of the solute molecules. He also found that the physiological conditions that affect the streaming affect the rate

of translocation of the solutes as well. His theory seems to explain the mechanism of translocation. But this streaming, if at all it takes place, is very slow and cannot account for the rather rapid translocation of food through the phloem. Mason and Phyllis have rejected this view.

2. Diffusion Theory. Mason and Maskell reported in 1929 that nitrates move up in the transpiration current, and the elaborated food material —sugars and amino-acids—moves down the phloem. On the basis of the 'ringing' experiments carried out by them, they found that the total inorganic nitrogen in the leaf still increased during the daytime and decreased at night, and that sugars and amino-acids accumulated above the girdle. From the nature and rate of diffusion of sugars and nitrogenous compounds, they concluded that the movement of the solutes in the phloem is not due to any mass flow in it. They inferred that the solute movement is due to a kind of diffusion process, not clearly understood, at an accelerated or decelerated rate, depending on the energy released by respiration as a result of metabolism and the activity of the protoplasm, also inexplicable. Even then, the rate of diffusion is far too slow to fully explain the rapid transport of the solutes through the sieve-tubes.

3. Gradient Pressure. Munch held in 1929 that the movement of the solvent (water) and the solutes (organic food material) takes place simultaneously and at the same rate. According to him, there is an area of high turgor pressure in the leaf and an area of low turgor pressure in the root. The former is due to the formation of osmotically active substances (like sugar) in the leaf through photosynthesis. The latter is due to the presence of osmotically inactive substances like starch (sugar either converted into starch or utilized in metabolism). Phloem, as is known, is continuous from the leaf to the root. Because of the difference in the turgor pressure (turgor gradient), there is a mass flow of the solutes and the solvent from the region of higher concentration (leaf) to the region of lower concentration (root) through the phloem. The cytoplasmic strands extending through the sieve-plates are supposed to facilitate the move-

ment. Later in the season, as in spring, higher turgor pressure develops in the root cells as a result of conversion of the starch into sugar, and the flow starts in the reverse direction, i.e. upwards. To maintain the turgor pressure in the leaf cells, there is a continuous flow of water into them through the xylem. According to this view, the movement is unidirectional at a time. This view was, however, strongly criticised by Mason and his colleagues in 1936.

Although Munch's theory gives a plausible explanation for the mechanism of solute movement in the phloem, it is open to some serious doubts. Crafts, who believed in the simultaneous transport of all organic solutes and water in the phloem through the lumen of the sieve-tubes as well as through the walls, raised strong objections to Munch's hypothesis in 1931 and 1938 on the following grounds : (1) The resistance offered by the cytoplasmic strands extending through the sieve-plate, almost plugging the pores, is not conducive to the mass flow of the solutes. (2) Innumerable sieve-plates occurring at frequent intervals may, in fact, act as so many road blocks, interfering with the speed of the mass flow. (3) Turgor pressure cannot be so high a driving force as to account for the movement of the solutes over such a long distance—leaf to root—particularly at the rate known. (4) The movement, as far as known, is bidirectional at a time. (5) Sometimes translocation has been noted to take place towards the region of higher turgor pressure. (6) The activity of the protoplasm is not accounted for by this theory, although it is known that killing the phloem markedly affects or even stops translocation. Munch's hypothesis is no doubt a satisfactory physical theory. But it is presumed that the protoplasm plays a more prominent role than hitherto known. Finally, it may be said that the translocation of food is a complex problem which remains to be solved.

STORAGE

Food is prepared in excess of the immediate need of a plant. This surplus food exists in two conditions—either *suitable for travelling* or *suitable for storage*. The travelling form is characterized by *solubility* and the storage form by *insolubility* in the cell-sap.

Storage Tissues. Tissues meant for storage of food have thin cellulose walls. The cells are mostly parenchymatous in nature. If the walls are thick, they are provided with many simple pits. Storage cells are also living so that the protoplasm can secrete the enzymes required and render the food materials soluble or insoluble, depending on whether translocation or storage is required. All parts made of large-celled parenchyma always contain a certain amount of stored food. The cortex of the root is particularly rich in stored food, and so is the large pith of the monocotyledonous root. There is also a quantity of food stored up in the endodermis, pith, medullary rays and xylem parenchyma of the stem. The border parenchyma of the leaf also contains stored food.

Storage Organs. Food material is stored up in the endosperm or in the thick cotyledons of the seed for the development and growth of the embryo. A considerable amount of food is stored up in the fleshy pericarp of the fruit. Food is specially stored up in fleshy roots—fusiform, napiform, conical and other roots, and in underground modified stems like the rhizome, tuber, corm, etc. All fleshy stems and branches, e.g. many cacti and spurges (*Euphorbia*), succulent leaves, e.g. Indian aloe (*Aloe vera*), American aloe (*Agave*), purslane (*Portulaca*) etc., and fleshy scales of onion always contain stored food. The swollen stem-base of kohl-rabi (*Brassica caulorapa*) and the gouty stem of *Jatropha podogarica* also contain stored food. The growing regions and floral organs may also store food.

FORMS OF STORED FOOD. The various forms in which food material is stored in these different organs and tissues may now be considered. The food may consist of carbohydrates, proteins, or fats and oils (see also pp. 130-40).

A. CARBOHYDRATES

Starch (see FIGS. II/14-5). This is of universal occurrence in plants with the exception of fungi. As soon as sugar is formed in the leaf, it is converted into starch. This starch is in the form of minute bodies without any definite structure. In the absence of carbon assimilation at night, starch is converted into sugar which travels down to the storage organs and is reconverted there into starch by the leucoplasts. The starch grains deposited by the leucoplasts are much bigger and have a distinct, stratified appearance. Starch is insoluble in water and is stored up as such for a longer or shorter period. When the plant is growing, starch is again converted into sugar, which then travels from the storage organs to the growing regions and is eventually used by the protoplasm for its nutrition and growth.

Glycogen. Fungi store carbohydrate in the form of glycogen. It is allied to starch and is readily converted into sugar. Glycogen is a white amorphous powder that dissolves in hot water. It is coloured reddish brown by iodine solution [see also p. 135].

Inulin (see FIG. II/13). This is a soluble carbohydrate and has the same chemical composition as starch. It is found in the underground parts of some *Compositae*, *Liliaceae* and *Amaryllidaceae*. It may be converted into some form of sugar.

Sugars. Grape-sugar is the first carbohydrate formed in the green leaves of plants. But it is usually converted into starch as soon as it is formed. It is only in a few cases, as in grape, onion, etc., that grape-sugar is stored up as such. Cane-sugar occurs as reserve food in sugarcane, banana, pineapple, beet, etc. Grape contains 12-15% glucose and sugarcane contains 10-15% sucrose.

Hemicellulose (see FIG. II/7). This occurs as a thickening matter in the cell-wall of the endosperm of the date seed. It may be converted into some form of sugar by the action of the enzyme, *cytase*.

B. NITROGENOUS MATERIALS

Proteins. These are the most complex, and at the same time, the most important substances. Proteins are the chief constituents of protoplasm and the nucleus, and consist of carbon, hydrogen, oxygen, nitrogen and, sometimes, sulphur and phosphorus. However, their exact chemical composition is not known. Various kinds of proteins occur in plants as food. They are found in three distinct conditions, viz. as definite oval or rounded granules known as the aleurone grains, as amorphous proteins (i.e. with no definite shape), and as soluble proteins which occur in solution in the cell-sap. Aleurone grains (see FIG. II/16) occur abundantly in seeds associated with starch, as in pea, bean, etc., or with oil, as in castor. They are fairly large when they occur with oil. The other two kinds of proteins occur in bulbs, tubers and in other storage organs.

Amino-acids and **Amines**. These are much simpler nitrogenous substances than proteins, and occur in solution mostly in the growing regions. Less frequently, they occur in the storage tissue. (See also p. 139).

C. FATS AND OILS

Fats and oils are found in all groups of plants and in almost all living cells of the plant body. In angiosperms, they are specially common in the seeds and fruits. Very little carbohydrate is present when oil occurs in abundance. Similarly, little oil is found when starch occurs in abundance. Big aleurone grains often accompany fats and oils, as in castor seed. Fats are solid and oils are liquid at ordinary temperature. They are not soluble in water or in alcohol (except castor oil). All of them are, however, soluble in ether, petroleum, chloroform, etc. They occur in the form of globules in the protoplasm, often saturating it. They are formed from fatty acids and glycerine. (See also pp. 139-40).

It is known that these substances enter into the composition of protoplasm, but they undergo many chemical changes before they are utilized by the protoplasm. They are decomposed by the enzyme, *lipase*, into fatty acids and glycerine. A large amount of heat is released during decomposition. When oily seeds germinate, a considerable quantity of fatty acids may be found in them, while

glycerine disappears almost immediately. But these substances are finally converted into sugar. Fatty acids and glycerine may also be translocated to the **growing regions**, where they are utilized by the **protoplasm**. Both these substances readily pass through cell-walls.

Food Stored in the Seed. There is always a considerable amount of food stored up in the cotyledons and endosperm of the seed for the use of the growing embryo. Food occurs there in insoluble forms and is first digested, i.e. rendered soluble and chemically simpler under the action of specific enzymes (see next chapter). It is then utilized by the growing parts of the embryo for various purposes, such as nutrition and growth of the protoplasm, cell-formation, development of the embryonic parts and also vigorous respiration. The food occurs in the following forms: (1) **Starch** is a very common form of carbohydrate stored up in the seed. Cereals like rice, wheat, maize, oat, barley, etc., are particularly rich in starch. (2) **Hemicellulose** is deposited as a thickening matter in the cell-walls of the endosperm of many palm seeds, e.g. date palm, betel-nut palm, nipa-palm, vegetable ivory-palm, etc., and also in some other seeds, e.g. coffee, mangosteen, etc. (3) **Oils** are deposited to a greater or less extent in most seeds. There is a special deposit of oils in seeds like groundnut, gingelly, coconut, castor, safflower etc. (4) **Proteins** also occur in all seeds in varying quantities. They occur in a high percentage in seeds like pulses. The protein content of soya-bean is 35% or more. Oily seeds also contain a high percentage of proteins e.g. castor seed. When the seed germinates, storage proteins break down under the action of proteolytic enzymes into amino-acids, which then migrate to the embryo, and synthesis of new proteins takes place.

CHAPTER 9

ENZYMES

Enzymes are organic (biological) catalysts, each being a certain kind of protein, secreted by the living cells to bring about thousands of biochemical reactions in various metabolic processes (e.g. photosynthesis, respiration, digestion of food) etc., in both plants and animals. Their significance is that they initiate a particular biochemical reaction in a substrate and actually accelerate and regulate the rate of this reaction by their surface energy, without themselves undergoing any chemical change in the process. So enzymes are regarded as biological catalysts which catalyze thousands of chemical compounds, often within the cells. Each enzyme is a special protein, usually bringing about one particular reaction. It is apparent that but for the activity of enzymes, life would have been very slow or even still. Their importance in plant life and animal life, thus, cannot be overstimated. It is now definitely known that the mitochondria and chloroplasts are the main seats of enzyme synthesis. All the enzymes connected with the oxidation of pyruvic acid in the Kerbs cycle of respiration are synthesized in the mitochondria. Those required for fixation of CO_2 in photosynthesis (dark reactions) are synthesized in the chloroplasts. Further, it may be noted that the synthesis of each enzyme is controlled by a gene. This is the 'single gene—single enzyme' hypothesis of Beadle and Tatum, (1959). A large number of enzymes are involved in hydrolysis. This means that the elements of H_2O enter into such a reaction. They are mostly the digestive enzymes. The substance on which an enzyme acts is called the *substrate*. All living cells secrete enzymes, always in small amounts, to act on a number of products simultaneously or one after the other in a regulated manner, effecting reaction after reaction. The term 'enzyme' was first applied by Kuhne in 1876 to the plant juice which, as he found, could bring about digestion of certain chemical compounds. In 1897, Buchner first discovered that extract from crushed yeast cells could bring about fermentation in sugar solution. In

1903, he isolated the first enzyme. (Buchner was a winner of Nobel Prize). Many other enzymes have been discovered since then and it is now definitely known that thousands of chemical reactions in plants and animals are due to them. The enzyme, 'urease', was first isolated by Summer in 1926 in crystalline form. Since then, several enzymes have been obtained in pure crystalline form. Enzymes are very complex chemical substances made of large and heavy molecules. They occur in the form of colloids in the protoplasm, which may secrete one or more enzymes at a time. All enzymes are destroyed at high temperatures. Apart from the mitochondria, several other structures of the plant cell, such as the nucleoli, plastids, ribosomes and lysosomes, are also involved in the manufacture of specific types of enzymes. They are soluble in water, alcohol, dilute glycerine, and in dilute acid or alkali. Some enzymes consist entirely of proteins, e.g. certain proteolytic enzymes and amylases which act directly on the substrate. However, many enzymes have two components that act together for any enzymic activity—a protein part and a non-protein part (a prosthetic group or a coenzyme). When the non-protein part is firmly attached to the protein part and is not separable from it, it (the non-protein part) is called a **prosthetic group**, and when it can be readily separated from the protein part by dialysis, it is called a **coenzyme**. Neither is active without the presence of the protein. All the oxidizing-reducing enzymes have a prosthetic group. The latter may be a metal or an organic compound with a metal. Thus the enzymes tyrosinase and ascorbic acid oxidase have a protein portion and a copper atom. Cytochrome oxidase, catalase and peroxidase contain iron (as iron porphyrin). Likewise, zinc, manganese, cobalt, nickel, magnesium, calcium, potassium, etc., may form prosthetic groups of certain enzymes. In such cases, the prosthetic groups act as specific *activators*. Some oxidizing enzymes (respiratory and fermenting) contain organic compounds as prosthetic groups. The coenzyme components of many enzymes include a variety of compounds. The protein portion and the coenzyme may occur separately in the same cell, but they must be linked together or closely associated for the whole enzyme to be effective. The same prosthetic group or coenzyme may combine with different kinds of proteins and form different kinds of enzymes. Several vitamins (e.g. vitamin B complex) are now considered as forming coenzyme components of many enzymes. Similarly NAD (formerly called DPN), NADP, ATP, FAD, coenzyme A, etc. act as coenzymes. **Zymogen.** Cells sometimes do not directly produce an enzyme, but at first, the chemical precursor of an enzyme known as zymogen or proenzyme is secreted by the protoplasm. The zymogen then becomes converted into an active enzyme. Many kinds of zymogens have been identified so far. They are now known to combine with different protein components as prosthetic groups or coenzymes to form different kinds of enzymes.

PROPERTIES OF ENZYMES. (1) *Specificity.* Each enzyme is a specific catalyst, i.e., there is a particular enzyme for a particular substance. For instance, the enzyme that acts on starch will not act on protein or any other substance. This is expressed as 'lock and key' action. Some enzymes (e.g. emulsin) can, however, act on a number of substances that have a certain molecular pattern. Conversely, different enzymes may act on the same substrate with the formation of different end-products. Thus, pyruvic acid may be converted into a number of compounds under the influence of different enzymes. (2) *Catalytic Property.* The enzyme acts as a catalytic agent. This means that the enzyme induces some chemical reaction in a particular substance without itself undergoing any chemical change. Thus, the enzyme may be regarded as an organic catalyst. After the chemical change is over, it is released unchanged and used again. (3) *Inexhaustibility.* The enzyme is never exhausted while it works, i.e. a small quantity of it can act on an almost unlimited supply of the substance, provided that the products of its action are removed from the seat of its activity. Finally, of course, the enzyme breaks down and disappears.

(4) *Colloidal Nature.* Enzymes occur in the protoplasm in the form of colloids. Enzyme molecules are very large and fall within the colloidal system. They have high molecular weights, and being very large, diffuse slowly and can be more or less easily separated by dialysis in many cases. (5) *Reversible Action.* Some enzymes can bring about reactions in both directions. For example, lipase can bring about synthesis of fats from glycerine and fatty acid, and can, under certain other conditions, decompose fats into glycerine and fatty acid. This is also true of some proteolytic enzymes, dehydrogenases and transferring enzymes. (6) *Sensitivity to Heat.* Enzymes in a liquid medium are destroyed at a temperature of 60-70°C. In dry seeds and spores they can often stand a temperature of 100-120°C., at least for some time. Enzymes extracted from plant tissues can also stand such high temperature. (7) *Activators and Inhibitors.* There are certain compounds (particularly the prosthetic group) which accelerate the activity of certain enzymes. There are others which inhibit their action or even destroy them.

CLASSIFICATION OF ENZYMES. Enzymes have been classified in different ways by different authors. They are too numerous and our knowledge about the chemical structure of most of them is still imperfect. This being so, a perfect classification has not been possible yet. A simple classification based on the kinds of reactions that they catalyze may be as follows :

1. Hydrolytic Enzymes or Hidrolases

A. Carbohydrases. (1) *Diastase* (or *amylase*) hydrolyses starch to dextrin and maltose. (2) *Maltase hydrolyses* maltose to glucose. (3) *Invertase* (or *sucrase*) hydrolyses sucrose to fructose and glucose. (4) *Inulase* hydrolyses inulin to fructose. (5) *Cellulase* hydrolyses cellulose to cellobiose to glucose. (6) *Cytase* (or *hemicellulase*) hydrolyses hemicellulose to glucose. (7) *Emulsin* hydrolyses glucosides to glucose and a non-sugar.

B. Proteolytic Enzymes. (*a*) *Proteos* : (1) *Pepsin* hydrolyses proteins to peptones. (2) *Trypsin* hydrolyses proteins to polypeptides and amino-acids. (3) *Papain* hydrolyses a wide variety of proteins to polypeptides and amino-acids. (*b*) *Peptidases*: (4) *Erepsin* hydrolyses polypeptides to amino-acids. (*c*) *Amilases*: (5) *Asparaginase* hydrolyses asparagine to aspartic acid and ammonia. (6) *Glutaminase* hydrolyses glutamine to glutamic acid and ammonia.

C. Esterases. (1) *Lipase* breaks down fats into fatty acids and glycerine. Lipase also brings about reversible reaction, i.e. it can synthesize fats from fatty acids and glycerine. (2) *Pectase* converts pectin to pectic acid. (3) *Tannase* converts tannin to glucose and digallic acid.

2. Oxidizing - Reducing Enzymes

D. Oxidases are a group of respiratory enzymes which bring about oxidation of certain chemical compounds in the presence of oxygen. *Cytochrome* (cell-colour), a pigmented member of this group closely related to chlorophyll, acts as a hydrogen-carrier. During certain oxidation-reduction processes, certain compounds become oxidized with the transfer of hydrogen to cytochrome (hydrogenated or reduced). Under the influence of *cytochrome oxidase*, the reduced cytochrome is again oxidized (dehydrogenated) and it goes back to its original condition. Other common oxidases are *tyrosinase* and *ascorbic acid oxidase*.

E. Catalases decompose hydrogen peroxide, H_2O_2, to water and molecular oxygen. They are very widely distributed in plants. They do not allow H_2O_2, a toxic compound, to accumulate in cells.

F. Peroxidases decompose H_2O_2 to water and active oxygen, causing oxidation of many compounds. They are very widely distributed in plants.

G. Dehydrogenases act on many organic compounds, particularly organic acids. For example, they convert ethyl alcohol to acetaldehyde, malic acid to oxalacetic acid, lactic acid to pyruvic acid, etc. These enzymes are probably present in all plants and act by transferring hydrogen from one compound to another, accompanied by electron transfer. The compound that releases hydrogen (i.e. dehydrogenated or oxidized) is said to be a *hydrogen-donor* and the one that receives hydrogen (i.e. hydrogenated or reduced) is said to be a *hydrogen-acceptor*. Their action is reversible.

H. Carboxylases convert pyruvic acid to acetaldehyde and carbon dioxide, oxalacetic acid to pyruvic acid and carbon dioxide, and amino-acids to amines and carbon dioxide.

I. Zymase is an enzyme complex, consisting of a complex mixture of several enzymes, coenzymes and also inorganic ions. It is involved in oxidation-reduction processes. A familiar example is the conversion of glucose to ethyl alcohol and carbon dioxide. Harden (1923, 1932) discovered over a dozen enzymes and a number of coenzymes in the zymase complex. Zymase works in the presence of inorganic phosphate.

3. Transferring enzymes or Transferases

J. Phosphorylases (in the presence of inorganic phosphate—H_3PO_4) catalyze starch or glycogen to glucose phosphate, and sucrose to fructose phosphate + glucose phosphate.

K. Transphosphorylases (e.g. *hexokinase, phospho-hexokinase, phospho-pyruvate,* etc.) transfer the phosphate group from one compound to another, for example, glucose or fructose+phosphate to glucose or fructose-phosphate, glucose-phosphate to fructose-phosphate, phosphoglyceric acid to phosphopyruvic acid, phosphopyruvic acid to pyruvic acid+phosphate, etc.

CHAPTER 10

DIGESTION AND ASSIMILATION OF FOOD

DIGESTION

The reserve material is generally insoluble in water or cell-sap and also indiffusible, but when translocation is necessary, it is rendered soluble and diffusible by the action of specific enzymes. It is only in the soluble form that food material is absorbed by the protoplasm. *This rendering of insoluble and complex food substances into soluble and simpler forms suitable for translocation through the plant body and assimilation by the protoplasm is collectively known as* **digestion.**

The process of digestion is chiefly intracellular, that is, it takes place inside the cell. Extracellular digestion occurs in a few cases, as in carnivorous plants, parasites, fungi and bacteria. In such cases, the digestive agent or enzyme is secreted by the protoplasm outside the body, where it digests or splits up the complex food material. The products of digestion are then absorbed by the cells. Digestion, like all other physiological functions, is performed by the protoplasm. For this purpose, it secretes different kinds of digestive agents or **enzymes** to act on different kinds of food substances. Enzymes involved in intracellular digestion are called *endoenzymes* and those involve in extra-cellular digestion, *exoenzymes*.

ASSIMILATION

Assimilation *is the absorption of the simplest products of digestion of foodstuff by the protoplasm into its own body, and conversion of these products into similar complex constituents of the protoplasm (the term 'assimilate' means to make similar).* It is as a result of assimilation that the protoplasm increases in bulk and the cell-walls are built up. Assimilation is a constructive process by which the protoplasm is continually reconstructing itself out of the nutritive substances, like sugar and simple products of proteins, supplied to it. The various kinds of carbohydrates are converted into sugar, particularly glucose, and the various complex proteins are converted on rapid hydrolysis into peptones, polypeptides and amino-acids. These products of digestion travel to the growing region, where the protoplasm is very active. Glucose is mostly broken down by the living cells during respiration, releasing energy. A part of the glucose supplies new material, particularly cellulose, for growth of cells and another part is precipitated as starch for future use. The digested products of proteins, viz. peptones, etc., are directly assimilated by the protoplasm into its own body, and new complex protoplasmic proteins and nucleoproteins are built out of them. We know that the protoplasm itself is a living substance, composed of very complex proteins. The food is, therefore, changed into complex protoplasmic proteins. The protoplasm being living, it is natural to suppose that food is changed into 'live' proteins, or, in other words, food passes from non-life into life, that is, protoplasm. This is the goal of nourishment. How this change takes place we do not know. We know only that the protoplasm has the power to bring it about.

Nutrition of the Embryo. The embryo lies within the coat of the seed and consists of an axis (the future plant) and the cotyledons. A seed remains in a (semi) dry condition. Its dry coat is impermeable to gases. When a dry, mature and functional seed is supplied with water, it absorbs water and swells considerably. The seed coat becomes permeable to atmospheric carbon dioxide and oxygen. As the seed swells, it exerts a pressure on the outer coat and the latter ruptures. Meanwhile, the cell walls and protoplasm become saturated with water. Absorption of water by the cells now takes place by osmosis. In exalbuminous seeds, the cotyledons are the storehouse of food and they also contain enzymes. These enzymes become active and digest the stored food, converting them to simpler soluble forms. Various types of stored food, such as starch, proteins, fats, etc., are hydrolysed by hydrolytic enzymes, which are probably aided by gibberellins.

Carbohydrates are broken down to sugar by amalases. β-amylase is present in seeds, but β-amylase is synthesized later. Enzyme proteases digest proteins into amino acids. Fats go through β-oxidation and the glyoxylate cycle to be converted into oxaloacetic acid, malic acid, pyruvic acid and phosphoenol pyruvic acid, in succession. Phosphoenol pyruvic acid is converted into sugar through the process, which is the reverse of glycolysis. Hemicellulose, which occurs as a thickening matter in the cell-wall of the endosperm of many seeds, may be converted to some form of sugar by the action of the hydrolytic enzyme, cytase. The digested food is supplied to the growing axis, i.e., the tips of the radicle and plumule. In albuminous seeds, the food is stored in the endosperm. The enzymes contained in the cotyledon-cells migrate to the endosperm and help break down the stored food to simpler, soluble forms. The digested food is transported to the cotyledons, which pass on the food to the growing axis for various purposes, such as nutrition, growth of protoplasm, cell formation, development of embryonic parts and vigorous respiration.

CHAPTER 11

RESPIRATION AND FERMENTATION

RESPIRATION

Respiration is essentially a process of oxidation and decomposition of organic compounds, particularly simple carbohydrates such as glucose, in the living cells with the release of energy. The most important feature of respiration is that by this oxidative process, the *potential* energy stored in the organic compounds in living cells is released in a step-wise manner, in the form of active or *kinetic* energy, under the influence of a series of enzymes and is made available, at least partly, to the protoplasm for its manifold vital activities. Often, a considerable amount of energy escapes from the plant body in the form of heat, as seen in germinating seeds. The reserve food materials that undergo oxidation are mostly simple carbohydrates, principally glucose, and sometimes also, particularly in the absence of glucose, other substances such as complex carbohydrates, proteins and fats. These are, of course, first hydrolysed and then oxidized. The main facts associated with respiration are: (1) Consumption of atmospheric oxygen. (2) oxidation and decomposition of a portion of the stored food, resulting in a loss of dry weight, as seen in seeds germinating in the dark. (3) Liberation of carbon dioxide and a small quantity of water (the volume of CO_2 liberated being equal to the volume of O_2 consumed). (4) Most important, release of energy by the breakdown of organic food. The overall chemical reaction may be stated thus: $C_6H_{12}O_6 + 6O_2 = 6CO_2 + 6H_2O +$ Energy (sugar + oxygen = carbon dioxide + water + energy). This shows that for oxidation of one molecule of sugar, six molecules of oxygen are used and that six molecules each of CO_2 and H_2O are formed. By burning sugar at a high temperature, CO_2 and H_2O are also formed, but in living cells, this process is carried out by a series of enzymes at a comparatively low temperature. Oxidation may be complete, as shown in the formula, with the formation of carbon dioxide and

water as end-products, the former escaping from the plant body and the latter getting mixed up with the general mass of water in the cells. Otherwise, it may be incomplete with the formation of some organic acid or ethyl alcohol and carbon dioxide, as shown by the equation: $C_2H_{12}O_6 = 2C_2H_5OH + CO_2$ (sugar = ethyl alcohol + carbon dioxide). In respiration of plants, the oxygen gas, after entering through the stomata and lenticels, diffuses through the intercellular spaces into the living cells and slowly oxidizes not only glucose and other carbohydrates, but also (though less frequently) other organic materials—like fats, proteins, organic acids and even protoplasm under extreme conditions. The carbon dioxide that is formed in respiration diffuses through the intercellular spaces and finally escapes through the stomata and the lenticels into the surrounding air. A portion of it may be retained in the cells and used for photosynthesis. In submerged aquatic plants, the surrounding water containing dissolved air supplies the gases required for respiration and carbon-assimilation.

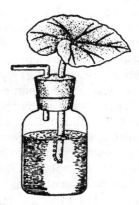

FIG. 33. Experiment on aeriferous system

All the living cells of a plant, however deeply seated they may be, must respire day and night in order to live. If the supply of air to a plant is cut off (by growing it in an atmosphere devoid of oxygen), it soon dies. The growing organs like the floral and vegetative buds, germinating seeds, and stem and root tips, respire actively, while the adult organs do so comparatively slowly. Gases normally enter the plant through the stomata. But these are closed at night. So, to facilitate the interchange of gases the concerned, special structures are developed on the branches. These are the lenticels. Unlike the stomata, they remain open. For easy diffusion of gases in the interior of the plant body, plants have developed a network of air-cavities and intercellular spaces which are connected throughout and are continuous with the stomata and the lenticels (see Experiment 28).

In respiration the cells are continually exhaling carbon dioxide and in photosynthesis, the green cells are continually making use of this gas during the daytime and giving off oxygen. But the latter process goes on more vigorously than the former and practically masks it. Thus, in the green parts of plants, the composition of the intercellular air varies, becoming much richer in oxygen during the daytime, and richer in carbon dioxide at night. The amount of nitrogen varies very little, as this gas is not made use of by the protoplasm. Since plants are continually exhaling carbon dioxide in respiration, the atmosphere has a tendency to become richer in this gas, especially at night. Carbon dioxide is a suffocating gas and tends to vitiate the atmosphere. But then during the day, the green plants absorb it for photosynthesis and give out oxygen, which goes back to the atmosphere. The atmosphere is, thus, purified and the composition of the air remains constant.

Experiment 28. Aeriferous system of the plant (FIG. 33). Take a wide-mouthed bottle and a cork of appropriate size with two holes bored in it. Partially fill the bottle with water and insert the long petiole of the leaf selected (e.g. *Begonia*) into the water through a hole in the cork. Through the other hole, introduce a bent tube with its inner end clear above the surface of the water. Make all the connections air-tight by applying paraffin-wax, and draw the air out from the bottle through the bent tube, preferably with a vacuum pump. As this is done, a series of minute bubbles are seen to escape through the cut end of the petiole and rise upwards. Repeat the experiment after applying a coat of vaseline

on the surfaces of the leaf and note that no air bubbles appear. The escape of air bubbles indicates that there is an intercommunicating system of intercellular spaces connected with the stomata, forming as a whole the aeriferous system of the plant.

AEROBIC AND ANAEROBIC RESPIRATION (*aer*, air; *an*, not; *bios*, life). Normally, free oxygen is used in respiration, resulting in complete oxidation of stored food and formation of carbon dioxide and water as end-products. This is known as **aerobic respiration**. A considerable amount of energy is released by this process, as represented by the equation—$C_6H_{12}O_6 + 6O_2 = 6CO_2 + 6H_2O + 674$ kilo-cal (sugar+oxygen=carbon dioxide+water+674 kilo-cal. of energy). Under certain conditions, as in the absence of free oxygen, many tissues of higher plants, seeds in storage, fleshy fruits and succulent plants like cacti temporarily take to a kind of respiration called **anaerobic respiration**. Such respiration results in incomplete oxidation of stored food and formation of carbon dioxide and ethyl alcohol, and sometimes also various organic acids, such as malic, citric, oxalic, tartaric, etc. The energy released by this process is not sufficient to maintain the activity of the protoplasm. It may be represented by the equation—$C_6H_{12}O_6 = 2C_2H_5OH + 2CO_2 + 28$ kilo-calorie (sugar=ethyl alcohol+carbon dioxide+28 kilo-calorie of energy). It is otherwise known as *intramolecular respiration* because in this process, intramolecular oxidation of sugar and other compounds takes place without the use of free oxygen. Anaerobic respiration may continue for only a limited period of time, at most a few days, after which death ensues, evidently due to low production of energy and accumulation of toxic substances in the cells. In certain micro-organisms (certain bacteria, yeast and some other fungi), however, the fundamental process of energy-release is anaerobic respiration. Anaerobic respiration resulting in the production of alcohol is otherwise called alcoholic fermentation.

MECHANISM OF RESPIRATION. Chemical changes in respiration (from the breakdown of glucose to the release of CO_2 and H_2O) are more or less definitely known. It is known that the whole

process is controlled by a group of different kinds of complex enzymes, the respiratory enzymes, which work step by step. We also know that it is complete in two distinct phases: an anaerobic phase and an aerobic phase. The first phase, which is incomplete oxidation of glucose to pyruvic acid through a chain of intermediate reactions, is called **glycolysis**. This phase, takes place in the absence of oxygen (to be more precise it does not require oxygen). The second phase, which involves complete oxidation of the pyruvic acid to CO_2 and H_2O, is called **Krebs cycle**, and it takes place in the presence of oxygen. Several reactions occur in the whole process, each reaction being controlled by a specific enzyme.

Anaerobic Phase. In this phase of respiration, a simple carbohydrate like glucose or its isomer, fructose, is first phosphorylated (a phosphate group added by ATP, an energy-rich phosphate compound now known to be formed in the mitochondria). In this process, ATP is converted into ADP. This is a very important step, initiating the process of respiration and leading to the formation of phosphoglyceric acid and, finally, pyruvic acid. Other common reserve materials used in respiration are starch and sucrose. Each, however, is first hydrolysed to glucose, as follows:

$$starch—2n(C_6H_{10}O_5) + nH_2O \xrightarrow{amylase} nC_{12}H_{22}O_{11}$$

(maltose), $C_{12}H_{22}O_{11} + H_2O \xrightarrow{maltase} 2C_6H_{12}O_6$

(glucose); and sucrose—$C_{12}H_{22}O_{11} + H_2O$ $\xrightarrow{sucrase} C_6H_{12}O_6$ (glucose) $C_6H_{12}O_6$ (fructose).

Glucose with supply of ATP becomes activated in the presence of the enzyme *hexokinase*, and glucose-6-phosphate is formed. Glucose-6-phosphate is immediately converted to fructose-6-phosphate under the action of the enzyme, *hexose phosphate isomerase*. Phosphorylation further continues with the supply of ATP, and, thus, in the presence of the enzyme, *phosphofructokinase*, fructose-6-phosphate is again phosphorylated to fructose-1, 6-diphosphate by the addition of a molecule of ATP. Then under the action of the enzyme, *aldolase*, the above compound splits into two 3-carbon fragments, one of which is 3-phosphoglyc-

eraldehyde. The other fragment does not take part in respiration but may be converted to 3-phosphoglyceraldehyde, which follows the pathway of anaerobic respiration. The next step in the series is the conversion of 3-phosphoglyceraldehyde to '1, 3-diphosphoglyceric acid under the action of the enzyme, *phosphoglyceraldehyde dehydrogenase*. This reaction involves addition of inorganic phosphate to form ATP from ADP for the next reaction, and also reduction of NAD to $NADH_2$. Then, under the action of the enzyme *phosphoglyceric kinase* plus ADP 1, 3-diphosphoglyceric acid is converted to 3-phosphoglyceric acid, and simultaneously ADP converted to ATP. Then, by a shift (migration) in the position of the phosphate group in the presence of the enzyme, *phosphoglyceromutase*, it is further converted to 2-phosphoglyceric acid. It should be noted that the transfer of energy from one compound to another takes place through the transfer of a phosphate molecule from one to the other. The next step in the series of reactions results in the formation of phospho-enol-pyruvic acid from 2-phosphoglyceric acid. This, in fact, is a dehydration reaction (removal of H_2O) in the presence of the enzyme, *enolase*. Finally, with the removal of all phosphate from this compound by the action of the enzyme *pyruvic kinase* and ADP the pyruvic acid stands as the end-product in glycolysis, and ADP is converted to ATP for further action. The following points may be noted: (1) 1 mol. of glucose yields 2 mols. of pyruvic acid, (2) the phosphate group as a source of energy is donated mainly by ATP, (3) 8 mols. of ATP are synthesized for every mol. of glucose converted to pyruvic acid, (4) each reaction is catalysed by a specific enzyme, (5) all the reactions are reversible, and (6) pyruvic acid holds an intermediate key position between the two phases of respiration.

Anaerobic Oxidation of Pyruvic Acid. Pyruvic acid, as it is formed, holds a key position from which, under different conditions, reactions proceed in several directions in various tissues and organisms. In the absence of O_2, pyruvic acid is converted to acetaldehyde and CO_2 under the action of pyruvic carboxylase. Acetaldehyde is now the starting point from which reactions lead to

Pathway of Glycolysis

glucose ($C_6H_{12}O_6$)

⇅   hexokinase + ATP

glucose-6-phosphate + ADP

⇅   hexose phosphate isomerase + ADP

fructose-6-phosphate

⇅   phosphofructokinase + ATP

fructose-1, 6-diphosphate + ADP

⇅   aldolase

3-phosphoglyceraldehyde (a 3-carbon compound)

⇅   phosphoglyceraldehyde dehydrogenase + DPN

1, 3-diphosphoglyceric acid + $DPNH_2$

⇅   phosphoglyceric kinase + ADP

3-phosphoglyceric acid + ATP

⇅   phosphoglyceromutase

2-phosphoglyceric acid

⇅   enolase

phosphoenolpyruvic acid

⇅   pyruvic kinase + ADP

pyruvic acid ($C_3H_4O_3$) + ATP

the production a of number of compounds. It is known that several bacteria and some fungi thrive normally under anaerobic conditions. It is seen in them that, in the absence of O_2, pyruvic acid becomes converted to certain compounds under the action of different enzymes with the release of a certain amount of energy, which, however, is small for the activity of such micro-organisms. Thus, in certain bacteria, pyruvic acid is reduced to lactic acid as the end-product, while in certain others, it is butyric acid. In the fermentation of glucose by yeast cells, pyruvic acid is reduced to ethyl alcohol and CO_2. The energy released in all such cases is of low order. In higher plants anaerobic respiration may continue only for a short period because the end-products formed in this process are mostly toxic. In them, the pyruvic acid may be converted to acetaldehyde, oxalacetic acid, some amino-acids, fatty acids and several other organic acids, e.g. oxalic acid, malic acid, tartaric acid, lactic acid, etc., under the action of different enzymes.

Aerobic Phase. This immediately follows the first phase with the supply of oxygen, and most of the pyruvic acid is completely oxidized to CO_2 and H_2O with the liberation of a maximum of energy. The ATP formed in this process is about four times greater than that formed in glycolysis. Several organic acids and some amino-acids (derived from α ketoglutaric acid) are formed during the process of aerobic respiration. A series of reactions takes place in a step-wise manner in the whole process under the action of distinct complex enzymes. In fact, there is a specific enzyme for each reaction. Some such enzymes have been extracted from plants and have been found to bring about reaction *in vitro*, similar to those *in vivo*. The sequence of reactions in this phase may be divided into two groups. The first is the oxidative decarboxylation (removal of a molecule of CO_2) of pyruvic acid to form acetyl-coenzyme A. The second is the citric acid cycle or Krebs cycle.

Formation of Acetyl-Coenzyme A. With the access of sufficient oxygen, the pyruvic acid ($C_3H_4O_3$) undergoes oxidative decarboxylation and is converted to acetyl-coenzyme A. The chemical process leading to this conversion is, however, very complex, involving a series of reactions. Several complex enzymes and 4 or 5 co-enzymes are involved in the whole process. Briefly speaking, under the action of *pyruvate decarboxylase*, the pyruvic acid reacts with TPP (thiamine pyrophosphate), with the result that TPP-acetaldehyde complex is formed and a molecule of CO_2 released. The 'activated' acetaldehyde portion of this complex reacts with lipoic acid under the action of *lipoyl reductase*, and acetyl-lipoic acid complex is formed. Next, the acetyl group is released from this complex and transferred to coenzyme A (CoA) under the action of

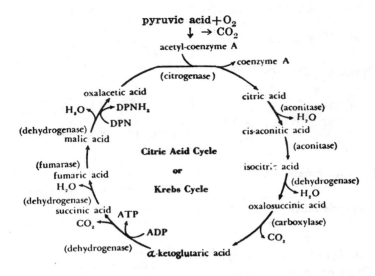

FIG. 34. Citric acid cycle or Krebs Cycle

transacetylose, forming acetyl-co-enzyme A (acetyl-CoA, also called 'active' acetate—C_2H_3O-CoA). It serves as a connecting link between the anaerobic phase (glycolysis) and the aerobic phase (Krebs Cycle) of respiration.

Krebs Cycle or Citric Acid Cycle. The Krebs Cycle consists of a series of chemical reactions under aerobic conditions, proceeding step by step in a cyclic order. This cycle of reactions, each regulated by a specific enzyme, is collectively called the **citric acid cycle** or **Krebs Cycle**, as first worked out by H. A. Krebs, an English biochemist, in 1943 (FIG. 34). It is otherwise called the **tricarboxylic acid cycle** since citric acid and some other compounds of this cycle have three carboxyl groups (—COOH) in them. It may be noted that the cycle as a whole goes only in one direction. The first step in the cycle is the combination of the acetyl portion of acetyl-coenzyme A with **oxalacetic acid** ($C_4H_4O_5$) under the action of the enzyme, *citrogenase*, to form **citric acid** ($C_6H_8O_7$), and coenzyme A is released. With the formation of citric acid, reactions follow in quick succession. By the dehydration process (removal of H_2O), citric acid is converted to **cis-aconitic acid** ($C_6H_6O_6$) and immediately by the hydration process (addition of H_2O), the latter converted to

isocitric acid ($C_6H_8O_7$). Both reactions are catalyzed by one and the same enzyme, *aconitase*. (Cis-aconitic acid may, however, be omitted in the process). Dehydrogenation (oxidation) of the isocitric acid in the presence of *isocitric acid dehydrogenase* results in the formation of **oxalosuccinic acid** ($C_6H_6O_7$). TPN (triphosphopyridine nucleotide) as a coenzyme is essential for this process. It may be noted that this is the *first oxidation step* in the Krebs Cycle. It may also be noted that each of the above four acids (citric to oxalosuccinic) is a 6-carbon compound and, therefore, CO_2 is not released in any of the above reactions. Oxalosuccinic acid is a keto acid and is readily decarboxylated (a CO_2 molecule released) to **α ketoglutaric acid** ($C_5H_6O_5$) under the action of a *carboxylase*. α ketoglutaric acid plays a very useful role in the metabolism of plants, particularly in the synthesis of some amino-acids (see pp. 263-4). By further oxidation and decarboxylation of α-ketoglutaric acid in the presence of *α-ketoglutaric dehydrogenase*, **succinic acid** ($C_4H_6O_4$) is formed rapidly through succinyl-CoA. This is the *second oxidation step*. Oxidation of succinic acid ('2H' removed) leads to the formation of **fumaric acid** ($C_4H_4O_4$). The reaction is catalyzed by *succinic dehydrogenase* with FAD (flavin adenine dinucleotide) firmly attached to it as a prosthetic group. This is the third *oxidation step*. By the hydration process, fumaric acid is converted to **malic acid** $(C_4H_6O_5)$ in the presence of *fumarase*. Then oxidation of malic acid by NAD (nicotinamide adenine dinucleotide) in the presence of *malic dehydrogenase* leads to the formation of **oxalacetic acid** $(C_4H_4O_5)$. In the process, '2H' is removed and NAD reduced to NADH$_2$. This is the *fourth oxidation step*. Oxalacetic acid is the end-product of the Krebs Cycle. After it is regenerated, it again reacts with acetyl-coenzyme A, and the cycle is kept going without interruption. Oxalacetic acid is present in plant cells for this purpose, and it may also be formed from pyruvic acid, aspartic acid, glutamic acid, etc. The enzymes and ATP required for the whole process are formed in the mitochondria. Aerobic respiration, thus, appears to be restricted to the mitochondria. It may be noted that complete oxidation of 1 mol. of glucose yields 2 mols. of pyruvic acid, 6 mols of CO_2 and 38 mols of ATP, as follows:

(pigmented bodies containing iron). NAD and FAD are reduced (hydrogen or electrons received) NAD—NADH$_2$—FAD FADH2, and later the energy released in the oxidation of NADH$_2$ and FADH$_2$ is used in the conversion of ADP to ATP (ADP + inorganic phosphate + energy = ATP). Hydrogen ions are released to the cytoplasm, while electrons pass down through coenzyme Q to the cytochromes (a, b and c). In the oxidation of cytochromes, more ATP is synthesized in the cells. It may be noted that the synthesis of ATP from ADP in the mitochondria at the expense of chemical energy through oxidation-reduction reactions of the electron transport system is otherwise called *oxidative phosphorylation* (as opposed to *photophosphorylation* which is synthesis of ATP in the chloroplasts at the expense of light energy). For each pair of electrons passed from one compound to another, 3 ATP are usually formed (only 2 ATP in certain reactions). In respiration, as stated before, most of the energy is released through the Krebs Cycle. With the reduction of cytochromes the electrons pass down to oxygen and the 'activated' oxygen freely combines with hydrogen (already released to the cytoplasm) to form H_2O.

See Appendix III for Chemical steps.

glycolysis (See Appendix III)	...	—	8 ATP
pyruvic acid to acetyl-CoA	...	2CO$_2$	6 ATP
Krebs cycle (See Appendix III):			
(a) isocitric acid to oxalosuccinic acid	...	—	6 ATP
(b) oxalosuccinic acid to α-ketoglutaric acid	...	2 CO$_2$	—
(c) α-ketoglutaric acid to succinyl CoA	...	2 CO$_2$	6 ATP
(d) release from succinyl CoA	...	—	2 ATP
(e) succinic acid to fumaric acid	...	—	4 ATP
(f) malic acid to oxalacetic acid	...	—	6 ATP
		2 CO$_2$	38 ATP

Electron Transport System. As stated before, oxidation of a compound means removal of electrons from it, usually accompanied by removal of hydrogen, and reduction means addition of electrons to a compound, usually accompanied by addition of hydrogen. The metabolic pathway through which the electrons pass from one compound to another is called the electron transport system or cytochrome system. In oxidation-reduction processes, specific enzymes are always connected with the transport of electrons from one compound to another. In respiration, the electron transport system consists commonly of NAD, FAD, coenzyme Q (a quinone compound) and cytochromes

Experiment 29. Aerobic respiration (FIG. 35A). Respiration in plants can be experimentally proved in a very simple but efficient way by the following method. The appliances required for this experiment are: a flask with a bent bulb, called **respiroscope** (an ordinary long-necked flask will also do), a beaker, a suitable stand with a clamp, a quantity of mercury (according to the size of the beaker), a caustic potash stick and some germinating seeds or opening flower-buds. Introduce some germinating seeds into the respiroscope. Pour a quantity of mercury into the beaker and invert the respiroscope over it. The respiroscope is fixed in this vertical position with a stand and a clamp. The air enclosed in the flask is

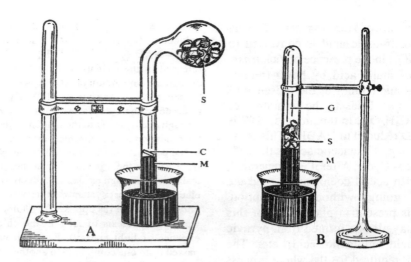

Experiments on respiration. FIG. 35. *A*, aerobic respiration; *B*, anaerobic or intramolecular respiration. *S*, seeds; *C*, caustic potash stick; *M*, mercury; *G*, gas

thus cut off from the surrounding atmosphere. With the help of the forceps, introduce a small piece of caustic potash stick into the respiroscope. This will float on the mercury. Leave the apparatus in this position for some hours, preferably till the next day. *Observation.* It will be seen on the following day that the level of mercury in the respiroscope has risen to the extent of nearly one-fifth of total volume. *Inference.* Since caustic potash [abs]orbs carbon dioxide, we may conclude that the gas [abs]orbed is carbon dioxide.

[T]he atmospheric connection being cut off, it may be [safe]ly assumed that the CO_2 must have been exhaled by [the] germinating seeds. The gas (4/5th in volume) [rem]aining in the respiroscope is nitrogen, while the [oxy]gen (originally 1/5th the total volume) must have [been] absorbed by the seeds in the process of respiration [sinc]e it had no chance to escape. It may also be noted [that] the rise of mercury will be immediate and quick [if th]e caustic potash stick is used at the end of the [expe]riment.

[N]*ote.* The experiment may be carried out in the fol-[lowi]ng way. Instead of mercury, water may be poured [in] the beaker, and the respiroscope with the germinat-[ing s]eeds inverted over it. A short test-tube containing [a sm]all piece of caustic potash stick may be floated on [the] water inside the respiroscope. Subsequently, the [wate]r level in the respiroscope rises.

Experiment 30. Anaerobic respiration (FIG. 35B). Fill a short narrow test-tube to the brim with mercury (*M*), close it with the thumb and invert it over mercury contained in a beaker. Keep the tube in a vertical position with a suitable stand. Take some germinating seeds and remove their seed-coats to get rid of the enclosed air (oxygen). With the help of the forceps, hold the skinned seeds under the test-tube and release them into it one by one. The seeds will rise to the closed end of the tube. Introduce five or six seeds in this way. They are now free from oxygen. It is better to soak the seeds in distilled water before introducing them into the test-tube. This keeps the seeds moist. Note on the following day that the mercury column has been pushed down, owing to the exhalation of a gas (G) by the seeds. Within one or two days, nearly all of the mercury is pushed out of the tube. Introduce a small piece of caustic potash stick into the test-tube with the help of the forceps. It floats on the mercury, and on coming in contact with the gas, it quickly absorbs it. The mercury rises again and fills up the test-tube. Evidently, the gas is carbon dioxide.

Experiment 31. To prove that carbon dioxide is released in the respiration of a green plant. Set up the apparatus as shown in FIG. 36. *A* contains soda-lime; *B* contains KOH solution; *C* encloses a pot plant—the bell-jar stands on a smooth, flat plate stuck with vaseline to prevent leakage of air; *D* contains baryta (or lime) water. Other connections are also made airtight. The experiment is carried out in a semi-dark room, with the bell-jar covered with a black cloth. The bent tube on

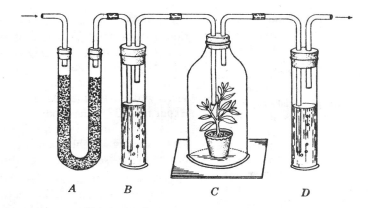

FIG. 36. Experiment on the respiration of a green plant

the extreme right is connected to an aspirator bottle (not shown in the figure). The stopcock of the aspirator bottle is slightly opened. As a result a partial vacuum is produced and a slow current of air, freed of CO_2, is drawn in through the other end of the series. After some time, as the air-current slowly passes into D, it will be seen that the baryta water in it turns milky (barium carbonate is formed). Evidently this CO_2 has been released

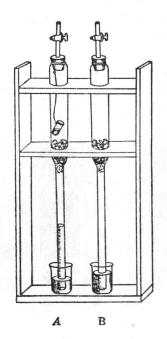

FIG. 37. Respiratory quotient—
$CO_2:O_2$ (see Experiment 32a)

by the plant. Note that carbon dioxide is absorbed by caustic potash, baryta water and lime water, but only the latter two turn milky in contact with carbon dioxide.

Experiment 32. The volume of CO_2 evolved in respiration is approximately equal to the volume of O_2 absorbed. (a) Set up the apparatus as shown in FIG. 37. The small test-tube in A contains KOH solution; B does not. The beaker at the bottom contains water in each case. Both the respiroscope tubes contain some germinating seeds. The stopcock is closed. After some time it is seen that the water rises in A, the CO_2 released by the seeds being absorbed by the KOH. There is no rise of water in B as no vacuum has been produced in it. B, therefore, shows that the total volume of air in it (whatever be the gaseous interchanges) is constant. As we know, only O_2 and CO_2 are invloved in respiration, and it may be taken for granted that the volumes of the two gases are equal. Then replace B by a new respiroscope tube (or use the same one after washing) without seeds and dip it into pyrogallate of potash (instead of water). As it absorbs O_2, the solution soon rises to the same extent as in A. We may, therefore, conclude that in respiration, the volume of CO_2 given out is equal to the volume of O_2 absorbed.

Note that if starchy seeds like pea, gram, etc., are used, the respiratory quotient is unity. If, however, oily seeds like castor are used, the R.Q. is less than unity, i.e. they absorb more O_2 and give out less CO_2.

(b) **Ganong's respirometer.** Arrange the apparatus, as shown in FIG. 38. Put 2 cc. of germinating seeds (or any other respiring material) into the bulb and pour 10% KOH solution into the side (or levelling or reservoir) tube after opening the hole at the neck of the bulb. By adjusting the height of the side-tube, the KOH solution may be brought to the 100 cc. mark in the graduated manometer tube. Now close the hole by turning the stopper. The volume of the enclosed air is 100 cc. and it is at atmospheric pressure. Pour more solution into the side-tube to maintain equal levels in the two tubes. As respiration takes place, the CO_2 liberated by the seeds is absorbed by the KOH solution, and it rises and stands at the 80 cc. mark. Evidently, 1/5th of the air (which is oxygen) has been absorbed by the seeds during respiration, and this is the volume of CO_2 exhaled by the seeds during the process, as indicated by the rise of the KOH solution. If saturated common salt solution is used instead of KOH solution its level is seen to remain constant in the tubes, evidently indicating that the volume of oxygen absorbed is the same as that of carbon dioxide exhaled.

Respiration is a destructive process consisting of the decomposition of some of the food material, more particularly glucose, brought about by the action of specific enzymes secreted by the protoplasm. Nevertheless, it is highly beneficial to the life of the plant for the reason that respiration sets free *energy* by which work is performed. This energy is absolutely necessary for the various synthetic processes, growth, movements, etc. If we think of the enormous development of a large tree,

it is apparent we can at once realize that a vast amount of energy has been utilized in its construction. A considerable amount of energy, of course, escapes from the plant body in the form of heat. Heat is generated during vigorous respiration. A thermometer thrust into a mass of germinating seeds will show a marked rise of temperature (see Experiment 33). The production of heat is an easily observed form of energy. Respiration causes a loss in the dry weight of a plant. This is believed to be due to the escape of carbon dioxide.

Experiment 33. Heat generated in respiration (FIG. 39). Take two Thermos flasks and fill one (A) of them with germinating seeds. Fill (B) with germinating seeds that have been killed being boiled for a few minutes and then soaked in 5% formalin to prevent any fermentation which would generate heat. Insert a sensitive thermometer in each, as shown in the figure, and pack the mouth of the flask with cotton. It is better to place, half immersed in the lump of seeds, a small test-tube containing a small piece of caustic potash stick. Wait for some time and note the remarkable rise of temperature in the case of flask A, which contains the germinating seeds. There is no rise of temperature in flask B with killed seeds, (the dotted line indicating the original temperature). This evidently proves that heat is evolved in respiration.

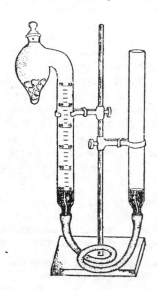

FIG. 38. Ganong's respirometer (see Experiment 32b)

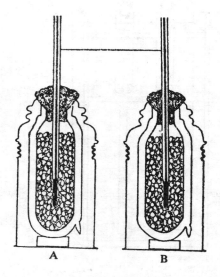

FIG. 39. Experiment to show that heat is generated in respiration (see text)

CONDITIONS AFFECTING RESPIRATION

1. **Oxygen.** The presence of oxygen is essential for respiration. But it must be noted that it is required for the reactions of the Krebs Cycle only (and not for the anaerobic phase—glycolysis). Therefore, there are marked changes in the rate of respiration under varying conditions of oxygen concentration, affecting R.Q. values (see below). If the concentration goes below 5%, the process rapidly falls off. Under this condition, the amount of CO_2 evolved is greater than the O_2 absorbed. If the oxygen supply is cut off, only CO_2 is produced as a result of anaerobic respiration. With a gradual increase in the oxygen concentration, there is a corresponding, steady increase in the rate, and the R.Q. value approaches unity, i.e. $CO_2:O_2 = 1$. But the rate does not go far beyond the normal rate at atmospheric concentration of O_2.

2. **Temperature.** This distinctly affects the rate of respiration. The minimum rate is reached at 0°C or even at 10°C. With a rise in temperature, the rate increases and reaches a maximum at 45°C. or even 40°C. Beyond this point, the protoplasm is injured and enzyme activity, in particular, is affected, causing a decrease in the rate of respiration. The optimum temperature range is 30°C. to 35°C.

3. **Light.** The effect of light is only indirect. Respiratory activity is greater in bright sunlight than in subdued light. This may be due to the fact that in bright light the stomata remain wide open and oxygen is easily and quickly absorbed.

4. **Supply of Water.** Protoplasm saturated with water respires more vigorously than that in a desiccated condition, as in the dry seed. Thus, the rate of respiration increases with the supply of water.

5. **Vitality of cells.** Respiration in young, active cells is more rapid than in old cells. Vegetative buds, floral buds and germinating seeds respire more vigorously than the older parts of a plant.

6. **Carbon Dioxide Concentration.** If, during respiration, carbon dioxide is allowed to accumulate inside the plant as a result of stomatal closure, or around the plant, respiration slows down and comes to a standstill. If the carbon dioxide is removed, respiration proceeds normally again. Concentration of CO_2 has a depressing effect on respiration.

7. **Nutritive Material.** Food material, more particularly soluble carbohydrates, affects respiration to a considerable extent. With the supply of oxygen, food material is quickly broken down.

Respiratory Quotient (R.Q.). There is a relation between the volume of carbon dioxide evolved and the volume of oxygen consumed in the pocess of respiration, and the ratio of these two volumes is known as respiratory quotient. Thus, when sugars are consumed in respiration, as mostly in cereals, the respiratory quotient (R.Q.), i.e. the ratio of $CO_2: O_2$ is equal to unity. This means that for one molecule of CO_2 given out, one molecule of O_2 is used. Sugars are by no means the only compounds consumed in respiration. Fats, proteins, organic acids and other materials are also consumed, and the R.Q. in such cases may be far from unity. When fats are consumed in respiration, as in oily seeds, the R.Q. is less than unity. Fats are poorer in oxygen than are sugars and, therefore, a correspondingly greater amount of oxygen is required for combustion of fats, or, in other words, less CO_2 is evolved for a particular volume of O_2 taken up. Likewise, when proteins are used in respiration, the R.Q. is less than unity since the proportion of oxygen to carbon in them is less than in carbohydrates. When organic acids are oxidized, the R.Q. is found to be more than unity. Such compounds are relatively rich in oxygen in comparison with carbohydrates. At night, succulent plants like cacti absorb oxygen without giving out carbon dioxide. In these plants, it is not carbon dioxide but organic acids (malic, citric, oxalic, etc.) are formed as a result of incomplete oxidation of sugar. During the daytime, however, they give out CO_2. The concept of respiratory quotient is important because it serves as a clue to the nature of the compounds used in respiration, and also to the nature of the process itself.

RESPIRATION AND PHOTOSYNTHESIS

1. In respiration, plants utilize oxygen and give out carbon dioxide, while in photosynthesis, plants utilize carbon dioxide and give out oxygen. One process is just the reverse of the other.

2. Respiration is a destructive (catabolic) process, but photosynthesis is a constructive

(anabolic) process. In the former, sugar is broken down into CO_2 and H_2O with the liberation of energy, while in the latter CO_2 and H_2O are utilized to build up sugar with the storage of energy. Respiration is, thus, a *breaking-down process*, and photosynthesis a *building-up process*.

3. The intermediate chemical reactions in the breakdown of sugar in respiration (anaerobic phase) and those in the synthesis of sugar in photosynthesis are much the same. In both processes, phospho-glyceric acid holds a pivotal position from which reactions proceed in different directions under different conditions.

4. Respiration is performed by all the living cells of a plant at all times, i.e. it is independent of light and chlorophyll. On the other hand, photosynthesis is performed only by the green cells, and that too, only in the presence of sunlight. Although photosynthesis proceeds for just a limited period, this process is much more vigorous than respiration.

5. The seat of respiration is the mitochondria present in the living cells of both plants and animals, while the seat of photosynthesis is the chloroplasts, (at least partly), present in only the green cells of plants.

6. Respiration results in a loss of the dry weight of a plant due to breakdown of food material and the production of carbon dioxide which escapes from the plant body, but photosynthesis results in a gain in the dry weight, due to formation of sugar, starch, etc., which accumulate in the plant body.

FERMENTATION

Fermentation is the incomplete oxidation of sugar (particularly glucose) into alcohol and carbon dioxide, brought about by several species of bacteria and yeast (and certain other fungi) in the absence of oxygen. Although fermentation by yeast cells leading to the production of commercial alcohol was known for a long time, it was Louis Pasteur who first studied the process elaborately and showed clearly (around 1857) that it is a process of life, and not of death. Pasteur actually applied many of his discoveries to the making of different kinds of liquors by using different species and strains of yeast. Other fermentative processes brought about by different types of bacteria were also elaborately studied by him. It later came to light through the work of Buchner in 1897 that the change of sugar into alcohol and carbon dioxide is due to the action of *zymase* (an enzyme complex) secreted by the micro-organisms, and not due to their direct action on sugar. Under the action of specific enzymes (see pp. 282-83), sugar becomes converted to pyruvic acid. The latter is then reduced to ethyl alcohol (through acetaldehyde) and carbon dioxide by the enzyme *carboxylase*. Fermentation processes are mostly anaerobic and although much less energy is liberated by such processes, organisms living under anaerobic conditions have to depend on this energy for their vital activities. Fermentation is most readily seen in date-palm juice, where sugar is broken up by the yeast cells in the absence of oxygen into alcohol and carbon dioxide. The frothing on the surface of the liquid is due to the formation of this gas. Fermentation may be defined as an enzyme action on sugar in the absence of free oxygen, splitting it (sugar) into carbon dioxide and alcohol and, sometimes, organic acids. The process is analogous to anaerobic respiration and may be represented by the same equation—$C_6H_{12}O_6$ + zymase $=2C_2H_5OH$ (ethyl alcohol) + $2CO_2$ + zymase + energy (28 kilo cal.). The equation shows that 1 molecule of glucose produces 2 molecules of ethyl alcohol and 2 of carbon dioxide. The amount of energy released in fermentation is no doubt small, but it suffices for the activity of anaerobic micro-organisms. Other common examples of fermentation are: acetic acid fermentation, which is the souring of alcoholic liquors such as wine, beer, etc. due to the conversion of alcohol to acetic acid (vinegar) by acetic acid bacteria; lactic acid fermentation, which is the souring of milk due to the conversion of milk sugar into lactic acid by lactic acid bacteria; butyric acid fermentation, which is the rancidity of butter due to the conversion of sugar into butyric acid by butyric acid bacteria, etc. Some fermentation processes are of great commercial importance, e.g. the production of alcohol by different species and strains of yeast,

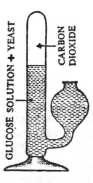

FIG. 40. Kuhne's fermentation vessel
(see Experiment 34)

the manufacture of vinegar (acetic acid) from alcohol by species of *Acetobacter*, the manufacture of flavoured butter and cheese, the retting of jute and flax, tanning (conversion of hide into leather), etc. It may be noted that the organic products formed by the fermenting micro-organisms act as toxic to them. This checks their unlimited growth and multiplication.

Experiment 34. Fermentation. Experiments on fermentation may be easily carried out with the help of a Kühne's fermentation vessel (FIG. 40) and the procedure is as follows. Prepare a 5% glucose solution in water and add to it a small quantity of fresh brewers' yeast, or collect a quantity of date palm juice early in the morning. Fill the closed upright tube of the fermentation vessel completely with this solution or the juice and partially fill the side-tube, up to or below the base of the bulb. Warm the solution to about 25°C and leave the apparatus in a warm place for a few hours. It will be seen that a gas collects at the upper end of the closed tube, displacing the solution, which now accumulates in the bulb of the side-tube and overflows it. The evolution of gas continues so long as the sugar in the solution is not exhausted. Then introduce a piece of caustic potash stick into the fermentation vessel and shake it gently to dissolve the piece, taking care that the gas collected in the closed tube does not escape. Place the fermentation vessel in the vertical position again. Within a few minutes, it will be seen that the gas is absorbed by the solution, which rises and again fills up the tube. The gas, evidently, is carbon dioxide evolved during fermentation.

RESPIRATION AND FERMENTATION. Both respiration and fermentation are oxidation processes by which energy stored up in carbohydrates and other compounds is set free, and carbon dioxide given out. The two processes depend upon whether free oxygen is available or not, and to what extent oxidation (complete or incomplete) proceeds. Recent research shows that respiration in higher plants takes place in two stages: an anaerobic phase resulting in complete oxidation of sugar, and an aerobic phase resulting in complete oxidation of the intermediate products formed in anaerobic respiration, into carbon dioxide and water. Fermentation is that type of anaerobic respiration in which alcohol is produced (Palladin). Generally speaking, respiration includes only aerobic respiration, while fermentation is regarded as a synonym for anaerobic respiration. On this basis, the following distinctions can be drawn between respiration and fermentation:

(1) Respiration takes place in the presence of free oxygen. Fermentation takes place in the absence of free oxygen, which is derived from rearrangement of molecules of some carbohydrates. Thus, fermentation is also known as intramolecular respiration. The initial or anaerobic phase is the same in both processes.

(2) Respiration takes place in all the living cells of a plant and, at times, in the presence of carbohydrates. Fermentation takes place only in the presence of some easily available carbohydrates such as various sugars under the action of certain micro-organisms, such as yeast, bacteria, fungi, etc.

(3) In respiration, carbohydrates are completely oxidized into carbon dioxide and water, while in fermentation, carbohydrates are incompletely oxidized, forming carbon dioxide, alcohol and various other products.

(4) Respiration is more efficient than fermentation so far as release of energy is concerned. In respiration, a much larger amount of energy is liberated as a result of complete oxidation, while in fermentation, much less energy is liberated as a result of incomplete oxidation, as may be seen from the following equations:

Respiration—$C_6H_{12}O_6 + 6O_2 = 6CO_2 + 6H_2O +$ 674 kilo-cal.

Fermentation—$C_6H_{12}O_6 = 2C_2H_5OH + 2CO_2 + 28$ kilo-cal.

CHAPTER 12

METABOLISM

Two series of chemical changes or processes take place simultaneously in a plant cell, one leading finally to the construction or building-up of the protoplasm, and the other to its decomposition or breakdown. These two processes, which are constructive on the one hand and destructive on the other, are together known as **metabolism**. Metabolism takes place only in the living cells and is one of the characteristic signs of life. The processes that lead to the construction of various food materials, other organic compounds and finally, of protoplasm, are together known as **anabolism**. Those leading to the destruction or breakdown are known as **catabolism**.

Anabolism. The main anabolic or constructive changes are: formation of sugars and other carbohydrates, formation of proteins and formation of fats and oils. These changes are regarded as anabolic because the protoplasm continually reconstructs itself with these nutritive substances. By anabolism, a considerable amount of potential energy is stored in these substances for future use by the protoplasm.

Catabolism. Side by side with anabolism, catabolic or destructive changes or processes take place in a plant's living cells. The main catabolic processes are digestion, respiration and fermentation. By these processes, complex food substances are gradually broken down into simpler products, e.g. carbohydrates into glucose, proteins into amines and amino-acids, and fats and oils into fatty acids and glycerine. The potential energy already stored in them is released by catabolism into kinetic energy for the protoplasm's manifold activities. Carbon dioxide and water are formed as a result of complete oxidation of glucose in aerobic respiration, and alcohols and organic acids as a result of incomplete oxidation of glucose in anaerobic respiration or fermentation. Amino-acids sometimes result from the decomposition of protoplasm. Besides, the secretory products, such as enzymes, vitamins, hormones, cellulose, nectar, etc., are also the results of catabolic processes. Catabolism also leads to the formation of many *by-products* in plants. Various waste products, such as tannins, essential oils, gums, resins, etc., belong to this category. These being useless or even harmful to the protoplasm are removed from the sphere of protoplasmic activity and mostly stored up in special cells, bark, old leaves, heartwood and glands. In this sense, the various kinds of waste products may also be regarded as excretory products. Besides, many other substances, such as some of the vegetable (organic) acids, aromatic compounds, anthocyanins, lignin, cutin, etc., are formed in the plant body as a result of catabolic processes.

CHAPTER 13

GROWTH

The growth of a plant is a complex phenomenon associated with numerous physiological processes—both constructive and destructive. The former lead to the formation of various nutritive substances and the protoplasm, and the latter to their breakdown. The protoplasm assimilates the protein food and increases in bulk (see p. 279), while the carbohydrates are mainly utilized in respiration and in the formation of the cell-wall substance, viz. cellulose. The cells divide and numerous new cells are formed. These increase in size and become fully turgid, and the plant grows as a whole. Growth is, thus, a complex, vital phenomenon brought about by the protoplasm. *It may be defined as a permanent and irreversible increase in size and form, attended by an increase in weight.* Sometimes a loss in weight is noticed at an early stage of growth, as, for example, when a potato tuber sprouts, it shows a loss of weight in the beginning due to transpiration and respiration. But that is soon made good as new materials begin to be formed by the sprouting shoot. Growth is usually very slow in plants, and is difficult to detect and measure accurately within a short space of time without the help of a suitable instrument. There are, however, certain plants which show very rapid growth. For instance, some climbers like morning glory and wood-rose grow at the rate of about 20 cm. per day. The young shoots of giant bamboo show a growth of over 40 cm. per day, while the tendrils of some *Cucurbita* show an extraordinary growth of 6 cm. per hour. However slow the growth of a plant may be, it can be measured accurately with the help of an instrument, called the **auxanometer**.

Experiment 35. Growth in Length of the auxanometer is an instrument by means of small increase in length can be magnified many t From the total known magnification recorded by t auxanometer, the actual length attained by a plant within a specified time can be easily calculated. Two types of auxanometers are in common use. The first and simplest type is the **lever auxanometer** or **arc indicator** (FIG. 41), and the second is the **pulley auxanometer** or simply **auxanometer** (FIG. 42). The principle is the same in both. (*a*) The **lever type** has a movable lever or indicator fixed to a wheel, round which passes a cord. One end of the cord is tied round or gummed to the apex of the stem. A small weight is suspended from the other end to keep the cord taut. As the stem increases in length, the wheel slowly rotates under the weight and the indicator moves down the graduated arc. The growth in length is thus recorded by the instrument on a magnified scale. The actual increase in the length of the stem is calculated from the record thus obtained. For instance, if the lever has transversed a distance of 45 cm. in 24 hours and the magnification is 90 times, the actual growth in the same period is 45/90 cm., i.e. 0.5 cm. or 5 mm. Therefore, the actual growth of the plant is 5/24 mm., i.e. 0.2 mm. in 1 hour.

(*b*) With the **pulley auxanometer** a permanent record of growth within a specified time is obtained on a smoked paper, which is wrapped round a drum or cylinder. The drum is rotated by means of a clockwork

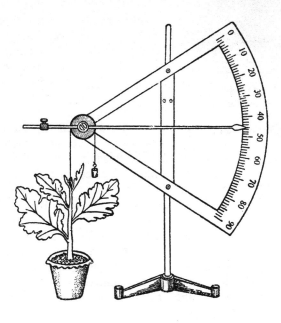

FIG. 41.
Arc indicator
or lever
auxanometer

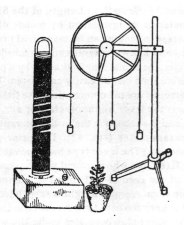

FIG. 42. A pulley auxanometer

mechanism. A cord with one end attached to the plant is passed round a small wheel, and a small weight suspended from the other end. Round the bigger wheel, which is fixed to the smaller one, passes another cord with two small weights at the two ends. There is a horizontal pointer attached to the cord with the tip in contact with the smoked paper. As growth takes place and the drum rotates, the pointer, being attached to the cord of the bigger wheel, leaves a mark on the paper on a maginfied scale. After a period of growth, the paper is removed and dipped into varnish, and the smoke or soot becomes fixed on the paper. If growth proceeds continuously, a diagonal curve is traced on the paper (FIG. 42). A horizontal curve is the result if growth ceases. It is easy to calculate the actual growth within a specified time from the magnification, which is now known.

Crescograph. The late Sir Jagadish C. Bose constructed a very delicate apparatus known as crescograph which is an electric device. With the help of this apparatus, the growth of a plant can be magnified one thousand to ten thousand times and accurately measured. At this high magnification, it is possible to measure the progress of growth even in seconds.

Conditions Necessary for Growth. Since growth is brought about by the protoplasm, the conditions necessary for growth are the same as those that maintain the activity of the protoplasm. The condition are as follows:

(1) **Supply of Nutritive Material.** Growth can only take place when the protoplasm of the growing region is supplied with nutritive material. The protoplasm assimilates these materials and builds up the body of the plant. Food mterial is also a source of energy.

(2) **Supply of Water.** An adequate supply of water is absolutely necessary to maintain the turgidity of growing cells. Turgidity is the first step towards growth. The protoplasm can work only when it is saturated with water. An abundant supply of water makes good the loss caused by transpiration. It is a fact, however, that only a small quantity is required for actual growth.

(3) **Supply of Oxygen.** Supply of free oxygen is indispensable for the respiration of all living cells. Respiration is an oxidation process by which the *potential* energy stored in the food is released in the form of *kinetic* energy and utilized by the protoplasm for its manifold activities.

(4) **Suitable Temperature.** The protoplasm requires a suitable temperature for its activities. It ceases to perform its functions or does so very slowly at a low temperature, while a temperature of 45°C coagulates and kills it. The protoplasm conducts its activities within a certain range of temperature. This is said to be due to the **thermotonic** effect of temperature. The optimum temperature ordinarily averages from 28° to 30°C, and the minimum lies at about 4°C.

(5) **Light.** Light is not absolutely necessary for the initial stages of growth. In fact, plants grow more rapidly in darkness than in light. Although light has a retarding effect on growth, the protoplasm remains healthy and the plant becomes sturdy, the stem and green leaves developing normally, when there is a certain intensity of light. Moreover, as we have already learnt, the stomata remain open and the chloroplasts function normally preparing food substances only in the presence of light. All this is said to be due to the **phototonic** or stimulating effect of light. Continued absence of light is very harmful to plants. Plants grown in the dark or in very weak light have delicate, soft and slender stems. Their branches have elongated internodes, are pale-green or pale-yellow and sickly in appearance, and they seldom produce flowers and fruits. The leaves of such plants are small, pale-yellow and often remain undeveloped and their roots are poorly developed. Plants showing

FIG. 43. Effect of light and darkness on growth of seedlings. *Left*, gourd seedlings; *right*, gram seedlings; *A*, grown in light; *B*, grown in darkness

these characteristics are said to be **etiolated** (FIG. 43B). The relative length of day and night has a profound influence on the production of flowers and fruits (see photoperiodism, p. 300). The effect of particular rays of light on a plant's growth can be easily seen when a pot plant is grown within a double-walled bell-jar which has been filled with red, yellow, green or any other solution (see also p. 261). The effect of unilateral light on growth and movements is discussed on p. 304.

(6) **Force of Gravity.** This factor determines the direction of growth of particular organs of the plant body (see p. 304). The root grows towards the force of gravity, and the stem away from it.

PHASES OF GROWTH (FIG. 45). Growth does not take place throughout the whole length of the plant body, but is localized in special regions called *meristems*, which may be apical, lateral, or intercalary. The growth in length is due to gradual enlargement and elongation of the cells of the apical meristems (root-apex and stem-apex) In dicotyledons and gymnosperms, the growth in thickness is due to the activity of the lateral meristems, i.e. interfascicular cambium, fascicular cambium and cork-cambium. Three phases can be recognized in the growth of any organ of a plant:

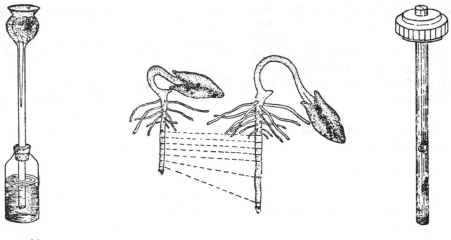

FIG. 44   FIG. 45   FIG. 46

FIG. 44. Measurement of growth of root. FIG. 45. Phase of growth of root. FIG. 46. A space marker wheel

(1) **The Formative Phase**. This is restricted to the apical meristem of the root and the stem. The cells of this region are constantly dividing and multiplying. They are characterized by abundant protoplasm, a large nucleus and a thin cellulose wall.

(2) **The Phase of Elongation**. This lies immediately behind the formative phase. The cells no longer divide, but increase in size. They begin to enlarge and elongate until they reach their maximum dimension. In the root, this phase is a few millimetres long and in the stem, a few centimetres. In some climbers, it may be much longer.

(3) **The Phase of Maturation**. This phase lies farther back. The cells have already reached their permanent size. The thickening of the cell-wall takes place in this phase.

GRAND PERIOD OF GROWTH. Every organ of the plant body, in fact every cell that the organ is composed of, shows a variation in the rate of its growth. The growth is slow at first. Then it accelerates reaching a maximum after which it falls off rather quickly and gradually slows down until it comes to a standstill. The entire period of growth of each organ, cell, or the plant as a whole is called the **grand period of growth**. Within the grand period, variations in growth occur due to external and other causes. For instance, there is the *diurnal variation of growth*. Light inhibits growth, and light that is too intense even checks it altogether. Thus, plants grow faster during the night than during the day. There is also *seasonal variation of growth*. During winter, the growth of many plants comes to a halt or becomes very slow, but proceeds rapidly during spring.

Experiment 36. Distribution and Rate of Growth. (*a*) Root. With the help of a space marker wheel (FIG. 46), mark the root of a germinating seed with transverse lines that are equidistant from each other. Waterproof Indian ink should be used for the purpose. Next pack the germinating seed in wet cotton and place it in the bulb of a thistle funnel, which should be made to stand in a bottle containing water. Cover the stem of the funnel with black paper to prevent curvature of the root owing to light. After a few days, it is seen that the lines

that are a bit behind the tip become widely separated from each other, while those higher up and at the tip remain more or less intact. This evidently shows that the growth is fastest behind the apex. The *rate of growth* may easily be measured from day to day with the help of a scale (*b*). Stem. The distribution of growth in the stem is also determined similarly, except that the thistle funnel need not be used. The stem shows the same phases of growth as the root. The rate of growth of the stem may be accurately measured with the help of an auxanometer. (*c*) Leaf. The distribution of growth of a flat organ like the leaf may be determined with the help of an instrument called the **space marker disc**.

Sigmoid curve. If the growth of a plant is measured at periodic intervals throughout its life and the readings are graphically plotted (growth against time), the graph shows an 'S' shaped curve, known as the Sigmoid curve. The shape of the curve is always the same, whether it is the growth length (height of the plant) that is being measured, or the growth of individual organs, such as root, fruit, etc. This curve indicates that a plant's rate of growth is slow in the initial phase (lag phase), accelerates in the middle (log phase or grand period of growth) and slows down in the last phase (senescent phase).

Hormones. It is now definitely known that certain chemical substances formed in very minute quantities as a result of metabolic processes within the plant have a profound influence on the *growth* of the plant's organs and on the various kinds of *tropic movements* exhibited by such organs. They also have a marked effect on certain physiological processes. These substances are known as **hormones** or **phytohormones** or **growth hormones**. Of the various kinds of plant hormones discovered to date, **auxins** (auxin-A and auxin-B) and **heteroauxin** (indole-acetic acid—IAA, first obtained from human urine) are known best so far their occurrence, composition and action are concerned. They are formed in one part of the plant body (chiefly in the apical meristem of the stem and the root, and also in the tip of the leaf) and transported to another part to produce a particular physiological effect there. Their movement is strictly longitudinal, normally from the apex downwards

(Went, 1928 and Thimann, 1934). Upward translocation is also possible through transpiration current. The presence of hormones was first demonstrated by experimental methods.[1] It is now possible to extract them from plants by appropriate chemical methods. Hormones stimulate growth at low concentration while they retard growth, at high concentration. Auxins cause the formation of roots in stem-cuttings and grafting. They are responsible for fruit development, seed germination, seedling growth and growth of plant organs. They also stimulate cell division and elongation, and influence certain physiological processes. Besides, the role of hormones in tropic responses is now well established.

Thus *phototropism* and *geotropism* are now explained on a hormonal basis. In the case of phototropism, in the course of their downward movement from the apex, hormones accumulate in the shaded side, which then grows more rapidly than the illuminated side. This results in a phototropic curvature, i.e. the shoot bends towards the light. In the case of geotropism, hormones accumulate on the lower side of the horizontally placed shoot. Thus, the growth of this side is stimulated and the stem bends upwards. In the horizontally placed root, hormones similarly accumulate on the lower side but the root reacts in a different way. It is probable that the growth of the root is stimulated by lower concentration of hormones. Therefore, the particular concentration that has stimulated the growth of the stem checks the growth of the root on its lower side. As a consequence, the root bends downwards. Hormones responsible for the development of the root, stem, leaf, flower, fruit, etc., have also been discovered. For example, *rhizocaline*, formed in the leaf, is necessary for root formation; *caulocaline*, formed in the root, is necessary for stem elongation; *phyllocaline*, formed in the cotyledon, is necessary for leaf growth; *florigen*, formed in the leaf, induces flower formation; *wound hormone* (traumatic acid) is necessary for the healing of wounds, etc. Traumatic acid induces cell division in the undamaged cells bordering a wound, resulting in callus formation which covers the wound and heals it. **Kinins** (kinetin and analogous compounds), first isolated from yeast DNA as *kinetin* (possibly a degradation product of DNA), promote cell division (as was first noted in tobacco pith culture), cell enlargement, seed germination, seedling growth, development of roots and buds, breaking of dormancy, etc. In some cases, kinetin works better in association with IAA. Kinins have not been isolated from plants as such, although they appear to be present in them in some form or the other.

---

[1] The term hormone was first used by Starling in 1906 in connection with certain secretions in the animal body. In the case of plants, the action of hormones (auxins) was first demonstrated on oat coleoptile by Boyes-Jensen (1910), Stark (1920) and, more elaborately, by Went (1926) and Thimann (1934). The tip of the oat coleoptile was cut off some millimetres behind the apex. This evidently checked the growth of the coleoptile. But when the decapitated tip was affixed to the cut surface, it was found that growth resumed at almost the normal rate. Evidently, the tip contained something which, when transmitted to the main coleoptile, induced growth. Further experiments carried out in 1928 and later made this clearer still. The cut off tip of an oat coleoptile was placed on agar (3%) for about an hour. The agar was then cut into small blocks and one such block placed on the cut surface of the coleoptile. It was then seen that the growth of the coleoptile was normal, as if nothing had happened. Evidently, something was transmitted from the cut off tip to the agar medium and thence, to the main coleoptile. That something is now known to be an auxin. Further experiments were carried out. Another agar block treated in the same way was placed on the cut surface on one side and it was seen that growth was more rapid on this side, causing the coleoptile to curve. Evidently, it was the auxin that accelerated that growth of this side. By 1934, at least three such growth substances or hormones were isolated : auxin-A, auxin-B, and heteroauxin. All these are widely distributed in plants. These are catalyzed into active hormones by specific enzyme action. For example, the amino-acid 'tryptophan' is the precursor to heteroauxin (indole-acetic acid—IAA). Around 1942 and later, it was found that certain synthetic compounds (not formed in plants) induce reactions similar to those induced by natural hormones. These are indole-butyric acid, naphthalene-acetic acid, etc.

Gibberellins. Gibberellins were first isolated from a fungus, *Fusarium moniliforme* (=*Gibberella fujikuroi*), by Japanese scientists (Sewada in 1912, Kurosawa in 1926, Yabuta in 1938, and several other later), and their effects on many higher plants studied. Many years back, Japanese farmers first noticed that many rice plants in their rice fields had grown abnormally tall and then died out without producing grains (bakanae disease of rice or foolish seedling disease), evidently resulting in heavy losses. Japanese scientists soon started investigations on the cause of this abnormal growth. They succeeded in tracing the above-mentioned fungus as the cause of the disease and finally isolating from it at least three gibberellins (gibberellic acid and others as natural plant hormones). Since this discovery was made, several compounds (hormones) similar to gibberellins have been found to occur in higher plants. Experiments with them on a number of plants have shown much quicker growth of the stems and leaves. Further investigations have revealed many other physiological effects of gibberellins, covering far wider grounds than auxins, viz. seed germination, seedling growth, flowering, fruit formation, parthenocarpy, cambial activity, cell elongation, breaking dormancy or dwarfism, and better responses to light and temperature.

SENESCENCE. Senescence is a decline in the physiological processes that take place in the body of a plant as it ages. In both plants and animals, ageing is accompanied by decreased RNA synthesis, and protein synthesis together with increased histone synthesis. This suggests that gene repression is a vital factor in ageing, which may, therefore, be delayed by hormones.

Vitamins. Vitamins (*vita*, life) are a heterogenous group of organic (biological) products of plants. They have proved to be invaluable for normal growth and development of the body, maintenance of health, vigour, nervous stability and proper functioning of the digestive system. They are also essential in preventing or curing certain deficiency diseases such as scurvy, beriberi, rickets, malnutrition, loss of appetite, poor physical growth, eye infection, nervous breakdown, etc., caused by the absence of vitamins in food or their faulty absorption due to intestinal trouble. For some centuries, scurvy (livid spots on the skin and general debility) was a dreaded disease among sailors. Vasco da Gama lost 100 sailors on this account during his voyage round the Cape of Good Hope in 1498. In 1757, Lind's discovery of the value of *Citrus* fruits (oranges and lemons) and green vegetables in the treatment of scurvy, as emphasized in his book, *A Treatise on the Scurvy*, brought new hope. Captain Cook, who included fruits and vegetables in his sailors' rations, lost none during his voyage to Australia in 1772. Around 1793, it was established that the use of orange or lemon juice prevented the occurrence of scurvy among sailors. Evidently, it contained something (now known to be vitamin C) which could prevent and cure the disease. It was only from the year 1906 that investigations on vitamins were made from the biological standpoint. In 1910, Hopkins' work in England on rats fed on pure food-stuff and that with fresh milk or fresh fruit juice added to it definitely proved the importance of vitamins for healthy growth. By now, several vitamins have been discovered and their value established. It is known that they do not take any direct part in body-building, nor are they a source of energy. But they play a very important role in the metabolism of proteins, fats and carbohydrates, and their proper assimilation into the body. They also facilitate the proper utilization of certain minerals by the body. Some vitamins act as prosthetic groups or coenzymes and help synthesize certain enzymes, or are even components of them, controlling many important biochemical reactions in both plants and animals. Vitamins are, however, always required only in minute quantities for a particular effect, and are used up in the metabolic processes. They are mostly synthesized by plants and stored up in different organs of plants. Some vitamins are also formed by several bacteria and certain fungi. Animals, including human beings, cannot synthesize vitamins in their bodies (a partial exception being vitamin D). Plants are, therefore, the source of vitamins for them. It is now possible to synthesize some of the vitamins, particularly vitamins A, C and D, on a commercial scale. Some common and important vitamins are as follows:

Vitamin A is a growth-promoting and anti-infective vitamin. It is soluble in fats and oils (sparingly soluble in water) and fairly resistant to heat. It is especially good for children being essential for healthy growth, physical fitness and good vision. It helps the development of bones and teeth, and healthy skin. Vitamin A also helps build resistance to bacterial infections of the lungs and intestines, and plays a part in the normal functioning of different organs. Its deficiency results in eye-diseases, particularly night-blindness, loss of weight, skin diseases, nervous weakness and respiratory diseases. Carotene of plants is the source of this vitamin. Animals can synthesize it by taking food containing carotene. Excess of vitamin A is stored in the liver and utilized whenever a deficiency occurs. The main sources of this vitamin are carrots, green leafy vegetables, cereals (particularly their pericarp), sprouting pulses, many fruits (particularly yellow ones, e.g. tomato, mango, orange, banana, apple, papaw, etc.), milk, butter, meat, liver of mammals, egg-yolk, fish, fish-liver oils (e.g. cod-liver oil and halibut-liver oil), etc.

Vitamin B consists of a group of closely allied vitamins, commonly called *vitamin B complex*. On a whole, it is indispensable for proper maintenance of health throughout life. Its deficiency results in digestive trouble, loss of appetite, diarrhoea, constipation, beriberi and neuritis. Its absence also interferes with proper metabolism of carbohydrates. Some of the vitamins of this group, e.g. thiamine, riboflavin, pyridoxine, niacin, etc., form important constituents (prosthetic groups or coenzymes) of certain enzymes. The folowing are the important members of this group. **Vitamin B_1** (or thiamine—an anti-beriberi and antineurotic vitamin) is soluble in water and, therefore, easily removed with rice-broth. It is not easily destroyed by heat. It prevents and cures beriberi, heart disease, neuritis and some forms of anaemia. For a long time beriberi was a dreaded disease in the rice-eating countries, viz. India, Malaya, China and Japan. Eating polished rice is now known to be the cause of this disease (when rice is polished, vitamin B, is removed from the pericarp.). **Vitamin B_2** (or riboflavin) is slightly soluble in water, relatively stable to heat, but destroyed by light. It is formed by all parts of the plant. It promotes growth and removes digestive trouble prevents and cures nervous and general debility, low vitality, soreness of tongue and lips, and some forms of eye-disease. It works in combination with other B vitamins. **Vitamin B_6** (or pyridoxine) is soluble in water and resistant to heat. It is distributed in all parts of the plant. It has clinical value in treating certain nervous and muscular disorders and certain types of anaemia. It helps metabolism of proteins and fats. **Vitamin B_{12}** is sparingly soluble in water and resistant to very high temperature. It helps to form red blood and thus cures symptoms of pernicious anaemia, and also diseases of the nervous system. It is linked up with protein metabolism. Several species of bacteria have the ability to synthesize this vitamin. **Nicotinic Acid** (niacin) is soluble in water and resistant to very high temperature. It is widely distributed in plants, and is common in milk, meat and yeast. It prevents pellagra (a kind of skin disease), frequent or persistent diarrhoea, loss of appetite and mental illness like insanity. **Folic Acid** is sparingly soluble in water. It helps form red blood corpuscles. Its deficiency may cause macrocytic anaemia and retardation of growth. **Biotin** (vitamin H) is soluble in water and resistant to heat. It cures scaling-off of the skin, muscular pain, distress of the heart and loss of appetite. Vitamin B complex is very widely distributed in plants in almost all their parts, and occurs in nearly all natural foods; rich sources, however, are dried yeast, whole grains (unpolished), pulses, most vegetables (particularly green ones like spinach, lettuce and cabbage), many fruits (e.g. tomato, orange, banana, apple, etc.), nuts, milk, cheese, egg-yolk, meat, liver, fish, etc.

Vitamin C (or ascorbic acid—an anti-scurvy vitamin) is soluble in water. It is sensitive to heat and, therefore, lost by cooking and it is destroyed when exposed to sunlight. It prevents scurvy, mental depression, swelling and bleeding of gums, degeneration of teeth, cold, and sore mouth. It raises power of resistance to infection, helps healing of wounds and formation of blood, and removes intestinal trouble. Vitamin C is a general activator of the metabolic processes. It cannot be stored in the body and, therefore, a daily supply of this vitamin is a must. It is found in high concentrations in most fresh fruits (particularly orange, lemon, pummelo, tomato, pineapple, emblic myrobalan, banana, guava, papaw, etc.), green vegetables (e.g. lettuce, spinach, cabbage, etc.), sprouting pulses and cereals, and milk.

Vitamin D (or calciferol—an anti-ricket vitamin) is soluble in fats and oils. It cannot stand strong light and is otherwise sufficiently stable. Its deficiency causes rickets and dental caries in children, and osteomalacia (softening of bones) in adults. The absence of this vitamin inhibits proper absorption of calcium and phosphate. It is essential for normal development of bones and teeth, and for general growth. It is commonly found in dried yeast, milk (irradiated), butter, egg-yolk, fish and fish-liver oils. Vitamin D can also be produced in the human body by the action of ultra-violet rays (in sunlight or electricity) on the skin. Ergosterol, commonly prepared from yeast but known to be widely distributed in plants and animals, is transformed into Vitamin D on irradiation, i.e. on exposure to sunlight.

Vitamin E (or anti-sterility vitamin) is soluble in fats and oils, resistant to heat and light, but destroyed by ultra-violet rays. Its deficiency causes sterility in animals (not yet definitely proved in the case of human beings), degeneration of muscles and falling of hair. It is found in green vegetables, germinating grains, wheat embryo, milk, egg-yolk, meat, etc.

Vitamin K is fat-soluble. Its deficiency causes lowering of the pro-thrombin value of blood, i.e. inhibits proper blood-clotting in wounds and cuts. It is found in green vegetables (concentrated mostly in the chloroplasts), fresh fruits and yeast.

Vernalization and Photoperiodism. The influence of temperature and of day-length on the sexual reproduction of plants, particularly in the case of annuals and biennials, has been investigated for a period of over 40 years by several scientists. These investigations have led to the discovery of very two important phenomena, known as vernalization and photoperiodism. It it inter-

esting to note that some plants, mostly from the temperate regions, require a period of low temperature before flowering takes place, others require treatment at a much higher temperature. But for this condition, the plants would not produce flowers. The same effect, in addition to another described below, can be noticed if soaked seeds are subjected to a particular temperature over a certain period during an early stage of germination. The procedure is as follows. The seeds are soaked in water and allowed to germinate till only the radicle has emerged. Further growth is artificially arrested by the temperature method for a period varying from a few to several days depending on the kind of seed. For certain types of seeds, the temperature requirements usually vary from 1°C (or even less) to 10°C. This applies to certain varieties of wheat. For other types, e.g. rice millets, cottons and soya-bean, the temperature requirement is much higher—20° to 25°C, and the treatment period extends over several days. The seeds are then dried and sown in the usual way. The effect of such treatment is the arrest of growth during germination, but accelerated growth of seedlings and early flowering. This method of inducing earlier flowering by pre-treatment of seeds at temperatures specific to different groups of plants was developed in Russia by Lysenko (1932), and is known as **vernalization**. (The Russian term is *jarovizacija,* meaning pre-sowing treatment). The practical benefits of vernalization are earlier flowering, earlier maturing of the crop, escaping frost, drought and flood, and extension of cultivation to regions with very low temperature. This method has helped Russian farmers grow crops in Siberia, where the soil is ice-bound and unfit for any cultivation for ten months a year. For the remaining two months, only early-maturing crops can be grown.

The influence of the day-length on reproduction was studied in America by Garner and Allard (1920). According to them, some plants require a day-length longer than 12 hours for flowering, while others require less than 12 hours. The former are known as long-day plants and the latter as short-day plants. There are some plants that are day-neutral, as they flower at any day-length. The relation of the time of flowering to the daily duration of illumination is known as **photoperiodism**. Photoperiodism has helped control the flowering of a large number of agricultural and horticultural plants. Artificial shortening of the day-length by shading, or lengthening of the day-length by electric illumination has induced plants to flower earlier than normal. By reducing the day-length by shading, Dr S. M. Sircar of Calcutta University (formerly Director of the Bose

Research Institute, Calcutta) has been able to induce flowering of a winter variety of rice (AMAN) in 50 days, compared to the normal of 140 days. The phenomenon of photoperiodism is of considerable practical importance in growing plants during seasons in which the natural day-length is not suitable for flowering. Flowering of various annual and biennial plants during different seasons depends mainly on seasonal day-length. This is of particular importance in agriculture as artificial control of day-length (daily illumination) can facilitate simultaneous flowering of two crop varieties which would normally flower in different seasons. Cross-pollination for the purpose of crop-improvement can thus be effected.

CHAPTER 14

MOVEMENTS

Living beings are distinguished from non-living ones by their power of movement. Protoplasm is sensitive to various external agencies, such as heat, light, electricity, gravity, certain chemicals, etc., which act as stimuli. Plants or plant organs often respond to such stimuli by moving in a particular direction. The capacity of plants or their particular organs to receive stimuli from without and to respond to them is spoken of as **irritability**. Irritability expresses itself in some kind of movement and is a decided advantage to the plant since, by this movement, it can adjust itself according to environmental conditions.

Conditions Necessary for Movements.
(1) **Water.** An adequate supply of water to the organs concerned is essential for certain kinds of movements. A turgid condition of the cells is indispensable for the purpose. (2) **Temperature.** Movement can only occur within a certain range of temperature. (3) **Oxygen.** A steady supply of air (oxygen) is necessary for respiration which releases energy for work. (4) **Hormones.** Hormones (see pp. 296-97) are now known to have a profound influence on growth and certain kinds of movements. (5) **Non-fatigue.** Continued stimulation brings about fatigue. No response can be evoked from a fatigued organ or tissue.

KINDS OF MOVEMENT. Plants display different kinds of movement, which may be broadly classified as (*I*) movements of locomotion and (*II*) movements of curvature.

A. MOVEMENTS OF LOCOMOTION

Movements of the protoplasm within a cell, free movements of naked masses of protoplasm and those of unicellular or multicellular organs and entire organisms are expressed as movements of locomotion. These movements may again be (1) spontaneous (or autonomic) and (2) induced (or paratonic).

1. Spontaneous Movements of Locomotion. These are movements which occur *of their own accord*, that is, without the influence of external stimuli. They may be of the protoplasm or of minute free organs, or entire organisms. These movements may be due to some internal causes, not clearly understood. Common instances are: ciliary movement of free ciliate protoplasmic bodies, such as the ciliate gametes and zoospores; amoeboid movement of free non-ciliate protoplasmic masses; rotation or circulation of protoplasm within the cell; oscillating movement of *Oscillatoria* (see FIG. V/2); and brisk movements of many unicellular algae, like desmids and diatoms.

2. Induced Movements of Locomotion are the movements of minute free organs or entire organisms *induced by external factors*, which may be in the nature of certain chemical subtances, light and heat. These factors act as stimuli. Movements thus influenced by external stimuli are otherwise called **taxes** or **taxisms,** and depending on the nature of the stimulus, taxic (or tactic) movements may be (1) chemotaxis when influenced by chemical substances, (2) phototaxis when influenced by light, and (3) thermotaxis when influenced by temperature.

(1) **Chemotaxis.** Chemotaxis is the movement of free organs or organisms, the movement being brought about by the presence of certain chemical substances. There are certain bacteria which are strongly attracted by the presence of free oxygen and they move towards the source of supply. Chemotaxis is best exhibited by the male gametes (antherozoids) of many 'flowerless' plants. Thus, in mosses, cane-sugar is secreted by the archegonium for the purpose of attracting the antherozoids towards it. Malic acid is secreted in ferns for the same purpose.

(2) **Phototaxis.** Phototaxis is also the movement of free organs or organisms in response to the stimulus of light. Algae afford very good examples of phototaxis. They move towards sources of weak light, being attracted by it. Very strong light, however, repels them and they turn away from it. Another striking example of phototaxis is afforded by the chloroplasts of leaves. Light that is too intense decomposes chlorophyll and, therefore, under this condition the chloroplasts arrange themselves one over the other alongside the lateral walls of the palisade cells of the leaf. This arrangement or movement of the chloroplasts is called **apostrophe.** In subdued light, however, they arrange themselves alongside the outer and inner walls. This arrangement or movement is called **epistrophe.**

(3) **Thermotaxis.** Thermotaxis is the movement of free organs or organisms in response to the stimulus of heat. In case of a difference in temperature, they move towards the warmer side. Protoplasm shows more rapid rotation or circulation if the tissue is gently warmed. Thus, if a section from a *Vallisneria* leaf is slightly warmed over a burning match-stick and then examined under a microscope, the protoplasm is seen to rotate more rapidly.

B. MOVEMENTS OF CURVATURE

Being fixed to the ground, higher plants are incapable of any locomotion. Some of their organs, however, show different kinds of movement. The organs may move and change position or direction by means of curvature. They move in order to get into positions that will enable them to perform their functions more effectively. Movements in curvature may be mechanical or vital. Vital movements are broadly of two kinds: spontaneous (or autonomic) and induced (or paratonic).

1. Mechanical Movements. Mechanical movements are exhibited by certain non-living organs of plants. Examples are the bursting of explosive fruits (see pp. 114-15), bursting of the sporangia of ferns and some other structures. Some fruits burst suddenly when they dry up, e.g. *Phlox, Barleria, Bauhinia vahlii* (see FIG. I/183), *Andrographis,* etc., and others burst on absorbing water, e.g. *Ruellia* (see FIG. I/182). The dry, long awn of certain grasses—wild oat (*Avena sterilis*), for example—begins to twist and roll on contact with water. The elaters of *Equisetum* spore are very hygroscopic: they roll up spirally round the spore when the air is moist, and uncoil and stand out stiffly from the spore when the air is dry. Mechanical movements of this nature, having a definite relation with moisture (by imbibition or by loss of it), are otherwise known as hygroscopic movements.

2. Spontaneous Movements. Spontaneous movements are movements of certain living organs of plants occurring *of their own accord,* that is, without the influence of external factors. Such movements may be of two kinds: (1) movement of variation and (2) movement of growth.

(1) **Movement of Variation.** Movements of variation are movements of *mature* organs, caused by *variation in the turgidity* of the cells of these organs. Thus movement is fairly rapid. The spontaneous movement of variation is rather rare. In the majority of plants, the movement of cellular organs is induced by external factors. Spontaneous movement is, however, remarkably exhibited by the *pulsation* (rising and falling) of the two lateral

FIG. 47. A leaf of Indian telegraph plant

leaflets of the Indian telegraph plant (*Desmodium gyrans*; FIG. 47). The terminal leaflet, however, remains fixed in its position. Normally, these two leaflets move up and down from morning to evening, so long as sunlight is available, but sometimes they continue to move till late at night, depending on the energy they have conserved from the sunlight during the day.

Turgor Movements. Certain plant organs display these movements, which are due to changes in the turgidity of certain cells of these organs, commonly the pulvinus in the case of the leaf. Turgor movements are often rapid and may occur again and again. They may be spontaneous (movement of variation), as exhibited by the Indian telegraph plant, or induced by contact, light, heat, etc., as exhibited by the sensitive plant, sensitive woodsorrel, carambola (*Averrhoa*; B. KAMRANGA; H. KAMRAKII), most species of *Leguminosae*, some species of wood-sorrel (*Oxalis*), and by the opening and closing of the stomata.

(2) **Movement of Growth.** The movement of growth is the movement of *growing* organs and is *due to unequal growth* on different sides of these organs. This kind of movement is very slow. It is seen in some trailers and creepers in which growth occurs only on one side (of the stem) at a time. The stem tip then moves from one side to the other. In such a case, the stem moves in a zigzag course as it elongates. Movement of this kind is known as (1) **nutation.** If the growth passes regularly around the stem, it then moves in such a way as to form a spiral, as in tendrils and twiners. Movement of this kind is said to be (2) **circumnutation.** Another kind of growth movement is exhibited by most of the young leaves. In these the initial stage of growth is more rapid on the undersurface and, therefore, they remain rolled or folded on the upper surface. This kind of growth movement is called (3) **hyponasty.** Due to more rapid growth on the upper surface later, the leaves unfurl and become flat and straight. This is called (4) **epinasty.** A striking example is afforded by fern leaves which are at first closely coiled due to hyponastic growth. They later uncoil and become straight due to epinastic growth.

3. Induced Movements. The movements of certain living organs of plants may be induced by external factors which act as stimuli. Induced movements are broadly of two kinds: (*a*) tropic and (*b*) nastic. The stimuli may be in the nature of (1) contact, (2) light, (3) gravity, (4) temperature, (5) certain chemical substances, and (6) moisture.

(*a*) **Tropic Movements** or **Tropisms.** Tropic movements of plant organs are, like taxisms, always directive, i.e. the direction of movement is determined by the direction from which the stimulus is applied, and the organs move either towards the source of the stimulus or away from it. The nature of the stimuli like (1) contact, (2) light, etc., as stated above, and the corresponding tropic movements are as follows:

(1) *Contact with a Foreign Body.* Movement stimulated by contact with a solid object is called **haptotropism** or **thigmotropism.** Twining stems and tendrils are good examples of haptotropism. These organs are sensitive to contact with foreign bodies but the reaction is rather slow and, therefore, the contact must be of long duration to bring about the movement. Some tendrils, however, respond very quickly, often within a few minutes. When such organs come in contact with any support or any hard object, the growth of the contact side is checked while the other side continues to grow. The result is that the organs slowly coil round that object. This is a mechanism for climbing. Some climbers move clockwise, e.g. white

yam (*Dioscorea alata*), while others move anti-clockwise, e.g. wild yam (*D. bulbifera*). Growth is arrested if the direction is artificially altered. Haptotropism is also exhibited by the tendrillar leaf-apex of glory lily (*Gloriosa*) and the petiole of pitcher plant (*Nepenthes*), garden nasturtium (*Tropaeolum*) and virgin's bower (*Clematis*).

(2) *Light*. Movement as determined by the direction of incidence of rays is called **heliotropism** or **phototropism**. Some organs grow towards the light and are said to be *positively heliotropic*, as the shoot. Others that grow away from it are said to be *negatively heliotropic*, as the root. Dorsiventral organs like leaves, runners, etc. grow at right angles to the direction of incidence of rays, so that their upper surface is exposed to light. Such organs are said to be *diaheliotropic*. Positive heliotropism is seen clearly in potted plants, particularly the seedlings, when they are grown in a closed room or box (**heliotropic chamber**; FIG. 48) with one open window on one side. They tend to grow towards the window, i.e. towards the source of light, and in the case of the box, they ultimately come out through it. The cause of phototropic curvature is now explained on the basis of *hormones* (see pp. 296-97). The effect of this unilateral light may be eliminated by vertically placing a potted planted on a **clinostat** (FIG. 50) and rotating it. The plant grows vertically upwards and does not bend towards the window. The flower-stalk of ground-nut (*Arachis hypogaea*; FIG. 49) grows towards light, but after pollination, it becomes negatively heliotropic and positively geotropic like the root. The stalk bends down and quickly elongates, pushing the fertilized ovary into the ground, where the ovary gradually ripens into a pod (fruit). In *Eucalyptus*, the edge of the leaf is turned towards intense light and when the light is diffuse, the surface is exposed to it. Some species of *Trifolium* also exhibit the same phenomenon.

(3) *Force of Gravity*. Movement in response to the force of gravity is called **geotropism**. Geotropism has a marked effect on the direction of growth of plant organs. The primary root is seen to grow towards the centre of gravity and the primary shoot away from it. The former is said to be *positively geotropic* and the latter, *negatively geotropic*. The lateral roots and branches usually grow at right angles to the force of gravity and are said to be *diageotropic*. That the direction of growth is determined by the stimulating action of the force of gravity is clearly seen in a seedling which has been placed in a horizontal position, away from light. Both the stem and the root become curved (in their growing region behind the apex), passing through an angle of 90°. The root curves and grows vertically downwards, and the stem grows upwards. It is the very tip of the root, for a distance of 1 to a few mm. in length, that is sensitive to this stimulus. This is the region of cell division (see FIG. I/3). The actual bending, however, takes place bit behind the tip, in the region of elongation. Bending does not take place if the tip of the root is decapitated. Under the force of gravity, the root of a germinating seed can grow downwards even through mercury, overcoming considerable pressure. It is possible to eliminate the effect of geotropic stimulus on the root and the shoot by introducing a centrifugal force with the help of a **clinostat** (FIG. 50). This is done by rotating the seedling in a horizontal plane and thus, subjecting all sides of the growing and sensitive regions to this force. The force of gravity cannot act on any definite part under this condition and, therefore, no geotropic movement is possible. The cause of geotropic curvature is now explained on the basis of *hormones* (see pp. 296-97).

Experiment 37. Geotropism. A clinostat (FIG. 50) may be used to demonstrate geotropism. This is an instrument by which the *effect* of lateral light and the force of gravity on a plant's organ—root or stem—can be eliminated. It consists of a rod with a disc mounted

FIG. 48. Heliotropic chamber

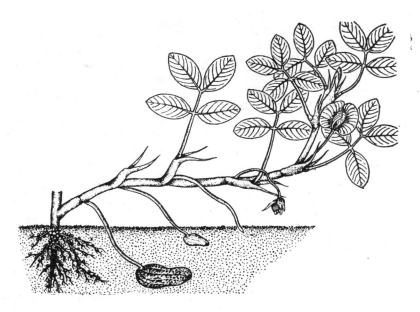

FIG. 49. Groundnut or peanut plant (*Arachishypogaea*) showing that the
flower stalk is negatively heliotropic and positively geotropic after pollination of the flower

on it, to which a small potted plant may be attached, and a clockwork mechanism for rotating the rod and the disc. The clinostat works slowly, its rotation being ordinarily 1/4th to 4 turns per hour. A plant, preferably a potted plant, may be fixed in the clinostat in any position—vertical, horizontal or at an angle—and made to rotate by the clockwork mechanism of the clinostat. When the plant is horizontal, the root and the stem grow horizontally, instead of the root curving downwards and the stem upwards. This is due to the fact that all sides of the growing axes are, in turn, directed downwards, upwards and sideways so that the force of

gravity cannot act on any definite position. This eliminates the effect of the force altogether. The root and the stem cannot, therefore, bend. If, however, the plant is fixed in the vertical position and the clinostat rotated, it grows in the vertical direction—the root downwards and the stem upwards.

(4) *Temperature.* The movement or curving of a plant's organ in response to the stimulus of heat or cold is called **thermotropism**. If a closed box containing seedlings is warmed on one side, the seedlings curve towards the warm side.

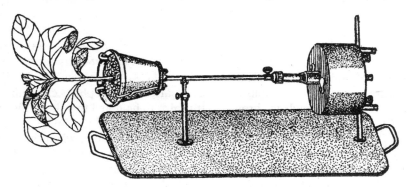

FIG. 50. Clinostat in the horizontal position to eliminate the effect of force of gravity

(5) *Chemical Substances.* Movement induced by the presence of certain chemical substances is called **chemotropism**. The tentacles of sundew respond to various nitrogenous substances placed on its leaf. Thus, a drop of soluble protein or a bit of raw meat induces movement only after a portion of it has been absorbed. On absorption, the protoplasm gets stimulated and sends a motor impulse to the surrounding tentacles, which bend down on the protein or meat from all sides. The pollen-tube grows towards the ovule, being stimulated by the sugary substance secreted by the stigma, style and ovary. The sucking roots of parasites and the hyphae of parastic fungi penetrate into the tissue of the host plant in response to the stimulus of certain chemical substance. Similarly, the respirator roots of many plants growing in estuaries curve upwards from the soil into the air, that is, towards the source of oxygen, which stimulates them (see FIGS. IV/2-3).

FIG. 51. Experiment on hydrotropism

(6) *Moisture.* The movement of an organ in response to the stimulus of moisture is known as **hydrotropism**. Roots are sensitive to variations in the amount of moisture. They tend to grow towards the source of moisture, and are said to be *positively hydrotropic*. The roots of seedlings growing in a hanging basket made of wire-netting and filled with moist sawdust first project downwards, coming out of the basket under the influence of the force of gravity, but they soon turn

back in response to the stimulus of moisture (moist sawdust in the basket) and pass again into the basket, having formed loops.

Experiment 38. Hydrotropism. A porous clay funnel, covered around with a filter paper, is placed on a wide-mouthed glass bottle (or hyacinth glass) filled with water, as shown in FIG. 51. The filter paper is thus kept moist. The porous funnel is filled with dry sawdust and the soaked seeds arranged in a circle, each near a pore. It is necessary to add a few drops of water now and then to the seeds to help them germinate. As they germinate, it will be seen that the roots, instead of going vertically downwards in response to the force of gravity, pass out through the pores towards the moist filter paper and grow downwards, alongside the paper, into the bottle. The roots thus show movements towards moisture, or, in other words, they are positively hydrotropic.

(*b*) **Nastic Movements** or **Nastics.** Like tropisms, nastic movements of plant organs are induced by stimuli like contact, light and heat, but these movements are not directive, i.e. the direction of movement in such cases is not determined by the direction from which the stimulus is applied. In other words, from whichever direction the stimulus acts, it affects all parts of the organs equally and they always move in the same direction. Their direction is largely determined by the structure or anatomy of the organs concerned. Nastic movements are mostly exhibited by flat, dorsiventral organs like leaves and petals. The following kinds of nastics are common :

(1) *Seismonasty.* Movement brought about by mechanical stimuli, such as contact with a foreign body, poking with any hard object, drops of rain, a gust of wind, etc., is called **seismonasty**. Movements of the leaves (leaflets) of sensitive plant (*Mimosa pudica*; FIG. 53), sensitive wood-sorrel (*Biophytum sensitivum*: FIG. 52), *Neptunia*, carambola (*Averrhoa*), etc., are familiar examples. The leaflets of such plants close up when touched. It is also to be noted that the degree of movement varies according to the intensity of the stimulus applied. For example, when the leaf-apex of the sensitive plant is touched lightly, only a few pairs of leaflets close up. When rather roughly touched or pinched, all the leaflets react in the same way from the apex downwards: they close up

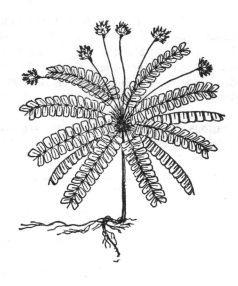

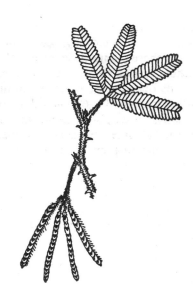

FIG. 52   FIG. 53

FIG. 52. Sensitive wood-sorrel (*Biophytum sensitivum*).
FIG. 53. Sensitive plant (*Mimosa pudica*)

simultaneously and the leaf as a whole droops. Venus' fly-trap (*Dionaea*; see FIG. 28) is another very interesting example. The two lobes of the leaf of this plant are provided with three hairs each. The hairs are extremely sensitive to touch, and in contact with a foreign body, particularly a flying insect, the two lobes close up suddenly. In *Bignonia, Mimulus* and *Martynia*, the two stigmatic lobes close up when touched or when pollen grains fall on them. In the sunflower family (*Compositae*) and China rose family (*Malvaceae*) the stigmas bend down and touch the anthers to achieve self-pollination, in case cross-pollination fails. Sweet sultan (*Centaurea moschata*) is a very interesting case. Its stamens are very sensitive to contact with any foreign body. Thus, when pollinating insects touch them, they begin to twist and oscillate and the florets also move. This movement may be observed if the stamens are gently poked with any hard object. The stamens of barberry (*Berberis*), purslane (*Portulaca*), prickly pear (*Opuntia*), etc., are also sensitive to contact.

(2) *Photonasty*. Movement induced by changes in the intensity of light is called **photonasty**. Many flowers open when there is strong illumina-

tion and close in the dark or when artificially shaded, e.g. noon flower (*Pentapetes*). Some flowers open in the weak light of the morning, but close with the increasing intensity of light as the day advances, e.g. garden purslane (*Portulaca grandiflora*). Some flowers open at night, that is, in darkness, but close at daybreak, e.g. night-blooming cacti (*Cereus* and *Phyllocactus*). The stomata open when light appears but close up again when light fails.

(3) *Thermonasty*. Movement induced by temperature variation is called **thermonasty**. Many flowers open rather quickly when the temperature rises and close up when it falls. A similar effect is produced in the case of the leaves of most *Leguminosae*, and also of *Oxalis*. The leaves close up when the temperature rises high or falls low, and they open at optimum temperature.

(4) *Nyctinasty*. The movement induced by alternation of day and night is called **nyctinasty** (or nyctitropism) or **sleep movement**. Nyctinasty has a marked effect on leaves and flowers, particularly the former. Nyctinasty is caused by the simultaneous action of light and temperature, but always

more by light. This kind of movement is most remarkably exhibited by *Leguminosae*. The leaflets of these plants close up and often the leaf as a whole droops in the evening when the light fails. They open up again in the morning light. A few other plants like *Chenopodium*, carambola (*Averrhoa*), etc., also exhibit the same phenomenon. The upper surfaces of the leaflets normally fold up to prevent excessive radiation of

heat during the night. Movement of this nature is due to difference in the turgidity of the cells of the pulvinus at the base of the leaf and the leaflets. *Gerbera* (a garden herb) and *Portulaca* (wild or garden variety) are examples of flowers that exhibit nyctinasty.

The various kinds of movements that have already been described are tabulated below.

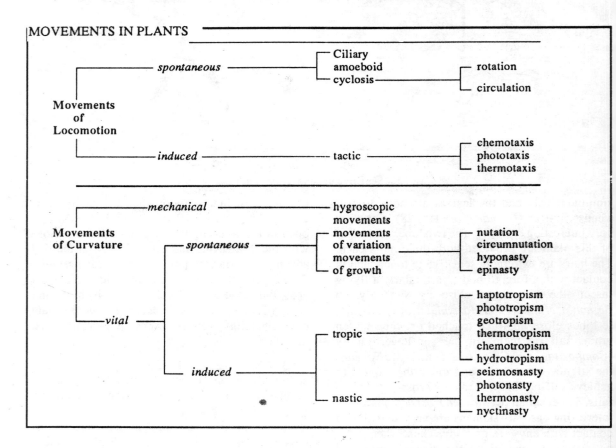

MOVEMENTS IN PLANTS

Movements of Locomotion
- spontaneous — Ciliary, amoeboid, cyclosis — rotation, circulation
- induced — tactic — chemotaxis, phototaxis, thermotaxis

Movements of Curvature
- mechanical — hygroscopic movements
- vital
  - spontaneous — movements of variation, movements of growth — nutation, circumnutation, hyponasty, epinasty
  - induced
    - tropic — haptotropism, phototropism, geotropism, thermotropism, chemotropism, hydrotropism
    - nastic — seismosnasty, photonasty, thermonasty, nyctinasty

CHAPTER 15

REPRODUCTION

Since the life of an individual plant is limited in duration, it has developed certain mechanisms by which it can reproduce itself in order to continue the perpetuation of the species and also, to multiply in number. The following are the principal methods of reproduction: **vegetative, asexual** and **sexual.**

1. VEGETATIVE REPRODUCTION

A. *NATURAL METHODS OF PROPAGATION*

In any of these methods, a portion gets detached from the body of the mother plant and this detached portion embarks on a new life under suitable conditions. Gradually, it grows into a new, independent plant. The methods by which vegetative propagation takes place are many and varied.

(1) **Budding.** In the case of yeast (see FIG. II/25), one or more tiny outgrowths appear on one or more sides of the vegetative cell immersed in sugar solution. These outgrowths soon get detached from the mother cell and form new individuals. This method of outgrowth formation is known as budding. Budding often proceeds continuously so that finally one or more chains, sometimes sub-chains, of cells are formed. All the individual cells of the chain separate from one another and form new yeast plants.

(2) **Gemmae.** In some mosses and liverworts (e.g. *Marchantia*; see FIGS. V/118 and 120), special bodies known as gemmae develop on the leaf, branch or thallus for the purpose of vegetative propagation.

(3) **Leaf-tip.** There are certain ferns, commonly called 'walking' ferns (e.g. *Adiantum caudatum, A. lunulatum* and *Polypodium flagelliferum*), which propagate vegetatively by their leaf-tips (FIG. 54). As the leaf bows down to the ground, the tip strikes roots and forms a bud. This bud grows into a new, independent fern plant. However, ferns normally reproduce vegetatively by their rhizomes.

In 'flowering' plants, the methods of vegetative propagation are diverse. The resulting offspring resembles the parent form in almost all respects. Therefore, gardeners often use these methods for multiplying the number of flowers in their gardens.

(1) **Underground Stems.** Many 'flowering' plants reproduce by means of the rhizome (e.g. ginger), the tuber (e.g. potato), the bulb (e.g. onion) and the corm (e.g. *Gladiolus*). New buds are produced on these modified stems, which gradually grow into new plants.

(2) **Sub-aerial Stems.** The runner, the stolon,

FIG. 54. Walking fern (*Adiantum caudatum*)

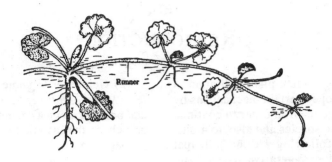

FIG. 55. Runner of Indian pennywort (*Ceniella*)

the offset and the sucker are used by plants like the Indian pennywort (*Centella*; FIG. 55), taro (*Colocasia*), water lettuce (*Pistia*) and *Chrysanthemum* for vegetative propagation (see FIGS. I/32-5).

(3) **Adventitious Buds.** In sprout-leaf plants (*Bryophyllum pinnatum*; see FIG. I/16A), *Kalanchoe daigremontiana* (FIG. 56) and *Crassula*, rows of adventitious (foliar) buds are produced on the leaf-margin, each at the end of a vein. These buds may drop from the leaf and grow into new plants, or they may drop together with the leaf and then grow. In *Kalanchoe verticillata* (FIG. 57) bud-formation is restricted to the apical part of the leaf. In elephant ear plant (*Begonia*; see FIG. I/16B), a few adventitious buds are produced on the surface of the leaf, from the veins and also from the petiole, particularly when lightly incised. Similarly, the roots of some plants may produce adventitious (radical) buds for the same purpose, as in sweet potato (see FIG. I/9A), *Trichosanthes* (B. PATAL; H. PARWAL), wood-apple (*Aegle*), ipecac (see FIG. I/10B), etc.

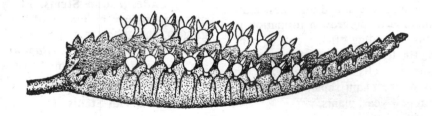

FIG. 56. A leaf of *Kalanchoe diagremontiana* with adventitious buds

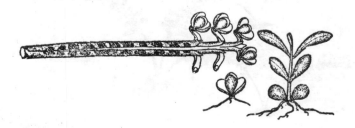

FIG. 57. A leaf of *Kalanchoe verticillata* with adventitious buds

FIG. 58. *Globba bulbifera. B,* bulbil

(4) Bulbils. In *Globba bulbifera* (FIG. 58) and garlic (*Allium sativum*), some of the lower flowers of the inflorescence become modified into small multicellular bodies known as bulbils. They fall to the ground and grow into new plants. Sometimes they grow to some extent on the plant itself. In American aloe (*Agave*; FIG. 60) and certain species of *Crassula*, reproductive buds or bulbils often take the place of many flowers of the inflorescence. In *Marica northiana*, 1 or 2 large leafy bulbils develop on the green, flat scape near its apex. The scape soon bends down to the ground, and the bulbils strike roots and grow into new plants. Bulbils, big or small, are also produced in the leaf-axil of wild yam (*Dioscorea bulbifera*; FIG. 59) and *Lilium bulbiferum*. In wood-sorrel (*Oxalis*; FIG. 61), a cluster of small buds (bulbils) may be seen on the top of the swollen tuberous root. These buds, being brittle at the base, fall off easily and grow into new plants. In pineapple (*Ananas*), the inflorescence generally ends in a reproductive bud, but in some varieties of pineapple (FIG. 62) the inflorescence becomes surrounded at the base by a whorl of such buds and also crowned by a few of them.

B. ARTIFICIAL METHODS OF PROPAGATION

In any of these methods, a portion can be separated out by a special method from the body of the mother plant and grown independently. There are several such methods:

(1) Cuttings. (*a*) *Stem-cuttings*. Many plants such as rose, sugarcane, tapioca, garden croton, China rose, drumstick (*Moringa*), *Duranta, Coleus* (see FIG. I/6), etc., may be easily grown from stem-cuttings. When cuttings from such plants are put into moist soil, they strike roots at the base and develop adventitious buds which grow. (*b*) *Root-cuttings*. Sometimes, as in lemon citron, ipecac (see FIG. I/10B), tamarind, etc., root-cuttings put into moist soil sprout, forming roots and shoots.

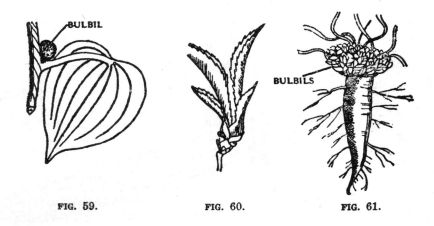

FIG. 59.   FIG. 60.   FIG. 61.

FIG. 59. *Dioscorea bulbifera.* FIG. 60. Bulbil of American aloe (*Agave*).
FIG. 61. Wood-sorrel (*Oxalis*)

FIG. 62. Pineapple with a crown and a whorl of bulbils

(2) **Layering** (FIG. 63). In this case, a lower branch is bent down, a ring of bark 2.5-5 cm. long removed and this portion pushed into the soft ground, keeping the upper part free. The bend is covered with soil and a stone or brick placed on it. When it strikes roots, usually within 2-4 months, the branch is cut out from the mother plant and grown separately. Lemon, *Ixora*, rose, jasmines, grape-vine, etc., readily respond to this method.

(3) **Gootee** (FIG. 64). This method is usually employed for propagating lemon, orange, pummelo, guava, litchi, *Magnolia*, etc. During early rains, a healthy, somewhat woody branch is selected and a ring of bark, 2.5 to 5 cm. long, is sliced off from it. A sufficiently thick plaster of grafting clay[1] is applied all round the ringed portion, which is then wrapped up with straw or arag and tied securely. It should be wetted with water every morning and afternoon. In drier climates, an earthen pot with a hole at the bottom may be hung over the bandage in a convenient position, and the two connected by a long piece of cloth or soft cotton cord. As the pot is filled with water, the latter trickles down the cloth or cord and keeps the bandage constantly moist. Usually, within 1-3 months the gootee is ready, as indicated by its striking roots. It is then cut out below the bandage.

(4) **Grafting.** This consists of inserting the small branch of a plant into a rooted plant of the same or allied species in such a way as to bring about an organic union (fusion of tissues) between the two and, finally, make them grow as one. The branch that is inserted is known as the *scion* or *graft*, and the plant that is rooted to the soil as the *stock*. The scion grows, retaining all its qualities, while the stock which may be of inferior quality but physically sturdy supports it by supplying

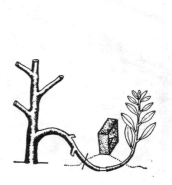

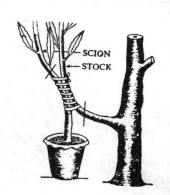

FIG. 63.   FIG. 64.   FIG. 65.

Artificial Methods of Propagation. FIG. 63. Layering. FIG. 64. Gootee. FIG. 65. Inarching or approach grafting

[1]Grafting Clay. Clay (2 parts), Cowdung (1 part) and some finly cut hay mixed with water.

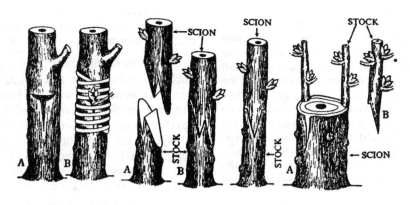

FIG. 66.   FIG. 67.   FIG. 68.   FIG. 69.

Artificial Methods of Propagation (*contd.*). FIG. 66. Bud grafting. FIG. 67. Whip or tongue grafting.
FIG. 68. Wedge grafting. FIG. 69. Crown grafting

water and food material. Grafting, thus, ensures the production of particular desired characteristics in the scion or graft, characteristics originally exhibited by the scion-mother. Grafts are prepared for the purpose of propagation of certain fruit and ornamental shrubs and trees. Some of the common methods are as follows:

(*a*) **Inarching or Approach Grafting.** (FIG. 65). By this method, the branch (scion) of a plant is made to unite with a seedling (stock) or a small plant in a pot by firmly tying them together with a cord. Before this, a small portion of the bark is sliced off from each to ensure closer contact and quicker union between the two. When proper fusion has taken place, usually within 2-3 months, the stock is cut above the joint and the scion below, thus leaving the scion standing on the stock. Some fruit trees, like mango, litchi, guava, sapodilla plum, etc., readily respond to this method.

(*b*) **Bud Grafting** (FIG. 66). For this method, a T-shaped incision is made in the bark of the stock, and a bud cut out clean from a selected plant is inserted into the T-shaped slit and bandaged properly. This method makes it possible to grow several varieties of rose on one rose stock, good varieties of orange, lime, lemon, citron, pummelo, etc., on inferior stocks, several varieties of *Hibiscus* on one, several varieties of cactus on one, and so on. Luther Burbank of California was able

to grow several varieties of prune and allied species on one stock by bud grafting.

(*c*) **Whip or Tongue Grafting** (FIG. 67). The stock, usually 1 to 1.5 cm. thick, is cut down above the ground. Sloping cuts, a few centimetres long, are made in it, as shown in the figure. The scion is of the same thickness and is also cut in such a way that it fits exactly into the stock. It is then inserted into the stock and tied firmly. The wound is of course covered with grafting wax[2]. All buds are removed from the stock, but not from the scion.

(*d*) **Wedge Grafting** (FIG. 68). The stock is cut 20 to 25 cm. above the ground and the wood of the stem incised with clean cuts in the form of a hollow V. The scion, cut obliquely downward into a solid V so as to fit closely into the stock, is inserted into the stock and tied firmly. Grafting wax is used to cover the wound.

(*e*) **Crown Grafting** (FIG. 69). An old tree may be rejuvenated by this method. The stem is cut across 20 to 25 cm. above the ground. The bark of the stock is cut through from the surface downward to a length of 12 to 15 cm. The bark is partially opened on either side. Prior to this, a small branch cut out from another tree of the same species is incised at the base with a sloping cut and this is now inserted into the slit in the bark and tied firmly. The wound is of course covered with grafting wax.

[2]Grafting Wax. A mixture to tallow (1 part), beeswax (1 part) and resin (4 parts), melted together and worked into a soft dough under water.

Chimaera (or **Chimera**). Chimaera refers to a fabulous monster with a lion's head, goat's body and serpent's tail. That is why chimaera is an organism which is made of two or more genetically distinct tissues. Grafting sometimes produces chimaeras, otherwise called graft hybrids. Here, genetically distinct tissues (cells) of the two (stock and scion) become associated, evidently producing a mingling of two sets of characters. As a result, the new buds that appear on the junction of the two plants (stock and scion) possess mixed characteristics. The branches developing from such buds show such mixtures, in the leaves or flowers, or in both. Chimaeras may be produced on normal plants by bud mutations as well.

2. ASEXUAL REPRODUCTION

This commonly takes place by means of asexual reproductive units, called spores, produced by the mother plant, or sometimes by the division (fission) of the mother cell in the case of unicellular plants. Asexual reproduction, thus, takes place by two methods: fission and spore formation.

1. By Fission. In the simplest cases, as in many unicellular algae and fungi and in bacteria, the mother cell splits into two new cells. The new cells thus formed contain all the materials of the mother cell and soon grow to the size of the latter, becoming independent plants. The method of reproduction by the division of mother cell is called fission (see FIG. V/62A).

2. By Spore Formation. Spores are asexual reproductive units which can grow independently, i.e.

without fusing with another unit, and are always unicellular and microscopic in size. They may be motile or non-motile.

(1) Ciliate motile spores called **zoospores**, produced by many algae and fungi, swim about in water for some time with the help of their cilia, like minute aquatic animalcules, then directly develop into new, independent individuals. Zoospores are commonly formed in large numbers, as in *Ulothrix* (see FIG. V/20). In *Vaucheria* (FIG. 70), however, the whole mass of protoplasm escapes from the mother cell as a single large multiciliate and multinucleate zoospore. It swims in water for some time and then comes to rest. Almost immediately, it germinates into a new *Vaucheria* filament. This is a case of **rejuvenescence**.

(2) Non-ciliate, non-motile spores of various kinds are most common among terrestrial fungi. Such spores are light, dry and provided with a tough coat, and are well adapted for dispersal by wind. At the same time, they are resistant to unfavourable atmospheric conditions.

(3) True spores are always borne by a sporophyte. Thus, the sporogonium (sporophyte) of moss reproduces asexually by spores. Similarly, ferns, *Lycopodium* and *Equisetum* bear spores and reproduce asexually through them. It should also be noted that these plants are **homosporous**, i.e. they bear only one kind of spore. The more advanced types of plants, e.g. *Selaginella* and

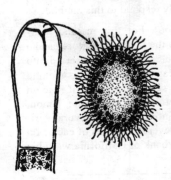

FIG. 70. Rejuvenscence in *Vaucheria*

'flowering' plants (both gymnosperms and angiosperms), are **heterosporous**, i.e. they bear two kinds of spores: microspores (male) and megaspores (female).

3. SEXUAL REPRODUCTION

This consists of the fusion of two sexual reproductive units, called **gametes**, which, like spores, are also unicellular and microscopic. To reproduce sexually, two similar or dissimilar gametes fuse together to give rise to a zygote. The zygote develops into a new plant. Sexual reproduction in which the pairing gametes are similar is known as **conjugation**, while that in which the pairing gametes are dissimilar is known as **fertilization**. The zygote is called **zygospore** in the case of conjugation, and **oospore** in the case of fertilization.

(1) **Conjugation**. In lower algae and fungi, the pairing gametes are essentially similar, i.e. not differentiated into male and female. The union of such similar gametes, i.e. **isogametes** (*isos*, equal), is known as **conjugation**. The zygote thus formed is called the **zygospore**. This grows into a new plant.

(2) **Fertilization**. In all the higher forms of plant life, on the other hand, the pairing gametes ar dissimilar, i.e. differentiated into male and female. The union of dissimilar gametes, i.e. **heterogametes** (*heteros*, different), is known as **fertilization**. The zygote thus formed is called the **oospore**, which grows into a new plant. In Bryophyta and Pteridophyta, and in many algae and fungi, the male gametes are *ciliate, motile* and *active*, and are called **antherozoids** or **spermatozoids**. They are very minute. The female gamete, on the other hand, is much larger, *nonciliate, stationary* and *passive*, and is called **egg-cell, ovum** or **oosphere**. The corresponding male and female reproductive units in the 'flowering' plant are the **two gametes** of the pollen-tube and the **egg-cell** or **ovum** of the embryo-sac within the ovule.

Gametes are always borne by the gametophyte. Moss is a gametophyte; it directly bears the gametes. In Pteridophyta, the gametes are borne by a small, green body called the prothallus, so the prothallus is the gametophyte. In 'flowering' plants, the gametophyte is an extremely reduced body.

4. SPECIAL MODES OF REPRODUCTION

1. Apomixis. Apomixis is an irregular mode of reproduction resulting in the development of an embryo without the act of fertilization. It may be (*a*) parthenogenesis, (*b*) apogamy and (*c*) sporophytic budding. (*a*) **Parthenogenesis** is the development of a zygote from the egg-cell without the act of fertilization, as seen in many lower plants, e.g. *Spirogyra, Chara, Mucor, Saprolegnia*, certain ferns and certain species of *Selaginella* and *Marsilea*. In some 'flowering' plants, as in *Thalictrum*, *Alchemilla*, certain species of *Compositae* and *Solanaceae*, the embryo, too, may develop by parthenogenesis, i.e. without fertilization. In them the embryo may develop from a haploid egg-cell or diploid egg-cell. In the former case, although germination is more or less normal, the plant becomes small and sterile. In the latter case, the plant is normal in all respects. Sometimes the ovary develops normally into a fruit without fertilization. This type of fruit development is called **parthenocarpy**. Parthenocarpic fruits are almost always seedless. Natural parthenocarpy is found in many plants, as in certain varieties of banana, pineapple, guava, grape, apple, pear, papaw, etc. It is rather peculiar that fruit formation may sometimes be induced by artificial pollination with foreign pollen (pollen from another species or even genus), or even by the application of pollen extracts, but without subsequent fertilization. In such cases, as later found, auxins formed in the ovary appear to be involved in the setting of the fruit (Gustafson, 1939). Sometimes, mere spraying with certain growth-promoting chemicals like indole-acetic acid and naphthalene-acetic acid results in the setting of fruits without fertilization (induced parthenocarpy; Gustafson, 1936). (*b*) **Apogamy** is the development of an embryo from any cell of the gametophyte (prothallus) other than the egg-cell, evidently without the intervention of gametes. The embryo so formed grows into the sporophyte. It is of common occurrence in ferns. In 'flowering' plants, it is sometimes seen that one or more embryos may be formed from the synergids, as in onion (*Allium*), lily (*Lilium*), aconite (*Aconitum*) and *Iris*, or from an antipodal cell, as in onion (*Allium*). The synergid or antipodal cell may be haploid or diploid. (*c*) **Sporophytic budding** may sometimes occur, resulting in the development of an embryo. This means that an embryo may be formed from the diploid cells of the nucellus, as in orange, mango, prickly pear (*Opuntia*), etc., or even from those of the integument, as in onion (*Allium*). The embryo thus formed is pushed into the embryo-sac during the course of its development.

2. Apospory (*apo*, off or without). Apospory is the development of the gametophyte directly from the vegetative cells of the sporophyte, without the intervention of a spore. In ferns, the prothallus may develop from certain vegetative cells of the leaf instead of the spores, or it may develop from one or more cells of the sporangium other than a spore. Apospory has been found in *Pteris, Asplenium, Osmunda* and certain other ferns. The gametophyte that develops by this method is commonly diploid and may bear both antheridia and archegonia. Apospory is

sometimes seen in some mosses as well.

Polyembryony. The occurrence of more than one embryo in the seed is known as *polyembryony*. Many species of both dicotyledons and monocotyledons exhibit this phenomenon. Polyembryony is, however, particularly common among conifers (see FIG. VI/18H). These embryos may be formed in the seed in a variety of ways: (1) There may be more than one egg-cell in the embryo-sac or more than one embryo-sac in the ovule, and all the egg-cells may be fertilized, (2) A number of embryos may develop simultaneously from different parts of the ovule. Thus, they may be formed from the synergids and antipodal cells (vegetative apogamy), from the fertilized egg-cell or unfertilized egg-cell (parthenogenesis), and from the tissue of the nucellus and the integument by sporphytic budding (apospory). Examples have been found in onion, groundnut, mango, lime, lemon and orange (but not in shaddock and citron). Polyembryony is commonly found in conifers the ovules of which contain many archegonia. All the archegonia may be fertilized, resulting in the formation of as many embryos as there are archegonia, but ultimately, only one embryo reaches maturity while the others die off. In addition, one or four embryos may be formed in *Pinus* from the fertilized egg-cell.

4   ECOLOGY

PRELIMINARY CONSIDERATIONS

ECOLOGY (*oikos,* home; *logos,* discourse or study) deals with the study of interrelationships between living organisms (plants and animals) as they exist in their natural habitats, and the various environmental factors that affect them. Ecology, therefore, is a detailed study of the flora and fauna (together called **biota** or biotic community) of a particular region and also the environmental conditions prevailing in that region. This is expressed as ecological complex or **ecosystem.** Ecology deals with the principal aspects of life from birth to death, as influenced by the environment. It investigates various structural peculiarities (external and internal), all vital functions including growth and reproduction, survival capacity of the offspring, adaptations for distribution, migration, colony formation, etc., of the various species of plants and animals of a particular region, and also various environmental factors influencing these aspects of plant and animal life. Ecology is, thus, a vast and intricate subject, requiring a good preliminary knowledge of morphology, taxonomy, anatomy, physiology, climatology, soil science, geography, etc. Apart from the physical features of the environment, the influence of plants and animals upon one another is also of considerable importance. It is known that all animals including human beings are directly or indirectly dependent on plants, particularly for food and shelter; while the effects of animals and human communities on plants are also manifold. A study of ecology necessarily includes both plants and animals, and the interactions between them.

In different climatic regions (that often cover vast areas), particular species of plants and animals living together under identical environmental conditions display a considerable amount of interdependence. In such areas, both plants and animals form distinct communities, major and minor. The major or climax communities are one or more dominant species that have permanently established themselves there, while the minor communities consist of species that are still unstable. The complex of communities (major and minor) of plants and animals existing under identical climatic conditions in a particular region is called a **biome.** The major communities always constitute the main features of a biome, but they are associated with minor communities, whatever be the composition of the biome in different regions. Biomes may be aquatic, e.g. freshwater biome and marine (salt-water) biome, or terrestrial, e.g. evergreen forests, deciduous forests, coniferous forests, thorn forests, grasslands, scrubs, deserts, Arctic tundra, etc. Most of the above biomes are well represented in India. Tundra is an exception, while coniferous forests are restricted to the hills, developing there in successive stages according to the altitude.

Interdependence between Plants and Animals.
(1) **Food.** Green plants manufacture food and store it in their body, while animals depend mostly on this stored food. (2) **Oxygen.** Green plants purify the atmosphere by absorbing carbon dioxide and giving out pure oxygen. (3) **Shelter.** Plants provide shelter to a variety of animals, particularly birds, wild beasts and forest dwellers. (4) **Clothing.** Many plants furnish material for clothing. Silk worms, MUGA worms and ENDI worms are reared on mulberry plant, SOM plant (*Machilus bombycina*) and castor plant, respectively. (5) **Drugs.** Many plants have curative value and are used extensively in the manufacture of drugs to treat various illnesses. (6) **Vitamins.** These are almost exclusive

products of plants, required by human beings, other animals and by plants themselves, for healthy growth. (7) **Pollination**. Many animals, particularly insects, aid pollination, resulting in the setting of seeds and fruits. (8) **Dispersal of Seeds**. Similarly, many animals are useful agents in disseminating seeds and fruits. (9) **Parasitism**. Certain animals lead a parasitic life upon plants, while many plants do likewise on animals. (10) **Disintegration of Soil**. Many lower organisms (the soil-dwellers) disintegrate and sometimes chemically after the soil, making it more suitable for higher plants. (11) **Civilization**. Plants have contributed to the growth of civilization, as a whole, in innumerable other ways.

ENVIRONMENT. Environment includes all the factors that affect the form and growth of not only individual plants, but also plant associations. Environmental or ecological factors may be (1) climatic, (2) edaphic, (3) biotic, and (4) topographic. The climatic factor concerns includes rainfall, temperature, light, wind and humidity. The edaphic factor concerns the physical and chemical properties of the soil and its water and air content. The biotic factor concerns bacteria, protozoa, etc., in the soil, and other living plants and animals including human beings, which directly or indirectly affect vegetation. The topographic factor includes undulation, elevation (altitude), slope, and exposure to sun, rain and wind. The vegetation of an area depends on the combined action of these factors.

1. Climatic Factor. Atmospheric conditions, such as rainfall, temperature, light, wind etc., fall under the climatic factor. These affect primarily the shoot system of the plant.

(a) **Rainfall.** Water is the most important factor. It is responsible for various structural modifications of plants and is also indispensable for all the vital functions of a plant. Protoplasm is saturated with water and often over 90% of the total weight of the active tissues is water. The source of water for terrestrial plants is rain. Rainfall has a marked effect on the geographical distribution of plants. Thus, depending on the amount of precipitation, vegatation may be broadly of the following types: evergreen forest (with abundant rainfall), deciduous forest (with moderate or low rainfall) grassland (with low rainfall) and thorn scrub (with scanty rainfall). Availability of rain water depends on the water-retaining capacity of the soil, as also often on the plants themselves. The soil may be *physically dry,* or sometimes *physiologically dry* due to the cold state of the ground or the preponderance of salts in it. Topographical factors are also very important in this respect. Cherrapunji and Mawsynram in the Khasi Hills, the rainiest spots in the world with an annual rainfall of over 11,500 mm., have a very luxuriant vegetation, while the Rajputana, which has very little or no rain, is extremely arid. It should also be remembered that abundance or scarcity of water determines the life-cycle of the plant, the duration of plant growth and the time of reproduction, in addition to certain well-marked features of the plant. Two extremes are hydrophytes and xerophytes.

(b) **Temperature.** A plant requires a certain temperature to carry out all its vital functions. Temperature markedly affects germination, growth, reproduction and movements. However, different plants growing in different climatic regions of the earth require varying ranges of temperature. Under certain conditions, some organs of the plant are thermotropic. For instance, the opening and closing of flowers and the stomata, the drooping of leaves at night, etc., are caused partly by heat. In many cases, temperature helps the dehiscence of fruits and thus, the dissemination of seeds. Plants normally prefer a temperature ranging from 20°C. to 40°C. Active tissues filled with water are unable to withstand the extremes of temperature that many dry seeds and spores can. Most flowering plants die below 0°C. and above 45°C., while seeds remain uninjured at temperatures far beyond these limits. Freezing temperature or frost kills plants, but plants become unusually resistant at high altitudes where frosts frequently occur. Temperature has an important bearing on plant geography. There is a considerable difference between the flora of tropical, sub-tropical, temperate, Arctic and Alpine regions.

(c) **Light.** Physiologically, light is a very important factor. It is responsible for the formation of chlorophyll and for carbon assimilation. It also accelerates transpiration. Although strong light checks growth, it has a tonic effect on plants. Light induces certain kinds of movements, like photonasty and phototropism. The relative length of day and night has a marked effect on the development of flowers and maturation of fruits. Of all parts of the plant, the leaves undergo by far the greatest modification under the action of light. Plants growing in shady places are called **sciophytes**. These usually have large, thin leaves which are sparsely distributed on the stem. The stem is thin with long internodes. Both the stem and the leaves are glabrous. The palisade tissue is poorly developed and the leaf consists largely or entirely of spongy tissues. The epidermis often contains chlorophyll and the cuticle is thin. Stomata may be present on both sides. Common examples are *Begonia*, aroids, wood-sorrel, ferns, mosses and liverworts. Plants which grow well only in the light are called **heliophytes**. These have small leaves which are thicker and crowded together on the stem. The stem is stouter and has short internodes. The stem and sometimes the leaves are very hairy. The palisade tissue is well developed. The epidermis is provided with a thick cuticle, but no chlorophyll. Stomata are present on the lower side and are often sunken or occluded. Aqueous tissue is often present. Most thick-leaved plants are heliophytes.

(d) **Wind.** Wind usually has a destructive action on vegetation. It enhances transpiration. Very strong, dry wind is often fatal to plants, particularly to young seedlings. It has been seen that in forests, some plants can resist the action of wind far better than others. On the seashore, coconut-palms are exposed to strong gusts of wind but these plants can withstand strong wind because their leaves are cut into narrow segments and have stout mid-ribs. The cuticle is also very thick. Wind is useful in disseminating seeds and fruits, particularly those provided with some kind of appendage (see pp. 110-11). When the air is dry, certain species in the desert roll up into balls and are driven by the wind to other places, where they strike roots and grow when conditions are favourable (See p. 327).

2. Edaphic Factor: Soil. Most plants are fixed to the ground and draw their supply of essential food from the soil. Only carbon dioxide and some nitrogen in a few cases, are obtained from the air. It is evident from this that there is an intimate relationship between plants and soils, particular types of soil favouring the growth of particular species of plants. Thus, the structural peculiarities and distribution of plants over different regions of the earth are largely determined by edaphic factors. This being so, a study of the different aspects of soils is as important as the study of plants themselves from the ecological point of view. These aspects of soils have been dealt with in Part III, Chapter 2.

3. Biotic Factor. The term 'biotic factor' includes all influences exerted by living organisms to bring about any change in the vegetation of a locality. The most important in this respect are human beings and grazing animals. Man acts as a powerful agent, influencing profoundly the original vegetation of a locality in a number of ways : cultivation, terrace cultivation in the hills, reclamation of land, cutting down trees for wood and fuel, deforestation, afforestation, etc. Grazing by domesticated animals destroys many herbaceous plants in pastures and areas surrounding the villages of agriculturists. Grazing constantly interferes with the normal development of vegetation. The relation of a species to other living organisms is apparent in many cases. Neighbouring species compete for food, water and sunlight. A particular species may be attacked and sometimes wholly destroyed by parastic plants or animals, or it may be fed upon by animals. In some cases, plants are of mutual help to each other, e.g. symbionts. Symbiosis between bacteria and leguminous plants may be mentioned in this connection. Soil bacteria, protozoa, earth-worms, rats, etc., are useful agents in altering the soil. They also damage vegetation. The above are examples of how closely interwoven the lives of plants and animals are (see also pp. 317-18).

4. Topographic Factor. This has an important bearing on vegetation, particularly in mountainous regions such as the Himalayas. Altitude is the qualifying factor here, determining the zonal distribution of vegetation, e.g. tropical, sub-tropical, temperate, sub-temperate and alpine. Rainfall plays an important part within the zone. Slope is another important factor that determines whether water is retained in the soil or drained down after rainfall. This, in turn, influences the type of vegetation. Exposure to sun, monsoon rain and wind also affect vegetation. Thus, the southern slope of the Himalayas has luxuriant, deciduous and evergreen forests, whereas the northern side develops only dry forests.

UNITS OF VEGETATION. Vegetation is not uniform in any country. Depending on climatic and edaphic factors, the vegetation of an area, big or small, may be divided into a number of natural units with different and distinct compositions. A large unit of natural vegetation under identical climatic conditions in a particular area is called a **plant formation**. Formations are controlled by their own climate, and may be of the following types : deciduous forest, evergreen forest, coniferous forest, Arctic tundra, Alpine tundra, grassland, etc. A formation is said to be a **climax** (or climax formation) when it is dominated by one or more species. For example, there may be certain dominant tall trees in evergreen forests, certain dominant shrubs in scrub vegetation, and certain dominant grasses or sedges in grasslands. A climax is the direct effect of the climate.

A major subdivision of a plant formation is called an **association**. There may be a number of associations within the formation, depending on sub-climates and the nature of the soil. An association is similar in general outward appearance, ecological structure and floristic composition, e.g. marsh association, or hydrophytic, halophytic or xerophytic association. A plant association may have one or more dominant species. There may be **communities** of closely associated plants within the association. Examples are *Acacia-Dalbergia* (KHAIR-SISSOO), found along the banks of large streams, and different species of *Quercus* or *Rhododendron*, found in the Himalayas. When a community invades a new area, it is termed a **colony**.

The study of ecology from the community point of view (i.e. a mass of vegetation) is called **syne-**cology and that from the standpoint of component (individual) species, **autecology**. The distribution of plants over the surface of the earth, including hills, rivers, lakes and seas, and the factors concerned in their distribution and migration are together known as plant geography or **phytogeography**.

SUCCESSION. The primitive vegetation of an area is never stable. It passes through a series of changes until a stable form or climax is reached. It may start in water, on barren rock, or elsewhere.

(*a*) **Hydrosere.** The series of changes in the vegetation of a pond, lake, marsh or stream are together known as hydrosere. The vegetation starts with some submerged plants rooted to the soil, e.g. *Ceratophyllum*, *Vallisneria*, *Hydrilla*, *Naias*, *Chara*, *Potamogeton*, etc. These proliferate and form a sort of underwater garden. As older plants and animals die, a thin substratum is formed at first. This is thickened with the accumulation of soil particles resulting from erosion and transportation. Soon various floating plants, some rooted to the soil, e.g. water lily (*Nymphaea*), lotus (*Nelumbo*), *Euryale* (B. & H. MAKHNA), *Limnanthemum*, water chestnut (*Trapa*), etc., and some entirely floating, e.g. water lettuce (*Pistia*), water hyacinth (*Eichhornia*), duckweed (*Lemna*), bladderwort (*Utricularia*), *Salvinia*, *Ceratopteris* (a water fern), etc., invade the area. Some of these proliferate very rapidly and cover the water surface. They often kill the submerged plants by either cutting off light or by competition. With the death of one set of plants, the ground is prepared for the next set, i.e. succession continues. The pond, in the meantime, is being silted up. At this stage, when the pond still has sufficient water, plants like *Phragmites*, *Arundo*, *Typha*, *Scirpus*, etc., which are partly submerged, begin to invade the area and establish themselves. Besides, plants like *Sagittaria*, *Jussiaea*, *Alisma*, several sedges and rushes occupy the available space. They grow and eventually die, and further sedimentation takes place. The substratum rises and the depth of the water decreases. The next stage is the appearance of wet soil and then dry soil. By now the hydrophytes have disappeared and given place to mesophytes. Only those species of shrubs and trees that can stand water-logging during the rainy season make their appearance. Further invasion takes place. Finally a permanent, forest stage is reached. This is the climax. The type of forest is determined by the amount of annual rainfall. If succession takes place in saline areas, the hydrosere is called *halosere*.

(*b*) **Xerosere.** This is another interesting feature of succession. The series of changes in the vegetation of bare rocky beds, rocky hill-slopes, sand beds and other areas with extreme scarcity of water are together known as xerosere. The first invasion on rocks under such extreme conditions is that of crustose lichens, which grow only for a short period during wet weather and then undergo desiccation. They gradually spread and disintegrate the rock into soil, at least to some extent. Foliose lichens soon make their appearance. In due course, humus accumulates and the soil becomes receptive for the next series. Some forms of hardy mosses now invade the area. Soil is in the process of formation as humus accumulates and water is retained. The next series is the appearance of hardy, short-lived annuals, followed by biennials and perennials. These help further the disintegration of rock into soil, accumulation of humus and retention of soil water. As herbaceous plants multiply, the lichens and mosses become scarce. The stage is now set for invasion by hardy shrubs, which gradually come to form the dominant vegetation. The depth of the soil increases further and soon becomes suitable for tree growth. At this stage, however, trees are stunted in growth, xeromorphic in habit and sparsely distributed. If conditions are favourable, xeromorphic plants are soon replaced by mesophytes. The trees proliferate and new types of herbs grow in their shade. The invading trees soon become dominant, forming a climax. If succession takes place in sandy areas, the xerosere is called *psammosere*.

Ecesis. The successful establishment of a form of vegetation that has migrated from one locality to another is known as ecesis. Ecesis refers to all the factors (climatic and edaphic) prevailing in the new locality, and the adaptability of a plant to the new environment and conditions. It includes, therefore, all the factors favouring seed germination, plant growth and reproduction, leading finally to the successful establishment of a plant. It is evident that any one factor inhibiting any of the above processes may stand in the way of complete ecesis. Competition with neighbours and also among the invading plants may be another setback. Ecesis is next in importance to the migration of plants to a new locality because migration cannot give rise to new vegetation in the absence of ecesis. In other words, a particular form of vegetation cannot establish itself in a new environment unless the conditions required for ecesis are present.

Commensalism. When members of two species become closely associated with each other, temporarily or permanently, each being self-supporting so far as food and nutrition are concerned, the relationship between the two is expressed as commensalism (*com*, together; *mensa*, table). Literally, it means 'eating together at the same table, without causing any harm or inconvenience to the other'. Commensalism involves growing together on the same substratum, or one on the body of the other for shelter or support, or even for transport, or often for facility of food manufacture. Epiphytes, total or partial, are typical commensals. Examples of epiphytes are various orchids, Spanish moss (*Tillandsia usneoides*, an American plant that hangs in festoons from the branches of trees and is usually carried by the wind from tree to tree), *Scindapsus*, *Pothos*, *Dischidia*, several ferns (e.g. *Drynaria*), *Lycopodium phlegmaria*, *Usnea* (a lichen), etc. Those use the branches of trees for support and adequate light. Other examples of commensalism are *Nostoc*, which lives in the cavities of cycad root, certain bacteria (e.g. *Escherichia coli*) that live in the intestines of animals and consume undigested food, and *Protoccoccus*, which lives on tree trunks.

ECOSYSTEM. Every biotic community exists in an abiotic environment and there is constant interaction between the two. A living organism and the environment surrounding it cannot be separated from each other. The system arising from the interactions of a biological community with its non-living surroundings is called an **ecosystem**, e.g. a pond, a forest, etc. The concept of the ecosystem was first advanced by A. G. Tansley in 1935. An ecosystem is an ecological unit, which has both structure and function.

The study of the structure of an ecosystem

includes an analysis of the biotic communities living in the habitat and the physical features of the environment, including edaphic factors, nutrients, climate conditions, energy source, etc. Structurally, an ecosystem can be divided into (a) abiotic components and (b) biotic components. Abiotic componets include soil, water, moisture, wind, solar radiation, basic inorganic elements, organic compounds, gases, etc., present in the habitat. Biotic components include autotrophic components (green plants, which can trap radiant energy and systhesize food) and heterotrophic components (non-green plants and all animals which cannot manufacture food and depend on autotrophic components). Biotic components can be divided into three groups, namely: (a) producers, (b) consumers and (c) decomposers and transformers.

The green plants in an ecosystem are called producers as they can manufacture food, on which the heterotrophs depend. Producers trap solar energy, assimilate carbon dioxide, evolve oxygen and prepare food. Algae, green aquatic plants, grasses and trees are all examples of producers. The other living organisms which feed on the autotrophs are called consumers as they consume the food manufactured by the producers. Consumers can be divided into primary, secondary and tertiary consumers. Herbivorous animals, such as insects, rodents, deer, cows, etc., which feed on plants are called primary consumers. Secondary consumers can be further classified into carnivores (only flesh eating animals) and omnivores (animals which eat flesh as well as green plants). Tertiary consumers, such as lions, tigers, etc., prey upon herbivorous, carnivorous and omnivorous animals. Decomposers, such as fungi and bacteria, decompose dead organisms and convert the organic substances present in them into simpler forms, which are then transformed into inorganic compounds by transformers. The dynamic nature of an ecosystem is maintained in this way.

The study of the functional aspects of an ecosystem consists of an analysis of the energy flowing into the system and the flow of energy through the different trophic levels. The inorganic constituents of the system are converted into organic substances by green plants. Green plants are eaten by primary consumers, primary consumers by secondary consumers, and secondary consumers by tertiary consumers. Finally, decomposers convert the organic substances present in the body of dead organisms into simpler forms, which are, in turn, transformed into simple inorganic substances and returned to the environment by transformers. Energy from the sun is trapped by green plants and transferred to primary consumers (through food). From primary consumers, it is transferred to secondary consumers and so on. Thus, energy flows through the different trophic levels of the food chain, decreasing gradually. Energy is also released during the decomposition of dead organisms. The flow of energy and the cycling of nutrients are the two most important functions of an ecosystem. The flow of energy is always unidirectional, while nutrients follow a cycle.

Types of Ecosystems. There are two basic types of ecosystems, namely (i) terrestrial (forest ecosystems, grassland ecosystems, desert ecosystems, man-made ecosystems, such as agricultural ecosystems, etc.) and (ii) aquatic (fresh-water ecosystems, like pond ecosystems, river ecosystems, etc. and marine ecosystems).

Flow of Energy in an Ecosystem. Energy is defined as the capacity for doing work. There are two forms of energy, namely, kinetic energy and potential energy. The energy possessed by a body at rest is called potential energy, while energy in motion is kinetic energy. One form of energy can be converted into another. The chemical energy stored in food is the source of energy for all living organisms. Green plants can trap solar energy and convert it into chemical energy. Thus, all life on earth depends on solar energy. The unidirectional flow of energy is based on two important laws of thermodynamics. The first law states that the total amount of energy in the universe is always constant. It may change from one form to another, but it can never be destroyed or created. The second law states that energy flows from higher to lower levels.

On the basis of these two laws, the flow of energy may be explained as follows. Solar energy cannot be created but it can be transformed into other forms. During the conversion of energy from one form to another, a part of it gets lost (released) in the form of heat energy. Green plants trap radiant energy and convert it into chemical energy, which is then stored in food. During this process of transformation of light energy to chemical energy, a part of energy is lost in the form of heat.

Every other living organism depends on green plants for food as also for the chemical energy stored in it. All living organisms, including green plants, carry on various activities during which some amount of chemical energy stored in the food is converted into kinetic energy, resulting in the loss of a part of energy in the form of heat.

Hence, as energy passes from one organism to another through the food chain, it is constantly being lost from the living system.

Eventually, all the energy captured by the producers is returned to the non-living world, mainly in the form of heat and not in the same form (i.e. light) in which it was absorbed by the green plants.

Energy released (or lost) in this way (in the form of heat) cannot be utilized. In other words, the flow of energy is unidirectional.

Further, the capacity of energy to perform work decreases gradually as it is constantly being lost when converted from one form to another while passing through various consumer levels.

While performing their activities, plants use up some of the energy captured from sunlight. Herbivorous animals eat these plants and obtain a supply of energy, but not the same amount of energy that was originally captured from the sunlight by the green plants. This is because the plants have aready utilized a portion of energy originally stored by them. Likewise, herbivorous animals use up a portion of the energy they have received from plants. Therefore, there is further degradation of energy when the carnivorous animals capture and eat the first-order-consumers. In this way, each consumer level obtains smaller and smaller amounts of the original energy that was trapped by the producer. This forms an energy pyramid which shows that energy flows from higher to lower levels.

Food chain. The transference of food from one trophic level to another is called the food chain. Thus, the food chain may be defined as the transfer of energy stored in food from producers to consumers by the repeated process of eating and being eaten. For example, plants are eaten by rodents, rodents are eaten by snakes, snakes by hawks, and so on.

Plants → Rodents → Snakes → Hawks

Food web. In nature, food chains are usually not simple and linear, but branched, because at every stage or trophic level, consumers have several alternative forms of food to choose from. For example, in the above case, rodents may be eaten directly by hawks or other predators. Similarly, snakes feed on small animals. There is plenty of variation in the diet of herbivores, as well. Rodents may eat more of grass, snails may consume juicy herbs, deer may feed on the leaves of herbs and shrubs or they may shift from one species of plants to another during food shortages. As a result, food chains become branched and interlinked at various stages, leading to a reticulate or web-like structure. This is called **a food web.** Food webs make a community more stable, as the number of alternative pathways is greater.

CHAPTER 2

ECOLOGICAL GROUPS

Although plants sometimes occur as isolated individuals, more commonly we find that they adapt to the same environment and are associated together in groups. The groups may include various plant species, belonging to different families, differing in shape, size, form and relationship, but they live under the same conditions of the soil, moisture, heat and light. Some of the common groups are described below.

1. Hydrophytes. Hydrophytes are plants that grow in water or in very wet places. They may be submerged or partly submerged, floating or amphibious. Their structural adaptations are mainly the result of high water content and deficient supply of oxygen. The various adaptations found in hydrophytes are as follows.

Adaptations. The main features of aquatic plants are the reduction of protective tissue (epidermis here is meant for absorption, not for protection), supporting tissue (lack of sclerenchyma),

conducting tissue (minimum development of vascular tissue) and absorbing tissue (roots mainly act as anchors and root-hairs are lacking), and the special development of air-chambers for aeration of internal tissues.

The root system in hydrophytes is feebly developed and root-hairs and root-cap are absent. No roots are developed at all in some floating plants, such as bladderwort (*Utricularia*) and hornwort (*Ceratophyllum*). In submerged plants such as *Vallisneria*, *Hydrilla*, and *Naias*, water-dissolved mineral salts and gases are absorbed by the entire surface. In plants like water lettuce (*Pistia*), water hyacinth (*Eichhornia*), duckweed (*Lemna*), no root-cap develops, but an analogous structure called root-pocket is found instead.

The stem is soft and more or less spongy, owing to the development of a large number of air cavities filled with gases. The leaf also contains air cavities. These cavities, on the one hand, give buoyancy to the plant, allowing it to float, and on

FIG. 1. Giant water lily (*Victoria amazonica* = *V. regia*)

the other, serve as stores of air (oxygen and carbon dioxide). They store the carbon dioxide given off in respiration for photosynthesis, and also the oxygen given off in photosynthesis during the daytime for respiration. There is a minimum development of the mechanical and vascular tissues. The xylem is reduced to only a few elements, while the phloem is reduced to a few narrow sieve-tubes. The epidermis has no cuticle but contains some chloroplasts. The stem and the leaf-stalk are in some cases provided with prickles and spines for defence against attacks by aquatic animals.

Aquatic plants may be fixed to the substratum or they may float freely. Likewise, leaves may be submerged or floating. Submerged leaves are thin and often become elongated in order to cope with the subdued light under water. They are generally ribbon-shaped, finely dissected or linear. There is no cuticle. The stomata are also usually absent and if present, they are functionless. The exchange of gases and absorption of water and mineral salts take place through the epidermis of the leaf. The mesophyll is thin and not differentiated into palisade tissue and spongy tissue, and the epidermis contains chloroplasts to utilize the weak light under water. Floating leaves are well developed and have a thick cuticle. Their upper surfaces contain a large number of stomata while the lower surfaces have no stomata or only functionless ones. Exchange of gases takes place through the upper surface, and absorption of water through the lower. Floating leaves have many air cavities to provide buoyancy and for the purpose of aeration. Amphibious plants are subjected to alternate flooding and drying. They usually grow at the edge of a pool of water, their lower leaves submerged and the upper ones above water. Many such plants often show **heterophylly** (*heteros*, different; *phylla*, leaves). This means that the same plant bears different kinds of leaves (see p. 45).

Some Common Aquatic Plants. (*a*) **Submerged:** *Vallisneria, Hydrilla, Naias, Ottelia, Potamogeton*; (*b*) **Floating:** *Wolffia* (smallest plant with frond like a sand grain), *Hydrocharis*, bladderwort (*Utricularia*), hornwort (*Ceratophyllum*), duck-weed (*Lemna*), water lettuce (*Pistia*), water hyacinth (*Eichhornia*), water chestnut (*Trapa*), *Neptunia, Azolla, Salvinia, Ceratopteris*; (*c*) **Plants with floating leaves:** water lily, giant water lily (FIG. 1), *Euryale* (B. & H. MAKHNA), *Limnanthemum*. In the case of lotus (*Nelumbo*), the leaves stand above the water; (*d*) **Amphibious plants showing heterophylly:** water crowfoot (*Ranunculus aquatilis*), water plantain (*Alisma*), arrowhead (*Sagittaria*), *Limnophila heterophylla, Cardanthera triflora*.

2. Hygrophytes. These are plants that grow in constantly moist areas. They occur in moist, shady places, in forests, or in the moist soil near water-logged localities. The root system and the vascular system in hygrophytes are poorly developed. The growth of these plants is stunted and their parts are generally soft and spongy. The stem is usually an underground rhizome. The mechanical tissues are only feebly developed. The leaves on the whole are well developed, fully expanded and have numerous stomata. They are smooth, shiny and have a thin cuticle. Since these plants grow in moist areas transpiration is not active, but to get rid of the excess water, their leaves are provided with hydathodes (see FIG. II/42) through which water is exuded in liquid form. Common hygrophilous plants are aroids, ferns, begonias and some grasses.

3. Mesophytes. These plants grow under average conditions of temperature and moisture. The soil in which they grow is neither saline nor water-logged, and the temperature of the air is neither too high nor too low. Mesophytes are, therefore, intermediate between hydrophytes and xerophytes.

Adaptations. The root system is well developed. Dicotyledonous mesophytes have tap roots with branches and monocotyledonous mesophytes have clusters of fibrous roots. There is an abundance of root-hairs for absorption of water from the soil. The stem is solid (and not spongy, as in water plants), erect and normally branched. There are few or no thorns on the stem. All the different kinds of tissues, particularly the mechanical and conducting tissues, are fully developed in mesophytes. The cuticle is present in the aerial parts, such as the leaves and branches. In dorsiventral leaves, the lower epidermis has numerous stomata; there are few or none on the upper surface. In erect leaves, as in monocotyledons, the stomata are more or less equally distributed on both surfaces.

4. Epiphytes. Epiphytes grow perched on the trunks and branches of other plants, but only for the purpose of support, i.e. they are not parasitic. They grow on almost all kinds of trees and shrubs, rarely exhibiting a preference. They are normally green and autotrophic in habit. However, considering the conditions under which they grow, they seem to lead a very hard life for want of adequate supply of nutrients, more particularly water which is the principal factor for the sustenance of life. In tropical climates, they have to depend mainly on rain water and in temperate climates and in the hills, they depend on dew. They normally obtain their food material from dead bark, wind-borne debris, humus and the rain water that collects in the network of their roots. They also absorb the water trickling down the hanging roots. Although they are seen to grow on isolated trees here and there, epiphytes grow luxuriantly in tropical rain forests, often thickly covering the tree trunk. As they have to depend on rain or dew, their existence is precarious during the dry season when they mostly go into a dormant, often defoliated state to tide over the difficult period. They begin to thrive again with a few showers of rain. Epiphytes commonly show the following adaptations to the conditions under which they live: (*a*) they can quickly attach themselves to their support by the formation of clasping roots soon after the germination of the seeds, (*b*) many of them have xeromorphic characteristics so that they can stand droughts, and (*c*) the mechanism for seed dispersal is efficient in angiosperms; in orchids, a large quantity of extremely minute seeds is produced in a single capsule. The xeromorphic types may continue to grow without drying up even through the bad season. They may be leaf-succulent or stem-succulent. Many orchids have succulent pseudo-bulbs. Besides, in many such epiphytes, the cuticle is

thick, the stomata are sunken and the leaves are smaller and fewer. Some plants, particularly many orchids, spend their entire lives on supporting plants. These are total epiphytes or holoepiphytes. Some plants, particularly the rootlet climbers, are initially terrestrial and later epiphytic, having lost their connection with the soil. These are partial epiphytes or homoepiphytes, e.g. *Cereus triangularis* (see FIG. VII/35A) and *Scindapsus* (B. GAJPIPAL). Conversely, some plants are initially epiphytic at first and later terrestrial, being rooted to the soil, e.g. banyan and peepul.

Examples. Among angiosperms, orchids are the most common epiphytes, e.g. *Vanda* (see FIG. I/13), *Dendrobium* (see FIG. VII/79), *Cymbidium*, *Eria*, etc.; and also certain plants of *Araceae*, e.g. *Scindapsus officinalis*, *Pothos scandens*, etc.; *Bromeliaceae*, e.g. *Tillandsia usneoides*—a peculiar American plant hanging from branches and looking like *Usnea* (a lichen; see FIG. V/109); *Asclepiadaceae*, e.g. *Dischidia raflesiana* (see FIG. I/70) and *D. nummularia*; *Cactaceae*, e.g. *Cereus triangularis* (see FIG. VII/35A)—a large climbing epiphyte with triangular stem often reaching tree-tops, etc. Among Pteridophyta, several ferns are epiphytes, e.g. bird's nest fern (*Asplenium nidus*), *Drynaria quericifolia* with dimorphic leaves, many species of *Polypodium*, e.g. *P. fissum*—all growing in tufts on tree-trunks, and *Cyclophorus adnascens*—creeping, branching and almost covering the whole tree, etc.; a few species of *Lycopodium*, e.g. *L. squarrosum* and *L. phlegmaria* (see FIGS. V/150-51A), are also somewhat common epiphytes. Among Bryophyta several forms of mosses often cover tree-trunks as cushions; *Porella* (see FIG. V/128), one of the Junger manniales, is also fairly common. Among algae mention only be made of *protococcus* and *Trentepohlia* growing on barks of trees, the latter on leaves also.

5. Xerophytes. These are plants that grow in deserts or in very dry places. They can withstand a prolonged period of drought uninjured. For this purpose, they have certain peculiar adaptations. It is not that xerophytes thrive under desert conditions. The property of drought-resistance is not attributed to the anatomical features of such plants, but to the capacity of the protoplasm to endure a high degree of desiccation with practically no injury. The dominant features of deserts or very dry regions are scarcity of moisture in the soil and extreme atmospheric conditions, such as intense light, high temperature, strong wind and aridity of the air. Therefore, xerophytic plants have to guard against excessive evaporation of water. This is achieved by the reduction of evaporating surfaces. They also have to adopt special mechanisms to absorb moisture from the soil and to retain it. Xerophytic characteristics are also found in plants growing in cold regions, such as temperate and sub-arctic zones, high altitudes, rocky beds, sandy regions, dry places with scanty rainfall and salt marshes.

Adaptations. These plants produce a long tap root which goes deep into the subsoil in search of moisture. Many desert plants which live for a short period produce a superficial root system to absorb moisture from the surface soil after a passing shower of rain. To retain the water absorbed by the roots, the leaves and stems of some plants become very thick and fleshy, as in Indian aloe (*Aloe*) and American aloe or century plant (*Agave*). Sometimes, the roots also become fleshy, as in *Asparagus*. They develop aqueous tissue to store up water. This is further facilitated by the abundance of mucilage contained in them. For the same purpose, the leaves often develop a multiple epidermis, as in oleander (*Nerium*). Many desert plants have phylloclades, which are modified stems that store water and food and also perform functions of a leaf. Most cacti and several species of *Euphorbia* are examples of this.

The leaves and stems are provided with a thick, sometimes very thick, cuticle. The epidermal cells are often strongly cutinized to prevent excessive loss of water through transpiration. Tannins and gums are frequently found in the epidermal layer. In many cases, the stem is smaller and provided with prickles, as in *Euphorbia splendens*. The leaves are also smaller so that the evaporating surface is minimized. Thus, they may be divided into small segments, as in *Acacia*, or modified into

spines, as in many cacti and spurges (*Euphorbia*). Sometimes, they are reduced to small scales, as in *Tamarix* and *Asparagus*. In some plants, as in *Gnaphalium* and *Aerua*, there is a dense coating of hairs. There are fewer in stomata—usually 10-15 per sq. mm.—and these remain sunken in grooves and occluded, sometimes covered by hairs. The sclerenchyma is strongly developed in most xerophytes. In Australian *Acacia* (see FIG. I/67), the leaf is modified into a phyllode, and it turns its edge in the vertical direction in strong sunlight to minimize transpiration. Under conditions of extreme dryness, the leaves of most xerophytic grasses and of many other plants as well roll up, considerably reducing their evaporating surfaces. In such cases, the stomata also close up.

Many xerophytic herbs lie prostrate on the ground, completing their life history within a short time, e.g. *Solanum surattense*, *Tribulus terrestris*, *Trianthema monogyna* and *Suaeda fruticosa*. Some are perennial in habit. Many xerophytes are elaborately armed with prickles and spines.

Two very peculiar cases showing special xerophytic adaptations may be mentioned here. These are certain species of *Selaginella* and *Anastatica*. During the dry season in the desert, these plants curl up into a sort of ball and are driven about by the wind. They are fixed only when they reach wet soil or the rains begin.

Some Common Xerophytic Plants. Many spurges (*Euphorbia*) are xerophytic, e.g. *Euphorbia splendens*, *E. royleana*, *E. neriifolia* and *E. tirucalli* (see FIG. I/40A). Prickly pear (*Opuntia*), *Cereus* and *Pereskia* are among the xerophytic cacti. Other xerophytes are the dagger plant (*Yucca*; see FIG. I/81), Indian aloe (*Aloe*), American aloe (*Agave*), *Capparis aphylla*, *Tamarix*, prickly poppy (*Argemone*), Jew's slipper (*Pedilanthus*), globe thistle (*Echinops echinata*), safflower (*Carthamus*), amaranth (*Amaranthus*), wild plum (*Zizyphus nummularia*), purslane (*Portulaca*), Indian spinach (*Basella*), saltwort (*Salsola*), sea-blite (*Suaeda*),. *Asparagus*, gum tree (*Acacia nilotica*), *Prosopis spicigera* (B. & H. SHOMI), camel thorn (*Alhagi*), *Solanum surattense* (B. KANTIKARI; H. KATELI), *Tribulus terrestris* (B. GOKHRIKANTA; H. GOKHRU), *Gnaphalium*, and

Aerua. Common xerophytic grasses are *Stipa*, *Sporobolus*, Saccharum *spontaneum* (B. KASH; H. KANS), *S. munja* (B.SAR; H. MUNJA) and *Aristida*.

6. Halophytes. These are special types of plants growing in saline soil or saline water which contain a high concentration of salts. Hence, halophytes show some special characteristics (or adaptations). The cells of ordinary land plants or fresh-water plants maintain a low osmotic pressure which may be equal to, or more often slightly higher than, the osmotic pressure of the medium (soil or water) in which they are growing, i.e. the pressures inside and outside these plants are more or less in a state of equilibrium. But when the medium is definitely saline, as in the sea, sea coast or salt-lake, the water balance between the plants and their habitat becomes disturbed, much to the disadvantage of the former. The osmotic pressure of the saline water is very high. Under this condition, water tends to be extracted from the plant tissues rather than absorbed by them since their osmotic pressure is lower than that of the medium. The saline water or soil, thus, behaves as a *physiologically dry* medium for such plants. To meet this exigency, the plant tissues must maintain a higher osmotic pressure than that of their saline medium. Therefore, the only plants that can adapt to such a situation are those whose tissues have a high concentration of salts and consequently an exceptionally high osmotic pressure—as high as 35-40 atmospheres or even much higher. Such plants are called **halophytes**. These show the following characteristics (or adaptations).

Xeromorphic Adaptations. The majority of halophytes show xeromorphic characteristics, i.e. the characteristics of xerophytes. The relationship between the two groups is not, however, clearly understood. Many of them have fleshy leaves, e.g. sea-blite (*Suaeda maritima*) and glasswort (*Salsola foetida*). They often have no leaves and the stem is fleshy and jointed, e.g. saltwort (*Salicornia brachiata*) and *Arthrocnemum indicum*. Sometimes the stem is fleshy and mucilaginous, e.g. Indian spinach (*Basella rubra*—wild or cultivated). The epidermis is often strongly cutinized and thickened, sometimes even hairy. Spines and prickles are present in several cases, e.g. *Acanthus ilicifolius* (B. HARGOZA; H. HARKUCH-KANTA), *Asteracantha longifilia* (=*Hygrophila spinosa*; B. KULEKHARA; H.

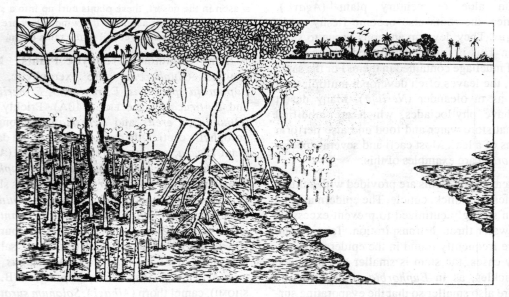

FIG. 2. Mangrove plants showing (a) pneumatophores for respiration, (b) stilt roots for support, and (c) viviparous germination for survival

GOKULA-KANTA) and *Solanum surattense* (=*S. xanthocarpum*; B. KANTIKARI; H. KATELI, KATITA). The internal structure is often like that of xerophytes. Other common examples of halophytes are *Pluchea indica*, *Blumea maritima*, *Azima tetracantha*, *Vigna luteola*, *Caesalpinia nuga*, *Flagellaria indica*, *Tamarix indica* and nipa-palm (*Nipa futicans*), etc.

Special Adaptations. Halophytes form a special type of vegetation, known as the **mangrove**, to cope with the more or less daily tides that inundate the muddy swamps of the tropical estuaries and sea-coasts that they grow in. Mangrove vegetation is most extensively represented in the Sundarbans (West Bengal). Mangrove plants show some special adaptations: (1) A large number of **stilt roots** (FIG. 2) grow out of the main stem and the branches. (2) In several cases, in addition to the stilt roots, special roots called **respiratory roots** or **pneumatophores** (FIGS. 2-3) are also produced in large numbers. They develop from underground roots and project beyond the water level. They look like so many conical spikes distributed all round the trunk of the tree. In some places, they grow so thickly that it becomes difficult for a boat to pass through them. Their upper parts have several pores or respiratory spaces through which exchange of gases for respiration takes place. (3) Mangrove species also show **vivipary** (FIG. 4), i.e. the seed germinates inside the fruit while it is still on the parent tree and is nourished by it. Germination is almost immediate, without any period of rest. The radicle elongates to a certain length and its lower portion swells up. Finally, the seedling separates from the parent tree and falls down. The radicle presses into the soft mud, keeping the plumule and cotyledons clear above the saline water. Lateral roots are quickly formed for proper anchorage. The advantage is that the fruit cannot be swept by tidal waves. Typical mangrove plants are *Rhizophora* (B. KHAMO), *Ceriops* (B. GORAN), *Kandelia* (B. GORIA), *Bruguiera* (B. KANKRA) *Sonneratia* (B. KEORA), *Heritiera* (B. SUNDRI), *Excoecaria* (B. GEO) *Avicennia* (B. BAEN or BINA), etc. (see also p. 334).

7. Marsh Vegetation. A marsh is a tract of low, wet land which remains covered with water for the greater part of the year. A marsh is made of

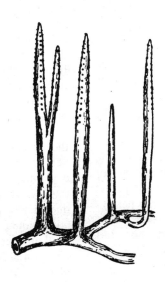

FIG. 3

FIG. 3. Pneumatophores growing vertically upwards from an underground root.

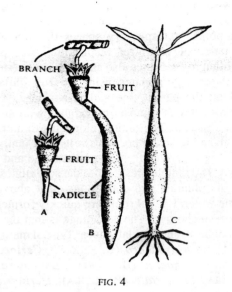

FIG. 4

FIG. 4. Viviparous germination

stagnant mud, which contains plenty of mineral salts. The water is alkaline, or even neutral, but not acid. The peculiarity of marsh vegetation is that the submerged parts show hydrophytic adaptations, while the aerial parts have the characteristics of land plants. From the margin to the mid-marsh, the vegetation often shows three zones with, of course, a certain amount of overlapping. The first or outermost zone, lying nearest the dry land, is composed of plants which have only their roots or rhizomes in waterlogged areas. This zone exhibits the characteristics of hygrophytes to some extent. The leaves are usually well developed, have several stomata and thin cuticle. The stem is usually spongy. There is a predominance of low herbs in this zone, the commonly found plants being water dropwort (*Oenanthe*), marsh pennywort (*Hydrocotyle*), various sedges (*Scirpus, Carex*, etc.), rush (*Juncus*), and horsetail (*Equisetum*).

The second or intermediate zone lies between the first zone and the mid-marsh. Here, the roots or rhizomes are in the wet soil under water. Parts of the stem are submerged in the water, and the leaves and flowers are either floating or above the water. This zone is characterized by tall herbs of upright growth. Plants typical of this zone are reed (*Phragmites*), *Arundo domax* and elephant grass (*Typha*). etc. This zone is often called reed-swamp association. Low herbs or floating plants associated with them are water plantain (*Alisma*), water crowfoot (*Ranunculus*), water lilies (*Nymphaea*), lotus (*Nelumbo*), duckweed (*Lemna*), water lettuce (*Pistia*), arrowhead (*Sagittaria*), hornwort (*Ceratophyllum*), *Hydrilla, Vallisneria, Utricularia*, as well as some floating grasses, such as *Hygrorhiza, Vossia* and *Panicum proliferum*, and some sedges, such as *Scirpus* and *Cyperus*.

The third or the innermost zone is submerged, and the vegetation typically hydrophytic. Plants commonly found in this zone are *Potamogeton, Vallisneria, Hydrilla* and *Ceratophyllum*. Besides, many of the aquatic plants of the second zone extend into this zone.

Eutrophication. The complex sequence of changes taking place in an aquatic ecosystem due to the addition of excessive nutrients to the water is called eutrophication. Eutrophication leads to a dense growth of phytoplankton (mostly green and blue-green algae) in the water. Filamentous algae and other rooted submerged plants may grow in abundance at the bottom of the water, specially in the shallow areas. This leads to (i) an increase in productivity at all levels of the food chain, (ii) various changes (in succession) in the kinds of organisms growing in the body of water, and (iii) a reduction in the level of dissolved oxygen. When the process takes place naturally, it occurs at a very slow rate, but in the case of man-induced eutrophication, the changes take place at a rapid rate. Many lakes and rivers have become polluted due to the addition of nitrogen and phosphorus compounds from municipal sewage and agricultural and farm operations. Due to eutrophication, clear water bodies have become filled wih phytoplankton and other aquatic vegetation. As a result, drinking water that was once clear and pure now tastes different. Many such water bodies are now unfit for even swimming and boating.

CHAPTER 3

TYPES OF VEGETATION IN INDIA

On the basis of rainfall, temperature, altitude and topography, the types of vegetation found in India may be broadly classified as follows. However, there is a certain amount of overlapping of types, both in the plains and the hills. It is interesting to note that *Orchidaceae* is the largest family in the Indian flora, being represented by about 1,700 species, while *Compositae* (the largest dicotyledonous family) is represented in India by only about 674 species. According to Calder, the following is the classification of families in their order of occurrence in the Indian flora taken as a whole : *Orchidaceae, Leguminosae, Gramineae, Rubiaceae, Euphor-biaceae, Acanthaceae, Compositae, Cyperaceae, Labiatae* and *Uraticaceae*. The proportion of dicotyledons to monocotyledons is 7 : 1.

1. Tropical Evergreen or **Rain Forests.** These occur in areas with a heavy annual rainfall, exceeding 2,000 mm. The western parts of the Western Ghats and the eastern parts of the subtropical Himalayas fall under this category. Evergreen forests are composed of tall and medium-sized trees, many shrubs, several climbers and epiphytes, different types of bamboos and ferns, all growing luxuriantly. They do not shed their leaves annually, at least not all together. Such forests generally have a 3-storeyed appearance (see p. 335). The families that dominate such forests are *Dipterocarpaceae, Guttiferae, Annonaceae, Meliaceae, Burseraceae, Sapotaceae, Euphorbiaceae* and *Pelmae.* Families like *Ebenaceae, Sapotaceae, Capparidaceae, Rhamnaceae* and *Myrtaceae* are also well represented. *Tetrameles nudiflora, Dipterocarpus macrocarpus, Hopea odorata, Artocarpus chaplasha, Terminalia myriocarpa* and *Cedrela toona* are typical of the tallest trees of evergreen forests and are of considerable economic value. Other trees that are common are ebony (*Diospyros*), ironwood tree (*Mesua*), *Mimusops*, rosewood (*Dalbergia*), *Chikrassia, Pterospermum,* *Calophyllum*, several species of *Terminalia* and *Cinnamomum, Amoora* and *Alstonia*.

2. Tropical Deciduous or **Monsoon Forests.** Such forests (see pp. 335-36) occur in areas with a moderate or low annual rainfall (1,000-1,500 mm.) as in the eastern parts of the Western Ghats, Deccan plateau, Madhya Pradesh, Uttar Pradesh, Bihar, West Bengal (western parts) and the lower slopes of the Himalayas (forming tropical hill forests). SAL (*Shorea*) is dominant in certain areas, as in Assam and central India extending to Orissa, while teak (*Tectona*) is dominant in the Deccan plateau, and sandalwood (*Santalum*) in the Mysore area. The trees commonly found in such forests are JARUL (Lagerstroemia), redwood (*Dalbergia*), GAMHAR (*Gmelina*), *Bombax*, *Terminalia, Sterculia, Dipterocarpus, Butea, Cassia, Bauhinia, Acacia, Albizzia,* PADAUK (*Pterocarpus macrocarpus*), red sandalwood (*P. santalinus*), *Adina* and *Odina*.

3. Tropical Thorn Forests. Such forests (see pp. 335-36) are restricted to areas with very low rainfall (500-760 mm.), as in south Punjab, Rajputana, North Kutch and the Deccan plateau. Thorny shrubs and low trees are characteristic of these forests. The commonly found plants are SHOMI or JHAND (*Prosopis*). *Acacia nilotica Zizyphus, Capparis, Balanites, Euphorbia, Flacourtia* and *Tamarix*. In saline soil, as in Punjab, thick-leaved species of *Salsola, Suaeda, Chenopodium,* etc. are found. The principal families are *Leguminosae, Capparidaceae, Tamaricaceae* and *Rhamnaceae*.

4. Mangrove or **Littoral Forests.** These forests (see p. 334) are characteristic of the deltas of large rivers (Ganges, Mahanadi, Godavari, Krishna, Kaberi and Indus), some sea coasts and marine islands.

5. Riparian Forests. These are found along the banks of rivers (see p. 336), and consist mainly of

KHAIR (*Acacia catechu*) and SISSOO (*Dalbergia sissoo*), mixed with *Bombax*, *Trewia*, *Barringtonia*, *Populus*, *Tamarix*, etc.

6. Grasslands. These are not common in India. Some grasslands, however, occur in the Gangetic plain and in the plains of Assam. Elsewhere they are sporadic. Hill grasslands are found in the Khasi Hills, south Indian hills and the tropical Himalayas. Grasslands dotted with open forests of low trees and shrubs, called **savannahs**, are found in Uttar Pradesh and Gujarat.

7. Temperate Evergreen or **Coniferous Forests.** These occur in the temperate eastern and western Himalayas and in the Nilgiri Hills at an altitude of 1,600-3,500 metres. Such forests are mainly composed of Coniferae, such as pine (*Pinus*), deodar (*Cedrus*), spruce (*Picea*), silver fir (*Abies*), etc. and Cupuliferae (*Fagaceae* and *Betulaceae*) such as oak (*Quercus*), beech (*Fagus*), and birch (*Betula*) mixed with poplar (*Populus*), elm (*Ulmus*), *Rhododendron*, chestnut (*Castanopsis*), walnut (*Juglans*), maple (*Acer*), etc. Other than Coniferae and Cupuliferae, the dominant families are *Sapindaceae*, *Lauraceae*, *Magnoliaceae*, *Salicaceae* and *Urticaceae* [see also p. 337].

8. Alpine Forests. These occur in the Alpine area of the Himalayas beyond the limit of tree growth (3,500 metres), and consist of the dwarf shrubs of juniper (*Juniperus*), silver fir (*Abies*), *Betula* and *Rhododendron* (several species). At still higher altitudes Alpine scrub consisting of low herbs is the only type of vegetation found (see pp. 337-38).

CHAPTER 4

PHYTOGEOGRAPHICAL REGIONS OF INDIA

The division of India into certain phytogeographical regions was first proposed by Clarke in 1898. It was revised by Hooker in 1904. Based on recent publications on provincial and local flora, the following division was proposed by Calder[1] in 1937. With more information flowing in, it was further modified by Chatterjee[2] in 1939. An outline of the above divisions is given below:

Clarke (1898)— 1. West Himalaya 2. India Deserta 3. Malabaria 4. Coromandalia 5. Gangetic Plain. 6. East Himalaya 7. Assam.

Hooker (1904)—1. Eastern Himalaya 2. Western Himalaya 3. Indus Plain 4. Gangetic Plain 5. Malabar 6. Deccan.

Calder (1937)—1. Western Himalaya 2. Eastern Himalaya 3. Indus Plain 4. Gangetic Plain 5. Deccan 6. Malabar.

Chatterji (1939)—1. Deccan 2. Malabar 3. Indus Plain 4. Gangetic Plain 5. Assam 6. Eastern Himalaya 7. Central Himalaya 8. Western Himalaya.

The main factor in the distribution of species is the amount of annual rainfall in a particular region. The type of soil within the region is another important factor. In mountainous regions like the Himalayas, altitude is the primary factor, coupled with rainfall, in determining zonal vegetation. Where rainfall is heavy (over 2,000 mm.), sometimes very heavy, as in Assam, north Bengal and Malabar, luxuriant vegetation with **evergreen forests** and diversity of species is the rule. Where rainfall is low (usually 1,000-1,500 mm.), as in the Deccan, central India and parts of Punjab, sparse vegetation with **deciduous forests** and uniformity of species is the rule. Where

[1] *An Outline of the Vegetation of India* by C. C. Calder, 1937.
[2] *Studies on the Endemic Flora of India and Burma* by D. Chatterjee, 1939.

rainfall is very low (500-760 mm.), sometimes much less, as in south Punjab, Rajasthan and Sind (Pakistan), the vegetation is thin, sparse and xerophilous, with **thorny scrubs** predominating. Based on the above factors, India may be divided into the following phytogeographical regions:

1. Deccan : This consists of the Deccan plateau, Tamil Nadu, Andhra and a major part of Karnataka— these form a hilly tract of land with an annual rainfall of 840-1,000 mm.— and central India (Madhya Pradesh, Orissa and part of Gujarat), which has an annual rainfall of 840-1,400 mm. The following types of vegetation are found here : (a) predominance of dry deciduous forests with teak (*Tectona*), mahogany (*Swietenia*), *Acacia*, nux-vomica (*Strychnos*), *Lagerstroemia*, Indian rosewood (*Dalbergia*), *Dillenia*, *Cassia*, *Terminalia*, sandalwood (*Santalum*) in Karnataka, red sandalwood (*Pterocarpus*), *Butea*, *Bauhinia*, *Dillenia*, *Odina*, *Grewia*, *Buchanania*, *Chloroxylon*, *Chikrassia*, etc., and also many epiphytic orchids; (b) SAL (*Shorea*) forests, extending from Orissa to central India; (c) thorny scrubs, consisting mainly of *Zizyphu*, *Acacia*, *Capparis*, *Balanites*, *Euphorbia*, *Flacourtia* and *Prosopis*, are widespread; (d) an almost unbroken mass of coconut-palms along the coasts extending to Karnataka; (e) estuarian vegetation of the mangrove type covering a small area. In the above region, black soil covers a wide area and is used extensively for the cultivation of cotton. On the whole, the following families are well represented in this area : *Sterculiaceae*, *Meliaceae*, *Leguminosae*, *Combretaceae*, *Bignoniaceae*, *Urticaceae*, *Acanthaceae*, *Labiatae*, *Commeli-naceae* and *Gramineae*.

2. Malabar : This consists of the Western Ghats, which extend from Gujarat to Travancore. It has an annual rainfall of over 2,500 mm. and shows luxuriant vegetation of the following types : (a) tropical evergreen forests with luxuriant growth of trees, mainly *Heavea* and *Ficus elastica* (both rubber-yielding), *Dipterocarpus*, *Artocarpus*, sandalwood (*Santalum*), red sandalwood (*Pterocarpus*), nutmeg (*Myristica*) ebony

(*Dyospyros*), toon (*Cedrela*), Alexandrian laurel (*Calophyllum*), *Michelia*, *Ternstroemia*, coconut-palm (*Cocos*), talipot palm (*Corypha*), *Mimusops*, *Hopea*, and *Sterculia*. There is also a rich growth of shrubs, climbers and epiphytes; (b) deciduous forests occurring in strips with an annual rainfall of 1,500-2,000 mm. The vegetation is sparse and the trees mostly deciduous. The trees commonly found are mountain ebony (*Bauhinia*), teak (*Tectona*), Indian redwood (*Dalbergia*), *Adina*, *Lagerstroemia*, *Terminalia*, *Grewia* and bamboo (*Bambusa*); (c) temperate evergreen forests at higher elevations (to a maximum of 2,670 metres) with a rich vegetation of evergreen trees, mainly *Michelia*, *Eugenia*, and *Ternstroemia*. The following families dominate this area: *Guttiferae*, *Dipterocarpaceae*, *Palmae*, *Sterculiaceae*, *Anacardiaceae*, *Meliaceae*, *Myrtaceae*, *Melastomaceae*, *Scitamineae*, *Orchidaceae*, *Araceae*, etc.

3. Indus Plain. The average rainfall is very low—Punjab 630-760 mm., Rajasthan 250-500 mm. and Sind (Pakistan) 200 mm. North-eastern Punjab, however, is comparatively wet. Thar, the great Indian desert, covers a large tract of land in Rajasthan. The vegetation in its outskirts is typically xerophytic. The mean humidity of the plain is 50-52 or less, and is responsible for very hot summers and very cold winters. **Soils.** Tracts of land impregnated with salts, called KALLAR, are widely distributed. In the Sind Sagar doab, the southern districts of Punjab and Rajasthan, the soil is very sandy and highly unstable, often forming dunes. Along the banks of larger rivers, the soil, though sandy, has plenty of subsoil moisture. Black saline soil, called RAPAR, is devoid of any vegetation.

Vegetation. (a) **Desert Thorn Forest.** *Prosopis spicigera*, *Salvadora oleoides*, *Capparis aphylla*, etc., are the dominant species. They usually grow in clumps, leaving the ground bare in between. Such forests are commonly called RAKHS. Associated with the dominant species are commonly found *Tamarix articulata*, *Acacia leucoploea*, *A. nilotica*, *A. modesta*, *Albizzia lebbek*, *Morus alba*, *Zizyphus jujuba*, *Boswellia*, *Odina*, *Dalbergia*, *Salix*, etc. There are saline tracts covering wide areas. *Sporobolus arabicus*, an Arabian grass, associated with saltwort (*Salsola foetida*), sea-blite (*Suaeda fruticosa*), *Chenopodium*, etc., is seen to remain confined to the saline soil. Plants like *Acacia nilotica*, *Tamarix articulata*, *Butea monosperma*, etc., also withstand saline conditions well. The undergrowth is formed by plants like *Calotropis procera*, *Kochia indica*, *Chenopodium album*, *Zizyphus nummularia*, *Asparagus gracilis*, *Ephedra foliata*, etc. (*b*) **Dune Scrub**. In Sind, southern Punjab and Rajasthan, the vegetation is open, irregular and xerophytic. Stunted trees and bushes, thorny in character, form the only type of vegetation. The dominant species are *Leptadenia spartium*, *Euphorbia royleana*, *Acacia jacquemontia* (the only tree form), *Crotalaria burkia*, *Sericostoma pauciflorum*, *Calligonum polygonoides*, and *Calotropic procera*. (*c*) *Acacia-Dalbergia* (KHAIR-SISSOO) **Forest**. This is found along large rivers on sandy or gravelly alluvium. The dominant species are *Dalbergia sissoo*, *Acacia catechu*, and poplar (*Populus euphratica*), associated with *Tamarix dioica*, *Acacia farnesiana*, *A. nilotica*, *Saccharum spontaneum*, *S. munju*, etc.

4. Gangetic Plain : The Gangetic plain has (*a*) an upper dry region extending from Punjab (average annual rainfall about 500 mm.) to Allahabad (average annual rainfall about 1,000 mm.), (*b*) a lower humid region extending from Allahabad to West Bengal with a rainfall gradually increasing to 1,900-2,500 mm., and (*c*) Gangetic delta, including the vast expanse of the Sundarbans. The Gangetic plain is now mostly under cultivation and, therefore, the original flora is lost to a considerable extent. In the upper Gangetic plain, plants like *Peganum*, *Acacia*, *Moringa*, *Prosopis*, *Tecoma*, *Boswellia*, *Anogeissus*, *Rhus* and some palms still exist. *Salvadora* is common in the alkali land. Some grasslands or savannahs also occur here, dotted with trees like *Bombax*, *Zizyphus*, *Randia*, and *Butea*. *Leguminosae*, *Gramineae*, *Cyperaceae* and *Compositae* are the dominant families. There is a vast area of rice fields in the lower Gangetic plain. Groves of *Mangifera*, *Artocarpus*, *Ficus*, *Areca*, *Borassus*, *Phoenix*, etc. flourish in the uncultivated areas. Several species of aroids are very common. Certain plants introduced into the area have acquired a strong foothold. These are *Lagerstroemia*, *Pterospermum*, *Bombax*,

Polyalthia, *Casuarina*, etc. This area abounds in 'jheels' and large tanks, where aquatic plants like *Nymphaea*, *Nelumbo*, *Euryale*, *Limnanthemum*, *Vallisneria*, *Hydrilla*, several grasses and sedges grow luxuriantly. Several families of 'flowering' plants are represented in this area.

Mangrove or Littoral Forests. The lower Gangetic plain nearest the sea—a large tract of land, called the Sundarbans, with a network of water channels, sea creeks and swampy islands—is densely covered with extensive tidal swamp forests of evergreen trees and shrubs of the Malayan type. The mangrove forest of the Sundarbans stretches over an area of about 6,000 sq. miles and is the largest in the world. This tract of land spontaneously separates itself from the upper alluvial plain. The vegetation is dense and compact, and consists of species that are distinctly different from those of the rest of the Gangetic plain, except its northern boundary which has mixed types. The rivers are subject to tidal influence and are, therefore, saline. The numerous islets are mostly covered with savannahs composed of reed (*Phragmites karka*), associated with other tall grasses and tall sedges, and often dotted with trees. Throughout much of the Sundarbans, the vegetation is of the mangrove type, which is more pronounced towards the sea-face. The dominant feature of the mangrove is *Rhizophoraceae* , which consist of the following typical mangrove trees: *Rhizophora mucronata* (BARRA-KHAMO), *R. conjugata* (KHAMO), *Ceriops roxburghiana* (GORAN), *Kandelia rheedei* (GORIA), *Bruguiera gymnorhiza* (KANKRA), etc. Associated with these are other mangrove species like, *Heritiera minor* (SUNDRI—*Sterculiaceae*) which is very widespread in the area, *Excoecaria agallocha* (GEO—*Euphorbiaceae*) which is also plentiful, *Aegiceros majus* (KULSI—*Myrsinaceae*), *Sonneratia epetala* (KEORA—*Lythraceae*) and *Avicennia officinalis* (BAEN or BINA—*Verbenaceae*) which is the largest tree in the Sundarbans. There are 36 species of mangrove trees in the Sundarbans. Palms like *Nipa fruticans* (GOLPATA) and *Phoenix paludosa* (HITAL) are typical mangrove species. Coconut-palm (*Cocos nucifera*) and cane (*Calamus tenuis*) grow extensively, and are often planted. Elephant grass (*Typha angustata* and *T. elephantina*), *Alpinia allughas*, screwpine (*Pandanus fascicularis*), etc., are very common along the edges of ponds, canals, streams and swamps. *Panicum repens* and *Ipomoea pes-caprae* are two important sand and mud binding species. *Acanthus ilicifolius* (HARGOZA), *Asteracantha longifolia* (KULEKHARA), sea-blite (*suaeda maritima*), *Salicornia brachiata*, *Arthrocnemum indicum*, *Tamarix gallica* (BAN-JHAU), *Allophyluscobbe*, *Crotalaria retusa*, *Derris sinuata*, etc., are some of the other plants common in the area. Thirteen species of *Orchidaceae*, 14 species of terrestrial and epiphytic ferns, *Lycopodium phlegmaria* (SEE FIG. V/151 A), *Aldrovanda vesiculosa* (see FIG. III/29) and *Psilotum* (in the eastern Sundarbans) have also been found in this area. It may be noted that in his *Flora of the Sundarbans*, Prain has recorded 334 species belonging to 75 families. Some of these families are *Leguminosae* (38 species), *Gramineae* with 29 species, *Cyperaceae* (19 species), *Euphorbiaceae* (16 species), *Orchidaceae* (13 species), and *Asclepiadaceae* (12 species). The rest of the families have less than 10 species. Apart from being a matter of botanical interest, the flora of the Sundarbans is economically very important, being the source of timber and firewood. Many medicinal plants also grow in this area.

5. Assam[1]. The climatic factors of north-east India are high humidity (80-90), frequent rainfall and moderate to mild temperature without extremes of heat or cold (generally 29°-19°C.) in the plains, and mild to cold in the hills. As for the edaphic factor, the soil is highly fertile. The average rainfall is heavy but varies—2,000 mm. in lower Assam, 3,200 mm. in upper Assam, 2,900 mm. or more in Cachar and 2,700 mm. Mizo hills in the Garo Hills, 5,800 mm. in Khasi and the Jaintia Hills (in Shillong, however, 2,000 mm.), with the heaviest in Cherrapunji (11,440 mm. or more) and its neighbourhood (Mawsynram—11,900 mm. or more). This region consists of plains and hills, criss-crossed by several rivers. The Brahmaputra flows through the whole length of the Assam valley with alluvial deposits on either side. Assam is a country of rivers, hills and plains, extraordinarily rich in vegetation. A region of the Khasi Hills above the pine zone (2,000 metres) is considered the richest, not only in India but perhaps in the whole world (see *Flora of Assam*, vol. I). The flora of Assam may be divided into the following types:

(*a*) **Evergreen Forests.** With abundant rainfall, this type of forest extends in a more or less continuous belt from the north-east corner of Arunachal to the Darrang district along the foothills of the Himalayas. Such forests also occur in the Nowgong district, Cachar district and greater part of the Khasi Hills. Elsewhere, they are found only in isolated patches. These forests are composed of a very large number of species and present a 3-storeyed appearance. The top storey consists of some isolated tall, evergreen or deciduous trees (some 46 metres high) towering above others. The following are common—*Dipterocarpus macrocarpus* (HOLLONG), *Artocarpus chaplasha* (CHAM), *Tetrameles nudiflora* and *Terminalia myriocarpa* (HOLLOK). The middle storey consists of several medium-sized trees (up to about 23 metres), such as *Colophyllum*, *Mesua* (NAHOR), *Amoora* (AMARI), *Cinnamomum* (GONSEROI), *Phoebe* (BONSUM), *Machilus* (SOM), *Duabanga* (KHOKAN), *Ficus elastica* and other species, *Michelia*, *Magnolia* and *Schima*. The lowest storey is made up of several shrubs. Climbers and lianes are very common, and so are epiphytes (many orchids, some ferns and aroids). The pine forests in the Khasi Hills are evergreen, but they have no climbers or undergrowth. Here, pine is associated with several species of oak (*Quercus*), *Pieris*, chestnut (*Castanopsis*), birch (*Betula*), etc., and in some places, with yew (*Taxus*), *Cephalotaxus*, *Araucaria*, spruce (*Picea*), silver fir (*Abies*), deodar or cedar (*Cedrus*), *Tsuga*, *Cryptomeria*, cypress (*Cupressus*) and juniper (*Juniperus*). The following conifers occur at high altitudes in Arunachal, particularly in the Aka and Dafla Hills : *Podocarpus*, *Taxus*, *Abies*, *Pinus longifolia*, *P. excelsa*, *Tsuga* and *Cupressus*.

(*b*) **Deciduous Forests.** These forests occur mainly in the lower Assam valley, Garo Hills and North Cachar Hills (particularly in the angle formed by the Mikir Hills and the Naga Hills), often mixed with some evergreen species. These tracts, except the North Cachar Hills, are composed mainly of *Shorea robusta* (SAL) forests and scrub forests, commonly associated with or surrounded by *Careya arborea* (KUMBHI), *Lagerstroemia* (AJAR), *Schima wallichii* (evergreen), *Dillenia pentagyna* (AKSHI), *Kydia calycina* (KOTRA), *Terminalia belerica* and *T. chebula*, *Cassia fistula* (SONARU), *Albizzia* (KOROI and MOZ), *Gmelina* (GUMHAR), *Stereospermum* (PAROLI), *Alstonia*, walnut (*Juglans*), *Engelhardtia* (LEWA), *Dalbergia*, *Bombax* and *Sterculia* (ODAL). In Lakhimpur, there are forests

---

[1]This refers to flora of north-east India which includes Assam, Nagaland, Meghalaya, Arunachal (NEFA), Mizoram, Manipur and Tripura.

which have only *Shorea assamica* (MAKAI), often over 30 metres high. In the North Cachar Hills and the dry regions of Cachar, where SAL is absent, the forests are of mixed types and consist of *Dipterocarpus turbinatus* (GARJAN), *Bombax, Adina, Stephegyne*, several species of *Ficus, Cassia nodosa*, several grasses and bamboos (*Bambusa* and *Melocanna*). Further, *Coffea bengalensis* with white flowers, *strobilianthes* with blue flowers, *Mussaenda* with a white or yellow leaf-like (modified) sepals and *Holmskioldia* with scarlet-red flowers adorn the deciduous forests as undershrubs and shrubs. The storeys characteristic of evergreen forests are absent in deciduous forests.

(c) **Swamp Forests.** Cachar abounds in swamps. Small swamps are not uncommon in the Assam valley. Various aquatic and semi-aquatic grasses, e.g. *Panicum* (many species), *Phragmites, Arundo, Erianthus, Vossia* and *Hygrorhiza*, and sedges, e.g. species of *Scirpus* and *Cyperus*, occur here. Besides, *Ceratopteris* (an aquatic fern), *Azolla, Salvinia, Marsilea*, etc., and among 'flowering' plants *Euryale, Alipinia*, water lilies (*Nymphaea*), lotus (*Nelumbo*) etc., are quite common. *Barringtonia* (HIJAL) *Cephalanthus* (PANIKADAM), *Clinogyne* (SITAL-PATI), *Ficus heterophylla*, and *Dracaena spicata* are commonly found at the edges of such swamps.

(d) **Grasslands.** These are widespread in low-lying areas, riparian tracts, and dry lands with low rainfall. The genera characteristic of the wet tracts are *Phragmites, Arundo, Erianthus* and *Saccharum*. They often cover extensive areas along the banks of large rivers and some of them often grow to a height of 6 metres. In the dry lands, the grasses are low and hardy. *Imperata, Andropogon, Erianthus, Panicum, Apluda, Saccharum* and *Isachne* are the commonly found grasses.

(e) **Riparian Forests.** These forests extend along large streams at the foothills of the Bhutan range from Goalpara district to Darrang district. *Acacia catechu* (KHAIR) and *Dalbergia sissoo* (SISSOO) are the two major species that occurr abundantly in such forests. Such forests are generally known as *Acacia-Dalbergia* (KHAIR-SISSOO) forests. The two species occur mixed up with *Duabanga* (KHOKAN), *Bombax* (SIMUL), *Trewia* (PITULI), *Barringtonia* (HIJAL), *Salix tetrasperma* (PANI-HIJAL) and *Anthocephalus* (KADAM).

Interesting Aspects of the Flora of North-East India (Assam and neighbouring states and territories). A few of the multitude of interesting plants occurring in this region deserve special mention. Their morphological

and physiological features and their economic importance have been described in the text; only a general survey is given here. Many of these plants are rare and found only in this region. Among the carnivorous plants are found the—pitcher plant (*Nepenthes khasiana*) in the Garo Hills and Khasi-Jaintia Hills, *Drosera burmanni* in Jorhat *Drosera peltata* in the Khasi and Garo Hills, *Pinguicula alpina* on the Shillong peak, *Aldrovanda vesiculosa* in tanks in Manipur, and land *Utricularia* on hill-sides in Shillong. Among saprophytes are found the Indian pipe (*Monotropa uniflora*) and *Burmannia* (4sp.) in the Khasi Hills. The root parasites, *Balanophora dioica* and *Sapria himalayana* (akin to *Rafflesia*) are found in the Khasi Hills and the Aka, Dafla and Naga Hills, respectively. Orchids (abound, as do well over 400 species) many beautiful ferns and some tree ferns. Other interesting plants : *Coptis teeta* (a medicinal plant) in the Mishmi Hills, *Aquilaria agallocha* (AGARU) in Sibsagar, *Mussaenda* (9 sp.), lady's umbrella or Chinese hat (*Holmskioldia*) and *Cycas pectinata* in the lower hills, *Rhododendron arboreum* (a tree with deep red flowers) and a few other species in the Khasi Hills (alt. 1,624-1,830 m.) and several species in the Naga Hills (alt. 2,438-3,048 m), *Gnetum gnemon* (a shrub) in Sibsagar and some other districts, and *Gnetum montanum* (a climber) throughout the state. The following epiphytic lycopods are found : *Lycopodium phlegmaria* in the plains districts, and *L. squarrosum* in the Khasi Hills. *Equisetum debile* (often 4 metres in length) is found among bushes beside hill streams. About 56 species of timber trees (of which about 32 are used for various purposes) are also found. About 20 species of bamboo (*Bambusa, Metocanna, Arundinaria, Dendrocalamus*, etc.), 14 of cane (*Calamus, Zalacca, Daemonorops*, etc.) and *Aldrovanda* occur in Manipur. This region is famous for oranges, pineapples, bananas, papaws, apples, plums, pears, etc.

6. The Himalayas. The Himalayas are more or less sharply divisible into (a) the eastern Himalayas, extending from Darjeeling (West Bengal) to the Mishmi Hills (Arunachal) including Sikkim and Bhutan. The average rainfall here is 3050 mm.; (b) the central Himalayas— the region of Nepal— with much less rainfall; and (c) the western Himalayas, extending from the Kumaon Hills to Peshawar (Pakistan), with rainfall gradually decreasing from 1,100 mm. to about 500 mm.

Altitude (and, consequently, decreasing temperature) is the single major factor determining the zonal vegetation of the Himalayas. Each zone has its characteristic flora with, of course, a little or considerable overlapping, i.e. there is no line of demarcation between one zone and the next. However, three broad zones can be more or less distinctly recognized, viz. (a) tropical zone with warm to mild climate, (b) temperate zone with mild to cold climate, and (c) alpine zone with intensely cold climate, merging into the snow-line. Within the zone, rainfall and topography are the next important factors, the western wing of the Himalayas being drier and the eastern wing wetter. Two sub-zones are often distinguishable within each zone.

(a) **Tropical Zone** (500-1,600 metres). This forms the submontane belt of the Himalayas, called Terai, and is covered by dense forests. Depending on the rainfall two types of forests develop in this zone : **evergreen** (with abundant rainfall—over 2,500 mm.) in the eastern wing, and **deciduous** (with scanty rainfall—1,100 mm. or much less) in the western wing. On the whole, SAL (*Shorea robusta*) forests dominate this zone (uninfluenced by rains). Other trees common in this zone are *Lagerstroemia*, *Bauhinia*, *Bombax*, *Cassia fistula*, flame of the forest (*Butea*), *Sterculia*, *Schima*, *Mangifera*, *Anghocephalus*, *Dillenia*, and *Michelia*. A good number of timber trees occur in this zone. Several species of *Melastoma*, *Osbeckia*, *Strobilanthes*, *Mussaenda*, *Coffea bengalensis*, many grasses and plenty of ferns, form the undergrowth. Climbers and lianes are abundant, and so are clumps of bamboos and wild bananas. Tree trunks are densely covered with mosses and lichens, and orchids are found in abundance. Several families are represented in this zone, the dominant ones being *Orchidaceae*, *Gramineae*, *Cyperaceae*, *Leguminosae*, *Compositae*, *Scrophulariaceae*, *Urticaceae*, *Rasaceae*, *Rubiaceae*, and *Euphorbiaceae*. Above 1,000 metres, pines gradually become the dominant form of vegetation (see next zone).

(b) **Temperate Zone** (1,600-3,500 metres). Coniferae and Cupuliferae (*Betulaceae* and *Fagaceae*) dominate this zone. This zone is otherwise called the **coniferous zone** because of the predominance of conifers. In the lower temperate sub-zone, pine forests predominate (*Pinus khasya* in the east and *P. longifolia* in the west), associated with *Podocarpus* at places.

With increasing altitude, the composition of the flora changes rapidly. Deodar (*Cedrus deodara*) dominates the higher temperate sub-zone. Associated with pines and other conifers (see below) occur oak (*Quercus*), beech (*Fagus*), *Pieris*, *Castanopsis*, birch (*Betula*), alder (*Alnus*), poplar (*Populus*), willow (*Salix*), maple (*Acer*), elm (*Ulmus*), walnut (*Juglans*), *Magnolia*, etc., most of which are as high as 3,500 metres or even more. Orchids and ferns abound, and *Bucklandia*, a handsome tree, can be spotted at places. *Rhododendron* (125 sp., mostly in the eastern Himalayas) deserves special mention. At lower elevations of this zone, the species (e.g. *R. arboreum*) are trees or large shrubs. Higher up, they are mostly shrubby (e.g. *R. companulatum*, *R. triflorum*, etc), and in the cold temperate sub-zone still higher, they become further stunted in growth (e.g. *R. glaucum*). The temperate zone as a whole is rich in vegetation and abounds in several species of herbs and shrubs. Special mention may be made of *Rosa*, *Rubus*, *Berberis*, *Pyrus*, *Sambucus*, *Hydrangea*, *Strobilanthes* and *Impatiens* among shrubs, and *Potentilla*, *Anaphalis*, *Senecio*, *Aster*, *Anemone*, *Aonitum*, *Ranunculus*, *Saxifraga*, *Sedum*, *Meconopsis*, *Primula*, *Digitalis*, and *Podophyllum*, among herbs. There are plenty of mosses and lichens. The dominating families in this zone are: *Orchidaceae*, *Compositae*, *Leguminosae*, *Rubiaceae*, *Euphorbiaceae*, *Urticaceae* and *Ranunculaceae*. At higher altitudes, there is a predominance of *Rosaceae*, *Labiatae*, *Cruciferae*, *Ericaceae*, *Umbelliferae*, *Primulaceae* (e.g. *Primula* with 148 sp., mostly eastern, and *Androsace* with a few species, mostly western), and *Saxifragaceae* (e.g. *Saxifraga* and *Hydrangea*). The conifers occurring at higher altitudes in this zone are blue pine (*Pinus excelsa*), spruce (*Picea*), silver fir (*Abies*), deodar (*Cedrus*), cypress (*Cupressus*), yew (*Taxus*), *Cephalotaxus*, *Tsuga* and juniper (*Juniperus*).

(c) **Alpine Zone** (3,500-4,500 metres). This zone extends beyond the limit of tree growth up to the perpetual snow-line, and is characterized by the dominance of small herbaceous dicotyledons, spotted with low shrubs or undershrubs (mainly species of *Juniperus*, *Betula*, *Rhododendron*, *Ephedra*, *Berberis*, *Rosa*, and *Lonicera*). The vegetation here is sparse. Extreme conditions prevail in this zone, viz. freezing temperature, snow-cover for the greater part of the year, powerful sunlight, strong gales and low atmospheric pressure. These conditions reduce absorption but enhance transpiration. This being so, the vegetation tends towards xeromorphism: short growth season, stunted growth, hairy covering, thick cuticle, reduced leaves, and often fleshy storing of water, etc. Several shrubby and herbaceous species of *Rododendron* (many gregarious in habit) appear in their exquisite beauty from 3,500 metres to the alpine meadows, particularly in the eastern Himalayas. Higher up, at 4,500-4,800 metres, their height diminishes to 0.6-0.3 metres or less. Some of the other common genera represented in this zone are *Meconopsis, Podophyllum, Rosa, Rheum, Potentilla, Primula, Saussurea, Saxifraga, Nardostachys, Anaphalis, Artemisia, Astragalus, Aster, Chrysanthemum, Erigeron, Inula, Senecio, Aconitum, Anemone, Caltha, Delphinium, Ranunculus, Thalictrum, Androsace, Sedum* and *Corydalis.* The families dominating this zone are: *Compositae, Scrophulariaceae, Primulaceae, Saxifragaceae, Rosaceae, Ranunculaceae,* and *Leguminosae.* Alpine mosses and lichens are plentiful. In such a region, there is a preponderance of endemic species. *Polygonum viviparum* covers a wide range (1,500-5,400 metres) and *Erigeron* is distributed from the tropical to the temperate to the alpine zones, ascending up to the snow-line. It may be of interest to note that the following species ascend right up to the snow-line: *Thalictrum alpinum, Ranunculus pulchellus, Caltha scapiosa, Delphinium caeruleum* and *D. viscosum, Potentilla microphylla, Saxifraga cernua* and *S. saginoides, Sedum himalense, Corydalis crasifolia, Rhododendron anthopogon, R. lepidotum,* edelweiss (*Leontopodium alpinum* — covered with woolly hairs), *Nardostachys jatamansi* (B. JATAMANSI), and a few species of *Aster, Erigeron* and *Saussurea.*

The Eastern and the Western Himalayas. As already stated, the eastern side is wetter and the western side drier. Obviously there is some difference in the floristic composition of the two wings of the Himalayas. There are, however, several genera and species common to both, and both wings are divisible into the tropical, temperate and alpine zones. There is, however, a preponderance of European and Siberian flora in the western Himalayas, and of Chinese and Malayan flora in the eastern Himalayas.

Eastern Region. This region, particularly Sikkim, is very rich and contains over 4,000 species of 'flowering' plants and over 250 species of ferns (including 8 tree ferns). The ratio of dicotyledons to monocotyledons may stand at 2.5:1. The coniferous plants of the east are mainly : *Pinus Khasya, P. excelsa* and *P. longifolia* (the last two both eastern and western), *Cephalotaxus mannii* and *C. griffithii,* Himalayan silver fir (*Abies spectabilis = A. webbiana*), *Tsuga*

brunoniana (both eastern and western), *Juniperus recurva, Taxus baccata, Podocarpus neriifolia* and *P. latifolia, Picea morinda* (both eastern and western) and *Larix griffithii.* Orchid, palms and bamboos abound among the 'flowering' plants. Several species of *Rhododendron* appear in their brilliance. There is a profusion of epiphytes and climbers. Besides, the following flowering plants are well represented in this area: oak (*Quercus*), *Castanopsis,* birch (*Betula alnoides*), alder (*Alnus nepalensis*), walnut (*Juglans*), *Magnolia, Michelia, Bucklandia, Primula* (several species), *Photinia, Eriobotrya,* Himalayan poppy (*Meconopsis*—6 sp.), *Berberis, Impatiens* and *Saxifraga.* Of the many species of *Quercus* in the east, some common ones are *Q. lineata* and *Q.* H *glauca.* The dominant families of 'flowering' plants are *Orchidaceae, Gramineae, Leguminosae, Compositae, Cyperaceae, Urticaceae, Scrophulariaceae, Rosaceae, Rubiaceae* and *Euphorbiaceae.* Several other families are also well represented in this area.

Western Region. The flora of this region is much poorer than that of the east. The ratio of dicotyledons to monocotyledons may stand at 3:1. The coniferous plants of the west are mainly : *Pinus longifolia, P. excelsa* and *P. gerardiana, Juniperus communis, J. recurva* and two other species, *Abies pindrow, Cupressus torulosa, Cedrus deodara* and *Picea morinda.* Cycadaceae, however, disappears in the west. There is a decrease in the number of orchids, palms and bamboos among the 'flowering' plants. A stemless palm, *Nannorhops,* is special feature of this region. There are fewer species of *Rhododendron,* but there are some common alpine species in both the east and the west, e.g. *R. campanulatum, R. lepidotum* and *R. anthopogon.* There are considerably fewer epiphytes and climbers, but many more grasses and leguminous plants than in the east. The following 'flowering' plants, however, are well represented in this area : *Astragalus, Artemisia, Saussurea, Ranunculus, Rubus, Rosa, Prunus, Pyrus,* willow (*Salix*), poplar (*Populus*), elm (*Ulmus*), maple (*Acer*), barberry (*Berberis*), birch (*Betula utilis*), alder (*Alnus*), *Potentilla, Punica, Rhamnus, Polygonum, Nepeta,* and *Pistacia.* A few species of *Quercus* in the west are *Q. incana, Q. dilatata,* and *Q. semecarpifolia.* The following families of 'flowering' plants gain dominance in the west : *Gramineae, Compositae, Cyperaceae, Leguminosae, Labiatae, Ranunculaceae, Cruciferae, Orchidaceae, Rosaceae,* and *Scrophulariaceae.* It should also be noted that some families of the east, like *Dilleniaceae, Guttiferae, Passifloraceae, Burmanniaceae* and

Pandanaceae, practically disappear in the west, while certain new families like *Salvadoraceae* and *Polemoniaceae* make their appearance.

Endemism. Certain species and even genera remain confined to a small area, a small section of a country or an island from generation to generation. Such species and genera are said to be **endemic**. They cannot migrate and spread out owing to certain natural barriers, e.g. high mountains, deserts and seas. Oceanic islands have a high percentage of endemic species, for example, 82% in the Hawaiian Islands and 72% in New Guinea. Although isolated, endemic species multiply and often freely give rise to new species. There are two views on endemism. Some are of opinion that endemism represents the remnants of once flourishing flora, e.g. tree ferns, *Ginkgo biloba*, etc. Others believe that endemic flora is of recent origin, e.g. *Gentiana, Impatiens, Primula*, and *Rhododendron*. The latter view is generally more favoured. According to Chatterjee (*Studies on the Endemic Flora of India and Burma*), the Himalayas (temperate and alpine) and the Indian peninsula have the largest number of endemic species in India (3,169 species in the former region and 2,045 species in the latter, and only 533 species in the general area). In India, 'wides', i.e. those that have spread in from outside, may consist of approximately 4,000 species. Working on the above basis, endemism in India comes to almost 59% (varying, however, from 50-70% from region to region, the Himalayas showing the highest percentage).

5 CRYPTOGAMS

Divisions and General Description

Cryptogams or 'flowerless' or 'seedless' plants are lower and more primitive plants. They form three main groups, viz. **Thallophyta, Bryophyta and Pteridophyta.** Thallophyta include algae, fungi, bacteria and lichens. Bryophyta include liverworts, horned liverworts and mosses, while Pteridophyta include ferns and their allies. All these have been futher divided and subdivided into smaller groups. [See also Introduction].

Reproduction. A particular plant may take to one or more of the three methods of reproduction, viz. vegetative, asexual and sexual. Vegetative reproduction commonly takes place by cell division or by fragmentation. Asexual reproduction takes place by fission or through various types of spores. Sexual reproduction takes place by the fusion of two gametes, and the degree of sexuality passes through progressive stages—isogamy to anisogamy to oogamy. In the primitive forms of plants, fusion of two gametes of similar shape, size and behaviour (isogametes) occurs. The fusion of such gametes is called **isogamy.** In other forms, the two gametes may be slightly different in size and behaviour (anisogametes), and the fusion of such gametes is called **anisogamy.** In the advanced forms, the gametes become differentiated into male (microgametes) and female (megagametes). Their fusion is called **oogamy.** In oogamous forms, the male gamete is small, motile, ciliate, active and initiative and is called an **antherozoid** (spermatozoid or simply sperm), while the female gamete is large, non-motile,

non-ciliate, passive and receptive, and is called an **egg** (egg-cell, ovum or oosphere). In isogamous and anisogamous forms, both types of gametes may be discharged from the body of the plant and gametic union may take place outside the plant body. In oogamous forms, on the other hand, only the antherozoids are discharged, the egg-cell is retained within the plant body and fertilization takes place in the oogonium within the body of the mother plant.

Alternation of Generations.[1] The life history of many plants (higher algae, liverworts, mosses, ferns and their allies) is completed in two alternating stages or generations. These two generations differ not only in morphological characteristics, but also in modes of reproduction. One generation reproduces by the asexual method, i.e. by spores, and the other by the sexual method, i.e. by gametes. The former is, therefore, called the **sporophytic** or asexual generation, and the latter the **gametophytic** or sexual generation. To complete the life history of a particular plant, one generation gives rise to the other—the gametophyte to the sporophyte and the sporophyte to the gametophyte; or to put it another way, the two generations regularly alternate with each other. This alternation is spoken of as alternation of generations.

Cytological Evidence of Alternation of Generations. In order to keep the chromosome number the same through successive generations, plants reproducing sexually (fertilization), evidently with the doubling of chromosomes in

---

[1] In 1851, Hofmeister was the first to give a clear shape to the idea of alternation of generations in mosses and ferns. He also tried to extend the idea to gymnosperms and angiosperms.

the zygote as a result of fusion of two gametes, must have a counter-stage (meiosis) involving reduction of chromosomes. It is a fact that the gametophyte always possesses half as many chromosomes as the sporophyte. In other words, if the sporophyte bears $2n$ or *diploid* chromosomes, the gametophyte would bear n or *haploid* chromosomes (n signifying the number of chromosomes). At the time of reproduction, the sporophyte bears spore mother cells (each with $2n$ chromosomes). These undergo meiosis or reduction division and the chromosome number is reduced to half in the spores, evidently with n or *haploid* chromosomes. The spore, therefore, represents the beginning of the gametophytic generation. The gametophyte, evidently with n chromosomes, bears gametes in due course. When the two gametes (male and female, each with n chromosomes) fuse to form the zygote, the chromosome number is doubled, i.e. it becomes $2n$. The zygote develops into the sporophyte with $2n$ chromosomes in all its cells. The zygote, therefore, represents the beginning of the sporophytic generation, which continues right up to the formation of the spore mother cells.

We may summarize the matter, therefore, by saying that spores, gametophytes, sexual organs and gametes, all with n chromosomes (i.e. the phase between fertilization and meiosis), represent the gametophytic generation. The zygotes, sporophytes, sporangia and spore mother cells, all with $2n$ chromosomes (i.e. the phase between meiosis and fertilization), represent the sporophytic generation. The haploid (n) or gametophytic generation begins with the spore and ends with the formation of the gametes, while the diploid ($2n$) or sporophytic generation begins with the zygote and ends with the formation of the spore mother cell.

In most green algae and fungi, the $2n$ or diploid phase is represented only by the zygote and not by any definite structure developing from it, which may be regarded as a sporophyte (any structure). Therefore, there is no true alternation of generations in them. But in the higher green algae, some fungi, most brown algae and red algae, and more particularly in the higher cryptogams—liverworts, mosses, ferns and their allies—alternation of generations is very regular. In these, progressive stages in the development of the sporophyte and reduction of the gametophyte can be traced, culminating in the 'flowering' plants. In the latter, the main plant body is always a sporophyte, and the gametophyte is represented only by a few cells (gymnosperms) or by a few nuclei (angiosperms).

CHAPTER 2

ALGAE

Differences between Algae and Fungi. (1) Algae are green thallophytes that contain *chlorophyll*. In many algae, other colours may mask the green colour, but chlorophyll is always present in all of them. Fungi, on the other hand, have no chlorophyll. (2) Algae are *autotrophic* plants, i.e. they manufacture their own food with the help of chlorophyll, whereas fungi are *heterotrophic* plants, i.e. their modes of nutrition are diverse. They have to depend on the supply of prepared food material. They are either parasitic or saprophytic. (3) The body of an alga is composed of a *true parenchymatous tissue*, but the body of a fungus is composed of a *false tissue*, or pseudoparenchyma, which is an interwoven mass of fine, delicate thread, known as *hyphae*. (4) The cellwall of an alga is composed of true cellulose, and that of a fungus of fungus-cellulose or chitin mixed with cellulose, callose, pectose, etc., in different proportions. (5) Algae live in water or in wet substrata, whereas fungi live as parasites on other plants or animals, or as saprophytes on decaying animal or vegetable matter. (6) Reserve carbohydrate in algae usually consists of starch, while it consists of glycogen in fungi.

As for the structure, both groups may be unicellular, multicellular, filamentous or thalloid. Reproduction in them may take place vegetatively by cell division or by detachment of a portion of the mother plant, or asexually by spores, or sexually by gametes.

Classification of Algae (20,000 sp.)

Class I	Myxophyceae or Cyanophyceae or blue-green algae (1,500 sp.), e.g. *Gloeocapsa, Oscillatoria, Nostoc, Anabaena, Rivularia*, etc.
Class II	Euglenophyceae (350 sp.), e.g. *Euglena*.
Class III	Chlorophyceae or green algae (6.500 sp.). **Order 1.** Volvocales, e.g. *Chlamydomonas, Pandorina, Eudorina* and *Volvox*. **Order 2.** Chlorococcales, e.g. *Chlorococcum, Chlorella, Pediastrum, Proto-siphon* and *Hydrodictyon*. **Order 3.** Ulotrichales, e.g. *Ulothrix* and *Ulva*. **Order 4.** Chaetophorales, e.g. *Chaetophor, Coleochaete* and *Protococus*. **Order 5.** Conjugales (or Zygnematales), e.g. *Spirogyra, Zygnema* and desmids (e.g. *Cosmarium*). **Order 6.** Oedogoniales, e.g. *Oedogonium*. **Order 7.** Cladophorales, e.g. *Cladophora* and *Pitho-phora*. **Order 8.** Siphonabs, e.g. *Vaucheria* and *Cauterpa*. **Order 9.** Charales, e.g. *Chara* and *Nitella*.
Class IV	Bacillariophyceae or diatoms (5,300 sp.).
Class V	Phaeophyceae or brown algae (about 1,000 sp.), e.g. *Ectocarpus, Laminaria, Fucus* and *Sargassum*.
Class VI	Rhodophyceae or red algae (about 3,000 sp.), e.g. *Polysiphonia* and *Batrachospermum*.

CLASS I CYANOPHYCEAE OR MYXOPHYCEAE

(or blue-green algae; 1,500 sp.)

General Description. Cyanophyceae or Myxophyceae or blue-green algae are a small group of primitive algae characterized by the presence of a blue pigment, *phycocyanin*, in addition to chlorophyll (together making a blue-green colour), simple construction of the body, not clearly differentiated protoplast and simple method of reproduction. Some species are truly unicellular, while in others, the daughter cells after divisions adhere together to form a chain of cells (filament) or a flat or spherical colony. A great majority of them are fresh-water dwellers and are often found in plenty in almost every stagnant pool of water, wet ground or in the form of road slime after rains. The cell structure is of a primitive type. There is no definite nucleus, nor any plastid, and the protoplast is differentiated into a peripheral coloured zone—the **chromoplasm**, and an inner colourless portion—the **central body** (see FIG. 2C). The cell-wall is made of cellulose and pectic compounds. Carbohydrate occurs in the form of glycogen, starch being altogether absent. A gelatinous sheath is a common feature in most of them. Some filamentous forms, particularly *Oscillatoria*, exhibit a slow, spontaneous movement. Blue-green algae never reproduce sexually, nor do they bear any kind of ciliated body. The common methods of vegetative reproduction are cell division in unicellular forms, breaking up of the colony in colonial forms, and fragmentation of the filament into short pieces called **hormogonia** (see FIG. 2B) in filamentous forms. In some filamentous forms (except *Oscillatoria*), a vegetative cell may act as a resting spore, called **akinete** (see p. 345). One or more enlarged vegetative cells with transparent contents and thickened walls may be seen in such forms; these are called **heterocysts** (see p. 345).

Origin of Cyanophyceae. Cyanophyceae or blue-green algae are supposed to have originated from some non-ciliate, unicellular ancestor. Cyanophyceae is a very primitive group that has not given rise to higher plant forms, but has remained confined within its own group. Its primitive nature is evident from the simple construction of the plant body and the lack of organized protoplast (cytoplasm, nucleus and plastids). Further, sexual reproduction is altogether absent and so is the asexual reproduction of the ciliated bodies (zoospores). Cyanophyceae, however, bears some resemblance to

Rhodophyceae, it sometimes possesses *phycoerythrin* (the red pigment of the latter) and lacks ciliated motile cells at any stage of its life history. Blue-green algae seem to be related to bacteria, both being ancient groups with some characteristics in common.

1. *GLOEOCAPSA*

Occurrence. *Gloeocapsa* (family *Chroococcaceae;* FIG. 1) represents a simple, primitive form of unicellular blue-green algae. It is the commonest alga, occuring abundantly on wet rocks, wet ground, pools of water and often in laboratory aquaria, and forming small masses of jelly and road slime. It flourishes during the rainy season and dries up in winter. A small mass of jelly examined under a microscope reveals a large number of single cells or small colonies of cells, oval or spherical, lying embedded in a mucilaginous matrix. *G. quarternata* is a very common species of the road slime.

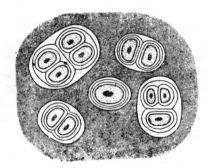

Gloeocapsa. FIG. 1. A cell and four colonies embedded in gelatinous matrix

Structure. A single cell, more or less spherical, represents a *Gloeocapsa* plant. The protoplast of the cell is generally differentiated into two regions: a blue-green peripheral region which has chlorophyll and phycocyanin diffused through it (the **chromoplasm**) and a central region with a mass of chromatin granules constituting an incipient nucleus (the **central body**). The plant is always unicellular but often, 2 to 4, or sometimes several, daughter cells are held together in a colony by the mucilaginous sheath. The latter occurs in concentric layers surrounding the individual cells as well as the whole colony. Mucilage is always

derived from the walls of the individual cells.

Reproduction. *Gloeocapsa* reproduces vegetatively only by the process of cell division. In this process, the central chromatin matter first divides into two parts. This is followed by the formation of a ring-like wall across the cell and its growth inward, dividing the cells into two. Each daughter cell secretes its own mucilaginous sheath, grows and finally behaves as a new plant. Two or more such cells are frequently held together in a colony in a common mucilaginous matrix secreted by the individual cells. A few species sometimes form thick-walled resting spores.

2. *OSCILLATORIA* (100 *sp.*)

Occurrence and Structure. *Oscillatoria.* (family *Oscillatoriaceae;* FIG. 2A) is a dark blue-green alga. It consists of a slender, unbranched, cylindrical filament. It commonly occurs in ditches, shallow pools of water, sewers, and wet rocks and walls. *O. tenuis, O. princeps,* are some of the common species. Filaments of *Oscillatoria* float in water, either free or entangled in masses. Each filament is made up of numerous short cells. The individual cells are the *Oscillatoria* plants, and the filament is regarded as a colony. All the cells are alike, except the end cell. This is usually convex, and the filament is not differentiated into the base and the apex. Some dead and empty cells occur at places in some of the filaments. The protoplast of each cell is differentiated into two regions : a coloured peripheral zone—chromoplasm and an inner colourless zone (the central body—see FIG. 2C). The colour is due to the presence of chlorophyll and phycocyanin, which diffuse through the chromoplasm and are not associated with any kind of plastids. Both regions are granular in nature and have various spherical or irregular inclusions, which are mainly food grains, particularly glycogen and proteins. There is no true nucleus. The central body, however, is regarded as an incipient nucleus and has only some chromatin and no nuclear membrane and nucleolus. Cell division takes place in one direction only. Each filament remains enveloped in a thin mucilaginous sheath. When observed under

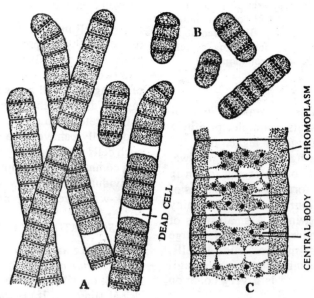

Oscillatoria. FIG. 2. *A,* filaments; *B,* hormogonia; and *C,* a portion of the filament magnified

the microscope, the filaments are seen to exhibit a slow, swaying or oscillating movement, their ends tossing from side to side.They may sometimes exhibit a twisting or rotating motion. This is a characteristic feature of *Oscillatoria.*

Reproduction. In the blue-green algae, reproduction takes place vegetatively by cell division or by fragmentation of the filament, or asexually by spores. Gametes and zoospores are altogether absent. In *Oscillatoria,* the filament breaks up into a number of fragments, called hormogonia (FIG. 2B). Each hormogonium consists of one or more cells and grows into a filament by uni-directional cell division.. The hormogonium has a capacity for locomotion.

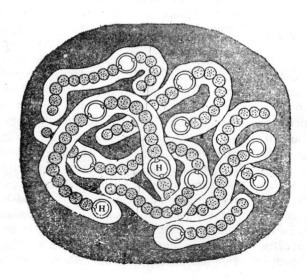

Nostoc.

FIG. 3.
Filaments
embedded in
gelatinous
matrix. Note
the heterocysts (H)
with the
polar nodules

3. *NOSTOC* (29 *sp.*)

Occurrence. *Nostoc* (family *Nostocaceae;* FIG. 3) is a common blue-green alga of filamentous form. Species of *Nostoc* may be terrestrial or aquatic, and generally occur in ponds, ditches and other pools of water, as well as in damp soil in the form of small, somewhat firm masses of jelly. A few species are endophytic in habit, occurring in the intercellular cavities of plants like *Anthoceros, Lemna,* and the root of *Cycas.* Some lead a symbiotic life in association with a fungus, forming a lichen.

Structure. Each gelatinous mass contains numerous slender filaments, which look véry much like strings of beads under a microscope. The filaments are interwoven, forming an intricate mass. Each filament is unbranched and consists of a colony of cells, like beads in a chain, and often has a gelatinous sheath of its own, in addition to the gelatinous matrix in which the tangled mass of filaments remains embedded. The sheath may be colourless or slightly tinged. The filament minus the sheath is commonly called a **trichome.** Each cell of the filament is blue-green, more or less spherical or oval (sometimes barrel-shaped or somewhat cylindrical). The constitution of the cell is very much like that of *Gloeocapsa.* The filament grows in length by cell division in one plane only. The divided cells grow and round off, and the filament elongates and appears like a beaded chain. A characteristic feature of *Nostoc* is the presence of some enlarged vegetative cells, terminal and intercalary, with thickened walls and transparent contents. These occur at frequent intervals and are called **heterocysts.** At the two poles of each heterocyst there are two pores, one at each end, through which cytoplasmic connection is maintained between the heterocyst and the adjacent vegetative cells. In the terminal heterocyst, however, only one such pore is formed. In either case, each pore is later closed by a button-like thickening of the wall—the *polar nodule.* The function of the heterocyst is not definitely known (see below).

Reproduction. *Nostoc* reproduces vegetatively by fragmentation, and sometimes asexually by resting cells (spores) called akinetes.

Fragmentation. In vegetative reproduction, the filament breaks up into several short segments, called hormogonia. Each hormogonium gives rise to a long filament by repeated cell division in one direction. A large number of such daughter filaments may be seen in the gelatinous matrix. The fragmentation of the filament into hormogonia takes place at the junction of the heterocyst and the adjoining cell. The function of the heterocyst is otherwise not definitely known. It may, however, sometimes act as a spore. It has also been suggested that the heterocyst is a food storage cell.

Akinetes. In a few species of *Nostoc,* certain vegetative cells of the filament become enlarged and thick-walled, containing reserve food, under adverse conditions like winter or drought. These cells are called resting cells (spores) or **akinetes,** and may be produced singly or in a chain. An akinete is regarded as a modified vegetative cell meant to act as a resting spore. It has no wall of its own, its wall being indistinct from that of the mother cell. According to the species, akinetes may develop anywhere in the filament or in a specific part of it, either close to or away from the heterocyst. Later, under favourable conditions, each akinete germinates and gives rise to a *Nostoc* filament.

4. *ANABAENA* (28 *sp.*)

Occurrence. *Anabaena* (family *Nostocaceae;* FIG. 4) is widely distributed, and is commonly found in fresh water, floating freely or in thin mucous layers, and also often in wet soil, rocks and tree trunks. Some species also grow as endophytes, e.g. *A. azollae* in the cavities of *Azolla* frond, and *A. cycadacearum* in *Cycas* roots.

Structure. *Anabaena* is a filamentous type of blue-green alga. The filament is a colony of individual cells (plants) in a chain-like formation that looks like a string of beads. *Anabaena* resembles *Nostoc* in this respect, but differs from it in certain other respects (see p. 346). The filament of *Anabaena,* like that of *Nostoc,* is unbranched and consists of a row of oval or spherical cells, bead-

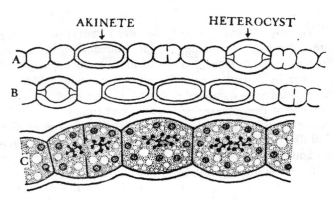

Anabaena. FIG. 4. A-B, two filaments; C, structure of cells (magnified);
note the central body, cyanophycin granules, and the division of some of the cells of the filaments

like in appearance, intermixed at frequent intervals with some heterocysts, and akinetes. Akinetes may develop singly or in series, and are more or less cylindrical or oval. They are considered important for diagnosis of species. The filament elongates by division of individual cells in one plane only, and their rapid enlargement. The protoplast of each cell is differentiated into a central body, which may correspond to an incipient nucleus, and the chromoplasm, which corresponds to the cytoplasm. The central body is irregular in shape, radiates into arms and contains many chromatin granules. The peripheral region contains chlorophyll in minute granules and phycocyanin in solution. The reserve food mainly occurs in the form of glycogen, fat globules and a varying number of cyanophycin granules, which are protein in nature. They usually occur in the peripheral region. There are also several minute *gas vacuoles* or *pseudovacuoles* whose function is not definitely known. Possibly, they give buoyancy to the filament. Each cell has a thin wall of cellulose and pectic compounds, surrounded by a thin, gelatinous sheath which helps retain moisture. In Anabaena, the heterocysts, sometimes many, are intercalary in position. Each heterocyst is connected with the adjacent cells of the filament by a pore at each end.

Reproduction. There is no sexual mode of reproduction in Cyanophyceae. The group also lacks in motile cells. *Anabaena* commonly reproduces vegetatively by fragmentation of the filament, and sometimes asexually by akinetes. Fragmentation of the filament usually takes place at the junction of the heterocyst and the adjoining vegetative cell. The filament, thus, breaks up into hormogonia, which, by cell division in one direction grow into normal filaments. Under extreme conditions, *Anabaena* may reproduce by akinetes which may ultimately separate from the filament and germinate.

Differences between *Nostoc* and *Anabaena*. Although both are characterized by unbranched, filamentous forms made of beaded cells and the presence of heterocysts, they differ from each other in the following respects. (1) *Nostoc* filaments are twisted and flexuous, forming a tangled mass, and have a thick (but not very firm) sheath, while *Anabaena* filaments are straight or slightly curved, more rigid, often free, and with a thin sheath. (2) *Nostoc* filaments often lie embedded in a more or less firm gelatinous matrix, while *Anabaena* filaments are often free or sometimes in a thin gelatin. (3) In *Nostoc,* the heterocysts are intercalary as well as apical, while in *Anabaena,* they are intercalary. (4) Akinetes are more frequent and much more elongated in *Anabaena* than in *Nostoc.* (5) *Nostoc* is equally terrestrial and aquatic, while *Anabaena* is mostly aquatic.

5. *RIVULARIA* (FIG. 5)

Rivularia (family *Rivulariaceae;* FIG. 5) is a filamentous type of blue-green alga. It commonly

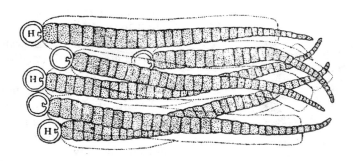

Rivularia. FIG. 5. A group of filaments; note the heterocysts (H) and the sheaths (dotted lines)

grows on submerged rocks, stones, aquatic plants, and sometimes on rocky cliffs. A few species are marine. The filaments form a colony which remains embedded in a gelatinous mass, sometimes encrusted with lime. They occur in a radiating manner and each filament has a distinct gelatinous sheath of its own. The filament, called trichome, is differentiated into (*a*) a basal heterocyst. (*b*) a narrow (attenuated) apical portion, which is whip or tail-like, consisting of a row of small cells, and (*c*) the main body, consisting of a series of more or less rectangular cells arranged in a row. *Rivularia* reproduces vegetatively by hormogonia. Each fragment or hormogonium then grows by cell division into a mature *Rivularia* filament.

CLASS II EUGLENOPHYCEAE
(over 18 sp.)

EUGLENA (*over 18 sp.*)

Euglena (family *Euglenaceae;* FIG. 6) is a most simple, unicellular organism. The evolution of the higher forms of plants possibly started from it. It belongs to the Flagellatae group, the organisms of which do not belong strictly to either the plant or the animal kingdom. It grows in large numbers in polluted water containing organic substances, and colours it bright green. It is a single-celled, naked, free-swimming organism. It is elongated, with one end blunt and the other tapering. It has a single cilium, i.e. a long, slender, whip-like projection, which

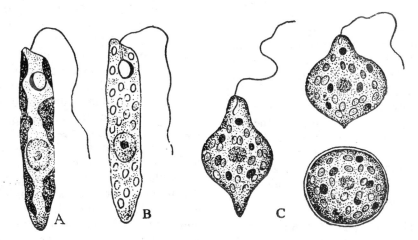

Euglena. FIG. 6-1. *A*, green form; *B*, colourless (saprophytic) form;
C, various forms (three shown) assumed by a single cell

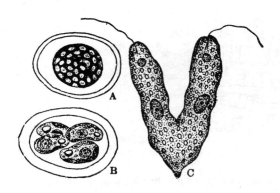

Euglena. FIG. 6-2. *A*, resting spore or cyst;
B, four daughter cells formed by division of the
cyst; *C*, longitudinal splitting of *Euglena* cell

vibrates and helps the plant swim. It can also crawl by changing its shape (FIG. 6-1C). The protoplast contains a central nucleus, several green plastids, a contractile vacuole that contracts and expands in a few seconds, and a red spot near the blunt end, called the *eye spot*. It feeds itself by photosynthesis and also ingests solid particles from the surrounding water. When grown in the dark, it loses its colour and leads a saprophytic life, obtaining nourishment from the aquatic medium in which it grows (FIG. 6-1B). It does not contain starch as the product of carbon assimilation.

Reproduction. There is no sexual mode of reproduction in this plant. It multiplies by dividing longitudinally into two, the nucleus taking the intitiative in the process (FIG. 6-2C). When the food supply falls short, the protoplasmic contents contract and are surrounded by a thick wall which can resist unfavourable conditions. This is known as the cyst or resting spore (FIG. 6-2A). The cyst germinates under favourable conditions. Then the wall becomes mucilaginous and the protoplast divides into 2, 4 or more bodies (FIG. 6-2B). The divided bodies are set free as naked, unicellular organisms.

CLASS III **CHLOROPHYCEAE**
(or green algae; 6,500 sp.)

General Description. Chlorophyceae or green algae are characterized by the presence of chlorophyll located in definite plastids (chloroplasts). They are mostly fresh-water algae, but some species are terrestrial and not a few are marine. Green algae exhibit a variety of forms: (a) unicellular or colonial, being motile or non-motile, (b) multicellular, being thalloid or filamentous, and (c) coenocytic. The protoplast in all Chlorophyceae is well organized, having a definite nucleus (usually one in each cell or several in a coenocyte), and one or more distinct chloroplasts. Depending on the species or genera, the chloroplasts vary in shape and size. They can be cup-shaped, plate-like, stellate, spiral, spherical, oval or discoidal, and contain one or more pyrenoids (rounded protein bodies surrounded by a starchy envelope). The cell-wall is made of cellulose and often has a layer of pectose around it. The gelatinous sheath may or may not be present. Most unicellular and colonial forms are provided with whip-like structures, called *cilia*—often 2, sometimes 4—or many—for motility of cells or colonies. In Chlorophyceae, the cilia are of uniform length and always formed at the anterior end of the cell. In higher forms of Chlorophyceae, the cilia are restricted to the reproductive bodies—zoospores and zoogametes. Primitive forms of Chlorophyceae have two or more contractile vacuoles and a small eye spot (see FIG. 7A).

Reproduction. Vegetative reproduction takes place ususlly by cell division or by fragmentation. Asexual reproduction takes place by spores of various types : (a) a motile, ciliate spore (zoospore), (b) a non-motile, non-ciliate spore with a distinct wall of its own but produced within a mother cell (**aplanospore**—abortive zoospore), and (c) and a vegetative cell acting as a spore having no wall of its own—the wall of the mother cell acting as the wall of the spore, (**akinete** or modified vegetative cell). Sexual reproduction takes place by isogamy, anisogamy or oogamy depending on the species (see p. 349). Whatever the mode of sexual reproduction, some species are **homothallic** (i.e, the pairing gametes come from the same parent), while others are **heterothallic** (i.e., the pairing gametes come from two separate parents). In many green algae, it has been observed that a gamete grows *parthenogenetical-ly* (i.e. without fusion with another gamete) into a new plant. The gamete thus behaves as a spore and is called **parthenospore** or **azygospore**. Sometimes, as in *Spirogyra*, the gamete has no cilia and is called **aplanogamete**.

Origin and Evolution of Sexuality in Chlorophyceae. The vegetative method of reproduction is the most primitive method of multiplication of individual plants. Asexual reproduction by zoospores appeared later in the early (lower) Chlorophyceae, possibly as a means of rapid multiplication. Sexual reproduction appeared later still and continued right up to the highest division of the plant kingdom, evidently to achieve something that was not possible by the other methods. This something is protection, for the thick-walled zygote—the result of the sexual act—is better equipped to withstand unfavourable environmental conditions before it starts a new life. Sexual reproduction has other advantages, too. It should be noted that when conditions are favourable for vegetative activity, neither spores nor gametes are produced; when conditions are less favourable, asexual cells or spores are produced; as the plant approaches the end of its life or when conditions are very unfavourable, sexual cells or gametes are produced. The mode of reproduction is, thus, greatly influenced by the changing environment and age of the plant.

The basic fact concerning the origin of sexuality in Chlorophyceae is that it appeared as a modification of the older asexual method, and is directly correlated with the origin of sexual cells or gametes from the asexual cells or spores (zoospores). Because of their small size (owing to repeated divisions), the gametes have lost the power of functioning individually. They have, thus, developed some kind of mutual attraction and freely come together in pairs and fuse. This is the earliest indication of sexuality. It may then be rightly said that gametes are derived from spores (zoospores). It is also seen that spores and gametes are similar in several members of Cholorophyceae, e.g. *Chlamydomonas*, *Ulothrix* and *Oedogonium*, excepting that the gametes are

smaller and more numerous.

Once sexuality appeared, it established itself and its evolution through isogamy to anisogamy to oogamy, based on the differentiation of sexual cells and sexual organs, proceeded towards a high degree of complexity, possibly towards a state of perfection through successivee stages. In the simple and primitive forms of Chlorophyceae, there is fusion of two gametes (zoogametes) similar in shape and size. This is called **isogamy**, as found in *Chlamydomonas*, *Ulothrix*, etc. The next stage in the evolution of sexuality is **anisogamy**, as found in *Pandorina*, certain species of *Chlamydomonas*, etc. Here, a slight difference is noticed in the size of the gametes or in their behaviour—the first indication of differentiation into male and female. A complete differentiation of gametes and gametangia into male and female is found in the advanced forms of Chlorophyceae. The union of such differentiated gametes is called **oogamy**, as is found in *Oedogonium*, *Vaucheria*, etc. In all Chlorophyceae, however, the gametangia are single-celled. It is also significant that the origin and evolution of sexuality ran parallel and along the same evolutionary lines, though following different trends of evolution, in different orders of Chlorophyceae. Some representative types of Chlorophyceae may now be considered to illustrate the above.

Chlamydomonas (see FIGS.7C & 8B). The simplest type of gamete formation is found in *Chlamydomonas*. Here, the vegetative cell divides and forms 2, 4 or 8 ciliate motile zoospores for asexual reproduction. In the same way, the vegetative cell forms 16, 32 or 64 (sometimes more) ciliate gametes for sexual reproduction. The zoospores and gametes are similar in structure, but the latter are smaller and more numerous. This suggests that gametes are derived from zoospores and that sexuality originates in the transformation of the asexual zoospores into sexual gametes. This is a case of isogamy.

Ulothrix (see FIG. 20). *Ulothrix* is another example of the origin of sexual cells or gametes (C) from asexual cells or zoospores (*C*). It produces zoospores of different sizes—large with 4 cilia, medium with 2 or 4 cilia, and small with 2 cilia. The large zoospore germinates into the normal filament, the medium one into a slow-growing filament, and the small one germinates, if at all, into a short filament. The small ones, however, freely come together into pairs and fuse into a zygote, which then germinates normally. The small spores, being unable to function individually, behave as gametes. The transition from spores to gametes and, therefore, from an asexual to a sexual condition, is thus clear. A reproductive unit is, thus, a spore or a gamete according to its behaviour, or in other words, the origin of sex is correlated with the behaviour of the spore as a gamete.

Spirogyra and *Zygnema*. The special feature of these is that the gametes do not have cilia and are *aplanogametes*. In some species of *Zygnema*, the gametes are truly isogamous, the two gametes meeting and fusing in the conjugation tube. However, in other species of *Zygnema* (see FIG.31B-C) and in all species of *Spirogyra* (see FIG.25), the gametes are morphologically isogamous but physiologically anisogamous. One gamete (male) is actively amoeboid and the other gamete (female) is passive. This order (Conjugales) does not form spores (zoospores) for asexual reproduction. But sometimes, when conjugation fails, the protoplast (gamete) of a cell behaves as a spore and is called the *azygospore*.

Oedogonium (see FIGS. 38 & 39). This shows a high degree of sexual differentiation (oogamy). It reproduces asexually by a solitary zoospore and sexually by highly differentiated gametes —antherozoid and ovum—borne by the antheridium and oogonium, respectively. The latter are only certain cells of the parent filament. Here, the zoospores and the antherozoids, each provided with a ring of cilia, are similar in appearance except that the latter are smaller.

Vaucheria (see FIGS. 41 & 42). This reproduces, as in the previous case, by a solitary zoospore and by highly differentiated male and female gametes and gametangia—oogamy. Here the antherozoids are quite distinct from the zoospores. The former are very minute, biciliate

and produced in large numbers, while the latter are large, solitary and multiciliate. The antheridium and the oogonium, bearing antherozoids and ova, respectively, are produced laterally by the vegetative filament, or they occur on special short branches borne by the parent filament.

Origin and Evolution of Chlorophyceae. It is presumed that Chlorophyceae or green algae have evolved from some motile (ciliate) uincellular ancestor of the type of *Chlamydomonas*. Several orders of Chlorophyceae seem to have evolved independently and followed different lines of development—progressive or retrogressive. Three such lines or trends of development (evolution) may be specially noted: one line has progressed towards the formation of a motile colony, culminating in *Volvox*; a second line towards the formation of a non-motile colony with multinucleate cells, e.g. *Chlorococcum*, *Protosiphon* and *Hydrodictyon*, and with a further tendency to form multinucleate siphonaceous or tubular types, e.g. *Cladophers*, *Vaucheria* and *Caulerpa*; and a third line towards filament-formation—first unbranched and later branched, as represented by Ulotrichales, which may have given rise to the Bryophyta, the next higher group. The first and second lines of evolution have ended blindly, without giving rise to higher forms. It is noticeable that there has been a parallel development in the methods of reproduction through the same stages in all the above three lines—first by cell division, later by zoospores, and still later by the sexual method, in progressive stages (isogamy to anisogamy to oogamy).

1. CHLAMYDOMONAS (43 sp.)

Occurrence. *Chlamydomonas* (family *Chlamydomonadaceae*; FIG. 7A) is a unicellular green alga found in ponds, ditches and pools of stagnant water. A few species are found in snow, forming blood-red patches owing to the development of a red pigment by such species.

Structure. *Chlamydomonas* cells (FIG. 7A) are unicellular, usually spherical or oval, and have a thin wall. *Chlamydomonas* may be regarded as an intermediate form between the flagellate algae and the higher algae. The protoplasm at the anterior end of the cell is clear. It gives off two cilia and contains two contractile vacuoles. The latter pulsate, undergoing alternate expansion and contraction, and their function may be respiratory or

D

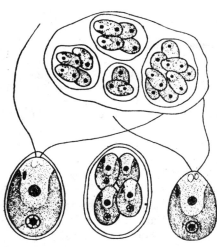

A   B   C

Chlamydomonas. FIG. 7 *A*, a mature cell—note the
two contractile vacuoles, eye spot, nucleus, plastid
and pyrenoid; *B*, four daughter cells (zoospores)
formed by asexual method; *C*, a zoospore after
escape; *D*, palmella stage

Reproduction

(*a*) *Asexual Reproduction. Chlamydomonas*
reproduces asexually by zoospores. In the formation of zoospores, the cilia of each cell are withdrawn and the contents divide into 2, 4 or 8 cells,
seldom more (FIG. 7B). The daughter cells grow,
develop two cilia each and become motile
zoospores. The wall of the mother cell dissolves
and the zoospores are set free (FIG. 7C). Each
zoospore enlarges and becomes a vegetative cell
again.

Palmella Stage. Under unfavourable conditions, the daughter cells divide repeatedly into
numerous cells instead of forming zoospores.
Their walls become gelatinous, and the cells are
held together in colonies by the gelatinous envelope of the mother cell. Thus, numerous colonies
are seen to lie embedded in a gelatinous matrix.
This is known as the palmella stage (FIG. 7D).
When conditions are favourable, the cells develop
cilia, swim out of the gelatinous matrix and
become motile again.

(*b*) *Sexual Reproduction.* Sexual reproduction
takes place by motile ciliate gametes, formed in
the same way as the zoospores. The gametes are
like the zoospores, but are somewhat smaller and
more numerous—16, 32 or 64, or even more (FIG.
8). In most species of *Chlamydomonas*, all the
gametes are similar and are called isogametes,
and their fusion is known as isogamy. A few
species, however, show anisogamy, i.e. slight
differentiation of gametes. Gametes of different

excretory. There is a lateral orange or red pigment
spot, commonly called the eye spot. This is sensitive to different intensities of light. In the posteri-
or region, there is a single, large, cup-shaped
chloroplast with a pyrenoid in it. The pyrenoid
consists of a central protein body surrounded by
many minute starch grains. The cell has a more or
less centrally placed nucleus. The cells swim
briskly by lashing their cilia.

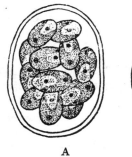
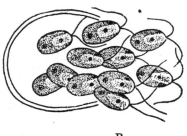

A   B

Chlamydomonas. FIG. 8. *A*, gametes formed; *B*, gametes escaping

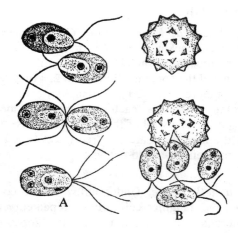

Chlamydomonas. FIG. 9. *A,* free-swimming gametes
and conjugation; *B,* (*top*) a resting zygote; (*bottom*)
four cells formed from the zygote

motile daughter cells (FIG. 9B). These grow,
escape from the mother cell and become individual motile *Chlamydomonas* cells.

It may be noted that in *Chlamydomonas,* the gametes
are mostly alike (isogametes), though there are cases
showing slight differentiation of gametes (anisogametes). This is an early indication of sexual differentiation. The similarity between the gametes and
zoospores suggests the origin of sexual cells (gametes)
from asexual cells (zoospores) by the transformation
of the latter into the former.

2. *PANDORINA* (3 *sp.*)

Pandorina[1] (FIG. 10) forms small oval colonies
of usually 16 biciliate cells (sometimes 4, 8 or 32
cells). The cells are similar and are arranged to
form a hollow sphere, i.e. the cells lie around a
small central cavity. The colonies lie embedded in
a gelatinous matrix. Being close together in the
colony, the cells become laterally compressed.
The individual cells of the colony are like those of
Chlamydomonas. The colony is propelled in
water by the vibration of the two widely divergent
cilia of each cell.

Reproduction. *Pandorina* reproduces both asexually and sexually. In asexual reproduction, the

parents usually conjugate in pairs (FIG. 9A). A
zygospore—the product of the fusion of two similar gametes—is formed. Their ciliate ends conjugate first. Soon after fusion, the cilia are
withdrawn and the zygospore clothes itself with a
thick wall (FIG. 9B). It goes through a period of
rest, and its contents then divide and form 2 or 4

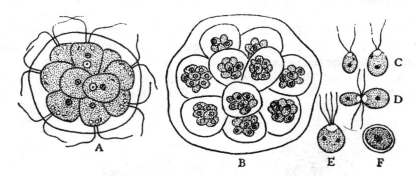

Pandorina. FIG. 10. *A,* a free-swimming colony of biciliate cells; *B,* asexual reproduction; daughter colonies
formed within the mother colony; *C,* gametes (large and small); *D-E,* anisogamy; *F,* zygote

[1] *Pandorina, Eudorina* and *Volvox* of the family *Volvocaceae* are motile, colonial, green algae that often grow abundantly in fresh water and float about in it. The cells of the colony lie embedded in a more or less spherical, hollow,
mucilaginous sphere. Each colony, known as the coenobium, usually consists of 16 cells in the case of *Pandorina,*
32 cells in the case of *Eudorina,* and a few hundreds, often many thousands, in the case of *Volvox. Volvocaceae*
follows a distinct line of evolution. Originating perhaps from *Chlamydomonas,* it passes through a simple type of
colony to more complex types, and through isogamy to anisogamy to oogamy, ending finally in *Volvox.*

individual cells of the colony divide simultaneously, each producing usually 16 daughter cells in a colony or as many cells as are present in the mother colony. Later, the new (daughter) colonies escape after the breakdown of the mother cells and swim away through the gelatinous envelope. In sexual reproduction, the cells of the colony form biciliate gametes, 16 or 32 in number, exactly in the same way as in asexual reproduction. The gametes are similar in shape but dissimilar in size, some slightly larger and less active than the others. They escape in groups, but sooner or later separate into free individual gametes and swim about. Soon, the dissimilar gametes (anisogametes) fuse in pairs, the process being known as anisogamy. It may be noted that anisogamy becomes more pronounced in *Eudorina*. The result of fusion is a zygote, which soon settles down and forms a wall round itself. Later, it divides and produces four zoospores, of which one divides and forms a new colony. The remaining three degenerate.

3. *EUDORINA* (4 or 5 sp.)

Eudorina (FIG. 11) forms a spherical colony of usually 32 cells (sometimes 16 or 64 cells), which are spherical and lie loosely towards the periphery of the mucilaginous sphere. The cells are arranged in five tiers—the three middle tiers having 8 cells each, and the anterior and posterior tiers having 4

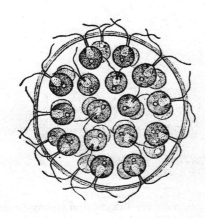

FIG. 11. *Eudorina* colony

cells each. The cells remain connected by fine protoplasmic strands, hardly visible except by proper staining. Each cell (12A) has a mucilaginous sheath and two cilia. There is a distinct reddish-brown eye spot which is sensitive to light. Besides, there are two contractile vacuoles at the base of the cilia, a nucleus somewhere in the middle, and a cup-shaped chloroplast with 1 or more pyrenoids.

Reproduction

(a) *Asexual Reproduction*. Each cell of the colony divides and forms its own small group of 32 cells. All the newly-formed small colonies are separated from one another with the disintegration of the mother colony. Each colony grows and forms a new mature coenobium.

(b) *Sexual Reproduction*. Sexual reproduction takes place by differentiated gametes. The coenobia are dioecious, being differentiated into male and female. The vegetative cells of the female colony enlarge to some extent, lose their cilia and come to lie near the surface of the mucilaginous sphere (12E). Each such cell is a single female gamete. The cells (often not all) of the male colony divide successively, giving rise to a packet of 64 male cells (12B). The packet of cells moves out of the colony and swims as a unit to the female colony (12C-D). The packet then splits up into individual male gametes or spermatozoids (as shown in 12E). The spermatozoids are more or less spindle-shaped and provided with two cilia. They swim into the female colony (12E) and each fuses with a female gamete to form an oospore. It should be noted that two dissimilar gametes (male and female) fuse in pairs. Therefore, this is a case of oogamy. Several such oospores are formed. They remain in the female colony.

4. *VOLVOX* (over 12 sp.)

Volvox. (FIG. 13) is a fresh-water, colony-forming, free-swimming, green alga occurring in ponds and other pools of water during and after rains. It often appears in abundance, colouring the water

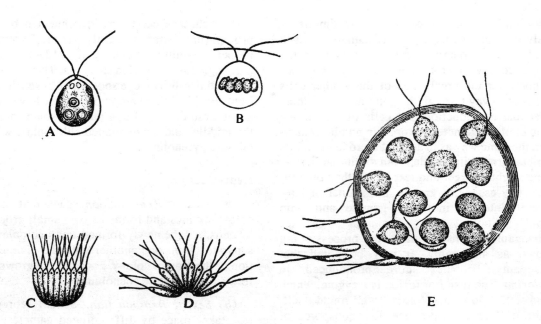

Eudorina. FIG. 12. *A,* a single cell of the colony (note the two contractile vacuoles, eye spot, nucleus and two pyrenoids; *B, C,* and *D,* stages in the formation of the male gametes; and *E,* a female colony with female gametes, and some free-swimming male gametes

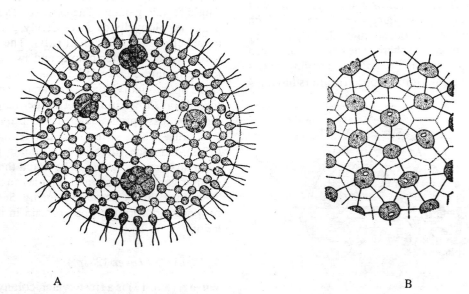

A   B

Volvox. FIG. 13. *A,* a colony showing vegetative cells connected by cytoplasmic strands, four colony-forming cells (including two daughter colonies) and outer sheath; *B,* a portion of a colony (magnified) showing vegetative cells connected by cytoplasmic strands (thick lines) and polygonal sheaths (dotted lines)

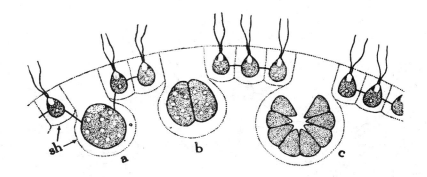

Volvox. Asexual Reproduction. FIG. 14. Formation of a daughter colony within a mother colony; *a,* an enlarged vegetative cell (gonidium); *b,* the same after first division; *c,* a young daughter colony developed from it; *sh,* sheath. *Redrawn after Fig.* 12 in Cryptogamic Botany, Vol. I

green, particularly during spring, then disappears abruptly in the summer. For the rest of the year, it lies dormant in the zygote stage. *V. globator,* which is found floating in tank water, is a common species.

Among the Volvocales, *Volvox* has reached the highest stage of colony formation. As a matter of fact, each colony or **coenobium** (*koinos,* common; *bios,* life), consists of a few hundreds to several thousands (500–40,000) of cells which are in a peripheral layer in such a way as to form a hollow sphere (FIG. 13A). They contain water or a dilute solution of a gelatinous material. Each cell (FIG. 13B) has a gelatinous sheath of its own. The cells are held together in a colony by the sheaths secreted by the individual cells. Delicate but distinct strands of cytoplasm connect the cells. The colonies, approximately 1 mm. in diameter, sometimes up to 2 mm., swim about freely in water. *Volvox* cells are very much like those of *Chlamydomonas.*

A mature colony (FIG. 13A) contains two kinds of cells : several small vegetative cells and a few (5-20) large cells. A vegetative cell has two cilia that protrude outwards and vibrate, 2 to 5 contractile vacuoles, a central nucleus, a cup-shaped or plate-like chloroplast with one pyrenoid, and an eye spot. The vegetative cells do not divide. The larger cells are reproductive and may behave as

exclusively asexual cells or sexual cells. Normally, they act as asexual cells in the beginning of the season and as sexual cells at the close of the season.

Reproduction

(a) *Asexual Reproduction* (FIG. 14). The enlarged cells (gonidia) of the mother colony retract their cilia and push back to the posterior side, then divide and redivide in the longitudinal plane. They thus give rise to a large number of cells in one plane, forming new young daughter colonies within the mother colony. When the cells stop dividing, they turn round, develop cilia and form hollow spheres. These float and slowly revolve within the much enlarged hollow portion of the mother colony. Soon, they escape from their imprisoned state through a rupture in the membrane of the mother colony, or through a pore in it, and swim away as independent colonies.

(b) *Sexual Reproduction* (FIG. 15). Sexual reproduction is oogamous in *Volvox.* In the monoecious species, both types of gametes (male and female) are borne by the same colony (*homothallic*), while in the dioecious species, they are borne by separate colonies (*heterothallic*). These gametes are borne by certain enlarged cells called gametangia (gamete-bearing cells) which lie in the posterior side of the colony. Some of these cells are antheridia or male reproductive

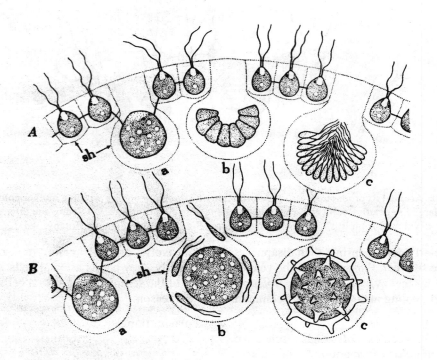

Volvox. Sexual Reproduction. FIG. 15. A, formation of antheridium and antherozoids; *a*, an antheridium; *b*, antherozoids being formed; *c*, the same already formed in a cluster; *sh*, sheath; *B*, formation of oogonium with an egg, fertilization, and zygote; *a*, a young oogonium; *b*, the egg about to be fertilized by one of the antherozoids; *c*, zygote; *sh*, sheath. (*Redrawn after Fig.* 13 *in* Cryptogamic Botany, Vol. I, *by G. M. Smith by permission of McGraw-Hill Book Company*)

organs. The protoplast of these divides many times and produces a cluster of minute, biciliate, male gametes called the **antherozoids** or sperms (FIG. 15A). The other cells are **oogonia** or female reproductive organs. The protoplast of these forms a single, large, female gamete called **egg** or **ovum** (FIG. 15B). The eggs are large, passive and nonmotile, while the sperms are very minute, active and motile. The latter may be in a plate-like colony, escaping from the mother colony as a unit, or they may be arranged to form a hollow sphere. In the former case, the unit breaks up into individual sperms as it approaches an egg, and in the latter case, the sperms are liberated singly. The mode of fertilization is oogamous. The sperms swim and enter through the gelatinous sheath into the oogonium lying in the mother colony. One of them

finally fuses with the egg (FIG. 15B*b*). Thus, fertilization is effected.

Zygote. After fertilization, the zygote clothes itself with a thick, spiny wall and turns orange-red (FIG. 15B*c*). It is set free from the mother colony only after the decay or disintegration of the latter. The zygote sinks to the bottom of the pool of water and after a period of rest, it germinates with the approach of the favourable season. The protoplast of the zygote undergoes reduction division prior to germination. In some species, the protoplast of the zygote divides and forms a new colony directly. In others it forms a single biciliate zoospore which escapes by the rupture of the zygote wall and swims away. The free-swimming zoospore divides and forms a new colony.

5. *PEDIASTRUM* (30 *sp.*)

Occurrence. *Pediastrum* (family *Hydrodic-tyaceae*; FIG. 16A) is a widely distributed green alga found floating in fresh-water ponds, ditches and other pools of water. It is a colony-forming alga. Each colony (coenobium) is small, usually consisting of 8, 16, 32 or 128 cells (rarely 4 or 2). The cells are often arranged around a central one in concentric rings, forming a thin flat plate, one layer thick. *P. simplex* is a common species.

Structure. The number of cells in a colony varies within wide limits, as stated above. All the cells are more or less alike and fit closely together into a compact colony. The peripheral cells, however, differ in shape and their outer walls usually bear 2 (rarely 1 or 3) narrow hair-like projections. Each cell has a distinct cell-wall and is initially uninucleate, later becoming multinucleate (2 to 8) by divisions (coenocytic). There is a single parietal chloroplast containing a pyrenoid. However, there may be many pyrenoids in old cells with diffuse chloroplasts.

Reproduction. *Pediastrum* usually reproduces by the asexual method, and sometimes by the sexual method.

(a) *Asexual Reproduction* (FIG. 16). The proto-plast of certain cells (not many cells simultaneously) divides into a varying number of segments, depending on the physiological condition of the cell. Thus, each parent cell in a 16-celled colony may produce 4, 8, 16, 32 or 64 zoospores. The division of the protoplast is accompanied by nuclear divisions. Each segment becomes converted into a biciliate, uninucleate and void zoospore. The zoospores escape as a packet, usually in the morning, into a vesicle formed from the inner layer of the mother cell. They swarm here for a while *(B)*, soon rearranging themselves within the vesicle, and grow and take the shape of the mother cells *(C)*. Cell-walls appear round them almost immediately and, thus, a new (daughter) colony is formed *(D)*. The cells of the daughter colony vary in number, depending on the number of zoospores formed in the mother cell.

(b) *Sexual Reproduction* (FIG. 17). This has been observed in a few species. The protoplast of a cell divides and forms a number of biciliate, spindle-shaped gametes *(A)* in the same way as the zoospores are formed. All the gametes are alike (isogametes) but are smaller than the zoospores. They escape from the mother cell, one at a time, into the surrounding water. Soon the gametes fuse in pairs *(A)*. The fusion product

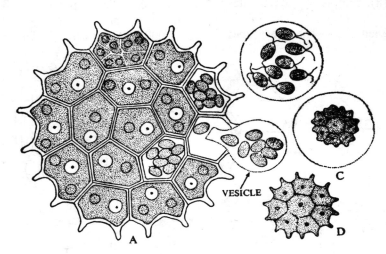

Pediastrum. FIG. 16. *A*, a mature 16-celled colony showing formation of zoospores, and escape of one group of them into a vesicle; *B*, zoospores swarming within the vesicle; *C*, zoospores rearranging themselves to form a daughter colony; *D*, daughter colony enlarging

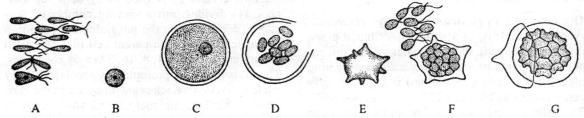

A   B   C   D   E   F   G

Pediastrum. FIG. 17. *A*, gametes and conjugation; *B*, zygote; *C*, zygote (magnified);
D, zoospores escaping from zygote; *E*, a thick-walled polyhedron formed from a zoospore;
F, zoospores within a polyhedron; *G*, zoospores forming a new colony

forms a smooth, spherical zygote (zygospore; *B-C*). The zygote grows and its protoplast divides into a large number of biciliate zoospores (*D*). These escape into the surrounding water, swim freely for a while, and come to rest. Each then develops into a thick-walled polyhedral cell (polyhedron; *E*). The latter grows and its contents divide into several zoospores (*F*). As they escape, a vesicle is formed, and the zoospores stream into it. The zoospores regroup themselves within the vesicle (*G*) as in asexual reproduction, grow and form a new colony.

6. *HYDRODICTYON* (2 *sp.*)

Hydrodictyon reticulatum (family *Hydrodictyaceae*; FIG. 18), commonly called water net (*hydro*, water; *diktyon*, net), is a common, fresh-water, netlike, green alga. The other species,

H. africanum, has been recorded only from South Africa. The net, a fairly big one, sometimes growing up to 25 cm. or so, is hollow within and floats freely on water. The plant body (net) consists of elongated cylindrical cells which anastomose to form a sac-like net. The cells are initially uninucleate and contain a single chloroplast with a pyrenoid, but they later become multinucleate and contain a reticulate chloroplast with many pyrenoids. A mature cell has a large central vacuole and a lining layer of cytoplasm. *Hydrodictyon* has reached the highest degree of non-motile colony formation.

Reproduction

(a) *Asexual reproduction* (FIG. 18 C) takes place through zoospores. The protoplast of a vegetative cell produces a large number of zoospores (7,000-20,000), which swim for a time within the

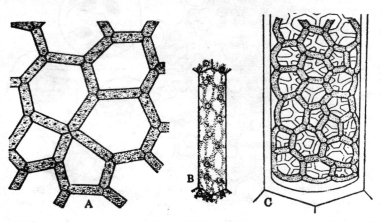

Hydrodictyon. FIG. 18. *A*, a portion of a net; *B*, a single cell (magnified);
C, a young net formed within the mother cell by asexual reproduction

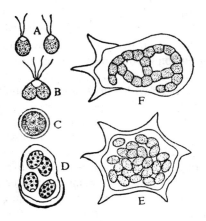

Hydrodictyon. FIG. 19.

A,   isogametes;
B,   conjugation;
C,   formation of zygote;
D,   zoospores escaping into a
        vesicle from the zygote;
E,   a zoospore forming a
        thick-walled polyhedral body,
        the protoplast of which has
        divided into numerous
        zoospores;
F,   a young net formed by
        rearrangement of zoospores

mother cell. Soon, they come together and form a new net within the mother cell. After the disintegration of the mother cell, the new (daughter) net grows into an adult one.

(b) *Sexual reproduction* (FIG. 19) is isogamous. A vegetative cell forms 30,000-100,000 minute, biciliate gametes (isogametes). These escape through an opening of the mother cell and fuse in pairs. The zygote, thus formed, divides by meiosis to form four biciliate zoospores. Each zoospore at first grows into a thick-walled, polyhedral case. Its protoplast rests for a few months, then divides to form many small zoospores which soon escape into a vesicle. Within the vesicle, the zoospores rearrange themselves in such a way as to form a short and irregular net, which soon grows into the adult size.

7. *ULOTHRIX* (30 *sp.*)

Ulothrix (family *Ultoricaceae*; FIG. 20) is a green, filamentous alga occurring in fresh-water in ponds, ditches, water reservoirs, horse or cow troughs, slow streams, etc., particularly in the spring. A few species grow in the sea. The filament of *Ulothrix* is unbranched and consists of a single row of more or less rectangular cells. It is fixed to the substratum or to any hard object in the water by the basal, elongated, colourless cell called the *holdfast*. The filament, if detached, may float freely on water. Each cell of the filament contains a nucleus and a peripheral, band-like chloro-

plast with entire or lobed margin. Usually, there are many (sometimes one or few) pyrenoids lying embedded in the chloroplast. These are rounded protein bodies with a starchy envelope.

Reproduction takes place asexually by zoospores, sexually by gametes, and vegetatively by fragmentation of the filament.

(a) *Asexual Reproduction (B-E).* (1) Zoospores with 4 cilia (megazoospores) are produced for the process of asexual reproduction, which takes place by the division of the protoplast of any cell of the filament, except the holdfast. They are larger than the gametes but produced in fewer numbers—2, 4, 8, or sometimes even 1, rarely as many as 16 or even 32—in each cell. Each zoospore is more or less pear-shaped and contains a distinct red *eye spot* on one side, a pulsating vacuole close to the flagellate end and a large chloroplast. The zoospores escape through an opening in the lateral wall of the cell and swim about briskly in the water for a few hours or even a few days. Then they come to rest and attach themselves by their colourless end to any hard object in the water. The cilia are withdrawn and a cell-wall is formed round each zoospore. Then it germinates directly into a new filament. (2) Sometimes smaller zoospores (but bigger than gametes), called **microzoospores**, are produced in the filament. These possess either two or four cilia. Either they germinate directly into new *Ulothrix* filaments, like the megazoospores, or they fuse in pairs like the gametes. This indicates that the origin of gametes lies in zoospores. (3) Sometimes the whole protoplast of a cell may round itself off and form a thick-walled spore known as the aplanospore (non-ciliate, non-motile, modified zoospore).

(b) *Sexual Reproduction (B-H)*. Sexual reproduction is isogamous and consists of the fusion of two similar biciliate gametes (*isogametes*). The gametes may be formed in any cell of the filament except the holdfast. They are smaller than the zoospores and biciliate. There may be 8, 16, 32 or 64 in each cell. Each gamete possesses a red *eye spot* and a chloroplast band. The gametes are set free from the cell in exactly the same way as the zoospores. They swim about with the help of their cilia for some time, till two gametes coming from different filaments (*heterothallic*) get entangled by their cilia. Gradually, a complete fusion (conjugation) of the two takes place laterally. The cilia are withdrawn towards the close of the process. Tthe fusion product moves around for some more time but soon comes to rest. It rounds itself off, clothes itself with a thick cell-wall, and forms into a zygospore. After a period of rest, the zygospore germinates into a unicellular *germ plant* which produces 4 to 16 zoospores or aplanospores. They are quadriciliate (zoospores) or nonciliate (aplanospores) and each develops into a new plant. If fusion fails, each gamete may behave as a zoospore. It withdraws its cilia, rounds itself off and clothes itself with a cell-wall. After a dormant period, it germinates directly into a new *Ulothrix* filament. The zygote nucleus has $2n$ or *diploid* chromosomes. It undergoes reduction division and the zoospores are povided with n or *haploid* chromosomes. This haploid number continues

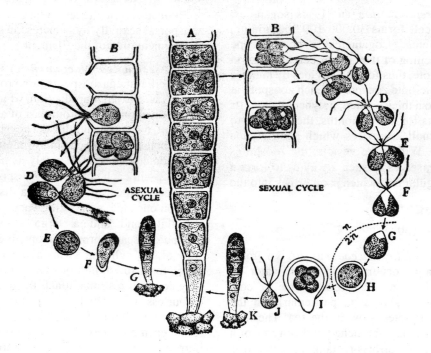

Ulothrix. FIG. 20. *Life-cycle*: sexual reproduction—*A*, vegetative filament; *B*, formation of gametes; *C*, gametes swimming; *D-G*, stages in the conjugation of gametes; *H*, zygospore; *I*, the germ plant with zoospores; *J*, a zoospore (quadriciliate); *K*, a young filament; asexual reproduction—*B*, a portion of the filament showing the formation of zoospores; *C*, a quadriciliate zoospore; *D*, zoospores swimming; *E*, a zoospore rounded off; *F*, zoospore germinating; and *G*, a young filament

throughout the life of the *Ulothrix* plant.

(c) *Vegetative Reproduction.* This takes place by fragmentation of the filament into short pieces consisting of a few cells each. Each piece or fragment grows into a long filament by transverse division of cells and their enlargement.

Note. Ulothrix provides a very early indication of the sexual differentiation which becomes so pronounced in the higher plants. The behaviour of gametes (or sexual cells) and zoospores (or asexual cells) suggests that the former were originally derived from the latter. The gametes are similar in appearance but not in behaviour. The passive one may be regarded as the egg-cell or female gamete, and the active one as the male gamete.

8. CHAETOPHORA (12 sp.)

Occurrence. *Chaetophora* (family *Chaeto-phoraceae*; FIG. 21) is a fresh-water green alga, growing attached to water plants, stones, pebbles, shells, etc., submerged in standing (rarely flowing) water, commonly found at the edge of ponds, lakes, marshes and bogs. *C. elegans* is a common species.

Structure. The vegetative body consists of two parts: a part made of erect, profusely branching, deep green filaments, and another made of a prostrate, sparingly branched, cushion-like thallus usually 2 or 3 cm. in diameter).The branching filaments are hardly visible to the naked eye. The prostrate part remains attached to some object in the water, and sometimes the older cells in it produce rhizoids. The erect part develops from the prostrate part, and its filaments (branches) are held together within a tough gelatinous envelope. The cells are somewhat cylindrical or barrel-shaped and are like *Ulothrix* in appearance. The cells gradually become smaller towards the apex of the filament, and in several species of *Chaetophora*, the filament ends in a long or short unicellular or multicellular, colourless hair (devoid of chloroplasts) which usually tapers to a point. Each cell of the filament contains a single plate-like, parietal chloroplast, which contains usually 1 or 2 pyrenoids and a single nucleus. *Chaetophora* follows the same sort of life cycle as *Ulothrix*, but structural differences between the two are con-

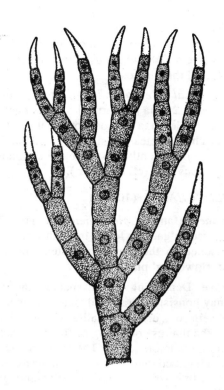

Chaetophora. FIG. 21. A branched thallus

spicuous. The branching habit of *Chaetophora* indicates an evolutionary advance over *Ulothrix* and other related unbranched forms.

Reproduction. *Chaetophora* reproduces both asexually and sexually. Both methods are much the same as those of *Ulothrix*. Occasionally, vegetative reproduction occurs by fragmentation of the thallus but is not a common feature because of its toughness.

(a) *Asexual Reproduction.* Large, motile zoospores with 4 cilia (megazoospores) are formed for this purpose by the division of the protoplast of any vegetative cell. They are usually formed singly in each cell and are much larger than the gametes. They escape from the mother cells by an opening in the lateral wall, swim briskly for some time, then come to rest, getting attached to some hard object in the water. The cilia are, of course, withdrawn. Soon the zoospores germinate directly into a new plant. Reproduction may also be effected by the resting cells, such as the aplanospores (1 to 4 each cell) and brownish akinetes (see p. 348) which usually develop in the upper part of the filament.

(b) *Sexual Reproduction.* Small, motile gametes with 2 cilia are formed for this purpose. They are smaller than the zoospores but greater in number. The gametes are similar in all respects (isogametes). Evidently, sexual reproduction is of the isogamous type (cf. *Ulothrix*).

9. *COLEOCHAETE* (10 *sp.*)

Coleochaete (family *Coleochaetaceae*; FIG. 22) is a small green alga. It is found in fresh water, usually attached to the leaves and stems of some aquatic 'flowering' plants.

Structure. Depending on the species, the plant body may consist of branched filaments made of rows of cells, or a disc-like thallus with lobed margin (*A*), the thallus consisting of filaments radiating from a common centre. The filaments are so close or adpressed together as to simulate a continuous disc. In certain species, the filaments grow vertically from a cushion-like, prostrate base. The disc-like thallus appears like a pinhead, varying from 2 to 5 mm., and is the thickness of one layer of cells. Many of the cells give out long, slender, hair-like bristles, called *setae*, which have a

gelatinous sheathing base and a linear thread of cytoplasm within. The seta is an outgrowth of the wall, arising from a pore in it (wall). Each cell of the thallus has a nucleus and a parietal chloroplast, the latter containing 1 or 2 pyrenoids. The growth is apical or marginal.

Reproduction. *Coleochaete* reproduces both asexually and sexually.

(a) *Asexual reproduction* takes place by zoospores (*B*). Any vegetative cell may act as a zoosporangium, producing a single, relatively large, ovoid, biciliate zoospore. During spring, often all the vegetative cells form zoospores simultaneously. The zoospore has a single chloroplast and a nucleus. It escapes through a pore in the wall of the mother cell and swims in the water for some time. Then it comes to rest and begins to produce a new thallus.

Sexual Reproduction. Sexual reproduction is of an advanced type and oogamous, the reproductive organs being differentiated into antheridium and oogonium, with motile antherozoids and non-motile eggs, respectively. The plant may be homothallic or heterothallic. Any vegetative cell may divide into a number of smaller cells, each cell being a male gametangium or antheridium (*C*), producing a single, small, motile, biciliate antherozoid. In the formation of the oogonium

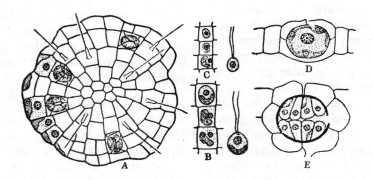

Coleochaete. FIG. 22. *A*, a disc consisting of numerous filaments growing close together (note the zygotes overgrown by the surrounding cells and some bristles with sheathing base); *B*, some vegetative cells showing the formation of zoospores; *right*, a biciliate zoospore; *C*, some antheridial cells showing the formation of antherozoids; *right*, a biciliate antherozoid; *D*, an oogonium within a thallus (in section); *E*, zygote (in section) showing a group of cells, each of which will develop into a zoospore

(*D*), some of the marginal cells of the thallus enlarge and become oogonia. The protoplast of the oogonium is converted into a large, passive (non-motile) egg. The remaining marginal cells not involved in the formation of the oogonia continue to grow, so that the oogonia soon come to lie away from the margin.

In the filamentous species, the antheridia and the oogonia are formed terminally at the ends of filaments, either by the same plant or by two different plants. In certain species the oogonium is provided with a beak-like projection, called the *trichogyne*, which receives the antherozoids and allows them to pass through it into the oogonium.

Fertilization. The antherozoids swim to the oogonium and one of them fuses with the egg nucleus. After fertilization, the egg clothes itself with a heavy wall which soon turns brown. This is the zygote (oospore; *E*). The adjoining vegetative cells of the thallus overgrow the zygote and completely enclose it. After a period of rest the zygote, still within the encased oogonium, divides and gives rise to 16 or 32 daughter cells, each of which is converted into a biciliate zoospore. The zygote wall and the encasing layer break and the zoospores are liberated. Each then directly develops into a new thallus.

The zygote is diploid, but its first division being reductional, all the zoospores formed as a result of successive divisions are haploid, and so is the plant body developed from each. Thus, there is no alternation of generations in *Coleochaete*. It should also be noted that the thalloid form of the plant body and the advanced form of reproduction (oogamy) raises *Coleochaete* to a very high position among green algae. It nearly approaches thalloid liverworts which may have arisen from Coleochaete in the remote past.

10. *PROTOCOCCUS* (14 *sp.*)

Occurrence. *Protococcus* (or *Pleurococcus*; family*Protococcaceae*) is a very common unicellular, green alga (FIG. 23). It is terrestrial and very widely distributed. Species of *Protococcus* (e.g. *P. viridis*) grow in moist, shady places and form a green covering on tree trunks, branches, posts, old damp bricks or brick walls, flower pots and other similar objects.

Structure. Each plant is represented by a single, more or less globose cell. The plants occur either as isolated individuals or form small groups (colonies) of 2, 3, 4 or sometimes more cells as a result of division of the solitary cell. The cells of a group become flattened on the contact side. Ciliate cells and gelatinous covering are conspicuously absent. Under conditions of excessive moisture and possibly certain other conditions, *Protococcus* may divide in one direction and form a short filament consisting of a few cells, usually 3 or 4, often many more. It has, thus, been suggested that *Protococcus* was orginally a filamentous form, but due to lack of vegetative growth as well as loss of normal reproductive function, it has become reduced to a unicellular stage. The cells are remarkably resistant to desiccation but their vital activity becomes very slow under such conditions. With the availability of rain water, dew or moist air, the cells are reactivated. Individual cells are very small, spherical or oval, filled with dense cytoplasm and covered by a rather heavy cellulose wall. Each cell has a single nucleus and a large

 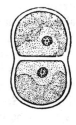 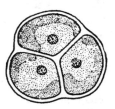 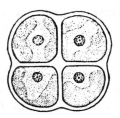

A   B   C   D

Protococcus. FIG. 23. *A* , a single cell; *B-D* , small colonies formed by divisions of the cell

parietal chloroplast with lobed margin but no pyrenoid.

Reproduction. The only method of reproduction is vegetative cell division, which is often very rapid. The first division of the cell is transverse (median) and the second, in one or both daughter cells, is at right angles to the first division. Succeeding divisions, if any, are at right angles to the first one. The daughter cells may remain attached to one another in a small group, or separate and form independent cells (plants). Each cell, thus, represents a plant. It begins to divide again under favourable conditions.

In the past, *Protococcus* was regarded as one of the most primitive forms of green algae but it is now regarded as a reduced form of some filamentous type, possibly of Ulotrichales or Chaetophorales. The occasional branching, short and irregular though it is, lends support to this view.

11. *SPIROGYRA* (100 *sp.*)

Occurrence. *Spirogyra* (family *Zygnemataceae*) is a green filamentous alga (FIG. 24) occurring in a tangled mass that floats about freely in water. It is a cosmopolitan plant of fresh water, and is found growing abundantly in ponds, ditches, springs, slow-running streams, etc. In some species growing in running water, a short, unicellular organ of attachment, called *hapteron*, is formed. *S. maxima*, *S. longata*, and *S. nitida* are some of the common species.

Structure. Each *Spirogyra* plant is an unbranched filament, a few to many cm. in length, consisting of a single row of cylindrical cells. The walls are made of cellulose and pectin. Pectin swells in water into a gelatinous sheath, which encases the *Spirogyra* filament. It is, therefore, slimy to touch. The filament is not differentiated into base and apex. Each cell has a lining layer of cytoplasm, in which one or usually more *spiral bands* of chloroplasts—the characteristic feature of *Spirogyra*—lie embedded. The nucleus is situated somewhere in the centre, suspended by delicate strands of cytoplasm, and there is one large, central vacuole. Each cell has 1 to 14 chloroplasts, which run along the whole length of the cell. The

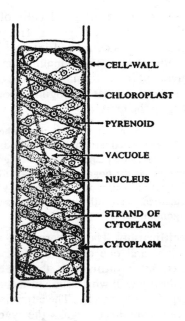

Spirogyra. FIG. 24. A cell of filament (magnified)

margin of each chloroplast may be quite smooth, or wavy or serrated. It contains several small, nodular, protoplasmic bodies—the **pyrenoids**. The pyrenoids are connected by a sort of ridge which develops on the inner side of the chloroplast, and minute starch grains are deposited around them. The nucleus usually has one large nucleolus, frequently more. Growth by elongation and cell division by mitosis usually take place at night. If the filament happens to be broken up into individual cells or short pieces, the cells divide and give rise to new filaments (vegetative propagation).

Reproduction. This takes place in *Spirogyra* by the sexual method, and consists in the fusion (conjugation) of two similar reproductive units or gametes, i.e. isogametes. Conjugation usually takes place between the cells of two filaments or even three. This is called scalariform (or ladder-like) conjugation. Sometimes, however, conjugation takes place between the cells of the same filament. This is called lateral conjugation.

Scalariform conjugation (FIG. 25). When two filaments come to lie in contact in the parallel

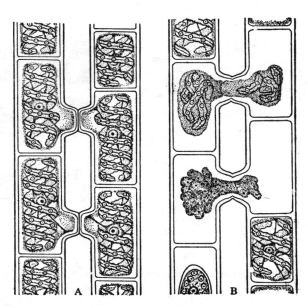

Spirogyra. FIG. 25. Scalariform conjugation. *A-B* are stages in the process

direction, they repel each other. As a result of this repulsion, tubular outgrowths develop from the corresponding points of contact of the two filaments. These tubular outgrowths are called **conjugation tubes**, and when all or most of the cells of the two filaments have formed such tubes, the whole structure looks more or less like a ladder. Hence, the name scalariform or ladder-like conjugation. Their end or partition walls dissolve and an open conjugation tube is formed. In the meantime,

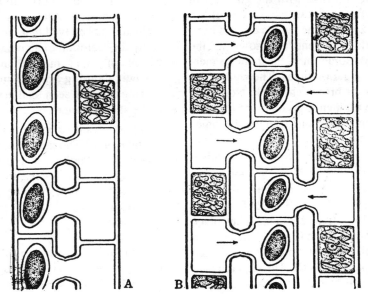

Spirogyra. FIG. 26. *A*, formation of zygospores after conjugation;
B, scalariform conjugation between three filaments

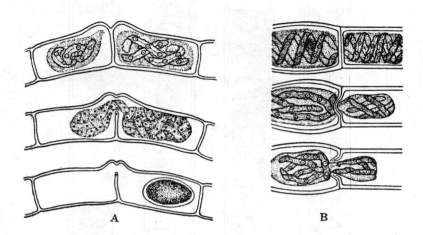

Spirogyra. FIG. 27. *A*, Lateral conjugation and formation of zygospore (chain type); *B*, direct lateral conjugation

the protoplasmic contents of each cell lose water, contract and become rounded off at the centre. Every contracted mass of protoplasm forms a gamete. All gametes are alike in appearance, (isogametes). By a kind of *amoeboid* movement, the gametes of one filament creep through the conjugation tubes into the corresponding cells of the adjoining filament and fuse with the gametes of that filament. The fusion of two gametes results in the formation of a zygote. The zygote clothes itself with a thick, dark wall, and is known as the zygospore (FIG. 26). Sometimes, the gametes meet and fuse in the conjugation tubes. The wall of the zygospore is black or brownish-black. Normally, the gametes of one filament pass on to the gametes of the other filament. Thus, one filament becomes practically empty, barring a few vegetative cells at places, while the other has a row of zygospores. Sometimes, three filaments are involved in the process of conjugation, the zygospores being formed in the middle filament (FIG. 26B).

Lateral conjugation (FIG. 27). This takes place between the cells of the same filament. (*A*) **Chain Type.** An outgrowth or conjugation tube is formed on one side of the partition wall. Through the passage thus formed, the gamete (male) of one cell passes into the gamete (female) of the neighbouring cell. (*B*) **Direct Lateral Conjugation.** In certain species, as in *S. jogensis* (as reported by

Iyengar, 1958), the male gamete passes into the female gamete by perforating the centre of the septum. The protoplast of one cell (male) tapers towards the next cell (female), which now swells considerably. The tapering end pushes and pierces the septum between the two cells and the whole protoplast of the male cell moves into the female cell through the perforation, fusing with the female gamete. After fusion, a zygospore is formed. It is believed that the perforation is effected by the secretion of an enzyme. In lateral conjugation, only the gametes of alternate cells move to the neighbouring cells. Thus, later on, zygote-bearing cells are seen to alternate with empty cells in the same filament.

Sometimes it so happens that conjugation does not take place. The gametangia then become converted into thick-walled bodies identical with zygospores. These bodies, formed parthenogenetically (see p. 315), are called **azygospores** or **parthenospores.** They germinate like the zygospores.

Note. In *Spirogyra,* there is no distinction between male and female gametes so far as shape and structure is concerned, but there is some difference in behaviour. One is active, motile and initiative and may be regarded as male, while the other is passive, non-motile and receptive and may be regarded as female. All the cells of one

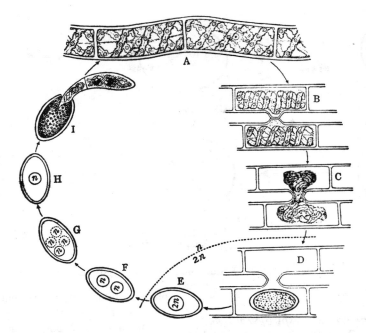

FIG. 28. Life cycle of *Spirogyra*. *A*, vegetative filament (portion);
B-C, stages in conjugation; *D*, zygospore formed; *E-II*, reduction division and nuclear
changes within the zygospore (see also FIG. 30); and *I*, zygospore germinates

filament behave as male, and those of the other as female. Moreover, the chloroplasts of the male gamete become disorganized, while those of the female persist as broken filaments.

Reduction Division (FIG. 30). The zygote is formed as a result of the fusion of two gametes, each with n (or x) chromosomes and, therefore, the zygote-nucleus has $2n$ (or $2x$) chromosomes. The nucleus of the zygote at first undergoes a reduction division and the resulting nuclei divide again to form four nuclei, each with n (or x) chromosomes. Three of these nuclei degenerate, so that the mature zygote contains a single nucleus with n (or x) chromosomes.

Germination of Zygospore (FIG. 29). The zygospore has a thick cellulose wall composed of three layers, of which the middle one contains some chitin. With the rapid decay of the parent filament, all the zygospores are set free and sink to the bottom of the pool of water. They undergo a period of rest and germinate during the next favourable season. The protoplast of each zygospore first increases in size. Then its outer layers burst and the inner one with the protoplast grows out in the form of a short tube, which ultimately forms into a new filament. The filament escapes and floats on the surface of the water. The length of the filament increases by division of cells. Soon, the floating filaments take to conjugation again (Life cycle of *Spirogyra* is depicted in FIG. 28).

Spirogyra. FIG. 29. Zygospore germinating

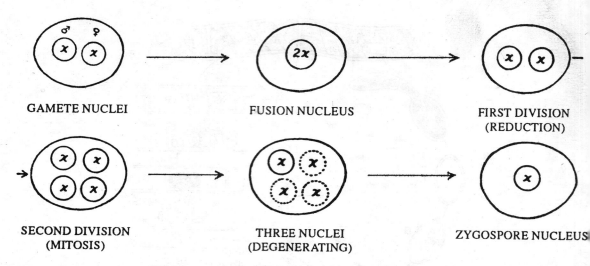

GAMETE NUCLEI   FUSION NUCLEUS   FIRST DIVISION
                                                                   (REDUCTION)

SECOND DIVISION   THREE NUCLEI   ZYGOSPORE NUCLEUS
   (MITOSIS)   (DEGENERATING)

Spirogyra. FIG. 30. Reduction division of zygospore nucleus

12. ZYGNEMA (95 sp.)

Occurrence. Zygnema and *spirogyra*, well-known members of *Zygnemataceae*, are widely distributed green algae floating in almost every pool of fresh water. Some species, however, produce rhizoid-like organs of attachment called haptera.

Structure. Each plant of *Zygnema* (FIG. 31) is an unbranched filament. The filament, which is not differentiated into base and apex, consists of a row of cylindrical cells. The protoplast of each cell is uninucleate. The nucleus lies embedded in a broad strand of cytoplasm connecting two star-shaped chloroplasts, which lie in the axial direction (*A*). Delicate strands of cytoplasm radiate outwards, often to the wall, from each chloroplast. The stellate chloroplast is characteristic of *Zygnema*. At the centre of each chloroplast lies a single chloroplast, which is surrounded by radiating starch grains. In the division of the cell, the nucleus first undergoes mitosis. This is followed by the furrowing of the cytoplasm in the middle of the cell. Each of the two chloroplasts, thus separated, divides and so does the pyrenoid. The different organs then take their respective positions, as in the mother cell.

Reproduction. Reproduction in *Zygnema* takes place vegetatively and sexually, as in Spirogyra. The total absence of ciliate gametes or zoospores is conspicuous in both. Vegetative reproduction takes place only by the accidental breaking-off of the old filament into short fragments, which grow by cell division and cell elongation.

Sexual Reproduction takes place by means of conjugation (*B-C*), usually in the spring. Both the scalariform and lateral methods of conjugation are found in *Zygnema*. These methods closely resemble those of *Spirogyra*. Scalariform conjugation is, however, the usual method. In some species, the gametes (isogametes) of the conjugating filaments migrate from their respective gametangia, meet and fuse in pairs in the conjugation tube, and form the zygospore there. In other species, however, the gametes (aplanogametes) of one filament (male) move through the conjugation tubes into the gametangia of the attached filament (female), and after gametic union, the zygospores develop in the latter (female) filament (*D*). The zygospore nucleus has diploid chromosomes but, on the eve of its germination, it undergoes reduction division (into four haploid nuclei). Three of them, however, degenerate. The zygospore initially has four chloroplasts but two of them soon degenerate (*E-H*). There are three layers covering the zygospore. The latter germinates only the year after by

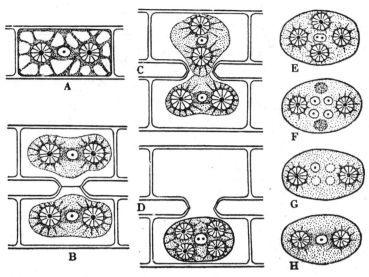

Zygnema. FIG. 31. *A*, a cell of *Zygnema* showing two star-shaped chloroplasts and a central nucleus;
B-C, formation of gametes and mode of conjugation; *D*, formation of zygospore after conjugation;
E-H, reduction division of zygospore nucleus; note that three nuclei degenerate and so do two chloroplasts

producing a short filament, which escapes from the zygospore. It divides and elongates into a mature filament.

When conjugation fails, the gametes may be converted into azygospores or parthenospores which are essentially identical with zygospores. Azygospores are rather common in some species of *Zygnema*.

13. *COSMARIUM* (*over* 800 *sp.*)

Cosmarium (family *Desmidiaceae*; FIG. 33). This faimily, commonly known as **desmids**, is a big group of unicellular plants comprising about 2,500 species. They exhibit a variety of peculiar, often exceedingly beautiful forms (FIG. 32), and are very widely distributed. They are found in plenty in almost every pool of fresh water. Often, the cells are held together in an unbranched filament or in an amorphous colony. Many desmids display a jerky movement, which is due to the secretion of mucilage through pores in the cell-wall. Like other desmids, Cosmarium is a fresh-water, free-floating alga.

Structure. *Cosmarium* (FIG. 33A) consists of a single cell with a median constriction, called *sinus,* which divides the cell into two distinct symmetrical halves (*semicells*). These are connected by a narrow zone, called *isthmus.* The cell-wall is smooth and consists of three concentric layers —(*a*) the innermost, thin layer made of cellulose, (*b*) a somewhat thicker median layer made of cellulose and pectic compounds, and (*c*) the outermost layer made of gelatinous sheath. The two inner walls have several pores. The protoplast contains a single nucleus, which lies at the isthmus, and usually a single chloroplast with 1 or 2 pyrenoids in each semicell. However, 2-4 chloroplasts, sometimes many, are not, uncommon. A large chloroplast often has many pyrenoids.

Reproduction. *Cosmarium* reproduces vegetatively and sexually.

Vegetative Reproduction (FIG. 33 B-C). During vegetative reproduction, which is a process of cell division, the nucleus of each cell divides into two and the isthmus elongates. A partition wall is formed across the isthmus. Each elongated portion of the isthmus then enlarges and gives rise to a new semicell. The chloroplast also divides. The

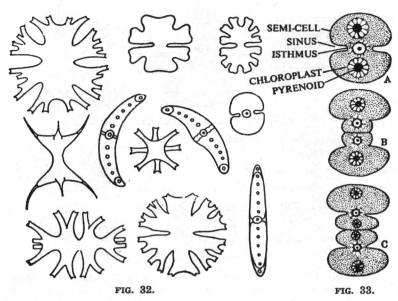

FIG. 32.   FIG. 33.

Desmids. FIG. 32. Various forms of desmids including *Cosmarium*.
FIG. 33. *Cosmarium*. A, a vegetative cell; B-C, mode of vegetative reproduction

pyrenoids may divide or may be newly formed. The daughter cells separate and, thus, two *Cosmarium* cells are formed. It is evident that each newly-formed semicell is always younger than the one belonging to the parent cell. No zoospore is formed in desmids.

Sexual Reproduction (FIG. 34). Sexual reproduction, though rare, is isogamous. During conjugation, two mature cells, or sometimes two newly-formed daughter cells, come in contact and are covered by a common gelatinous sheath. The protoplast of each cell forms a gamete. Each cell then breaks open at the isthmus, the two gametes escape and meet midway between the two. In some species, a distinct conjugation tube may be formed. In such cases, the zygote is formed in the conjugation tube. The two gametes fuse, forming the zygote. The zygote becomes thick-walled and spiny or warty, and remains enveloped by a gelatinous sheath, often with the four empty semicells adhering to it. It germinates after a period of rest and gives rise to two daughter protoplasts, each of which develops into a new *Cosmarium* plant. The zygote nucleus undergoes reduction division, with two haploid nuclei passing into each daughter

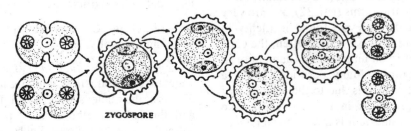

Cosmarium. FIG. 34. Sexual reproduction (conjugation), zygospore and mode of its germination

protoplast. One nucleus in each degenerates as do all the chloroplasts in excess of the specific number. Thus, a *Cosmarium* cell has only one nucleus and one or two chloroplasts. The two newly-formed *Cosmarium* cells escape after a rupture of the zygote wall.

14. *OEDOGONIUM* (300 *sp.*)

Occurrence. *Oedogonium* (family *Oedogoniaceae*) is a common green, filamentous alga living in fresh-water ponds and pools. The filaments usually attach themselves to any object in tne water by an irregularly lobed basal cell called the holdfast. Older filaments may, however, float freely.

Structure. Each plant is an unbranched filament consisting of a row of cylindrical cells (FIG. 35). The apex of the filament may be rounded or may end in a hair-like structure. Growth takes place by cell division, which may be apical or intercalary.

Method of Cell Division and Formation of Apical Caps. (FIG. 36). Only certain cells of the filament divide, and there is a corresponding formation of apical caps at the distal end of each such cell. The division may be intercalary or apical (never basal). With the initiation of cell division, the nucleus moves upward, elongates to some extent, and divides mitotically. As the nucleus begins to divide, a ring-like thickening of cellulose appears within the lateral wall of the cell, at its distal end. A small groove is formed in this ring, completely encircling it. A rent appears in the lateral wall, external to this groove. The result is that the wall splits transversely at this point. About this time or a little earlier, mitosis comes to an end. A thin transverse plate (wall) is formed immediately after cytokinesis, dividing the protoplasm into two. The lower cell now begins to elongate, rather rapidly, and within a very short time it reaches the size of the parent cell. With the elongation of the cell, the transverse wall is pushed up to about the level of the ring, where it unites with the lateral wall. The cellulose ring stretches longitudinally into a cylinder, contributing to the formation of the new wall and elongation of the new upper cell, which soon

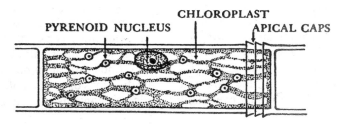

PYRENOID NUCLEUS CHLOROPLAST APICAL CAPS

Oedogonium. FIG. 35. A vegetative cell

The cell-wall is somewhat thick and rigid. It consists of cellulose internally, pectose in the middle, and chitin externally. Each cell contains a single nucleus, which lies in the peripheral layer of the protoplasm, somewhere in the centre of the cell. The cell has a single, large, peripheral chloroplast which takes the form of a cylindrical network, extending lengthwise from one wall to the other. Each chloroplast often contains several pyrenoids, which usually occur in the intersections of the network. Each pyrenoid is a protein granule that is surrounded by a sheath of starch plates. *Oedogonium* has certain special features : peculiar mode of cell division, formation of apical caps and development of dwarf males.

grows to the size of the lower cell. The strip of the old wall, which persists at the top of the upper cell, now appears as a distinct apical cap. A new cap is formed with each division of the cell. Thus, overlapping caps appear on successive divisions and many such caps may be formed.

Reproduction takes place asexually through large, solitary zoospores, sexually through highly differentiated male and female gametes, and vegetatively through fragmentation of filaments, which is often quite common.

(a) *Asexual Reproduction* (FIG. 37). This method of reproduction is brought about by zoospores. Any cell of the filament may form a

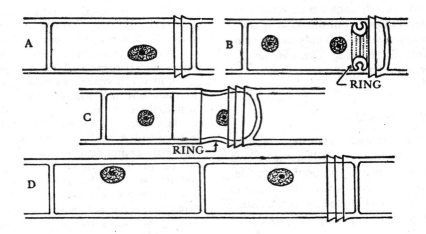

Oedogonium. FIG. 36. *A-D*, cell division and formation of apical caps

single zoospore by the process of **rejuvenescence** (see p. 314). The contents of the cell become rounded off and form a zoospore (*A-B*). This is a large, pear-shaped body. Its narrower end is clear and bears a ring of cilia, while its broader end is green and contains a chloroplast (*C*). The upper wall of the cell splits transversely, allowing the zoospore to escape. The zoospore then swims for a while and soon attaches itself to some object (*D*). The cilia are withdrawn. Next, the zoospore clothes itself with a cell-wall and eventually germinates into a filament.

(b) *Sexual Reproduction* (FIG. 38). Sexual reproduction takes place through differentiated male and female gametes, known as antherozoids and oospheres (or egg-cell), respectively. Many species are monoecious (homothallic) and some are dioecious (heterothallic). Antherozoids are borne in certain small cells, known as antheridia (*A*). Antheridia are produced in a series by repeated divisions of any cell of the filament. The protoplasmic contents of each antheridium divide once

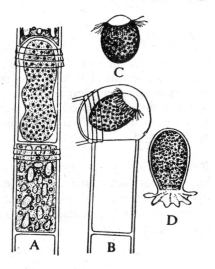

Oedogonium.
FIG. 37.
Asexual Reproduction.
A,   portion of a filament showing a chloroplast and a zoospore in the process of formation;
B,   zoospore escaping;
C,   zoospore swimming;
D,   zoospore attached to an object

and produce a pair of antherozoids. Each antherozoid has a ring of cilia and is like the zoospore, except that it is smaller. Antherozoids are liberated by a transverse slitting of the antheridial wall.

The egg-cell is borne in a large spherical cell known as the oogonium (*B*). Oogonia occur amongst the ordinary vegetative cells of the filament, either singly, or 2 or more in a row. The protoplasmic contents of the oogonium separate from the cell-wall and become rounded off, forming a single, large, non-motile egg-cell or oosphere. This egg-cell enlarges and becomes spherical or oval. There is a colourless, receptive spot at one end of it, and the oogonium opens close to this spot by a pore or a transverse slitting of the wall.

Fertilization. When the antherozoids are liberated, they swim to the oogonium with the help of their cilia. Then one antherozoid enters through the slit in the oogonium wall and fuses with the egg-nucleus at the receptive spot (B). The oosphere covers itself with a thick cell-wall and becomes a reddish-brown oospore (C). The oospore sinks to the bottom, goes through a period of rest, then germinates. The nucleus of the oospore has 2*n* chromosomes. It undergoes reduction division, giving rise to four zoospores (D), each with *n* chromosomes. The zoospores escape and swim about for some time. Then they rest for a while, attach themselves to some object, and each germinates into a new filament.

In certain dioecious species of *Oedogonium*, a complicated process of reproduction takes place. A special type of zoospore, called **androspore** (FIG. 39A), is produced by the same filament that bears the oogonia or by a distinct filament. Androspores are produced in special cells, called **androsporangia**. The latter formed either singly or in a row, like the antheridia, by division of the ordinary vegetative cells of the filament. Each androsporangium produces a single androspore which, like the antherozoid, is provided with a crown of cilia and is motile. The androspore is intermediate in size between the zoospore and the antherozoid. When liberated, the androspore swims for a while and soon attaches itself direct to the oogonium or to a cell close to it. It then produces a short, narrow filament, called the **dwarf male** or **nannandrium** (FIG. 39B). This consists of an elongated, basal cell, and a terminal cell or a row of cells (2 to 4). Each such cell is an antheridium. It bears a pair of small, motile antherozoids crowned with cilia. The antheridium opens by a lid at the apex or it ruptures by the wall and the antherozoids are liberated. They swim to the oogonium and fertilization takes place in the usual way.

15. *CLADOPHORA* (160 *sp.*)

Occurrence. *Cladophora* (family Cladophoraceae; FIG. 40) is a very widely distributed genus, commonly found in fresh-water ponds,

Oedogonium.
> FIG. 38. Sexual Reproduction.
A, portion of a filament
showing antheridia (A)
and antherozoids (B);
B, a filament showing
oogonium (C) and egg-cell
(D) with receptive spot (E);
C, an oospore;
D, formation of
zoospores from it

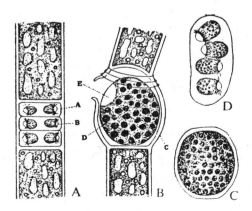

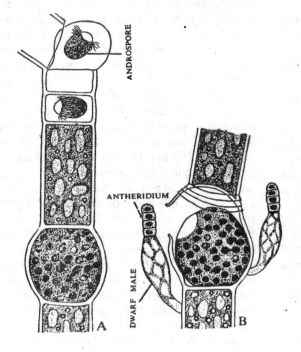

Oedogonium.
FIG. 39

A, portion of a filament showing an oogonium and two androspores;

B, a filament showing oogonium with a receptive spot and two dwarf males

lakes and streams. It attache to some object by rhizoid-like branches. A few species are marine.

Structure. The plant body consists of freely branched filaments. Each filament is made of a row of cylindrical cells that are united end to end (*A-B*). The branching is lateral, although sometimes it looks dichotomous. The cells are coenocytic in nature and contain numerous nuclei. The chloroplast of the young cell is parietal, encircling the cytoplasm, and reticulate. It also contains many pyrenoids. In the older cell, the chloroplast may break up into many discoidal ones, some containing pyrenoids. There is a large central vacuole. The cell-wall is made of three layers—the outer composed of chitin, the middle of pectic compounds and the inner of cellulose.

Reproduction. Vegetative reproduction is brought about by certain cells lying at the base of the plant. These cells are filled with a heavy store of food. After the filaments die, such cells grow into new filaments in the following season.

(a) *Asexual reproduction* is brought about by

quadriciliate zoospores (*C*), which are formed in large numbers in the apical cell and the other cells close to it (asexual plant). The zoospores are uninucleate. They escape one by one through a minute pore formed at or near the upper end of the cell-wall. After swarming there for a while, each secretes a wall, elongates rapidly and develops into a new plant (sexual plant).

(b) *Sexual reproduction*, which takes place only in the sexual plant, is brought about by isogametes borne by any of its vegetative cells. The gametes are biciliate (*D*) and are produced in large numbers, like the zoospores. Cladophora being hetcrothalhi, the gametes borne by two different plants fuse in pairs. The zygote formed as a result of fusion grows directly into a new plant (asexual plant) within a day or two. It reproduces through zoospores again. It should be noted that the spore (zoospore) bearing plant, i.e. the asexual plant, is diploid, and the gamete-bearing plant, i.e. the sexual plant, is haploid, but both are alike in appearance. Reduction division takes place

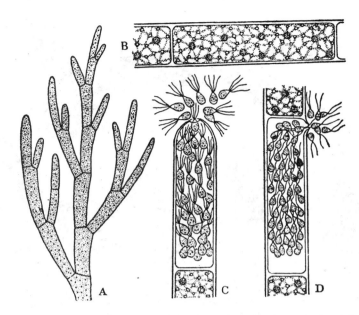

Cladophora. FIG. 40. *A*, a portion of the plant; *B*, a cell (magnified) showing peripheral reticulate chloroplast with many pyrenoids, and also several nuclei, *C*, quadriciliate zoospores escaping from the zoosporangium; *D*, biciliate gametes escaping from the gametangium

during the formation of the zoospores. *Cladophora* shows *isomorphic* alternation of generations. The stages in its life history are shown below:

1. Asexual plant $(2n)$ → zoospore (n) → sexual plant (n).

2. Sexual plant (n) → isogametes (n) (fusion in pairs) → zygote $(2n)$ → asexual plant $(2n)$

16. *VAUCHERIA* (35 *sp.*)

Occurrence. *Vaucheria* (family *Vaucheriaceae*; FIG. 41A) is a green freshwater alga, growing in ponds, ditches and wet soil. It is not free-floating like *Spirogyra*, but is mostly attached to a substratum by means of colourless rhizoids or holdfasts. It is deep-green and aways lives in a tangled mass.

Structure. The thallus consists of a single, branched, tubular filament. It is unseptate and contains many minute nuclei, which lie embedded in the lining layer of cytoplasm. Such a structure is known as a coenocyte. *Vaucheria* is, therefore, a coenocyte. There is a large central vacuole which

runs along the whole length of the coenocyte. Septa appear only in connection with the reproductive organs. The formation of septa also occurs during injury. The injured part, thus cut off, then develops into a new plant. The filaments increase in length by apical growth. There are several very small and discoidal chloroplasts. They lie embedded in the lining layer of cytoplasm and pyrenoids. The protoplasm contains plenty of oil-globules, but lacks in starch.

Reproduction. This takes place asexually as well as sexually.

(a) *Asexual Reproduction.* This is brought about by a large solitary zoospore. During its development, the apex of the filament swells up, becomes club-shaped and is partitioned off from the rest of the filament by a septum. This club-shaped body is known as the zoosporangium (FIG. 41B). Its protoplast becomes rounded off, forming a single zoospore. The wall of the zoosporangium ruptures at the apex. The zoospore escapes through the apical pore (FIG. 41C) and begins to

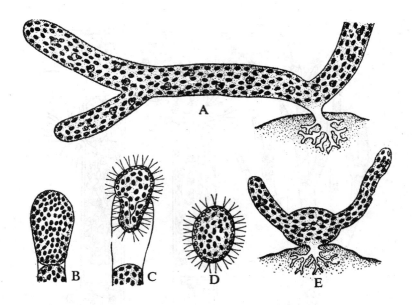

Vaucheria. FIG. 41. *A*, a *Vaucheria* filament; *B*, formation of zoosporangium;
C, zoospore escaping; *D*, free-swimming zoospore; *E*, zoospore germinating

rotate. The zoospore (FIG. 41D) is a large, oval body. Its central part is occupied by a large vacuole, and several small chloroplasts lie embedded in the surrounding zone of the cytoplasm, giving the zoospore an intensely deep-green colour. The whole surface of the naked (without cell-wall) zoospore is covered with numerous short cilia arranged in pairs and under each pair of cilia lies a nucleus. For this reason the zoospore is regarded as a compound one. The zoospores generally escape in the morning. They swim about freely for a while (half an hour or less), vibrating by the vibration of their cilia, and soon come to rest. The cilia are immediately withdrawn and a cell-wall is developed round each zoospore. The zoospore germinates (FIG. 41E) almost immediately after coming to rest. This is achieved by the protrusion of one or more tube-like filaments, one of which, at least, produces a colourless branched rhizoid and attaches the plant to the substratum. The protoplasm leaves the old cell and rejuvenates, i.e. it becomes young and active again. This method of asexual reproduction is known as rejuvenescence.

(b) *Sexual Reproduction.* This takes place by the method of fertilization, that is by sharply dif-

ferentiated male and female organs. The male organs are known as antheridia and the female as oogonia. These are developed at scattered intervals as lateral outgrowths. The antheridia and oogonia usually arise side by side on the same vegetative filament (FIG. 42B-C), or on short lateral branches of it (FIG. 42A). All fresh-water species of *Vaucheria* are homothallic.

The outgrowth that forms the oogonium swells out, assumes a more or less rounded form, and is cut off by a basal septum (FIG. 42A-C). The apex of the oogonium generally develops a *beak*, either towards the antheridium or away from it. The protoplasm of the oogonium contains much oil, several chloroplasts, but only one nucleus. There is a single egg-cell or oosphere which completely fills the oogonium. The oogonium is initially multinucleate, but before the partition wall is formed, all but one of the nuclei (the egg-nucleus) return to the main filament or degenerate.

Each antheridium arises as a short, tubular branch by the side of the oogonium, and simultaneously with it. Its terminal portion is cut off by a septum, and it then becomes the actual antheridium (FIG. 42A-C). It usually curves towards the

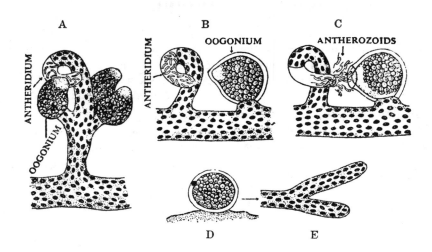

Vaucheria. FIG. 42. *A*, antheridium and oogonia on a short lateral branch; *B*, the same borne directly by the filament; *C*, mature antheridium and oogonium; antherozoids discharged and ovum about to be fertilized; *D*, oospore; *E*, a new filament developed from the oospore

oogonium as it matures. The protoplasm contains numerous chloroplasts and nuclei. Many male gametes (antherozoids) are produced inside each antheridium. They are very minute and biciliate. The cilia point in opposite directions.

Fertilization. The antheridium bursts at the apex and the antherozoids swarm to the vicinity of the oogonium, the beak of which opens at about the same time (FIG. 42C). Several antherozoids may enter through the beak, but only one fuses with the egg-nucleus, while the rest perish. *Vaucheria* is homothallic, and self-fertilization is the general rule. After fertilization, the oosphere, is surrounded by a thick cell-wall, and is known as the oospore (FIG. 42D). The oospore undergoes a period of rest, then germinates directly into a new *Vaucheria* filament (FIG. 42E). Reduction division has not yet been observed in *Vaucheria*.

17. *CAULERPA* (60 *sp.*)

Occurrence. All the species of *Caulerpa* (family *Caulerpaceae*) are marine, growing in shallow or deep water in tropical seas. They are attached to the mud or sand at the bottom of the water, rocks, coral reefs, or to the roots of mangrove plants.

Structure. The plant body is represented by a single-celled thallus with a slender, creeping rhizome. The latter bears colourless, root-like rhizoids on its lower surface, and erects leafy shoots on its upper surface. The plant body is a branched coenocyte (unicellular without any partition wall but multinucleate), usually 10-30 cm. in height. The cell-wall, made of callose and pectic substances, is comparatively thick. It has many ingrowths in the form of transverse and longitudinal rods, called the *trabeculae*, which give a degree of rigidity to the thallus. The cytoplasm forms a lining layer within the cell-wall and contains numerous nuclei and disc-shaped chloroplasts which do not contain any pyrenoids. There is a large vacuole at the centre, running lengthwise through the entire body of the plant.

Reproduction

Vegetative reproduction is effected by the fragmentation of the thallus into several parts, or by detachment of the leafy shoot from the rhizome. The details of asexual or sexual reproduction are not fully known.

Asexual reproduction takes place by means of zoospores. These are generally produced in any portion of the leafy shoot or sometimes in the rhizome. Numerous papilla-like outgrowths, called the *extrusion papillae* develop on the surface of the thallus. The zoospores are liberated through these, often in large quantities, like a mass of fine particles. The zoospores are pear-shaped and biciliate. Each has only one chloroplast without pyrenoids, and an eye spot.

Sexual reproduction has not been observed in all species. In *Caulerpa clavifera* and some other species, the mode of reproduction is anisogamous and the plants are dioecious (heterothallic). The gametes, formed in the erect, leafy shoot, are biciliate. The female gametes are somewhat longer and broader than the male gametes. As the zygote matures, the thallus disintegrates. However, the germination of the zygote has not been observed.

18. *CHARA* (90 *sp.*)

Occurrence. *Chara* (family *Characeae*; FIG. 43), a common stonewort, grows submerged in fresh-water ponds, lakes, streams and other pools of standing water. It is attached to the bottom by branched, filamentous rhizoids, and is gregarious in habit. Some species grow in brackish water. The body is often encrusted with lime, which often forms a thick deposit at the bottom. *Chara* and *Nitella* are two very common genera of *Characeae*. They are very widely distributed. About 20 species of *Chara* and 30 of *Nitella* have been recorded from India.

Structure. The plant body consists of an erect, branched stem, usually 20-30 cm. in height, differentiated into distinct nodes and internodes. Branching is of the following types: (*a*) a whorl of short branches, branchlets or leaves (of limited growth), consisting of usually 3-8 nodes and internodes at each node of the stem and the long branches (FIG. 43A), (*b*) whorls of short branches arising from the long branches (of unlimited growth), and (*c*) shorter branches or appendages with one internode and somewhat pointed ends (with complex sexual organs; FIG. 43B), called *bracts and bracteoles*, growing out of the branchlets or leaves. Besides, there may be some unicellular outgrowths, called *stipulodes* (or *stipuloids*), arising in 1 or 2 whorls from the basal node of each branchlet or leaf. The node consists of two or a few central cells and a definite number of

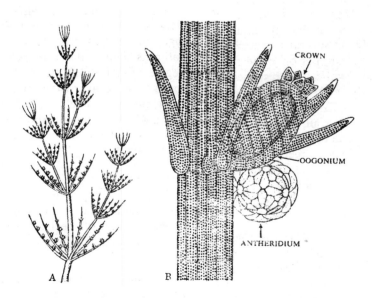

Chara. FIG. 43. *A*, a plant (upper portion) showing long and short branches; *B*, a branch showing an oogonium (or nucule) with sterile jacket and crown, and an antheridium (or globule) covered by shield cells

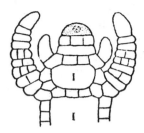

Chara. FIG. 44. Growing apical cell, nodes and internodes (*I*) in apex of stem

peripheral cells. The latter form a definite number of short branches or leaves (of limited growth). Their number is constant for a species. The central cells of the first node give rise to long branches (of unlimited growth). The internode consists of a single, large, cylindrical cell, ensheathed by a layer of narrow, vertical cells forming the cortex. The cortical cells arise partly from the upper node and partly from the lower node and meet somewhere in the middle of the internode. The stem grows in length by means of a dome-shaped apical cell (FIG. 44). All the cells contain numerous small chloroplasts but no pyrenoids, and the reserve food occurs in the form of spindle-shaped starch. Rotatory movement of the protoplasm round a large, central vacuole is very conspicuous in the internodal cells.

Reproduction. The plant normally reproduces sexually and sometimes vegetatively. Asexual reproduction is not known to take place. Vegetative reproduction is usually brought about by (*a*) bulbils—small masses of cells, usually spherical or star-shaped, formed on the stem, at the node or on the rhizoid, and (*b*) protonema-like outgrowths formed at the nodes.

(*a*) *Sexual Reproduction.* All species of *Chara* normally reproduce sexually. The male and the female fructifications—antheridium (otherwise called *globule*) and oogonium (otherwise called *nucule*)—are very complex structures with enveloping sheaths. They are borne at the nodes of short branches, which also bear still shorter, unicellular branches (FIG. 43B), and are visible to the naked eye. Most species of *Chara* are homothallic (monoecious), e.g. *C. zeylanica* and *C. fragilis*, and the antheridium and oogonium always occur in pairs with the latter lying just above the former. Only a few species are dioecious, e.g. *C. wallichii.*

The antheridium or globule (FIGS. 43B & 46A) is a very complex body. It is spherical and turns red or orange when mature. Its wall (jacket) is made of eight curved, plate-like cells, which are somewhat triangular, called **shield cells**. These have a peculiar thickening on the surface and their walls are folded with the joints fitting into one another. The shield cells expand rapidly, giving

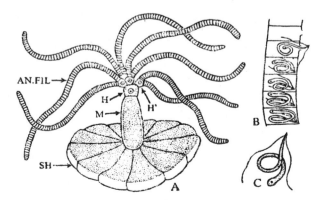

Chara. FIG. 45. *A*, a shield cell (*SH*) with manubrium (*M*), primary head cell or primary capitulum (*H*), secondary head cell or secondary capitulum (*H'*), and antheridial filaments (*AN, FIL*), each consisting of a row of minute antheridial cells; *B*, a few antheridial cells of a filament (magnified), each cell with a biciliate antherozoid; *C*, a free swimming antherozoid after escape

rise to a cavity within the antheridium. Besides, their outer walls form ingrowths, dividing the cells into a number of compartments. From the centre of each shield, an elongated, cylindrical cell, called the **manubrium** or handle cell, projects inwards. Evidently, there are eight manubria. Each of them terminates inwardly in a roundish cell, called the *primary capitulum* or primary head cell. The head cell cuts off six smaller cells, known as the *secondary capitula* or secondary head cells. The secondary head cell produces a pair of long, slender **antheridial filaments** (FIGS. 45A & 46A), of which consists of 100-200 tiny cells called **antheridial cells**. The antheridial filaments form a tangled mass in the cavity of the antheridium. The protoplast of an antheridial cell forms a single, coiled, biciliate antherozoid (FIG. 45B-C). A single antheridium may produce as many as 20,000-50,000 antherozoids. When the antheridium matures, the shields separate from one another. Besides, there is an elongated stalk cell, called the **pedicel cell**, projecting into the cavity of the antheridium.

The oogonium or nucule is an ovoid structure that is much bigger than the antheridium. Closely encircling the oogonium are five spiral bands of cells, called **jacket cells** (or tube cells or turning cells). These cells arise at the base. After they have surrounded the oogonium completely, they cut off at their tips five small cells, which form the **crown** or corona. The oogonium contains a single, large, uninucleate egg and plenty of food material.

Fertilization. When the antheridium matures, it gets ruptured at the junctions of the shield cells, which then fall apart. The antheridial filaments are exposed. The antherozoids escape through slits or pores in the walls of the antheridial cells and swim about. The crown cells of the oogonium separate slightly at the base, leaving five small slits through which the antherozoids enter. Finally, one of them fuses with the egg-nucleus. The zygote (oospore) clothes itself with a thick wall and the oogonium as a whole hardens. The zygote germinates after a period of rest. The zygote-nucleus undergoes reduction division, forming four haploid nuclei, three of which degenerate. On germination, the zygote gives rise to a rhizoid and a green filament (protonema). The shoot of the *Chara* plant arises from the protonema as a lateral bud.

The vegetative cells of the *Chara* plant are

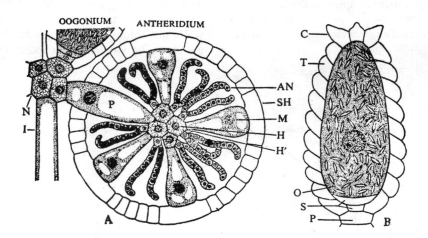

Chara. FIG. 46. *A*, antheridium (globule) in section. *AN*, antheridial filament; *SH*, shield cell; *M*, manubrium; *H*, primary head cell (or primary capitulum); *H'*, secondary head cell (or secondary capitulum); *P*, pedicel; *N*, node; *I*, internode; *B*, oogonium (nucule) in section; *C*, corona; *T*, tube cell (or turning cell); *O*, oogonium with an egg, and plenty of starch grains (spindle-shaped) and oil globules; *S*, stalk cells; *P*, pedicel cell.

haploid, with 28 chromosomes, while the zygote (oospore) is diploid.

Origin of *Characeae*. *Characeae* or stoneworts hold a unique position among the green thallophytes. They are possibly related to Chlorophyceae, but the degree of relationship cannot be ascertained. *Characeae* is an ancient group and may have arisen as an offshoot of some early Chlorophyceae. Their bright green colour (chlorophyll being the only pigment present in them), the storage of carbohydrates in the form of starch, the gametophytic nature of the plant body, the sporophytic stage being represented only by the zygote, etc., as in all green algae, indicate some relationship between *Characeae* and Chlorophyceae. That is why this group is often classified as an order of Chlorophyceae (see p. 342). But the erect, vegetative body with nodes and internodes, and the complex reproductive organs with sterile sheaths are distinctive features. The multicellular sex organs tend to raise this group to a higher level (bryophytic level), but the structure and development of these organs are very different in the two groups. Moreover, the sporophytic phase, so well developed in stages in bryophyta, is practically absent (except for the zygote). Therefore, some algologists still prefer to treat *Characeae* as a distinct and isolated group of green thallophytes. They classify the green algae (or Chlorophyta) into two separate classes: Chlorophyceae and Charophyceae.

CLASS IV **BACILLARIOPHYCEAE**
(or diatoms; 5,300 sp.)

General Description. Bacillariophyceae, commonly called **diatoms** (FIG. 47), constitute a big, isolated group of mostly one-celled algae. These are of an infinite variety of forms and often of exquisite beauty. The single cells may occasionally form filaments and colonies. They are universally distributed in fresh water, as well as in salt water, and also in wet ground. In some parts of the ocean, they occur in a vast assemblage as floating *plankton*. They often occur in huge numbers in a small space. Most diatoms are free-floating, but some are attached by a gelatinous stalk. Many free-floating diatoms exhibit a jerky movement that is visible under a microscope. There are over 5,300 living species of diatoms. Fossil diatoms are seen to have formed huge deposits of siliceous or diatomaceous earth, often of considerable depth, in various parts of the world.

Structure. Diatoms (FIG. 47) may be boat-shaped, rod-shaped, disc-shaped, wedge-shaped, spindle-shaped, circular, oval, rectangular, etc. The wall of the diatom cell is made of two halves or valves, one (older) fitting closely over the other

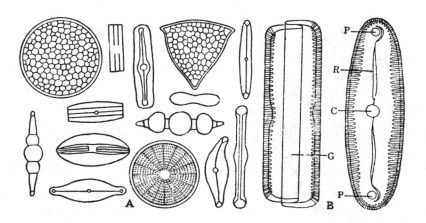

Diatoms. FIG. 47. *A*, various forms of diatoms; *B*, a diatom (*Pinnularia*): *left*, girdle view showing overlapping valves; *right*, valve view showing raphe; *G*, girdle; *P*, polar nodule; *R*, raphe; *C*, central nodule

(younger), very much like a pill-box or soap case. The outer valve is known as the *epitheca* and the inner as the *hypotheca*. The valves are made of pectin impregnated with silica. They are adorned with numerous fine lines, which are really a series of very fine *dots*. The ornamentation, a special feature of diatom valves, is radially symmetrical in the round or centric diatoms (called **Centrales**), which are of wide occurrence in the ocean. It is bilaterally symmetrical (in two series, one on each side of the valve) in the elongated or pinnate diatoms (called **Pennales**), which are frequently found in fresh water. In some genera, there are *ingrowths* of the wall. According to their position, these ingrowths are called central nodules or polar nodules. A longitudinal line or slit extends from the central to the polar nodule in many diatoms. This line, called the *raphe*, actually consists of a series of extremely minute openings. The jerky movement, seen only in diatoms with raphes, may be due to the streaming movement of the cytoplasm along the raphe. The movement of the cytoplasm pseudopodia through the openings of the raphe sets up a water current. Under the microscope, usually either the side with the valve is uppermost (*valve side*), or the side with the connecting band is uppermost (girdle side).

The protoplast consists of a thin, peripheral layer of cytoplasm lying just within the cell-wall, one large or many small yellow to golden-brown plastids of various shapes and sizes, a central nucleus suspended by distinct, slender cytoplasmic threads or by a broad cytoplasmic band, and a conspicuous central vacuole. The colour is due to the presence of a golden-brown pigment called *diatomin*, in addition to chlorophyll. Pyrenoids may or may not be present. When present, they do not have a starchy envelope. The reserve food consists of globules of fat and globules of an insoluble complex substance called *volutin*. No starch is formed in diatoms.

Reproduction. Diatoms may reproduce vegetatively (by cell division, generally at night), asexually (by auxospores), and sexually (by conjugation of gametes), but all these methods are unique. In vegetative reproduction, the protoplast

grows, resulting in the separation of the two valves. Each of the two half-cells forms a new valve against the old one, fitting into it. Division and valve formation proceeds continuously. As a result, one set of cells gradually becomes smaller and smaller. The reduction in size, however, does not apply to all forms. When a particular minimum size is reached, there is a reversion to the original size through the formation and activity of a special kind of cell called **auxospore**. The auxospore may be formed in a variety of ways. (1) In the first method, the protoplast of a cell may escape from the valves after the valves have separated. It grows to its maximum size and then forms new valves. The protoplast acts as an auxospore. (2) In the second method, the protoplast divides into two, each daughter protoplast (an auxospore) growing and forming new valves. (3) In the third method, which is a sexual one, the protoplasts of two cells escape and act as two gametes. They fuse to produce a zygote, which behaves as an auxospore. (4) In the fourth method, two contiguous diatom cells form two gametes each. These fuse in pairs, forming two zygotes which act as auxospores. The auxospore grows and helps the diatom return to its original size.

Uses. Diatomaceous earth has a variety of uses. It is used in metal polish, toothpaste, paints and plastics. It is extensively used as a filter in filtration of liquids, e.g. sugar refining. It is also used as a heat insulator in boilers and furnaces.

CLASS V PHAEOPHYCEAE
(or brown algae; 1,000 species)

General Characteristics. Phaeophyceae or brown algae are a very interesting group of seaweeds with a variety of peculiar forms and sizes, comprising about 1,000 species. They are widely distributed between tidal levels along sea coasts, predominantly of temperate seas. They are attached to rocks or some other substrata. In colder seas, they seldom go beyond a depth of 20 m., while in warmer seas, a few species may grow to a maximum depth of 90 m. Some also grow as epiphytes or endophytes on other algae. A few are free-floating. Their colour ranges from brown to olive-green due to the presence in the chloroplasts of a brown pigment, *fucoxanthin*, which masks the chlorophyll. There are no pyrenoids. The reserve food may be a kind of sugar (and not starch) or, more commonly, a complex carbohydrate called *laminarin*. Some, like *Ectocarpus*, are short filaments, while others, like *Fucus* and *Sargassum*, are usually a few cm. to 1 m. in length. Others are massive seaweeds, called giant kelps (*Laminaria*—2-9 m., *Nereocystis*—45 m., and *Macrocystis*— 60-90 m.). They grow at or below the low tide level, extending far into the sea to a depth of about 90 m. Small kelps are only about a metre long. Unicellular brown algae are not known to exist. The body of the kelp is differentiated into a basal, root-like, branched holdfast, a long or short stem called **stipe** and one or more leaf-like blades called **fronds**, which have air bladders to facilitate floating. Some species have fronds of massive size. Phaeophyceae (except *Fucus* and *Sargassum*) show a regular alternation of generations, with different degrees of development of the sporophyte and the gametophyte. The latter can be similar (isomorphic, as in *Ectocarpus*) or dissimilar (heteromorphic, as in *Laminaria*) in external appearance, and their motile cells (zoospores and gametes or sperms) are laterally biciliate, the two cilia being of unequal lengths, in contrast with the apically ciliate cells of most algae.

Reproduction. Motile reproductive bodies (zoospores and gametes or sperms) are universally present throughout Phaeophyceae. Several species reproduce vegetatively, by fragmentation of the thallus. Most of them reproduce asexually, through zoospores or aplanospores (except *Fucus* and *Sargassum*), and sexually, by isogamy, anisogamy or oogamy. The zygote germinates without any period of rest.

Uses. Kelps are sources of iodine. Many are rich in potassium and other minerals, and are used as fertilizers in coastal areas. They contain sugar and several are rich in vitamins. Some are consumed by the coastal people of China and Japan. Most of the brown algae form an important source of food for fish. Algin, another product obtained from kelps (particularly *Laminaria* and *Macrocystis*), is used in certain industries, as in the making of ice cream, in the rubber industry, baking industry, paint industry and in certain pharmaceutical preparations.

Origin of Phaeophyceae. Phaeophyceae or brown algae are supposed to have originated from some brown, ciliate, unicellular ancestor. The universal presence of motile, ciliate reproductive cells lends support to this view. The brown algae do not seem to be related to the green algae. Their vegetative body (thallus) is always multicellular, in contrast to various unicellular green algae. Then again, the presence of fucoxanthin and the formation of laminarin are exclusive to this group. However, because of the missing links, their origin and relationship with other algae cannot be traced. Like green algae, they show progressive stages of sexual reproduction—isogamy to anisogamy to oogamy. Phaeophyceae have remained confined to the sea and have not given rise to land forms. However, there seem to be two divergent lines of evolution within the group—in one, the two alternating generations (sporophyte and gametophyte) are similar in external appearance, while in the other, the two generations are dissimilar. The origin of Fucales and their relationship with other brown algae are also shrouded in mystery.

1. *ECTOCARPUS*

Occurrence. *Ectocarpus* (family *Ectocarpaceae*; FIG. 48A) is a simple brown alga. It is very widely distributed and found in plenty, attached to other bigger algae or rocks along the coasts of almost all seas.

Structure. *Ectocarpus* (FIG. 48A) occurs as tufts of branched filaments. Each filament is monosiphonous, i.e. it consists of a single row of cells. The plant body is differentiated into two portions: a prostrate portion that is irregularly branched, and an erect portion with much-branched filaments. The cells are uninucleate and contain a few band-shaped or many small, disc-shaped, brown plastids (chromatophores). Although all individual plants of a species look alike vegetatively, investigations have shown that there are actually two different kinds—one (asexual plant) is the sporophyte with diploid ($2n$ chromosomes) and the other (sexual plant) is the gametophyte with haploid (n chromosomes).

Reproduction. The sporophytic (diploid) plant

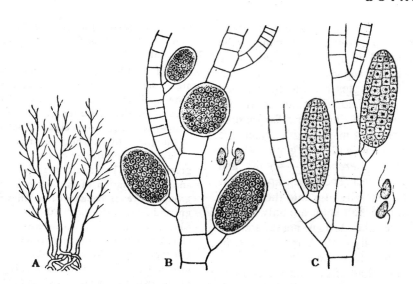

Ectocarpus. FIG. 48. *A*, habit of the plant; *B*, asexual plant (*n*) with unilocular
sporangia; two zoospores (*n*) shown separately; *C*, asexual plant (2*n*) with plurilocular
sporangia; two zoospores shown separately

reproduces asexually through two kinds of
zoospores. One kind, formed in a unilocular
zoosporangium, is haploid (FIG. 48*B*), and the
other kind, borne in a plurilocular zoosporangium,
is diploid (FIG. 48*C*). The gametophytic plant, on
the other hand, though very much like a sporophyte
and hardly distinguishable from it, reproduces
through gametes borne in plurilocular gametangia.
The gametangia with gametes and the plurilocular
zoosporangium with zoospores seeming alike, a
good deal of confusion arose as to whether the
structure concerned was really a gametangium or a
sporangium. Investigations on cytology and
behaviour of such reproductive bodies clarified the
position. It was found that the zoospores are
diploid and each grows by itself, whereas the
gametes are haploid and fuse in pairs. Therefore,
the zoospore-bearing organ is the sporangium and
the gamete-bearing organ is the gametangium. The
corresponding plants, though alike, are sporophyte
and gametophyte, respectively.

(a) *Asexual Reproduction.* Cytologically, there
are two kinds of zoospores (borne by the sporophytic or asexual plant)—some haploid (with *n*
chromosomes) and some diploid (with 2*n* chromosomes), borne respectively in unilocular sporangia

and plurilocular sporangia. Both kinds of sporangia may be borne by the same plant or by two different plants. The unilocular sporangium may be a
flattened cell of the filament, or it may develop at
the end of a short lateral branch. In any case, it
bears 32 or 64 zoospores which, as said above, are
haploid. These finally escape from the sporangium
through a terminal opening and give rise to the
gametophytes. The plurilocular sporangium, on
the other hand, borne likewise laterally, consists of
several hundreds of small cells arranged in several
(20–40) transverse tiers. Each cell of the sporangium develops a single zoospore. In both cases,
the zoospores are laterally biciliate, the cilia being
of different lengths. The zoospore gives rise to the
diploid sporophyte, which again bears plurilocular
sporangia. *Ectocarpus* may multiply indefinitely
by this method. Sometimes, depending on seasonal changes, the diploid zoospores borne in the
plurilocular sporangium develop plants that bear
unilocular sporangia with haploid zoospores. In
this case, reduction division takes place at an early
stage of sporangium formation. Such zoospores
grow into gametophytic plants.

(b) *Sexual Reproduction.* The gametophytic or
sexual plant (FIG. 49) is like the sporophyte in

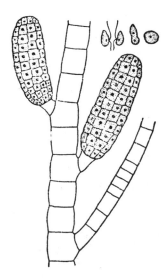

Ectocarpus. FIG. 49. Sexual plant (*n*) with
plurilocular gametangia; two gametes (*n*),
conjugation, and zygote (2*n*) shown separately

appearance. It produces (laterally) long, multicellular gametangia resembling plurilocular sporangia. Each cell of the gametangium produces a
single, laterally biciliate gamete. All gametes are
of the same size (isogametes), but there is some
difference in the behaviour (activity) of the pairing gametes. Ecotocarpus being heterothallic,
gametes coming from different plants fuse in
pairs. The gametes escape from the gametangium
and swim in the water. A particular gamete
(female) soon comes to rest, and one of the many
active gametes (male), which cluster round it,
fuses with it. The zygote that is formed is diploid.
It grows, without any period of rest, into a sporophyte bearing unilocular or plurilocular sporangia
or both, as described above. Often, some of the
gametes, particularly the female ones, develop by
parthenogenesis, i.e. without fertilization, into
new haploid plants (gametophytes). The gametes,
thus, behave as haploid zoospores.

Alternation of Generations. *Ectocarpus* shows
isomorphic alternation of generations. The two
generations are more or less equally developed.
The spore(zoospore)-bearing plant is the sporophyte (diploid), while the gamete-bearing plant is
the gametophyte (haploid). On sexual reproduction through gametes, the gametophyte produces a
diploid zygote which gives rise to the diploid
plant, i.e. the sporophyte. The sporophyte, on the
other hand, reproduces by haploid zoospores
borne in a unilocular sporangium and gives rise to
the gametophyte. Thus, the two generations
(diploid and haploid) alternate with each other.
But there are some discrepancies in the life-cycle
of *Ectocarpus*. It is seen that the diploid zoospores
borne in the plurilocular sporangium give rise to
sporophytes which bear only plurilocular sporangia with diploid zoospores. In this case, the gametophytic generation is omitted. Then again,
gametes may act as spores (zoospores) and develop parthenogenetically into gametophytes again.
In this case, the sporophytic generation is omitted.
The stages in the life history of Ectocarpus are
shown below :

1. Asexual plant (2*n*) → (*a*) zoospores (2*n*) in
plurilocular sporangium → asexual plant (2*n*);
(*b*) zoospores (*n*) in unilocular sporangium → sexual plant (*n*).

2. Sexual paint (*n*) → isogametes (*n*) in plurilocular
gametangium by fusion in pairs → zygote (2*n*) →
asexual plant (2*n*).

2. *LAMINARIA* (30 *sp.*)

Occurrence. *Laminaria* (family *Laminariaceae;*
FIG.50A) is widely distributed in cold waters along
the shores of the North Pacific Ocean and the
North Atlantic Ocean. Several species are found
below the low-tide level, often extending far out
into the sea to a depth of about 30 metres.

Structure. The plant body consists of a large
blade (frond), a stipe and a holdfast (FIG. 50A).
The blade represents the main part of the plant,
usually varying from 2m. to 4m. in length. In
some species, the thallus may be as big as 9m.,
while in a few others, it is only 0.5m. The blade
may be simple, with smooth or wavy margins, or it
may be palmately divided (*L. digitata*; FIG. 50B).
The stipe is a slender, long, flexuous stalk supporting the blade. The holdfast is a disc-like structure
at the base. It has root-like branches, which are
often provided with a dense mass of rhizoids. The

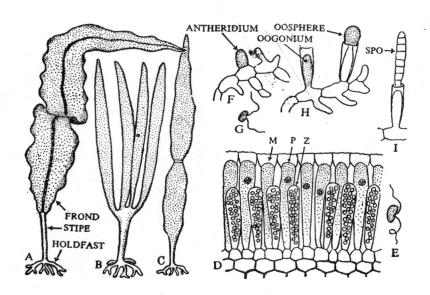

Laminaria. FIG. 50. *A*, a plant; *B*, *Laminaria digitata* with a palmate blade; *C*, a plant showing
old blade (*top*), meristematic zone (*middle*), and new blade (*bottom*); *D*, a portion of a sorus
in section (*M*, mucilage cap; *P*, paraphysis; *Z*, zoosporangium); *E*, a biciliate zoospore; *F*, a male
gametophyte; *G*, a biciliate antherozoid; *H*, a female gametophyte; and *I*, a young sporophyte (*SPO*) on oogonium

plant attaches itself to some submerged rock by means of the holdfast. A meristematic zone, lying at the base of the blade, annually produces a new blade, the old one dying off (FIG. 50*C*).

Thallus in Section (FIG. 51). A vertical section shows that the thallus (stipe or blade) is differentiated into three distinct zones: (*a*) externally, the **epidermis**—1 or 2 layers thick, with many chromatophores; assimilatory in nature, (*b*) a deep **cortex** made of vertically elongated cells arranged in radial rows, but slightly separated by an anastomosing system of mucilage ducts (except at certain points), and (*c*) centrally, an axis or **medulla**, consisting of (*i*) multicellular vertical filaments ('*hyphae*'), somewhat parallel to each other, (*ii*) some connecting filaments, also multicellular, running horizontally or diagonally through the medulla, and (*iii*) certain cells of the medulla modified into long filaments ('*trumpet hyphae*') with perforated transverse walls, as in sieve-plates. The perforations may be blocked by callus pads at a later stage. The trumpet hyphae may have spiral bands of thickening, like a spiral vessel, but

made of cellulose. The medulla, as a whole, conducts fluids.

Reproduction. Most species of *Laminaria* are perennial. Although there are specific differences in external form, the general life history, including modes of reproduction, is remarkably similar. *Laminaria* shows distinct alternation of generations. The main plant, which is large, is the sporophyte and it reproduces asexually. The gametophytes, male and female, are represented by very minute, filamentous bodies and they reproduce sexually.

(*a*) *Asexual Reproduction.* For this purpose, many unilocular zoosporangia develop in extensive sori on both surfaces of the blade, almost covering them. Each **sorus** (FIG. 50*D*) consists of a mass of zoosporangia intermixed with a large number of paraphyses. They develop from superficial (epidermal) cells on the surface of the blade. At first, an epidermal cell divides into two—a basal cell and terminal cell. The latter elongates and becomes more or less club-shaped. This is the **paraphysis**. It is capped by a mucilaginous layer.

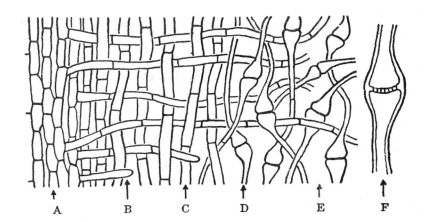

Laminaria. FIG. 51. Stipe in longi-section through the medulla. *A*, part of the
cortex (note the mucilage ducts); *B*, transverse connecting filament; *C*, vertical filament
('hypha'); *D*, trumpet hypha; *E*, mucilage ducts; and *F*, trumpet hypha showing perforations like a sieve-plate

All the paraphyses are held together by the mucilaginous caps in a distinct palisade. The zoosporangia develop in the same way, and are also more or less club-shaped. However, they are much shorter than the paraphyses. The nucleus of the sporangium divides repeatedly into 32 or 64 nuclei and finally, they become converted into a group of 32 or 64 zoospores, of more or less the same size. Each zoospore (FIG. 50*E*) is pear-shaped and biciliate. The two long cilia are placed laterally, and there may be an eye spot. The zoospores escape in a mass of mucilage through the apex of the sporangium. The mucilage dissolves and the zoospores are set free. They are motile and swim briskly in the water. Soon, however, a wall forms around each, and they settle and germinate.

(b) *Sexual Reproduction*. The zoospores germinate and produce two kinds of minute filamentous bodies—the gametophytes. At first, a zoospore grows into a *germ tube*, which soon enlarges at the tip. The zoospore nucleus divides into two and the protoplast, together with a nucleus, migrates into the enlarged tip. The other nucleus degenerates. The enlarged cell then divides, giving rise to a short filament with a few short branches. The whole structure is the gametophyte, male or female. The zoospores of the sporangium produce male and female gametophytes (FIG. 50*F* & *H*) in equal numbers. All the gametophytes are microscopic. The male gametophyte, however, has smaller cells than the female. The male and the female gametophytes bear antheridia and oogonia, respectively, in their lateral branches. The antheridium (FIG. 50*F*) is a small, spherical cell containing one antherozoid. The antherozoid (FIG. 50*G*) is extremely minute and has two long but unequal cilia, which are placed laterally. The oogonium (FIG. 50*H*) is an enlarged structure containing an oosphere. The oogonium is covered by a mucilaginous layer, which forms a sort of cup at the apex. The oosphere partly frees itself from the oogonium and rests on the mucilage cup. Fertilization is effected in the usual way. The antherozoids swim to the oogonium and one of them fuses with the oosphere. The oosphere surrounds itself with a wall and becomes the oospore. The latter soon divides and produces a short filament *in situ* (FIG. 50 *I*). With the formation of rhizoids at the base, the filament gets detached from the oogonium and soon attaches itself to a submerged rock. Gradually, it grows into a full-fledged *Laminaria* plant with a holdfast, stipe and blade.

Alternation of Generations. *Laminaria* shows a distinct heteromorphic alternation of generations—a large sporophyte and minute gametophytes. The main plant is the sporophyte, which reproduces asexually through zoospores, giving rise to the gametophytes, male and female, in equal numbers. They are extremely small and bear antheridia and oogonia, respectively. They reproduce sexually through the antherozoid and oosphere, giving rise to the sporophyte. The stages in the life cycle of *Laminaria* are given below:

itself to a rock, (*b*) a long or short stipe, i.e. the stem-like portion, and (*c*) leather fronds or laminae, i.e. the flattened portions, provided with a distinct mid-rib. The inflated tip of the frond is called the **receptacle**. It has some small openings, each leading into a cavity known as the **conceptacle**. The branches have some swellings along the mid-rib, often close to dichotomy. These swellings are filled with air and are known as air bladders. They give buoyancy to the plant, helping it float. The body of *Fucus* is composed of parenchymatous

$$\text{Laminaria plant } (2n) \rightarrow \text{sori } (2n) \rightarrow \text{zoosporangia } (2n) \rightarrow \text{zoospores } (n)$$
$$\uparrow \qquad\qquad\qquad\qquad\qquad\qquad\qquad\qquad\qquad\qquad\qquad\qquad\qquad \downarrow$$
$$\text{antherozoid } (n) \leftarrow \text{antheridium } (n) \leftarrow \text{male gametophyte } (n) \leftarrow$$
$$\text{oospore } (2n) \leftarrow \text{X oosphere } (n) \leftarrow \text{oogonium } (n) \leftarrow \text{female gametophyte } (n)$$

3. *FUCUS* (16 *sp.*)

Occurrence. *Fucus* (family *Fucaceae*) is a widely distributed marine alga, growing between the high tide level and low tide level along coasts. They are more abundant in temperate seas.

Structure. The *Fucus* plant (FIG. 52) consists of a dichotomously branched thallus, generally 0.3 to 1 m. in length. Some species growing below the low tide level may be as big as 4.5 m. The plant body is differentiated into three distinct parts: (*a*) a basal, disc-shaped holdfast by which the plant attaches

cells. Each cell contains a nucleus and several plastids, which contain *fucoxanthin* in addition to chlorophyll, the former masking the chlorophyll and giving the plant a brown appearance. As a result of photosynthesis, a carbohydrate called *laminarin* accumulates in the cells. No starch is formed.

The thallus in section shows a loose mass of elongated cells, collectively known as the medulla, which occupies the main bulk of the thallus. The interspaces in the medulla are filled with a gelatinous substance. Surrounding the medulla and lying towards the surfaces is a compact mass of cells known as the **cortex**. The thallus grows by means of a single, pyramidal, apical cell.

Reproduction. Asexual reproduction is absent in *Fucus*. Vegetative reproduction occurs through fragmentation of the thallus. The detached parts then float on the water and vegetate. *Fucus*, however, usually reproduces sexually through heterogametes—antherozoids and eggs borne by the antheridium and oogonium, respectively.

(*a*) *Sexual Reproduction.* Antheridia and oogonia are borne in special globose or flask-shaped cavities, known as the **conceptacles**, which lie embedded in the swollen tip or **receptacle** of the thallus. Externally, the conceptacles appear as small scars. Both antheridia and oogonia may occur in the same conceptacle or in two separate conceptacles borne by the same plant (monoecious), or they may be borne by two separate plants (dioecious).

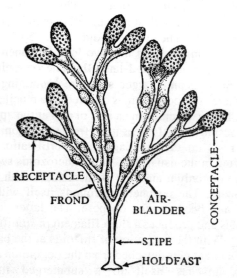

Fucus. FIG. 52. A *Fucus* Plant. (Dark dots on the receptacle are conceptacles)

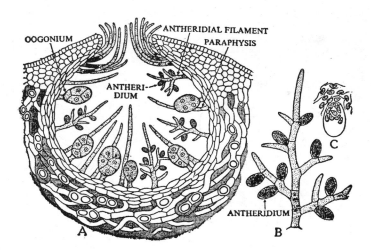

Fucus. FIG. 53. *A*, a conceptacle in longi-section showing oogonia in various stages of development, antheridial filaments with antheridia, and paraphyses; *B*, an antheridial filament (magnified) showing antheridia with antherozoids; *C*, an antheridium discharging biciliate antherozoids

A conceptacle (FIG. 53*A*) of monoecious species shows in section the following: (*a*) several unbranched, multicellular, sterile hairs called **paraphyses**, (*b*) an apical opening known as the **ostiole**, (*c*) numerous oval, sac-like **antheridia** borne on small, much-branched *antheridial filaments* (FIG. 53*B*), and (*d*) a number of isolated oval oogonia, each borne on a very short stalk-cell. The antheridium produces numerous, more or less pear-shaped **antherozoids**, generally 64 in number, each with two lateral cilia of unequal lengths. After they are liberated from the antheridium, the antherozoids (FIG. 53*C*) swim about freely in water. Each oogonium (FIG. 53*A*) is a single, large, oval cell. Its nucleus divides three times to produce *eight* nuclei. Each forms a large, round egg with the cleavage of the cytoplasm. The oogonial wall is made of three layers. The outer layer bursts and the oogonium, still surrounded by the two inner layers, is pushed out of the conceptacle as a result of the swelling of the gelatinous material within the conceptacle. Later the middle layer ruptures at the apex, and as the inner layer imbibes more water, it swells and the eggs become rounded off. The inner layer soon dissolves and the eggs are set free (FIG. 54*A-C*). Both antheridia and oogonia are liberated in packets, through the ostiole.

Fertilization. Eggs are large and passive, while the antherozoids are minute, ciliate and active. A length number of antherozoids swim to the oogonium, being attracted by some chemical substance, and each gets attached to it by one cilium (FIG. 54*D*). Their vibrations around the egg makes it rotate. One or more antherozoids may enter the egg, but only one fuses with the egg-nucleus. The fertilzied egg or zygote clothes itself with a wall, and almost immediately (within a few hours) divides and grows into a new thallus.

Alternation of Generations. There is no alternation of generations in *Fucus*. The plant itself is diploid, i.e. sporophytic. Reduction takes place during the formation of gametes (eggs and antherozoids); so the gametes are haploid, i.e. gametophytic. The diploid condition is restored in the zygote after the fertilization of the gametes. Stages in the life-cycle of the *Fucus* plant are shown below:

Fucus plant ($2n$) conceptacle ($2n$) → $\begin{cases} \text{antheridium}(2n) \rightarrow \text{antherozoid } (n) \\ \text{oogonium } (2n) \rightarrow \text{egg } (n) \text{ by } fusion \end{cases}$

(fertilization) with an antherozoid → zygote ($2n$) → *Fucus* plant ($2n$).

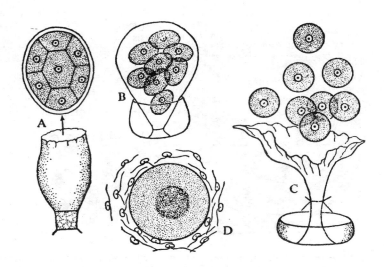

Fucus. FIG. 54 *A*, escape of oogonium with 8 (nearly mature) eggs from the outer layer;
B, oogonium with 8 mature eggs escaping from the middle layer which has burst and slipped down:
C, breaking of the inner layer setting free the 8 fully formed eggs; *D*, an egg surrounded by numerous
biciliate antherozoids just prior to fertilization. (*Redrawn partly after* FIG. 171 in Plant Morphology by
A. W. Haupt by permission of McGraw-Hill Book Company)

Note that the *Fucus* plant being a sporophyte with diploid chromosomes, the so-called antheridium is looked upon as a microsporangium producing small motile microspores which function as antherozoids, and the so-called oogonium as a megasporangium producing large immobile megaspores which function as eggs. *Fucus* is thus heterosporous.

4. *SARGASSUM* (250 *sp.*)

Occurrence. *Sargassum* (FIG. 55) is a common genus of *Sargassaceae* growing abundantly along the rocky coasts of tropical and sub-tropical seas. The plant grows to a length of about 6 m. or so and may remain attached to some rocks by a holdfast or as is common may be free-floating, often being drifted to the coast or far out into the sea. This plant grows aboundantly in the Sargasso Sea, which Columbus braved in 1492, despite the apprehensions of his sailors.

Structure. The plant body consists of an axis (stipe) with many branches. Branching is always monopodial. The stipe and the lateral branches bear a large number of green flattened or cylindrical leafy fronds with wavy serrated margins and a mid-rib. Berry-like air-bladders develop in small clusters from the axil of the frond or close to its base. These give buoyancy to the plant to facilitate floating. The species of *Sargassum* exhibits a range of forms. Growth takes place by a three-sided apical cell.

Reproduction. *Sargassum* is closely related to *Fucus* and follows the same life-cycle. **Vegetative reproduction** is most common and is brought about by the fragmentation of the thallus. There is no asexual mode of reproduction in *Sargassum*.

Sexual Reproduction. Receptacles with many branches are often borne into the axil of the frond or a little beyond. Sexual reproduction takes place through well-developed sex organs (antheridia and oogonia) which occur in hollow flask-shaped cavities called **conceptacles** at the ends of the branches of the receptacle. Plants of this species may be monoecious, bearing the sex organs in two distinct conceptacles on the same receptacle or on two separate receptacles, or they may be dioecious, the organs being borne by two separate plants. The monoecious condition is, however, more usual than the other. Each conceptacle has a minute opening at the apex, called the **ostiole**. Sterile conceptacles, called *cryptoblasts*, often occur scattered over the thallus. Several **oogonia** lie embedded in the wall of the female conceptacle. The nucleus of the oogonium divides thrice to form eight nuclei, but only one of them is functional, acting as the egg. The others degenerate. Nuclear divisions usually take place while the oogonium is still within the conceptacle. Sometimes they occur after the oogonium moves out of it. The oogonium wall is differentiat-

Fertilization. This takes place outside the plant body, as in *Fucus*, and the process is much the same in both the cases. Several antherozoids swim to each oogonium but only one fuses with the egg-nucleus. This results in the formation of a zygote which germinates immediately without any period of rest.

Alternation of Generations. *Sargassum*, like *Fucus*, shows no alternation of generations. The plant itself is diploid and the only gametes are haploid. The zygote ($2n$) grows into the plant without any reduction division. The life-cycle of *Sargassum* is as follows:

$$
\begin{aligned}
&Sargassum\ (2n) \rightarrow \text{receptacle}\ (2n) \rightarrow \male\ \text{conceptacle}\ (2n) \rightarrow \text{antheridium}\ (2n) \\
&\qquad\qquad\qquad\qquad\qquad\qquad\qquad\qquad \text{antherozoids}\ (n) \leftarrow \text{by meiosis} \\
&\qquad\qquad\qquad\qquad \rightarrow \female\ \text{conceptacle}\ (2n) \rightarrow \text{oogonium}\ (2n) \\
&\text{zygote}\ (2n) \leftarrow \text{(by fusion with an antherozoid) egg}\ (n) \leftarrow \text{by meiosis}
\end{aligned}
$$

ed into three layers, as in *Fucus*. All the oogonia are discharged from the wall of the conceptacle but each remains attached to it by a long slender mucilaginous thread. Numerous **antheridia** develop on branched antheridial filaments in the male conceptacle in much the same way as in *Fucus*. Each antheridium bears 64 antherozoids which are biciliate and more or less pear-shaped. The two cilia are of unequal lengths.

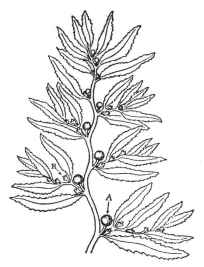

Saragassum. FIG. 55. A plant (portion) showing numerous green fronds, air-bladders (A) and receptacles (R)

CLASS VI RHODOPHYCEAE
or red algae (about 3,000 sp.)

General Characteristics. Rhodophyceae or red algae form a big group of highly specialized marine algae comprising about 3,000 species. They are very widely distributed in both temperate and tropical seas, particularly in the latter. Many species are found between the high tide level and the low tide level along coasts, a good number of species grow at depths of 60-90 m to a few at much greater depths, up to about 180 m. They are mostly attached to rocks. There are, however, some epiphytic and parasitic varieties, which grow on other algae. Although mostly marine, about 50 species have been found to occur in fresh water, mostly in hill streams. Red algae are characteristically red or purplish colour due to the presence of a red pigment called *phycoerythrin* which often marks the presence of chlorophyll. Many red algae contain a small amount of *phycocyanin*, the blue pigment of Cyanophyceae. Freshwater species are green in colour. Red algae have a variety of forms—filamentous, ribbon-shaped, distinctly leaf-like and marked with veins, etc. They are mostly a few to about 25 cm. in length, while a few are as long as 1 to 1.3 m. Deep-water ones are much longer. Gelatinous material is abundant in red algae, either occurring within the thallus or forming a sheath in the filamentous forms. Some red algae are heavily incrusted with lime. The cells may be uninucleate or multinucleate with one or more plastids, which may be with or without pyrenoids. A sugar or, more commonly, a special kind of starch called *floridean starch* accumulates in the cells as a result of photosynthesis. There is a total absence of motile ciliate cells, zoospores are altogether absent and the gametes are never ciliate. Members of Rhodophyceae are either haploid, or they show a regular alternation of similar haploid and diploid stages, as in *Polysiphonia*.

Uses. Red algae are very important from the economic point of view. Some of them (e.g. *Porphyra* and *Chondrus*) are eaten by the Chinese and the Japanese. In Europe, they are used to make soups and puddings. Many red algae are an important source of food for fish, and some of them are fed to cattle. An important commercial product known as **agar-agar** (or simply agar) is obtained from some red algae (e.g. *Gelidium* and *Gracilaria*). This jelly-like substance is used in laboratories as a medium of culture for fungi and bacteria. It is also used in medicines, commonly laxatives. It is widely used as a thickening material for soups, puddings and jellies. It is used extensively as a sizing material, an emulsifying agent and a dyeing and printing material in the textile industry. The agar industry was confined to Japan initially and then spread to the U.S.A., Canada, Australia, New Zealand and South Africa. Some red algae are used as a base for shoe-polish, shaving cream, cosmetics, etc. Many red algae contribute materially to the formation of coral reefs.

Origin and Relationship of Rhodophyceae. Rhodophyceae is the most highly specialized group of algae. The origin of this group and its relationship with other algae remain a mystery. This is indeed a unique group among the algae because of the unique type of female organ—the carpogonium, the mode of zygotic germination, and the absence of ciliate reproductive bodies. This group may have originated from some non-ciliate unicellular ancestor. Primitive red algae, however, bear some resemblance with blue-green algae to. Both have blue and red pigments, a primitive type of nucleus, and both lack ciliate

reproductive bodies. They differ, however, in many other important characteristics, particularly in the mode of reproduction.

1. *POLYSIPHONIA* (150 *sp.*)

Polysiphonia (FIG. 56A) is a common marine red alga. Its thallus is cylindrical and much branched (filamentous), attaining lengths of a few to about 25 cm. Many species commonly grow attached to the thallus of *Fucus* and other marine algae. The body is polysiphonous (FIG. 56B) i.e. composed of a central row of elongated cells—the central or axial siphons, and another layer of more or less similar cells encircling it—called the pericentral siphons. Hence the name *Polysiphonia*. The number of pericentral siphons varies from 4 to 24. There are distinct pores and protoplasmic connexions between the adjoining cells. The cells are uninucleate and with many red discoidal plastids. Growth takes place by a single apical cell.

There are three distinct forms of *Polysiphonia* representing three stages in its life-history. One form reproduces by four spores formed in a tetrad, called the **tetraspores**; the second form is male and bears only **antheridia** (or spermatangia); and third form is female and bears **carpogonia** and later carposporangia with carpospores. *Polysiphonia* is thus *heterothallic*. No motile ciliate cells develop at any stage. The three forms are alike in general appearance.

Male Plant (FIG. 56C). In the male plant, the antheridia are borne in dense clusters on one arm (fertile) of a dichotomous branching near the apex of the thallus. The other arm grows into a long forked sterile branch. The fertile arm is unbranched and considerably elongated, being several cells in length. These cells cut off a number of pericentral cells laterally in an encircling manner. Then each cuts off one or more unicellular antheridial mother cells towards the free surface. Each of them bears 2 to 4 **antheridia** (FIG. 56D). The protoplast of each antheridium functions as a single male gamete known as the **spermatium**.

Female Plant (FIG. 57A). The procarp (the complex female organ of Rhodophyceae—the carpogonium with the trichogyne and associated

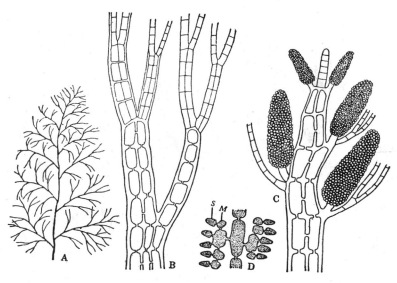

Polysiphonia. FIG. 56. *A*, a plant (portion); *B*, branching, and tubular or siphonic
cells with pores maintaining protoplasmic connexions through them; *C*, a male plant
(portion) with antheridial branches bearing clusters of antheridia; *D*, antheridial branching
showing antheridial (spermatial) mother cells (*M*) and spermatia (*S*)

ells) arises from a cell of the central axis a little
ehind the apex of the thallus. It produces a large
ell called the *supporting cell*, which gives rise to
short, curved, 4-celled branch, called the *car-
ogonial branch*. The terminal cell of the car-
ogonium branch is the **carpogonium**, with a
lender elongated projection at the apex, called the
richogyne. The supporting cell further cuts off a
asal cell and an upper cell (auxiliary cell). An
nvelope develops around the carpogonium and
ssociated cells as an outgrowth of the pericentral
ells adjacent to the supporting cell. The nucleus
f the carpogonium is the egg-nucleus.

Fertilization. The spermatiua on liberation
rom the antheridiua, are carried by water currents
o the trichogyne. The tip of the trichogyne dis-
olves to allow a spermatium to pass through it
nto the carpogonium. The spermatium then unites
ith the carpogonium-nucleus (egg-nucleus). The
richogyne is cut off by a wall at its base, and the
usion-nucleus (diploid) passes into the auxiliary
ell. The carpogonium and the branch cells break
own, while the auxiliary cell, supporting cell and
ther cells fuse into a large irregular cell—the pla-

cental cell. From this grow a number of large,
elongated single-celled **carposporangia**. The contents of each constitute a **carpospore**. The nucleus
of the carpospore is diploid. In the meantime, the
envelope grows and surounds the carposporangia.
The large, urn-shaped **pericarp** or envelope has a
small opening or **ostiole** at the apex. The whole
structure consisting of the carposporangia and the
pericarp is known as the **cystocarp** (FIG. 57*B*).

Tetrasporic Plant (FIG. 57*C*). Carpospores liberated from the carposporangia germinate and
develop into tetrasporic plants which are asexual.
A fertile central cell (siphon) of a tier produces a
short-stalked sporangium, which lies between the
central and the pericentral siphons. Its nucleus
undergoes reduction division and four **tetraspores**
are formed in a tetrad. A series of tetraspores may
thus be formed in the fertile filament. On liberation from the sporangium the tetraspores germinate, two of them developing into male plants and
two into female plants.

Alternation of Generations. The tetrasporic
plant is diploid (or sporophytic). Reduction division takes place during the formation of the

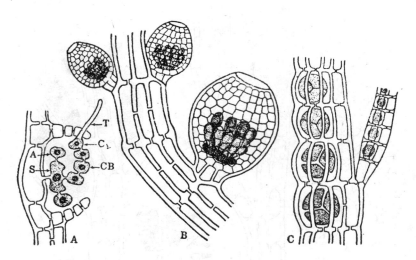

Polysiphonia. FIG. 57. *A*, a female plant (portion) with procarp (in section) showing carpogonial branch
(*CB*), carpogonium (*C*) with trichogyne (*T*), supporting cell (*S*), auxiliary cell (*A*) and a sterile basal cell;
note the envelope (pericarp) in the process of formation; B, cystocarps with a wall (pericarp) and
carposporangia (carpospores) inside; *C*, tetrasporic plant (portion) bearing tetraspores (old and young)

tetraspores, which are evidently haploid. They grow into haploid (or gametophytic) male and famele plants. With the fusion of the gametes, the diploid condition is restored in the zygote-nucleus. The carpospore is also disploid. The diploid carpospore grows into the diploid tetrasporic plant,. Stages in the life-cycle of *polysiphonia* are shown below:

1 Tetrasporic plant (2*n*) → tetrasporangia (2*n*) → tetraspores (*n*) → male and female plants (*n*).

2 Male plant (*n*) → antheridia (*n*) in clusters → spermatia (*n*) → fuse with egg-nuclei (*n*) of female plant.

3 Female plant (*n*) → carpogonium (*n*) → egg-nucleus (*n*) on fusion (fertilization) with spermatium (*n*) of male plant → zygotenucleus (2*n*) → carposporangium (2*n*) → carpospore (2*n*) → tetrasporic plant (2*n*).

2. *BATRACHOSPERMUM* (40 *sp*.)

Batrachospermum (FIG. 58*A-B*) is a fresh water red alga commonly found in hill streams. It occurs in clustered masses very close to springs. The filaments are carried a long way downstream. The colour is usually blue-green, but sometimes violet or brown. The cells are uninucleate with parietal lobed plastids, each with a pyrenoid. The thallus which is a few cm. in length, is filamentous, and shows monopodial branching. Whorls of short (or dwarf), delicate filaments arising from each node of the thallus give it a distinct beaded appearance (FIG. 58*A*), which is clear under a pocket lens or even to the naked eye. Each dwarf filament (FIG. 58*B*) is much branched, consists of a row of ellipsoidal or narrow and elongated cells and often bears some fine hairs at the tip. The thallus is attached to some hard object by a prostrate shoot from which arise many floating primary thalli. The basal cells of the whorl of short filaments develop threads of cells which grow downwards over the cells of the thallus, forming a cortex.

Reproduction. *Batrachospermum* reproduce both sexually and asexually. There are two distinct stages or forms in the life-history of the plant—the mature form reproducing sexually and the juvenile form reproducing asexually. The juvenile form is a simple protonema-like filament (FIG. 58*C*).

(a) *Asexual Reproduction.* Asexual reproduction of the juvenile form often takes place by the formation of **monospores** (FIG.58*C*). The

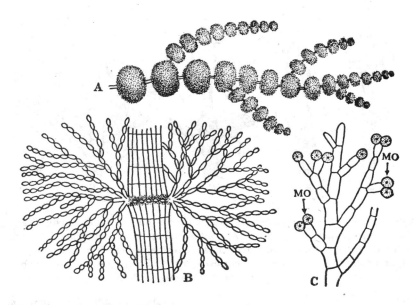

Batrachospermum. FIG. 58. *A*, a plant showing lateral branching and whorls of dwarf filaments; *B*, a whorl (magnified); *C*, the juvenile form producing monospores

monospore is always formed singly within the monosporangium and is really the terminal cell of a short lateral branch growing from the juvenile filament. The latter may reproduce by the formation of monospore year after year, or under suitable conditions of illumination, it may give rise to mature thalli by lateral branching.

(b) *Sexual Reproduction.* Antheridia or spermatangia, i.e. the male reproductive organs, develop in small groups at the end of a lateral (short or dwarf) filament (FIG. 59A). The antheridium mother cell produces one or more antheridia terminally. They are uninucleate and usually globose or ovoid. The protoplast of each antheridium forms a single male gamete known as the **spermatium**. The latter, when mature, escapes through a rupture in the antheridial wall. The **carpogonium** (FIG. 59B), i.e. the female reproducctive organ, may be borne by the same plant that ·produces the antheridia (homothallic), or, it may be borne by another plant (heterothallic). Short lateral branches, consisting of a few cells, called carpogonial filaments are produced from some of the short or dwarf filaments of the whorl. The terminal cell of the carpogonial filament is the **carpogonium**. The tip of the carpogo-

nium is prolonged into a distinct inflated cell, called the *trichogyne*. All the cells of the carpogonial branch have a dense mass of protoplasm and are uninucleate. The protoplast of the carpogonium forms a single uninucleate female gamete.

Fertilization. After its escape from the antheridium, the spermatium, which is carried to the carpogonium by water currents, gets attached to the trichogyne. The contact wall of the trichogyne dissolves and the spermatium passes through it into the carpogonium and fuses with the female gamete. The trichogyne is cut off by the formation of a plug. It is, however, persistent in *Batrachospermum.* The basal part of the fertilized carpogonium (FIG. 59C), now partitioned off, forms the zygote. This produces a mass of short branching filaments called *gonimoblasts.* The terminal cell of a filament is a *carposporangium* (FIG. 59D). The protoplast of each carposporangium is a **carpospore**. Some of the sterile cells at the base of the carpogonium form an envelope of loose filaments around the carposporangia. The whole structure consisting of the envelope, gonimoblasts, carposporangia and fertilized carpogonium is known as the **cystocarp** (FIG. 59D).

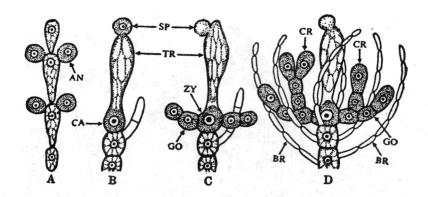

Batrachospermum. FIG. 59. *A*, an antheridial branch bearing antheridia; *B*, a mature carpogonium; *C*, fertilized carpogonium; *D*, cystocarp. *AN*, antheridium; *CA*, carpogonium; *TR*, trichogyne; *SP*, spermatium; *ZY*, zygote; *GO*, gonimoblasts; *BR*, enveloping branches (filaments); *CR*, carposporangium (with carpospore). *Redrawn after FIG. 76 in* Plant Morphology by *A. W. Haupt by permission of McGraw-hill Book Company*

Almost immediately after fertilization, the zygote-nucleus undergoes reduction division, followed by repeated mitotic divisions. Finally, a nucleus migrates into the carposporangium. The carpospore, when released, germinates into a pad of parenchymatous tissue. From this develop numerous short branching filaments (juvenile plants).

This stage is otherwise called *Chantransia* stage (resembling an alga of this name). Later special branches arise from the *Chantransia* filaments, as is more common, directly from the parenchymatous pad, and grow up into new *Batrachospermum* plants. The main plant including the juvenile forms is *haploid*, while the zygote is diploid.

CHAPTER 3

BACTERIA

A Short Historical Account. Anton van Leeuwenhoek (1653-1723) of Delft in Holland was the first to discover bacteria (1653-1723) with the help of the microscope considerably improved by himself (see also p. 117). Louis Pasteur (1822-1895), the famous French chemist and bacteriologist, thoroughly established the science of bacteriology. He carried out extensive work on fermentation and decay and the cause of hydrophobia. About the year 1875, Pasteur made importance of bacteria known to the world. He was the first to prepare vaccine and use it for the cure of the disease. He saved many Russians by the use of this vaccine, and the Tsar of Russia honoured him with a diamond cross and a hundred thousand francs to build a laboratory in Paris—now called the Pasteur Institute. About the same year, Robert Koch of Germany proved that anthrax disease, common among cattle, was caused by a kind of bacteria. In 1882, Koch discovered that tuberculosis and Asiatic cholera were caused by bacteria. After that, many scientists were attracted to this new science. Prominent among them were Emile Roux—helper of Pasteur, and Emil Behring—pupil of Koch who discovered the diphtheria antitoxin about the year 1894. In 1880s, Elic Metchnoikoff of South Russia proved that phagocytes eat up germs and protect the body. In 1893, Theobald Smith of America discovered germs of Texas fever in the blood corpuscles of cows. In 1870, Joseph Lister (1827-1912), an English surgeon, developed the technique of antiseptic surgery, and in 1929, Alexander Fleming, an English bacteriologist, discovered penicillin which proved to be an effective remedy for many dreadful infectious diseases.

Shapes of Bacteria

1 **Bacilli** (sing. bacillus)—rod-shaped bacteria, e.g. *Bacillus* (=*Mycobacterium*) *tuberculosis*, *B.* (=*Clostridium*) *tetani*, *B. typhosus*, etc.

2 **Cocci** (sing. coccus)—spherical bacteria, e.g. *Staphylococcus*, *Streptococcus*, *Azotobacter*, etc.

3 **Spirilla** (sing. spirillum)—bacteria with spirally wound body, e.g. *Spirillum*, *Spirochaete*, etc.

4 **Commas**—slightly twisted like a comma, e.g. *Vibrio cholerae*.

General Description. Bacteria (class Schizomycetes) are the smallest and the most primitive cellular organisms, and number over 2,000 species. They are single-celled, usually spherical, rodlike, or branched. In some forms the cells may be united into filaments or masses. They may be motile or nonmotile, and aerobic or anaerobic. There is no definite nucleus in the bacterial cell; chromatin granules representing an incipient nucleus are, however, often present. The cell-wall is made of chitin. Some forms of bacteria are provided with 1 cr more cilia (or flagella). Chlorophyll is altogether absent. Many of these microorganisms are as small as 1μ or even 0.5μ, particularly the spherical ones. The rod-like forms are usually 2μ to 10μ in length (1 micron=1/1,000 mm.). Being so minute in size, they are imperfectly seen even at the highest magnification of the ordinary microscope.

Occurrence. They occur almost everywhere— in water, air and soil, and in foodstuff, fruit and vegetables. Many of them float on dust particles in the air; many are found in water; and many are specially abundant in the soil, particularly up to a depth of 30 cm., and also in sewage. A few thousand may occur in 1 cc of water, and a few million in 1 gramme of soil. Many live within and upon the bodies of living plants and animals. The intestines of all animals always contain a good number of different kinds of bacteria.

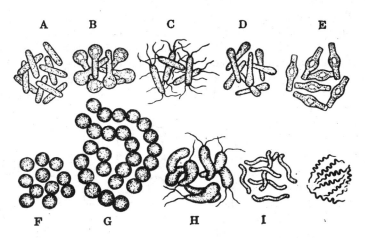

Bacteria. FIG. 60. Bacilli : A, *Bacillus* (=*Mycobacterium*) *tuberculosis*; B. *B.* (=*Clostridium*) *tetani*; E, *B. anthracis*. Cocci : F, *Staphylococcus*; G, *Streptococcus*; Comma : H, *Vibrio cholerae*. Spirlla : I, *Spirillum* (common in water); J, *Spirochaete*

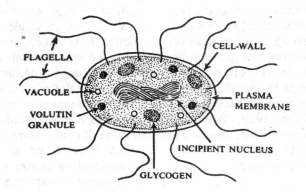

FLAGELLA

CELL-WALL

VACUOLE

PLASMA
MEMBRANE

VOLUTIN
GRANULE

INCIPIENT NUCLEUS

GLYCOGEN

FIG. 61. A bacterial cell (highly maginfied)

Structure. The electron microscope reveals the structure of bacteria in greater detail (FIG. 61) than the ordinary microscope. There is a distinct but complex cell-wall made of proteins and carbohydrates. Chitin is often present but seldom any cellulose. Surrounding the cell-wall there is frequently a layer of slime in the shape of a **capsule or sheath**. The encapsulated form is very resistant to adverse conditions and to treatments. Diseases are usually caused by the encapsulated form of bacteria. Several types of bacteria are provided with one or more slender, whip-like threads called *flagella* originating from the cytoplasm. Such bacteria are motile. There is a thin plasma membrane formed by the cytoplasm inside the cell-wall. The cytoplasm is spread uniformly throughout the cell and contains many small vacuoles, stored food granules such as volutin, glycogen fats and sometimes sulphur, too and an **incipient nucleus**. The active cell remains saturated with water, which makes up 90% of the contents. An organized nucleus, as found in higher plants, is absent. The nucleolus and nuclear membrane are absent. There is, however, a nuclear material (or chromatin) in the bacterial cell, in the form of 1 or 2 deeply staining bodies, possibly representing chromosomes. Chemically, these bodies are composed of twisted and folded strands of DNA (deoxyribonucleic acid), which is the genetic material of the chromosomes of living cells, responsible for the transmission of hereditary characteristics. The DNA bodies divide

prior to the division of the bacterial cell and are distributed equally among the daughter cells.

Reproduction. Bacteria commonly reproduce by **fission**. Sexual reproduction in them is not known to occur with any certainty.

Fission (FIG. 62A). Fission may take place in one two or three planes. This way they can multiply rapidly. Hay bacillus (*Bacillus subtilis*), for instance, divides two or three times an hour under favourable conditions. At the minimum rate of division, a single cell may give rise to over 16 million (16,777,216) offspring at the end of 12 hours.

Sexual reproduction in bacteria had not been known to occur until 1974, when Lederberg and Tatum reported that they had observed a sort of conjugation between two strains of the common intestinal bacterium (*Escherichia coli*) evolved by them by exposure to ultraviolet light. They were of the view that during the short period of

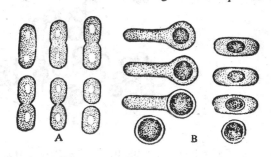

A   B

FIG 62. *A*, fission of a bacterial cell; *B*, spore formation in two types of bacteria

onjugation a part of the chromosome of one train was injected into the other. The new bacterial cell was seen to be capable of living under conditions which would not suit either of the parent cells. Evidently, it had received material from both the parent cells, and was better fitted for the struggle for existence. No multiplication of bacterial cells takes place by this method, however. Beyond this, sexual method of reproduction is unknown in bacteria.

Spore Formation (FIG. 62B). Some bacteria, particularly some rod-shaped ones, form spores which are always 'resting' spores. A small mass of protoplasm within the mother cell clothes itself with a thick membrane, forming an **endospore**. The mother cell soon dissolves. The endospore may remain dormant for months, or even several years, resisting adverse conditions, such as high temperature, freezing, extreme dryness, presence of poisonous chemicals, etc. Then, under favourable conditions of moisture, temperature and suitable food, the endospore enlarges, and its contents form a full-fledged bacterial cell. Spore formation is not a method of multiplication.

Nutrition. Bacteria, like other living organisms, require energy for their manifold activities. From the standpoint of nutrition, bacteria may be autotrophic (only a small number of them), or heterotrophic (majority of them). The former may be photosynthetic, having a pigment closely related to chlorophyll, or chemosynthetic. The latter obtain their energy for synthetic processes by the oxidation of inorganic compounds of sulphur, iron and nitrogen (see pp. 261-62). Most bacteria are, however, heterotrophic in their mode of nutrition. They may be saprophytic or parasitic in habit. The former usually live in water or soil containing organic compounds of plant or animal origin, in dead plants and animals, in vegetables and stored in a variety of other media. They secrete enzymes to digest complex organic compounds. Parasitic bacteria infect living plants and animals and absorb the food products from their hosts by the same process of enzyme-secretion and digestion.

Harmful Effects of Bacteria. Many parasitic (or pathogenic) bacteria infect living plants and ani-

mals, particularly the latter, and cause various diseases in them, sometimes in epidemic form. Normally they infect the host through wounds, or they may be breathed in or taken in with food, water and milk. After infecting the body they produce a toxin (poison) which causes many serious diseases in human beings and animals. Some comon disease-producing bacteria are: *Bacillus typhosus* causing typhoid fever, *B. anthracis* causing anthrax, *B.* (=*Clostridium*) *tetani* causing tetanus, *Clostridium botulinum* causing a dangerous type of food-poisoning (called **ptomaine** poisoning), *B.* (=*Corynebacterium*) *diphtheriae* causing diptheria, *B.* (=*Mycobacterium*) *tuberculosis*, causing tuberculosis, *Mycobacterium leprae* causing leprosy, *B. dysenteriae* causing dysentery, *B.* (=*Diplococcus*) *pneumoniae* causing pneumonia and *Vibrio cholerae* causing cholera. Some species of streptococci (the blood-poisoning bacteria) are possibly the deadliest enemy of mankind. They have the remarkable power of dissolving the red corpuscles of the human blood, and are responsible for erysipelas and extremely dangerous kinds of blood-poisoning.

Parasitic bacteria also attack plants and cause various diseases, such as fire blight of apple and pear, ring disease of potato, black rot of cabbage, canker of *Citrus* (korange), etc. In plants, however, fungal diseases are far more common than bacterial diseases, while in animals the reverse is the case. Many bacteria are also responsible for the decay of vegetables, fruit, meat, cooked food, etc., particularly during summer.

Beneficial Effects of Bacteria. Although some bacteria (the disease-producing ones) are most harmful, a large number of them are most useful in various ways, particularly in agriculture and some industries. Many bacteria are nature's scavengers.

(1) **Agricultural.** (a) **Decay of Organic Substances.** But for the most useful work of many bacteria, the dead bodies of plants and animals would remain unaltered, covering possibly the whole or at least a very large part of the earth's surface. In addition, the organic compounds contained in these dead bodies would remain permanently locked up without any further use.

Fortunately, bacteria act on these bodies, reduce the various organic compounds to simple forms, such as nitrates, sulphates, phosphates, and release them to the soil for utilization by green plants. Carbon dioxide, water, oxides of nitrogen, or even free nitrogen formed in the process, however, escape unused. (*b*) **Nitrification.** Proteins contained in the dead bodies of plants and animals are acted on by different kinds of bacteria and converted to ammonium compounds (ammonification) and then oxidized into nitrites and nitrates (nitrification) suitable for absorption by green plants (see p. 228). (*c*) **Nitrogen Fixation.** The fixation of free nitrogen by many soil bacteria like *Azotobacter* and *Clostridium* directly in their own bodies, and *Rhizobium* (nodule bacteria) in association with the roots of leguminous plants is very important from an agicultural standpoint (see pp. 229-30). (*d*) **Fertilizers.** The conversion of cowdung and animal excreta into manure, and the formation of humus or leaf-mould, are other examples of bacterial activity (see p. 223). Many chemical changes which make the soil fertile are mainly due to bacteria (and also of many other organisms in the soil). In fact the fertility of the soil may be largely attributed to the presence of bacteria in the soil. (*e*) **Plant Disease Control.** Some antibiotics obtained from bacteria can be used to control many plant diseases.

(2) **Industrial.** Many bacteria are very useful in various industries. They are used in the curing and ripening of tobacco leaves, fermentation of tea leaves, ripening of cheese, retting of fibres, formation of vinegar from alcohol (by acetic acid bacteria *Acetobacter aceti*), fermentation of sugar into alcohol, curdling of milk by lactic acid bacteria, conversion of hide into leather during the process of tanning, and silage preparation (a fermented nutritious food for cattle) are all examples of how bacteria are useful in industries.

(3) **Medical.** (*a*) Valuable antibiotic drugs have been obtained from a number of bacteria and fungi. Thus, antibiotics like penicillin (isolated from *Penicillium notatum*, a mould), streptomycin (isolated from *Streptomyces griseus*, a bacterium), chloromycetin (isolated from *S. venezuelae*,

another bacterium), etc., have been used successfully to control and cure pneumonia, diphtheria, wound infections, tuberculosis, typhoid, etc. (*b*) Bacteria always dwell in large numbers in the human system, particularly in the intestines. Although their activity is not clearly understood, some physiologists are of the view that these bacteria are in some way connected with digestive activities in the intestinal tracts. It is also believed that they check the growth of putrefactive and pathogenic bacteria. Thus, lactic acid bacteria in fermented milk (curd) are supposed to cure or prevent dysentery. In any case, bacterial flora in the human intestines is considered essential for the maintenance of normal health.

Hay Bacillus (*Bacillus subtilies;* FIG. 63) is a common saprophytic bacterium growing in a decoction of hay. It can be grown easily in the laboratory by soaking hay in water and boiling it. The spores of hay bacillus withstand prolonged boiling. The decoction may then be kept in a warm place for a day or two. One or two drops may then be examined under a microscope at high magnification. Hay bacillus is unicellular and rod-shaped, provided with a number of flagella all over its body. The cells may be held together in chains. There is a granular vacuolated mass of protoplasm with chromatin granules but no definite nucleus. While growing in the fluid, hay bacillus reproduces by fission. The cell undergoes constriction in the transverse plane and splits into two. The process of fission may be repeated several times within a short time. It is seen that the cells overcrowd the liquid and tend to come to the surface. They lose their cilia and become non-motile. Their walls become gelatinous and the cells are held together in long chains. Several such chains form a mucilaginous mass, called a *zoogloea*, which floats as a thin film or scum on the surface of the liquid. When food is exhausted, the bacillus cells form one or two spores, called *endospores*, within the mother cell. The protoplasm withdraws from the wall and clothes itself with a fresh firm wall which can resist the action of high temperature and many poisonous substances. Later, under favourable conditions, the

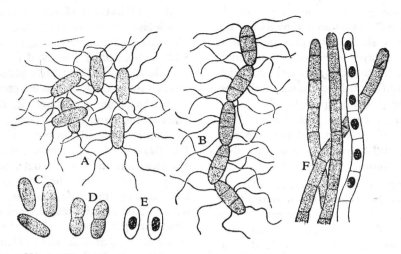

Hay bacillus (*Bacillus subtilis*), FIG. 63. *A*, motile forms; *B*, a chain of motile forms; *C*, nonmotile forms; *D*, fission; *E*, spore formation; and *F*, chains of nonmotile forms with spore formation in one chain

spores germinate in a suitable medium. The wall of the mother cell decays and the spore is liberated. The tough coat of the spore splits and the protoplasm escapes into the surrounding medium. Cilia are formed and the bacillus cell leads an active life.

VIRUSES. Viruses (*virus*, poison) are the smallest and possibly the most primitive living organisms yet known to science. They are very much smaller than bacteria, and cannot be detected under the most powerful common microscope. Their presence is revealed only when they produce certain diseased conditions in plants or animals. In, 1886, Mayer first described the virus disease of tobacco and called it 'tobacco mosaic'. In 1892 Iwanowski, a Russian biologist, first demonstrated that the sap of the affected tobacco plant strained through a bacteria-proof filter could infect healthy tobacco plants. Beijerinck, a Dutch microbiologist, in 1899 showed that the dried sap containing virus retains the power of infection. According to him, the virus is carried through the phloem from one part to another. By 1933-34, several virus diseases were discovered. As first shown by Takami in 1901, virus diseases may be transmitted from diseased plants to healthy ones through biting or sucking insects and also by any kind of contact, as

in grafting. They may be borne by seeds, leaves, or stems. Virus-containing sap may be injected into non-infected plants. The infection may then spread from cell to cell by diffusion. All viruses are entirely parasitic and are quite.inert in their free state in air or water. They grow, multiply and produce disease symptoms in the living cells of plants and animals. Bawden in 1936 and later others have shown that viruses are made of nucleoproteins resembling those found in the chromosomes of plants and animals. Viruses can be isolated, purified and obtained in the form of crystals (a unique feature in a living organism). In 1935, Stanley, an American microbiologist, first isolated tobacco mosaic virus (TMV) in the form of crystals. These crystals dissolved in water and when rubbed on tobacco leaves, rapidly produced disease symptoms. Many more viruses have been obtained in such forms since then.

Recent investigations using electron microscopes and X'-ray photography have revealed some detailed facts about viruses. Although virus particles have no cellular structure they are still complex organisms with a genetic mechanism. They are of varying shapes and sizes ranging in lengths from $10m\mu$ to $200m\mu$, sometimes up to $450m\mu$ ($1m\mu = 1/1,000\mu$). Further, a virus is now known to contain a core of nucleic acid, mostly DNA (sometimes RNA) surrounded by a thin film of protein (protein shell). The protein shell is mainly a protective layer and is often very complex. The DNA is a genetic (hereditary) material, and is responsible for all biochemical activities. The protein can be separated from the DNA in different strains and the DNA of one strain can use the protein of another strain and produce new hybrids. Subsequently, when they divide, they make their own protein.

There are three kinds of viruses infecting plants, animals and bacteria. A few hundred plant diseases caused by viruses have been recorded so far, such as mosaic diseases in apple, bean, beet, cabbage, cauliflower, cucumber, gourd, groundnut, mustard, pea, potato, radish, tapioca, tobacco, tomato, wheat, etc.; black ring spot of cabbage; leaf roll of potato; chlorotic diseases in *Abutilon*, apple, pepper, rose, snapdragon, etc.; Leaf curl as in bean, beet, cotton, gingelly, papaw, raspberry, soya-bean, tobacco, *Zinnia*, spike disease in sandalwood; yellow diseases in beet, carrot, marigold, peach, strawberry, sugarbeet, etc.; and necrosis (quick killing of affected tissues) as in potato and tomato. Some human diseases, such as mumps, smallpox, chicken-pox, measles, herpes, polio, yellow fever, scarlet fever, influenza, common cold, cancer, hydrophobia, etc., are supposed to be caused by viruses.

BACTERIOPHAGES. Some viruses also attack bacteria and destroy their nuclear material. They are called bacteriophages (*phagein*, to eat). Such viruses have a tail and a head, surrounded completely by a contractile protein sheath. The head contains DNA. When the protein sheath contracts, the tail end penetrates into the bacterial cell. Then all the virus DNA is injected into the latter, while the whole of the protein remains outside. The DNA of the virus now controls all the biochemical activities of the bacterial cell and, peculiarly enough, induces the latter to form more virus DNA and protein. The result is, the appearance, within about 20 minutes, of several new strains of virus particles, destruction of the bacterial chromosome (nuclear material) and finally, bursting of the bacterial cell. No such effect is produced if the protein portion of the virus is injected into the bacterium. Evidently, DNA is the genetic material (or gene).

Virus Reproduction. Outside the host body the virus is inactive. But inside, it is the virus DNA or RNA that controls the biochemical activities of the infected cells which now begin to make DNA or RNA and proteins characteristic of the invading virus. At the same time, the virus particle replicates itself several times, forming hundreds of particles like the original one with identical nucleic acids and proteins. The reproduction of virus has been studied in greater

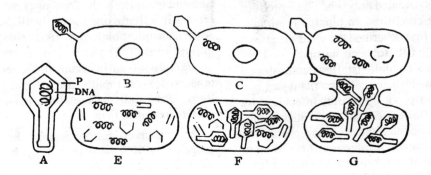

Bacteriophage. FIG. 64. A, a virus particle showing its structure and composition (*P*, protein; *DNA*, deoxyribonucleic acid); *B-G*, stages showing how a bacteriophage infects a bacterial cell, destroys the bacterial chromosome (shown here diagrammatically as an oval body), and replicates itself

detail in connection with the bacteriophage (see FIG. 64). Many types of viruses also undergo mutation, producing new kinds of disease symptoms in host plants and animals.

CHAPTER 4

FUNGI

A Short Historical Account. Among the earliest researchers mention may be made of **Gleditsch**, a German botanist, who, in 1753, attempted a short classification of fungi. **Fontana**, an Italian scientist, worked assiduously for several years on rusts of cereals and published his account in 1767. Serious studies on fungi started from the early part of the 19th century. **Persoon**, working in Paris, published his first account of fungi in 1793, *Synopsis Methodica Fungorum* in 1801, *Edible and Poisonous Mushrooms* in 1818, and *European Fungi* and a somewhat detailed classification of fungi from 1822-28. **Fries'** system of classification (1821-32) and later his elaborate work on Hymenmycetes of Sweden (1857-63) gave impetus to many for further study of mycology. **Berkeley** (1803-89), a great British mycologist, published his *Cryptogamin Botany* in 1857 and *Outlines of British Fungology* in 1860. Besides, **Cooke's** (1825-1914) *Handbook of British Fungi*, published in 1971, *Handbook of Australian Fungi* in 1892, Cryptogamic Journal *Grevillea* (1884-90), his extensive collections and elaborate drawings at Royal Botanic Gardens, Kew, are of outstanding merit. Special mention should be made of **De Bary** (1831-88), professor of botany at Halle and later at Strassburg, who did extensive work on mycology, mostly of a physiological and biological nature, and was the leading mycologist of the period. His new classification of fungi was published in 1884. His investigations on Uredinales and Ustilaginales cleared up many early misconceptions about them, and he was the first to establish heteroecism in rusts in 1864. He also introduced methods of culture of fungi. De

Bary also discovered an association of algae and fungi in lichens. He actually laid the foundation of modern mycology. **Saccardo** (1845-1920), a famous Italian mycologist, published his monumental work on systematic mycology, *Sylloge Fungorum*, in 18 volumes (1892-1906); some supplementary volumes were added later. The technique of culture was further advanced by **Brefeld** (1839-1925) and **Van Tieghem** (1839-1914); the former introduced the agar method and the latter the glass-cell method. **Dangeard**, about 1893 or so, discovered sexuality in Uredinales and Ustilaginales, and later in Ascomycetes and Basidiomycetes. **Blackman** in 1904 discovered a kind of alternation of generations in rusts. **Blakeslee** in 1904 discovered heterothallism in *Mucor* and allied fung, and he designated the two strains as + and − , subsequently other investigators noticed the same phenomenon in some other fungi. The importance of mycology in agriculture and certain industries and also as an academic study has been realized and many specialists all over the world have undertaken investigations on fungi in the current century.

CLASSIFICATION OF FUNGI (90,000 sp.)

Class I Myxomycetes or slime fungi (over 300 sp.).

Class II Phycomycetes or alga-like fungi (1,500 sp.). Sub-class (i) Oomycetes (or Biflagellatae)—reproduction oogamous. **Order 1.** Saprolegniales, e.g. *Saprolegnia* (water mould). **Order 2.** Perenosporales, e.g. *Pythium*, *Phytophthora*, *Albugo* (=*Cystopus*)

and *Perenospora*. Sub-class (ii) Zygomycetes (or Aplanatae)—reproduction isogamous. **Order 3.** Mucorales, e.g. *Mucor* and *Rhizopus*.

Class III **Ascomycetes** or sac fungi (25,000 sp.). Sub-class (i) Protoascomycetes (no ascocarp; asci naked). **Order 1.** Saccharomycetales, e.g. yeast (*Saccharomyces*). Sub-class (ii) Euascomycetes (asci in ascocarp). Series (1) Plectomycetes (closed ascocarp—cleistothecium; no hymenium; asci sacttered). **Order 2.** Aspergillales, e.g. *Penicillium* and *Aspergillus*. Series (2) Pyrenomycetes (ascocarp with an apical opening—perithecium; asci in hymenial layer). **Order 3.** *Erysiphales*, e.g. *Erysiphe* and *Uncinula*. **Order 4.** Sphaeriales, e.g. *Neurospora* and *Xylaria*. **Order 5.** Hypocreales, e.g. *Claviceps*. Series (3) Discomycetes (open ascocarp—apothecium; asci in hymenial layer). **Order 6.** Pezizales, e.g. *Peziza* and *Ascobolus*.

Class IV **Basidiomycetes** or club fungi (23,000 sp.). Sub-class (i) Hemibasidiomycetes (basidia septate or divided; teleutospore germinating into promycelium which bears basidiospores). **Order 1.** Ustilaginales or smuts (700 sp.), e.g. *Ustilago*. **Order 2.** Uredinales or rusts (4,600 sp.), e.g. *Puccinia*. Sub-class (ii) Holobasidiomycetes (basidium simple, club-shaped, directly bearing basidiospores; karyogamy and meiosis occur in the basidium). Series (1) Hymenomycetes (basidia on distinct hymenium). **Order 3.** Agaricales (7,000 sp.); it includes various forms of gill-fungi, e.g. mushrooms (*Agaricus*, *Amanita*, etc.), coral fungi (*Clavaria*), and various forms of pore fungi (*Polyporus*, *Polystichus*, *Fomes*, *Boletus*, etc.). Series (2) Gasteromycetes (hymenium indistinct; fruit body remains enclosed by peridium, i.e. distinct outer wall). **Order 4.** Lycoperdales, e.g. puff-balls (*Lycoperdon*). **Order 5.** Phallales, e.g. stinkhorns (*Phallus*). **Order 6.** Nidulariales, e.g. bird's nest fungi (*Nidularia* and *Cyathus*). Gasteromycetes are regarded as the highest of all fungi.

Class V **Deuteromycetes** or fungi imperfecti (over 24,000 sp.), i.e. fungi with imperfect life-history (sexual stages being unknown), e.g. *Helminthosporium* and *Fusarium*. They usually reproduce by conidia. Many of them cause major plant and animal diseases.

General Description. Fungi are a group of thallophytes lacking in chlorophyll. They may develop a variety of other pigments in the cell-wall or in the cell-cavity, and have an infinite variety of shapes and sizes, sometimes massive (fleshy or hard). Being non-green, they lead a heterotrophic mode of life, either as saprophytes or as parasites. The carbohydrate food is stored in the form of *glycogen* (and not starch). Saprophytic fungi grow in a variety of conditions, and thrive under an abundance of moisture, warmth and supply of organic food. Parasitic fungi, on the other hand, grow on living plants (wild or cultivated) and also on animals including human beings. They have the remarkable power to disintegrate or dissolve almost anything they attack by the secretion of suitable enzymes. Parasites that pass their entire life on living hosts are called *obligate parasites*, e.g. rusts; while those that normally live upon living hosts but may lead a saprophytic life, if need be, are called *facultative parasites*, e.g. some smuts. The plant body, except the unicellular forms, is commonly made of an interwoven mass of very fine and delicate threads called **hyphae**, collectively called **mycelium**. The wall of the hyphae may be made of chitin or pure cellulose.

Reproduction. *Vegetative reproduction* may take place by means of fragmentation of the body of the fungus, or detachment of a part of it, or budding, or in some cases through special bodies called sclerotia. A **sclerotium** is a compact, often hard and rounded, mass of hyphae, occasionally with a dark firm outer covering layer but normally without any spore in it. It varies in size from a small pin-head to a few or sometimes several cm. in diameter, and gives rise to mycelium or fruit-body.

Asexual reproduction takes place by means of spores of various natures: (*a*) ciliate spores or zoospores, (*b*) ordinary **spores**, sometimes called gonidia, borne often in large numbers in a case called sporangium, (*c*) **conidia**, formed singly or in groups or chains by specialized hyphae or conidiophores at their tips by the process of abstriction, (*d*) **chlamydospores**, which are thick-walled resting spores formed singly or in a chain by certain vegetative hyphae; (these are transformed vegetative cell), (*e*) **oidia** which are short segments of a vegetative hypha, functioning as spores (*f*) **ascospores**, usually 8 in number, formed in a sac called ascus, and (*g*) **basidiospores** are spores, usually 4 in number, formed externally by a club-shaped basidium on short slender stalks called sterigmata. There are also other kinds of specialized spores too.

Sexual reproduction in fungi shows three distinct phases: (*a*) **Plasmogamy** is the fusion of two protoplasts with or without nuclear fusion. In this process, two haploid nuclei (called a **dikaryon**) of opposite sexes are brought together in one cell. The dikaryotic condition may continue for a considerable length of time, as in higher fungi (e.g. *Puccinia*), or the two nuclei may fuse almost immediately, as in lower fungi (e.g. *Mucor* and *Phythium*), (*b*) **Karyogamy** is the fusion of the two nuclei of a dikaryon resulting in a diploid (zygote) nucleus. This is sooner or later followed by meiosis to revert to the haploid condition. (*c*) With the development of gametangia and gametes, sexual reproduction may be **isogamous, anisogamous** (rare), or **oogamous.**

CHARACTERISTICS OF THE MAIN GROUPS

Phycomycetes. (1) The mycelium is unseptate and coenocytic. (2) The **sporangia** has innumerable sporangiospores (zoospores or aplanospores) formed *endogenously*. (3) Sexual reproduction is oogamous in Oomycetes, and isogamous in Zygomycetes. (4) Biciliate motile cells (zoospores) are produced by many species. (5) The zygote is unicellular and simple.

Ascomycetes (1) The mycelium septate; primary mycelium is uni-or multinucleate, while ascogenous hyphae are always binucleate. (2) Conidia

formation is a common feature. (3) The ascus usually has 8 ascospores formed *endogenously*. (4) Sexual reproduction is reduced to the fusion (karyogmy) of two compatible nuclei (+ and –) in the young ascus, with gradual suppression of sex organs (or gametangia). Karyogamy is immediately followed by meiosis, resulting in usually 8 ascospores within the ascus. (5) Motile cells are absent. (6) The **ascocarp** (fruiting body) is multicellular and complex, bearing the asci. It is open and cup- or saucer-shaped (called **apothecium**), **oval** or flask-shaped with a small apical opening (called **perithecium**), or completely closed (called **cleistothecium**). (7) Hook or crosier is common (see below).

Basidiomycetes. (1) The mycelium is septate. The primary mycelium is multinucleate but secondary mycelium is usually binucleate. (2) Conidia formation is not a common feature. (3) The **basidium** usually has 4 basidiospores formed *exogenously*. (4) Sexual reproduction is reduced to the fusion (karyogamy) of two compatible nuclei (+ and –) in the young basidium. There are no sexual organs (except spermatia and receptive hyphae in rusts). Karyogamy is immediately followed by meiosis, resulting in usually 4 basidiospores borne exogenously by the basidium. (5) Motile cells absent. (6) The **basidiocarp** (fruiting body) is multicellular and complex, bearing the basidia— often open, sometimes closed (basidiocarp not formed in Uredinales and Ustilaginales). (7) Clamp connection is common (see pp. 406-7).

Resemblances between Ascomycetes and Basidiomycetes. (1) The binucleate ascogenous hyphae of Ascomycetro may be homologous with the bimucleate secondary hyphae of Basidiomycetes. (2) The asci may be homologous with the basidia; both are binucleate (dikaryotic) in the early stages. (3) Sexual reproduction is reduced to nuclear fusion (karyogamy) in the young ascus or the young basidium, as the case may be. (4) The ascospore may be homologous with the basidiospore. Both are uninucleate. Both pass through stages like plasmogamy, karyogamy and meiosis. The last two processes take place in

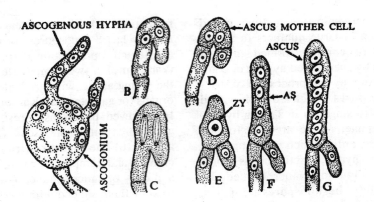

FIG. 65. Development of ascus by hook or crosier method. A cnium producing ascogenous hyphae;
B, k or crosier with a pair of nuclei (dikryon); C, conjugate nuclear division (mitosis); D, ascus mother
cell with a dikaryon; E, zygote (ZY) with diploid (2n) nucleus; F, young ascus (AS) after meiosis;
mature ascus with 8 ascospores

the young ascus or in the young basidium. (5) No motile cells are formed in any of these two groups. (6) The hook or crosier method in Ascomycetes, and the clamp connection in Basidiomycetes are hardly different in bringing together (dikaryotization) the reproductive nuclei of two opposite strains (+ and –).

Hook or Crosier Method (FIG. 65). The ascus in a majority of Ascomycetes is formed by the hook or crosier (meaning a crook or bend) method. The tip of the ascogenous hypha elongates and bends over, forming a sort of hook (*B*). The ascogenous hypha itself originates from the ascogonium after the pairing of nuclei (dikaryotic condition; *A*). The ascogenous hypha evidently contains pairs of nuclei received from the ascogonium. In each pair, one nucleus is male and the other female. Similarly, the tip of the hypha contains a complementary pair of nuclei (dikaryon; see p. 405). These two nuclei undergo mitotic division simultaneously, with the two spindles standing parallel to each other in the vertical direction (*C*). One pair of daughter nuclei (one male and one female) lies close together near the bend, while one nucleus (either male or female) of one spindle lies towards the tip of the hook and another nucleus (of opposite sex) of the other spindle lies towards the basal septum of the ascogenous hypha and another (*D*). Now two septa appear, resulting in

three cells. The middle or the hook cell is binucleate (one male and one female). This is the ascus mother cell. The two other cells are uninucleate (one male and the other female). The binucleate cell (ascus mother cell) soon develops into the ascus. Karyogamy (see p. 405), i.e. fusion of the two nuclei, takes place in the young ascus, and the zygote that is formed evidently conains a diploid nucleus (*E*) The zygote-nucleus undergoes divisions, the first one being meiotic (*F*). Usually the divisions cease when 8 nuclei are formed. Each nucleus clothes itself with a wall and becomes converted into an ascospore. The ascus simultaneously grows and elongates, containing the ascospores (*G*). Several asci may be formed from repeatedly branched ascogenous hyphae.

Clamp Connection (FIG. 66) This is a common feature in most types of Basidiomycetes except rusts. Clamp connection is a special mechanism by which the sister nuclei of a dikaryon get separated into two daughter cells. This mechanism is found in the secondary mycelia which usually consist of binucleate cells. The binucleate condition arises from the fusion of two uninucleate cells of two primary hyphae without, however, any karyogamy, i.e. without the fusion of nuclei. Clamp connection is usually formed in the terminal cells of the hyphae. In some cases, however, it occurs in most of the cells of the secondary hyphae, and in some

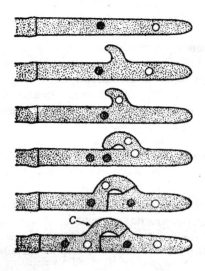

FIG. 66. Clamp connexion (*C*)

others only in some cells here and there. A short branch arises, between the nuclei forming a sort of hook (clamp cell). One nucleus passes into the clamp cell, and now both the nuclei divide simultaneously. The clamp cell bends over and its end touches the wall. This bridge-like short connection (branch) is called the clamp connection. Now one nucleus of each pair approaches the other, evidently passing through the bridge. After this migration, a septum is formed at the base of the clamp cell and another septum below the bridge, thus separating a pair of nuclei, one from each parent cell.

ORIGIN OF FUNGI. No definite statement can be made regarding the origin of fungi. There are two views on this matter. According to one view, fungi have been derived from algae. It is said that Phycomycetes have arisen from Chlorophyceae, possibly Siphonales, by the loss of chlorophyll, which has evidently brought about a change in the mode of nutrition but not in the process of development. The second view is that since primitive Phycomycetes (which are Chytridiales—unicellular) bear uniflagellate zoospores and gametes resembling protozoa (green algae are never uniflagellate) they may have been derived from some uniflagellate organisms like protozoa. If this is so, fungi must have followed an independent line of development (evolution), standing midway between animals and plants. Regarding the origin of Ascomycetes again, there are two views. According to one, Ascomycetes may have been derived from some red algae since there are marked similarities in the sexual characteristic of these two groups. Another view which is more generally accepted is that Ascomycetes have arisen from oogamous Phycomycetes. There is general Basidiomycetes agreement among mycologist that have been derived from Ascomycetes. There is a close resemblance between the two groups (see p. 405). Basidiomycetes are of course, more advanced than Ascomycetes.

CLASS I   MYXOMYCETES
or slime fungi (about 400 sp.)

Myxomycetes, commonly called slime fungi, form a peculiar group of organisms which are animal-like in their vegetative stages and plant-like in their reproductive stages. Slime fungi are widely distributed, growing in damp shady places, in soil rich in humus, damp old planks of wood, rotting logs of wood, decaying leaves, etc. and prefer moisture and darkness. They are saprophytic in habit and, like other fungi, lack chlorophyll. They may be colourless or variously coloured—yellow, orange, brown, red, violet, etc.

Plant Body. The body of the Myxomycete consists of a naked slimy mass of protoplasm with many nuclei. Such a body is otherwise known as plasmodium. The plasmodium forms pseudopodia and shows amoeboid movement, creeping over and within the substratum and growing in different directions, commonly towards moisture and avoiding light as far as possible. The diameter of the body varies from a few to several cm. The plasmodium engulfs solid particles of food. It also absorbs food material in solution. In the dry season, it passes into a hard sclerotium-like body.

Reproduction

Vegetative reproduction may take place by the breaking up of the plasmodium into fragments, each growing as an independent body. Two fragments may also unite and grow as a single organism.

Asexual reproduction. For this purpose, the plasmodium comes to the surface of the substratum in which it grows, and forms different kinds of sporangia according to the species. The sporangia and spores are formed in the presence of light. The plasmodium may form one or more large sporangia on the surface of the substratum or a number of small separate sporangia on long or short stalks. They may be cylindrical, oval (ovate) or spherical. The sporangium is multi-nucleate and consists of a tough network of plasmodium strands, known as the **capillitium**, enclosing numerous spores in its meshes. The protoplasm of the sporangium excretes waste material, which is deposited on the surface of the sporangium as a wall-layer known as the peridium. The spores are uni-nucleate and surrounded by a definite cellulose wall. The capillitium shows hygroscopic movement and the sporangium bursts irregularly at the apex. The spores which are liberated are scattered by the wind. The protoplast of the spore escapes from it by amoeboid movement and forms a zoospore, which develops a long cilium at its anterior end. Sometimes two or four zoospores are formed. The zoospores swim for a while, retract their cilium and pass into an amoeboid condition or into a resting stage. Theey may divide repeatedly and multiply vegetatively.

Sexual reproduction. Sooner or later the amoeboid zoospores behave as gametes and begin to fuse in pairs. The fusion product may be regarded as a zygote. It is amoeboid and as it develops into a plasmodium the fusion nucleus divides repeatedly. The young plasmodium seems to exert an attractive force upon the neighbouring zygotes, which move towards it and fuse with it (no nuclear fusion takes place), contributing to the growth of the plasmodium body. The plasmodium is multinucleate and coencytic. It creeps in different directions by the formation of pseudopodia and grows in size. The nuclei of the plasmodium are diploid. Rreduction division takes place at some stage prior to the formation of the spores.

CLASS II   PHYCOMYCETES
or alga-like fungi (1,500 sp.)

1. *SAPROLEGNIA* (25 sp.)

Occurrence. *Saprolegnia* (family *Saprolegniaceae*; FIG.67A), commonly called water mould, grows in water. It is saprophytic, living on the dead bodies of insects, fish and other animals, and on plant remains. Some species are parasitic on fish and eggs, causing diseases in them. They commonly occur in fish nurseries. Many species are also soil-dwellers. A dead insect placed in a pot of water shows a flocculent growth of this fungus within a few days.

Structure. The mycelium consists of much-branched, coenocytic (nonseptate and multi-nucleate) hyphae. Two types of hyphae are often distinguished: short, rhizodal hyphae, penetrating into the substratum to obtain food from it, and a mass of long, profusely branched hyphae spreading over the substratum and finally bearing the reproductive organs. This mass is distinctly visible to the naked eye. The hyphae vary considerably in width. Septa develop only in connection with the reproductive organs.

Reproduction. *Saprolegnia* reproduces asexually as well as sexually.

Asexual Reproduction. (FIG. 67 *B-E*). For this purpose, the end of a vegetative hypha swells and forms a **zoosporangium** (*B*). It is an elongated, tapering structure, separated from the vegetative hypha by a septum. When young, it is filled with a dense mass of protoplasm, and looks somewhat brownish under the microscope. Before the septum is formed, a large number of nuclei flow into the zoosporangium. Soon, by furrowing (cleavage) of the protoplasm, starting from the wall, small uninucleate masses appear, and each mass becomes converted into a uninucleate zoospore. The zoosporangium is closely packed with such zoospores. These are the **primary zoospores**. They are pear-shaped and apically biciliate. They escape into the surrounding water through an apical opening of the sporangium (*C*). There is proliferation of the sporangium, and this means that after the zoospores escape, a secondary sporangium

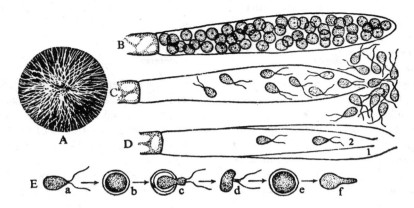

Saprolegnia. FIG. 67. *A*, growth of *Saprolegnia* on a dead insect; *B-E*, asexual
reproduction; *B*, a mature zoosporangium with primary zoospores; *C*, a zoosporangium
discharging primary zoospores; *D*, internal proliferation of zoosporangium
(·1, primary; 2, secondary); *E*, development of secondary zoospore from primary zoospore
(*a*, primary zoospore; *b*, encysted zoospore; *c*, secondary zoospore being formed;
d, secondary zoospore; *e*, encysted zoospore; *f*, and germinating zoospore)

grows from the base upwards within the primary
sporangium (*D*), sometimes projecting beyond the
latter. It is again filled with zoospores as before.
The process may be repeated three or four times.
The primary zoospores, after escape from the
sporangium, swim about in water for some time,
come to rest, withdraw their cilia, and encyst. After
a short period of rest, each cyst gives rise to a **secondary zoospore**, which is kidney-shaped and
laterally biciliate. The zoospores, thus formed,
swim for some time, encyst, and finally germinate
by producing a **germ tube** (*E*). *Saprolegnia* is
thus **diplanetic**, with two types of zoospores and
two swarming periods. **Diplanetism** is characteris-

tic of *Saprolegnia*. Asexual reproduction may also
be brought about by chlamydospores (or gemmae)
formed at the ends of the hyphae, singly or in a
chain; sometimes they are intercalary in position.

Sexual Reproduction (FIG. 68). Distinct male
and female gametangia are formed. The female
gametangium or **oogonium** may be the terminal
cell of a vegetative hypha or it may be intercalary.
It swells at the apex and becomes more or less
spherical or sometimes oblong. Its contents form
one, or more, spherical, uninucleate **oospheres** or
eggs. One or more oil drops are seen to occupy a
particular position in the egg according to the

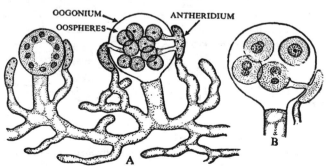

Saprolegnia. FIG. 68. Sexual reproduction; *A*, development
of antheridia and oogonia; *B*, fertilization and formation of zygote

species. The male gametangium or **antheridium** may arise from the same hypha that bears the oogonium, or from a different hypha close to the oogonium. A septum develops, separating the antheridium from the rest of the hypha. The antheridium is a multi-nucleate, elongated, somewhat tubular body, much smaller than the oogonium. One or more antheridia may be attached to the oogonial wall. A **fertilization tube** develops from the antheridium, penetrates the oogonial wall and reaches an oosphere (*A*). The fertilization tube may branch, within the oogonium each branch reaching an oosphere. Several non-motile antheridial nuclei (male gametes) migrate through this tube into the oogonium, and one such male nucleus passes into an oosphere and fuses with the egg-nucleus. The fertilized egg-nucleus or zygote-nucleus is evidently diploid (2*n*). It clothes itself with a thick, smooth wall and becomes an **oospore** (*B*). After a prolonged period of rest, the oogonial wall disintegrates and the oospore germinates by producing a **germ tube**. Reduction division of the zygote-nucleus takes place during the germination of the oospore. The oospore may also develop

parthenogenetically, i.e. without fertilization, in many cases. In some species, the antheridium is not formed at all.

2. *PYTHIUM* (40 *sp.*)

Occurrence. *Pythium* (family *Pythiaceae*) is a parasitic fungus, which usually attack seedlings of cress and mustard at the base of their hypocotyl (FIG. 69*A*) under conditions of overcrowding and over-watering. It causes the disease commonly known as the 'damping-off' of seedlings. Members of *Cruciferae* are particularly susceptible to this disease. Other crops like tobacco, ginger, etc., are also infected by this fungus. The most common species of *Pythium* causing 'damping-off' is *P. debaryannum*. When attacked, the seedlings become weakened at their base and soon fall over. At first the fungus is a parasite, but later, after the death of the host seedlings, it thrives on them as a saprophyte. The mycelium ramifies in all directions through the intercellular spaces, penetrating here and there into the living cells. At a still later stage, white, cottony threads (hyphae) may be seen on the surface of the seedlings. The

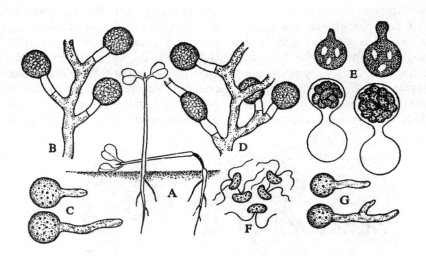

Pythium. FIG. 69. *A*, healthy and infected seedlings; *B*, hyphae (conidiophores) with conidia; *C*, conidium germinates by sending out a germ tube; *D*, hyphae with zoosporangia; *E*, zoosporangium germinating and finally forming a vesicle with zoospores; *F*, biciliate zoospores; and *G*, zoospore germinates by producing a germ tube

long, slender, much-branched hyphae are unseptate and coenocytic, enclosing many small nuclei (cf. *Mucor*).

Reproduction takes place both asexually and sexually.

Asexual Reproduction (FIG. 69 B-G). The mycelium sends out aerial hyphae through the stomata or the cuticle, here and there. The hyphae bear short lateral branches, each swelling into a spherical head. This head, which is partitioned off at the base by a septum, may act as a conidium (*B*) or as a zoosporangium (*D*) according to external conditions. Under moist conditions it acts as a zoosporangium. It bulges out into a bladder-like vesicle (*E*). The protoplasm migrates into it and divides to form a number of small naked uninucleate and biciliate zoospores. The zoospores, when set free, swim about in water for a short time (*F*). Soon they withdraw their cilia and clothe themselves with a wall. Eventually, they infect a new seedling and germinate by putting forth a short hypha or germ tube (*G*) which branches freely within the tissue of the host. Under dry conditions, the head, instead of forming zoospores, behaves as a conidium (or conidiospore). It infects a new seedling directly and produces a germ tube (*C*) which branches freely within the tissue of the host.

Sexual Reproduction (FIG. 70). After the death of the host, the fungus leads a saprophytic life and takes to sexual reproduction, possibly due to star-vation. Within the dead tissues of the host or outside them, the hyphal end swells into a spherical head due to migration of a large mass of protoplasm, forming the female organ, called **oogonium** (*A*). It is cut off from the supporting hypha by a partition wall. The oogonium may also be formed as an intercalary swelling of a hypha. The cytoplasm of the oogonium soon becomes differentiated into two distinct regions: a central denser region with a nucleus, constituting the egg or oosphere, and a peripheral region with many small nuclei, constituting the **periplasm**. A small branch arises from the same hypha or from another close to the oogonium. It swells and becomes more or less club-shaped, and is cut off by a septum at the base. This is the male organ, called **antheridium**. Its protoplast becomes differentiated into a central male gamete, which is uni-nucleate and an outer periplasm, which is multi-nucleate. The nuclei of the periplasm soon degenerate. The antheridium bends towards the oogonium and comes in contact with it. A short cylindrical tube, called the **fertilization tube** or *beak*, grows from it, and pierces the oogonium. The male gamete passes into the oogonium through this tube and fuses with the egg nucleus of the oosphere. This kind of fertilization (with the antheridium and the oogonium lying side by side on the same stalk) is known as **paragynous**. The fertilized oospore (*B*) forms a thick wall around itself and rests for some months in the soil. Infection takes place in the way described above. The oospore germinates by producing a germ tube or it forms a zoosporangium (*C*), the

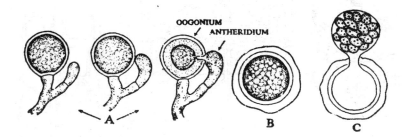

Pythium. FIG. 70. *A*, formation of sexual organs—oogonium with oosphere, and antheridium (note the beak); *B*, thick-walled oospore inside oogonium formed after fertilization; and *C*, oospore germinates and produces a vesicle (zoosporangium) with zoospores

protoplasmic contents of which divide to form a number of zoospores.

Control of the Disease. (1) Overcrowding and over-watering must be avoided. (2) Steam sterilization of the soil. (3) Heat sterilization of the soil by burning wood in the field. (4) Sprinkling dilute formalin solution over the soil. (5) Spraying with Bordeaux mixture.

3. *PHYTOPHTHORA* (13 *sp.*)

Occurrence. *Phytophthora* (family *Pythiaceae*) are widely distributed. Common species of the fungus occurring in India are: *P. infestans* which attacks potato plants, *P. palmivora* which attacks coconut-palm and palmyra-palm, *P arecae P. colocasiae* which attacks taro (*Colocasia*), and *P. parasitica* which attacks castor plants. *Phytophthora infestans* causes a serious disease in potato plants, known as 'late blight' (early blight being caused by *Alternaria solani*). The disease takes on more serious proportions in the hills than in the plains, sometimes spreading like an epidemic. The formation of black patches on the undersurfaces (less often on the upper) of potato leaves indicates the diseased condition of the plant (FIG. 71A). The disease may spread to the entire leaf and other parts, extending down to the underground parts, particularly the tubers. All the neighbouring plants may be similarly affected if the weather is warm and humid. The fungus causes 'wilting' of the leaves and 'rotting' of the tubers, either in the field or in storage. To begin with, brownish marks may be noticed below the skin in such tubers. Soon the underlying tissues soften and rot. The fungus may also attack and destroy plants like tomato, pepper, egg-plant, etc.

Structure. The mycelium is profusely branched, and the branches penetrate the intercellular spaces of the leaf, stem and tuber of the potato plant and send haustorial hyphae into the interior of the living, thin-walled cells to suck them (FIG. 71C). The haustorium may be hooked or sometimes spirally twisted, and simple or branched. The mycelium is non-septate and *coenocytic* (*cf. Pythium*). Septa may, however, develop later in old mycelia.

Reproduction. The fungus commonly reproduces asexually. Sexual reproduction, though not common, was first observed in pure culture and later in the infected tuber.

Asexual Reproduction. At the time of reproduction, long, slender, erect hyphae, called **sporangiophores**, grow out in small groups through the stomata on the lower surface of the leaf (FIG. 71B). On the tuber, however, they appear in large numbers. The sporangiophore becomes branched, and each at its apex branch bears a short-stalked, multinucleate, ovoid or lemon-shaped **sporangium** with a papilla-like tip. The tip of the sporangiophore continues to grow pushing the sporangium to one side, and then forms another sporangium.

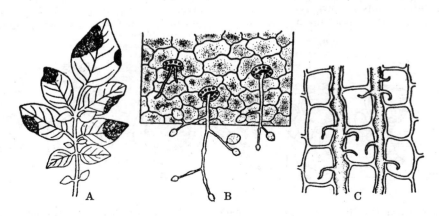

Phytophthora. FIG. 71. *A*, a potato leaf showing the infected areas; *B*, sporangiophores protruding through the stomata and bearing sporangia; *C*, haustorial hyphae

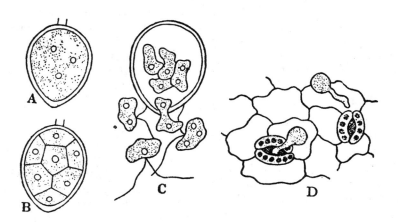

Phytophthora. FIG. 72. Asexual reproduction: *A*, sporangium; *B*, a sporangium becoming a zoosporangium; and *C*, zoospores escaping; *D*, zoospores germinating on the host plant (note the infection through the stomata)

Thus the sporangium, though terminal at first, soon becomes lateral on the sporangiophore, which shows a zig-zag growth (a sympodium). Further, a distinct nodular swelling of the branch appears just above the sporangial base. When mature, the sporangia are dispersed by the wind or washed away by the rain. Usually, when the temperature is high, the sporangium germinates directly on a potato plant, by pushing out a germ tube. However, when the temperature is low, the contents of the sporangium divide into several uninucleate segments. Each segment then develops into a biciliate **zoospore**, with the two cilia attached laterally (FIG. 72*A-C*). The tip of the sporangium bursts and the zoospores escape. The zoospore swims for a while, then comes to rest, loses its cilia and forms a wall around itself. Under favourable conditions of temperature and moisture, the zoospores germinate on the leaf by producing a germ tube, which penetrates through a stoma into the tissue of the leaf (FIG. 72*D*). The disease thus spreads rapidly from plant to plant. Sporangia and zoospores are short-lived, and the fungus hibernates in the tuber in the form of mycelia. Thus the infection of the plant starts from the diseased tuber.

Sexual Reproduction. This takes place by means of oogonia and antheridia which develop from two neighbouring hyphae (FIG. 73). The oogonium is spherical or pear-shaped with a smooth, reddish-brown wall. It contains a large oosphere or egg-cell, lying loose and free within it, surrounded by a scanty zone of protoplasm, called the periplasm. All the nuclei of the oogonium, except one egg-nucleus of the oosphere, degenerate. The antheridium is broadly club-shaped, and develops before the oogonium. It contains many nuclei but finally, only one male nucleus persists while the others degenerate. Peculiarly enough, the oogonium, as it grows, penetrates through the antheridium and swells above

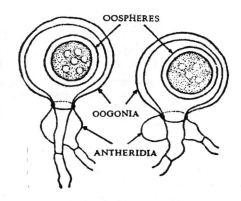

FIG. 73. Sexual reproduction in *Phytophthora*

it, becoming spherical or pear-shaped. The antheridium also swells and forms a funnel-shaped collar around the base of the oogonium. This kind of fertilization is called **amphigynous** (as opposed to paragynous, see p. 412). After fertilization, the oospore lies loosely in the oogonium. The oospore may also develop parthenogenetically, i.e. without fertilization.

Control of the Disease. (1) Spraying young plants every 10 or 15 days with Bordeaux mixture (copper sulphate and lime). (2) Selecting disease-free seed-tubers, particularly from non-infected areas. (3) Storing seed-potatoes at a low temperature – 4°C to 5°C.

4. ALBUGO (25 sp.)

Occurrence. *Albugo candida* (=*Cystopus candidus*; FIG. 74), commonly known as 'white rust', is a parasitic fungus, which attacks several plants of the mustard family, such as mustard, radish, cabbage, turnip, etc. White blisters on the stem and leaves (*A*) indicate the diseased condition of the plant. Later, the flowers and ovaries become distorted. However, the disease does not take on serious proportions in India. *Albugo* belongs to the family *Albuginaceae*.

Structure. The mycelia ramify through the inter-cellular spaces of the host plant and branch profusely. The hyphae are unseptate and multi-nucleate. They send globular or button-like haustoria (*B*) into the living cells of the host to absorb food from them.

Reproduction. *Albugo* reproduces both asexually and sexually.

Asexual Reproduction (FIG. 74*C*). The hyphae grow luxuriantly at certain points below the epidermis. They form erect, branched or unbranched, club-shaped, multi-nucleate sporangiophores in clusters. The latter begin to cut off spherical multi-nucleate sporangia in chains from their tips. The sporangia are separated from one another by short necks made of gelatin. The epidermis soon gets ruptured as a result of the internal pressure exerted by the increasing number of sporangia which then appear on the surface as a white powdery mass. The sporangia are now carried by the wind to other plants. The protoplasmic contents of each sporangium (FIG. 74*D*) divide to form a few (four or eight or more) kidney-shaped zoospores, each with two lateral cilia. The sporangium bursts and the zoospores escape. They swim about for some time in the water that collectes on the surface of

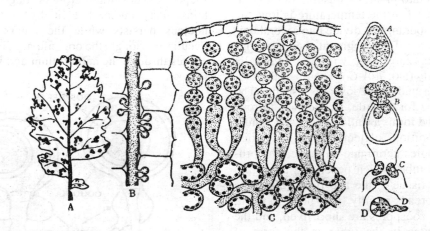

Albugo. FIG. 74. A, infected leaf of mustard; B, an intercellular hypha with button-like haustoria; C, an infected leaf in section, showing chains of multi-nucleate sporangia under the epidermis (note the neck separating the sporangia); D, germination of a sporangium—(a), sporangium dividing, (b), zoospores escaping; (c), biciliate zoospores swimming; and (d), a zoospore germinating

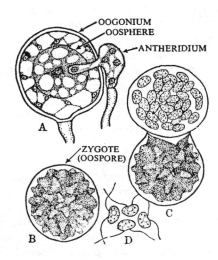

Albugo. FIG. 75. A, fertilization; *B*, zygote (oospore); *C*, germination of zygote—zoospores escaping into a vesicle; *D*, bicilate zoospores after escape

the host plant. They soon lose their cilia, cover themselves with a wall and come to rest. Later, they germinate by producing a germ tube which enters the host through a stoma. Sometimes a sporangium germinates directly without the intervention of the zoospores.

Sexual Reproduction (FIG. 75). Later in the season, the hyphae produce male and female gametangia within the intercellular spaces of the host (*A*). To form the female gametangium or oogonium a hypha swells at the tip and becomes spherical. A septum appears at the base. The oogonium is multi-nucleate, and its cytoplasm becomes differentiated into two distinct zones: a central zone called the **ooplasm** which is the egg or oosphere, and a peripheral zone called the periplasm. The central zone is a dense mass of cytoplasm with an egg-nucleus (other nuclei of this zone usually degenerate), while the peripheral zone is lighter and multi-nucleate. To form the male gametangium or antheridium a hypha close to the oogonium swells at the tip and becomes more or less club-shaped. It is cut off at the base by a septum. The antheridium is multi-nucleate. Soon it comes in contact with the oogonium and produces a fertilization tube, which penetrates the

oogonial wall and the periplasm and goes deep into the oosphere. One or more male nuclei are set free from the antheridium through this tube, but only one of them fuses with the egg-nucleus. If more egg-nuclei be present, all of them may be fertilized. The zygote (oospore; *B*) formed thereby clothes itself with a thick wall, the periplasm taking part in its formation. The zygote is set free only after the decay of the host tissue. It undergoes a period of rest and then produces numerous (over 100) zoospores. The zygote bursts and the zoospores escape into a vesicle (zoosporangium; *C*). The vesicle dissolves and the zoospores, each with two lateral cilia, are set free to swim about in water (*D*). The zoospore germinates under appropriate conditions by producing a germ tube.

5. *MUCOR* (50 *sp.*)

Occurrence. *Mucor* (family *Mucoraceae*), commonly called 'pinmould', is a saprophytic fungus (FIG. 76). It grows on animal-dung, wet shoes, stale, moist bread, rotten fruit, decaying vegetables, shed flowers and other organic media, spreading like a cobweb. It can be grown easily in the laboratory on a piece of moist bread kept under a bell-jar in a warm place for three or four days.

Structure. The plant body is composed of a mass of white, delicate, cottony threads collectively known as the **mycelium** (FIG. 76). It is always

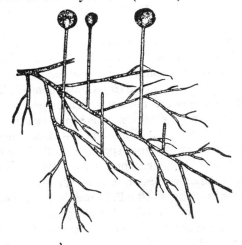

Mucor. FIG. 76. Ramifying mycelia with some sporangia (or gonidangia)

much-branched, but is coenocytic, i.e. unseptate and multi-nucleate. Each thread of the mycelium is known as the hypha.

Reproduction. This takes place both sexually and asexually. The asexual method is most common.

Asexual Reproduction (FIG. 77). This method of reproduction takes place by means of spores (or gonidia) which develop in a case, called sporangium (or gonidangium), under favourable conditions of moisture and temperature. Numerous slender, *erect* hyphae, called sporangiophores, arise from the mycelium. Each ends in a spherical head—the sporangium (FIG. 76). The apical portion of each of these hyphae swells out into a spherical head (FIG. 77) to form the sporangium. As the hypha begins to swell, the protoplasmic contents migrate to its tip, and accumulate more

quantity of fluid and exerts a considerable pressure on the wall of the sporangium. As a consequence the sporangium bursts, setting free the spores. The spores are blown about by the wind. The columella persists for some time after the bursting of the sporangium. Being very minute, light and dry, the spores float about in the air, and under favourable conditions, they germinate in a suitable medium directly into the *Mucor* plant. Hyphae often develop from the columella when the **sporangiophore** (i.e. the slender, erect stalk of the sporangium) happens to fall over. These hyphae then bear the sporangia.

Sexual Reproduction (FIG. 78). Sexual reproduction takes place by the method of conjugation, only under certain conditions, particularly when the food supply becomes exhausted. Conjugation

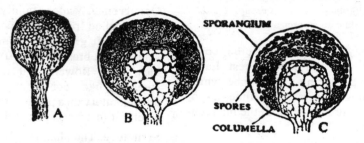

Mucor. FIG. 77. Development of sporangium, spore and columella. *A*, the end of the hypha swells; *B*, two regions—dense and light—are apparent with a layer of vacuoles between them; and *C*, mature sporangium (or gonidangium) with spores (or gonidia) and dome-shaped columella

densely towards the periphery, the central part remaining comparatively thin and vacuolate (*A*). Later, a row of vacuoles appears around the central part and these soon fuse (*B*). Consequently, a cleft is formed between the outer, denser portion and the inner, thinner portion, thus separating the two (*C*). The central portion, which is dome-shaped and sterile, i.e. without spores, is called the **columella.** The peripheral protoplasm now gives rise to a number of small, multi-nucleate, angular masses by cleavage (*B*). Each multi-nucleate mass becomes rounded off and is covered by a wall, forming a spore (*C*). Its wall thickens and darkens. The wall of the sporangium is thin and brittle. The columella swells due to the accumulation of a

consists in the fusion of *two similar* gametes, i.e. isogametes (cf. *Spirogyra*). The process is as follows: When two hyphae borne by two different plants of opposite sexes (called the + strain and the − strain) come close together, two short, swollen protuberances, called the conjugating tubes or *progametes* (FIGS. 78 *A-B* & 80), develop. These form a contact at their tips. As they elongate, they push the parent hyphae apart from each other. Each progamete enlarges and becomes club-shaped. Soon it is divided by a partition wall into a basal **suspensor** and a terminal gametangium (FIGS. 78*C* & 80). The protoplasmic contents of each gametangium constitute a gamete. The gametes are multi-nucleate and are called

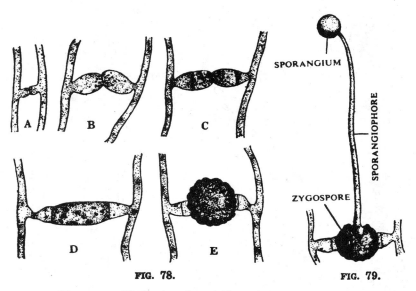

FIG. 78.   FIG. 79.

Mucor. FIG. 78. Conjugation: *A-E* are stages in the process;
note the thick-walled zygospore at *E*. FIG. 79. Germination of zygospore

coenogametes. The two gametes are identical in all respects. The end- (or common) walls of the two gametangia dissolve, and the two gametes fuse together (FIG. 78*D*) forming a zygospore (FIG. 78*E*). The zygospore swells into a rounded body, and its wall thickens, turns black and becomes warted. It contains plenty of food, particularly fat globules.

It has been observed that sometimes, sexual reproduction does not take place even though the fungus grows under all favourable conditions. The investigations of the American botanist, Blakeslee (1904), have revealed the fact that there are two different strains or races of the fungus (the + strain and the − strain), and that sexual reproduction takes place only between the hyphae of these two different strains, apparently of opposite sexes. These two strains are evidently formed from separate spores—some giving rise to the *plus* strains and others to the *minus* strains—and they must grow together (FIG. 80). Morphologically, there is no difference between the two strains, except that the + strain (regarded as female) show a slightly more vigorous growth than the − strain (regarded as male). Physiologically, they are different and

behave as two opposite sexes. Such species are said to be **heterothallic**, and the condition is designated as heterothallism. Heterothallism has also been found in certain Ascomycetes (e.g. *Ascobolus* and *Aspergillus*) and Basidiomycetes (e.g. rust fungi). There are, however, many species which form zygotes by the conjugation of the hyphae of the same mycelium. Such species are said to be **homothallic**.

Sometimes it so happens that the gametes do not fuse even though the conjugating hyphae meet. The gametangia then develop parthenogenetically (see p. 315) into thick-walled bodies called **azygospores** or **parthenospores** (cf. *Spirogyra*). The azygospore looks similar to the zygospore. Often the free end of a hypha may produce a solitary azygospore. Germination of the azygospore in *Mucor* has not been followed.

Germination of Zygospore (FIG. 79). The zygospore undergoes a period of rest and then germinates. The outer wall bursts and the inner wall grows out into a tube, called the sporangiophore or **promycelium**, which ends in a single sporangium. The sporangiophore may be branched, each branch

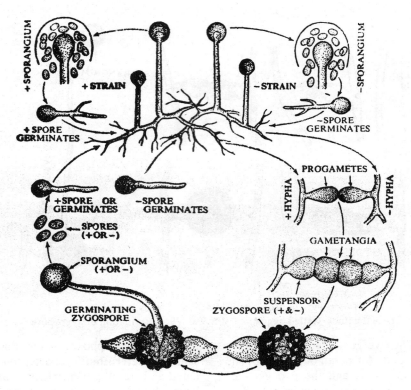

FIG. 80. Lifecycle of *Mucor*

bearing a sporangium. The sporangium contains several small **spores** but no columella. The spore germinates, giving rise to the *Mucor* plant.

Blakeslee also found that in heterothallic species, all the spores of a sporangium give rise to either + mycelia or – mycelia, but not both. The zygote is diploid and contains material of both the + strain and the – strian. It undergoes reduction division at the initial stage of germination. Three of the four nuclei so formed degenerate. Evidently, the surviving one (+ or –) gives rise to + spores or – spores by repeated mitotic division, and finally to + strains or – strains, as the case may be.

Torula Condition (*torula*, a small swelling). It is sometimes seen that under favourable conditions, the mycelium of *Mucor* becomes segmented into a short chain of cells. These cells either swell up, becoming thick-walled and large (chlamydospores), or remain thin-walled and small (oidi-

um cells). Chlamydospores are resting spores which germinate normally, giving rise to the mycelium. Oidium cells, on the other hand, separate from each other, multiply by budding like the yeast cells, and, like the latter again, set up alcoholic fermentation. The formation of oidium cells and their activity take place specially when the hyphae are immersed in a nutritive liquid.

Rhizopus nigricans (family *Mucoraceae*), a common black mould, is found growing on moist, stale bread, decaying vegetables and fruits, jelly, male inflorescence of jack and other organic media. Its life history is the same as that of *Mucor*.

CLASS III ASCOMYCETES
sac fungi (25,500 sp.)

1. *SACCHAROMYCES* (40 sp.)

Occurrence. Yeast (*Saccharomyces*—family *Saccharomycetaceae*, now called *Endomy-*

cetaceae) grows abundantly in organic substances rich in sugar, such as date-palm juice, vineyard soil and grapes. Yeast has the property of changing sugar into alcohol. This property has been used in developing certain important industries, particularly brewery and bakery (see below).

Uses. Yeast has a variety of economic uses. (1) It is used for various fermentation processes, such as the manufacture of beer from germinating barley grains, of wine from grapes, of country liquor (toddy) from date-palm and palmyra-palm juices, etc. (2) Yeast is used in the preparation of industrial alcohol from different kinds of cereals and also from potato. (3) It is used in making bread. Dough mixed with yeast gives sponginess and flavour to the bread. (4) It has medicinal value, being rich in vitamins and enzymes. (5) It has nutritive value, being rich in digestible compounds, specially proteins and fats.

Structure (FIG. 82). [Yeast was first microscopically examined by Leeuwenhoek in the year 1680. Its true nature was discovered by Schwann in Germany as late as 1836.] The structure of yeast is very simple. A single cell represents the whole body of the plant. It is very minute and looks like a pinhead under the microscope (FIG. 81A). Each cell is colourless, oval or almost spherical or slightly elongated, and has a distinct cell-wall, possibly made of *chitin*, and contains a mass of cytoplasm and a single nucleus. The nucleus contains a large vacuole (FIG. 82) This nuclear vacuole is a peculiarity in yeast. In the vacuole lies the nuclear reticulum with a nucleolus, and a centrosome on the side. Embedded in the cytoplasm are granules of glycogen, protein and volutin as well as several oil globules. Mitochondria are common in the yeast cell.

Reproduction. This takes place mostly by budding and sometimes by fission. Sexual reproduction is rare and found in a few species.

By Budding (FIG. 81B). The process of budding takes place under normal conditions when the yeast cells grow in sugar solution. As they grow two changes are noticed—one in the yeast cells and the other in the sugar solution. The former change is the *budding* of yeast cells, leading to vegetative reproduction. The latter is *alcoholic fermentation* (see pp. 421-2), leading to the breakdown of sugar into alcohol and carbon dioxide. In the process of budding, each cell gives rise to one or more tiny outgrowths which gradually grow and are ultimately cut off from the mother cell. These then lead a separate existence. The nucleus divides amitotically and one passes on to each outgrowth. This method of reproduction is known as vegetative **budding** or **gemmation** (*gemma*, a bud; pl. gemmae). Budding may be repeated, resulting in the formation of one or more chains and even subchains of bead-like cells. These chains and subchains are sometimes called *pseudomycelia*. The cells ultimately separate from one another and each leads an independent life.

By Fission (FIG. 83). Some yeast cells, called 'fission' yeasts, multiply by division. In this process, the mother cell first elongates. Its nucleus then divides into two. The two nuclei move apart

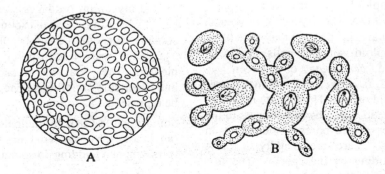

Yeast. FIG. 81. *A*, yeast cells as seen under the microscope; *B*, budding or gemmation

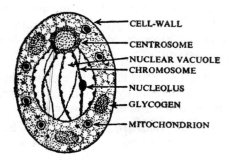

FIG. 82. One yeast cell (magnified)
showing the nuclear vacuole

and a transverse partition wall is formed somewhere in the middle of the mother cell, dividing it
into two parts. The two parts, each of which has a
nucleus, then separate from each other along the
partition wall, forming two independent yeast
cells.

Sexual Reproduction (FIGS. 84 & 85). Some
species of yeast also reproduce sexually (conjugation). In this connection, it, should be noted that
the somatic (i.e. vegetative) cells of yeast may be

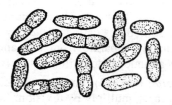

FIG. 83. Fission in yeast cells.

diploid ($2n$) or haploid (n), while the ascospores
are always haploid (n). The zygote is, of course,
diploid ($2n$). Sexual reproduction may take place
between two haploid somatic cells, as in *S.
octosporus* and *S. cerevisiae*, or between two
ascospores, as in *S. ludwigii*, resulting in all cases
in a zygote (diploid or $2n$). This zygote may give
rise to diploid somatic cells by budding, as in the
last two species, or to ascospores by meiosis, as in
the first species. There are usually 8 or 4
ascospores, depending on the species. The few
species of yeast in which sexual reproduction has
been observed so far go to show that the process

may take any of the following three patterns
(Guilliermond, 1940).

(a) In certain species, as in *S. octosporus*, the
diploid phase is very short, while the haploid
phase is prolonged. Here, two somatic cells (n)
come in contact. At the point of contact, they send
out short, neck-like protuberances (conjugating
tubes), which unite by their tips. The two nuclei
then pass on to the conjugating tubes. The partition is dissolved and the two nuclei fuse at the
neck. The conjugating tubes widen and the contents of the two cells unite, resulting in a zygote
($2n$). The zygote behaves as an ascus. Its nucleus
now divides thrice, the first division being meiotic, and 8 nuclei are thus formed (each haploid or
n). Each nucleus forms a wall around itself,
enlarges and becomes an ascospore (n). The wall
of the ascus breaks and the ascospores are set free.
Each ascospore enlarges and becomes a somatic
cell (n). The ascospores may again take to conjugation under suitable conditions. Usually, however, they multiply by budding. The sexual cycle
may be represented as follows:

Somatic cells (n), by fusion in pairs ($n + n$) →
zygote ($2n$), by meiosis → 8 ascospores (n) in
ascus. by budding → somatic cells (n).

(b) In certain other species, as in *S. ludwigii*,
the diploid phase is prolonged while the haploid
phase is very short. Here, the four ascospores (n)
unite in pairs within the ascus, resulting in two
zygotes (each $2n$). The zygote cell produces a
germ tube ($2n$), which grows into a separate
mycelium ($2n$) called *sprout mycelium*. Each cell
of this mycelium produces somatic (yeast) cells
($2n$) by budding. The cells soon get detached. The
somatic cells enlarge and become converted into
asci, each with 4 ascospores (n) produced by
meiosis. They may again take to conjugation
under suitable conditions. The sexual cycle may
be represented as follows:

Somatic cells ($2n$), by meiosis → 4 ascospores
(n), in ascus, by fusion in pairs → zygote ($2n$), by
sprouting and budding → somatic cells ($2n$).

(c) In still other species, as in the common
bread yeast (*S. cerevisiae*), both phases (haploid

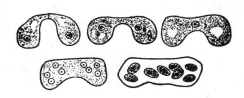

Yeast. FIG. 84. Conjugation of yeast cells and
formation of ascospores

and diploid) are more or less equally important
since each phase may continue for an indefinite
period by budding. Two such haploid somatic cells
(+ and –) may fuse, giving rise to a diploid cell, i.e.
the zygote ($2n$). The zygote continues to multiply
by budding, giving rise to a large number of well-
developed yeast cells ($2n$). Eventually, these may
behave as asci, each with 4 haploid ascospores
formed by meiosis. After liberation from the ascus,
the ascospores continue to multiply by budding,
giving rise to several haploid yeast cells (+ or –).
These are somewhat smaller than the diploid cells.
The sexual cycle may be represented as follows:

Somatic cells (n + or –), by fusion in pairs→
zygote ($2n$ + –), by budding → somatic cells ($2n$ +

–), by meiosis → 4 ascospores (n, 2 + and 2 –) in
ascus, by budding → somatic cells (n, + or –).

Alcoholic Fermentation. The process of fermentation was first studied elaborately by Louis
Pasteur during the fifth decade of the 19th century.
Many of his discoveries were actually applied to
the making of different kinds of liquor on a commercial basis through the use of different species
and strains of yeast. When yeast cells grow in
sugar solution, as in date-palm juice, palmyra-
palm juice or grape juice, they set up fermentation
(see p. 290) in the solution.This process   es
place in the absence of oxygen under the action of
the enzyme, *zymase complex* , which is secreted by
them, as first shown by Buchner in 1897. Sugar is
decomposed, and ethyl alcohol and carbon dioxide
are the chief products formed. Carbon dioxide
escapes, and causes frothing on the surface of the
solution. Ethyl alcohol is poisonous, and the yeast
cells cease functioning if the concentration of
alcohol reaches 14-18%. Comparatively little
alcohol is formed when oxygen is abundantly supplied, but when the supply of oxygen is cut off,
alcohol is produced more freely. The following
chemical change takes place in sugar:

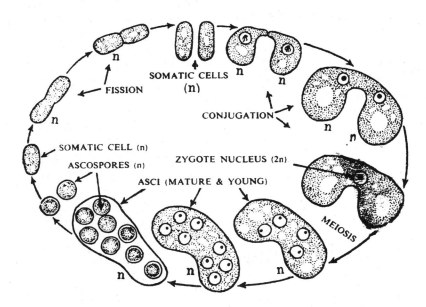

FIG. 85. Sexual cycle in a yeast (*Saccharomyces octosporus*)

$$C_6H_{12}O_6 + \text{zymase} = 2C_2H_5OH + 2CO_2 + \text{zymase} + \text{energy}$$

(sugar + zymase = alcohol + carbon dioxide + zymase + energy)

2. *PENICILLIUM* (137 *sp.*)

Penicillium and *Aspergillus* are two common and important genera of the family *Aspergillaceae*. They are common green and blue moulds. Both have a similar life-history but their morphological structures are different. They can be readily distinguished from each other by the nature of conidiophores, which they produce in abundance. There are about 800 species, belonging to the order Aspergillales.

Occurrence. *Penicillium* (FIG. 86), a blue or green mould, is a very common and widely distributed fungus. Most species of *Penicillium* are saprophytic in habit, and they commonly grow on bread, vegetables, fruit, jams and other foodstuff, and also on leather, shoes, fabrics, paper, books, etc. Spores of this fungus are present almost everywhere in the air and soil, and are often sources of contamination, resulting in huge spoilage. A few species are parasitic on animals, including human beings. *P. italicum*, a blue mould, and *P. digitatum*, a green mould, are com-mon parasites of *Citrus* fruits. *P. notatum*, a blue-green mould, is the source of the world-famous **penicillin**, an antibiotic first isolated from this fungus by the late Sir Alexander Fleming, a bacteriologist, in 1929. Certain species of *Penicillium* are used industrially in making various organic acids, and in making special types of flavoured cheese.

Structure. The mycelium consists of an interwoven mass of hyphae which spread on the surface of the substratum, penetrating deep into it at places. The hyphae branch freely and are septate and multi-nucleate.

Reproduction. *Penicillium* freely reproduces asexually by means of conidia. A few species take to sexual reproduction.

Asexual Reproduction. A number of hyphae stand erect from the undifferentiated vegetative mycelium. These are the **conidiophores** (*A*). They branch repeatedly near the apex, regularly or irregularly, in a broom-like fashion, and are septate. The slender, ultimate branches, known as the **sterigmata** (sing. sterigma), cut off chains of cells by the process of budding. These are the spores called **conidia**, which are formed in countless numbers. They are spherical or oval, and usually bluish or greenish. The branched conidiophores

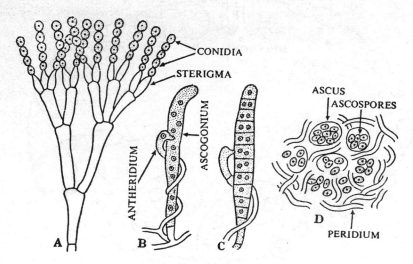

Penicillium. FIG. 86. *A*, branched conidiophore ending in sterigmata with conidia in chains (penicillus); *B*, sex organs: antheridium and ascogonium; *C*, ascogonium with binucleate cells; *D*, cleistothecium

including the sterigmata and the conidia are together called **penicillus** (a little brush). The conidia are easily dispersed by the wind. Under favourable conditions, they germinate by producing a *germ tube*.

Sexual Reproduction. This has been observed only in a few cases, first by Dangeard in 1907. The stages, however, are not known perfectly yet. In certain species, the development of the antheridium (male) and the ascogonium (female) has been observed (*B*). In others the antheridia are absent or do not function. The ascogonium is a long, straight and somewhat club-shaped body. It is at first uninucleate but becomes multinucleate (with as many as 64 nuclei) later, by repeated divisions of the nuclei. The **antheridium** arises as a slender hypha (antheridial branch) from a separate vegetative hypha and grows to a certain height, twining round the ascogonium. A septum appears in it, separating a terminal cell which is the antheridium. It swells and becomes more or less club-shaped, and is uninucleate. Its tip touches the ascogonial wall laterally. The contact walls dissolve and the protoplast of the antheridium migrates into the ascogonium. However, some scientists are in doubt about whether the antheridium nucleus at all passes into the ascogonium. Commonly, however, the ascogonial nuclei approach each other in pairs. After the pairing of the nuclei, the ascogonium divides into a number of binucleate cells (*C*), which now produce many hyphae—the **ascogenous hyphae**. The pairing nuclei pass into the ascogenous hyphae. They develop septa, each cell containing a pair of nuclei (dikaryon), and their terminal cell develops into a more or less globose **ascus**. The two nuclei fuse in the young ascus (or ascus mother cell). The fusion (or zygote) nucleus ($2n$) divides thrice (the first division being meiotic) and finally gives rise to 8 ascospores (n) in each ascus.

In the meantime, a closed 'fruiting' body or **ascocarp** (see p. 405), called the **cleistothecium** (*D*), is formed from the surrounding vegetative hyphae, evidently enclosing a number of asci. It has a protective sheath, called the **peridium**, which is pseudoparenchymatous in nature. The inner layer of the peridium is nutritive. As the ascospores mature, the asci dissolve away, leaving the ascospores free and scattered within the cleistothecium. The peridium decays and the ascospores are liberated. Finally, they are blown away by the wind.

3 *ASPERGILLUS* (78 *sp.*)

Occurrence. *Aspergillus* (=*Eurotium*; FIG. 87), commonly called blue mould, is a very widely distributed fungus like *Penicillium*, and its spores are found all over the air and soil. Species of *Aspergillus* grow on almost all kinds of foodstuffs, including butter, bread, fruit, vegetables and jams, and on leather goods, fabrics and books, sometimes causing considerable damage to them, particularly during the rainy season. Air-borne spores (conidia) often cause decay and contamination of foodstuff. *A. niger*, a black mould, often infests foodstuff. *Aspergillus* species are mostly saprophytic in habit, but a few (e.g. *A. fumigatus*) are parasitic on animals, including human beings, and cause diseases of the ears and lungs.

Aspergillus can produce a large number of enzymes which enable them to grow on a variety of organic media. *Aspergillus* is economically an important fungus. Some (e.g. *A. oryzae*) are used industrially in the manufacture of alcohol from rice starch, and some species used in the manufacture of certain organic acids (e.g. citric, gluconic, etc.) on a commercial basis. They have also been used in some enzyme preparations. Some species are sources of certain antibiotics.

Structure. The mycelium consists of an interwoven mass of hyphae which branch freely and spread through the surface of the substratum as well as deeper into it. The hyphae are hyaline, septate, much branched and multi-nucleate.

Reproduction. *Asperigillus* freely reproduces asexually through conidia. Only a few species reproduce sexually.

Asexual Reproduction. Several hyphae stand erect from certain cells (called **foot cells**) of the vegetative hyphae. These are the conidiophores (*A*). They are long and erect but unseptate. Each conidiopore swells at the apex into a more or less

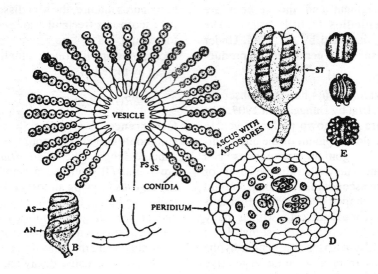

Aspergillus. FIG. 87. A, conidiophore with primary sterigmata (*PS*), secondary sterigmata (*SS*), conidia, vesicle and foot cell (at the bottom); *B*, sex organs: antheridium (*AN*) and ascogonium (*AS*); *C*, sterile hyphae (*ST*) enclosing the ascogonium; *D*, cleistothecium; *E*, ascospores of different species

spherical, multi-nucleate head called the **vesicle**. Growing from the entire surface of the vesicle are innumerable cells in 1 or 2 layers depending on the species. Those of the first are short, and are called the *primary sterigmata*. The cells of the second layer are long and bottle-shaped, and are known as the *secondary sterigmata*. If only one layer is present, the cells become bottle-shaped. Each such sterigma produces spores, called conidia, in a chain in basipetal order. The conidia are spherical or oval and usually multi-nucleate (rarely uninucleate). They are always formed in great profusion. The colony as a whole may then appear bluish, greenish, blackish or brownish, according to the species. The mature conidia eventually become loose and are blown away by the wind. They germinate in a suitable medium by producing a germtube.

Sexual Reproduction. Sexual reproduction has been observed in a few species of *Aspergillus*, but the stages are not perfectly known. Antheridia (male) and ascogonia (female) may be formed for sexual reproduction (*B*). They develop from separate, specialized vegetative hyphae lying close together, or from the same hypha at different levels. Both the antheridium and ascogonium are unicellular and multi-nucleate. As it grows, the ascogonial hypha soon becomes differentiated into three parts: a unicellular, tightly coiled structure—the ascogonium, a terminal cell (which is the receptive neck of the ascogonium)—the **trichogyne**, and a multicellular **stalk**. The antheridial hypha, growing by the side of the ascogonium, climbs it. It soon cuts off a terminal cell—the **antheridium**. It climbs some more and its tip reaches the trichogyne. The contents of the antheridium migrate through the trichogyne into the ascogonium, where pairing of nuclei (male and female) takes place. Their actual fusion has not been observed. Usually, however, the sister nuclei of the ascogonium come together in pairs. The antheridium may also remain undeveloped or functionless, or it may not reach the trichogyne. After pairing of the nuclei, whatever be the method, the ascogonium becomes septate and forms several binucleate cells. These cells now produce many **ascogenous hyphae** of diffferent lengths. These branch within the 'fruiting' body (see below). They become septate, with binucleate cells, and produce asci at their tips. The asci are spherical, oval or pear-shaped, and binucleate (dikaryotic). Fusion of the nuclei (karyogamy) takes place in the young ascus, and the zygote nucleus ($2n$) divides thrice (the first division being meiotic) to form 8 nuclei. Each nucleus surrounds itself with a wall and becomes an ascospore. Thus there are ascospores in each ascus. The ascospores have a peculiar shape, somewhat like pulley wheels (E). In flat view, however, they appear mostly spherical, oval or star-shaped.

In the meantime, soon after the formation of the sex organs, a number of sterile vegetative hyphae grow up the ascogonium (C), and enclose it as a 2-layered sheath called the peridium. This is pseudo-parenchymatous in nature, the outer layer being protective and the inner nutritive. The peridium enclosing the asci appears as a small globose body. This is the 'fruiting' body or ascocarp of the fungus, and being closed, is also known as the cleistothecium (D). The asci within the cleistothecium soon dissolve away, leaving the ascospores free and scattered within it. The peridium decays and the ascospores are blown away by the wind. They germinate under suitable conditions by producing a germ tube.

4. ERYSIPHE (10 sp.)

Occurrence and Structure. Erysiphe. (family *Erysiphaceae*; FIG. 88) is an obligate parasite causing a disease commonly called powdery mildew. Powdery mildews are mostly superficial parasites which first appear as small, white spots on leaves, then rapidly spread on the entire leaf-surface, usually the upper. The surface then appears to be coated with a fine, white powder that can be easily brushed off. Common hosts of *Erysiphe* are cucurbits, cereals, some grasses, pea, bean, rose and several other plants. *E. polygoni* is almost omnivorous, growing on a wide range of hosts, wild or cultivated. In India, this species is commonly found on pea and some other leguminous plants, and *E. graminis* is found on barley and other cereals, as well as many grasses. The mycelium of the fungus is superficial and consists of a matted mass of colourless, septate hyphae (A). These send haustoria into the epidermal cells of the host. The haustoria swell or branch off within the host cells. The hyphae are hyaline at first, but later they turn greyish, brownish or reddish. The mycelium produces many simple, erect conidiophores on the surface of the leaf. Each conidiophore cuts off (from the top downwards) a chain of oval conidia, having the appearance of a powdery coating. The fungus multiplies rapidly by means of the conidia.

Later, when conidia formation ceases, the fungus produces uni-nucleate sex organs—ascogonium (female) and antheridium (male). The latter is more slender than the former. They develop side by side at the tips of hyphae, pressing together closely (B). The male nucleus enters the ascogonium through a perforation made in its wall and pairs with the female nucleus of the

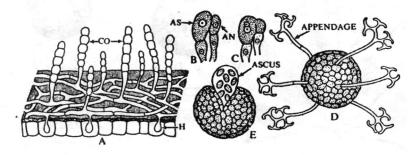

Erysiphe. FIG. 88. *A*, conidiophores and conidia (*CO*) on leaf-surface, and haustoria (*H*) in epidermis; *B*, sex organs: ascogonium (*AS*) and antheridium (*AN*); *C*, the same showing pairing of male and female nuclei; *D*, cleistothecium with dichotomously branched appendages; and *E*, the same bursting with the liberation of asci (appendages not shown)

ascogonium (*C*). It is now generally agreed that karyogamy (see p. 405) takes place in the young ascus mother cell. After this, the ascogonium forms into a row of cells. The penultimate cell of this row produces ascogenous hyphae (which then form asci, usually 2-8) within a closed ascocarp (see p. 405) called cleistothecium (*D*). From the stalk cells of the ascogonium and the antheridium, sterile hyphae arise forming a sheath for the ascocarp. From the sheath cells, peculiar hooked, branched, bulbous or simple *appendages* develop around the ascocarp. These are important diagnostic characteristics. The ascocarps appear on the leaf-surface as minute, spherical, dark bodies that look like so many black dots. The ascus commonly bears 8 ascospores, sometimes less (2-6) in some species. The ascospores are liberated after the bursting of the ascocarp and the ascus (*E*).

The source of infection may be the dormant mycelium in the seed, or the ascocarp which remains in the soil. *Control.* (*a*) The seeds may be soaked in hot water (50°C) for about 10 minutes; (*b*) the plants may be dusted with fine sulphur dust.

5 *UNCINULA* (20 *sp.*)

Occurrence. Uncinula necator (family *Erysiphaceae*; FIG. 88) is an obligate parasite like *Erysiphe*, causing a powdery mildew disease on grape-vine (*Vitis vinifera*). The disease is prevalent in the vineyards of India, as at Nasik. Sometimes, the disease takes on epidemic proportions. The disease was first noticed in Kent (England) in 1845, and in 1851 almost all the vineyards in France were seriously affected. The disease is also common in America and Australia.

Nature of the Disease. The vine may be attacked at any stage of its growth. The disease appears mainly on the leaves (*A*) and berries as white, diffuse, powdery or dusty patches, which soon turn grey and finally dark. Microscopic examination shows that the dusty patches are made of mycelia and conidia. All parts of the plant may be infected. Infected flowers do not produce fruit, while the young infected fruit drop off. Comparatively old fruit, if infected, become distorted in shape. Their skin cracks and they seldom ripen. Diseased leaves curl up and become discoloured and deformed. Black marks are seen on the stem when the fungus is rubbed off. Diseased plants, on the whole, show stunted growth and may wilt. Moderately high temperature and cloudy, sultry weather are conducive to the growth of the fungus.

Morphology of the Fungus. *Uncinula necator*, like other powdery mildews, is superficial

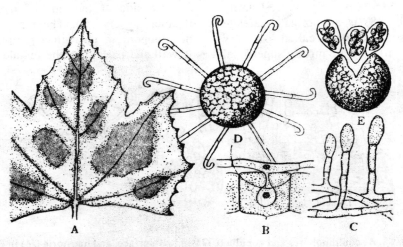

Uncinula. FIG. 89. *A*, an infected leaf of grape-vine; *B*, a haustorium penetrating an epidermal cell of the host; O, hyphae with conidiophores and conidia (on the top); *D*, a cleistothecium with hooked appendages; and *E*, a bursting cleistothecium showing the liberation of asci

(ectophytic). The mycelia together with the conidiophores gradually spread on the surface of the affected parts. The hyphae send sucking organs or haustoria (*B*) into the epidermal and even sub-epidermal cells of the host plant. These enlarge within the host cell and become pyriform in shape. The hyphae are branched and septate, forming initially a white web on the surface and darkening later.

Reproduction. The fungus usually reproduces asexually by means of conidia, and sometimes sexually, resulting in the formation of cleistothecia (closed fruiting body) enclosing asci. This, however, is not a common feature in India. Environmental factors may be responsible for this.

Asexual Reproduction. For this purpose, conidia appear in abundance on leaves and fruit, forming a dense, powdery film (*A & D*). Conidia, usually 3 or 4, are produced in a chain at the end of each simple, erect conidiophore. They are oval. When mature, they are easily dispersed by wind or rain. They are resistant to cold and dry atmospheric conditions. Under warm, moist conditions, the conidia readily germinate on the host (grape-vine) and grow vigorously on it in shady areas.

Sexual Reproduction. The stages in sexual reproduction are not known perfectly although cleistothecia (*D*) have been abundantly found in some countries. They lie embedded in the ectophytic mycelia on the surface of the leaf or shoot. They are hyaline when young but soon turn black, usually appearing in early winter or sometimes much earlier. They are almost spherical but somewhat flattened on top. Each cleistothecium has 8 to 25 septate appendages growing from its surface cells. Each appendage is curled inwards or hooked at the tip. The fruiting body contains 4 to 8 ovoid asci, each of which usually bears 4 to 6 oval ascospores (*E*), rarely 8 or even 2. When mature, the cleistothecia are washed down by the rain or blown away by the wind, either singly or in clusters. They rupture and the asci are liberated. The asci then burst and the ascospores are dispersed by the wind. Under suitable conditions, they infect new hosts.

Mode of Infection. (*1*) Fresh infection normally takes place through conidia which have survived winter. (*2*) The cleistothecia may remain on the vines and leaves or on the ground. Later, in spring, the ascospores may infect the leaves and shoots. (*3*) Dormant mycelia remaining in buds through winter may also be a source of infection.

Control. (*1*) Sulphur dusting is a universal treatment against this vine mildew. Timely dusting (once when the shoots are still young and again when the flowers are about to appear; a third application some time later may also be necessary) effectively controls the disease. (*2*) Pruning and removing all diseased parts. (*3*) Washing the vines with an acid solution of iron sulphate. (*4*) Coating the stems with a paste of sublimed sulphur and soft soap.

6. *NEUROSPORA* (3 *sp.*)

From the academic standpoint, *Neurospora* is considered very important since a considerable amount of genetical work, possibly next to that done on yeast, has been done on this fungus. Dodge first worked on it in 1927-28 and later. Reseach was done on it also by Lindegren in 1932, Beedle in 1944, Beedle and Tatum in 1945, Tatum in 1950, and others. The three species of this genus are *N. sitophila*, *N. tetrasperma* and *N. crassa*. All of them have been thoroughly studied.

Occurrence and Structure. *Neurospora* (family *Fimetariaceae*; FIG.90A), commonly called pink bread mould, is a saprophytic fungus, frequently seen in bakeries. It often contaminates cultures of fungi and bacteria in laboratories. The mycelium consists of a mass of branched, septate, somatic hyphae that spread on the substratum. The aerial hyphae produce countless *pink* spores (conidia) making the fungus easily recognizable. *Neurospora* is mostly heterothallic, and is differentiated into + strain and – strain (cf. *Mucor*).

Reproduction. The most common method of reproduction is asexual. Sexual reproduction was first discovered by Dodge in 1927-28. Since the discovery of this phenomenon, much work has been done on the genetics of this fungus.

Asexual Reproduction. This takes place freely through conidia, which are produced in great

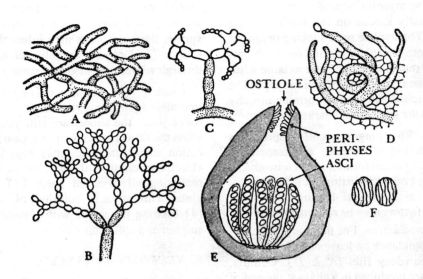

Neurospora. FIG. 90: *A*, branched and septate mycelia; *B*, a branched macroconidiophore with beaded macroconidia; *C*, a branched microconidiophore with microconidia; *D*, ascogonium (a coiled fertile branch); *E*, a mature perithecium with asci; and *F*, ascospores (2 shown) with ridges on the wall

numbers by the somatic aerial hyphae. There are two kinds of conidia: large (*macroconidia*) and small (*microconidia*). The former are borne in huge numbers in beaded chains on branched conidiophores, and are oval in colour (FIG. 90*B*). They are easily dispersed by the wind. The microconidia are minute in size and occur singly or in very short chains (each consisting of a few conidia), on special, branched conidiophores (FIG. 90 *C*). The fungus reproduces itself indefinitely by means of the conidia, generation after generation. Under favourable conditions, they germinate and give rise to somatic hyphae (+ or −) again.

Sexual Reproduction. Neurospora, as stated before, is mostly heterothallic, and this being so, sexual reproduction occurs only when two opposite strains (+ and −) happen to come together. No antheridia or sperm cells have been found in *Neurospora.* The female gametangium, as in other Ascomycetes, is the ascogonium. It is seen that a loose mass of somatic hyphae forms into a flask-shaped body—the **perithecium**. The young perithecium contains a somewhat coiled, fertile body—the ascogonium (FIG. 90 *D*). From the ascogonium grow out certain curved hyphae—the

trichogynes or receptive hyphae. Plasmogamy, i.e. the union of two protoplasts of opposite strains, may take place in any of the following ways, leading to the production of asci and ascospores and the maturation of perithecia or 'fruiting' bodies. The mycelia of any strain (+ or −), though hermaphroditic in nature (bearing both conidia and ascogonia), are mostly self-sterile. Plasmogamy may be as follows:

(1) Two hyphae of opposite strains may fuse (somatogamy).

(2) A hypha of one strain may come in contact with a trichogyne of the opposite strain.

(3) A macroconidium of one strain may come in contact with a trichogyne of the opposite strain and act as a male cell or gamete (spermatium)

(4) A microconidium of one strain may come in contact with a trichogyne of opposite strain and act as a male cell or gamete (spermatium).

Perithecia, Asci and Ascospores. After plasmogamy, the perithecia begin to mature, each perithecium containing several asci formed from the ascogonium. The young ascus is binucleate (one + and one −). But at an early stage of ascus formation, the two nuclei within it fuse (karyo-gamy) and thus, the ascus becomes uni-nucleate (+ −). This fused nucleus is the zygote, which represents the only diploid (2n) phase of *Neurospora*. Next, by meiosis followed by mitosis, 8 ascospores (only 4 in *N. tetrasperma* by meiosis) are formed in each ascus. Sexual differentiation, i.e. differentiation into + strain and − strain, occurs mostly during the first division, (sometimes the second) of the ascus nucleus in the young ascus (see below). The mature perithecium (FIG. 90*E*) is pyriform, beaked and dark, and has a thin wall and a long neck with an apical pore—the **ostiole**. The perithecium is superficial on the substratum, i.e. not on or within a stroma (see p. 431). It encloses several cylindrical asci, each opening by a minute apical pore. There may be hair-like growths (**peri-physes**) forming an inner lining on the ostiole. Paraphyses are, however, absent in a mature perithecium. Each mature ascus contains 8 brown-ish or blackish, oval ascospores, of which 4 are of one sexual strain and 4 of the other strain. Dodge also found that the 4 ascospores formed in *N. tetraspora* are binucleate (+ and −) and, therefore, self-fertile, i.e. abundant perithecia are formed when such spores are germinated. The ascus has a definite apical pore, very minute though, through which the ascospores are expelled with some force. The asci mature at different times within the perithecium. Each ascospore (FIG. 90*F*) is provid-ed with distinct nerves or ridges on its wall, and hence the name *Neurospora* (*neuron*, a nerve). The scospores germinate easily in suitable medium into + mycelia or − myycelia, as the case may be.

Segregation of Strains. Cultures from the ascospores of an ascus are seen to produce an abundance of perithecia. Evidently the spores are of two strains (+ and −). Using a special technique in 1928, Dodge was able to isolate tne spores of an ascus one by one, and grow them separately into mycelia. He found that the first 4 spores at the bottom of an ascus gave rise to mycelia of one strain (+ or −), while the 4 spores at the other end gave rise to mycelia of the opposite strain (− or +), thus indicating that the segregation of sex factors took place in the *first division* (meiotic) of the ascus-nucleus in the young ascus (FIG. 90-1*A*). In addition, his work showed that sex segregation might also take place to a certain extent in the *second division* (FIG.90-1*B*). Dodge experimen-tally proved the above facts by growing the spores of specific locations in the ascus and observing the extent to which the mating of + strain and −

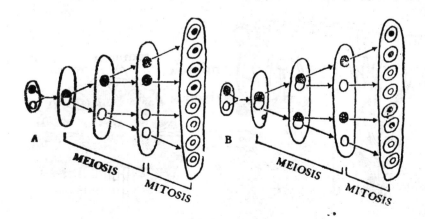

Neurospora. FIG. 90.-1. Segregation of sex in ascospores. *A*, segregation of alleles (paternal and maternal) in the first meiotic division (but no crossing over between two genes) − the result is 4:4 distribution of ascospores in the ascus; *B*, segregation of alleles in the second meiotic division (with crossing-over between two genes) − the result is 2:2:2:2 distribution of ascospores in the ascus

strain took place, i.e. whether both the strains were represented in each culture or only one strain. Dodge was also able to bring about crossings between different species of *Neurospora*. These results were corroborated by Lindegren and later, by Beedle and Tatum. Lindegren also found that the *first division* of the *ascus-nucleus* was meiotic in about 85% cases, while the *second division* was so in about 15% cases.

7. CLAVICEPS (12 sp.)

Claviceps (family *Clavicipitaceae*) belongs to the order Hypocreales, which consists of over 800 species.

Claviceps purpurea (FIG. 91), commonly called ergot fungus, grows as a parasite on rye (*Secale cereale*) and other grasses. It is well known for the ergot disease it produces on the ovaries of rye, for its poisonous effect on many herbivorous animals and human beings, and also for its universal use as a medicine known as ergot. If the ascospores of the fungus happen to fall on the flowers of rye, during spring, as they always do under natural conditions, they germinate into germ tubes which penetrate the ovary. Thus, the ovary becomes infected and the mycelium within it ramifies and forms into a compact, cottony mass of septate hyphae. The mass grows, hardens and turns dark purple or violet. The body thus formed is the **sclerotium** of the fungus (91A). Its length usually ranges from 1 to 3 cm. (see p. 404). It is pseudoparenchymatous in nature. The ovary gets completely destroyed and the sclerotium takes its place. Finally, it appears through the spikelet as an elongated, often somewhat curved and dark purplish body. Sclerotia are common in affected rye fields but so far it has not been possible to induce their formation in artificial culture.

Economic Importance. The sclerotium of rye is called the ergot. It contains seven alkaloids, of which **ergotamine** and **ergotoxine** are powerful. Ergot is distinctly poisonous, its poisonous effect being known as ergotism. Grazing animals that feed on diseased grains suffer badly. Their hoofs, tails and horns are affected due to contraction and thickening of the blood vessels supplying blood to these parts, finally leading to a gangrenous condition. Ergot poisoning also causes paralysis, nervous disorders and abortion. Bread or food contaminated by ergot is very harmful to human beings. Nevertheless, ergot is a universal drug. It is used to control haemorrhages and induce uterine contraction after childbirth. Ergot is collected from naturally diseased rye in Russia, Spain, Portugal and Poland. A large quantity is exported to Britain and America.

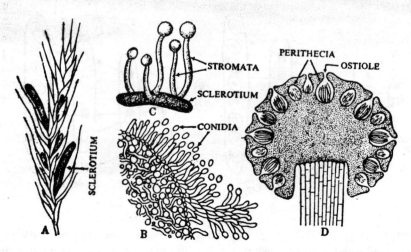

Claviceps. FIG. 91. *A*, sclerotia on spikelets of rye; *B*, conidia (*Sphacelia*)stage on the ovary; *C*, germinating sclerotium producing stromata; *D*, a stroma in vertical section showing numerous perithecia

Reproduction

Asexual Reproduction. The mycelium extends to the surface of the ovary and spreads over it as an interwoven mass of hyphae. Their tips behave as short slender conidiophores, which cut off from their ends a profusion of minute, oval or spherical conidia (91*B*). Conidia formation takes place within two days of infection. A sweet, yellow, sticky fluid—also called 'honeydew'—which emits an odour, is secreted by the infected flowers. The fluid bathes the conidia. This stage is otherwise known as the *Sphacelia* stage of the fungus and indicates an early sign of infection. The liquid attracts insects, which carry the conidia to other rye flowers and other grasses, infecting them. In due course, they may produce sclerotia again.

The sclerotium (FIG. 91*A*) is a hard, compact mass of hyphae, dark outside and white inside. When conidia formation cases, the sclerotia begin to grow and take shape. When fully formed, many of them fall to the ground or are harvested along with the grains. They contain plenty of food—proteins and fats—and pass into a dormant stage during winter. In the next spring, they grow and each gives rise to a number of mushroom-like bodies with long stalks and more or less globose heads, which are initially yellowish-brown but turn pink or violet later. These bodies are called **stromata** (91*C*). (A **stroma** is a compact mass of hyphae, like the sclerotium, but it bears perithecia). The stroma is also pseudoparenchymatous in nature, like the sclerotium. A broken sclerotium may grow normally, like the intact one. Sunken in the stromatic head and lying in a single, ring-like layer are several flask-shaped perithecia (91*D*).

The perithecium (FIG. 92*A*) has a thin wall, which has an opening called the ostiole. Within the perithecium develop many elongated, cylindrical asci, interspersed with slender paraphyses. Each ascus contains 8 acicular (needle-like) ascospores (FIG. 92*B*). The growth of the perithecium is simultaneous with the formation of the asci. When mature, the ascospores are forced out of the asci and finally dispersed by the wind. The ascospore germinates by putting forth germ tubes (92*C*).

Sexual Reproduction. Asci must have been

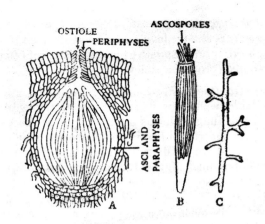

Claviceps. FIG. 92. *A*, a perithecium in vertical section (magnified); *B*, an ascus discharging ascospores; *C*, an ascospore germinating

formed as a result of sexual union, as in other members of Ascomycetes, but details of their formation in *Claviceps* are not known yet. The sexual organs arise from certain hyphae at the base of the peritheceum. These hyphae have much denser protoplasmic contents and are, therefore, easily distinguishable from the rest of the hyphae. They are branched. An ascogonium (female) and one or more antheridia (male) develop side by side from the terminal cell of a branch. Both are multinucleate, but the ascogonium is broader than the antheridium. The male nuclei of the antheridium migrate into the ascogonium, and plasmogamy (see p. 405) takes place. The nuclei are thus arranged in pairs, each pair being called a dikaryon (see p. 405). The ascogonium then produces ascogenous hyphae. Ascus formation takes place at the tips of such hyphae by hook or crosier method (see p. 405).

8. *PEZIZA* (150 *sp.*)

The family *Pezizaceae* is represented by a number of genera, of which *Peziza* and *Ascobolus* are described in the following pages. Both look alike with well-developed, fleshy, cup-shaped fruiting bodies but they differ mainly in the following ways: in *Peziza*, the ripe asci do not project beyond the level of the hymenium, and the ascospores are uniseriate and colourless. In

Ascobolus, the ripe asci elongate greatly and project beyond the level of the hymenium, and the ascospores are biseriate or multiseriate and often coloured (brown or violet).

Peziza (family *Pezizaceae*) belongs to the order *Pezizales which has about 500 species.* (FIG. 93A) is a cup fungus. It has a fleshy, cup or saucer-shaped, superficial fruiting body, usually ranging from 1-10 cm. in diameter. Some may be much smaller or much bigger. The cups are mostly regular in form, sometimes irregular and often contorted. *Peziza* is saprophytic in habit. It grows abundantly during the rainy season on heaps of semi-decomposed cow dung, decaying wood in heavily manured soil or soil rich in humus.

The hyphae are much branched and grow extensively, penetrating the substratum. The interwoven hyphae are massed together, forming the aerial, fleshy, cup-shaped reproductive or fruiting body, known as the **apothecium** (see p. 405). The apothecium (*A*) may be variously coloured, but often brownish, particularly on the inner surface.

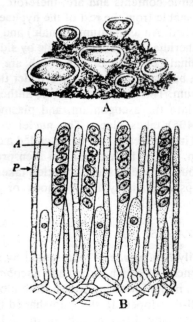

Peziza. FIG. 93.A, fruit bodies or cups (apothecia); B, a portion of apothecium (in section) showing asci (*A*) with ascospores and paraphyses (P)

It is usually sessile or short-stalked. It decays soon after the spores mature and shed. The inner wall of the apothecium is lined with a continuous layer (hymenium) consisting of countless asci, intermixed with slende, sterile hyphae—paraphyses (*B*). Each ascus is a cylindrical body and contains 8 distinct, hyaline ascospores. The latter are arranged obliquely in a row (uniseriate). When mature, they are liberated from the ascus through a terminal pore. They germinate under suitable conditions and in an appropriate medium, producing new mycelia.

Sexuality. There are no sexual organs in *Peziza* but nuclear fusion of two vegetative hyphal cells has been observed in a few species. Thus, prior to the formation of the apothecium, the nuclei of certain hyphal cells fuse in pairs, indicating reduction of sexuality. These cells then give rise to the ascogenous hyphae from which asci are subsequently formed. If this is true, the nucleus of the young ascus must be diploid. Next, 8 ascospores are formed in the ascus. The wall of the apothecium and the paraphyses are formed from vegetative hyphae.

9. ASCOBOLUS (25 sp.)

Occurrence. *Ascobolus* (FIG. 94A) is a cup fungus like *Peziza* and both belong to the same family, i.e. *Pezizaceae*. Most species of *Ascobolus* are coprophilous like *Peziza*, usually growing on the dung of certain animals. For example, *A. magnificus* grows on horse dung. Some species grow in soil rich in organic manures, and break up organic compounds for use by green plants. Certain species are also seen to grow on rotten wood, or on burnt ground, which has carbon deposit. All species of *Ascobolus* are saprophytic in habit.

Structure. The mycelium consists of hyaline hyphae, which ramify through the substratum. The hyphae are septate and have may branches. Within a few days of the germination of the spore, a soft fleshy, cup-shaped body, which is initially closed, appears on the surface. This is the most conspicuous part of the fungus, and is its fruiting body (ascocarp). The ascocarps (*A*) can be small or large.

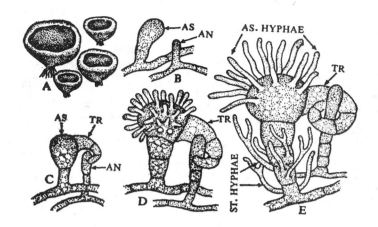

Ascobolus. FIG. 94.*A*, fruiting bodies; *B-E*, stages in the development of sexual organs; *AS*, ascogonium; AN antheridium; *TR*, trichogyne; *AS. HYPHAE*, ascogenous hyphae; *ST. HYPHAE*, sterile hyphae

Reproduction

Sexual Reproduction. A. magnificus and other species as well as are monoecious, bearing both male and female sexual organs, but are self-steile, as first shown by Dodge in 1920 and by others later. The ascocarps are produced only after two complementary strains (i.e. those of opposite sexes) are brought together. Morphologically, however, there is no difference between the two. When the two strains (*A* strain and *B* strain) grow mixed together, sexual branches grow and become differentiated into male (antheridium) and female (ascogonium) organs (*B*). Cross-fertilization takes place between these two organs, borne by two separate strains. A few species of *Ascobolus*, however, are self-fertile. In certain species the antheridia may not develop at all and a single strain produces the fruiting body by fusion of hyphae. The antheridial branch (*C*) consists of a multicellular stalk and a terminal antheridium, which is cylindrical or somewhat club-shaped. It bears numerous nuclei, sometimes as many as 400. The female branch (*C*) consists of unicellular or multicellular stalk and an ascogonium (oogonium), which is more or less globose. The ascogonium is uni-nucleate at first and forms, terminally, a receptive outgrowth called the trichogyne. This usually consists of a few cells. As the female branch elongates, the trichogyne becomes twisted around the antheridium. Thus, communication is established between the two sexual organs.

Fertilization. This takes place between the antheridium and the ascogonium which are borne by two separate strains. The male nuclei pass into the trichogyne and move towards the ascogonium by perforating the septa of the trichogyne. Each male nucleus has two distinct chromatin bodies by which it can be distinguished from the female nucleus even at later stages. Around this time, the female nucleus of the ascogonium divides repeatedly by mitosis and the newly-formed nuclei spread out near the periphery. The male nuclei enter the ascogonium and the sexual nuclei fuse in pairs (actually a close association). Each such pair, called a *dikaryon* (see p. 405), otherwise called *definitive nucleus*, is a functional unit (2*n*). It now undergoes repeated conjugate divisions mitotically, resulting in several nuclei (each 2*n*). The ascogonium produces several filaments called ascogenous hyphae (*D-E*). The contents of the ascogonium pass into them. The ascogenous hyphae elongate and become septate, each cell having a pair of diploid nuclei. The ascogenous hypha produces terminally an ascus by the hook or crosier method (see p. 406), and a pair of nuclei

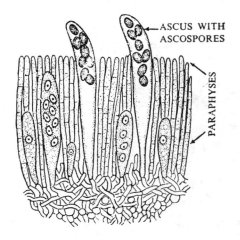

ASCUS WITH ASCOSPORES

PARAPHYSES

Ascobolus. . FIG. 95, section through apothecium showing asci (in several stages of development) and paraphyses

move into it. The young ascus is always binucle-ate. It is here that actual nuclear fusion (second fusion) takes place and the zygote nucleus becomes tetraploid ($4n$). Almost immediately, the zygote nucleus undergoes meiosis, forming four nuclei (each $2n$). A second reduction called *brachymeiosis* follows. Thus, finally 8 nuclei are produced (each n). The ascus simultaneously grows and becomes cylindrical. Cytoplasm col-lects round each nucleus and a wall is formed round each. Thus, altogether 8 ascospores appear in each ascus. They are brown or violet.

Ascocarp. With the development of the asci, the **ascocarp** (94A) is formed. In *Ascobolus,* the ascocarp is open and cup-shaped, and is called apothecium. It is formed of an interwoven mass of sterile vegetative hyphae growing around the sex-ual organs. The apothecium (FIG. 95) has a fleshy protective wall (pseudoparenchymatous in nature), known as the peridium and a hymenium on its inner surface. The hymenium bears many asci and paraphyses (sterile hyphae) arranged in a parallel series. The asci elongate and protrude beyond the level of the hymenium. Their tips bend towards the source of light (positively pho-totropic). Eventually, the asci burst and the ascospores are discharged. If the air is dry, 'puff-ing' of the spores may be noticed.

CLASS IV BASIDIOMYCETES or CLUB FUNGI
(23,000 sp.)

1. *USTILAGO* (300 *sp.*)

Ustilago (family *Ustilaginaceae*) belongs to the order Ustilaginales or smuts, which consists of about 700 species.

Ustilago or smut (FIG. 96) is a parasitic fungus which usually attacks members of *Gramineae*. It may also grow as a saprophyte in soil rich in organic material. Some crops commonly attacked by *Ustilago* are maize, wheat, barley, oat, rice and sugarcane. The harmful effect of corn smut by *U. zeae* on maize (*A*), of oat smut by *U. avenae* on oat, of loose smut by *U. tritici* on wheat (*B*), etc., often causes heavy losses.

The plants may be infected in different ways. Infection usually takes place through teleutospores or basidiospores. Dormant mycelia, which become active later, may exist in the seed or plant in the following ways: (1) The teleutospores may fall on the stigma or feathery style, germinate and pro-duce a promycelium (*D, top*). The latter forms infective hyphae (but no basidiospores), which penetrate into the ovary. Subsequently, as the ovary develops, the mycelia remain dormant in the grain (seed). As the latter germinates, the mycelia grow and ramify. In such a case, as in *U. tritici* (on wheat), the disease is internally seed-borne. (2) The spores may also adhere to the grains exter-nally. They are usually released after threshing of the ears. As they get scattered, they may infect new hosts through their young parts—roots, stems, leaves and more particularly, spikelets, as in *U. zeae* (on maize) and *U. avenae* (on oat). (3) The basidiospores may produce uni-nucleate hyphae which may infect the host, or grow on the surface of the host body, but two such hyphae must fuse in the tissue of the host or just outside, pro-ducing a binucleate mycelium. This then grows normally and causes the disease. Two basid-iospores may also unite to give rise to a binucleate mycelium. (4) A binucleate mycelium may pro-duce binucleate conidia on the surface of the host body. These are dispersed by the wind and become

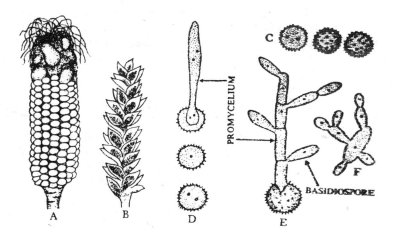

Ustilago. FIG. 96. *A*, maize cob infected; *B*, wheat spikelets infected; *C*, teleutospores;
D, teleutospore germinating: *bottom*, teleutospore (binucleate); *middle*, the same (uninucleate and diploid on
fusion of the two nuclei); *top*, the same germinating into promycelium (note the four nuclei on reduction division);
E, mature promycelium bearing basidiospores; and *F*, basidiospore budding

sources of infection. Uninucleate conidia formed
by a uninucleate hypha do not survive long. But
they may unite with a hypha of the opposite strain
to produce a binucleate mycelium first.

The binucleate mycelia may be local or
widespread in the body of the host, and are sparsely septate but profusely branched. The hyphae
ramify through the intercellular spaces, producing
a few haustoria in some species. The haustoria
penetrate the living tissue of the host to absorb
food material from it. As a consequence, the
growth of the host plant becomes stunted. The
hyphae tend to grow towards the meristematic
regions, drying up the older parts. During the flowering stage of the host plant, the hyphae extend to
all parts of the ears (spikelets) and cover them with
black, soot-like masses of spores—hence, the
name 'smut'. All the floral parts except the awns
are soon replaced by the black powdery mass of
spores. The spores are called teleutospores (or
chlamydospores; *C*). They are formed in countless
numbers and are somewhat thick-walled. The
ovaries often become very swollen and usually
distorted, and are desotryed.

The teleutospores are blown about by the wind.
They may germinate in the soil, or if they are carried over to the stigmas and styles of healthy

plants, they germinate there by producing a short
germ tube called the promycelium (or basidium;
D, *top*). The promycelium becomes septate (characteristic of *Ustilago*) and consists of 4 uninucleate cells (*E*). Young teleutospores are binucleate
(*D*, *bottom*). When they mature, nuclear fusion
(karyogamy) takes place within them (*D*, *middle*).
This is the only *diploid condition* of the fungus.
The diploid nucleus of the zygote divides meiotically while the promycelium is being formed (*D*,
top). Each cell of the promycelium is provided
with a haploid nucleus (*E*).

The next stage may follow any of the patterns
described below, according to the species. (1) From
each cell of the promycelium, one or more thin-
walled elongated, uninucleate (haploid) basidiospores (also called sporidia) may be formed
through budding (*E*). Each such basidiospore may
take to budding again, before or after it is shed
from the promycelium, forming secondary basidiospores (*F*). The nuclei correspondingly divide
meiotically to supply each spore with a nucleus.
Two such basidiospores of opposite strains (+ and
−) unite (but no karyogamy, i.e. nuclear fusion,
takes place), and produce a binucleate mycelium
(dikaryon, + and −). (2) A basidiospore may germinate into a uninucleate hypha (+ or −). Two such

hyphae unite and produce a binucleate mycelium (dikaryon). (3) A basidiospore may germinate into a uninucleate hypha (+ or –). Then a basidiospore of the opposite strain may unite with this hypha, producing a binucleate mycelium (dikaryon). (4) The promycelium may directly produce infective hyphae without the intervention of basidiospores. Two such hyphae of opposite strains unite and produce binucleate mycelium (dikaryon).

It is only after the attainment of the dikaryotic condition is attained by any of the above methods that the binucleate mycelium grows vigorously and spreads through the body of the host, initiating the parastic phase of the fungus and finally producing teleutospores—a distinct symptom of the disease.

Control. (1) Rotation of crops in the case of maize. (2) Hot water treatment of grains in the case of wheat, and then drying them under strong sunlight. (3) Spraying the grains with equal parts of commercial formalin and water in the case of oats, or dusting them with copper carbonate powder. (4) Cross-breeding with types resistant or immune to smut;—possibly the best method.

2. *PUCCINIA* (700 *sp.*)

Puccinia (family *Pucciniaceae*) belongs to the order Uredinales or rusts, which are destructive parasites, and coimprise about 4,600 species. *Puccinia* species may be *heteroecious* , requiring two distinct hosts to complete their life cycle, or *autoecious*, requiring only one host to complete their life cycle. *Puccinia* attacks a variety of host plants, particularly members of *Gramineae*. *Puccinia graminis*, commonly known as the 'black rust' of wheat, is a *heteroecious* species which attacks wheat plants and common barberry plants in rotation. This species is also **polymorphic**, bearing different kinds of spores and spore structures on wheat and barberry.

Life history. This species is a virulent parasite. It attacks wheat plants and often damages them very seriously. The disease sometimes breaks out in an epidemic form. It also attacks barley, oats and rye.

Stages on Wheat Plant.

(*a*) **Uredium and Uredospores** (FIG. 97). In late spring or early summer, the spores (aeciospores; see FIG. 100) carried by the wind from barberry to wheat germinate on the latter, each producing a germ tube through a stoma (*A*). Within 10-12 days of infection, reddish-brown streaks appear on the stem, leaf-sheath and leaf (*B*), indicating the diseased condition of the plant. A section through the infected part shows a mass of mycelia ramifying through the intercellular spaces, penetrating at places the living cells of the

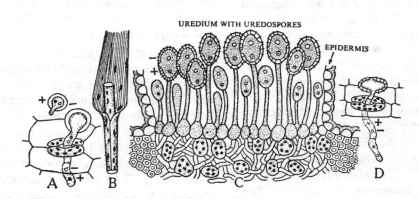

UREDIUM WITH UREDOSPORES

EPIDERMIS

Puccinia. FIG. 97. *A*, germination of acciospore (binucleate) on wheat plant—germ tube entering through a stoma; *B*, wheat leaf and leaf-sheath showing uredia; *C*, a uredium (in section) showing binucleate uredospores (+ and –) and also the infecting hyphae; *D*, germination of a uredospore on wheat plant again

host to absorb food from them, and on the surface a number of spore clusters known as **uredia** (or uredosori). The hyphae of the mycelium are septate and the cells binucleate (+ and –). As they grow, the uredia break through the epidermis and appear on the surface as reddish-brown streaks (*C*). The uredium bears many slender hyphae that project outwards, each ending in a one-celled, rough-walled, brownish or reddish, binucleate (+ and –) spore called the **uredospore**. This stage is known as the 'red rust' of wheat. When mature, the spores are blown about by the wind over a wide area, and they directly infect other wheat plants (*D*). The disease may thus appear in an epidemic form, destroying the whole or major part of the crop. The uredospores may be produced successively throughout the summer infecting the wheat plants each time. These spores cannot usually withstand a very severe winter.

(*b*) **Telium and Teliospores** (FIG. 98). In late summer, the mycelia still existing in the wheat plant after the formation of the uredospores grow and mass together below the epidermis. They give rise to black spots or streaks at places on the stem (*A*), leaf-sheath and leaf. Each such spot or streak is a sorus, called the **telium**. The telium produces several slender stalks, each ending in a black or dark-brown, elongated, two-celled, heavy-walled spore called the **teliospore** (*B*). This stage is the 'black rust' of wheat. The teliospores are resting spores that help the fungus tide over the winter period. Each cell of the young teliospore is binucleate (+ and –) but soon the two nuclei fuse together (a reduced form of the sexual act), and the mature teliospore has two uni-nucleate cells (+ –). The spores, evidently diploid, remain dormant on the wheat plant or in the soil till the following spring. They do not infect the wheat plant again.

(*c*) **Basidium and Basidiospores** (FIG. 98*C*). One or both cells of the teliospore germinate independently, each producing a slender, elongated hypha called the **basidium**, which consists of four terminal cells. Each cell produces a short slender stalk called the **sterigma**. Its end dilates and forms a spore called the **basidiospore**. The diploid nucleus (+ –) of the teliospore undergoes

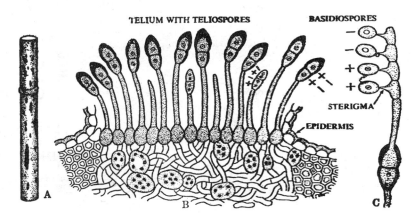

Puccinia. FIG. 98. *A*, an infected wheat stem showing telia; *B*, a telium (in section) showing young binucleate teliospores (+ and –) and mature uninucleate teliospores (+), and also the infecting hyphae; *C*, germination of a teliospore (on old dry wheat plant or in the soil) producing four basidiospores (uninucleate, + or –), each on a short sterigma

Nomenclature. Uredium, uredosorus or uredinium → uredospore, urediospore or uredinospore. Telium or teleutosorous → teliospore or teleutospore. Spermogonium, pycnium or pycnidium → spermatium, pycnospore or pycniospore. Aecium or aecidium → aeciospore or aecidiospore.

reduction division so that the basidial cells and the basidiospores become haploid. They are, of course, uninucleate but are of opposite strains (two + and two −). *Puccinia* is. thus, *heterothallic* (see p. 417). The basidiospores do not infect the wheat plant. They are blown about by the wind, many of them being carried over to barberry (*Berberis vulgaris*) bushes where the next stage takes place.

Stages on Barberry Plant

(*d*) **Spermogonium and Spermatia** (FIG. 99 *B-C*). The basidiospore germinates on the barberry leaf by producing a germ tube, which enters the leaf through the cuticle (*A*). The mycelia grow extensively in the leaf tissue and soon mass together beneath the epidermis (usually upper). Within about 7-10 days of infection, slightly raised yellowish or reddish spots, called **spermogonia** (or pycnia), are formed on the leaf surface (*B*). The cells of the mycelium as well as

those of the spermogonium, are uninucleate. They are of either the + strain or the − strain, and are produced correspondingly from a + basidiospore or from a − basidiospore. In section, the spermogonium is more or less flask-shaped (*C*). Its inner wall is lined with many fine, ferile hyphae (spermatial hyphae). These successively cut off from their ends very minute, uninucleate cells called **spermatia** (or pycnospores; *D*). Several sterile hyphae, called **periphyses**, also grow from the upper part, projecting outwards through the narrow pore or ostiole. Besides, there are certain special hyphae called **receptive hyphae**, protruding outward through the ostiole. The spermatia are exuded through the ostiole in a drop of sweet fluid. The sweet fluid attracts insects, which carry the spermatia from one spermogonium to another possibly of the opposite strain. The spermatia come in contact with the receptive hyphae of the opposite strain and their contents pass into them, but no nuclear fusion takes place (*E*). The receptive

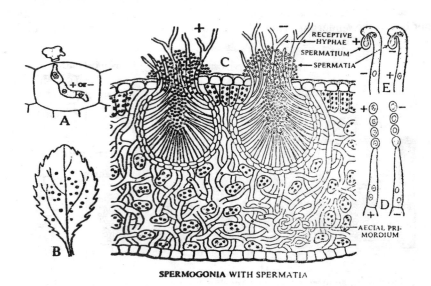

SPERMOGONIA WITH SPERMATIA

Puccinia. FIG. 99. *A*, germination of a basidiospore (uninucleate) on barberry leaf through the cuticle; *B*, barberry leaf infected showing spermogonia on the upper surface; *C*, section through the infected part showing two spermogonia (one + and one −), mass of infecting hyphae and some receptive hyphae which have become binucleate (+ and −) after the entry of spermatial nuclei (see *E*); the receptive hyphae are now extending towards the aecial primorodium; *D*, spermatial hyphae cutting off spermatia (+ or −); *E*, spermatia and receptive hyphae of opposite strains uniting (nuclei, however, do not fuse) hyphae, now with binucleate cells (+ and −), extend to the *aecial primordium* formed near the lower epidermis from an interwoven mass of primary hyphae which have already penetrated the entire leaf area. Some of the periphyses, too, may behave as receptive hyphae. There is also evidence that a + spermatium may unite with a − spermatium, giving rise to hyphae with binucleate (+ and −) cells. The receptive hyphae with binucleate cells eventually form the basal cells of the aecium (FIG. 100C).

(*e*) **Aecium and Aeciospores** (FIG. 100). The elongated, binucleate basal cells (+ and −) of the aecium now give rise to clusters of comparatively large cup-like blisters, called **aecia** or clustercups, on the lower surface of the leaf (A-B). As the aecium grows, it breaks out of the epidermis (C). The basal cells begin to cut off from the bottom chains of binucleate cells (+ and −). These immediately divide, producing large, orange or yellow binucleate cells (spores) called **aeciospores** (+ and −) and small sterile cells (also binucleate, + and −) in an alternating manner (D). The latter soon disintegrate. Aeciospores are the first *binucleate spores* to appear in the life cycle of the fungus. A protective layer called the **peridium** also

develops from the basal cells of the aecium. Soon, the peridium bursts and the spores are liberated. These are shed in late spring and early summer, and are blown about by the wind. If they happen to fall on a wheat plant, they infect it (FIG. 97A) and the life cycle is repeated.

Sexuality, Diplophase and Haplophase. Sexuality in *Puccinia* is reduced to the fusion of two nuclei in the young teliospore. Diplophase (binucleate condition) begins with the cells of the receptive hyphae after spermatization (FIG. 99E) and continues through aecium and aeciospores on barberry and later, on wheat through infecting mycelia, uredium, uredospores and finally, young teliospores (where the actual fusion of nuclei takes place). The haplophase (uninucleate condition) begins with the mature teliospores on wheat and continues on barberry through germinating basidiospores, infecting mycelia and finally, spermogonium and spermatia. *Puccinia* is heterothallic, the basidiospores being distinctly of two opposite strains (+ and −). It should also be noted that in the whole life-cycle of *Puccinia* the diploid (2n) condition is represented by the mature teliospores only.

Control. No special method has been discovered

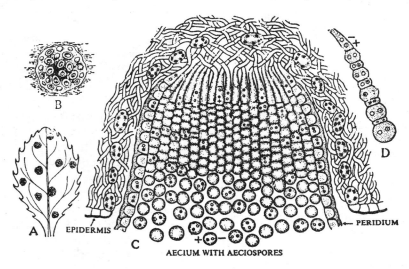

AECIUM WITH AECIOSPORES

Puccinia. FIG. 100. *A*, barberry leaf showing clusters of aecia on the lower surface; *B*, a cluster (magnified); *C*, an aecium (in section) showing binucleate (+ and −) aecial cells, aeciospores and peridium, and a tangled mass of infecting hyphae; *D*, a chain of aeciospores and sterile cells produced in an alternating manner

so far to prevent or radically cure the disease. Certain methods have, however, been devised to control its intensity. (1) Eradication of the barberry bush near a wheat field is a good established practice. (2) By cross-breeding with rust-resistant varieties, it has been possible to evolve new types of wheat which are immune to the rust for at least some years and for a particular locality. (3) Elimination of cultivation of wheat in the hills during summer may reduce the spread of the disease to the plains through uredospores. (4) Cultivation of rust-resistant varieties.

3. AGARICUS (about 70 sp.)

Agaricus (= *Psalliota*; family *Agaricaceae*), commonly called mushroom (when edible) or toadstool (when poisonous), is a fleshy saprophytic fungus. It grows on damp, rotten logs, tree trunks, decaying organic matter, and in damp soil rich in organic substances. The family *Agaricaceae* has about 5,000 species. Other common genera of the family are *Amanita*, *Lepiota*, *Coprinus*, *Marasmius*, etc.

Edible and Poisonous Forms. There are about 200 species of fleshy fungi that are edible; many are non-edible, and over 12 species distinctly poisonous. All puff-balls are edible, particularly when they are young. Other common edible fungi are *Agaricus campestris* (*Psalliota campestris*), *Morchella esculenta*, *Volvaria terastria*, *Lepiota mastoides*, etc. Certain species of *Amanita* which resemble edible *Agaricus* are extremely poisonous. These, however, are usually distinguished from the latter by a cup-like structure (called volva) at the base, which is absent in *Agaricus*. Edible types cannot be easily distinguished from poisonous ones except by critical examination. Generally speaking, (1) most of the species which have bright colour are to be regarded as poisonous; (2) those bearing pink spores, and (3) those with a cup at the base are also poisonous; (4) a hot burning taste or acid flavour should, as a rule, be avoided; (5) those growing on wood, and (6) those whose stems do not break easily, when touched, are non-edible; and (7) non-edible types do not generally grow in open, sunny places.

Structure (FIG. 101). The mycelium consists of a mass of much-branched hyphae, which unite (anastomose) at their points of contact and form a network in the substratum in which the fungus grows. The hyphae are very slender, hyaline and septate, mainly consisting of binucleate cells (+ and –). Frequently, several hyphae are seen to be massed together here and there into thick twisted

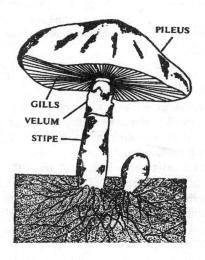

Agaricus. FIG. 101. Two plants, young and old, with ramifying mycelia

strands, called **rhizomorphs**, covered by a sheath. To start with, as the uninucleate basidiospore germinates, it produces a primary mycelium (+ or –). Soon, however, it becomes multi-nucleate by repeated nuclear divisions. Septa appear between the nuclei, dividing the mycelium into a number of uninucleate cells. This stage is short. Soon, however, two such hyphae (one + and one –) come into contact and fuse. The fusion is in the nature of plasmogamy (i.e. fusion of two protoplasts without nuclear fusion or karyogamy. This takes place through a pore punctured in the hyphal wall.) The new hypha, thus formed, is the secondary mycelium, and its cells are typically binucleate (+ and–). This is followed by clamp connexion (see FIG. 60) in some cells, at least. The secondary mycelium spreads in all directions through the substratum, perennates from year to year, and in season, produces the main, fleshy, aerial body which is the **fructification** or fruit body of the fungus, otherwise called **basidiocarp** (basidia-forming body) or **sporophore** (spore-producing body).

Basidiocarp (FIG. 101). This consists of a fleshy stalk known as the **stipe** (a stem) and an umbrella-like head or cap known as the **pileus** (a cap or hat). The stalk and the head are composed of an interwoven mass of hyphae, and in section they have the appearance of a tissue—known as *pseudoparenchyma*. The stipe is stout and cylindrical, while the pileus is expanded, roundish and convex. When young, the fructification is spherical (button stage) and is completely enveloped by a thin membranous covering called the **veil** or **velum**. With the rapid growth of the fruit body, specially the pileus, the velum gets ruptured, while the lower part of it remains attached to the stipe in the form of a ring (annulus). The pileus soon spreads in an umbrella-like fashion on the top of the stipe. On the undersurface of the pileus, a large number of thin, vertical, plate-like structures, extending radially from the stipe to the margin of the pileus, are seen. These are known as the **gills** or **lamellae**.

Gills. Gills occur in large numbers, between 300 to 600 for each fructification. Each gill bears innumerable spores (basidiospores) on both surfaces. A gill (FIGS. 102-3) in section shows three distinct portions: trama, sub-hymenium and hymenium. The **trama** is the central portion of the gill and consists of an interwoven mass (false tissue or pseudoparenchyma) of long, slender hyphae. The hyphal cells of the trama curve outward on either side of the gill and terminate in a layer of small rounded or oval cells. This layer is the **sub-hymenium**. External to it lies the **hymenium** which is composed of a compact layer of club-shaped cells—basidia and paraphyses. The spore-bearing ones are the basidia and the sterile ones are the **paraphyses**; The latter are somewhat shorter than the basidia and are regarded by some mycologists as immature basidia. Each basidium bears four basidiospores (sometimes two, as in cultivated mushroom) on short, slender stalks known as the sterigmata (sing. sterigma). When mature, the basidiospores fall off and germinate under suitable conditions.

Reproduction. Asexual reproduction is not a regular feature in the life cycle of *Agaricus*. Sometimes, however, it may take place through a kind of 'resting' spores called **chlamydospores** which are enlarged, thick-walled vegetative cells of a hypha, formed singly or in chains. They germinate by producing a germ tube. Sometimes, hyphae break up into small unicellular fragments called **oidia** (uni-nucleate or bi-nucleate). Accordingly, they grow into primary or secondary mycelia. A uninucleate oidium may also directly fuse with a primary mycelium. In some species, a basidiospore may give rise to a large number of conidia by budding. Each conidium then germinates into a mycelium.

Sexual Reproduction. We have already seen how plasmogamy takes place between two primary hyphae of opposite strains (+ and −), leading to

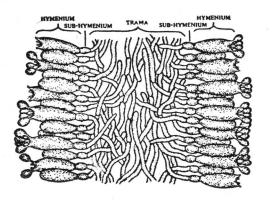

Agaricus. FIG. 102. A gill in section

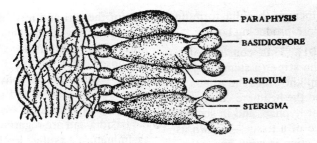

Agaricus. FIG. 103. A portion of a gill in section

dikaryotic (bi-nucleate) secondary hypha. A short but distinct sexual phase is, however, represented by the complete fusion (karyogamy) of two haploid nuclei of opposite strains (+ and –) in the young basidium. This produces a diploid zygote (+ –), the nucleus of which divides by meiosis to form 4 haploid nuclei (2 + and 2 –) in the basidium. Each nucleus (+ or –) pushes into a basidiospore through a sterigma. Evidently, 2 basidiospores are of + strain and the other 2 of – strain. On germination, the + basidiospore produces a + primary mycelium, and the – basidiospore produces a – primary mycelium, as described before. There are, however, no sex organs in *Agaricus.*

Development of Basidium and Basidiospore (FIG. 104). The basidium is initially bi-nucleate (*A*). The two nuclei, each with *n* chromosomes, fuse to form the zygote nucleus (*B*). The latter,

evidently provided with $2n$ chromosomes, undergoes reduction division, giving rise to four daughter nuclei, each with *n* chromosomes (*C-D*). Slender projections or sterigmata—usually 4, sometimes 21—are formed at the end of each basidium (*D*). Each sterigma swells at the end, and a nucleus migrates into it from the basidium (*E*). The swollen end-cell containing a nucleus is the basidiospore (*F*). A small outgrowth, called hilum, is formed at the junction of the basidiospore and the sterigma. A drop of water accumulates on the hilum, and then the basidiospore, together with the drop of water, suddenly shoots off from the sterigma (*G*). This explosive mechanism is not, however, understood.

4. *POLYPORUS* (about 500 sp.)

Polyporus (FIG. 105), a pore fungus, belongs to the family *Polyporaceae*, which has over 1,000

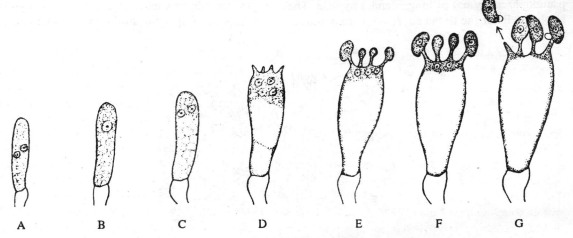

A   B   C   D   E   F   G

Agaricus. FIG. 104. Stages in the development of basidium and basidiospore. (For explanation see text)

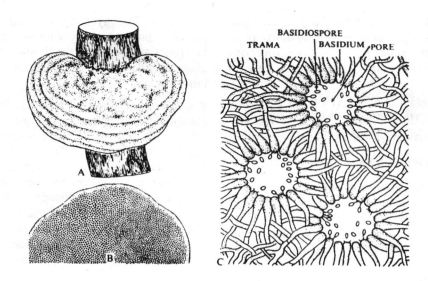

Polyporus. FIG. 105. *A*, the fungus growing on a dead branch; *B*, lower surface of the fungus (a portion) showing pores; *C*, fruit body (in transection through the pore-tubes)

species. Other common genera of this family are *Polystichus*, *Formes*, *Daedalea* and *Lenzites*. Many species of *Polyporus* grow as bracket or shelf fungi, either singly or in groups, on various forest trees, stumps and logs, and are responsible for wood decay, sometimes causing heavy damage. This has necessitated the use of wood preservatives, particularly in the case of timber. *Polyporus* is usually annual. The mycelia develop within and below the bark, and eventually form on it a more or less flat fruit body (*A*) called **basidiocarp** (basidia-bearing body) or **sporophore** (spore-bearing body). The fruit body is leathery, corky or woody, and is whitish or slightly greyish or brownish. The upper surface may be smooth, rough or warted, often undulating, and in some species, distinctly striated, particularly towards the outer margin. The lower surface is porous (*B*). The fruit body in section (*C*) is seen to consist of (*a*) a **context**, which is the upper or outer fibrous part made of thick-walled hyphae; (*b*) a trama, which is a loose mass of much-branched, septate and anastomosing hyphae; (*c*) a series of **pores** or **tubes** which extend from below the context to the lower surface, on the lower surface the pores appear as innumerable, minute holes, practically

covering it; and (*d*) a **hymenium**, which is a distinct layer of basidia lining each pore. The basidia are club-shaped and project slightly into the pore. Each basidium bears four short, slender sterigmata. Each sterigma forms a basidiospore at its end by abstriction. The basidiospores are discharged continually for some weeks into the pores, through which they escape freely and are blown about by the wind. The basidiospore shoots from the sterigma exactly in the same way as in *Agaricus* (see FIG. 104). An enormous quantity of basidiospores is produced by a fruit body. They germinate under favourable conditions.

It may be noted that the primary hyphae formed from the basidiospores have uni-nucleate (*monokaryotic*, + or –) cells, while the secondary hyphae have binucleate (*dikaryotic*, + and –) cells. The basidiospores (+ or –) germinate close together and the hyphae freely anastomose, with the result that the + or – nucleus of one primary hypha passes into another primary hypha of the opposite strain. A dikaryon (see p. 405) is the result. The secondary hyphae that develop from dikaryotic hyphae have bi-nucleate (*dikaryotic*, + and –) cells. The basidium, which is the terminal cell of a secondary hypha, is similarly bi-nucleate (+ and −). One nucleus goes to a basidiospore, which is evidently either + or −, finally giving rise to a + hypha or a − hypha.

CLASS V   DEUTEROMYCETES OR FUNGI IMPERFECTI
(over 24,000 sp.)

1. *HELMINTHOSPORIUM* (175 *sp.*)

Helminthosporium (FIG. 106) belongs to the family *Dematiaceae*. Several diseases are caused by this fungus. The 'leaf spot' disease of rice (*A*) due to the attack of *H. oryzae* is fairly common in Assam and West Bengal, and occasional in other areas. The fungus usually attacks all parts of the rice plant, particularly the leaves, mostly their lower surfaces, causing brown to dark brown spots with yellowish halos. The spots rapidly increase in number. The ears may also be affected (*B*), becoming distorted and sterile. Other common diseases caused by the fungus are: 'foot rot' of barley due to the attack of *H. sativum*, which also attacks wheat and many other grasses; 'leaf stripe' of barley caused by *H. gramineum*; 'leaf spot' of oats *H. avenae*; and 'eye spot' of sugarcane caused by *H. sacchari*.

Structure. The mycelium consists of branched, septate hyphae which grow through the intercellular spaces and penetrate the living cells of the host plant, i.e. the hyphae are intercellular as well as intracellular.

Reproduction. The only method of reproduction known so far is by means of **conidia** (*C*). Erect, stout **conidiophores** emerge in groups, mainly through the stomata. They are unbranched. Sometimes, however, branches appear at their base. The conidiophores bear conidia towards the top. The conidia are multiseptate, the septa ranging from 5 to 10. They are dispersed by the wind. The disease spreads in rainy and cloudy weather. It is usually a seed-borne disease. Successful control of the disease has not been possible yet.

2. *FUSARIUM* (65 *sp.* and several varieties)

Fusarium (FIG. 107) belongs to the family *Tuberculariaceae*. Species of this genus are often very deceptive because of the great variety of forms. Two common species of *Fusarium* which cause wilt-diseases in India are *F. udum* (attacks pigeon pea) and *F. vasinfectum* (attacks cotton). The wilt-disease of linseed caused by *F. lini* and that of cabbage by *F. conglutinans* are also fairly common. Infection of the host plant takes place

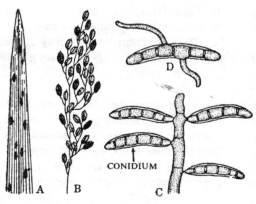

FIG. 106

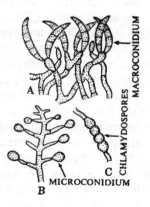

FIG. 107

Helminthosporium. FIG. 106. *A*, rice leaf infected; *B*, rice spikelets infected; *C*, conidiophore bearing conidia; *D*, a germinating conidium

Fusarium. FIG. 107. *A*, sporodochium (a portion) with macroconidia; *B*, conidiophore with microconidia; *C*, hypha with chlamydospores

through tender roots. The mycelium penetrates the vascular tissues. Black streaks are formed and these soon spread to the stem and the branches. The fungus remains restricted to the vascular tissues. The mycelium grows profusely within the vessels and plugs them. The result is wilting followed by death.

Reproduction. The fungus reproduces by macroconidia, microconidia and chlamydospores (see p 405). Sclerotium formation is also not uncommon. Macroconidia (FIG. 107A) are long, septate and crescent-shaped, and are formed on short conidiophores. The latter are borne on a sporodochium on the surface of the host plant. The **sporodochium** is a cushion-shaped stroma, i.e. a compact mass of vegetative hyphae much like a mattress, covered with conidiophores on the surface of the host plant. Microconidia (FIG. 107B) are small, usually oval and unseptate or uniseptate. They are formed within the tissue, but on the surface of the plant they are held together in groups in a drop of liquid. Chlamydospores (FIG. 107C) are formed in chains within the tissue. The conidia and the spores, when shed, remain in the soil and are viable for long periods. No direct treatment has been found to control the disease. Long periods of rotation have, however, been found effective.

PLANT PATHOLOGY

A Short Historical Account. Work on plant pathology was initiated by **Tillet**, whose experimental investigations on the bunt (stinking smut) of wheat elucidated the cause of the disease and its prevention. He published the results of his work in 1755, and was awarded the first prize offered by the Academy of Bordeaux. **Provost's** work in Geneva in 1807 threw more light on the causal fungus (*Tilletia tritici*) and the effective treatment (by copper sulphate). In the meantime **Andrew Knight's** work on wheat rust in 1804 established the fact that spores from barberry infect wheat plants. Plant pathology was actually founded as an important branch of study through the extensive work carried out by **Persoon** (1761-1836), **Fries** (1794-1878), **De Bary** (1831-88) and **Kuhne** (1825-1910). **Sir Edwin J. Butler** (1874-1943), Imperial Mycologist, Pusa Agricultural Institute, India (1905-19), and later, Director of the Imperial Mycological Institute, **Kew** (1920-35), did very valuable work on fungal diseases of plants. His *Fungi and Diseases in Plants*, published in 1918, was a notable contribution to mycology. A revised and enlarged edition of the book was published in 1949 under the title, *Plant Pathology*, by **Butler** and **Jones**.

PLANT DISEASES CAUSED BY FUNGI.[1] *Symptoms*, *Causes* and *Effect*. Abnormal symptoms or outward signs are indications of the diseased conditions of plants. There is a variety of symptoms, such as leaf spots, leaf curl, discolouration, blights, rots, smuts, rusts, mildews, wilts, blisters, hypertrophies, cankers, damping off, etc. These symptoms are caused mostly by parasitic fungi, commonly called **pathogens**, which attack field crops, cultivated plants, ornamental and useful plants, and also many wild plants. The fungi plunder the food stored in the host plants, block the conducting tissues, destroy the affected cells and tissues, produce toxins (poisons) in them and finally, cause their decay and death. The spores of the fungi may be seed-borne, wind-borne or insect-borne, and a particular disease may spread from field to field, sometimes appearing in an epidemic form unless controlled in time. The annual loss in agricultural crops on this account alone is very heavy. In India, the loss of foodgrains due to diseases, pests and rodents is roughly 10%, often much more, of the total annual production. It may be noted that a plant, as an animal, may suffer from one or more diseases at a time. Some of the diseases are listed below:

A. **Late Blight of Potato.** This is a common and often a serious disease of potato plants, frequently appearing in a severe form in the hills. The disease is caused by *Phytophthora infestans* (see

---

1 References: *Plant Pathology* by Sir Edwin J. Butler and S. C. Jones, *Fungi and Plant Disease* by B. B. Mundkur, *Introduction to Plant Pathology* by F. D. Heald, and *Plant Pathology* by J. C. Walker.

p. 412). Black patches appear on the undersurface of the leaves, less often on the upper. The disease may spread to the entire leaf and to all parts of the plant body, including the tubers. If the weather is warm and humid, and the soil water-logged, the disease spreads rapidly to neighbouring plants through the multi-nucleate sporangia of the fungus. The fungus finally causes 'wilting' of leaves and 'rotting' of tubers. An early indication of the disease in such tubers is brownish stains below the skin. **Control.** (*a*) Spraying the young plants with Bordeaux mixture. (*b*) Selection of seed tubers from non-infected areas. (*c*) Storage of seed tubers at a low temperature—4-5°*C*.

B. Smuts. Smuts (soot-like diseases) are common and serious diseases of wheat, barley, maize, oats and sugarcane, caused by different species of *Ustilago*. The **loose smut of wheat** is caused by *Ustilago tritici* (see p. 434). The disease is common in the wheat-growing areas of India, as elsewhere. The fungus mainly attacks the stem, flowers and often the whole inflorescence. The infected parts turn black and all the grains are often totally destroyed. The disease becomes manifest only when a black, sooty mass appears on the infected parts, particularly the 'ears'. The fungus is seed-borne and as the seed (grain) germinates, the mycelia lying dormant in the grain grow and ramify through the intercellular spaces of the young plant and pass on to the flowers, forming sooty masses of spores (teleutospores). The ovaries first swell up, then get distorted and destroyed. Finally the spikelets become deformed and covered by a black, powdery mass of spores, replacing all the floral parts and the glumes (except the awns). When the spores are blown away by the wind or washed away by the rain, only the stalk stands, bare of grains. The spores may, thus, spread over wide areas, and the flowers may be infected afresh. The spores germinate on the stigma and infect the grains of healthy plants. In this way, the disease is carried over to the next generation. **Control.** (*a*) Varieties of wheat already immune and resistant to smut should be cultivated. (*b*) Cross-breeding with types immune or resistant to smut is possibly the best method.

(*c*) Hot water treatment of wheat grains and then drying under strong sunlight may reduce the intensity of the disease.

C. Rusts. Wheat suffers from a variety of rust diseases, caused by different species of *Puccinia*, viz. black or stem rust of wheat caused by *Puccinia graminis*, yellow rust caused by *P. glumarum*, and brown rust caused by *P. triticina*. All these rusts are common almost throughout India. *P. glumarum* appears on the leaves as yellow rusty spots or stripes, and in case of severe attack, the crop may dry up. *P. triticina* appears as brown or orange spots (not stripes) on the leaves in clusters, often irregularly scattered. Losses on account of this disease seem to be insignificant. *P. graminis* (see p. 436), however, is a virulent type of parasite, often causing a serious disease of wheat plants in both the hills and plains. The disease is manifested by the appearance of reddish-brown spots and streaks on the stem, leaf-sheath and leaf as a result of the formation of *uredia with uredospores*. This stage is known as the 'red rust' of wheat. As the uredospores mature, the uredia burst and the brown, oval uredospores are blown about by the wind over large areas. They may directly infect other healthy wheat plants, often causing an epidemic. Later, dark spots appear on the stem, leaf-sheath and leaf as a result of the formation of *telia with teliospores*. This stage is known as the 'black or stem rust' of wheat as it is the stem that is most severely affected. The final effect of the disease is weakening of the plant, reduction of grains in size and number, and shrivelling up. The teliospores do not infect wheat plants again, their next hosts being barberry plants. **Control.** (see p. 440).

D. Mildews. These diseases appear as whitish, yellowish or brownish spots on the leaves and other parts. There are two kinds of mildews: downy and powdery. The former are caused by *Cystopus*, *Plasmopara* and *Peronospora*. They are endophytic and, therefore, only some damage is caused to the crops. Powdery mildews, on the other hand, are caused by *Erysiphe* and *Uncinula*. Since the fungus is ectophytic, damage to the crops is often not heavy. Common mildews are:

(a) **White rust of crucifers** (e.g. mustard, radish, cabbage, cauliflower) is caused by the downy mildew called *Cystopus candidus* (see p. 414). White or yellow blisters of variable shapes and sizes appear on the leaves (mainly), branches and even inflorescences. *Cystopus* is often associated with *Peronospora*. In case of heavy attack, it is seen that the nutrient cells collapse, the soft parts disintegrate, the infected parts turn brown and dry up, and the flowers become deformed. The disease, though common in India, is not a serious one as it usually appears only in a mild form. Therefore, no control measures are taken.

(b) **Powdery Mildew of Grape-vine** is caused by *Unicinula necator*. The disease is common in India as well as in some other countries. It appears mainly on the leaves, flowers and berries as white, powdery or dusty patches, which soon turn grey and finally dark. When severely infected, the crop suffers heavily (see p. 426).

(c) **Powdery Mildew of Cereals** (e.g. barley, oats, rye and wheat), and also several grasses is a very common but not serious disease caused by *Erysiphe graminis* (see p. 425). The mycelia and conidia form superficial growths on the upper surface of the leaves, stem and sometimes flowers. The growth have a sort of powdery appearance, which is initially white and turns reddish afterwards. The plant's growth becomes stunted and the leaves shed or become deformed and twisted. The fungus being ectophytic, much damage is not caused to the crop. The disease is not widespread in India and, therefore, no control measures are taken.

It may also be noted that many moulds damage vegetables, fruits and food, particularly in storage. They also damage fabrics, paper, books, leather, shoes, etc., particularly during the rainy season.

CONTROL. *Prevention and Check.* Considering the heavy economic losses caused by various plant diseases, it is imperative to devise proper control measures. Some of the common methods of destroying or controlling the causative fungi are as follows: (1) Spraying or dusting the affected plants with certain poisonous chemicals, called fungicides, e.g. copper sulphate, copper sulphate and lime (Bordeaux mixture), sulphur, sulphur-lime, quick-lime, mercury compounds, formaldehyde, etc., or a mixture of them. (2) Fumigation by sulphur dioxide gas. (3) Seed treatment—cautious application of hot water, formaldehyde or certain compounds of copper, sulphur or mercury. (4) Soil sterilization by burning wood in the field, or by application of steam or some poisonous chemicals. (5) Selection disease-free seeds and plants. (6) Eradication and destruction of diseased plants. (7) Destroying disease-carrying insects. (8) Breeding of disease-resistant varieties of plants. (9) Rotation of crops—growing some other crop in place of the existing one for one or more years.

PLANT DISEASES CAUSED BY BACTERIA. Some plant diseases are also caused by pathogenic bacteria listed below: (a) **Canker**. This appears as a dead area on the surface of the stem, leaves and fruit. There is a crater-like depression in the centre, usually surrounded by a raised margin. This disease may be caused by bacteria as well as by certain fungi. Canker of *Citrus* (orange and lemon) is a common example, caused by *Pseudomonas* (= *Xanthomonas*) *citri*. It occurs in most of the *Citrus* orchards in India, sometimes taking a serious turn. It appears on the leaves, branches and fruits, under conditions of moderate temperature, adequate rainfall and humid weather. The cankerous spots soon turn corky and brownish, or sometimes pinkish, affecting the shape, size, quality and appearance of the fruit. The disease may spread through the wind, rain and insects, as well as human beings. Canker of plum, peach and prune is caused by *Xanthomonas pruni*. (b) **Black rot of cabbage** is caused by *Pseudomonas campestris*. (c) **Wildfire of tobacco** is caused by *Pseudomonas tabaci*. (d) **Fire blight of apple and pear** is caused by *Bacterium* (=*Erwinia*) *amylovorum*. (e) **Ring disease of potato** is caused by *Bacterium* (=*Corynebacterium*) *solanacearum*. (f) **Soft rot of potato** is caused by various bacteria. There are many other such bacterial diseases. Fungal diseases, however, are more common than bacterial diseases.

PLANT DISEASES CAUSED BY VIRUSES. A few hundred viral diseases affecting plants have been recorded so far (see pp. 401-2).

ANTIBIOTICS

Antibiotics (*anti*, against; *bios*, life) are certain chemical substances, possibly enzymes, secreted by a good number of soil bacteria and soil fungi, which have been found to check the growth of particular types of infective bacteria (germs) and even destroy them. Antibiotics are the miracle drugs of modern times. They act like magic bullets shooting down the germs that have invaded the human body and caused infectious diseases, often of a virulent nature, e.g. pneumonia, typhoid, diphtheria, tuberculosis, cholera, boils, abscesses, erysipelas, etc., They act within a very short time. Over the last 20 years or so, some 300 antibiotics have been isolated and studied at an almost incredible cost. Of these, about 13 have an established therapeutic value in different bacterial diseases. The first antibiotic was an accidental discovery. The painstaking labour and perseverance, the skill and cost involved in the examination of several thousand soil samples, the culture and isolation of the bacteria present in them, the study of their secretions and curative value, etc., involved in the discovery of other antibiotics are almost unimaginable. It is indeed a miracle that lay hidden in a spoonful of good earth for the benefit of mankind.

The first, best-known and most widely used antibiotic is **penicillin**[1], isolated by the late Sir Alexander Fleming, an English bacteriologist, in 1929 from a blue-green mould of the soil, called *Penicillium notatum*. It has a powerful antibacterial action and is amazingly effective against certain types of bacteria, called Gram-positive bacteria, which cause some virulent diseases like scarlet fever, tonsilitis, sore throat, rheumatic fever, erysipelas, wound infections, abscesses, carbuncles, tetanus, pneumonia, meningitis, etc. Penicillin really acts like a shotgun on a wide range of targets It has come into general use since 1943-44 when mass production first got under way.

Another antibiotic, **streptomycin**, was isolated in 1944 by Waksman, a microbiologist, from a species of soil bacteria, called *Streptomyces grisesus*. It mainly attacks some of the Gram-positive germs, particularly tubercle bacilli, and has proved to be very valuable against tuberculosis. A vigorous search for more antibiotics was on at this time and in 1947, another antibiotic, **chloromycetin**, was discovered by Burkholder, a microbiologist, in 1947. It was isolated from *Streptomyces venezuleae*. It has a powerful action on a wide range of infectious bacteria—both Gram-positive and Gram-negative—and is very effective against severe types of dysentery, intestinal infection and whooping cough. It has proved to be a magic drug in the treatment of typhoid fever caused by typhus bacilli. Next in the chain of antibiotics were **aureomycin**, isolated in 1948 by Duggar, a botanist and world authority on mushrooms, from *Streptomyces aureofaciens*, and **terramycin**, isolated in 1950 or a little earlier from *Streptomyces rimosus* under the auspices of the Pfizer Company of Brooklyn, the world's largest producers of antibiotics. Both are yellowish powders, and are very effective against a wide

---

[1] One morning in September, 1928, Fleming noticed some strange change in a culture of *Staphylococcus* (pus-forming bacteria) and found a blue-green mould in the plate of culture. It seemed to him that some deadly substance had been secreted by the mould, which wrecked havoc on his fresh *Staphylococcus* culture. Fleming next cultured the mould, extracted a crude juice from it and injected it into mice after infecting them with some disease germs (*Staphylococcus*, and *Pneumococcus*). To his great amazement, he found that the mice were cured. That was the age of sulpha drugs and this wonderful discovery lay unheeded for many years, possibly forgotten. Fleming, however, continued his research and in February, 1941, he gave his first injection to a human patient, a dying man unaffected by sulpha drugs. Amazingly enough, the patient showed immediate improvement but unfortunately for him, only a teaspoonful could be prepared at that time. This was too little to effect a radical cure. A second patient was treated similarly, but again, the stock was insufficient. The future of penicillin could, however, be foreseen, and soon some British and American pharmaceutical firms undertook to manufacture it on a large scale.

range of disease germs, particularly on penicillin-resistant cases, cholera and some viruses. **Erythro-mycin**, another antibiotic discovered by McGuire in 1925 from *Streptomyces erythreus*, has proved to be particularly effective on drug-resistant *Staphylococcus*. It is also remarkably active against whooping cough, diphtheria, large viruses, etc. Its range of action is wide, like that of penicillin.

Over the years some more hitherto unknown soil bacteria have been discovered, and antibiotics manufactured and released to the market. These wonder drugs have already saved and are still saving millions of human lives.

A recent discovery in the series of antibiotics is **jawaharene**, discovered in 1963 by Dr. D. K. Roy at the Institute of Biochemistry and Experimental Medicine in Calcutta, from a species of *Aspergillus* growing on rotten potato tuber. This antibiotic has proved to be very effective against various diseases, such as pox, poliomyelitis, influenza, etc., and against amoebic dysentery, leukaemia (or blood cancer—a deadly disease) and various forms of tumours.

CHAPTER 5

LICHENS

General Description. Lichens, comprising over 15,000 species, form a large, peculiar and interesting group of plants, being associations of specific fungi and algae. The former constitute the greater part of the lichen body. They were first discovered by **Tulasne** in 1852 and a few years later, **De Bary** studied the two constituent organisms in detail. The association of different fungi and algae give rise to distinct species. Lichens commonly occur as greyish-green, greenish-white or brightly coloured incrustations, one to several cm. in diameter, on the stems and branches of shrubs and trees, wooden posts, logs, rocks, stones, old walls and the ground. Sometimes, they hang in shaggy tufts, a few to several cm. long, from the branches of shrubs and trees. They can be also coloured: white, yellow, orange, brown, red or black. Many of them grow under extreme conditions of humidity and temperature, and may survive long periods of desiccation. They are extensively distributed, being more common in cold, even extremely cold regions and high altitude (up to the snowline), as well as in tropical rain forests. In lichens, fungi and algae live together in an intimate relationship, leading a symbiotic life. The fungi absorb water and mineral matter from the substratum and supply these to the algae, while the latter in their turn prepare food and supply it to the fungi. Lichens are, thus, typical examples of symbiosis. If separated from their associations, they lead a precarious life, more particularly the fungi. It has been possible to synthesize several lichens by bringing together appropriate fungi and algae (**Bonnier**, 1886).

Classification. Depending on the nature of the fungi, lichens have been classified into two main groups: (1) **Ascolichens** and (2) **Basidiolichens**. In Ascolichens, the fungi are members of Ascomycetes, reproducing by means of ascospores. They may be further divided into (a) **Discolichens**, when the fungi in them are members of Discomycetes (or cup fungi), producing open, cup- or saucer- shaped apothecia (see FIG. 112A), and (b) **Pyrenolichens**, when the fungi in them are members of Pyrenomycetes (or flask fungi), producing closed, flask-shaped perithecia (see FIG. 92A) with an apical opening (ostiole). Ascolichens far outnumber Basidiolichens. In the latter, the fungi are certain simple members of Agaricales, reproducing through basidiospores.

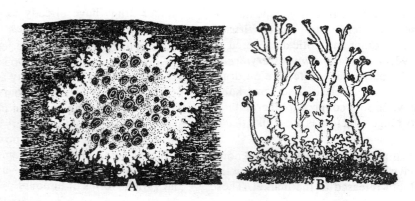

Lichens. FIG. 108. *A*, a foliose lichen (*Parmelia*); *B*, a fruticose lichen (*Cladonia*)

There are only three genera of Basidiolichens, viz. *Cora*, *Corella* and *Dictyonema*. The best known genus is *Cora*, which is widely distributed in America. It is somewhat like a bracket fungus.

Thallus. Lichen thalli follow three different patterns of growth in different genera, as follows: (*a*) **Crustose lichens**— These form hard, granular crusts and adhere very tenaciously to rocks, barks of shrubs and trees and certain soils, e.g. *Graphis* and *Lecanora*. They show very little differentiation into the upper and lower surface. (*b*) **Foliose lichens** (FIG. 108*A*)— These form definite, flattened leaf-like thalli with lobed margins, and adhere to walls, tree trunks, rocks and the ground by means of delicate rhizoids (**rhizines**), e.g. *Parmelia* and *Physcia*. Such lichens show distinct differentiation into the upper and lower surface. (*c*) **Fruticose lichens** — These form much-branched, shrub-like bodies which remain attached by their narrow basal portion only. The branches may be flat and ribbon-like, or slender and filamentous. Such lichens may stand erect, e.g. reindeer moss (*Cladonia*; FIG. 108*B*) or hang on the branches of shrubs and trees, e.g. old man's beard (*Usnea*; FIG. 109*A*). The main framework of the thallus is made of an interwoven mass of the hyphae of a fungus, usually an ascomycete (ascolichen), or, in a few cases, a basidiomycete (basidiolichen). Ascolichens enclose mostly unicellular or sometimes filamentous, blue-green algae (e.g. *Chroococcus*, *Gloeocapsa*, etc.—unicellular, and *Nostoc*, *Rivularia*, *Scytonema*, etc.—filamen-

tous), or certain green algae (e.g. *Chlorella*, *Pleurococcus* and some other less known forms—unicellular, and usually *Trentepohlia*—filamentous). Basidiolichens enclose similar blue-green algae. The type of fungus and alga associated in a lichen is always constant. In some lichens, the algae are scattered in the thallus, while in others, they occur in 1 or 2 layers.

A section through the thallus (FIG. 110) of a foliose lichen shows a loose mass of hyphae in the central region—the so-called **medulla**, and compact mass of hyphae in the peripheral region—the so-called **cortex**. Between these two regions usually lies the algal layer (usually called the **gonidial layer**). This has many algal cells (usually called the **gonidia**) held together in the meshes of the hyphae. In *Usnea*, a fruticose lichen, the thallus (FIG. 109*B*) is differentiated into a central, compact core of hyphae, a region of loosely interwoven hyphae, an algal region and, externally, another compact region of hyphae.

Reproduction. Lichens reproduce in a variety of ways: vegetative, asexual and sexual. But it must be noted that reproduction is predominantly fungal in character.

Vegetative Reproduction. This may take place by various methods. The first three methods, as described below, are peculiar to lichens. (*a*) **Soredia** (FIG. 109*C*). These are tiny, granular bodies occurring in large numbers on the upper surface of the thallus as a greyish coating of

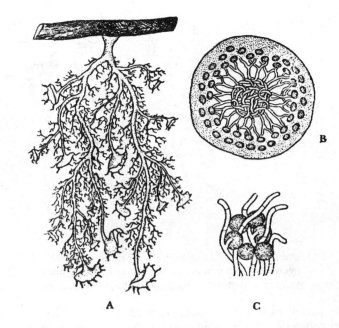

FIG. 109.
A, a fruticose
     lichen (*Usnea*);
B, a section
     through the
     thallus of
     Usnea;
C, a soredium

powder. Each soredium consists of one to many algal cells wrapped up in a weft of fungal hyphae, as in *Usnea* and *Cladonia*. The soredia are blown about by the wind, and under appropriate conditions, they germinate directly into lichen thalli. Sometimes they form new soredia. This is the most common method of reproduction in lichens. (*b*) **Isidia.** In many lichens these are formed as minute outgrowths on the surface of the thallus. Each isidium consists of both algal cells and fungal hyphae, as usual, but is surrounded by a layer of cortex. Isidia are primarily photosynthetic in function. Sometimes they get detached from the parent thallus and develop into new thalli. (*c*) **Cephalodia.** These appear as dark swellings on the upper surface of the thallus, sometimes internally as well. Each cephalodium consists of algal cells and fungal hyphae, as in the previous cases, but here the algal cells are different from those that normally occur in the thallus. Evidently, they are foreign algae and may have been carried over to the young lichen thallus, ultimately forming such abnormal bodies. (*d*) **Oidia.** In a few lichens, the hyphae may break up into short segments called oidia. An oidium germinates like a spore, producing normal hyphae. (*e*) **Fragmentation.** In many

lichens, the thallus may be divided into long or short fragments. Each fragment may grow to the size of the parent thallus. In *Usnea* (FIG. 109*A*), the branches may be broken up by the wind into several fragments. Some of them get attached to the branches of trees and grow normally.

Asexual Reproduction. In Ascolichens, reproduction takes place by means of spores formed by

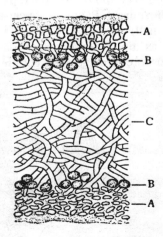

FIG. 110. A section through the thallus of a foliose lichen. *A*, cortex; *B*, gonidial layer; and *C*, medulla

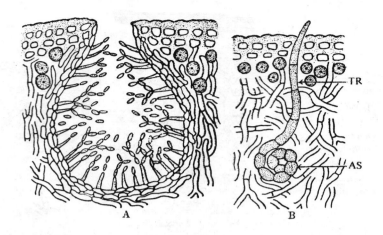

Lichen. FIG. 111. *A*, a pycnidium (or spermogonium) of *Physicia* in section showing pycnidiospores (or spermatia) formed in large numbers; *B*, a coiled ascogonium (*AS*) embedded in the thallus, with tube-like trichogyne (*TR*) protruding outwards

the fungal partner. On germination, each spore sends out hyphae in different directions. If any of them happens to come in contact with the requisite alga, it (the hypha) branches freely and covers up the algal cell. The combined body then grows into a lichen thallus. Some scientists have reported the formation of conidia in certain lichens. But this is disputed. Many lichens, e.g. *Physcia*, produce small, spore-like bodies in large numbers within a flask-shaped cavity, called the **pycnidium** (FIG. IIIA). The spores are called **pycnidiospores (or pycnospores)**. Pycnidia appear in large numbers as small, black dots on the surface of the thallus, or as tiny protuberances on its margin. Pycnidiospores are known to germinate in certain

species, producing a hypha. Coming in contact with an appropriate alga, the combined body grows and forms into a lichen thallus. (It may be noted that in certain other species, the so-called pycnidia behave as male organs, then called spermogonia, and the so-called pycnidiospores behave as male cells, then known as spermatia; see below). Basidiolichens, e.g. *Cora* (a common American genus), as stated before, reproduce by means of basidiospores, very much like *Agaricus*.

Sexual Reproduction. This has been observed in certain Ascolichens, as in *Collema*. The fungus alone takes part in the process. Sexual reproduction results in the formation of an ascocarp, usual-

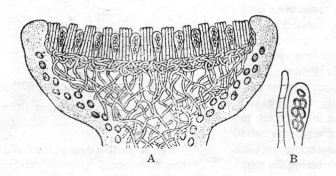

FIG. 112.
A, a section through an apothecium; note the asci and the paraphyses;
B, an ascus and a paraphysis

ly an apothecium (FIG 112A) and sometimes a perithecium, with many asci in each case. The sex organs are differentiated into male and female, and develop in close proximity to facilitate fertilization. The female organ is a multicellular, stout filament of large cells, known as the carpogonium (FIG. 111B). It consists of a coiled, basal portion, called the ascogonium, lying within the thallus, and a tube-like, upper portion, called the trichogyne, usually protruding beyond the thallus. The male organ, the spermogonium, is a flask-shaped chamber (FIG. 111A) with an apical opening (ostiole). The minute, non-motile male cells formed within it are known as the spermatia[1] (cf. pycnidiospores). Several spermogonia (pycnidia) may be formed in the thallus, with the inner wall of each lined with a layer of short, slender hyphae. Spermatia are formed from them by abstriction, like conidia, and occur in large numbers. Spermatia are very minute and cylindrical. They are liberated through the ostiole in slimy masses to float on the thallus.

Fertilization. This takes place when a spermatium comes in contact with the sticky, protruding tip of a trichogyne. Its protoplast migrates into the trichogyne and apparently fuses with the ascogonium nucleus (though the process has not been observed yet). Thus, fertilization is effected. Several ascogenous hyphae now begin to grow out from the basal portion of the ascognium; these hyphae branch freely and develop an ascus, always at the end of a branch. The ascogenous hyphae may also develop parthenogenetically in some cases. A mature ascus usually has 8 ascospores (FIG. 111B), but the number varies from 1 to 8. A complex ascocarp (see p. 405), bearing the asci, develops simultaneously. As stated before, the ascocarp usually takes the shape of an open cup or saucer, called the apothecium (FIG. 112A), very much like that of *Peziza*. The apothecium consists of an investing tissue made of vegetative tissue and an interwoven mass of hyphae, with a surface layer (hymenium) containing a compact mass of slender, sterile hyphae (paraphyses) and club-shaped asci, occurring together in a palisade-like layer. The asci have been pushed to this position by the elongation of the ascogenous hyphae. In some cases, however, the ascocarp develops into a flask-shaped chamber called the perithecium, with an apical opening (ostiole). The wall of the perithecium is lined with a layer of asci and paraphyses. On liberation, the mature ascospores germinate, producing hyphae. Those coming in contact with the right type of alga grow rapidly and eventually produce lichen thalli.

Uses. Lichens growing on rocks disintegrate them to form soils, thus preparing the ground first for mosses and subsequently for higher plants. Lichens have a variety of uses. Some are a valuable source of food for wild animals and cattle, e.g. reindeer moss (*Cladonia*; FIG. 108B), which grows in clumps to a height of about 30 cm. in the arctic tundra. Iceland moss (*Cetraria*) of the northern regions is used as food and medicine. In some countries, certain lichens are fried for cattle feed and to some extent, for human food as well. Some types are used as medicines. Some yield beautiful dyes. Litmus is prepared from certain lichens. Some species are used in cosmetics, perfumes and soaps. Lichens are also used in brewing liquor, and certain lichens containing tannins are used in tanning hide into leather.

---

[1] References: *Plant Pathology* by Sir Edwin J. Butler and S. C. Jones, *Fungi and Plant Disease* by B. B. Mundkur, *Introduction to Plant Pathology* by F. D. Heald, and *Plant Pathology* by J. C. Walker. The nature of spermatia is a disputed point. Although, in some cases, the spermatia act as male cells, they have been found to act as spores (pycnospores) in others, germinating independently.

CHAPTER 6
BRYOPHYTA

CLASSIFICATION OF BRYOPHYTA
(23,725 sp.)

Class I Hepaticae or liverworts (8,450 sp.). **Order 1.** Marchantiales (400 sp.), e.g. *Riccia* and *Marchantia* (thalloid liverworts). **Order 2.** Jungermanniales (8,050 sp.): (*a*) **anacrogynous**, e.g. *Pellia*, and (*b*) **acrogynous**, e.g. *Porella*. In the former, the archegonia always develop behind the apical cell (never from the apical cell itself) and the gametophytes are thalloid, while in the latter, the archegonia always develop from the segments of the apical cell and later from the apical cell itself; the gametophytes are leafy. The latter far outnumber the former.

Class II Anthocerotae or horned liverworts (300 sp.). **Order 1.** Anthocerotales (only order), e.g. *Anthoceros* (gametophyte simple and thalloid but sporophyte complex).

Class III Musci or mosses (14,975 sp.). **Order 1.** Sphagnales or bog mosses (350 sp.), e.g. *Sphagnum.* **Order 2.** Andreaeales (125 sp.), e.g. *Andreaea.* **Order 3.** Bryales or true mosses (14,500 sp.), e.g. *Funaria, Polytrichum, Barbula* and *Dicranella* (gametophyte distinctly leafy and sporophyte very complex).

ORIGIN AND EVOLUTION OF BRYOPHYTA.

Bryophyta do occupy an intermediate position between the higher algae and the lower pteridophyta, but their ancestors and descendants are not known. It is, however, most likely that bryophytes have evolved from some algal stock, possibly Ulotricales. But because of the missing links between the higher algae and the lower bryophytes, the actual position in regard to the origin of the latter cannot be ascertained. Having originated from some aquatic ancestor, the bryophytes were pioneers in establishing themselves on land. This was crucial in the evolution of plants gowing on land. Having established themselves on land, they followed their own course of development, culminating in an individualistic group without giving rise to higher forms. Among bryophytes, the liverworts are more primitive than the mosses, and the latter may have been derived from the former. According to another view, the bryophytes have diverged from pteridophytes; later, they followed an independent line of evolution, ending in a blind alley without giving rise to higher forms. Bryophyta show an advance over algae by the development of archegonia, multicellular antheridia, and a distinct alternation of generations. By virtue of these characteristics, they approach pteridophytes, but the absence of vascular tissue and their dependence on the gametophyte distinguish them from pteridophyties. Fertilization through ciliate antherozoids in an aquatic medium has persisted from algae to bryophytes to pteridophytes and to certain lower gymnosperms. This may indicate a link between these groups.

Development of the Sporophyte. The sporophyte is a distinct structure which has evolved from the zygote. It is diploid (with $2n$ chromosomes) and reproduces asexually through spores. It is a product of sexual reproduction and represents the stage between fertilization and subsequent meiosis (reduction division). In most green algae, the zygote represents only a passing diploid ($2n$) phase and does not rise to a sporophyte. In them, the zygote is only a resting body with a protective covering to tide over unfavourable conditions. The true sporophyte developed in plants after they invaded the land in the remote past and began to live under new and adverse environmental conditions. After its appearance it grew more and more complex and has established itself as the main plant body. From ferns onwards, all plants are sporophytes. Certain factors seem to be connected with the gradual development of the sporophyte: immediate germination of the zygote without any rest, prolongation of vegetative period and delay in meiosis leading to the formation of spores, alternation of generations, land habit, facility of dispersion of spores by wind, sterilization of sporogenous tissue for other functions, and segregation of the spore-producing region from the vegetative region.

To start with, the sporophyte is a simple structure lying embedded in the gametophytic thallus as a parasitic body. Nearly all its cells produce spores, e.g. *Riccia*. A more complex type of sporophyte is formed in *Marchantia*. Here, the sporophyte grows from the ray of the female receptacle and is already differentiated into a foot, seta and capsule. Some of the potentially sporogenous cells in it give rise to sterile cells—the elaters—and others to spores. Thus, a partial sterilization is evident. Besides, the capsule of *Marchantia*, unlike that of *Riccia*, dehisces irregularly or by an apical lid to liberate the spores for dispersal by the wind. In *Anthoceros*, the sporophyte has reached a high degree of complexity in many respects: relatively large size, continued growth in length through a basal meristem, extensive sterilization of the capsule leading to the development of the central axis—(the columella), development of chlorophyllous cells and other cellular differentiation in response to division of labour, partial sterilization of the sporogenous tissue leading to elaters and spores alternately, and all this on a simple primitive type of gametophyte, i.e. thallus. The mechanism of liberation of spores by dehiscence of the capsule into two valves is also very efficient. In moss, the sporophyte has reached a high degree of specialization, on a highly developed gametophyte. In this plant, the extensive amount of sterilization has resulted in an enlarged seta and a very complex capsule. The sporophyte of moss is still not quite an independent plant. *Anthoceros* and moss have, however, followed two independent lines of evolution. At the next higher stage, that is, in ferns and allied plants, the table is turned. The sporophyte in them has become the main or all-important body and is quite independent of the gametophyte, which has dwindled down to a simple structure—the prothallus. The sporophyte has elaborately developed roots, stem (often branched) and leaves (or sporophylls), with a distinct spore-producing region. Ferns and their relatives, like *Equisetum* and *Lycopodium*, are homosporous. At a higher level, *Selaginella* is heterosporous. At the highest level, the 'flowering' plants are all sporophytes and heterosporous, reaching the highest degree of complexity, while the corresponding gametophytes have become reduced to only a few cells or nuclei. Thus, from a simple beginning several millions of years ago, the sporophyte has finally established itself as the highest form of plants—the angiosperms, which now dominate the vegetation of the earth. On the other hand, the gametophyte, once the predominant feature of the early age, has now become reduced to almost nothing.

ROLE OF BRYOPHYTA IN SOIL CONSERVATION. From the ecological point of view, bryophytes play a significant role in soil conservation. Bryophyta comprises land-inhabiting, autotrophic plants which prefer moist and shady habitats. The gametophytic plant body is either thalloid or a leafy shoot. True roots are absent. There are root-like structures called rhizoids, which are often intervened with multicellular scales. They help in anchorage and absorption of water and nutrients from the soil.

Bryophytes are widespread in distribution. Members belonging to class *Hepaticae* (liverworts), such as *Riccia*, *Marchantia*, *Pellia*, etc., and to class *Anthocerotae* (horned liverworts), e.g., *Anthoceros*, have a dorsiventrally flattened thallus which grows densely, forming a covering like a green carpet on the ground. Other leafy members, such as different kinds of moss belonging to the class *Musci*, are also gregarious in habit. Wherever they grow, they multiply rapidly due to their extensive spore-producing capacity and form a continuous patch, or a soft velvet-like cover on the substratum.

The dense and extensive mat-like cover of these plants on the surface of the soil or substratum plays a significant role in soil conservation, It prevents soil erosion, which is caused primarily by water, the most powerful denuding agent in nature.

During the monsoon, rain water falls on the ground with tremendous force, washing away large quantities of exposed soil. During and after a rain storm, water runs down the slopes in sheets (sheet floods). Every year, sheet floods drain away huge amounts of exposed soil from the higher altitudes to the plains. Thin layers of fertile top soil, which have taken many years to form, are thereby lost with every shower of rain.

The dense mat formed by bryophytes prevents the rain from striking the soil surface directly. Besides, bryophytes bind the soil particles together with the help of their rhizoids and scales. Even after death and decay, the remains of bryophytes form humus on the soil surface, adding fertility to the soil and contributing to soil formation. In the dry season, bryophytes protect the soil surface form the effect of strong winds, which may blow away loose soil particles.

Members belonging to *Anthocerotales*, such as *Anthoceros*, have within their thalli colonies of blue-green algae, which can fix atmospheric nitrogen and enhance soil fertility. This facilitates the colonization of the area by higher plants, leading to increased vegetal cover and minimizing soil erosion.

1. *RICCIA* (135 *sp.*)

Riccia (family *Ricciaceae*; FIG. 113) is a thalloid liverwort showing distinct dichotomous branching and taking on a rosette form (*A*). There are about 22 species of *Riccia* in India, of which *R. discolor* (= *R. himalayensis*) is a fairly common one. The thallus is a flattened structure the dorsal (upper) surface of which has a longitudinal groove along the whole length of the mib-rib. The ventral (lower) surface usually has a row of scales at the apex and a number of unicellular, hairy structures known as the **rhizoids**. The rhizoids are of two kinds—smooth and tuberculate. The thallus is

thicker in the middle and thinner at the two margins. The growth of the thallus takes place through a single wedge-shaped, apical cell situated in an apical notch. The segments of the thallus are obcordate or linear, their margin sometimes ciliated. Species of *Riccia* are terrestrial and grow as a green carpet on wet ground, old damp walls, old tree trunks and moist rocks. The only aquatic species is *Riccia fluitans*.

A cross-section of the thallus (FIG. 113C) shows the following structure: (*a*) a discontinuous upper epidermis, (*b*) an assimilatory tissue consisting of rows of cells with chloroplasts, with narrow, irregular air spaces between the rows to facilitate diffusion of gases between the atmosphere and the thallus, (*c*) a lower colourless tissue consisting of fairly big, thin-walled cells for storage of water and food, and (*d*) a lower epidermis with many rhizoids.

Vegetative Reproduction. The vegetative propagation of *Riccia* is common. It takes place by progressive decay of the older portion of the thallus, evidently at its base, and its separation into branches (FIG. 113B). These then grow into new thalli.

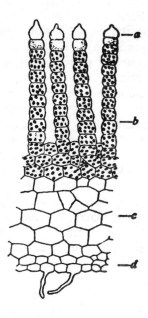

FIG. 113C. *Riccia* thallus in section (see text)

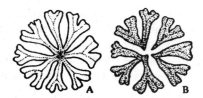

FIG. 113. *A*, a *Riccia* plant;
B, vegetative propagation

Sexual Reproduction. The plant is a gametophyte, i.e. it reproduces sexually through gametes. The two kinds of gametes—male and female—are borne in special structures known as the antheridia and the archegonia, respectively. Some species (e.g. *R. robusta*) are monoecious, while others (e.g. *R. discolor*) are disecious. In the monoecious species, the antheridia and archegonia develop together in the median groove on the dorsal (upper) side of the thallus. They grow in acropetal succession from the base of the thallus to its apex. Each **antheridium** (FIG. 114*A*), which is more or less pear-shaped, develops in a deep chamber formed by the overgrowth of the surrounding tissue of the thallus, and consists of a short stalk, a sterile wall and a compact mass of antherozoid mother cells. By a single division each mother cell forms two cells, each of which is metamorphosed into a small, twisted, biciliate male gamete or **antherozoid** (FIG. 114*B*). Each archegonium (FIG. 114*C-D*) also lies sunken in a similar chamber. It is a short-stalked, flask-shaped body with a swollen basal portion known as the **venter**, and a narrow, tubular upper portion known as the **neck**. The latter often projects beyond the epidermis and turns purplish. The neck contains a few neck canal cells (usually four) surrounded by six vertical rows of jacket cells. The venter is occupied by a large cell—the egg-cell, and a little higher up, a small cell—the ventral canal cell. The egg-cell contains a distinct large nucleus which is the **egg-nucleus** (female gamete). As the archegonium matures, the neck canal cells and the ventral canal cell degenerate into mucilage.

Fertilization takes place in the usual way. The antherozoids swim to the archegonium. The mucilage swells and forces out the cover cells of the neck canal (FIG. 114*D*). As the mucilage dissolves, an open passage is established through the neck. The antherozoids enter the archegonium and one of them fuses with the egg-nucleus. After fertilization, the ovum clothes itself with a wall and becomes the **oospore**.

Development and Structure of Sporophyte. The fertilized egg, i.e. the oospore, gives rise to the sporophyte, which reproduces asexually through spores. The sporophyte is a simple, spherical body called the **capsule** (FIG. 115). It consists of a spore-sac with a surrounding wall, the latter made of a single layer. The capsule develops *in situ* within the venter of the archegonium. With the growth of the capsule, the venter also grows and invests it. This investing structure is called the **calyptra**. The spore-sac contains a central mass of spore mother cells. Each mother cell undergoes reduction division and forms a *tetrad of spores* (FIG. 116*A*). Eventually, the spores are set free with the rupture of the calyptra and the wall of the capsule. Each spore (FIG. 116*B*) has a coat of two layers (three layers according to some authors). The outer layer is cutinized and the inner one

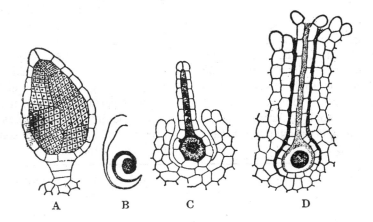

Riccia. FIG. 114. *A*, an antheridium; *B*, an antherozoid; *C*, a young archegonium; *D*, a mature archegonium

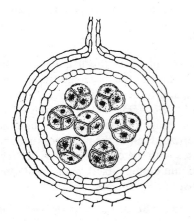
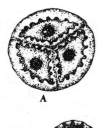

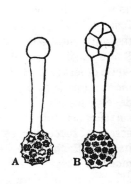

FIG. 115.   FIG. 116.   FIG. 117.

·*Riccia*. FIG. 115. Sporophyte (capsule) with sporetetrads within enlarged archegonium
FIG. 116. Spores—*A*, spores in a tetrad; *B*, a single spore
FIG. 117. *A-B*, early stages in the germination of spore

made of pectose and callose. The whole coat is irregularly thickened and folded. In the germination of the spore, the outer layer bursts and the inner one grows into a germ tube which gradually develops into the thallus (FIG. 117). The sporophyte develops within the gametophyte and is wholly dependent on it for nutrition. *Riccia* has no special mechanism for spore dispersal.

Alternation of Generations. The plant passes through two successive generations—gametophytic with *n* chromosomes and sporophytic with *2n* chromosomes—to complete its life history. The gametophytic generation begins with the spore and ends in the gametes—antherozoid and ovum—prior to fertilization. The sporophytic generation begins with the oospore and ends in the spore mother cells. The gametophyte gives rise to the sporophyte through sexual reproduction, and the sporophyte to the gametophyte through asexual reproduction. Thus, there is a regular alternation of generations, given below.

2. *MARCHANTIA* (65 sp.)

Marchantia (FIG. 118) is a rosette type of thalloid liverwort with conspicuous dichotomous branching, dorsiventral symmetry and a distinct mid-rib. It belongs to the family *Marchantiaceae*, of which there are about 11 species in India. *M. polymorpha* is common and widespread species, and *M. palmata* is common in the western Himalayas. *Marchantia* grows on damp ground or old walls and spreads rapidly during the rainy season, forming a sort of green carpet. It occurs abundantly in the cold climate of the hills. The thallus bears on its undersurface (ventral) many unicellular rhizoids of two kinds—tuberculate and smooth-walled, a row of scales along the mid-rib, and 2 or 3 rows of scales on either side of the mid-rib (the outer row being near the margin of the thallus). On the upper surface (dorsal), it bears a number of cup-like outgrowths, known as the **gemma-cups**, on the mid-rib. The thalli of some plants bear special *male* reproductive branches known as

Riccia (gametophyte-*n*) → archegonium (*n*) → ovum (*n*) x → oospore (*2n*)
↑   → antheridium (*n*) → antherozoids (*n*)   ↓
Spore ← spore-tetrad ← spore mother cells ← capsule ← sporophyte
(*n*)   (*n*)   (*2n*)   (*2n*)   (*2n*)

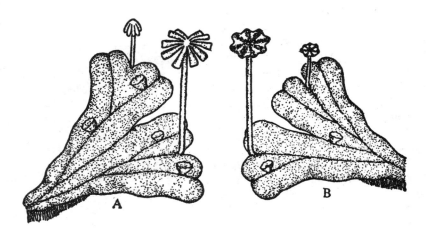

Marchantia. FIG. 118 *A*, female plant with archegoniphores and
gemma-cups; *B*, male plant with antheridiophores and gemma-cups

antheridiophores (FIG. 118*B*) and those of other plants bear special *female* reproductive branches known as **archegoniophores** (FIG. 118*A*). The two can be easily recognized—the former has a flat, circular, brownish, lobed disc on the top, and the latter has a green smooth disc projected into distinct rays, at first bending downwards and later becoming horizontal. The growing point of the thallus lies in the notch of dichotomy and is represented by one or a few cells.

A section through the thallus (FIG. 119) shows: (1) A single-layered upper epidermis which is interspersed with several air-pores; the cells of the epidermis contain chloroplasts. (2) Air chambers lying below the epidermis and communicating with the exterior through a centrally placed air pore. Externally the chambers often appear as polygonal areas on the thallus. Each air pore is surrounded by a few tiers of cells. From the floor of the air chamber arise short chains of cells, branched or unbranched, each cell containing several chloroplasts. These chains of green cells constitute the assimilatory tissue. (3) Storage tissue consisting of several layers of large, thin-walled (parenchymatous cells without chloroplasts) except a few upper layers. The cells contain mostly starch grains but there are some mucilage and oil-containing cells at places. (4) A single-layered lower epidermis without chloroplasts but with many rhizoids and some scales.

Reproduction

Vegetative reproduction. This may take place (*a*) by the decay of the old basal portion of the thallus, thus separating the branches, (*b*) by the formation of adventitious branches which get

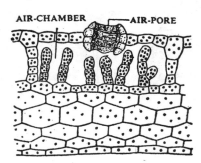

Marchantia. FIG. 119. Section
through the thallus

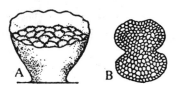

FIG. 120. *A*, gemma-cup;
B, a gemma

detached from the thallus, or (*c*) by **gemmae** (FIG. 120*B*) which develop in the gemma-cup or **cupule** (FIG. 120*A*). Each gemma is a small, more or less circular, flattened structure with a conspicuous depression on each side. The growing point lies in the depression. When the gemma gets detached from the gemma-cup, it grows out into a dichotomously branched thallus. It is green.

Sexual Reproduction. The thallus is the gametophyte, i.e. it reproduces sexually through gametes. *Marchantia* is dioecious, i.e. the male and female plants are distinct and separate. The male plants bear antheridia or male reproductive organs on special erect branches called antheridiophores (FIG. 118*B*), and the female plants bear archegonia or female reproductive organs on almost similar branches called archegoniophores (FIG. 118*A*). The **antheridiophore** (FIG. 121) consists of an erect cylindrical **stalk** and a more or less circular, usually 8-lobed disc or **receptacle** on the top. The stalk has two longitudinal channels on one side from which rhizoids and scales develop. The receptacle bears on its lower side a number of rhizoids and scales, and on the upper, several small air chambers and rows of antheridia. Each air chamber communicates with the exterior through a minute air pore and contains chains of

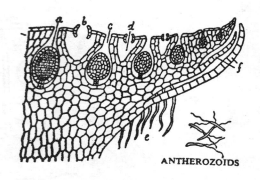

Marchantia. FIG. 121. Section through the antheridiophore. *a*, antheridium; *b*, air pore; *c*, ostiole; *d*, air chamber; *e*, hairs; *f*, scales. Some antherozoids (*on the right*)

green cells, as in the thallus. The antheridia are produced in acropetal order (the oldest towards the centre and the youngest towards the margin) from the segments of 8 growing points, which are located at the tips of lobes. Each antheridium (FIG. 121) develops in a cavity lying embedded in the receptacle, and is more or less ovoid in shape. It communicates with the exterior through a narrow canal known as the ostiole. The antheridium is composed of a mass of small, cubical cells (antherozoid mother cells) surrounded by a single-layered wall. Each antherozoid mother cell

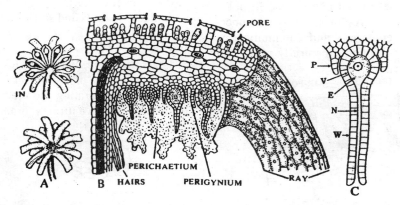

Marchantia. FIG. 122 *A*, (*top*) undersurface of the archegoniophore; *In*, involucre; (*bottom*) upper surface of the same; *B*, section through the archegoniophore showing air chambers with chains of green cells and air-pores, ray, archegonia, etc.; *C*, an archegonium; *P*, perigynium or pseudo-perianth; *V*, venter; *E*, egg-cell; *N*, neck; and *W*, wall

develops a minute, biciliate, spindle-shaped male gamete known as the **antherozoid** or **spermatozoid**. The archegoniophore (FIG. 122), similarly, consists of a stalk (often longer than that of the antheridiophore) and an 8-lobed, star-shaped disc or **receptacle** with mostly 9 radiating **rays** or arms, somewhat like the ribs of an umbrella. The rays alternate with the lobes of the disc. The growing point is located at the tip of the lobe of the disc between two rays. Evidently, there are 8 such growing points. A group of archegonia develop from the segments of each growing point in acropetal order, at first on the upper side. There are altogether 8 groups of archegonia alternating with the rays. By rapid elongation of the cells of the upper side of the disc, the growing points are, however, pushed downwards and inwards with the result that the groups of archegonia come to lie underneath the disc. Each growing point and the youngest archegonium are brought close to the stalk, while the oldest archegonium lies near the margin. The stalk of the receptacle has two longitudinal channels on one side with rhizoids and scales, as in the male stalk. The receptacle has many air chambers, on the upper side, as in the male receptacle. Groups of archegonia develop on the lower side, hanging downwards. A membranous, curtain-like outgrowth, known as the **involucre** (or perichaetium), fringed at the edges, is formed. This surrounds a group of archegonia as a protective covering (FIG. 122A-B). Moreover, at the base of each archegonium (ultimately surrounding it after fertilization) is a cup-shaped outgrowth known as the **pseudo-perianth** or **perigynium** (FIG. 122B-C). The archegonium (FIG. 122C) is a flask-shaped body consisting of a swollen basal portion—the venter, a narrow, elongated portion—the neck, and a very short stout multicellular stalk. The neck of the archegonium, when young, is covered by a lid made of a few 'cap' or 'cover' cells. The venter contains a large cell—the egg-cell or ovum with a distinct large nucleus—the egg-nucleus (female gamete), and a small, ventral canal cell, while the neck contains a row of usually 4-8 neck canal cells. The wall of the archegonium is made of six vertical rows of *jacket cells*.

Fertilization. When the antheridium bursts, the ciliate antherozoids swim out of the antheridial chamber through the ostiole and frisk about in the water, lashing it with their cilia: As the archegoni-

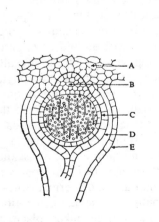

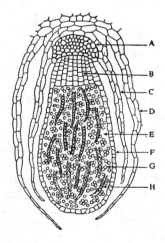

FIG. 123   FIG. 124   FIG. 125

Marchantia. FIG. 123. A young sporogonium; *A*, tissue of the gametophyte; *B*, foot; *C*, capsule (wall); *D*, archegonium (wall); and *E*, perigynium or pseudo-perianth. FIG. 124. A mature sporogonium; *A*, foot; *B*, seta; *C*, remnant of venter (calyptra); *D*, perigynium or pseudo-perianth; *E*, capsule; *F*, wall of the capsule; *G*, spore, and *H*, elater. FIG. 125. An elater (enlarged)

um matures, the neck canal cells and the ventral canal cell degenerate into mucilage. The mucilage swells up in contact with moisture and the lid is forced open. A clear passage is thus formed. The mucilage contains some protein matter which attracts the antherozoids. They swim to the archegonium through the medium of dew or rain water and many enter the venter through the neck. Finally, one of them fuses with the egg-nucleus in the venter. After fertilization, the ovum develops a ., all around itself and becomes the oospore.

Development and Structure of Sporogonium

(FIGS. 123-24). The oospore germinates *in situ* and gives rise to the **sporogonium**. The sporogonium is the sporophyte, i.e. it reproduces asexually by spores. The oospore divides into an upper cell and a lower. The lower cell divides further and produces a foot and a short stalk, called the seta, which elongates later. The foot penetrates the tissue of the receptacle and absorbs nutritive material from it. The upper cell divides and forms the **capsule**. The capsule consists of a single layer of wall-cells and a central mass of small cells (**archesporium**). Some of the archesporial cells grow into elongated, spindle-shaped structures with internal spiral thickenings. These are known as the **elaters** (FIGS. 124-25). Other cells of the archesporium form **spore mother cells**. Each spore mother cell divides by meiosis to form *four* **spores** in a tetrad. After fertilization, other parts of the archegonium also grow. Thus the wall of the venter grows, forming the calyptra, which surrounds the capsule (FIG. 124C). The neck withers and disappears. The **perigynium** (FIGS. 123E & 124D) grows rapidly and ultimately surrounds the sporogonium. The sporophyte is, thus, adequately protected by the calyptra, perigynium and involucre. As the seta elongates, it pushes the capsule through the calyptra. A remnant of the calyptra may be seen around the capsule (FIG. 124C). As the capsule matures, the seta elongates further and pushes it (the capsule) beyond the perigynium and the involucre. Finally, the capsule dehisces, rather irregularly, from the apex to about the middle into a number of segments, and the spores are discharged (FIG. 126). Under humid conditions, the

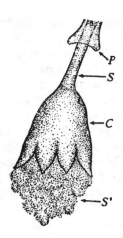

Marchantia. FIG. 126. Sporogonium dehiscing and discharging spores; *P*,. perigynium; *S*, seta; *C*, capsule; and *S*, spores

elaters adopt a twisting movement and push the spores out of the capsule. The spores germinate immediately after they shed, and each gives rise to a short, irregular filament consisting of a few cells. Through further cell divisions this filament develops into a *Marchantia* thallus. Two spores of a tetrad (FIG. 127G) give rise to male thalli and the other two to female thalli.

Alternation of Generations. (FIG. 127). There are two stages or generations in the life history of *Marchantia*. The plant itself is the gametophyte, having haploid or *n* chromosomes, and the sporogonium is the sporophyte with diploid or 2*n* chromosomes. The gametophyte reproduces sexually through gametes and gives rise to the sporophyte, and the sporophyte reproduces asexually through spores and gives rise to the gametophyte. Thus, the two generations alternate regularly with each other. All the stages from the oospore to the spore mother cells represent the sporophytic or asexual generation, and all the stages from the spores to the gametes—the ovum and the spermatozoid—represent the gametophytic or sexual generation. The alternation of generations takes place as shown below.

3. *PORELLA* (*180 sp.*)

Occurrence. *Porella* (family *Porellaceae*; FIG. 128) is a common acrogynous (see p. 476), leafy

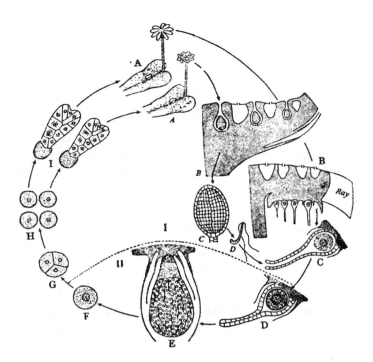

FIG. 127. Life cycle of *Marchantia*. *I*, gametophytic generation (haploid or *n*) and
II, sporophytic generation (diploid or 2*n*). *A*, male thallus with antheridium; *B*, antheridiophore
with antheridia (in section); *C*, an antheridium; *D*, an antherozoid; A, female thallus with archegoniophore;
B, archegoniophore with archegonia (in section); C, an archegonium with egg-cell; D, zygote within archegonium;
E, sporogonium; F, spore mother cell; G, spore-tetrad; H, spores; and I, young sporophytes (male and female)

liverwort. There are about 35 species in India, mostly in the Himalayas. *P. platyphylla* is a common species in the plains. *Porella* grows on moist rocks, tree trunks and old walls, and forms a compact greenish patch, practically covering the medium on which it grows.

Structure. The plant body consists of a slender, dorsiventral, prostrate stem and leafy branches. The lower side of the stem bears several rhizoids, primarily for anchorage. The leaves are arranged in **three rows**: two rows of dorsal leaves and a row

of ventral, small leaves called *amphigastria*. The dorsal leaves are unequally bi-lobed and overlapping. The plant grows by means of an apical tetrahedral cell, which evidently cuts off segments on three sides. (FIG. 128*B*).

Reproduction

Vegetative reproduction may take place by the breaking-off of some of the branches, or by the formation of unicellular or multicellular gemmae on the margin or at the apex of the leaf.

Marchantia (   )→ receptacle (*n*) → antheridia (*n*) → antherozoids (*n*)
Marchantia (   )→ receptacle (*n*) → archegonia (*n*) → antherozoids (*n*) X —

↑ ↑

spores (*n*) ← spore mother cells ← sporogonium (sporophyte) ← oospore

(2*n*)   (2*n*)   (2*n*)

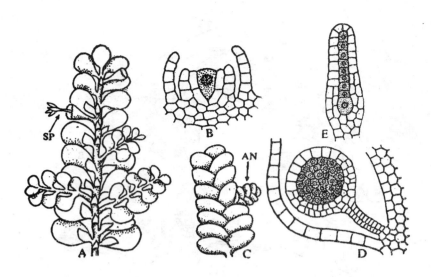

Porella. FIG. 128 *A*, female plant (dorsal view): *SP*, sporophyte; *B*, apex in longi-section
showing the growing apical cell; *C*, male plant (ventral view); *AN*, antheridial branch;
D, a portion of the same in section showing an antheridium filled with
antherozoid mother cells; and *E*, an archegonium

Sexual Reproduction. The plant is a gameto-phyte and evidently reproduces sexually through gametes. *Porella* is dioecious. The male plants (FIG. 128*C*) are usually smaller and produce special short and lateral antheridial branches (FIG. 128*D*). These bear antheridia, each in the axil of a leaf (or bract). Paraphyses may be present. The female plants (FIG. 128*A*) are larger and produce lateral archegonial branches. The archegonia on these are always borne terminally, either singly or in a group. Paraphyses may be present. Each antheridium (FIG. 128*D*) is a globoular body surrounded by a wall (jacket) and provided with a long, muticellular stalk. It is packed with antherozoid mother cells (androcytes), each giving rise to a minute biciliate antherozoid. Each archegonium (FIG. 128*E*) has a short, multicellular stalk, a venter with an egg-cell and an egg-nucleus, a ventral canal cell, a long neck with 6-8 neck canal cells, and a wall. The neck is nearly as broad as the venter. Fertilization takes place in the usual way. The antherozoids, when liberated, swim in water to the archegonium. They enter through the apical opening and finally, one of them fuses with the egg-nucleus. The fertilized egg forms a zygote.

Sporophyte (FIG. 129). The zygote secretes a wall round it and soon grows in size. It divides and redivides and soon gives rise to the sporophyte. This consists of a foot, seta and capsule. The capsule is globose and surrounded by a wall (jacket), 2 or 4 layers thick. It encloses short, slender, spirally thickened elaters and many spores. The sporophyte is surrounded by a calyptra, perianth and involucre. The **calyptra** is the envelope developed from the venter. The other two envelopes are formed by united leaves (or bracts). When mature, the capsule dehisces by four valves, and the spores are liberated.

Germination of the spore. Under favourable conditions, the spore germinates and gives rise to a small, multicellular body—the **protonema**. Soon its apical cell becomes active and produces the shoot and leaves of a new *Porella* plant.

4. *ANTHOCEROS* (60 *sp.*)

Anthoceros (FIG. 130), commonly called horned liverwort, is a very interesting plant particularly because certain special features in its life history, help one understand the course of evolution in

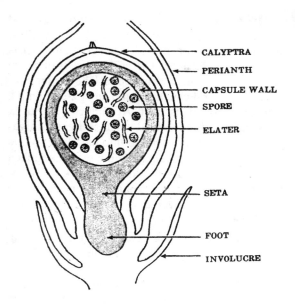

FIG. 129. Sporophyte of *Porella* in
longi-section (semi-diagrammatic)

higher plants. While its gametophyte is of a simple
and primitive type, its sporophyte has already
reached a high degree of development and complexity. The classification of *Anthoceros* is, therefore, uncertain. At present, it is treated as
belonging to a separate class, Anthocerotae, and
order Anthocerotales of Bryophyta. The features
of interest are mostly connected with the sporophyte. (*a*) The sporophyte exhibits a tendency
towards an independent life, with the development
of a considerable amount of green tissue and stomata. (*b*) Another indicator of independent life is
the massive foot to facilitate greater absorption of
water and mineral salts from the gametophyte.
With the decay of the gametophytic tissue, the foot
may even touch the ground and absorb water and
mineral salts directly from the soil. (*c*) The complexity of the sporophyte with a considerable
development of sterile tissue is an early indication
of a more complex and quite independent sporophyte at a later stage in the evolution of higher
plants. (*d*) The development of the sterile axis
(columella) represents the beginning of a conducting system. (*e*) The method of shedding spores
can be compared to that of ferns and allied plants.

Gametophyte. *Anthoceros* (FIG. 130) is a cosmopolitan plant and grows abundantly both in the
hills and plains in damp soil, hill sides, rotten tree
trunks, damp walls, etc. There are about 25 species
of *Anthoceros* in India, of which *A. punctatus* is a
common one. The plant body of *Anthoceros* is a
very simple type of gametophytic thallus, usually
2-3 cm. in diameter, with the reproductive organs
lying sunken in it. Species of *Anthoceros* may be
monoecious or dioecious. In the monoecious
species both the male and female organs develop
in the same thallus but separately, while in the
dioecious species these organs develop in separate
thalli. At a later stage, a number of cylindrical,
deep green sporophytes can be seen standing erect
on the thalli bearing the female organs. The thallus
is a small, dark green, plate-like, dorsiventral
structure, often very irregularly lobed and without
a mid-rib. There are many smooth-walled rhizoids
developing on the ventral (lower) surface and
scales are altogether absent. There are some intercellular, mucilage-filled cavities opening on to the
ventral (lower) side of the thallus. These are occupied by colonies of *Nostoc*. The internal structure
of the thallus is very simple, consisting of a mass
of thin-walled parenchyma without any differentiation of tissues. Each cell usually contains a *single*
large chloroplast with a large pyrenoid in it—a
feature not found in other Bryophyta. The

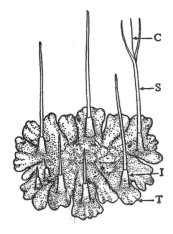

Anthoceros. FIG. 130. Thallus of *Anthoceros*
with sporophytes; *C*, columella; *S*, sporophyte
(capsule); *I*, involucre; and *T*, thallus (gametophyte)

pyrenoid consists of a mass of minute, disc or spindle-shaped bodies, which are the rudiments of starch grains.

Reproduction

Vegetative reproduction. This may take place by the continued growth of the thallus and its separation into segments. In dry regions, tubers may be formed on the margin. These may grow into new thalli under favourable conditions.

Sexual reproduction. The *Anthoceros* thallus is the gametophyte which reproduces sexually by means of gametes. Species of *Anthoceros* may be monoecious (homothallic), bearing both antheridia and archegonia, or dioecious (heterothallic), bearing either of the two. The sexual organs lie embedded in the dorsal (upper) surface of the thallus. The antheridia appear first in the monoecious species.

The **antheridia** (FIG. 131) grow in small groups (usually 2-4) within closed chambers, called antheridial chambers, which are filled with mucilage. Each chamber is covered over by a sort of roof made of 1 or 2 layers of cells. Each antheridium consists of a short, multicellular stalk, a sterile outer layer (one or more cells thick), and a compact mass of antherozoid mother cells. Each mother cell gives rise to a single, minute, biciliate antherozoid.

The **Archegonia** (FIG. 132) develop singly and separately, lying partially embedded in the thallus. When fully developed, each archegonium consists of a venter and a neck. The neck consists of a vertical row of 4-6 neck canal cells. The venter consists of a ventral canal cell and an egg-cell with a distinct egg-nucleus in it. At maturity, the neck canal cells and the ventral canal cell get disorganized and become converted into mucilage. While the major part of the archegonium remains sunken in the thallus, the upper end of the neck only protrudes out of it. When young, the neck of the archegonium is covered by four 'cover' cells, which separate out later.

Fertilization. This is effected in the following way. By the breakdown of the roof of the antheridial chamber, an outlet is formed for the antherozoids to escape. They swim to the archegonium and enter through its neck. Finally, one antherozoid fuses with the egg-nucleus in the venter. After fertilization, a zygote (oospore) is formed. Being diploid (with $2n$ chromosomes) the zygote represents the beginning of the sporophytic generation.

Sporophyte. The sporophyte develops from the zygote and consists of a **foot** and a **capsule**. For a time, it is surrounded at the base by a sheath or involucre formed by an upward growth of the archegonium. Soon after fertilization, the zygote

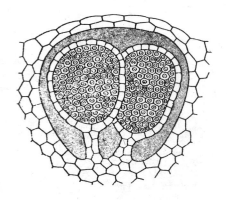

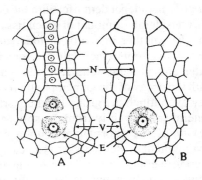

FIG. 131

FIG. 132

Anthoceros. FIG. 131. Two antheridia in an antheridial chamber (each with a stalk, wall and numerous antherozoid mother cells). FIG. 132. Two archegonia; *A*, an almost mature archegonium with egg-cell, ventral canal cell and neck canal cells; and *B*, a mature archegonium with egg-cell ready for fertilization; *N*, neck; *V*, venter; and *E*, egg-cell

grows and completely fills up the venter. It clothes itself with a wall and first divides vertically into two cells. The second division, which is transverse, cuts them off into four cells. The third division, at right angles to the first one, cuts them off into two tiers of four cells each. By further divisions, the lower tier finally gives rise to a bulbous, sterile structure at the base, thus increasing the absorbing surface. This is the foot, which looks more or less like an inverted cap (FIG. 133A). The upper tier finally gives rise to the **capsule**. There is

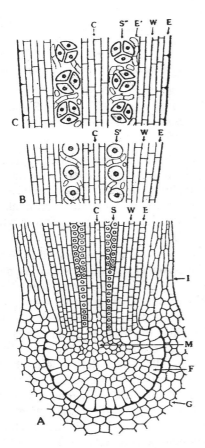

Anthoceros. FIG. 133. Longitudinal section of sporophyte (in three segments)—A, basal; B, middle and C, higher; *C*, columella; *S*, sporogenous tissue; *S'*, spore mother cell; *S"* spore-tetrad; *E'*, elater; *W*, wall of the capsule; *E*, epidermis; *I*, involucre or sheath; *M*, meristematic tissue; *F*, foot; and *G*, gametophytic tissue

no seta (stalk) of the capsule in *Anthoceros.* The capsule (FIG. 130) is a slender, cylindrical, deep green structure, usually 1-3 cm. long, sometimes much longer in a few species. The following regions can be seen in a longitudinal section through the capsule (FIG. 133). (*a*) A **meristematic tissue** at the base of the capsule, through the activity of which the sporophyte continues to elongate and the sporocytes, i.e. the spore mother cells, continue to be formed. (*b*) Centrally there is a sterile tissue—the **columella**; consisting of four rows of elongated cells each way. In transverse section, a solid square block of 16 rows of cells (FIG. 134) can be seen. The sterile columella is an early indication of the differentiation of the conducting system at a later stage in higher plants. (*c*) Surrounding the columella is a cylinder of **sporogenous tissue** (or archesporium). (*d*) The latter is surrounded by the **capsule wall**, which is a jacket of green, sterile tissue, 4-8 layers of cells in thickness, each cell having 2 or sometimes more chloroplasts in each cell. The outermost layer of this is the epidermis, which is strongly thickened and cutinized, and provided with stomata. Because of the presence of chloroplasts, the sporophyte can manufacture most of its food and is dependent on the gametophyte only for water and mineral salts. The sporophyte is, therefore, a semi-independent body. The sporogenous tissue may extend down to the base of the capsule or only half-way down, and may be 1, 2, 3 or 4 layers of cells in thickness. The sporophyte matures from the apex downwards, i.e. the base is younger than the apex. The sporogenous cells develop into small groups of sterile cells, called elaters, and small groups of spores in an alternating manner. The **elaters** are mostly smooth-walled and rarely with spiral bands. Each spore mother cell undergoes reduction division and four spores are formed in a tetrad (FIG. 134). The sporophyte reproduces asexually by means of these spores. The gametophytic generation begins with the formation of the spores. The mature capsule dehisces from the apex downwards into two horn-like valves, with the slender columella standing free in the centre (FIG. 130), and the spores are thrown out. The spore germinates and gives rise to an *Anthoceros* thallus.

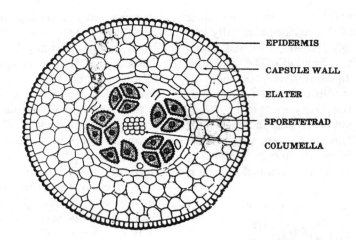

EPIDERMIS

CAPSULE WALL

ELATER

SPORETETRAD

COLUMELLA

Anthoceros. FIG. 134. Transection of sporophyte through the mature (upper) portion

Alternation of Generations. The life cycle of *Anthoceros* is completed in two generations—gametophytic and sporophytic, which regularly alternate with each other. The *Anthoceros* thallus is the main gametophytic body with haploid or *n* chromosomes, and the capsule with the foot represents the sporophyte with diploid or 2*n* chromosomes. The gametophyte reproduces sexually by gametes and gives rise to the sporophyte, and the latter reproduces asexually through spores and gives rise to the gametophyte.

5. *SPHAGNUM* (350 *sp.*)

General description. *Sphagnum* (FIG. 135A), commonly called bog moss or peat moss, is the only genus of the family *Sphagnaceae*. It is widely distributed all over the world, occurring mostly at the edges of bogs, swamps, lakes, tanks, and waterfalls, often in dense cushions. It is gregarious in habit and sometimes covers large areas. It normally grows in acidic water, the pH ranging from 3.7 to 4.9. *Sphagnum* has a special capacity for retaining water in its body and is, therefore, extensively used as a good stuffing material for pot herbs and hanging plants, like orchids, to keep them moist. Being soft and antiseptic it makes a good surgical dressing. It forms peat, which may be used as a fuel. It is also added to alkaline soil to neutralize it. Altogether 17 species of *Sphagnum* have been recorded from the temperate eastern Himalayas, mostly in Sikkim, Bhutan, the Khasi Hills and the Assam Hill ranges. Some species are *S. khasianum*, *S. plumosum*, *S. papillosum* and *S. contortum*.

Life Cycle. There are two distinct generations in the life cycle of *Sphagnum*. The main plant is the gametophyte, which later bears on its top a stalked capsular body (varying, however, in number from 1 to 5), known as the sporogonium which is the sporophyte.

Sphagnum may be distinguished from mosses by the following characteristics. (1) The stem has no rhizoids. (2) There is a great deal of branching, with two kinds of branches—long and short. (3) The leaf consists of two kinds of cells—green and hyaline. (4). The sex organs are borne on special lateral branches near the apex. In this way, they do not limit the indefinite growth of the main axis. The antheridia are solitary, each in the axil of a leaf, while the archegonia grow terminally, usually in a group of three. They do not have paraphyses. (5) The capsule is borne on a false stalk or pseudopodium (instead of a seta). (6) The capsule has no peristome. (7) The prothallus is thalloid.

Gametophyte. The gametophyte (FIG. 135A) consists of a long or short, slender, erect axis (usually a few centimetres on land and sometimes about two metres in water), a profusion of slender branches, a dense mass of minute, greenish leaves,

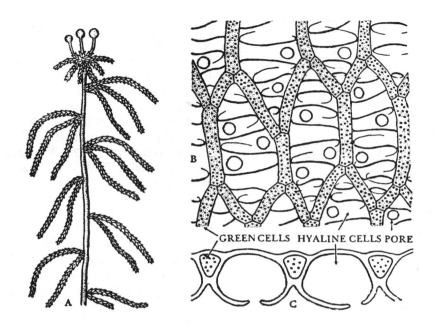

Sphagnum. FIG. 135. *A*, a stem with branches and leaves, and three terminal sporogonia; *B*, a mature leaf (surface view) showing narrow green cells, broad hyaline cells with pores, and spiral thickenings; *C*, the same in section (green cells may be triangular or rectangular)

and sex organs on special short branches near the apex. This is called the **gametophore**. The branches are lateral, profuse and of two kinds: short ones (of limited growth) crowded near the apex and long ones (of unlimited growth) lower down in tufts. The plant is perennial in habit and continues to grow almost indefinitely by a tetrahedral apical cell. The older parts always die off from below. The leaves cover the whole plant, but are more closely set on the branches than on the main stem. They appear in three rows from the apical cell. Later, with the growth and twisting of the axis and the branches, this arrangement is disturbed. The leaf is ovate or linear, is composed of a single layer of cells, and has no mid-rib. Under the microscope, the leaf is seen to be composed of a network of elongated, narrow, green cells containing chloroplasts, interspersed with large, broad, hyaline, dead cells filled with water (FIG. 135*B-C*). Such cells are spongy in nature (cf. velamen of orchid), absorbing and retaining water in enormous quantities. Some of the long, strong branches often get detached from the older parts after

their death and vegetate normally. The big mass of dead parts accumulating year after year forms peat, which in the course of time, may cover up a bog or even a lake. The acid of water in which the plant grows discourages bacterial activity and retards the decay of the dead parts.

Anatomy of the Stem. Internally, the stem is differentiated into three distinct regions: (*a*) a central pith or medulla made of thin-walled colourless cells, (*b*) a narrow cylinder of thick-walled cells acting as a supporting tissue; the cell-walls of this tissue may be of various colours—red, brown, yellow, blackish or greenish, and (*c*) externally a spongy cortex consisting of one layer (varying, however, from 1 to 5 according to species) of dead, hyaline cells with circular or oval pores in their walls and sometimes spiral thickenings. These features are not, however, constant. The cortex absorbs and retains water.

Sexual Reproduction. The *Sphagnum* plant is the gametophyte, reproducing sexually by differentiated gametes—male and female, borne

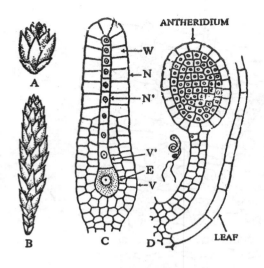

Sphagnum. FIG. 136.*A*, an archegonial branch;
B, an antheridial branch, *C*, an archegonium
(*V*, venter; *E*, egg; *V*', ventral canal cell;
N', neck canal cell; *N*, neck; *W*, wall or jacket);
D, an antheridium on a long stalk, developing
from a branch, with antherozoid mother cells
bounded by a jacket layer (wall);
an antherozoid shown separately

respectively by the antheridia and archegonia.
Sphagnum may be monoecious, bearing both the
antheridia and archegonia on the same plant, or
dioecious, bearing the sex organs on separate
plants. The antheridia (FIG. 136*D*) are borne
singly, each in the axis of a coloured leaf (reddish,
purplish or brownish), on special short, stout, lateral branches (antheridial branches) near the apex
of the shoot (FIG. 136*B*). They are produced in
acropetal succession. Each **antheridium** is ovoid
or spherical and has a slender, long stalk. It
consists of a mass of antherozoid mother cells
(androcytes), each enclosing a biciliate antherozoid, bounded by a jacket layer (wall). The two
cilia are of equal length. The archegonia (FIG.
136*C*) grow in a group of three (varying, however,
from 1 to 5) at the apex of very short branches
(archegonial branches) just below the apex of the
axis (FIG. 136*A*). Each archegonium consists of a
swollen venter with an egg and a long, slightly
twisted neck with neck canal cells, surrounded by
a wall, and has a long, multicellular stalk.

Fertilization. The antheridium bursts irregularly at the apex into valves and the antherozoids are
liberated. They swim to the mature archegonium
and enter it through the open neck (neck canal cells
dissolve into mucilage). One of the antherozoids
then fuses with the egg-nucleus. Thus, fertilization
is effected. The ventral canal cell may often act as
an oosphere, and fertilization takes place with it.
The zygote thus formed first divides transversely
into a short filament, 5-12 cells long. Longitudinal
divisions follow. Finally, a spherical or ovoid
spore-bearing body, the **sporogonium**, is formed
on the top of the branch. Usually one zygote of an
archegonial branch develops into a sporogonium.

Sporophyte. The sporogonium (FIG. 137*A*) is the
sporophyte reproducing asexually by means of
spores. It consists of a **capsule**, developing fom
the upper part of the filament (see above), a very
short neck-like stalk called the **seta** (often
remaining undeveloped), a large bulbous **foot**,
developing from the lower part of the filament
and a pseudopodium (see p. 471). The
sporogonium in longitudinal section (FIG. 137*A*)
shows the following regions. There is a compact
mass of colourless, sterile cells forming the
columella at the centre. A dome-shaped **spore-
sac** containing numerous spores formed in tetrads
occurs on the top of the columella. There is a lid
or cover known as the **operculum** on the top of
the capsule; it has a ring-like layer of thickened
cells known as the **annulus**. The capsule-wall is
made of a layer of thick-walled, cutinized
cells—the **epidermis**, and a few layers of thin-
walled cells internal to it—the **sub-epidermis**.
Rudimentary stomata (two guard cells only,
without any chloroplast or opening) are present in
the epidermis. The capsule, however, is greenish
in colour, containing some chloroplasts. The
whole capsule is bounded by a loose cap or
calyptra, which is the enlarged and stretched
archegonium wall. Soon, however, it is torn off
The seta being very short (almost absent), a false
stalk or **pseudopodium** develops from the stem at
the base of the capsule. As the spores begin to
mature, this stalk elongates rapidly and pushes up
the capsule. When the capsule is ripe, the

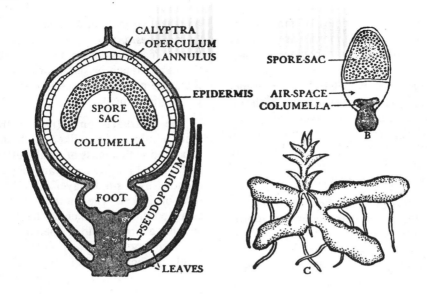

Sphagnum. FIG. 137. *A*, sporogonium in longi-section; *B*, the same showing the stage
prior to bursting (diagrammatic); *C*, thalloid protonema with a young gametophore

columella shrinks away from the spore-sac, leaving an air-cavity in between (FIG. 137*B*). The spore-sac now assumes a cylindrical form. The compressed air contained in the air-space exerts a heavy pressure on the spore-sac, with the result that the capsule explodes, blowing off the lid and scattering the spores.

Germination of the Spore. The spore, tetrahedral in shape, on germination gives rise to a vey short filament or germ tube. Its terminal cell divides in two directions, finally forming a green flat, irregularly-lobed thallus, called the **primary protonema** (FIG. 137*C*). It is a single layer of cells and bears many septate rhizoids. Any marginal cell of the primary protonema may divide and grow into a filament, finally becoming thalloid; this is the **secondary protonema**. A bud appears on the protonema from a tetrahedral cell on the margin of a lobe near its base. Leaves occur on the bud in three rows. The bud elongates rapidly and soon grows into an erect, leafy, much-branched gametophore. Usually one plant develops from a protonema. The latter soon disappears, and the mature plant, which has no rhizoids, absorbs water through its whole surface.

Alternation of Generations. The life-cycle of *Sphagnum* has two stages: gametophytic and sporophytic. The main plant is the gametophyte (haploid or *n*), which reproduces sexually by gametes and gives rise to the sporophyte. The sporogonium is the sporophyte (diploid or 2*n*), which reproduces asexually by means of spores and gives rise to the gametophyte again. Thus, the two generations alternate to complete the life cycle.

Vegetative Propagation. This is very common in *Sphagnum*, helping the plant to multiply rapidly and spread over large areas. The methods are: (*a*) separation of some of the long and strong branches after the death of the older parts; (*b*) development of secondary protonema by some of the short apical branches; (*c*) splitting of the protonema; and (*d*) formation of secondary protonema from the primary protonema.

6. *MOSS* (14,200 sp.)

Moss (FIG. 138*A*) occurs most commonly on old damp walls, trunks of trees, and damp soil during the rainy season, while in winter it dries up. It is gregarious in habit; wherever it grows it forms a green patch or a soft, velvet-like, green carpet.

There are about 14,200 species of mosses and allies. Some common Indian mosses are *Funaria hygrometrica*, *Polytrichum commune* and *Barbula indica*.

The moss plant is small, usually a few centimetres in height, and consists of a short axis with spirally arranged minute green leaves, which are crowded towards the apex. True roots are absent; it bears a number of slender multicellular branching rhizoids which perform the functions of roots. The axis may be branched or unbranched.

Life-cycle. The life-cycle of a moss plant is completed in two stages—gametophytic and sporophytic. The plant itself is the gametophyte, which is followed by another structure, called sporogonium, that grows dependent on the moss plant and is the sporophyte (FIG. 139*C*).

Gametophyte. The moss plant is a **gametophyte**, i.e. it bears gametes and reproduces sexually. Highly differentiated male and female organs are developed at the apex of the shoot. The male organ is known as the **antheridium** and the female organ as the **archegonium**. These organs are sometimes intermixed with some multicellular

hair-like structures, known as the **paraphyses** (*para*, *beside*; *physis*, growth = offshoot). Antheridia and archegonia may occur together on the same branch or shoot, or on two branches of the same plant (monoecious) or on two separate plants (dioecious).

The **antheridium** (FIG. 138*B-C*) is a multicellular, short-stalked, club-shaped body. It is packed with a mass of small cells known as the antherozoid mother cells (androcytes) and is surrounded by a single layer of cells known as the wall or jacket. The mother cells are regularly arranged in 5-15 segments (FIG. 138*B*), while the wall has a terminal lid or operculum, consisting of one to many cells. Each mother cell develops a single antherozoid (or male gamete). As the antheridium matures, the lid is forced open by the internal pressure of the contents and the mother cells are liberated through the apical opening in a mass of mucilage (FIG. 138*C*). The mucilaginous walls of the mother cells get dissolved in water and the **antherozoids** are set free. They are very minute in size, spirally coiled and bicilate. After liberation, they swim in the rain-water that collects at the apex of the moss plant.

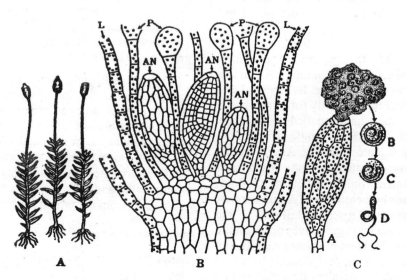

Moss FIG. 138. *A*, three moss plants with capsule; *B*, apex of the male shoot in longi-section showing antheridia (*AN*), paraphyses (*P*) and leaves (*L*); *C*, a mature antheridium discharging antherozoid mother cells in a mass of mucilage (*a*), antherozoid mother cell (*b*), wall of the same getting dissolved (*c*), and biciliate antherozoid (*d*)

The **archegonium** (FIG. 139*A-B*) is a multicellular body, but is flask-shaped. It is provided with a short, multicellular stalk and consists of two portions: the lower swollen portion, known as the **venter** (belly) and the upper tube-like portion or the **neck**. It is surrounded by a wall or jacket, which is single-layered higher up and double-layered in the region of the venter. The neck is long, narrow and straight. Within the venter lies a large **egg-cell** or ovum with a distinct nucleus—the egg-nucleus (female gamete). Above this lies a small ventral canal cell, and higher up in the neck, there are many neck canal cells. All the cells mentioned above except the ovum are functionless and soon degenerate into mucilage. The neck is at first closed at the apex by a sort of lid, but as the archegonium matures, the lid opens as a result of the internal pressure exerted by the mucilage and allows the antherozoids to pass through it.

Fertilization. It is effected through the medium of water—rain-water or dew—that collects on the plant. When the archegonium matures, it secretes mucilage with cane-sugar. This attracts a swarm of antherozoids which enter through the neck canal and pass down into the venter. One of them fuses with the egg-nucleus and the rest degenerate. After fertilization, the zygote clothes itself with a wall and is then known as the oospore. The latter germinates *in situ* and gives rise to the sporogonium on the moss plant (FIG. 139*C*). Although all the archegonia of a shoot or branch may be fertilized, ultimately one zygote (oospore) develops into the sporogonium.

Sporophyte. The sporogonium is the sporophyte, i.e. it bears spores and reproduces asexually. The sporogonium consists of **foot, seta** and **capsule.** The seta is the slender stalk which bears the capsule. The foot is the small conical structure which buries itself in the tissue of the moss plant. The sporogonium is not an independent plant; it grows as a semi-parasite on the moss plant. It draws its food partly from the moss plant (gametophyte) and partly manufactures its own food. The oospore divides into two cells—the upper and the lower; the lower cell, by repeated divisions, forms the seta with the foot, and the upper cell forms the multicellular, complex body of the capsule. As the oospore grows into the sporogonium, the archegonium gets ruptured somewhere in the middle. The upper half of the ruptured archegonium then forms

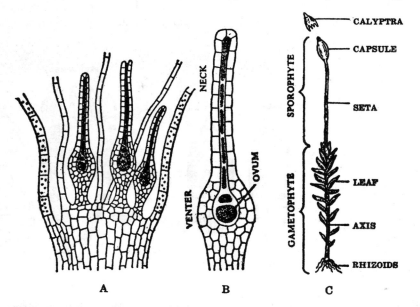

A   B   C

Moss. FIG. 139. *A*, apex of a female shoot in longi-section showing three archegonia, three paraphyses and two leaves; *B*, an archegonium; *C*, a moss plant showing the sporophyte growing on the gametophyte

a loose cap almost covering the capsule and is know as the **calyptra** (FIG. 140). Later, it is blown away (FIGS. 141-42).

Sporogonium. It is (FIG. 143) a complex body, which is more less pear-shaped. A longitudinal section through it shows the following regions.

(1) **Operculum.** This is the lid of the capsule, and lies on top of it. It is a few layers in thickness. When the capsule dehisces, the operculum comes away as a circular, cup-shaped lid.

(2) **Annulus.** This is a special ring-like layer of epidermal cells, lying around the capsule at the base of the operculum. It is by the rupture of the annulus that the capsule dehisces.

(3) **Peristome.** When the operculum falls off, the top of the capsule is seen to be furnished with one or two rows of thickened, tooth-like projections, constituting the peristome. These teeth are hyrgroscopic. When they are dry, they open out and facilitate the dispersion of spores (FIG. 142).

(4) **Columella.** This is the solid central column of the capsule. It is sterile, i.e. it contains no spores. Water and food material accumulate here for the developing spores.

(5) **Spore-sac.** This lies around the columella and contains numerous small cells. It is bounded externally by a few layers of cells, and internally by one layer. Each cell of the spore-sac is a spore mother cell. Each mother cell undergoes reduction division to form four spores. The capsule dehisces at the annulus, with the lid falling off. The capsule, being seated on a long stalk, is disturbed by the wind and the spores are thrown out of the spore-sac.

(6) **Air-cavity.** This is a cylindrical cavity surrounding the spore-sac, and is traversed by delicate strands of cells, known as the **trabeculae** (sing. trabecula).

(7) **Capsule Wall.** This is composed of (*a*) a few layers of chloroplast-bearing cells just outside the air-cavity, (*b*) a few layers of bigger cells, containing water—the sub-epidermis, and (*c*) externally, a distinct layer—the epidermis.

(8) **Apophysis.** This is the solid basal portion of the capsule with (*a*) a distinct epidermis, bearing a few stomata, (*b*) a sub-epidermis, containing chloroplasts, and (*c*) a central region of elongated cells, containing water—the water-conducting tissue.

Germination of the Spore. After dehiscence of the capsule, the spores are scattered by the wind and germinate under favourable conditions. The

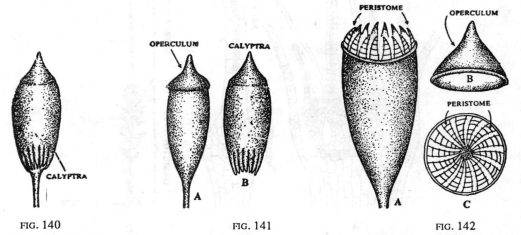

FIG. 140   FIG. 141   FIG. 142

Moss Capsule. FIG. 140. A capsule covered by calyptra. FIG. 141. *A*, a capsule without calyptra *B*, detached calyptra. FIG.142. *A*, a capsule showing peristome—open; *B*, opeculum; *C*, peristome— closed (surface view)

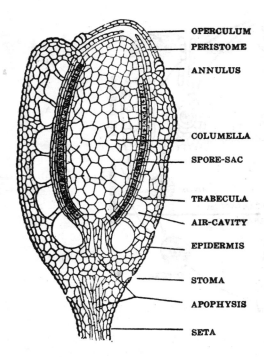

FIG. 143. Sporogonium of moss
in longitudinal section

OPERCULUM
PERISTOME
ANNULUS

COLUMELLA
SPORE-SAC

TRABECULA
AIR-CAVITY
EPIDERMIS

STOMA
APOPHYSIS
SETA

FIG. 144. Protonema of moss
(note the buds and rhizoids)

spore grows out into a short tube, which lengthens and ultimately forms a green, much-branched filament. This is known as the **protonema** (FIG. 144). It produces long, slender, brown rhizoids, and a number of small, lateral buds. These lateral buds develop into new moss plants, which form a colony again.

Alternation of Generations. (FIG. 145). The plant shows two generations, which alternate regularly. The plant itself is the gametophyte (or gamete-bearing plant), and the sporogonium is the sporophyte (or spore-bearing plant). Through sexual reproduction by gametes (antherozoid and ovum) the gametophyte gives rise to the sporophyte, and through asexual reproduction by spores the sporophyte gives rise to the gametophyte. In the life-history of the moss plant, the reduction of chromosomes to haploid or n takes place during the formation of spores from the spore mother cell. The spore is, therefore, the beginning of the sexual or gametophytic generation, and the various stages from the spore to the antherozoid and ovum repre-

sent the **gametophytic or sexual generation.** The antherozoid and the ovum fuse, and the chromosome number is doubled, i.e. $2n$ is restored in the oospore. The oospore, therefore, represents the beginning of the asexual or sporophytic generation, and the oospore, sporogonium and spore mother cells represent the **sporophytic** or **asexual generation** because in all of them the chromosome number is $2n$.

Vegetative Reproduction. The gametophytic plant reproduces vegetatively in a variety of ways: (1) by the formation of multicellular 'gemmae' which develop in groups, usually at the apex of the leaf or at the apex of a comparatively long branch; they get detached and germinate in moist soil, producing a protonema; (2) by protonema which develops from any part of the plant—stem, leaf or even rhizoid; (3) by the production of resting buds on the protonema; they get detached from the protonema and develop into new moss plants; and (4) by separation of protonemal branches.

Any part of the sporogonium (foot, seta or capsule) may also develop protonema and give rise to moss plants. This is a case of **appospory.**

COMPARISON BETWEEN LIVERWORTS AND MOSSES

(1) In liverworts the gametophyte is mostly thalloid (except leafy Jungermanniales) and dorsiventral; whereas in mosses it is leafy and radial. In both, the gametophytes are the main plants and are green in colour, performing photosynthesis, and they take to sexual reproduction through highly developed gametes and gametangia. Both show regular alternation of generations.

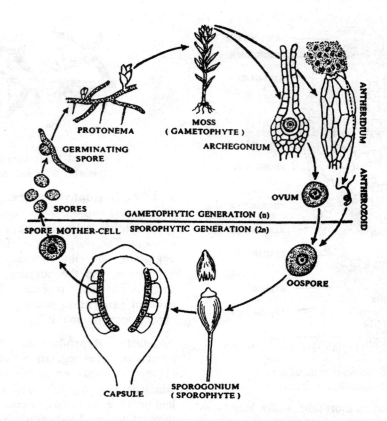

PROTONEMA
MOSS
(GAMETOPHYTE)
GERMINATING
SPORE
ARCHEGONIUM
ANTHERIDIUM
OVUM
ANTHEROZOID
SPORES
GAMETOPHYTIC GENERATION (n)
SPORE MOTHER-CELL   SPOROPHYTIC GENERATION (2n)
OOSPORE
CAPSULE
SPOROGONIUM
(SPOROPHYTE)

FIG. 145. Life-cycle of moss showing alternation of generations

(2) Leaves in the leafy liverworts (e.g. *Porella* of Jungermanniales) have no mid-rib; while those in mosses have mid-ribs (with some exceptions).

(3) In liverworts the rhizoids are unicellular and commonly not branched; while in mosses they are multicellular and generally branched.

(4) In liverworts the protonema is mostly absent or small; while in mosses it is distinct and well developed.

(5) The sporophyte in *Riccia* is simple and lies embedded in the thallus. In *Marchantia* it is differentiated into foot, seta and capsule; it comes out of the thallus and shows the beginning of sterilization of sporogenous tissue in the form of elaters. In both, the sporophyte is non-green and is wholly parasitic upon the gametophyte. The sporophyte of *Anthoceros* is a green, elongated, complex body with foot, seta and capsule, and it shows further sterilization of sporogenous tissue (elaters and a small columella); it is only partially parasitic upon the gametophyte. In mosses the sporophyte has reached a high degree of development and complexity with distinct foot, seta and capsule; it shows further differentiation into sterile tissue (columella) and sporogenous tissue; and being green it is only partially parasitic upon the gametophyte.

(6) Elaters are mostly present in liverworts; while they are absent in mosses.

CHAPTER 7

PTERIDOPHYTA

CLASSIFICATION OF PTERIDOPHYTA
(9,000 sp.)

Class I   Psilotopsida (or Psilophytinae)— 8 sp. **Order 1.** Psilotales (8 sp.), e.g. *Psilotum* and *Tmesipteris*.

Class II Lycopsida (or Lycopodinae)—963 sp. **Order 1.** Lycopodiales (186 sp.) e.g. *Lycopodium*. **Order 2.** *Selaginellales* (700 sp.), e.g *Selaginella*. **Order 3.** Isoetales (77 sp.), e.g. *Isoetes*.

Class III Sphenopsida (or Equisetinae)—25 sp. **Order 1.** Equisetales (25 sp.), e.g. *Equisetum*.

Class IV Pteropsida (or Filicinae)—7,800 sp. Sub-class Eusporangiate. **Order 1.** Ophioglossales (70 sp.), e.g. *Ophioglossum*, *Botrychium* and *Helminthostachys*. **Order 2.** Osmundales (19 sp.). e.g. *Osmunda*. **Order 3.** Marattiales (over 200 sp.), e.g. *Marattia* and *Angiopteris*. *Sub-class.* Leptosporangiate. **Order 4.** Filicales (7,600 sp.), e.g. *Dryopteris*, *Nephrolepis*, *Pteris*, *Polypodium*, *Adiantum*, etc. **Order 5.** Marsileales (67 sp.), e.g. *Marsilea*. **Order 6.** Salviniales (16 sp.), e.g. *Salvinia* and *Azolla*.

Leptosporangiate ferns are those in which the entire sporangium develops from a single superficial cell of the sporophyll; while **eusporangiate ferns** are those in which a row or group of superficial cells divide to form an outer and an inner layer of cells, the outer giving rise to the wall of the sporangium and the inner to the sporogenous tissue.

ORIGIN AND EVOLUTION OF PTERIDO-
PHYTA. The origin of Pteridophyta cannot be stated with any amount of certainty. It is, however, known that among the vascular plants, the oldest and the most primitive group is **Psilophytales** which grew abundantly in the early Palaeozoic. The group soon declined, and before it disappeared (leaving only two genera as its living representatives) it gave rise to three indepedent lines of

evolution as represented by Lycopodinae, Equisetinae and Filicinae. Each of them followed its own course of evolution. The origin of Psilophytales is again speculative; it may have been derived from algal ancestors or from some bryophytes. Of the three groups mentioned above, Lycopodinae seems to be comparatively primitive although it has given rise to heterosporous condition (e.g. *Selaginella* and *Isoetes*). Equisetinae is more advanced than the former; while Filicinae is the most advanced group. Among the orders of the latter, the eusporangiate ferns are regarded as ancient and the leptosporangiate ferns as modern.

TYPES OF STELES IN PTERIDOPHYTA
(FIG. 146). The vascular tissues as a whole, together with the associated tissues making up the central column of the root, stem and leaf constitute the **stele** (*stele* means a column). The stele thus consists of all the tissues, mainly, however, the vascular, from the centre to the pericycle, and is surrounded by the cortex (endodermis). The different types of stele that have developed during the course of evolution are differentiated mainly according to the relative positions of the xylem and phloem and the presence or absence of the pith. Pteridophyta are of special interest in this respect, since they show, often with natural gradations, all the stelar types, as described below. A certain amount of variation or gradation is noticed within each type. In 1875, **Sachs** gave an account of xylem and phloem (distribution and composition) and of cambium (origin and activity) in roots and shoots. But the theory of stele was formulated in 1886 by **Van Tieghem** who laid the foundation for the study of this very important structure. He could not, however, show that different stelar types had arisen from a single original type. In 1897, **Jeffrey** modified Van Tieghem's concepts of the stele and introduced the terms siphonostele and protostele. He concluded that the former and, as a matter of fact, all types of stele, had arisen from the latter.

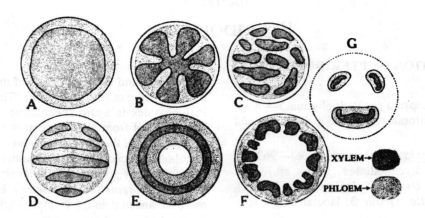

Types of Steles. FIG. 146. *A*, haplostele in *Gleichenia*; *B*, actinostele in *Lycopodium serratum*;
C, mixed protostele in *L. cernuum*; *D*, plectostele in *L. clavatum*; *E*, amphiphloic siphonostele
in *Marsilea*; *F*, ectophloic siphonostele in *Osmunda*; *G*, dictyostele in *Dryopteris*

(1) **Protostele** (*protos*, first). This is the most
simple and primitive type of stele, in which the
vascular tissues—xylem and phloem, particularly
the former—form a solid, central column *without
any pith*. Protostele is present in the stems of several members of Pteridophyta and in the roots of
almost all of them. It has, however, certain types.
In the simplest and earliest type the xylem forms a
solid central core, circular in outline, surrounded
by a ring of phloem. This type is called **haplostele**
(FIG. 146*A*), as in certain species of *Selaginella*
and *Gleichenia*. In the latter, however, the xylem
occurs mixed up with some parenchyma. In the
more advanced and complex types xylem appears
as a star-shaped structure with phloem alternating
with its rays. This is the radial type of stele, otherwise called **actinostele** (FIG. 146*B*), as in
Lycopodium serratum, *L. phlegmaria* and
Psilotun. In the most advanced type, xylem and
phloem occur in more or less parallel bands, alternating with each other. This is the parallel-banded
stele, otherwise called **plectostele** (FIG. 146*D*), as
in *Lycopodium clavatum*. In *L. cernuum*, the xylem
forms several small irregular groups, which lie
embedded in the ground mass of phloem. This is
called **mixed protostele** (FIG. 146*C*). Protostele is
also found in the pithless roots of many angiosperms and stems of some aquatic angiosperms.

With the development of the pith and the presence of leaf-gap; (see below) the pattern of distribution of the xylem and phloem changes, and the
stele becomes differentiated into distinct types.

(2) **Siphonostele** (*siphon*, hollow or tube).
With the appearance of the pith the vascular tissues are pushed away from the centre. The xylem
forms a cylinder around the pith and the phloem
lies on both sides of the xylem, often surrounding
it, or only on the outside of the xylem.
Siphonostele is thus a hollow or tubular stele.
There are two types.

(*a*) *Amphiphloic Siphonostele* (*amphi*, on both
sides). Here the xylem forms a cylinder around the
pith, and the phloem (together with the pericycle
and endodermis) forms two cylinders, one on the
outside and another on the inside of the xylem
(FIG. 146*E*). This type of stele is also called
solenostele. This is seen in certain ferns, e.g.
Adiantum, *Dicksonia*, etc. *Marsilea* typically
shows this type of stele (see FIG. 190). Among
angiosperms, it is found in *Cucurbitaceae*.

(*b*) *Ectophloic Siphonostele* (*ectos*, outisde).
Here, too, the xylem forms a cylinder around the
pith, as in the previous case, but only the external
cylinder of the phloem (together with only the
external pericycle and endodermis) is present.

(FIG. 146*F*). This is found in some ferns, e.g. *Osmunda*, *Helminthostachys*, *Botrycium*, and also in *Equisetum*. Gymnosperms and dicotyledons show an advanced type of ectophloic siphonostele, with endarch collateral bundles. In these, the leaf-gaps are large and indistinguishable from the interfascicular areas, and the pith and the cortex are connected by wide bands of parenchyma. Hence the vascular system is broken up into separate vascular bundles.

Origin of Siphonostele. It is an acknowledged fact that siphonostele develop from protostele. But there are two diametrically opposite views regarding the origin of the pith: *intrastelar origin* and *extrastelar origin*. According to **Boodle** and others supporting the intrastelar view, the pith developed from the gradual metamorphosis of the inner elements (tracheids) of the protostele and the consequent shifting of the vascular tissues outwards. According to them, therefore, the pith is intrastelar in origin, gradually expanding outwards in the form of medullary rays (expansion theory). This is the generally accepted view. According to **Jeffery**, however, the pith is extrastelar in origin; the obliteration of the inner endodermis, and the intrusion of the cortical tissue inwards, gave rise to the pith in the centre (invasion theory). This is not, however, a very convincing view.

(3) Dictyostele (*dictyo*, net). This is a much-dissected type of stele derived from the siphonostele, i.e. the stele is broken up into a number of separate vascular strands. This is the most advanced type of stele. The presence of numerous leaf-gaps caused by leaf-traces breaks up the stele into a network of separate strands, each constituting a concentric bundle (FIG. 146*G*). This is found in many species of *Polypodiaceae*, e.g. *Pteris*, *Pteridium*, *Polypodium*, *Aspidium*, etc., and some species of *Selaginella*.

Leaf-traces and Leaf-gaps. The vascular cylinder is continuous through the whole plant body. At the node, a strand of vascular tissue leaves the cylinder, passes out through the cortex and goes into the leaf; this strand of vascular tissue is called the **leaf-trace**. The leaf-trace, while leaving the vascular cylinder of the stem, causes small breaks or openings in it. Each break in the vascular cylinder of the stem is called a leaf-gap. The leaf-gap occurs in the vascular cylinder just above the leaf-trace and is filled up with parenchyma. Above the leaf-gap, the vascular cylinder becomes continuous again so that a transection at the node of the stem shows the break in the vascular cylinder, while a section at the internode, above the leaf-gap, shows a continuous ring-like cylinder. The presence of numerous leaf-gaps breaks up the vascular cylinder into a sort of network.

A reduction of vascular tissues is noticed from gymnosperms and woody dicotyledons where the activity of the cambium is at its maximum, to herbaceous dicotyledons with much less or no activity of the cambium and sometimes absence of interfascicular cambium, to monocotyledons without cambium (except in a few cases). This reduction series indicates the trend of evolution from woody types (primitive condition) to herbaceous types (advanced condition).

1. *PSILOTUM* (2 *sp.*)

General Description. *Psilotum* (FIG. 147*A*) of the (family *Psilotaceae*) and *Tmesipteris* belong to the living order Psilotales, which is closely related to the extinct order Psilophytales of the Devonian (see FIG. X/1). Psilophytales were the earliest land plants and the oldest pteridophytes. The above two genera of Psilotales are regarded as the living representatives of the extinct order. *Tmesipteris* is confined to Australia while *Psilotum* is somewhat common in the tropics. In India, *Psilotum nudum* (= *P. triquetrum*) is found in Pachmarhi (Madhya Pradesh), the Sundarbans and a few other places.

Structure. *Psilotum* is a slender, tufted, perennial herb, 15 to 60 cm. or more in length. It grows as an epiphyte on tree trunks, or on rocky slopes, often hanging downwards, or on the ground, or rocks, or bases of trees, often standing erect. The plant shows conspicuous dichotomous branching. It consists of a slender, subterranean rhizome, and slender, green aerial branches. The rhizome (*B*) is much-branched, coralloid and brown and bears many rhizoids but no roots. The stem is unbranched at the base, but higher up, it becomes

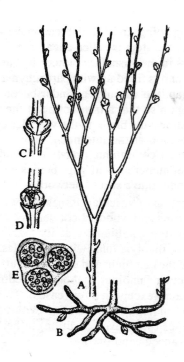

Psilotum. FIG. 147 *A*, a shoot with sporangia
(synangia); *B*, much-branched rhizome;
C, synangium closed; *D*, the same open; *E*, young
synangium in section showing spore mother cells

profusely branched in a dichotomous manner,
bearing minute, bifid scale-leaves singly at the
nodes. The branches are somewhat angular in
outline. The rhizome and the branch grow by
means of a large pyramidal apical cell. Internally,
the rhizome is protostelic, with scanty development of phloem around. The stem, on the other
hand, shows a siphonostelic structure, with star-
shaped xylem around a central, fibrous pith, and
indistinct phloem between the xylem arms. The
xylem is always exarch. Vegetative reproduction is
common and takes place by means of oval, multicellular gemmae, which develop in large numbers
on the surface of the rhizome, and sometimes also
on the prothallus.

Sporangia (FIG. 147*C-E*). A short stalk in the
axil of the scale-leaf bears a trilocular sporangium
(or a union of three sporangia, i.e. a synangium)
terminally. *Psilotum* is homosporous, i.e. it bears
only one kind of spores. A section through the
sporangium shows a central mass of sporogenous
cells, which produce minute, oval spores with
finely reticulated walls. The cells surrounding
them disintegrate and offer nourishment to the
developing spores. As the spores mature, the sporangium bursts longitudinally from the apex to the
base, and the spores are scattered.

Prothallus (FIG. 148*A*). Each spore germinates
into a cylindrical, branched prothallus. It is brownish in colour, and bears numerous rhizoids (but no
roots) all over its body. The presence of an endophytic, mycorrhizal fungus is a common feature.
Several antheridia and archegonia develop super-
ficially, projecting outwards, on the prothallus.
Each antheridium (*B*) is spherical and provided
with a distinct wall, and produces numerous spiral
and multiciliate antherozoids (*C*). The **archegonium** (*D*) is somewhat flask-shaped, with a neck
and a venter. Fertilization takes place in the usual
way. After fertilization, the oospore that is formed
grows into an embryo with a foot (buried in the
prothallus) and an axis which shows dichotomy
from the beginning. The axis grows into a
branched rhizome, from which aerial shoots soon
develop **nation of Generations**. *Psilotum* shows
a distinct alternation of generations but it is of
the *homomorphic* type, the prothallus and the
sporophytic rhizome being somewhat similar in
appearance.

Note. The primitive characteristics of *Psilotum*
which indicate its close relation to the extinct
group Psilophytales are: (*a*) axial nature of the
plant body; (*b*) dichotomous branching; (*c*) complete absence of roots; (*d*) terminal sporangia;
(*e*) homospory; (*f*) xylem made of annular and
spiral tracheids only; (*g*) protostelic condition of
the rhizome; (*h*) no cambium and, therefore, no
secondary growth; and (*i*) homomorphic type of
alternation of generations.

2. *LYCOPODIUM* (185 *sp.*)

Occurrence and Structure. *Lycopodium* (family
Lycopodiaceae; FIGS. 149-51), commonly called
club-moss, is a much-branched, herbaceous plant
found abundantly in the hills at a comparatively
high altitude. There are about eight species in

dichotomous branching, but some species are monopodial. Most species of *Lycopodium*, e.g. *L. cernuum* (FIG.149) and *L. clavatum* (FIG. 151) are terrestrial, while in the tropical forests there are some epiphytic species with pendent branches, e.g. *L. squarrosum* (FIG. 150) and *L. phlegmaria* (FIG. 151A), both common in north-east India.

Internal Structure of the Stem.
(1) **Epidermis**—This is the outermost layer of small cells with the outer and often radial walls thickened and cutinized. It is provided with numerous stomata. (2) **Cortex**—This is a wide region lying in between the epidermis and the stele. It varies considerably from species to species in its width, structure and composition. In *L. cernuum* (FIG. 152) the cortex is differentiated into (*a*) inner cortex made of parenchyma (*b*) middle cortex made of sclerenchyma, and (*c*) outer cortex made of one to a few layers of parenchyma which may be absent altogether. In some species the inner cortex and the middle or outer cortex may may be sclerenchymatous. (3) **Endodermis**—This is a single layer of small thin-walled cell surrounding the central stele. However, it is not well defined in all cases (4) **Stele**—This is the central cylinder of the vascular system, i.e. the xylem and phloem, surrounded by a few-layered, thin-walled parenchyma comprising the pericycle. The stele of the *Lycopodium* stem is a protostele with a central

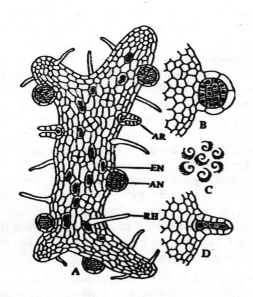

Psilotum FIG. 148. *A*, prothallus (gametophyte) with sex organs; *AR*, archegonium; *EN*, endophytic fungus; *AN*, antheridium; *RH*, rhizoid; *B*, an antheridium; *C*, antherozoids; *D*, an archegonium

India. The plant body consists of creeping rhizomes, which give off slender, elongated, aerial branches from the upper side and adventitious roots from the lower. The branches are densely covered with numerous small, narrow, pointed leaves. *Lycopodium* mostly shows characteristic

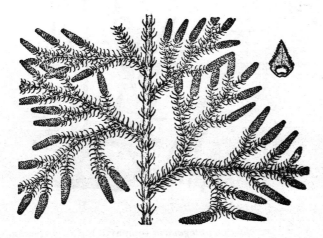

FIG. 149. *Lycopodium cernuum* (terrestrial); a sporophyll with a sporangium shown separately

vascular cylinder but no pith. There are commonly three types of steles in different species of *Lycopodium*. In some species, as in *L. serratum* and *L. phlegmaria*, the xylem forms radiating arms or rays from the centre, with the phloem alternating (radial arrangement). This is called actinostele (see FIG. 146B). In other species, as in *L. cernuum* (FIG. 152), the xylem is broken up into isolated strands, which lie embedded in the ground mass of phloem. This is called mixed protostele (FIG. 152). In some other species, as in *L. clavatum* and *L. complanatum*. Thr xylem and phloem occur in alternating, more or less parallel bands. This is called **Plectostele** (see FIG. 146D). In *Lycopodium*, the xylem is always exarch with the protoxylem towards the pericycle, and metaxylem towards the centre. The protoxylem consists of a few narrow, annular and spiral tracheids, and metaxylem of large, scalariform tracheids. The phloem consists of sieve-tubes and phloem parenchyma.

Sporophyte. The *Lycopodium* plant is the sporophyte, i.e. it reproduces asexually by means of spores, which are borne by specialized leaves, called **sporophylls** (spore-bearing leaves). The sporophylls resemble the vegetative leaves but are smaller in size. They are aggregated together, being spirally arranged, at the apex of a vegetative branch or of a special reproductive branch in the form of a *cone*, called **sporangiferous spike or strobilus** (FIG. 153). All the sporophylls are of the same kind and so also are the sporangia and the spores. *Lycopodium* is thus homosporous. The

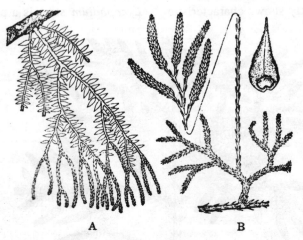

A   B

FIG. 151. A, *Lycopodium phlegmaria* (epiphytic); B, L. clavatum (terrestrial); a sporophyll with a sporangium shown separately

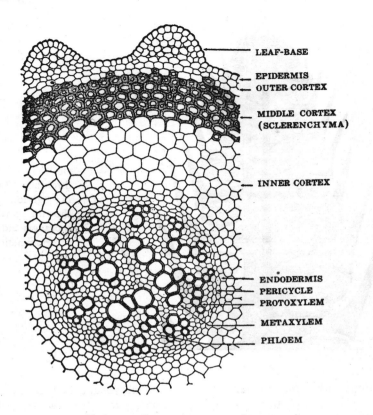

FIG. 152. *Lycopodium cernuum* stem in transection

sporangium has a short, multicellular stalk and is borne on the upper surface of the sporophyll—close to its base. It consists of a wall commonly made of a few (three or more) layers of cells and an inner mass of sporogenous cells or spore mother cells. Spores are formed in tetrads from these cells by reduction division.

Gametophyte (FIG. 154A-B). After the dehiscence of the sporangium the spores are scattered by the wind. The spores are remarkably long-lived, often retaining the form to germinate for a number of years. In many species the spores do not germinate for several months or sometimes even years after shedding. Even after germination begins, the rate of growth is slow. In *L. cernuum*, a common Indian species, the spores germinate within a few days and the growth of the gametophyte is completed in the same season. The spore, on germination, gives rise to the gametophyte or prothallus. The gametophyte may be subterranean, or sub-aerial, and vertical, or partially horizontal. In the sub-aerial type, the aerial portion turns green and bears the sexual organs. It is about 2 or 3 mm. in length. The subterranean type is much bigger but non-green. The gametophyte may be a cylindrical or tuberous body with a lobed crown or it may be broad and irregularly cup-shaped. The crown bears the sexual organs. The tuberous portion shows a complicated internal structure, being differentiated into distinct regions, and is always associated with an endophytic (symbiotic) fungus which infects a definite region of it at an early stage of gametophyte-development. But for this fungal infection the growth of the gametophyte becomes arrested. Some rhizoids are produced from the epidrmal layer. (For detailed structure of the gametophyte see FIG. 154B and caption). The gametophyte of *Lycopodium* is monoecious, bearing both antheridia and

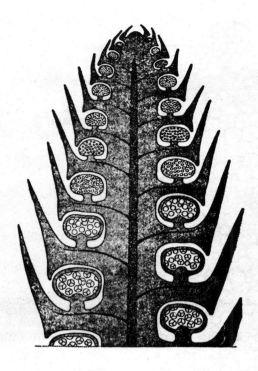

FIG. 153.
Strobilus of *Lycopodium*
in longitudinal section
showing sporophylls,
sporangia and spores
(diagrammatic)

archegonia. Numerous antheridia and archegonia are formed in the upper lobed portion (crown) of the gametophyte. The antheridium is more or less spherical, consisting of a wall made of one layer of cells and a central mass of spermatogenous cells (antherozoid mother cells). It lies wholly or partially sunken in the tissue of the prothallus. The spermatozoids (antherozoids) are minute, broadly rounded at the base, slightly curved, and biciliate. The archegonium is a narrow, elongated structure and lies almost wholly embedded in the prothallus except for the upper portion of the neck which projects beyond it. It consists of a narow **venter** and a long **neck** with a variable number of neck canal cells (1 to 16, commonly 4-6). The venter contains a single large egg-cell with a distinct egg (egg-nucleus or female gamete), and a ventral canal cell. All the canal cells soon get disorganized.

Embryo (FIG. 154*D*). After fertilization, which takes place in the usual way, the fertilized egg or oospore divides into two cells—outer and inner. The outer cell is the suspensor cell which is elongated but not functional, while the inner one is the embryonal cell. The latter, by successive divisions, gives rise to two tiers of four cells each, of which the outer tier, i.e. the one next to the suspensor, produces the foot, and the inner tier produces the stem on one side and the leaf on the other side. The root develops later from the inner tier close to the leaf, and then the foot becomes disorganized (FIG. 154*E*).

Alternation of Generations. *Lycopodium* passes through two generations to complete its life cycle. The main plant is the sporophyte (diploid or 2*n*). It bears one kind of spore (homosporous) and reproduces asexually through these spores to give rise to the next generation, i.e. the gametophyte (haploid or *n*). On germination, each spore of the sporophyte produces a minute body—the prothallus, which is the gametophyte. It bears sex organs and reproduces sexually to give rise to the sporophyte again. These two generations (the sporophyte including all the stages from the oospore to the spore mother cells, and the gametophyte including all the stages from the spores to the gametes) regularly alternate with each other.

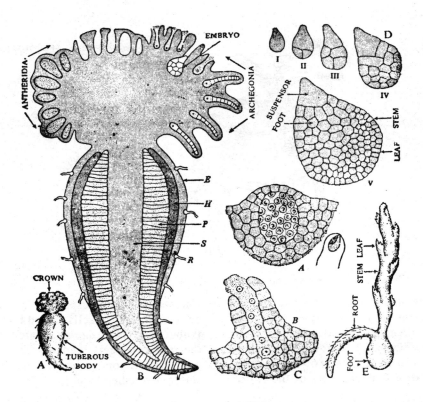

Lycopodium. FIG. 154 *A*, gametophyte; *B*, the same in longitudinal section *E*, epidermis, *H*, hyphal tissue; *P*, palisade tissue; *S*, storage tissue; and *R*, rhizoid; *C*, reproductive organs—(a),a mature antheridium with many antherozoid mother cells; an antherozoid on the right; (b), a mature archegonium (open); *D*, stages in the development of the embryo (I-V); *E*, a young sporophyte (developing on the gametophyte). *Redrawn after* FIG. 182 and FIG. 186 in Plant Morophology by *A. W. Haupt by permission of McGraw-Hill Book Company. Copyright* 1953

3. *SELAGINELLA* (700 *sp.*)

General description. *Selaginella* (family *Selaginellaceae*; FIG. 155) grows in damp places in the hills and plains. There are about 66 species in India, some common ones being *S. caulescens* and *S. kraussiana* (commonly planted in gardens), and *S. repanda* and *S. subdiaphana* (small and slender), *S. willdenovii* (very long and creeping). In habit, *Selaginella* may be prostrate, sub-erect, erect or rarely climbing; *S. lepidophylla* is xerophytic in habit (see p. 327). *Selaginella* plants are usually slender, much-branched and creep on wall or the ground. The slender stem bears four rows of leaves—two rows of small leaves on the upper surface and two rows of larger leaves at the two sides. A scaly structure, called **ligule** (FIG. 157),

develops on the upper (ventral) surface of each leaf, above its base. A long, slender, root-like organ is given off from the undersurface of the stem at the point of branching. This is known as the **rhizophore** (root-bearer). In some species, the rhizophore bears small, fibrous roots at the tip. The rhizophore resembles a true root in its internal structure, having a single protostele, bearing no leaves and being positively geotrophic. It resembles a stem, having no root-cap or root-hairs, and growing exogenously. It may be regarded as a leafless shoot that behaves like a root in some respects. It is often seen to bear some scaly leaves and even cones.

Internal Structure of the Stem. (FIG. 156). The epidermis is a single layer with a cuticle. There

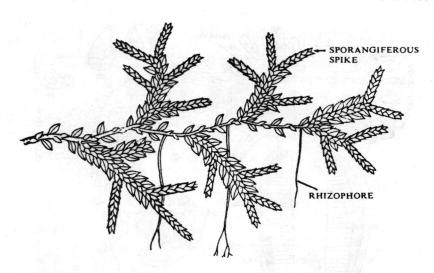

Selaginella. FIG. 155. A portion of a plant showing four rows of leaves, a number of spikes and three rhizophores

are a few layers of sclerenchyma below the epidermis. **The Ground tissue**—is a continuous mass of thin-walled, polygonal cells. There are usually 2 or 3 steles, each surrounded by an air space which is formed as a result of the breaking-down of some of the inner layers of the cortex.

The steles remain suspended in the air space by delicate strands of cells, called **trabeculae** (sing. **trabecula**). Casparian strips are often present in the trabecular cells and appear as dots or thin walls. When young, the stele is surrounded by a single-layered endodermis. Later on, the cells of

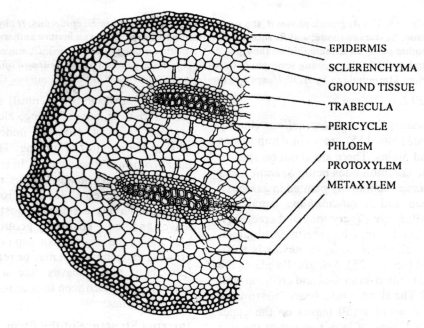

FIG. 156. *Selaginella* stem in transection

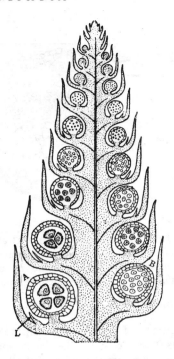

Selaginella. FIG. 157. A spike in longi-section;
A, megasporophyll with megasporangium and
B, microsporophyll with microsporangium and
microspores; L, ligule

the endodermis separate laterally and elongate considerably in the radial direction. These long radiating cells, formed as a result of stretching of the endodermal cells, are the trabeculae. In the mature stele, they act as bridges across the air space. Each stele, which is concentric in nature, consists of (*a*) pericycle, (*b*) phloem, and (*c*)xylem. Internal to the air space is a layer (sometimes two) of rather large but thin-walled cells—the pericycle. Phloem surrounds the central spindle-shaped xylem. Protoxylem lies at the two ends and metaxylem in the middle.

LIFE CYCLE. The life cycle of *Selaginella* is completed in two stages—sporophytic and gametophytic—the former much more complicated and the latter far simpler than in other pteridophytes. The *Selaginella* plant is the sporophyte and this is followed by another *two* structures, called prothalli, which are the gametophytes (male and female).

Sporophyte. The *Selaginella* plant is het-erosporous bearing *two* kinds of spores—microspores and megaspores—and reproduces asexually through them.

Sporophylls, Sporangia and Spores. *Selaginella* bears two kinds of sporophylls—**microsporophylls** and **megasporophylls**. These may occur together in the same cone, or may be borne in two separate cones, either on the same plant (monoecious) or on two separate plants (dioecious). All the sporophylls are nearly of equal size and spirally arranged, usually in four rows, round the apex of the reproductive shoot, in the form of a more or less distinct four-angled *cone* called the **sporangiferous spike** (FIGS. 155 & 157) or **strobilus**. The sporophylls are similar to the vegetative leaves in appearance, but are smaller. Each megasporophyll bears in its axil a single megasporangium with usually 16 megaspore mother cells. Only one of them divides, while the others become disorganized. The surviving cell undergoes reduction division and forms a tetrad of spores (FIG. 158A). Thus, the megasporangium contains *four large* megaspores. A considerable amount of food material, chiefly oil, is stored up in the megaspore. Like the megasporophyll, the microsporophyll bears in its axil a microsporangium with usually 16 microspore mother cells. All these undergo reduction division and give rise to 64 *small* microspores (FIG. 161) in groups of four (tetrads). *Selaginella* is thus **heterosporous**. The sporangia consist of a short, stout stalk and a capsule. The wall of the capsule is composed of three layers of cells. The megasporangia are some-what larger than the microsporangia. It should be noted that heterospory in *Selaginella* is an important step in the evolution of the 'seed' in higher plants, i.e. gymnosperms and angiospoerms (see Part VI, Chapter I).

Gametophytes. The two kinds of spores (micro and mega) germinate within their spore-coat and give rise to male and female prothalli, respectively. The prothalli are the gametophytes, i.e. they bear male gametes or antherozoids, and the female gamete or egg-cell, and reproduce sexually through the fusion of these two differentiated gametes (antherozoid and egg-cell).

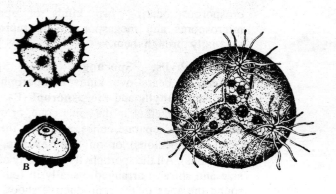
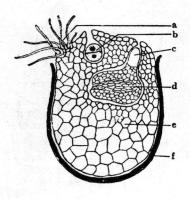

FIG. 158   FIG. 159   FIG. 160

Selaginella. Megaspore and development of female prothallus. FIG. 158. *A*, megaspores in a tetrad;
B, a megaspore in section. FIG. 159. Germinating megaspore with female prothallus protruding through
the triradiate fissure of the wall. FIG. 160. Female prothallus in longitudinal section: *a*, rhizoids; *b*, oospore
after first division; *c*, suspensor; *d*, embryo; *e*, tissue of the prothallus; and *f*, wall of the megaspore

Germination of the Megaspore: Female Prothallus (FIGS. 159-60). The megaspore-nucleus undergoes repeated free divisions, producing a number of free nuclei within the megaspore. Then walls appear around them and a cellular mass of tissue is thus formed. This is the female prothallus, i.e. the female gemetophyte. *The megaspore begins to grow before it is set free from the megasporangium*, but the formation of the female gametophyte is completed after the spore has fallen to the ground. At an early stage of gametophyte formation, a cavity appears at one end of it and is filled with reserved food, chiefly oil. This cavity subsequently becomes filled with cells. Further development of the gametophyte exerts pressure on the spore-wall which ruptures by a triradiate fissure, and the gametophyte become partially exposed (FIGS. 159-60). *The gametophyte is partially endosporous. It is a much reduced structure* compared to that of fern and allied plants. It is also *not an independent structure* like that of fern and allied plants, being enclosed by the spore-coat and nourished by the food stored in the spore. A number of **archegonia** and some groups of rhizoids develop in the exposed green portion of the prothallus. The inner, larger, non-green portion acts as a food reservoir. Each archegonium is also very small, consisting of a short neck with one neck canal cell, and a venter with an egg-cell and a ventral canal cell.

Germination of the Microspore: Male Prothallus (FIGS. 162-63). The microspore germinates and gives rise to the male prothallus, i.e. the male gametophyte. It begins to divide after it is set free from the microsporangium. A small cell is cut off at one end of the microspore. This is the **prothallus cell**, representing an extremely reduced male gametophyte. The rest of the microspore forms a single **antheridial cell**, which by a series of divisions, forms a small mass of cells. These are differentiated into a layer of peripheral sterile cells—the **jacket cells**, enclosing about 128 or 256 **antherozoid mother cells**. Each mother cell encloses a single biciliate slightly twisted **antherozoid**, or male gamete (FIG. 164).

Fertilization. After fertilization, which is essentially the same as in fern and allied plants, the egg-cell becomes the **oospore**; this divides and forms the **embryo** which gradually develops into the *Selaginella* plant. Thus the life-cycle is completed.

Alternation of Generations (FIG. 165) of *Selaginella* passes through two generations which regularly alternate with each other. The plant itself is the sporophyte, and the two prothalli—male and female—are the gametophytes. The sporophyte reproduces asexually through two kinds of

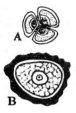

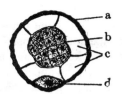

FIG. 161.　　　　　　FIG. 162.　　　　　　FIG. 163.　　　　　　FIG. 164.

Selaginella. Microspore and development of male prothallus. FIG. 161. *A*, microspores in a tetrad; *B*, a microspore in section. FIG. 162. Germinating microspore with prothallus cell. FIG. 163. Male prothallus in section: *a*, wall of microspore; *b*, antherozoid mother cells; *c*, jacket cells; and *d*, prothallus cell. FIG.164. Two antherozoids

spores—microspores and megaspores—which give rise to the male prothallus and the female prothallus, respectively. The male prothallus bears antherozoids in the antheridium, and the female prothallus bears an egg-cell in the archegonium. The two prothalli (gametophytes) reproduce sexually by means of these two gametes, giving rise to the sporophyte again. The two gametes fuse together and give rise to the oospore. The oospore is the beginning of the sporophytic generation, having 2*n* chromosomes. All the stages from the oospore to the spore mother cells represent the sporophytic generation. Reduction division takes place in the formation of the spores, so all the stages from the spores (micro and mega) to the gametes (antherozoid and egg-cell) with *n* chromosomes represent the gametophytic generation.

4. *ISOETES* (75 *sp.*)

General description. *Isoetes* (FIG. 166A), commonly called quillwort, is the only genus of the family *Isoetaceae*. Species of this genus are mostly confined to temperate regions. There are about 6 species of *Isoetes* in India, of which *Isoetes coromandeliana* is fairly common. *Isoetes* usually grows at the edge of tanks, ditches, streams or in shallow pools of water, partly or completely submerged, and looks like a tuft of grass. The activity of the apical meristematic cells causes growth in the length of the stem.

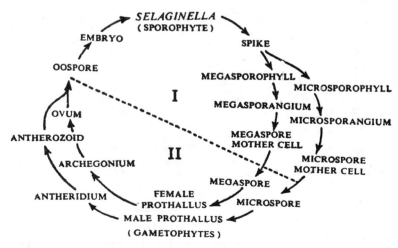

FIG. 165. Life cycle of *Selaginella* (diagrammatic) showing alternation of generations. *I*, sporophytic generation (diploid or 2*n*) and *II*, gametophytic generation (haploid or *n*)

Sporophyte. The *Isoetes* plant (FIG. 166A) is the sporophyte, bearing two kinds of sporangia and spores (micro and mega) on the same plant, i.e. it is heterosporous and monoecious. It consists of a short, 2- or 3- lobed corm-like stem, and a rosette of linear leaves arising from the upper surface. Many slender, often dichotomously branched roots develop from the lower sides. Each leaf has a persistent ligule (FIG. 166B), as in *Selaginella*, and internally, there are some longitudinal air chambers (FIG. 168). The base of the leaf is spoon-shaped and swollen owing to the development of a large sporangium on its concave inner surface, just below the ligule (FIG. 166B). Most of the leaves except the central ones are potential sporophylls, the outer ones bearing megasporangia (FIG. 167A) and the inner ones microsporangia (FIG. 167B-C). Each sporangium is wholly or partially covered over by a membranous flap known as the **velum**, which arises below the ligule (FIGS. 166B & 167)

and grows downwards. The sporangium (micro or mega) is traversed by strands of cells called the **trabeculae** (FIG. 167), which may be complete or incomplete. The two kinds of sporangia cannot be distinguished from each other when young. When mature, the microsporangium produces very minute microspores (150,000-1,000,000). The megasporangium produces only a limited number of large megaspores (50-300). The have a variety of shapes. Both microspores and megaspores are formed in tetrads, as usual.

Gametophytes. The spores are liberated after the decay of the sporangium wall. The micro-spore gives rise to the male gametophyte, and the megaspore to the female gametophyte. The **male gametophyte** (FIG. 169A-D) remains enclosed within the microspore coat, as in *Selaginella*, and consists of (*a*) a prothallus cell, (*b*) an antheridium of four antherozoid mother cells, and (*c*) a sterile jacket of

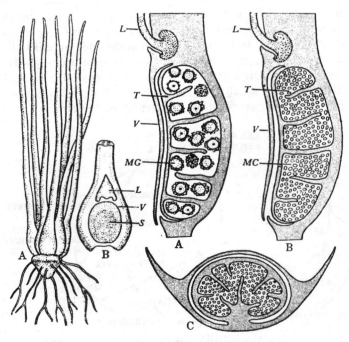

FIG. 166.   FIG. 167.

Isoetes. FIG. 166. *A*, a plant; *B*, leaf base (inner side). FIG. 167. *A*,megasporangium in longi-section with megaspores; *B*, microsporangium in longi-section with microspores; *C*, microsporangium in transection. *L*, ligule; *V*, velum; *S*, sporangium; *T*, trabecula; *MG*, megaspore; *MC*, microspores

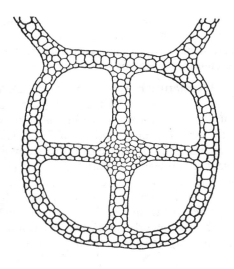

Isoetes. FIG. 168. Leaf in transection

four cells. Each antherozoid mother cell gives rise to a single, large, coiled, multiciliate antherozoid (FIG. 169E). Thus altogether four antherozoids are produced by each male gametophyte, the lowest among all pteridophytes. The wall of the microspore bursts and the antherozoids are liberated. The **female gametophyte** (FIG. 170A) develops inside the megaspore and does not protrude but, as in *Selaginella*, a triradiate fissure is formed in the megaspore wall, exposing the rhizoids and

the archegonia. The latter vary in number from one to many. The megaspore nucleus lying at one end begins to divide repeatedly and gradually, the whole female gametophyte becomes cellular. This is the female prothallus. Archegonia develop in that region of the prothallus that was formed first (that is if the previous one is not fertilized). The archegonium (FIG. 170B) consists of (a) a neck with 3 or 4 tiers of cells, (b) a neck canal cell (sometimes binucleate), (c) a venter with a ventral canal cell, and (d) a conspicuous egg.

Embryo. The fertilized egg (oospore) divides transversely. After further repeated divisions, the lower cell gives rise to a massive foot. The upper cell divides vertically. One of the two cells thus formed gives rise to the first leaf (cotyledon), and the other cell to the root. The stem arises later.

5. *EQUISETUM* (25 *sp.*)

General description. Equiesetum (FIG. 171), commonly called horsetail, is the only genus of the family *Equisetaceae*. It is a much-branched herb, often not exceeding a metre in height. It is widely distributed, especially in cool and temperate regions, and is usually abundant in marshy places or by the sides of springs and stream in the hills. Common Indian species are *E. arvense*, *E. ramosissimum* and *E. debile*. The last one, common in

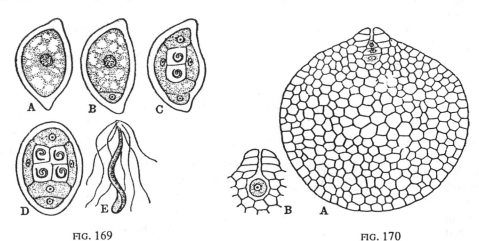

FIG. 169   FIG. 170

Isoetes. FIG. 169. *A-D*, male gametophyte in stages of development; *E*, an antherozoid. FIG. 170. *A*, female gametophyte; *B*, an archegonium. *Redrawn after figs 203 & 204 in* Plant Morphology *by A. W. Haupt by permission of McGraw-Hill Book Company*

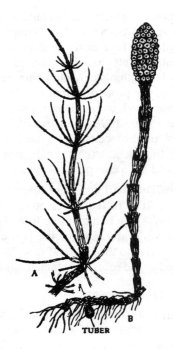

Equisetum. FIG. 171. *A,* A vegetative shoot with whorls of branches; *B,* a fertile shoot with a spike

Assam, grows to a height of 3-4 m. It may be noted that an American species, *E. giganteum*, climbs neighbouring trees and grows to a length of about 12 m. *Equisetum* consists of a long, slender, horizontal underground rhizome, giving rise at intervals to erect, aerial shoots. The rhizome often develops short, tuber-like bodies which serve as reservoirs of food material. The outline of the stem is wavy, with ridges and furrows which alternate at the next node. Each aerial shoot is simple or branched, distinctly articulated (jointed) and provided with nodes and internodes. The branched shoots are usually sterile and vegetative in function, while the unbranched shoots are fertile and short-lived. They soon dry up after the production of spores. In some species, however, the branched shoots are fertile. The leaves are minute and scaly, and form a whorl at each node. These leaves are free and pointed at the tips, but united below to form a sheath round the base of the internode. The lateral branches alternate with these leaves and grow upwards, piercing the sheath. As a result of

the reduction of the leaf laminae, the branches become green and perform photosynthesis. The roots are slender, adventitious and much-branched, developing from each node of the rhizome.

Internal Structure of the Stem. (FIG. 172). The stem has distinct nodes and internodes, with longitudinal ridges and furrows. The internal structure is as follows: (1) **Epidermis**—This is a single outer layer of cells with a deposit of silica in their outer and lateral walls. Its outline is wavy and its furrow has stomata in two rows. (2) **Sclerenchyma**—The sclerenchyma, specially the ridges, develops below the epidermis, interrupted in the furrows by the underlying cortex. (3) **Cortex**—This is many-layered and large air canals (*vallecular canals*), each corresponding to a groove, are formed in its middle. The outer layers of the cortex contain chloroplasts. The leaves being scaly, carbon assimilation is performed by the cortex (chlorenchyma) of the stem. The assimilating tissue extends up to the epidermis in the furrow, where the stomata lie. (4) **Endodermis**— This is the innermost layer of the cortex, often with a distinct Casparian strip in it. (5) **Pericycle**—This lies internal to the endodermis as a single layer. (6) **Vascular bundles**— These are closed, collateral, and arranged in a ring, each opposite to a ridge. Each bundle is made of xylem and phloem, with some parenchyma. There is a water-containing cavity in it, called the *carinal cavity*, which has been formed lysigenously by the breaking down of some of the protoxylem elements (cf. maize stem). The **xylem** occurs in separate strands—the *protoxylem* (made of annular and spiral tracheids), lying in isolated strands against the carinal cavity, and the *metaxylem* (usually made of scalariform and reticulate tracheids), lying in two strands laterally outwards. The **phloem** lies between the two metaxylem strands and consists of sieve-tubes and phloem parenchyma. (7) **Pith**—This lies on the inner side of the bundles, but a major portion of it forms a large central cavity (pith cavity).

LIFE CYCLE. The life cycle of *Equisetum* is completed in two stages—sporophytic and gametophytic. The plant itself is the sporophyte (FIG.

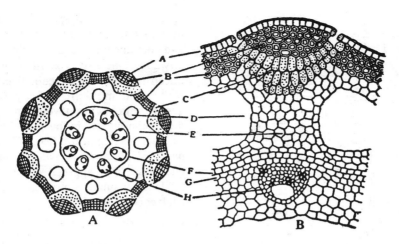

Equisetum. FIG. 172. A, section of stem (diagrammatic); B, a portion of the section (magnified).
A, epidermis; B, hypodermis (sclerenchyma); C, outer cortex with chloroplasts (note the stomata);
D, air cavities; E, general cortex; F, endodermis; G, pericycle; H, vascular bundle
(see text; note the pith and the pith cavity)

171), which is followed by another independent structure called the prothallus (FIG.174), which is the gametophyte.

Sporophyte. The *Equisetum* plant (FIG. 171) is the sporophyte, i.e. it reproduces asexually by spores which are borne by specialized leaves called sporophylls.

Sporophylls, Sporangia and Spores. The structure of the sporophylls is greatly specialized. They take the form of somewhat flattened, hexagonal or circular discs, each supported by a short stalk. They are aggregated together in whorls at the apex of a usually unbranched, non-green, aerial shoot in the form of a *cone*, called the **sporangiferous spike** or **strobilus** (FIGS. 171B & 173A). The lowest whorl is sterile and forms a **ring** at the base of the spike. In *Equisetum*, as in all higher plants, the reproductive region is quite distinct from the vegetative region. Each sporophyll (FIG. 173B) has the form of a stalked peltate disc. Its undersurface bears a group of **sporangia** (5-10) which contain numerous small **spores**. *Equisetum* is homosporous, bearing only one kind of spore. Each spore is green, contains many minute chloroplasts, and has a large central nucleus. In addition to intine and exine, the spore has a third layer called the **perinium**, which, when mature, ruptures into

two spirally wound bands, called **elaters** (FIG. 173-D-E). These are attached to the centre of the spores at their centre; and appear as four distinct appendages. They are extremely hygroscopic; when the air is dry, they unwind and stand out stiffly from the spore and when the air is moist, they roll up spirally round it. *Functions of Elaters*. The elaters expand and help in the dehiscence of the sporangium. The spores become entangled by the elaters and are carried away in clusters by air currents. This helps the spores germinate close together, facilitating fertilization.

Gametophyte. The prothallus (FIG. 174A) is the gametophyte, i.e. it bears gametes—male (antherozoid) and female (ovum), and reproduces sexually. The spores remain alive only for a few days. Under favourable conditions, their germination begins within 10 or 12 hours of liberation from the sporangium. The spores can be easily grown in culture in the laboratory. On germination, they give rise to prothalli which are small, dull brownish-green and much-branched (lobed). The prothalli in most species are usually 3-6 mm. in diameter. In *E. debile*, however, they may be as big as 3 cm. in diameter. When growing under favourable conditions, the prothalli are normally monoecious, bearing both antheridia and

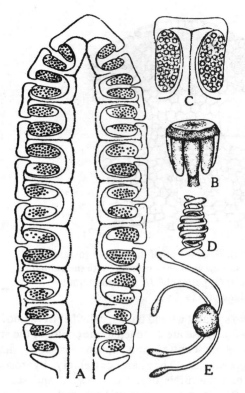

Equisetum. FIG. 173. *A*, a spike in longi-section showing sporophylls, each with sporangia, spores, stalk (sporangiophore) and peltate disc; *B*, a sporophyll with a whorl of sporangia; *C*, the same in longi-section; *D*, a spore with elaters coiled; and *E*, the same with elaters uncoiled

archegonia. If, however, they grow crowded together in the field or in culture, they are dioecious, the smaller ones being male and the bigger ones female. It has been seen that the latter bear antheridia as they age. This imperfect dioecism may be due to unfavourable conditions of growth. In *E. arvense*, however, about half the spores give rise to male prothalli and the remaining half to female prothalli. If no fertilization takes place, the latter may produce antheridia. The prothalli usually live long, sometimes more than two years. The prothallus is the **gametophyte**, bearing antheridia or archegonia, or normally both. The sexual organs begin to appear in the gametophyte within 30-40 days of growth, the archegonia first and antheridia later. The **antheridia** develop at the apex of a branch (lobe) of the prothallus, or on its margin. Each antheridium is more or less spherical and contains many antherozoid mother cells (usually 256). One **antherozoid** or male gamete is produced in each mother cell. It is a large, spirally coiled and multiciliate body (FIG. 174*B*). The **archegonia** always develop in the axial region of the prothallus and in the axil of one of its branches. Each **archegonium** (FIG.174*C*) is flask-shaped, has a swollen venter and a narrow neck, and encloses a large **egg-cell** with a distinct **egg** (egg-nucleus), a small ventral canal cell and a narrow neck canal cell.

Fertilization. The method of fertilization is the same as that of ferns. After fertilization, the **oospore** gives rise to an **embryo** which develops into a branching rhizome. This then produces erect, aerial shoots and several adventitious roots.

Alternation of Generations (FIG. 175). There is a regular alternation of generations in the life cycle of the *Equisetum* plant. The plant itself is the sporophyte, and the prothallus—monoecious or dioecious—is the gametophyte. As in fern, the sporophyte reproduces asexually by means of spores and gives rise to the gametophyte or prothallus. The prothallus reproduces sexually by means of gametes—anotherozoid and ovum—and gives rise to the sporophyte. Thus, the two generations regularly alternate with each other. The sporophytic generation in which the number of chromosomes is $2n$, begins with the oospore and ends in the spore mother cells. The gametophytic generation, in which the number of chromosomes is n, begins with the spores and ends in the gametes (antherozoid and ovum).

6. *FERN*

Ferns (FIGS. 176-7) are a group of highly developed cryptogams and are widely distributed all over the world. They are shade and moisture loving plants and, therefore, grow abundantly in cool, shady and moist places, both in the hills and plains. Ferns are mostly perennial herbs, with the stem often in the form of a rhizome, by which they usually reproduce vegetatively. In **tree ferns** (e.g. *Cyathea*, *Alsophila*, *Dicksonia*, etc.). however,

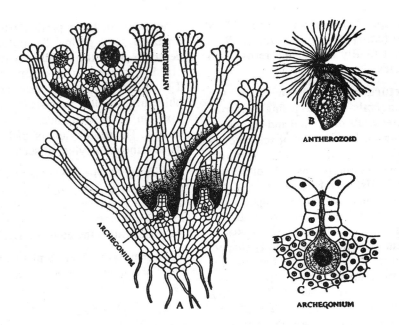

Equisetum. FIG. 174. *A*, prothallus (monoecious); *B*, an antherozoid; *C*, a mature archegonium

the stem is stout, erect and aerial. The roots are adventitious (fibrous) and usually grow in clusters from the rhizome. The leaves are mostly pinnately compound and consist of two parts: the frond (leafy portion) and the stipe (stalk). Young fronds are **circinate**, i.e. coiled inwards on the upper surface (FIG. 177), and are characterized by great apical growth. The lateral leaflets, borne by the axis or rachis, are known as the pinnae (sing. pinna). Sometimes these are more or less deeply pinnately lobed, and then each lobe is known as the pinnule. The stem and the petiole are covered with many brownish scales, known as the **ramenta**. There are about 7,600 species of ferns. Some of the common genera are *Asplenium* (650 sp), *Pteris* (250 sp.), *Adantum* (200 sp.), *Dryopteris* (150 sp.), and

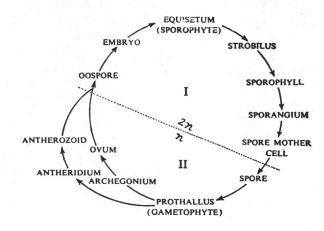

FIG. 175. Life cycle of *Equisetum* (diagrammatic) showing alternation of generations. *I*, sporophytic generation (diploid or 2*n*); and *II*, gametophytic generation (haploid or *n*)

Polypodium (75 sp.), *Nephrolepis* (30 sp.). They all belong to the family *Polypodiaceae*, which is by far the biggest family among the ferns, with about 3,000 species.

Internal Structure of the Fern Stem (or Petiole). (1) **Epidermis**—This is a single layer of cells with the outer walls thickened and cutinized. (2) **Sclerenchyma**—A few layers of sclerenchyma occur below the epidermis. (3) **Ground tissue**—This is a continuous mass of polygonal, parenchymatous cells. (4) **Endodermis**—This is a single layer of narrow, barrel-shaped cells surrounding each stele. This layer is often thickened, particularly on the inner side. (5) **Steles**—In the young stem or petiole, the stele is shaped more or less like a horse-shoe, but in the older part, it is broken up into usually two or three smaller steles. Each stele consists of (*a*) **pericycle**, (*b*) **phloem** and (*c*) **xylem**. The pericycle surrounds the stele as a single layer (some-

times a double layer, particularly at the sides) and contains starch grains. The phloem surrounds the central xylem, the bundle being concentric, and consists of sieve tubes and phloem parenchyma. The xylem lies in the centre, surrounded by the phloem. It usually consists of two groups of protoxylem at the two ends, and metaxylem in the middle. The protoxylem is made of spiral tracheids, and the metaxylem of scalariform tracheids.

Life cycle. The life cycle of a fern is completed in two stages—sporophytic and gametophytic. The fern plant is the sporophyte, which is followed by another small, green, flat structure called the prothallus—the gametophyte (FIG. 181).

Sporophyte. The fern plant, as stated above, is the sporophyte, i.e. it bears spores and reproduces by the asexual method.

Sporangia and Spores. On the undersurface of the fertile frond, i.e. the spore-bearing leaf or

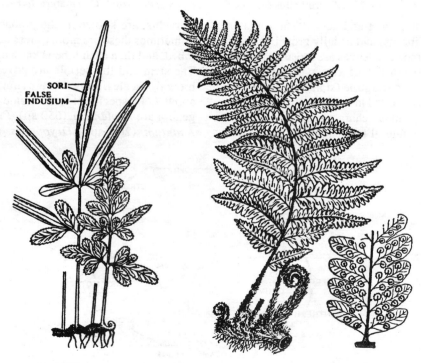

FIG. 176

FIG. 177

Fern Plants. FIG. 176. *Pteris* with continuous, linear sori and false indusium.
FIG. 177. *Dryopteris* with sori on veins of the pinna and reniform indusium

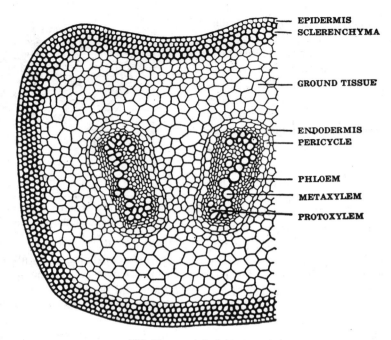

FIG. 178. Fern petiole in transection

sporophyll (as it is called), a number of dark brown structures, pale green when young, may be seen. These are called **sori** (sing. sorus). In *Dryopteris* (and also in *Polystichum*, *Nephrodium*, etc.), the sori develop on the veins on the undersurface of the sporophyll, and are arranged in two rows in each leaflet or pinna (FIG. 177). Each sorus (FIG. 179) consists of several **sporangia** which are covered over and protected by a reniform (i.e. kidney-shaped) or rounded shield, called **indusium**. The sporoangia and the indusium develop from a papilla-like outgrowth or **placenta** of the leaf.

In *Pteris* (FIG. 176), the sori are marginal, linear and continuous. There is a thin, membranous, scaly indusium on the inner side of the sori. However, the reflexed margin of the pinna forms a continuous, overlapping indusium, called the *false indusium*, which covers the sori. The indusium may be of

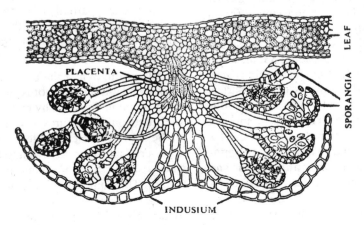

Fern. FIG. 179. Sorus in section

other types. For example, in *Adiantum*, the sori are distinct and separate on the margin of the pinna, usually in rounded groups, each covered by a *false indusium*. In *Cyathium* the indusium is cupshaped, while it is curved or shaped like a horseshoe in *Asplenium*. There are other types too. The indusium may also be absent, as in *Polypodium* and *Gleichenia*. The indusium is, in fact, an important feature often used in the classification of ferns.

Each **sporangium** (FIG. 180) consists of a long, slender, multicellular **stalk** and a **capsule** which is biconvex. Inside the capsule lies a mass of very small grains—the **spores**. The capsule initially contains 16 spore mother cells. These undergo reduction division into 32 daughter cells, which then divide mitotically, forming 64 spores. The wall of the capsule consists of a single layer of thin-walled cells, with a specially thickened and cutinized band or ring running round the margin of the capsule. This ring, which is incomplete and thin walled on one side, is called the **annulus**, and its unthickened portion the **stomium**. When the spores mature, they grow in size, and under dry conditions the capsule bursts at the stomium, liberating the spores. When the capsule bursts, the annulus bends back, exposing the spores, then suddenly returns to its original position, thus ejecting the spores with a jerk. The fern plant is **homosporous**.

Gametophyte. The prothallus (FIG. 181) is the gametophyte. The spore germinates under favourable conditions of temperature and moisture. At first, it gives rise to a short, green filament (germ tube) resembling an alga or moss protonema. By further division of cells later, it produces a small, green, flat, heart-shaped body, about 8 mm. wide. This is known as the **prothallus**. Its margin is very thin and single-layered, while its central part is comparatively thick and many-layered. Unicellular, hairy processes, called **rhizoids**, come out from the undersurface of the prothallus. These fix the prothallus to the soil and absorb water and mineral salts. Highly specialized **antheridia** and **archegonia** are produced on the undersurface of the prothallus for reproduction. The former develop amongst the rhizoids and the latter near the groove.

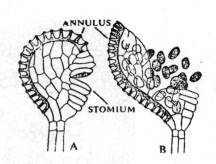

Fern. FIG. 180. Sporangia (capsule and stalk); *A*, capsule just opening at the stomium; *B*, capsule has burst with the annulus bending back

The **antheridium** (FIG. 182*A-B*) is a spherical or oval body consisting of a wall or jacket, with 1 or 2 caps or cover cells at the apex and a number of antherozoid mother cells (20-50). Each mother cell develops a single antherozoid or male gamete, which consists mostly of nuclear material. The antherozoid is comparatively large, spirally coiled and multiciliate (FIG. 182*C*).

The **archegonium** (FIG. 183) is a flask-shaped body. The swollen basal portion is known as the **venter**, and the slender tube-like upper portion as the **neck**. The venter encloses a single large **egg-cell** with an egg (egg-nucleus), and slightly higher up, a small ventral canal cell. The neck consists of a narrow neck canal, cell which is usually binucleate, and a wall made of four vertical rows of cells. The neck is short and curved. The venter lies embedded, partially or completely, in the prothallus. Before fertilization, the ventral canal cell and the neck canal cell disintegrate into mucilage, which forces open the mouth of the archegonium.

Fertilization. When the antheridium matures, it bursts and the antherozoids are liberated. They swim about in the water by means of their cilia. As the archegonium matures, it secretes mucilage and malic acid. Attracted by these substances, a large number of antherozoids swim to the archegonium, enter it through the neck and pass down into the venter. They quickly vibrate around the egg-cell and one of them soon fuses with the egg-nucleus. After this fusion (fertilization), the rest of the antherozoids die out. The fertilized ovum clothes

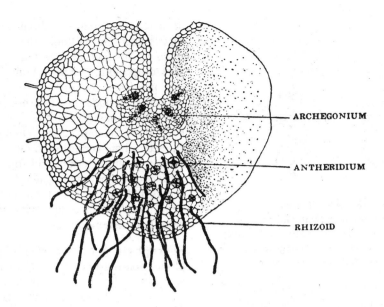

FIG. 181. Prothallus of fern

itself with a cell wall and becomes the **oospore**. The oospore divides and gives rise to an **embryo**. The embryo grows into a young sporophyte (with a green leaf and a root), still attached to the prothallus (FIG. 184). As the root penetrates the soil and the prothallus decays the young sporophyte develops into an independent fern plant.

Alternation of Generations. (FIG. 185). The fern plant passes through two stages or generations. The plant itself is the sporophyte, and the prothallus the gametophyte. The sporophyte reproduces asexually by means of spores and gives rise to the gametophyte or the prothallus. The latter reproduces sexually by means of gametes (antherozoid and ovum) and gives rise to the sporophyte or the fern plant. Thus, the generations regularly alternate with each other. In the life-history of the fern plant $2n$ chromosomes occur for the first time in the oospore. Therefore, this is the beginning of the sporophytic generation, which includes all the stages from the oospore to the spore mother cells. The reduction of chromosomes to n takes place during the formation of spores from the spore mother cells. Therefore, the spore represents the beginning of the gametophytic generation, which

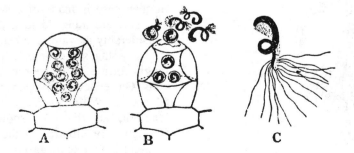

Fern. FIG. 182. Antheridium. A, a young one with antherozoid mother cells; B, a mature one after bursting; and C, an antherozoid

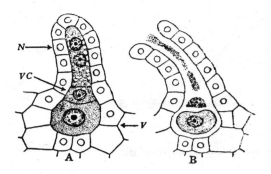

Fern. FIG. 183. Archegonia.
A, a young one; *N*, neck (wall and neck
canal cell with two nuclei); *VC*, ventral canal cell;
V, venter with an egg-cell and an egg-nucleus;
B, a mature one ready for fertilization

includes all the stages from the spores to the gametes (antherozoid and ovum). The sporophyte (fern plant) has already reached a high degree of development and complexity, and with the formation of roots and green leaves with chloroplasts, has become independent of the gametophyte. As a matter of fact, the sporophyte of fern is the all-important body, while the gametophyte is very insignificant.

7. *MARSILEA* (60 *sp.*)

Marsilea (family *Marsileaceae*; FIG. 186) is a slender, prostrate herb, growing roots in the mud

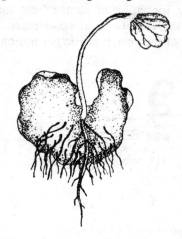

FIG. 184. Prothallus of fern with young sporophyte

at the edges of tanks or ditches. It is very widely distributed throughout the world. *Marsilea quadrifolia* and *M. minuta* are two common species in India. The plant body consists of a slender, prostrate, dichotomously branched rhizome with distinct nodes and internodes. It usually roots at the nodes and gives off leaves alternately in two rows along the upper side. When young, the leaves show circinate vernation. A mature leaf consists of a long or short petiole and four obovate leaflets arranged in a peltate manner. Each leaflet (pinna) shows dichotomous venation connected by smaller veins. Growth of the stem is due to an apical, tetrahedral, meristematic cell.

Sporophyte. The *Marisilea* plant is the sporophyte, bearing two kinds of spores, i.e. it is heterosporous. Special structures, called **sporocarps**, grow in small groups of 2-5, sometimes singly, from the base of the petiole or a little above it as a segment of it (interpreted as modified fertile leaf-segment or entire leaf). Sporocarps develop only when the water recedes and the soil tends to dry up. A mature sporocarp has a long or short stalk and has a very hard outer covering. It is more or less bean-shaped (FIGS. 186-7) and is about 8 × 6 mm. in size. Each half of the sporocarp has distinct forked venation, alternating with that of the other half. The sporocarp (FIG. 187*B*) usually contains 14-20 sori, each in a cavity, arranged in two rows on a receptacle. The sori develop in basipetal order. Each sorus is covered by a thin, delicate layer—the **indusium**. The sporangia at the apex of the receptacle are megasporangia and those lower down are microsporangia. The sporangium wall in each case is made of a single layer of cells. The sori are attached to a tissue which swells considerably in water and becomes gelatinous. In the early stages of development both kinds of sporangia form 8 or 16 sporocytes or spore mother cells. On reduction division, these produce 32 or 64 spores. While in the case of the microsporangium, all the microspores are functional, (though very minute) in the case of megasporangium, only one megaspore grows larger and is functional. The others degenerate.

With the development of the sporangia, a stony

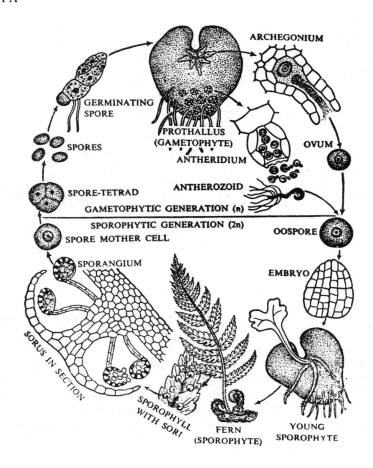

FIG. 185. Life cycle of fern showing alternation of generations

layer is formed on the outer surface of the sporocarp. The resisting power of the sporocarp and the longevity of the spores are remarkable. The spores have been seen to germinate even after many years of desiccation. If the sporocarp is cracked at the edge and kept in water for half an hour or so, it is seen that the gelatinized inner wall of the sporocarp pushes out of it in the form of a long, gelatinous ring (**sorophore**), with the sori attached to it in an alternating manner[1] (FIG. 187*C*). In nature, however, the decay of the sporocarp's stony layer takes at least 2 or 3 years. Thereafter, the spores are libeated on the conversion of the

indusium and the sporangium walls into mucilage. If the gelatinous ring is left in water, the development of the male and female gametophytes is seen to begin on the following day or the day after.

Gametophytes. The spores germinate very quickly, the microspore giving rise to the male gametophyte, and the megaspore to the female gametophyte. The development of the male gametophyte is complete within 12-20 hours, while the female gametophyte develops slightly slower.

The male gametophyte (FIG. 188*A-F*) is endosporous, developing within the microspore, as

---

[1]The sporocarp may be split open with a sharp scalpel into two valves, the contents gently scooped out and spread on a slide in water, covered with a cover-glass, and lightly tapped.

Marsilea. FIG. 186. A plant with sporocarps

in *Selaginella.* A cell cut off on one side is the pro-thallus cell, while the remaining cell of the game-tophyte divides into two halves. Each half is an antheridium. After further division, two primary spermatogenous cells are formed, surrounded by a jacket layer. Each cell then produces 16 anthero-zoid mother cells. Each mother cell is metamor-phosed into an antherozoid (FIG. 188G). The latter is much coiled, corkscrew-like and multiciliate,

with a mucilaginous vesicle containing some food.

The female gametophyte (FIG. 189B) consists of an archegonium protruding from the apex of the megaspore through its coat. The rest of the game-tophyte, which has no cellular differentiation, is a food reservoir. The archegonium consists of (a) a venter with a comparatively large egg and a small ventral canal cell, (b) a short neck with a neck canal cell, and (c) a sterile jacket of cells.

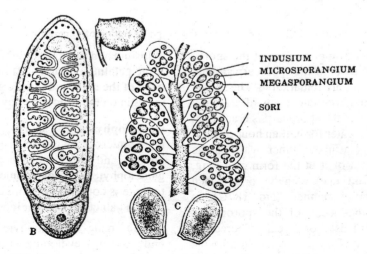

Marsilea. FIG. 187. A, a sporocarp; B, the same in longi-section showing young sori, in two rows, each sorus with megasporangium (terminal), microsporangia (lateral) and indusium (outer covering); C, part of the gelatinous ring carrying the sori; two empty valves of the sporocarp lying below

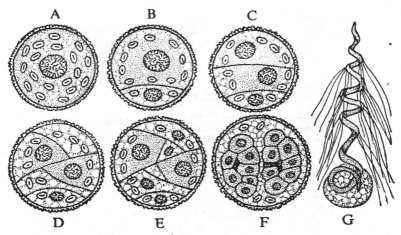

Marsilea. FIG. 188. *A-F*, development of the male gametophyte;
G, an antherozoid. *Redrawn after* Fig. 252 *in* Plant Morphology *by*
A. W. Haupt by permission of McGraw-Hill Book Company

Surrounding the female gametophyte is a broad, gelatinous envelope, which has a funnel-shaped portion that converges upon the archegonium.

Fertilization. Fertilization takes place almost immediately after the gametophytes are formed. Innumerable antherozoids swarm around the archegonium, many of them swim into the gelatinous envelope on the side of the archegonium and some pass down the neck. Finally, however, one antherozoid fuses with the egg-nucleus.

Embryo. The embryo is formed soon after fertil-ization. The oospore divides and redivides and the cells are arranged in four segments. The two segments (inner and outer) on one side give rise to the stem and the first leaf (cotyledon). The remaining two segments (inner and outer) on the other side give rise to the foot and the root. The adjoining cells of the gametophyte form a cap-like structure or calyptra around the developing embryo. The embryo grows rapidly by bursting the calyptra.

Internal Structure of Rhizome (*Marsilea*; FIG. 190). (1) **Epidermis**—This lies externally as

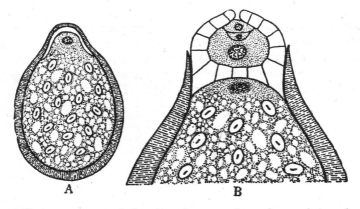

Marsilea. FIG. 189. *A*, a megaspore in longi-section; note the nucleus and several starch grains;
B, female gametophyte with an archegonium projecting out of the spore-coat; note the large
egg-cell with the egg-nucleus, ventral canal cell, neck canal cell and the sterile jacket

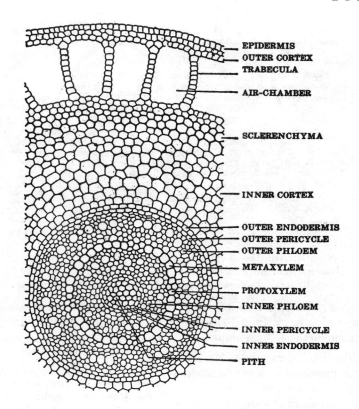

EPIDERMIS
OUTER CORTEX
TRABECULA

AIR-CHAMBER

SCLERENCHYMA

INNER CORTEX

OUTER ENDODERMIS
OUTER PERICYCLE
OUTER PHLOEM
METAXYLEM

PROTOXYLEM
INNER PHLOEM

INNER PERICYCLE
INNER ENDODERMIS
PITH

FIG. 190. Rhizome of *Marsilea* in transection (amphiphloic siphonostele)

a single layer. (2) **Cortex**—This usually consists of two layers of thin-walled parenchyma internal to the epidermis, a ring of fairly big air cavities traversed by trabeculae, usually 1 to 3 layers of thick-walled lignified cells, and internally several layers of thin-walled parenchyma containing starch grains. (3) **Stele**—This is an *amphiphloic siphonostele* with pith in the centre (see p. 478). It is bounded both externally and internally by phloem, pericycle and endodermis, which evidently occur twice. In the middle, xylem occurs as a ring with more or less distinct protoxylem and metaxylem. It consists of thick-walled tracheids surrounded externally by outer phloem, outer pericycle and outer endodermis. Internal to the xylem is the inner phloem, inner pericycle and inner endodermis in the reverse order. (4) **Pith**—This occupies the central portion and is parenchymatous or sclerenchymatous (growing in water or on dry mud).

6 GYMNOSPERMS

GENERAL DESCRIPTION

There are two subdivisions of **spermatophytes** ('seed' plants) or **phanerogams** ('flowering' plants)—angiosperms (*angeion*, case; *sperma*, seed) and **gymnosperms** (*gymnos*, naked). Gymnosperms are closely related to the higher cryptogams on the one hand, and to the angiosperms on the other. Thus, they form an intermediate group between the two. It should be noted that the lower gymnosperms like cycads have greater affinities with the higher cryptogams, while the higher gymnosperms—Coniferales and Gnetales—are closer to the angiosperms. The major similarities and differences are listed below. There are about 700 species of gymnosperms, of which a little over 50 occur in India.

GYMNOSPERMS AND HIGHER CRYPTOGAMS

Resemblances

(1) The general life history of both is identical with, of course, structural differences. Both groups show a regular alternation of generations, with gradual reduction and loss of independence of the gametophyte from the higher cryptogams to the gymnosperms, and a gradual increase in the complexity of the sporophyte.

(2) The plant body is clearly differentiated into root, stem and leaves.

(3) The leaves are of a compound nature and have circinate vernation, as in the earlier gymnosperms (cycads).

(4) The xylem of the vascular bundle has only tracheids (and no vessels, except in Gnetales) and phloem without companion cells.

(5) There occurs a gradual differentiation of the sporophylls (micro and mega) and of the spores—microspore and megaspore (heterosporous condition) in the higher cryptogams, leading to complete differentiation in the gymonosperms. The segregation of the sporophylls from the vegetative region and their arrangement in the form of cones (strobili) is another development.

(6) The gametophyte develop within the sporecoat as a dependent body (partially endosporous in *Selaginella* but completely endosporous in gymnosperms) for food supply and adequate protection by the sporophyte.

(7) Ciliate spermatozoids develop in the lower gymnosperms (cycads), as in cryptogams.

(8) The megaspore is retained within the megasporangium (permanently in gymnosperms but only for a short period in *Selaginella*) the archegonia develop in the female gametophyte.

(9) Formation of the suspensor in the gymnosperms during the stages of embryo development, as in *Selaginella*, is another similarity.

Differences

(1) Development of the ovule (and later the seed) in gymnosperms is a fundamental difference. The ovule and the seed are characteristic of all gymnosperms, while they are altogether absent in cryptogams.

(2) Formation of the pollen-tube in gymnosperms is another special feature which is conspicuously absent in cryptogams. The pollen-tube carries the non-motile male gametes to the

archegonium in most gymnosperms, while in all cryptogams, the motile spermatozoids swim by themselves to the archegonium in a drop of water. In *Cycas*, however, the pollen-tube is a sucking organ (haustorium) and not a sperm carrier.

(3) The megasporangium of the gymnosperm does not shed before fertilization and maturity; further, it is provided with a new structure in the form of a coat—the integument. The megasporangium covered by the integument is the ovule. The ovule is altogether absent in cryptogams.

(4) The megaspore of the gymnosperm remains permanently enclosed within the megasporangium. The female gametophyte is also completely endosporous (partially endosporous in *Selaginella*) and is consequently dependent on the mother sporophyte for nourishment. The embryo also remains enclosed within the megasporangium and is nourished by it.

(5) The gametophytes of gymnosperms are not green since they remain enclosed.

(6) The construction of the archegonia is much simpler in gymnosperms (shorter neck and no neck canal cells) unlike in cryptogams. Final reduction of the archegonia takes place in the higher gymnosperms, as in *Gnetum*—a feature closer to angiosperms.

(7) The presence of cambium leads to secondary growth in thickness in the gymnosperms, while its absence denies secondary growth to the cryptogams. Besides, tracheids with circular pits and those with sclariform markings are characteristic of gymnosperms and higher cryptogams, respectively.

GYMNOSPERMS AND ANGIOSPERMS

Resemblances

(1) The plant body is differentiated into a distinct root and shoot, the latter with many branches and leaves, however small they may be. In habit, the plants of both groups may be shrubs and trees. There are more herbs among angiosperms.

(2) The vascular system is well developed in both, with xylem and phloem (note, however, their differences described later).

(3) Both develop flowers for the purpose of reproduction. However, gymnospermic flowers are primitive and simple in construction, are always unisexual and have no perianth. Angiospermic flowers, on the other hand, are more advanced, often with both sepals and petals, and are unisexual or bisexual. Gymnospermic flowers are pollinated only through air currents, while angiospermic flowers are pollinated through various agents, particularly insects.

(4) The microspore or pollen grain grows into a pollen tube, which carries the male gametes to a position close to the egg-cell or ovum for the purpose of fertilization. In *Cycas*, however, the pollen tube is branching, the branches penetrate the nucellus and act as sucking organs (haustoria).

(5) The megaspore remains permanently enclosed in the megasporangium (nucellus of the ovule) and germinates into the female gametophyte or embryo sac (reduced prothallus) within the megasporangium.

(6) The megasporangium remains enclosed by the integument (1 in gymnosperms and usually 2 in angiosperms), giving rise to a more complicated structure—the ovule (and later the seed) for better protection of the embryo.

(7) The young sporophyte (embryo) develops at the expense of the food stored up in the parent sporophyte.

Differences

(1) In angiosperms, the xylem is composed mainly of vessels, and the phloem contains companion cells, while in gymnosperms the xylem is made exclusively of tracheids, and phloem contains no companion cells. In higher gymnosperms, however, as in *Gnetum*, there is a combination of gymnospermic tracheids and angiospermic vessels.

(2) The flowers are much simpler in gymnosperms. They have no calyx or corolla and are always unisexual, consisting of either microsporophylls (stamens) or megasporophylls (carpels) only. The plants are either monoecious or dioecious. The stamens and carpels are much simpler than in angiosperms. The sporophylls are borne in

strobili (except the megasporophylls of cycads), whereas in angiosperms they are borne in flowers.

(3) The only agency of pollination in gymnosperms is air current, while there are many pollinating agents in the case of angiosperms.

(4) In gymnosperms, the ovules are borne freely exposed on the megasporophyll (carpel), while in angiosperms, the ovules remain enclosed in the ovary, the carpel itself being differentiated into ovary, style and stigma.

(5) For pollination in gymnosperms, pollen grains enter the micropyle and are deposited on the nucellus; whereas in angiosperms they are deposited on the stigma.

(6) In angiosperms and higher gymnosperms, the male gametes contained in the pollen tube are two passive units, but in lower gymnosperms (*Cycas*, *Zamia* and *Ginkgo*), the male gametes are in the nature of ciliate spermatozoids.

(7) In gymnosperms, the male gametophyte is represented by a few cells (usually 2 or 3)—a vestigial prothallus. In angiosperms, it is reduced to two nuclei—the tube nucleus and the generative nucleus. In fact, there is very little evidence of a male prothallus in angiosperms.

(8) The female gametophyte in gymnosperms is a relatively large structure *with distinct archegonia* embedded in it, each with an ovum. In angiosperms, however, the female gametophyte is a vestigial prothallus represented by an 8-nucleate embryo-sac, and the ovum or egg-cell is free in it *without any archegonium*.

(9) The endosperm, when present in the angiosperm, is formed from the definitive nucleus only after fertilization and is triploid in nature. In gymnosperms, the endosperm is formed from the vegetative tissue of the female prothallus before fertilization (completed, however, after fertilization) and is haploid in nature. The seeds in all gymnosperms are endospermic.

(10) There are 2 to 15 cotyledons in gymnosperms, and 1 or 2 angiosperms.

DEVELOPMENT OF THE SEED IN GYMNOSPERMS.

The seed makes its appearance for the first time in gymnosperms. It develops from the ovule and the following factors are responsible for its development:

(1) Heterospory and differentiation of sporophylls and sporangia are the initial factors, as we find in *Selaginella*, leading towards seed production.

(2) Another factor is the retention of the megaspore within the megasporangium (nucellus of the ovule) and its germination into the female gametophyte (embryo-sac) within the megasporangium, so that the female gametophyte becomes completely endosporous. It is partially endosporous in *Selaginella*.

(3) Enclosure of the megasporangium and the female gametophyte within a new structure, i.e. the integument—the whole complex body so formed being known as the ovule—is another factor. After fertilization and maturity, this ovule gives rise to the seed.

(4) Attachment of the megasporangium (and the ovule) to megasporophyll till after its development into the seed.

(5) Development of the young sporophyte (embryo) within the tissue of the megasporangium

---

Homologous Structures in Cryptogams and Phanerogams

Megasporophyll	=	carpel	Microsporophyll	=	stamen
Megasporangium	=	nucellus of the ovule	Microsporangium	=	pollen-sac
			Microspore	=	pollen grain
Megaspore	=	embryo-sac mother cell	Male gametophyte	=	germinating pollen grain
Female gametophyte	=	embryo-sac			(pollen tube with the nuclei in it)

(nucellus), which belongs to the mother sporophyte, ensuring better feeding and greater protection.

(6) Development of the pollen tube for facility of fertilization under the new condition of ovule formation.

It is, thus, evident that the seed of the gymnosperm is a complex structure with three generations locked up in it: (1) the seed-coat or testa representing the parent sporophyte (old generation), (2) the female gametophyte representing the present generation, and (3) the embryo representing the new sporophyte (future generation).

CLASSIFICATION. Gymnosperms comprise 8 orders, of which 4 have become extinct. The orders are: (1) Cycadofilicales or Pteridospermales or seed ferns (extinct); (2) Bennettitales or Cycadeoideales (extinct); (3) Pentoxylales (extinct); (4) Cycadales (represented by the family *Cycadaceae* with 9 genera and 100 species); (5) Cordaitales (extinct); (6) Coniferales (largest order represented by 6 families with 41 genera and over 500 species); (7) Ginkgoales (represented by the family *Ginkgoaceae* with 1 genus and 1 species cultivated in China, Japan and India); and (8) Gnetales (represented by 3 families with China and Japan, sparingly cultivated in altogether 3 genera and about 71 species). An outline of classification is given in the following schedule:

ORIGIN AND EVOLUTION OF GYMNOSPERMS (see FIG.X/1). Evidence from fossil records goes to show that gymnosperms originated from the oldest and most primitive group of pteridophytes—the Psilophytales—which flourished during the Devonian period of the Palaeozoic age. The two oldest groups of gymnosperms, now extinct, viz. the Cordaitales and the Cycadofilicales, which had a common but independent origin from this group of Palaeozoic pteridophytes, became quite abundant during the mid-carboniferous period. Towards the close of the Palaeozoic or very early Mesozoic age both groups became extinct. The four groups of gymnosperms (leaving out Gnetales), viz. Bennettitales, Cycadales, Ginkgoales and Coniferales, which evolved independently from the two Palaeozoic extinct groups, formed the dominant vegetation of the earth during the mid-Mesozoic period. They, however, began to wane towards the late Mesozoic age. One group, viz. Bennettitales, became quite extinct, while a few descendants of only the other three groups continued through the Cenozoic age as the present-day living forms. Of the four groups of Mesozoic gymnosperms, contemporaneous and widely distributed, the Bennettitales originated from the Cycadofilicales, flourished and died during the same age. The Cycadales, which also originated from the Cycadofilicales but independently of the

Class A.	Cycadopsida			
Order 1	Cycadofilicales (or Pteridospermales)	—fossils only	e.g.	*Lyginopteris*
Order 2	Bennettitales (or Cycadeoideales)	—fossils only	e.g.	*Bennettites*
Order 3	Pentoxylales	—fossils only	e.g.	*Pentoxylon*
Order 4	Cycadales	—*Cycadaceae*	e.g.	*Cycas*
Class B.	Coniferopsida			
Order 5	Cordaitales	—fossils only	e.g.	*Cordaites*
Order 6	Coniferales	—*Abietaceae*	e.g.	*Pinus*
Order 7	Ginkgoales	—*Ginkgoaceae*	e.g.	*Ginkgo*
Class C.	Gnetopsida			
Order 8	Gnetales	—*Gnetaceae*	e.g.	*Gnetum*
		—*Ephedraceae*	e.g.	*Ephedra*
		—*Welwitschiaceae*	e.g.	*Welwitschia*

Bennettitales, have left some living representatives (about 100 species). Ginkgoales and Coniferales originated, independently of one another, from the Cordaitales. The former has left only one living representative (*Ginko biloba*) —a large tree in western China (now widely cultivated), while the latter has left over 500 living representatives (the biggest group of living gymnosperms). The remaining group of gymnosperms, viz. the Gnetales, is regarded as the most recent and advanced group, which comes close to the angiosperms. It has 3 genera and about 71 species. Fossil records of the Gnetales are rare and fragmentary, and not found earlier than the Tertiary. Evidently the group is of recent origin, possibly an offshoot of some Coniferales.

CHAPTER 2

CYCADALES

The family *Cycadaceae* comprises 9 genera with about 100 species. The genus *Cycas* is represented in India by a few species, of which *C. circinalis* (of Malabar and Western Tamil Nadu) and *C. revoluta* (a Japanese sp.) are widely cultivated in Indian gardens. Both yield a kind of sago. *C. rumphii* (of Malacca) is also widely cultivated in India. *C. pectinata* grows in the low hills of Assam and also in Sikkim, and *C. beddomei* in the forests of Eastern Peninsula.

CYCAS (20 *sp.*)

The stem of cycad (*Cycas*; FIG. 1) is unbranched, erect, stout and palm-like, with a crown of pinnate leaves arranged spirally round the apex. Small, dry, scale-like leaves alternate with the green pinnate leaves. Vernation (ptyxis) of the leaf is circinate like that of ferns. The plant has long primary (tap) root.

Cycads are dioecious, i.e. male and female flowers are borne by two separate plants. The male flower is a cone (FIG. 2), borne at the apex of the stem, which then grows by a lateral bud (the stem becomes a sympodium). In *Cycas pectinata*, the male cone may be as long as half a metre in length. The male cone consists of a collection of stamens or microsporophylls arranged spirally round the axis. Each sporophyll (FIG. 3*C*) is in the form of a

scale, narrowed below and broadened above. Its undersurface bears several pollen-sacs or microsporangia grouped in sori. There are usually 2 to 6 pollen-sacs in each sorus. Each pollen-sac contains many pollen grains or microspores. The

FIG. 1. A female plant of *Cycas circinalis* with carpels

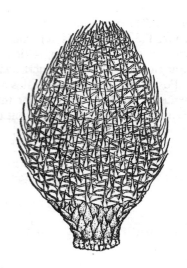

Cycas. FIG. 2. A male cone of *Cycas pectinata* consisting of innumerable microsporophylls arranged round the stout axis

nucleus of each microspore divides once and produces an extremely reduced **prothallus cell** (male gametophyte) on one side and a large **antheridial cell** on the other side (FIG. 5*A*). The latter divides again and produces a **generative cell** and a **tube cell** (nucleus). The pollen grain sheds at this three-celled stage, and subsequent changes take place after pollination.

In *Cycas,* there is no proper female flower. The plant bears near its apex a rosette of carpels or megasporophylls (FIG. 3*A*-*B*), which do not form a cone but are arranged alternately with the leaves. They are usually 15 to 30 cm. long, flattened or bent over like a hood, and often dilated above. In many species, they are covered all over with soft, brownish hairs. The margin may be entire, crenate or pectinate (pinnately divided). Usually 2-3 pairs of ovules (sometimes up to 5 pairs) are borne in an alternate or opposite manner in notches on either side of the stalk. These are mostly oval and large, sometimes very large, as in *C. circinalis* where they grow up to 6 cm. The carpel in gymnosperms is *always open*, i.e. it does not close up, as in angiosperms, to form the ovary, style and stigma. The ovules are borne, freely exposed, on the two margins of the carpel. The ovule (FIG. 4*A*) grows considerably even before fertilization. It consists of a single thick integument and a nucellus or megasporangium, fused practically throughout with the integument. The integument has an apical opening (the micropyle) and consists of three layers—a stony layer and a fleshy layer on either side. The inner layer merges into the nucellus lower down. A megaspore mother cell is produced within the nucellus of the ovule. This divides to form a row of four megaspores. Only one megaspore is functional; the other three disintegrate. The

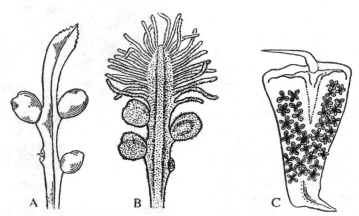

Cycas, FIG. 3. *A*, a carpel or megasporophyll of *Cycas circinalis*; *B*, the same of *Cycas revoluta*; *C*, a stamen or microsporophyll of *Cycas pectinata* with numerous pollen-sacs or microsporangia on the undersurface (slightly oblique view)

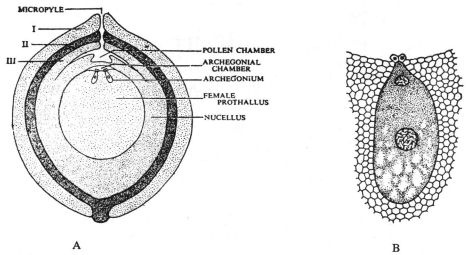

MICROPYLE

I

II

III

POLLEN CHAMBER

ARCHEGONIAL CHAMBER

ARCHEGONIUM

FEMALE PROTHALLUS

NUCELLUS

A

B

Cycas, FIG. 4. *A*, ovule in logitudinal section; *I*, *II*, and *III*, outer, middle (stony) and inner layers of the integument; *B*, an archegonium; note the neck with two neck cells, a large venter (egg-cell) with a central egg-nucleus, and a small ventral canal nucleus (higher up)

functional megaspore divides rapidly and gives rise to a cellular mass of tissue within it. This is the female prothallus or gametophyte (designated as the endospers). *The prothallus is completely endosporous.* The development of the gametophyte begins with repeated free nuclear divisions. The nuclei so formed are pushed towards the periphery by the appearance of an enlarging central vacuole. Cell-walls then develop round the nuclei from the peripheral region towards the centre. The fully developed gametophyte thus becomes cellular and large, occupying the major part of the nucellus. It has two distinct regions—a region of smaller cells towards the upper end and a region of larger cells, nutritive in function, with sugar at first and starch later. The endosperm grows rapidly after fertilization, invades the nucellus, and forms the major part of the seed. The small-celled region produces a few (2-8) archegonia towards the micropyle. Each archegonium (FIG. 4B) is extremely small and consists of a very short neck with two small neck cells (but no neck canal cell), and a large venter completely filled by an egg-cell. There is a distinct free egg-nucleus lying somewhere in its centre. The ventral canal cell is represented by only a nucleus which, however, soon becomes disorganized. The central cell

is invested by a special layer of cells, called the jacket, which is pitted. Food material enters the central cell through the pits. Just below the micropyle, a chamber or cavity is formed due to the breaking down of some of the nucellus cells. This cavity is called the pollen chamber. Just below this, another chamber is formed in the prothallus. This is the archegonial chamber.

Pollination and Fertilization. The pollen grains are carried by the wind. They fall on the micropyle and get bathed in the mucilage secreted by the latter. As the mucilage dries up, the pollen grains are drawn into the pollen chamber. The pollen grain (FIG. 5A) divides and forms (A) a small prothallus cell (male gametophyte) on one side, (b) a generative cell, and (C) a tube cell. The tube cell elongates into a long, branched pollen-tube (FIG. 5B) which enters the archegonial chamber, the membrane between the two chambers having broken down. The pollen-tube of *Cycas* is a sucking organ (haustorium) absorbing food from the nucellus, rather than a sperm-carrier. The generative cell divides into two—the stalk cell and the body cell. The stalk cell is sterile and the body cell divides into two male gametes (spermatozoids; FIG. 5C). These are remarkably large (in fact, the

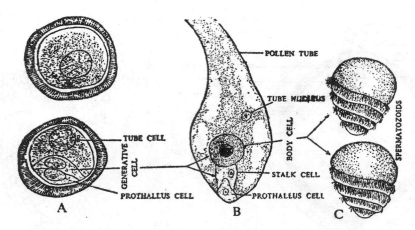

Cycas FIG. 5. *A*, *top*, a pollen grain or microspore; *bottom*, male
prothallus; *B*, pollen-tube (a portion); *C*, two spermatozoids

largest known being about 300 μ in length), top-shaped and multiciliate. The cilia are arranged in a spiral band. The pollen-tube bursts at the apex and the spermatozoids are set free. They swim to the archegonium by vibrating their cilia and enter the egg-cell. The male nucleus slips out of its cytoplasmic sheath, moves towards the egg-nucleus, and finally penetrates it. Fertilization is thus effected. The interval between pollination and fertilization is about four months.

Development of the Embryo. After fertilization, the egg-nucleus undergoes free nuclear divisions 8 or 10 times. As a result, a large number of free nuclei (without cell-walls) appear in the enlarged egg. A central vacuole is formed. This enlarges rapidly, pushing the free nuclei towards the periphery of the egg. Later, cell-walls are formed round the nuclei. A tissue thus appears and it soon fills up the whole of the vacuole. The cellular mass at the base of the egg constitutes the **proembryo**, while the upper cells form a large food reservoir. The proembryo soon differentiates into a suspensor and a terminal embryo. The suspensor elongates rapidly, becomes coiled and pushes the embryo deep into the nutritive tissue of the female gametophyte. As it takes shape, the embryo becomes differentiated into a radicle, a plumule and a pair of ctoyledons. Although there are a few archegonia, only one embryo matures in a seed.

Seed (FIG. 6). After fertilization, the ovule as a whole grows into the seed. The seed is large, globose or ovoid, 2.5-5 cm. across and usually orange or red. The mature seed bears only one embryo, differentiated into a hypocotyl, a radicle, a plumule and *two* cotyledons (a constant feature of all cycads). The cotyledons remain embedded in the copious endosperm and absorb food from it.

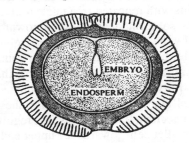

FIG. 6. *Cycas* seed in section

The seed-coat or integument surrounding the seed consists of a thick, fleshy outer layer and a stony inner layer. The endosperm stores a considerable quantity of food for the use of the embryo while the seed germinates. Its germination is prompt, without any period of rest.

Internal Structure of Cycad Leaf (FIG. 7). (1) **Epidermis**—The upper epidermis has a very thick cuticle, while the lower has a comparatively thin cuticl. There are a large number of sunken stomata, each arched over by epidermal

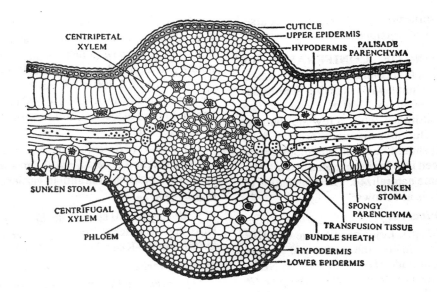

FIG. 7. *Cycas* leaf in transection

outgrowths. (2) **Hypodermis**—the upper hypodermis is highly thickened, while the lower is comparatively thin. (3) **Mesophyll**—This is differentiated into a distinct upper palisade parenchyma and spongy lower parenchyma. In between the two, there is a tissue of long, colourless cells, forming the **transfusion tissue** or conducting channel, which runs horizontally from the vascular bundle (mid-rib) to near the margin of the leaf. There being no veins in the cycad leaf, food and water are conducted through the transfusion tissue. (4) **Vascular bundle**—This has xylem on the upper side and phloem on the lower. The xylem is mesarch, i.e. protoxylem lies in the middle of the xylem. The xylem is well-developed towards the upper side and forms **centripetal xylem** (with distinct protoxylem and metaxylem). Towards the lower side, lying in the **parenchyma** of the bundle, small vascular strands detached from the centripetal xylem form **centrifugal xylem**. The vascular bundle is more or less completely surrounded by a sheath (**bundle sheath**). Some small, thick-walled cells and some clusters of crystals may be seen at places in the section.

CHAPTER 3

CONIFERALES

CONIFERALES (Coniferae or conifers) constitute the largest order among the gymnosperms and comprise six families, e.g. *Abietaceae* (=*Pinnaceae*), *Taxaceae*, and *Cupressaceae*. These are represented by 41 genera and over 500 species. They grow mostly in cold climates and at high altitudes in the hills (see below), and are evergreen trees or shrubs. *Abietaceae*, the largest family, is represented by 9 genera and about 230 species, a few genera being pine (*Pinus*), juniper (*Juniperus*), fir (*Abies*), Himalayan deodar (*Cedrus deodara*), Atlantic cedar (*Cedrus* *atlantica*) and spruce (*Picea*). *Pinus* is, of course, the typical genus of *Abietaceae*.

DISTRIBUTION OF CONIFERALES IN INDIA. There is a rich coniferous flora in the eastern and western Himalayas, occurring at altitudes ranging from 1,200 m. to 3,300 m. Many conifers grow at higher altitudes, while a few are found at lower heights. But investigations are far from complete yet. It should be noted that many exotic conifer introduced into Indian gardens and hill stations have become naturalized. The distribution of conifers in India is as follows:

Abeitaceae (=*Pinaceae*)

(1) *Pinus* (90 sp.): Long-needle pine or CHIR pine (*P. longifolia*) in both the eastern and western Himalayas at an altitude of 600-1,800 m.; in NEFA (Arunachal) at 1,200 m. and above; Khasi pine (*P. khasya*) in the Khasi Hills (Meghalaya) at 900-1,800 m.; blue pine (*P. excelsa*) in temperate Himalayan regions (both eastern and western) at 1,800-3,800 m.; in Arunachal Pradesh at 1,200 m. and above; *P. gerardiana* in the north-west Himalayas at 1,800-3,700 m; *P. insularis* in the Khasi Hills at 1,800 m.

(2) *Cedrus* (3 sp.): Himalayan deodar (*C. deodara*) in north-west Himalayas at 1,100-3,700 m. (planted in Shillong and other hill stations); Atlantic cedar (*C. atlantica*) cultivated in hill stations.

(3) *Picea* (35 sp.): Spruce (*P. morinda*) in eastern and western Himalayas at 1,800-3,700 m. (planted in Shillong and other hill stations).

(4) *Abies* (24 sp.): Himalayan silver fir (*Abies spectabilis* =*A. webbiana*) in eastern and western Himalayas at 2,100-3,700 m.; in Arunachal Pradesh at 3,000 m.

(5) *Tsuga* (9 sp.): *T. brunoniana* in eastern and western Himalayas at 2,400-3,300 m.; common in Arunachal Pradesh.

(6) *Larix* (8 sp.):larch (*L. griffithii*) in eastern Himalayas at 2,400-3,700 m.

Cupressaceae

(1) *Cupressus* (12 sp.): *C. torulosa* in western Himalayas at 1,800-2,400 m. (planted in Shillong); *C. funebris* (planted in Shillong).

(2) *Juniperus* (60 sp.): Juniper (*J. communis* —a shrub) in western Himalayas at 1,700-4,300 m.; *J. recurva* (a bush or small tree) in temperate and alpine Himalayas at 2,300-4,600 m.; in Mishmi Hills at 2,700 m.; *J. macropoda* (a tree) in western Himalayas at 1,500-4,300 m.; *J. pseudosabina* (a tree) in western and eastern Himalayas at 2,700-4,600 m.

(3) *Thuja* (=*Biota*; 6 sp.): *T. orientalis* (a Chinese sp.) and *T. occidentalis* (an American sp.) commonly cultivated in Indian gardens.

Podocarpaceae

Podocarpus (70 sp.): *P. neriifolia* in the Khasi Hills and Arunachal Pradesh at 900-1,200 m.; *P. latifolia* in the Khasi Hills at 900-1,500 m.

Araucariaceae

(1) *Araucaria* (15 sp.): *A. excelsa* (Australian) and *A. cunninghamii* (South American) commonly cultivated in Indian gardens.

(2) *Agathis* (20 sp.): *A. australis* (a source of copal varnish) planted in Indian gardens.

Taxaceae

(1) *Taxus* (8 sp.): *T. baccata* in temperate Himalayas at 1,600-3,300 m.; in the Khasi Hills and Mishmi Hills at 1,500 m.

(2) *Cephalotaxus* (6 sp.): *C. mannii* in the Khasi Hills and Naga Hills at 1,400-2,600 m.; *C. griffithii* in the Mishmi Hills and the Naga Hills at 1,800 m.

Taxodiaceae

Cryptomeria (1 sp.): Japanese cedar (*C. japonica*) is cultivated in Shillong and other hill-stations.

PINUS (90 *sp.*)

Pine (*Pinus*; FIGS. 11-12) grows abundantly in the temperate regions of the eastern and western Himalayas, at an altitude of 1,200 to 3,300 metres (see above). Common Himalayan species are Khasi pine (*P. Khasya*), long-needle pine or CHIR pine (*P. longifolia*), and blue pine (*P. excelsa*). *P. sylvestris*, a British pine, and a few others are exotic species.

Pine is a tall, erect evergreen tree, often growing to a height of 45 metres, with a basal girth of

3 m. The plant has a well-developed tap root and many aerial branches with green, needle-like leaves. The stem is rugged and covered with scale bark that peels off in strips at places. There are two kinds of branches—long (of unlimited growth) in apparent whorls, developing from lateral buds in the spring, and dwarf (of limited growth; see FIG. 11). The leaves are also of two kinds—long, green, needle-like foliage leaves (usually called needles) borne only on dwarf branches (or foliar spurs, as they are called), and small, brown, scaly leaves borne on both kinds of branches. The number of needles in a cluster varies from 1 to 5 (3 in *P. khasya*, *P. longifolia* and *P. gerardiana*, 5 in *P. excelsa*, 2 in *P. sylvestris*, and 4 or 1 in certain species.

Internal Structure of the Young Stem (FIG. 8). The young stem resembles the dicotyledonous stem in many respects. The general arrangement of the various tissues from the circumference to the centre is the same. However, it differs from the latter in having several resin ducts filled with the brownish substance of resin. These ducts are distributed almost throughout the stem. The epidermis has an irregular outline. The endodermis and pericycle are not marked out in the stem. The vascular bundles are not wedge-shaped, as in the dicotyledons. The phloem consists of sieve-tubes and phloem parenchyma, but no companion cells. The protoxylem consists of annular and spiral tracheids which are irregularly disposed towards the centre. Metaxylem consists exclusively of tra-

cheids with bordered pits. The tracheids are arranged in radial rows, as seen in the transverse section of the stem. The pits of the coniferous wood are large and mostly restricted to the radial walls. In angiosperms, on the other hand, they are much smaller but more numerous, and are not confined to particular walls. There are no true vessels in the coniferous stem.

STRUCTURE OF THE STEM

(1) **Epidermis.** This is a single layer with a very thick cuticle and an irregular outline. (2) **Hypodermis.** The hypodermis is few layers of large, sometimes thick-walled and lignified cells lying below the epidermis. (3) **Cortex.** This is made of many layers of more or less rounded cells, with conspicuous resin ducts. (4) **Medullary Rays.** These run from the pith outwards, between the vascular bundles. (5) **Pith.** There is a well-defined pith, consisting of a mass of parenchymatous cells. A few resin-ducts are also present in the pith. (6) **Vascular Bundles.** These are collateral and open, and arranged in a ring, as in the stems of dicotyledons. Each bundle consists of phloem, cambium and xylem. (*a*) The **phloem** consists of sieve-tubes and phloem parenchyma, but no companion cells. It lies on the outer side of the bundle. (*b*) The **cambium** is a few layers of thin-walled, rectangular cells lying between the xylem and phloem. (*c*) The **xylem** consists exclusively of tracheids. There are no true vessels in the wood. Resin ducts are also present. The protoxylem lies

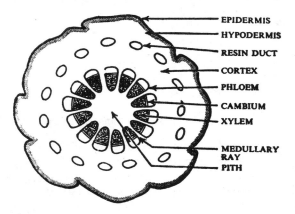

FIG. 8. Young pine stem in transection (diagrammatic)

towards the centre and consists of a few annular and spiral tracheids which are not disposed in any regular order. The metaxylem lies towards the cambium and consists of tracheids with bordered pits, which develop on the radial walls. These tracheids are roughly four-sided and arranged in definite rows.

the presence of conspicuous resin ducts distributed almost throughout the stem. The secondary wood consists exclusively of tracheids which have many bordered pits on their radial walls. As in the dicotyledonous stem, there are distinct annual rings, consisting of the autumn wood and the former consists of narrow and thick-walled

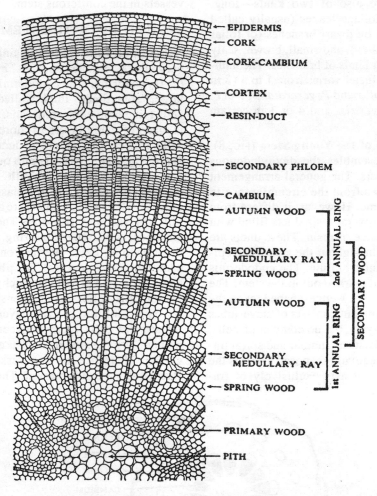

FIG. 9. A two-year old pine stem in transection (a sector)

Secondary Growth in Thickness of the Stem
(FIG. 9). The secondary growth in a coniferous (pine) stem takes place in exactly the same way as in a dicotyledonous stem. The following points may, however, be mentioned.

The coniferous (pine) stem is characterized by

tracheids, and the latter of wider and thinner-walled tracheids. Vessels or fibres are absent. There are many secondary medullary rays which run horizontally and are usually one layer of cells in thickness and a few (up to 12) layers in height. The xylem portion of each ray consists of (a) a few middle rows of rectangular, thick-walled cells (**ray parenchyma**) with numerous, comparatively large, simple pits, living contents and several starch grains, and (*b*) 1 to 3 marginal (upper and lower) rows of short tracheidal cells (**ray tracheids**) with bordered pits. The phloem portion of the ray consists of large, thin-walled cells extending upwards and downwards. These contain proteins, and are sometimes called *albuminous cells*. The **cork-cambium** soon arises in the cortex and gives rise to cork and bark on the outside, and some parenchyma on the inside. The scale bark that is formed peels off in strips.

projections of the cell walls extend into the cell cavity. Some resin ducts occur at places, adjoining the hypodermis, each surrounded by a layer (epithelium) of small, thin-walled cells (4) **Endodermis**—This occurs as a conspicuous layer of large, barrel-shaped cells. (5) **Pericycle**—This lies internal to the endodermis and is a many-layered tissue. It consists of some parenchyma, often some sclerenchyma, particularly on the phloem side, and transfusion tissue. The latter consists of (*a*) *albuminous cells*, which lie close to the phloem and are parenchymatous in nature, living and rich in protein and starch, and (*b*) *tracheidal*

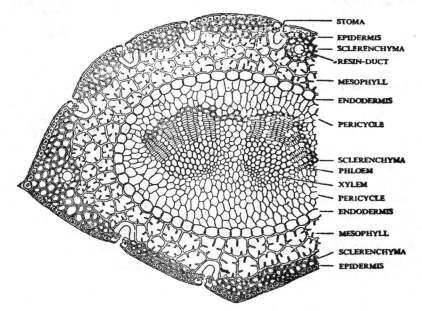

FIG. 10. Pine needle (leaf) in transection

INTERNAL STRUCTURE OF THE PINE NEEDLE (FIG. 10). (1) **Epidermis**—This is a single layer of very thick-walled cells with a strong cuticle. The cell cavity is nearly obliterated. Stomata lie slightly sunken in this layer, each stoma opening internally into a respiratory cavity. (2) **Hypodermis**— This occurs internal to the epidermis in 1, 2 or 3 layers, interrupted by the stomata. This tissue is deeper at the ridges. (3) **Mesophyll**—This consists of large, thin-walled, polygonal or irregular cells, containing plenty of chloroplasts and starch grains. Peg-like

cells, which lie adjoining the xylem and are thin-walled, elongated, dead cells, provided with bordered pits like tracheids. Albuminous cells serve to conduct food from the mesophyll to the phloem, and tracheidal cells conduct water and mineral salts from the xylem to the mesophyll. (6) **Vascular bundles**—There are 2 vascular bundles, which lie embedded within the many-layered pericycle. They are collateral and closed. The xylem, consisting of rows of tracheids, lies towards the angular side of the leaf, and the phloem, consisting of sieve-tubes, lies towards the convex side.

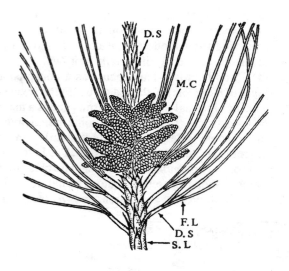

FIG. 11

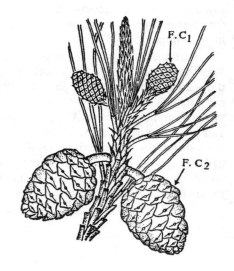

FIG. 12

Pinus. FIG. 11. A male shoot (branch) of unlimited growth showing male cones (*M.C.*), young dwarf shoots (*D.S.*) or shoots of limited growth (each in the axil of a scale), needle-like foliage leaves or needles (*F.L.*) borne only by dwarf shoots or foliar spurs (as these are called), and scale leaves (*S.L.*) spirally borne by both dwarf and long shoots. FIG. 12. A female shoot of unlimited growth showing two young female cones (*F.C₁*) of current year, two maturing female cones (*F.C₂*) of previous year (for the third year cone see FIG. 19A), and the rest as in FIG. 11

Pinus, like all other gymnosperms, is the sporophyte. It bears two kinds of cones or strobili (FIGS. 11-12)—male and female—on separate branches of the same plant (monoecious). The male cone consists of microsporophylls or **stamens**, while the female cone consists of megasporophylls or **carpels**. Cones always develop on the shoots of the current year, a little below their apex. Several male cones appear in a cluster of spikes, each in the axil of a scale leaf. They are 1.5 to 2.5 cm. long. The female cones may be solitary or in whorls of 2 to 4, each in the axil of a scale leaf. The male cones develop much earlier than the female cones. The flowers have no perianth.

Male Cone (FIGS. 11 & 13A). Several microsporophylls or stamens are arranged spirally round the axis of the male cone. (FIG. 13A). Each microsporophyll (FIG. 13B-D) is differentiated into a stalk (filament) and a terminal leafy expansion (anther), and its tip is bent upwards. Its undersurface bears two pouch-like Microsporangia or pollen sacs. Some conifers may have as many as 15. Each pollen sac contains many microspore

mother cells, each of which undergoes reduction division to produce a tetrad of microspores or **pollen grains.** Each pollen grain (FIG. 17A) has two coats—*exine* (outer) and *intine* (inner). The exine forms two wings, one on each side. A huge quantity of pollen is produced for pollination to be brought about by wind.

Female Cone (FIGS. 12 & 19A). This consists of a short axis with many a small, thin, dry, brownish scales, slightly fringed at the upper part, spirally arranged around it. These are known as the **bract scales** or **carpellary scales** (FIG. 14), corresponding to the carpels or megasporophylls. They are inconspicuous in the mature cone. On the upper surface of each bract scale, there is another stouter and bigger scale, woody and somewhat triangular known as the **ovuliferous scale** (FIG. 14). This is variously interpreted as an open carpel, a placenta or a ligular outgrowth. At the base of each ovuliferous scale, lying on its upper surface, are two sessile **ovules** with their micropyles turned downwards towards the axis of the cone. Each ovule (FIG. 15) is orthotropous and consists of a central mass of

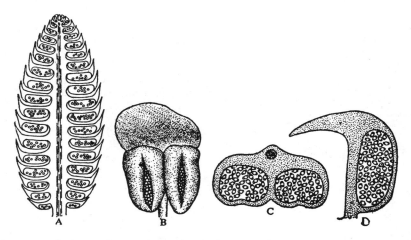

Pinus. FIG. 13. *A*, a male cone in longitudinal section; *B*, a microsporophyll showing two microsporangia (pollen-sacs); *C*, the same in transection; *D*, the same in longitudinal section. Note the microspores (pollen grains) with wings

tissue—the nucellus or megasporangium, surrounded by a *single* integument made of three layers. The integument leaves a rather wide gap known as the micropyle. A megaspore mother cell soon becomes apparent within the nucellus. It undergoes reduction division to produce four megaspores in a linear tetrad. Only one megaspore

is functional. The other three degenerate.

Male Gametophyte (FIG. 17A). The microspore or pollen grain begins to divide before it is set free from the microsporangium or pollen sac, and gives rise to the extremely reduced male prothallus (male gametophyte) within the microspore coat.

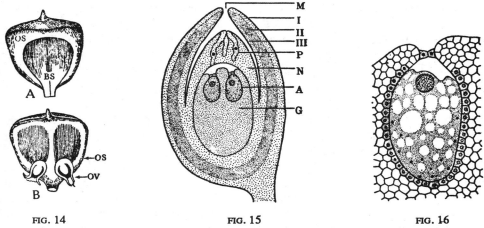

FIG. 14   FIG. 15   FIG. 16

Pinus. FIG. 14. Megasporophyll. A, lower surface; B, upper surface. *BS*, bract scale; *OS*, ovuliferous scale; *OV*, ovule with one integument. FIG. 15. Ovule in longisection. M, micropyle; *I*, *II*, and *III* are outer, middle (stony) and inner layers of the integument; *P*, pollen tube; *N*, nucellus; *A*, archegonium; and *G*, female gametophyte (endosperm). FIG. 16. An archegonium with two neck-cells and a large venter (egg-cell) enclosing a conspicuous egg-nucleus and many small food particles. (*Fig. 16 redrawn after Fig. 322 in Gymnosperms: Structure and Evolution by C. J. Chamberlain by permission of The University of Chicago Press.*)

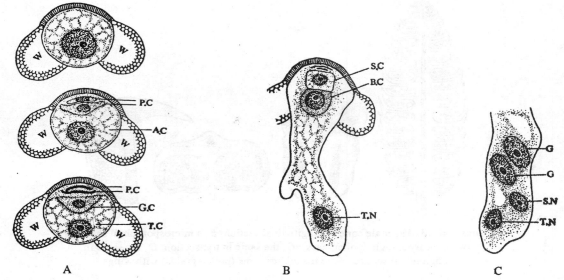

Pinus. FIG. 17. *A*, pollen and male gametophyte; *B*, pollen tube; *C*, portion of the pollen tube. *W*, wing; *P C*, prothallus cells; *A C*, antheridial cell; *G C*, generative cell; *T C*, tube cell; *S C*, stalk cell; *B C*, body cell; *T N*, tube nucleus; *G*, male gamete; and *S N*, stalk nucleus. (*Redrawn after Fig. 311 in Gymnosperm: Structure and Evolution by C. J. Chamberlain by permission of The University of Chicago Press.*)

The prothallus consists of (*a*) 2 or 3 small cells (**prothallus cells**) at one end, which soon become disorganized, and (*b*) an **antheridial cell**, which is the remaining large cell of the prothallus. The antheridial cell divides and forms a **generative cell** and a tube cell. The pollen grain sheds at this stage and subsequent changes take place after pollination.

Female Gametophyte (FIG. 15). The megaspore begins to divide after a period of rest, giving rise to the female prothallus (female gametophyte) within the nucellus. It digests a big portion of the nucellus and enlarges considerably. Soon it takes to free nuclear division, finally forming a solid mass of tissue—the female gametophyte (otherwise called the endosperm). It is completely *endosporous*, i.e. it remains permanently enclosed within the nucellus. The endosperm grows quickly after fertilization, invades the nucellus, and surrounds the embryo in the seed (FIG. 19*C*). At the micropylar end of the prothallus, lying embedded in it, develop 2 to 5 archegonia (FIG. 15). These are very small, as in *Selaginella*. As in the latter, each archegonium (FIG. 16) consists of a swollen venter

and a short neck. The venter encloses a large egg-cell (almost filling the cavity) with a distinct egg-nucleus in it, and also a small ventral canal cell which, however, soon gets disorganized. The neck consists of 2 or more (usually 8) neck cells but no neck canal cell. The archegonial wall is made of a layer of small but distinct cells called the jacket cells. The archegonia mature slowly and become ready for fertilization only in the following year.

Pollination. Pollination takes place through the agency of the wind, usually in May-June, soon after the female cone emerges from the bud. The pollen sacs burst and the winged pollen grains are blown about by the wind like a yellow cloud of dust. Some of them happen to fall on the young female cone. A huge quantity is wasted, however. The pollen grains pass between the two slightly opened scales and are deposited at their base. A quantity of mucilage is secreted at the micropyle, in which the microspores get entangled. After pollination, the scales close up and so does the wide, gaping integument. The mucilage is drawn in by the nucellus together with the microspores. The latter then lodge somewhere at the apex of the nucellus for about a year. Fertilization takes place in the following year at about the same time, the cone develops fully when the archegonia mature, and in the third year.

Fertilization (FIG. 18A). The mode of fertilization in *Pinus* was first discovered in 1883 by Goroschankin who observed the entry of both the male gametes into the embryo sac. Strasburger, however, discovered in 1884 the fusion of only one male gamete with the egg-nucleus. The process is as follows. The outer coat (exine) of the pollen grain bursts and the inner coat (intine) grows out into a slender tube, i.e. the pollen tube (FIG. 15). This pushes forward through the nucellus and finally reaches the neck of the archegonium. The pollen tube is characteristic of all gymnosperms and angiosperms. The tube nucleus passes into the pollen tube. The generative cell divides and forms a stalk cell and a body cell (FIG. 17B). Both these cells migrate into the pollen tube. The stalk cell is sterile, while the body cell divides and produces two male gametes (FIG. 17C). The male gametes are not ciliate, as in cycads. The pollen tube bursts at the apex and the two male gametes are liberated. The nucleus of the functioning male gamete slips out of the cytoplasm and passes on to the egg-nucleus[1]. The other male gamete, the stalk cell and the tube nucleus become disorganized.

Development of the Embryo (early stages;

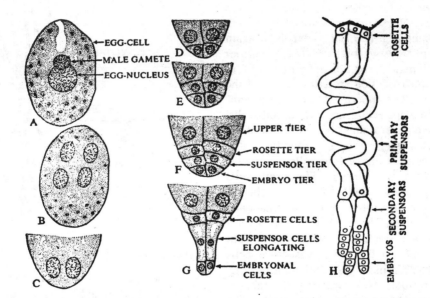

Pinus. FIG. 18. Fertilization and embryogeny. *A*, fertilization; *B-H*, development of the embryo by successive divisions of the fusion-nucleus; *B*, 4-nucleate stage; *C*, 2 of the 4 nuclei at the base; *D*, 8-celled proembryo; *E*, proembryo with 3 tiers of 4 cells each; *F*, proembryo with 4 tiers of 4 cells each; *G*, proembryo showing elongation of suspensor cells; *H*, 4 embryos (proembryos) separating, formation of secondary suspensors and rapid elongation of primary suspensors. At the next stage only one embryo matures (see FIG. 19C). (*Redrawn after Fig. 300 in Plant Morphology by A. W Haupt by permission of McGraw-Hill Book Company.*)

---

[1] The male and female gametes do not fuse in the resting stage but form two separate spindles with their respective chromosomes (12 in number) within the egg-nucleus. The two sets of chromosomes then orient themselves on a common spindle and their separate identity is lost. The chromosomes (24 in number) split longitudinally and the two sets move to the two opposite poles, forming two daughter nuclei which immediately divide into four.

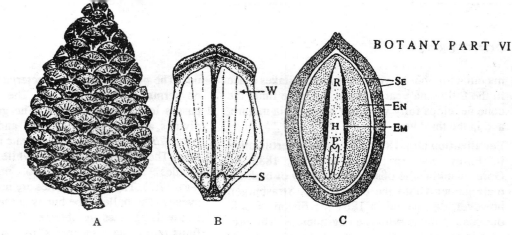

Pinus. FIG 19. *A* a mature female cone; *B*, a mature megasporophyll with 2 seeds (winged); *S*, seed;
W, wing; *C*, a seed in longisection; *EM*, embryo (*P*, plumule with many cotyledons; *H*, hypocotyl;
R, radicle); *EN*, endosperm; *SE*, seed coat (with outer and inner fleshy layers and stony middle layer)

FIG. 18*B-H*). By two successive divisions of the fusion-nucleus, four free nuclei are formed within the egg-cell (*B*). These then move to the bottom in a horizontal plane (*C*). The four nuclei divide again and walls appear between them (*D-E*). Further divisions result in the formation of four tiers of four cells each. This 16-celled structure is called the **proembryo** (*F*). The uppermost tier of the proembryo with its four open cells, i.e. without cell-walls, merges into the general mass of cytoplasm of the egg-cell and acts as a part of the surrounding nutritive tissue. The next tier of four cells constitutes what is called the '**rosette tier**'. The rosette cells may develop short and abortive embryos. Normally, they transmit food to the suspensor and the embryonal cells. The third tier forms a four-celled '**suspensor tier**'. The lowest tier of four cells is the '**embryo tier**'. The suspensor cells begin to elongate rapidly (*G*) and soon become very big and tortuous (*H*), thrusting the embryos into the gametophytic tissue (endosperm). The embryonal cells (*G*) divide and give rise to *four* potential embryos and also secondary suspensor cells (*H*). This polyembryony (see p. 316), i.e. the development of more than one embryo from an oospore, is characteristic of conifers. Of the four embryos thus formed only the strongest one survives and attains maturity, while the others degenerate. The mature seed, thus, has only one **embryo** (FIG. 19*C*). Besides, as there are a few archegonia in the ovule some more embryos may begin to develop but finally only one survives.

Seed. The megasporophylls grow considerably even before fertilization. After fertilization, how-

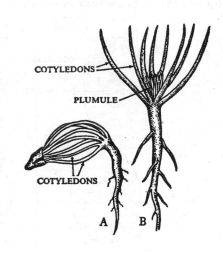

Pinus. FIG. 20. *A-B*, germinating seed and seedling

ever, the ovules develop into seeds (FIG. 19*B-C*), and the whole female flower into a dry, brown, woody cone (FIG.19*A*). The seed is albuminous in all gymnosperms. In *Pinus*, the seed-coat is provided with a membranous wing (FIG. 19*B*), which is formed from the ovuliferous scale. The seed-coat (integument) has three layers—the inner and the outer being thin, and the middle stony. The fully developed embryo of the seed (FIGS. 19*C* & 20) consists of an axis with a hypocotyl, radicle and a tiny plumule with many cotyledons (2-15) surrounding it. The seed germinates under suitable conditions (FIG. 20). The cotyledons are pushed upwards, germination being epigeal, and they turn green. The radicle grows downwards into a distinct tap root. The seedling thus becomes established.

CHAPTER 4

GNETALES

The Gnetales, which have reached the highest degree of development (evolution) among the gymnosperms, bear a close resemblance to the angiosperms. However, they cannot be regarded as the ancestors of angiosperms. The living Gnetales are so highly advanced and specialized, and the fossil forms so few, that their origin cannot be traced to any particular group of gymnosperms. They may have originated from an extinct group of gymnosperms and followed a parallel line of evolution with the angiosperms. The order Gnetales is represented by three families, each with a single genus: (a) Gnetaceae, e.g. Gnetum, (b) Ephedraceae, e.g. Ephedra, and (c) Welwitschiaceae, e.g. Welwitschia. Gnetum (35 sp.) is widely distributed in tropical Asia, Africa and South America. 2 sp. of Gnetum, viz. G. gnemon and G. montanum, are fairly common in Eastern India. G. gnemon grows in the Khasi Hills and Manipur Hills, while G. montanum grows in the eastern tropical Himalayas, Assam and the Deccan. Ephedra (35 sp.) is widely distributed in the Mediterranean, eastern Asia, and North and South America. In India, E. vulgaris grows in the temperate and alpine Himalayas at an elevation of 2,100-3,700 m., (in Sikkim, at 3,700-4,800 m.). E. platyclada grows in the western Himalayas at or below 4,700 m., E. peduncularis grows in the salt ranges of Punjab, Rajasthan and Sind (Pakistan). Welwitschia (1 sp.), viz. W. mirabilis, has been found in south-west tropical Africa.

GNETUM (35 sp.)

Gymnospermic Characteristics of Gnetum
(1) The ovules are naked, i.e. not enclosed in the ovary. (2) In pollination, the wind-borne pollen grains are lodged directly on the ovule, there being no style, stigma or ovary. (3) The male and female strobili are of gymnospermic types, although the flowers are more advanced with the development of the perianth. (4) The generative cell divides and produces a prothallus cell and a generative cell, the latter forming two male gametes. (5) Anatomically, there is a preponderance of gymnospermic tracheids with bordered pits. (6) The vascular bundles are in successive concentric rings, as in some cycads.

Resemblances with Angiosperms. Gnetum resembles angiosperms in many ways—vegetative, anatomical and reproductive. (1) Gnetum bears well-developed, broad, evergreen leaves with distinct reticulate venation, hardly distinguishable from those of angiosperms (FIG. 21). (2) The general climbing habit of Gnetum is more angiospermic than gymnospermic. (3) There are true vessels (of the angiospermic type) present in the secondary wood (though it also has tracheids of the gymnospermic type). (4) Both male and the female flowers have perianths. (5) There are two integu-

Gnetum. FIG 21. A branch with leaves
(reticulate venation)

ments surrounding the ovule. (6) There are no archegonia at all, as in the angiosperms. (7) The female gametophyte with many free nuclei closely resembles the embryo-sac of an angiosperm. (8) The stamen (microsporophyll) with a stalk (filament) and 1 or 3 anthers resembles that of an angiosperm. (9) The male gametophyte produces no prothallus cells, as in all angiosperms. (10) The endosperm is formed after fertilization. (11) The embryo has two cotyledons.

Life history. *Gnetum* is found only in the tropics. 2 common species are common in India—*G. montanum* and *G. gnemon*, both being widespread in Assam. The species of *Gnetum* are mostly woody climbers (e.g. *G. montanum*), or shrubs or small trees (e.g. *G. gnemon*). The leaves are simple, decussate, broad, evergreen, leathery, lanceolate-ovate and distinctly net-veined (suggestive of dicotyledons). The primary stem often produces two kinds of shoots—long and short. The latter bear one to a few pairs of leaves. Anatomically, the primary vascular bundles are formed in a ring, and the secondary vascular bundles are formed in successive concentric rings by successive cortical cambia, the primary cambium being short-lived. The secondary xylem is made of true vessels (as in angiosperms), associated with gymnospermic tracheids with bordered pits. A peculiarity of the phloem is that the sieve-tube and the companion cell are formed from two separate cells (and not by the division of a single cell, as in angiosperms).

Resin ducts are absent, unlike other gymnosperms.

Species of *Gnetum* are dioecious, one plant bearing male inflorescences (strobili) and another, female strobili. The strobili are usually branched (compound), pendulous and catkin-like, bearing numerous male or female flowers, as the case may be. The strobili are mostly axillary, sometimes terminal, and grow to a length of two to a few cm.

Male Strobilus. The male strobilus (FIG. 22A-B) is a slender axis growing between two connate bracts at the base. At short intervals higher up, bracts appear in several whorls. The bracts of a whorl, however, fuse together at an early stage to form a cup-shaped structure called the 'collar'. From a special tissue on the lower surface of the collar, several minute male flowers (apparently axillary) develop in 2-5 whorls round the axis. There may be a whorl of sterile female flowers (ovules) interposed between the whorls of male flowers. Each male flower (FIG. 22C) consists of a sheathing perianth (two segments fused into a tube), often surrounded at the base by jointed hairs, and a single stamen or microsporophyll. The latter consists of a stalk (filament) and two unilocular anthers containing pollen grains or microspores. Each anther opens by a terminal slit. The presence of the perianth is an angiospermic characteristic.

Female Strobilus (FIG. 23A-B). This is also a slender axis, branched or unbranched, growing between two bracts at the base. The female

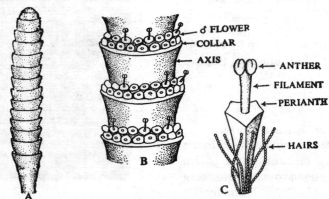

Gnetum FIG. 22. *A*, a male strobilus; *B*, a portion of the same (magnified) showing whorls of male flowers; *C*, a male flower

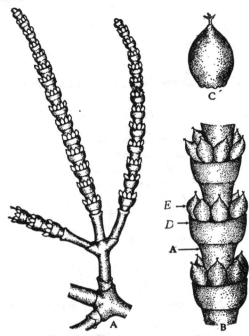

Gnetum.

FIG. 23.

A, a female strobilus;

B, a portion of the same (magnified) showing whorls of female flowers on an elongated axis;

E, a whorl of bracts forming the collar;

D, a whorl of bracts forming the collar;

C, a female flower (ovule) magnified

flowers, each represented by a single erect ovule, are arranged in successive whorls round the axis in the axils of connate, cup-shaped bracts (two bracts are fused into a cup). There are 4-10 female flowers or ovules in each whorl. Each ovule (FIG. 23*C*) is surrounded by a fleshy perianth (two outgrowths appearing from the base of the ovule get fused at a very early stage) forming the outer covering. The perianth finally turns orange-red in the seed. The ovule (FIG. 25*A*) consists of two envelopes or integuments, and a distinct nucellus or megasporangium, and is orthotropous in nature. Of the two integuments the outer one is stony and the inner one projects beyond the perianth into a sort of style or micropylar tube the tip of which is lobed or fimbriated. The embryo-sac or megaspore lies embedded in the nucellus towards the chalazal end. A fan-shaped nutritive tissue develops beneath the embryo. This tissue is called the *pavement tissue*, formed of radiating rows of cells and becomes disorganized after fertilization.

Male Gametophyte (FIG.24). The pollen grains often germinate while still in the micropylar chamber. Some of them, however, directly reach the nucellus and germinate there. On germination, the pollen grain gives rise to a very simple type of male gametophyte. The stages in the development of the male gametophyte, as worked out by Negi and Madhulata in 1957, are as follows (FIG. 24). The nucleus of the pollen grain or microspore (*A*) divides at first into two nuclei (*B*). The smaller one is the **prothallus cell** (*P*), and the larger, the **generative cell** (*G*). The latter divides again into two nuclei (*C*), one of which is the vegetative nucleus or **tube nucleus** (*T*), while the other is the generative cell (*G*). The former is without a wall, while the latter develops a distinct cell-wall. Thus, at this stage, the pollen grain has a prothallus cell (*P*), a tube nucleus (*T*) and a generative cell (*G*). It should be noted that the earlier view that a stalk cell and body cell are present and the prothallial cell absent has since been discarded. The pollen grain sheds at this stage and further development takes place after pollination. The pollen grains are drawn into the pollen chamber. Now the exine of the pollen grain bursts and the intine grows into a pollen tube (*D*). The generative cell divides and produces two male gametes (*E*) which migrate to the tip of the pollen tube.

Female Gametophyte (FIG. 25*B*). The megaspore mother cell divides and produces four megaspores, one or more of which may be functional. The

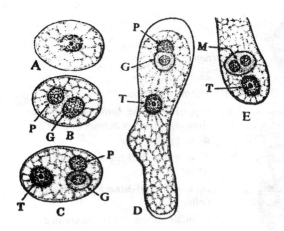

Gnetum.
FIG. 24.
Microspore and stages in the development of the male gametophyte
A, a microspore;
B, the same after the first division;
C, the same after the second division;
D, pollen tube formed;
E, lower end of the same;
P, prothallus cell;
G, generative cell;
T, tube nucleus;
M, male gametes

(Redrawn after Fig. 392 in Gymnosperms; Structure and Evolution by C. J. Chamberlain by permission of The University of Chicago Press.)

megaspore germinates with repeated free nuclear divisions and gives rise to the embryo-sac or female gametophyte, which lies deep within the nucellus. One or more of the free nuclei, particularly at the micropylar end, may be organized, with a mass of protoplasm surrounding them, into potential egg-nuclei and may be fertilized. No archegonium is formed in Gnetum (cf. angiosperms). In some species, as in G. gnemon, a multinucleate (later uninucleate) cellular tissue

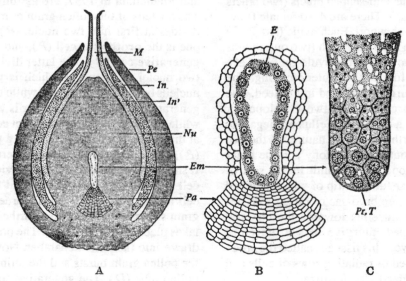

Gnetum. FIG. 25. A, ovule in longitudinal section showing micropylar tube (M), perianth (Pe), outer integument (In), inner integument (In'), nucellus (Nu), embryo-sac or female gametophyte (Em) and pavement tissue (Pa); B, female gametophyte (magnified) showing many free nuclei, a few eggs (E) and pavement tissue (Pa) beneath; C, development of prothallial tissue (Pr. T) at the base of the female gametophyte. (Redrawn after Figs. 391G, 395 and 394 in Gymnosperms: Structure and Evolution by C. J. Chamberlain by permission of The University of Chicago Press.)

(prothallial tissue), interpreted as homologous with the antipodal cells of angiosperms, is formed at the basal part of the female gametophyte (FIG. 25C). After fertilization, it fills up the entire gametophyte. The prothallial tissue in gymnosperms is designated as the endosperm. It is noticeable that the female gametophyte of *Gnetum*, with its many free nuclei and the absence of an archegonium, has almost reached the angiosperm level.

Fertilization and Development of the Embryo. One or more pollen tubes penetrate the micropylar chamber and the nucellus. Finally, the tubes reach the female gametophyte (FIG. 26A) and enter it. The male gametes are discharged through a terminal pore in the pollen tube. Both the male gametes are functional. Fertilization takes place when either of them fuses with any free egg-nucleus. Each fertilized egg-nucleus is surrounded with a wall and becomes the oospore (FIG. 26B). Some of the unfertilized nuclei divide and form a prothallial tissue (endosperm), while others become disorganized. The endosperm grows rapidly and soon invades the entire nucellus space. In *Gnetum*, most of the endosperm tissue is formed after fertilization. Many oospores or even embryos may be formed, but ultimately, one embryo comes to maturity. In the formation of the embryo the oospore divides and forms a two-celled proembryo (FIG. 26C). Each cell of the proembryo grows into a long slender tubular suspensor (FIG. 26D). Its nucleus divides into two. One of these undergoes free nuclear divisions, forming a group of four free nuclei at the end of the suspensor (FIG. 26E), while the other nucleus does not divide. These

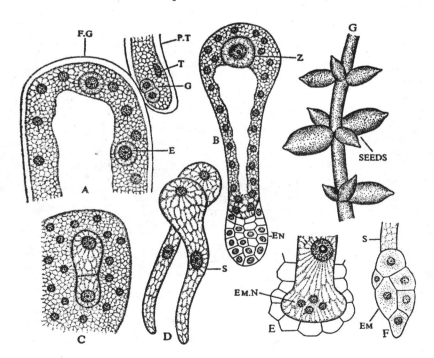

Gnetum. FIG. 26. *A*, pre-fertilization stage; female gametophyte (*F G*) and pollen tube (*PT*); *E*, egg-nucleus; *T*, tube-nucleus; *G*, male gametes; *B*, female gametophyte after fertilization showing zygote (Z), free nuclei, and development of endosperm (*EN*); *C*, proembryo; *D*, two suspensors (*S*) developing from the 2-celled proembryo; *E*, end of a suspensor showing four embryonal nuclei (*EM N*); *F*, embryo (*EM*) and suspensor (*S*); *G*, female strobilus with groups of seeds. (FIG. 26A-F *redrawn after Fig. 395 in Gymnosperms: Structure and Evolution by C. J. Chamberlain by permission of The University of Chicago Press.*)

four nuclei undergo further divisions. With the formation of walls around them, a multicellular embryo (with uninucleate cells) is produced (FIG. 26F). However, embryo formation is slightly different in *Gnetum gnemon*. In this species, the fertilized egg produces a single, long, tortuous suspensor, in which free nuclear divisions in both the earlier and later stages of embryo formation are more frequent. It should be noted that a cell containing a single nucleus associated with numerous starch grains is cut off at the tip of the suspensor. This is the **embryonal cell**. Its nucleus undergoes free nuclear divisions. Then, with the formation of walls round the free nuclei, a multicellular embryo is developed as in other species.

Seed. Although there are many ovules, not many seeds are formed. The seed (FIG. 26G) is albuminous. Its outer covering or perianth is fleshy and orange-red. Of the two integuments, the outer one is hard and stony. The embryo is with two cotyledons (dicotyledonous type).

7 ANGIOSPERMS

ORIGIN AND LIFE HISTORY

ORIGIN AND EVOLUTION. Fossil records indicate that angiosperms suddenly became abundant in a great variety of forms in the early Cretaceous period and have since then formed the dominant vegetation of the earth. It is probable that they evolved in the northern temperate regions in an earlier era, but were lost due to heavy glaciation in a later period. The flora of that era is lost forever with practically no chance of recovering the missing links. A part of the flora moved southward, and the survivors of the catastrophe, which were traced in the form of fossils, e.g. willow, beech, elm, fig, laurel, etc., show that the angiosperms of that period were already well advanced. It may, thus, be taken for granted that they originated much earlier, probably in the Triassic period or even earlier. But the missing links make it impossible to ascertain the ancestry of angiosperms. The views on this are divergent and speculative, the available data being meagre, fragmentary and isolated. Some of the theories proposed in this connection unsatisfactory though they may be in one or more respects, are as follows.

1. Bennettitales-Ranales Theory.

(*a*) **Hallier's** view (1906) regarding the origin of angiosperms is that Ranales (e.g. *Magnolia*) seems to be related to Bennettitales and may have been derived from *Cycadeoidea*, and that monocotyledons are an offshoot of dicotyledons. The elongated floral axis of Ranales with spirally arranged male and female sporophylls and the cone of *Cycadeoidea* are definitely alike. Both the groups were abundant in the Cretaceous period.

Ranales is regarded as the earliest stock, from which the polycarpic families of dicotyledons have arisen, as also have monocotyledons as an offshoot. But the differences in the anatomical structures of the wood, types of sporophylls, nature and position of the ovules, etc. in the two groups (Bennettitales and Ranales) have made it difficult for this view to be accepted. It is more likely that both the groups evolved from a common ancestor and developed in unrelated, parallel lines. (*b*) **Arber** and **Parkin** (1907), while strongly supporting Hallier, proposed the existence of an imaginary group (Hemiangiospermae) with cycadeoid type of flowers, linking the above two groups. According to them, the Ranalian type of flowers had originated from this imaginary group and all other angiosperms evolved from the Ranalian type. The anatomical structure of the wood, however, does not support the Bennettitalean origin of the angiosperms. They also found no valid reason for the assumption that monocotyledons had originated from dicotyledons. As a matter of fact, they held the view that the earliest monocotyledons were more primitive than the dicotyledons. (*c*) **Hutchinson** (1925) considered the origin of angiosperms as *monophyletic*, and supported the views of Hallier, and Arber and Parkin. He believed in the Bennettitalean origin of angiosperms and laid stress on two parallel evolutionary lines for the primitive dicotyledons—a woody (arborescent) line, called **Lignosae**, starting from Magnoliales, and a herbaceous line, called **Herbaceae** starting from Ranalas (see p. 538). He further held that the monocotyledons were derived from a primitive dicotyledonous order—the Ranales.

2. Coniferae-Amentiferae Theory. Engler and Prantl (1924) rejected the Cycadeoidean origin of angiosperms, as proposed by Hallier earlier. They held the view that dicotyledons and monocotyledons had arisen independently from a hypothetical group of extinct gymnosperms (allied to Coniferae) with unisexual strobilus, which developed in the Mesozoic age. Thus, according to them, the angiosperms had a *polyphyletic* origin, and evolution proceeded on several parallel lines. They also considered monocotyledons to be more primitive than dicotyledons. The unisexual, naked (without perianth) condition of the angiospermic flowers, as exemplified by Pandanales (monocotyledons) and Amentiferae (catkin-bearing dicotyledons, e.g. *Casuarina*, *Salix*, *Betula*) was most primitive. But according to the latest classification, these orders are regarded as definitely more advanced.

3. Gnetales-Casuarinales Theory. Wettstein (1935) held the view that angiosperms of the *Casuarina* type evolved from Gnetales (particularly *Ephedra*), a highly advanced group of gymnosperms, which branched off from the main gymnospermic line. There are, no doubt, some angiospermic features in Gnetales (see *Gnetum*, p. 523) but this group, as far as is known from the meagre fossil records, does not go further back than the Teritary period. **Fagerland (1947)** was, however, of the view that both Gnetales and Proangiosperms had had a common ancestor and that the modern angiosperms evolved from the latter group in polyphyletic lines.

4. Caytoniales-Angiosperm Theory. In 1925, **Thomas** suggested that Caytoniales, a small group of angiosperm-like plants discovered in Jurassic rocks of Yorkshire, might be the ancestor of angiosperms. **Harris (1932-33)**, who also studied Caytoniales, rejected this view. **Knowlton (1927)** in his book *Plants of the Past*, expressed the view that both Caytoniales and angiosperms evolved from the large extinct Palaeozoic group of pteridosperms. In his review of gymnosperms, **Arnold (1948)** expressed the view that Caytoniales were definitely allied to the pteridosperms rather than to

the angiosperms. In fact, according to him, they were the Mesozoic remnants of the Palaeozoic pteridosperms.

5. Pteridosperm-Angiosperm Theory. In reviewing the 'ancient plants' **Andrews (1947)** opined that the origin of angiospermic plants might lie in the 'seed-ferns' or pteridosperms, an ancient group of the Palaeozoic age. **Arnold** expressed a similar view in the same year. But it must be noted that the absence or scarcity of angiospermic fossils before the Cretaceous era, connecting them with the pteridosperms, makes this matter mere speculation rather than fact. Pteridosperms might be the ancestors of cycads and true ferns, but it is doubtful that they are ancestors of angiosperms.

There are other theories, too, but there is still no definite answer. The general consensus is that the angiosperms have evolved from some extinct group which has yet to be traced.

As is evident from the above, the question whether angiosperms are **monophyletic** (i.e. derived from a single ancestral stock) or **polyphyletic** (i.e. derived from several ancestral stocks) has not been satisfactorily solved. Generally speaking, the diversity of form of the primitive families of both dicotyledons and monocotyledons and their wide distribution in the early years suggest a polyphyletic. On the other hand, certain common and constant characteristics of early angiosperms, such as the 8-nucleate embryo-sac, formation of endosperm after fertilization as a result of triple fusion, types of flowers, stamens, carpels, ovules, etc., suggest a monophyletic origin.

LIFE CYCLE (FIG. 1). The life cycle of a plant is the series of progressive changes it undergoes, usually from the stage of zygote to the same stage (zygote) again. There are certain special features in the life cycle of an angiosperm, as compared with cryptogams. Some such features are the development of the pollen-tube, the seed and the $3n$ endosperms, absence of antheridia and archegonia, double fertilization, complexity of the sporophyte and extreme reduction and loss of independence of the gametophyte. To start with, the zygote grows rapidly into an embryo, and the latter gradually into

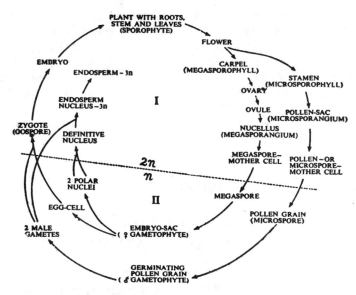

FIG. 1. Life cycle of an angiosperm. *I*, sporophytic or diploid (2*n*) generation; *II*, gametophytic or haploid (*n*) generation

a full-fledged plant with roots, stem, leaves and flowers. The flower bears a stamen or microsporophyll and a carpel or megasporophyll. The stamen bears a pollen sac or microsporangium and the carpel bears a nucellus or megasporangium within the ovule, which again develops within the ovary. The pollen sac and the nucellus, in their turn, produce the pollen (or microspore) mother cell and the embryo-sac (or megaspore) mother cell. By reduction division, the pollen mother cell gives rise to pollen grains or microspores, and the embryo-sac mother cell to the megaspore. (Of the four megaspores formed, three degenerate). The pollen grain germinates on the stigma of the carpel (pistil) and gives rise to the male gametophyte (the germinating pollen grain—the pollen tube with the three nuclei in it, i.e. the tube-nucleus and the two male gametes), and the megaspore to the female gametophyte (the embryo-sac with the eight nuclei). Both the gametophytes are extremely small. The female gametophyte is completely *endosporous* and entirely dependent on the mother sporophyte for protection and nutrition. Antheridia and archegonia are altogether absent in the gametophytes. The male gametophyte bears two male gametes and the female gametophyte bears a female gamete or egg-

cell. Pollination takes place mainly through the agency of insects and the wind, and this is followed by fertilization. One of the male gametes of the pollen-tube fuses with the egg-cell of the embryo-sac and the other male gamete fuses with the two polar nuclei or their fusion product, i.e. the definitive nucleus with 2*n* chromosomes. As a result of this *double fertilization*, rapid changes take place in the ovule and the ovary. The fertilized egg-cell becomes the zygote (oospore) which quickly grows into the embryo, the *triple-fusion* nucleus (two polar nuclei and one male gamete) grows into the endosperm (with 3*n* chromosomes), and the ovule and the ovary grow into the seed and the fruit, respectively. It should be noted that the zygote marks the end of the life cycle. Sooner or later, the next cycle begins from it (the zygote) and the same series of changes is repeated.

ALTERNATION OF GENERATIONS. In angiosperms, the sporophyte reaches a high degree of complexity, while the gametophytes become very small, simple and inconspicuous. The angiospermic plant is the sporophyte with 2*n* or diploid chromosomes. The embryo-sac with the eight nuclei and the germinating pollen grain, i.e. the pollen-tube with the three nuclei in it, are the female and male gametophytes, respectively, with n or haploid chromosomes. The endosperm with $3n$ chromosomes, formed as a result of triple fusion, is a unique structure in the angiosperm. All the stages from the zygote to the spore mother cells (mega and micro) represent the sporophytic generation (well-advanced), and all the stages from the spores (mega and micro) to the gametes (male and female) represent the gametophytic generation (extremely reduced). These two generations (sporophytic and gametophytic) alternate regularly to complete the life cycle of an angiosperm.

CHAPTER 2

PRINCIPLES AND SYSTEMS OF CLASSIFICATION

SYSTEMATIC BOTANY or TAXONOMY. This deals with the description, identification and naming of plants, and ther classification into different groups according to their resemblances and differences, mainly in their morphological characteristics. So far as angiosperms or higher 'flowering' plants are concerned, it has been estimated that over 199,000 species (dicotyledons—159,000 and monocytoledons—40,000) are already known to us, and that thousands more have yet to be discovered and recorded. Thus, there are not only numerous plants, but they are also of varied types, and it is not possible to study them unless they are arranged in some order. The object of systematic botany or taxonomy is to describe, name and classify plants in such a manner that their relationship with regard to their descent from a common ancestry may be brought out. The ultimate object of classification is to arrange plants in such a way as to give us an idea of their phylogenetic relationships, i.e. the sequence of their origin and evolution from simpler, earlier and more primitive types to more complex, recent and advanced types during different periods. The earlier classifications of plants were based on their economic uses, e.g. cereals, medicinal plants, fibre-yielding plants, oil-yielding plants, etc., or on gross structural resemblances, e.g. herbs, shrubs, trees, climbers, etc. These classifications were incomplete and fragmentary as plants that did not fit into such classifications or were of no economic value were usually ignored. Therefore, an ideal system of classification should not only indicate the actual genetic relationship but should also be reasonably convenient for practical purposes.

Units of Classification

SPECIES. A species is a group of individuals (plants or animals) having a very close resemblance with one another, structurally and functionally. The individuals of a species interbreed freely and successfully in nature so that they may be taken as having descended from the same parent stock. They also breed true to type, i.e. give rise to progeny of the same kind. They also normally have the same number of chromosomes in their cells—$2n$ in somatic cells and n in reproductive cells. Thus, all pea plants together constitute a species. Similarly, all banyan plants, all peepul plants, and all mango plants constitute different and distinct species. Species, however, often show a wide range of variations, with many intermediate forms or gradations, serving as connecting links between two allied species. It has, therefore, not been possible to draw a line of demarcation between one species and another allied one, nor to delimit the boundary of any one particular species.

This being so, it becomes very difficult to give an accurate and rigid definition of a species. Thus, taxonomists have often differed on the latitude of a species. Nevertheless, taxonomists have never ignored the importance of species, however vaguely and arbitrarily defined, as fundamental units of classification. It should also be noted that all the characteristics of a species are attributable to the behaviour of DNA in the chromosomes. DNA carries the same genetic code from generation to generation, controls the development of parental characteristics in the offspring and thus, normally limits the boundary of a species.

Under the influence of external conditions, certain individuals of a species may often show a marked degree of variation in form, size, shape, colour and other minor characteristics. Such plants are said to form **varieties**. A species may consist of one or more varieties, or none at all. Thus, we have different varieties of common garden pea, rice, potato, mango, etc. Varieties, however, are not permanent. They tend to revert to the species from which they were originally derived.

GENUS. A genus is a collection of species which bear a close resemblance to one another as far as the morphological characteristics of the floral or reproductive parts are concerned. For example, banyan, peepul and fig are different species because they differ from one another in their vegetative characteristics such as the habit of the plant, the shape, size and surface of the leaf, etc. But these three species are allied because of the similarity in their reproductive organs, namely, the inflorescence, flower, fruit and seed. Therefore, banyan, peepul and fig come under the same genus (*Ficus*).

Nomenclature. The name of a plant has two parts. The first refers to the genus and the second to the species. The system of designating every type of plant with a *binomial*, i.e. a name consisting of two parts, is known as binomial nomenclature. It was first established by Linnaeus and finally settled by the International Botanical Congress[1] held in Amsterdam in 1935. Thus, pea has been named *pisum sativum*, rice *Oryza sativa*, mango *Mangifera indica*, banyan *ficus bengalensis*, peepul *Ficus religiosa*, fig *Ficus carica*, and india-rubber plant *Ficus elastica*. As for cottons, they all belong to the same genus, *Gossypium*, which consists of about 20 or more species, such as BANI cotton of India (*Gossypium indicum*), KUMPTA cotton of southern Maharashtra (*G. herbaceum*), American cotton (*G. barbadense*), KIL cotton of Assam (*G. cernuum*), BURI cotton—the upland American cotton naturalized in India—(*G. hirsutum*), and so on. The name of the author who first described a species is also written in an abbreviated form after the name of the species, e.g. *Mangifera indica* Linn. Here Linn refers to 'Line' or 'Linnaeus', who first described the plant.

Family. A family is a group of genera which have general structural resemblances mainly in their floral organs. Thus, in the genera *Gossypium*, *Hibiscus*, *Thespesia*, *Sida*, *Abutilon Malva*, etc., we find free lateral stipules, epicalyx, twisted aestivation of corolla, monadelphous stamens, unilocular anthers, axile placentation, etc. So all the above-mentioned genera belong to the same family, and that is *Malvaceae*.

Systems of Classification

Systems of classification may be artificial, natural or phylogenetic. The systems have developed in a step-wise manner, from the earliest to the present times. Four periods, depending on the criteria used in classification, may be recoginized. *1st period*: This extends for about 2,000 years from about 1730s B.C. to the end of the 17th century. During this period, the systems were based on the **habit** of plants. *2nd period*: This extends from the thirties to the end of the 18th century. There is a definite change in the pattern of these systems. The habit

[1]International Rules of Botanical Nomenclature formulated by the International Botanical Congress at Vienna 1905, Brussels 1910, Cambridge 1930, Amsterdam 1935, and further revised by the American Society of Plant Taxonomists 1946-47, Stockholm 1950, Paris 1954 to synchronize with the centenary of the Botanical Society of France (1854-1954), Montreal 1959, Edinburgh 1964, Seattle 1969, Leningrad 1975, and Canberra 1980.

has given place to **sex organs** (stamens and carpels) of plants, and Linnaeus' sexual system of classification (1735) is specially remarkable. *3rd period*: this extends from the beginning to the eighties of the 19th century. Several famous botanists belong to this period. The systems propounded during this period were based on the **natural relationships** of forms. Bentham and Hooker's natural system of classification (1862-83) is of outstanding merit. *4th period*: This period extends from 1875 (possibly 1883) to the present times. The systems of this period have been based on the **phylogenetic relationships** of plants.

ARTIFICIAL SYSTEM. In the artificial system only one, or at most a few, characteristics are selected arbitrarily and the plants are arranged into groups according to such characteristics. As a result, closely related plants are often placed in different groups, while unrelated plants are often placed in the same group because of the presence or absence of a particular characteristic. This system enables us to determine readily the names of plants but does not indicate the natural relationship that exists among the individuals forming a group. It may, thus, be compared to the manner of arrangement of words in a dictionary in which, except for the alphabetical order, adjacent words are not necessarily connected with one another. Instead of being grouped together, they become widely separated. Nevertheless, the artificial system is of very great advantage in view of the fact that by following this system one can get to the name of an unknown plant without much difficulty. In other words, the identification of an unknown plant is rendered much easier by this system.

LINNAEAN SYSTEM (1735). The best-known artificial system is that put forward by Linnaeus (1707-78). It was published by him in the year 1735, and revised in his *Genera Plantarum* (1737) and *Species Plantarum* (1753). By 1760, his system became popular in Holland and Germany, and partly in England. Linnaeus classified plants according to the characteristics of their reproductive organs, viz. the stamens and carpels. Since these are regarded as the sexual organs of plants, Linnaeus' system is commonly called the 'Sexual

System'. According to it plants are divided mainly into 24 classes, including 23 of phanerogams and one of cryptogams. Phanerogams are further subdivided into groups with unisexual or bisexual flowers. Plants with unisexual flowers are again divided according to whether they are monoecious or dioecious. Further classification is based on the number of stamens. Plants with bisexual flowers are classified according to whether the stamens are united with the carpels, or free from them. The next consideration is whether the stamens are free or united. Then the number of stamens, their length, and ultimately, the number of carpels are taken into account.

NATURAL SYSTEM. In the natural system, all the important characteristics are taken into consideration, and plants are classified according to related characteristics. Thus, according to the resemblances and differences, mostly in the important morphological characteristics, plants are first classified into a few big groups. These are further divided and subdivided into smaller and smaller groups until the smallest division is reached and that is a species. All modern systems of classification are natural and supersede the artificial ones in that, on the one hand, they give us a true idea of the natural relationships existing between different plants, based on a detailed description of their characteristics and also of the sequence of evolution from simpler to more complex types, and on the other hand they meet the need to identify unknown plants. Plants arranged according to these systems also possess the same or identical properties in most cases.

According to the natural system, the plant kingdom has been divided into two *divisions*, viz. **cryptogams** or 'flowerless' plants (see part V) and **phanerogams** or 'flowering' plants. Phanerogams have again been divided into two *subdivisions*, viz. **gymnosperms** or naked-seeded plants (see part VI) and **angiosperms** or closed-seeded plants. Angiosperms have been subdivided into two *classes*, viz. **dicotyledons** and **monocotyledons**. The classes have been divided into *orders*, the orders into *families*, the families into *genera* and *species*, and sometimes, species into *varieties*. If a greater number of intermediate categories are required, the prefix *sub* is added to the particular term.

BENTHAM AND HOOKER'S SYSTEM (1862-83).

Bentham (1800-84) and Hooker (1817–1911), two English botanists who were contemporaries of Darwin, elaborated a natural system of classification of 'flowering' plants (dicotyledons, gymnosperms and monocotyledons), giving a more or less equal status to all three groups. Their system is based on (virtually an extension of) de Jussieu's system (1789) and de Candolle's system (1819). It was published in *Genera Plantarum*, in which dicotyledons are discussed first, then gymnosperms and finally, monocotyledons. They divided dicotyledons into 3 sub-classes and 14 series. The series were divided into cohorts (equivalent to orders), and cohorts into orders (equivalent to families). There are altogether 202 orders of angiosperms—165 orders of dicotyledons and 37 orders of monocotyledons. They started with the family *Ranunculaceae* (with polypetalous corolla and an indefinite number of free stamens and carpels), and ended with *Labiatae* (with gamopetalous corolla and a definite number of stamens and carpels), leaving out incomplete and an anomalous series. They divided monocotyledons into 7 series, and series directly into orders. They started with orders having epigynous flowers, e.g. *Orchidaceae* and Scitamineae, passed through orders with petaloid hypogynous flowers, e.g. *Liliaceae*, and then through orders with flowers which have lost their petaloid character, e.g. *Palmae* and *Araceae*. Finally, they came to *Gramineae* and *Cyperaceae* with simple construction of flowers and presence of glumes. The following is an outline of this system of classification.

CLASS I. DICOTYLEDONS

Sub-class I. **POLYPETALAE**. Flowers with both calyx and corolla; corolla polypetalous; both stamens and carpels present. Within the sub-class, progress is indicated through an polysepalous calyx to gamosepalous calyx, through an indefinite number of stamens to a definite number, and through hypogyny, perigyny and epigyny. This sub-class is divided into 3 series.

Series (*i*) **Thalamiflorae**. Calyx polysepalous, free from the ovary; stamens inserted on the thalamus, hypogynous; ovary superior. This series has 11 cohorts and 57 orders, beginning with Ranales and ending in Malvales.

Series (*ii*) **Disciflorae**. Calyx polysepalous or gamosepalous, free from or adnate to the ovary; disc usually conspicuous; stamens usually definite, inserted on or around the disc; ovary superior. This series has 5 cohorts and 21 orders (plus 2 anomalous orders), beginning with Geraniales and ending in Sapindales.

Series (*iii*) **Calyciflorae**. Calyx gamosepalous, often adnate to the ovary; stamens perigynous or epigynous, inserted on the disc; ovary superior or inferior. This series has 5 cohorts and 27 orders, beginning with Rosales and ending in Umbellales.

Sub-class 2. **GAMOPETALAE**. Flowers with both calyx and corolla; corolla gamopetalous; stamens almost always definite and epipetalous; carpels usually two or sometimes more, often united; ovary superior or inferior. This sub-class is also called Corolliflorae. It is divided into 3 series.

Series (*i*) **Inferae**. Ovary inferior; stamens usually as many as the corolla-lobes. This has 3 cohorts and 9 orders, beginning with Rubbiales and ending in Campanales.

Series (*ii*) **Heteromerae**. Ovary usually superior; stamens as many or twice as many as the corolla-lobes; carpels more than two. This has 3 cohorts and 12 orders, beginning with Ericales and ending in Ebenales.

Series (*iii*) **Bicarpellatae**. Ovary usually superior; stamens as many as or fewer than the corolla-lobes; carpels two. It has 5 cohorts and 24 orders, beginning with Gentianales and ending in Lamiales.

Sub-class 3. **MONOCHLAMYDEAE** or Incompletae or Apetalae. Flowers incomplete; either calyx or corolla absent, or sometimes both absent; flowers bisexual or unisexual. This sub-class includes the orders (families) which do not fall under either of the above sub-classes. It is divided into 8 series and 36 orders, beginning with *Nyctagineae*, *Amarantaceae*, etc., and ending with *Casuarineae*, *Cupuliferae*, *Salicaceae* and *Ceratophylleae*.

CLASS II. MONOCOTYLEDONS

Series (*i*) **Microspermae**. Inner perianth petaloid; ovary inferior, with 3 parietal placentae; seeds very minute, exalbuminous. This series has 3 orders—*Hydrocharitaceae*, *Burmanniaceae* and *Orchidaceae*.

Series (*ii*) **Epigynae**. Perianth petaloid, partly at least; ovary often inferior; seeds with copious endosperm. This series has 7 orders—*Scitamineae*, *Irideae*, *Amaryllideae*, etc.

Series (*iii*) **Coronarieae**. Perianth partly petaloid; ovary superior; seeds with copious endosperm. This series has 8 orders—*Liliaceae*, *Commelinaceae*, etc.

Series (*iv*) **Calycinae**. Perianth sepaloid; ovary superior; endosperm copious. This series has 3 orders—*Palmae*, etc.

Series (*v*) **Nudiflorae**. Perianth absent or represented by scales; ovary superior; carpels 1-∝, syncarpous; endosperm usually present. This series has 5 orders—*Pandaneae*, *Typhaceae*, *Aroideae*, *Lemnaceae*, etc.

Series (*vi*) **Apocarpae**. Perianth in 1 or 2 whorls or absent; ovary superior, apocarpous; endosperm absent. This series has 3 orders—*Alismaceae*, *Naiadaceae*, etc.

Series (*vii*) **Glumaceae**. Flowers solitary, sessile, in the axils of bracts or glumes, in spikelets; perianth absent or modified into scales; ovary unilocular, single-ovuled; endosperm copious. This series has 5 orders—*Cyperaceae*, *Gramineae*, etc.

Merits (1) Bentham and Hooker's system is a milestone in systematic botany. Some even go so far as to say that this system should have been further elaborated rather than replaced. (2) The placing of Ranales at the beginning of the system stand to logic. This is also Hutchinson's view. Engler, however, holds a different view. (3) It is a natural system, followed widely for its practical utility. (4) Monocotyledons are placed after dicotyledons, but the insertion of gymnosperms in

between the two is an anomaly. (5) The position of many cohorts (orders), though not the series, of Monochla-mydeae is natural, e.g. Cactales is regarded by them as well as by Hutchinson as related to Passiflorales, while Engler places the group near Myrtiflorae. (6) The system ends in *Verbenaceae* and *Labiatae* (leaving out Monochlamydeae). This view is shared by Hutchinson, but not by Engler.

Demerits. (1) The greatest drawback of this system is the unfortunate introduction of the Monochlamydeae group. As a whole, it is regarded as an artificial group, except its first series, Curvembryeae. In fact, the refuse of the other two sub-classes has gone into this group. Among achlamydeous families, there are many unrelated types. The achlamydeous condition is now regarded as one of reduction rather than of progress. It is largely on this score that the system has been criticized by later systematists. So this group has been broken up and the families have been redistributed. (2) Characteristics have often been selected arbitrarily so that related orders have become separated, often widely. (3) Microspermae (*Burmanniaceae* and *Orchideae*) is placed at the beginning of the monocotyledonous orders. Engler and Hutchinson have shifted them to the end. (4) The distinction between *Liliaceae* (with superior ovary), on the one hand, and *Irideae* and *Amaryllideae* (with inferior ovary), on the other, is no longer held valid, based as it is on merely one character. Engler has brought them together under *Liliflorae*. Hutchinson has, however, split it up into a number of smaller orders. (5) *Scitamineae* precedes *Liliaceae* and is placed together with *Bromeliaceae*, *Irideae* and *Amaryllideae*. Engler, on the other hand, raises it to the rank of an order with four families and places it after *Liliaceae*, from which it may have been derived. Hutchinson calls the order Zingberales, includes a number of small families in it and places it back to its former position.

PHYLOGENETIC SYSTEM. This is based on the phylogenetic relationships of plants. The systems of classification proposed in 1886 by Engler, a German botanist, in 1942, by Hutchinson, an

English botanist, and in 1942, by Tippo, an American botanist, are phylogenetic.

ENGLER'S SYSTEM. Engler's system is based on Eichler's system (1883), the major categories which Engler and his associates have accepted. Adolf Engler (1844-1930), Professor of Botany at the University of Berlin, first proposed his system in 1886 as a guide to the botanical garden at Breslau. The system was published in an expanded and elaborated form in *Die Naturlichen Pflanzenfamilien* (1887–1909) in 23 volumes covering the whole range of the plant kingdom, under the editorship of Engler and Prantl. Engler and Gilg's *Syllabus der Pflanzenfamilien*, published in 1892, is a comprehensive work on the systematic classification of 'flowering' plants and cryptogams, and is a very useful publication. According to Engler's system, the plant kingdom is divided into 13 divisions, of which the seed-bearing plants (Spermatophyta) form the last division named 'Embryophyta Siphonogama'. This has been further divided into two sub-divisions— Gymnospermae and Angiospermae. The latter are further divided into two classes—Monocotyledoneae and Dicotyledoneae. Monocotyledoneae has been directly divided into 11 orders with 45 families, while Dicotyle-doneae comprises two sub-classes—(*i*) **Archichlamydeae**, containing 30 orders with 190 families, representing the lower dicotyledons, and (*ii*) **Sympetalae** (or Metachlamydeae), containing 10 orders with 53 families, representing the higher dicotyledons. The orders have been further subdivided into sub-orders, families and genera. There are altogether 288 families. Monocotyledoneae begins with *Typhaceae* and ends with *Orchidaceae*, while Dicotyledoneae begins with *Casuarinaceae* and ends with *Compositae*.

The principle involved in this system is tracing the increasing complexity of flowers, particularly their accessory whorls, viz. achlamydeous flowers (no perianth), haplochlamydeous flowers (one whorl of perianth) and diplochlamydeous flowers (two whorls of perianth). Those with no perianth, or with only one whorl, or with polypetalous corolla form the sub-class Archichlamydeae. The gamopetalous condition with 1 or 2 whorls of perianth comes under the sub-class Sympetalae. The latter represents more advanced groups of dicotyledons. Progress within the sub-class is indicated through hypogyny, perigyny and epigyny, and the transition from a variable number of stamens and carpels to a definite number. Among dicotyledons, Engler starts with the *Casuarinaceae* family on the assumption that woody plants with unisexual, apetalous flowers borne in catkins are the most primitive.

Merits. (1) The whole plant kingdom has been classified with necessary sketches, records of numbers of species, and keys of identification of all known genera of plants. (2) It is a natural system based on relationships and is compatible with evolutionary principles. (3) The group have been built up step by step to form a generally progressional morphological series. (4) Many groups have been phylogenetically arrranged. (5) Apetalae (Monochlamydeae) have been abolished, being considered an artificial group, and amalgamated with Polypetalae into a new group, i.e. sub-class Archichlamydeae. (6) *Compositae* and *Orchidaceae* are considered, very reasonably, the highest families of dicotyledons and monocotyledons, respectively, in view of their highly evolved characteristics. Because of its merits, Engler's system was accepted by American and British botanists.

Demerits. (1) Monocotyledons gain precedence over dicotyledons. The higher dicotyledons and monocotyledons are believed to have developed from some primitive dicotyledonous stock. (2) *Casuarinaceae* is considered most primitive among dicotyledons and placed at the beginning of his system. This view is no longer acceptable. (3) Amentiferae, i.e. the catkin-bearing families with unisexual flowers, e.g. *Fagaceae*, *Salicaceae*, *Betulaceae*, are considered primitive among dicotyledons and placed early in his system. This group is now considered to be advanced rather than primitive. Ranales, like *Ranunculaceae*, and *Nymphaeaceae*, can never be derived from them. The primitive nature of Ranalean families is now almost universally accepted by taxonomists. Centrospermae, e.g.

Amarantaceae and *Caryophyllaceae*, cannot precede Ranales. (4) The derivation of dicotyledons from gymnosperms with unisexual strobili is another weak point of his system. (5) The system, as a whole, cannot be regarded as phylogenetic. (6) The position of Helobiae, e.g. *Potamogetonaceae*, *Alismaceaet Hydrocharaceae*, between Pandanales and Glumiflorae is very unsatisfactory. Both Pandanales and Glumiflorae are advanced groups. (7) Similarly, *Araceae*, *Lemnaceae* and *Typhaceae* are supposed to be derived from *Liliaceae*, and, therefore, cannot precede it.

HUTCHINSON'S SYSTEM. John Hutchinson, formerly Director of the Royal Botanic Gardens at Kew, England, is a leading exponent of a phylogenetic system of classification. He classified only the angiosperms in his famous work *The Families of Flowering Plants*, Vol. I (dicotyledons), which appeared in 1926, and Vol. II (monocotyledons) in 1934. The system has been revised in his *British Flowering Plants*, published in 1948, and in the second edition of *The Families of Flowering Plants* published in 1959. His system differs from all the previous ones in several fundamental respects. It is, however, closer to Bentham and Hooker's or Bessey's than to Engler's. The main features of his system are as follows.

It is based on a logical interpretation of the theory that the parts of an angiospermic flower are modified leaves. He held the view that the angiosperms, having strobilus-like, hypogynous, bisexual and polycarpellary flowers, originated in an extinct Mesozoic group of gymnosperms—the Bennettitales (e.g. *Bennettites =Cycadeoidea*). According to Hutchinson, two primitive orders of dicotyledons arose independently from this ancestral stock through an imaginary group of proangiosperms, and developed simultaneously on two distinct parallel lines (see p. 529). Thus, he considered the origin of angiosperms as *monophyletic*, and supported Hallier, and Arber and Parkin. Hutchinson emphasized the old view of woody (arborescent) and herbaceous types of primitive dicotyledons, of course, together with other related characteristics. Accordingly, he recognized two distinct divisions proceeding on two phyletic lines—woody and herbaceous. On one line evolved the fundamentally and predominantly *woody* orders, which he called **Lignosae**, and on the other line evolved the orders, fundamentally and predominantly *herbaceous*, which he called **Herbaceae**. The woody line started from the primitive order of Ranales (family *Magnoliaceae*), passed through *Annonaceae*, *Lauraceae*, *Dilleniaceae*, *Rosaceae*, etc., and ended in families like *Apocynaceae*, *Rubiaceae*, *Verbenaceae*, etc. The herbaceous line started from the primitive order of Ranales (family *Ranunculaceae*), passed through *Nymphaeaceae*, *Cruciferae*, *Caryophyllaceae*, etc., and ended in families like *Umbelliferae*, *Compositae*, *Solanaceae*, *Scrophulariaceae*, *Labiatae*, etc. Hutchinson recognized several climax orders in the phylogeny of the dicotyledons and rearranged them in proper sequences. Orders having both woody and herbaceous forms were considered polyphyletic, i.e. members originating from different ancestors, as found in Apetalae (without perianth), Urticales, Umbellales, Euphorbiales, etc. He also held that the monocotyledons were derived from a primitive dicotyledonous stock at a very early stage of evolution, the point of origin being the Ranales. His reshuffling of the monocotyledonous orders and families, and the elaborate descriptions of each has led to a better understanding of the group as a whole. Further, the splitting up of some families, particularly *Liliaceae*, on the basis of inflorescence characteristics, is very logical and sound. Monocotyledons began with the family of *Butomaceae* and ended in the family of *Gramineae*, with several climax orders, as in dicotyledons.

Primitive and Advanced Characteristics. These characteristics, which formed the basis of his classification, are described in the following list. (i) The polypetalous condition is more primitive than the gamopetalous condition. (2) Unisexual flowers are more advanced than bisexual flowers. (3) Apetalous forms have originated from petaliferous stock, and represent reduction and advance. (4) Free parts, on the whole, are considered more primitive than connate or adnate parts. Thus numerous free stamens preceded few or connate stamens. Similarly, the apocarpous pistil is more primitive than the syncarpous pistil. (5) Spiral arrangement of parts is more primitive than cyclic, etc.

Hutchinison's revised scheme of classification (1959) is as follows. He has divided the 'flowering' plants into two phyla: phylum I—**Gymnospermae** (not elaborated by him) and phylum II— **Angiospermae**. The latter are divided into two sub-phyla: sub-phylum I—**Dicotyledons** and sub-phylum II—**Monocotyledons**. Dicotyledons are divided into two big divisions: division I—**Lignosae** (with 54 orders and 246 families) and division II—**Herbaceae** (with 28 orders and 96 families). Monocotyledons are divided into three divisions: division I—**Calyciferae** (with 12 orders and 29 families), beginning with *Butomaceae* and ending in Zingiberales (*Scitamineae* of Bentham and Hooker), division II—**Corolliferae** (with 14 orders and 34 families) beginning with *Liliaceae* and ending in *Orchidaceae*; and division III—**Glumiflorae** (with 3 orders and 6 families), beginning with *Juncaceae* and ending in *Gramineae*. Thus, there are altogether 411 families of Angiospermae— 342 of Dicotyledons and 69 of Monocotyledons. In his classification, Hutchinson placed the Gymnospermae first, then the Dicotyledons, and finally the Monocotyledons.

Merits. (1) Most taxonomists believe that this system has given us a much better idea of phylogenetic conception and has stimulated rethinking on the subject. (2) The primitive or basic orders are Magnoliales, representing arborescent families, and Ranales, representing herbaceous families, giving rise to woody and herbaceous forms, respectively, on parallel lines. (3) Bisexual and polypetalous flowers precede unisexual and gamopetalous flowers. (4) Amentiferae (catkin-bearing families with unisexual, apetalous flowers), e.g. *Fagaceae*—oak, *Betulaceae*—birch, *Juglandaceae*—walnut, and *Salicaceae*—willow and poplar, is regarded as advanced (and not primitive, as by Engler) and thus has been transferred (including Urticales) to a new phyletic position

close to Rosales and Leguminosae. Their apparent simplicity represents reduction and speciliazation (and not primitiveness). (5) *Casuarinaceae* has been assigned an advanced position and placed at the top of the Amentiferae. (6) Several large orders have been split up into distinct small families, thus simplifying matters, e.g. Rosales, Perietales and Malvales. (7) Many families have been raised to the rank of orders, e.g. *Leguminosae* (now to an order), *Saxifragaceae* to Saxifragales and *Podostemaceae* to Podostemales. (8) Several orders and families have been reshuffled, e.g. Cactales (Opuntiales of Engler) placed close to Cucurbitales and Passiflorales. (9) The origin of monocotyledons has been traced to dicotyledons at an early stage of evolution, the point of origin being the Ranales. (10) Helobiae (of Engler) have been split up into separate orders and the order of Butomales (*Butomaceae* and *Hydrocharitaceae*) is considered to be the starting point of monocotyledons. (11) The genera of *Liliceae* and *Amaryllidaceae* have been reshuffled on the basis of inflorescence characteristics (and not on ovary position). (12) Several orders have been rearranged, ending in Cyperales and Graminales.

Demerits. (1) Many doubt the wisdom of Hutchinson's rigid bifurcation of dicotyledons into Lignosae (woody types) and Herbaceae (herbaceous types). (2) Many hold different views regarding the relationship between various orders and families. (3) The monophyletic view of the origin of angiosperms is not universally accepted. (4) The monophyletic origin of monocotyledons from the Ranales, as put forward by Hutchinson, clashes with the views of Lotsy (1911) and Hallier (1912), who put forward polyphyletic (diphyletic) views. (5) Urticales, Umbellales, Euphorbiales, etc. are said to originate from different ancestors.

Dicotyledons and Monocotyledons. The division of angiosperms into these two large classes is based on the following factors: (1) In dicotyledons, the embryo bears *two cotyledons*, whereas in monocotyledons, it bears *only one*. (2) In dicotyledons, the primary root persists and gives rise to the *tap root*, while in monocotyledons, the primary root soon perishes and is replaced by a cluster of *adventitious* (*fibrous*) *roots*. (3) As a rule, venation is *reticulate* in dicotyledons and *parallel* in monocotyledons. Among monocotyledons, aroids, sarsaparilla (*Smilax*) and yams (*Dioscorea*), however, show reticulate venation, and among dicotyledons, Alexandrian laurel (*Calophyllum*) shows parallel venation. Further, in dicotyledons, the veinlets end freely in the mesophyll of the leaf, whereas in monocotyledons, veins or veinlets do not end freely. (4) The dicotyledonous flower usually has a *pentamerous* symmetry, sometimes *tetramerous* (as in *Cruciferae*, and *Rubiaceae*), while the monocotyledonous flower has a *trimerous* symmetry. (5) In the dicotyledonous stem, the vascular bundles are *arranged in a ring* and are *collateral* and *open*, that is, they contain a strip of cambium which gives rise to secondary growth. In the monocotyledonous stem, however, the bundles are *scattered* in the ground tissue and are *collateral* and *closed*. Hence, there is no secondary growth (with but few exceptions). Also the bundles are more numerous in monocotyledons than in dicotyledons. Further, they are more or less oval in monocotyledons and wedge-shaped in dicotyledons. (6) In the dicotyledonous root, the number of xylem bundles varies from 2 to 6, seldom more, but in the monocotyledonous root there are many, seldom a limited number (5 to 8). It may also be noted that the cambium soon makes its appearance in the dicotyledonous root as a secondary meristem and gives rise to secondary growth, but in the monocotyledonous root, the presence of cambium is rare. Hence, there is no secondary growth.

Floral Diagram. The number of parts of a flower, their general structure, arrangement and the relation they bear to one another (aestivation), adhesion, cohesion, and position with respect to the mother axis may be represented by a diagram known as the **floral diagram**. The floral diagram is the ground plan of a flower. In the diagram, the calyx lies outermost, the corolla internal to the calyx, the androecium in the middle, and the gynoecium in the centre. Adhesion and cohesion (see p. 73) of members of different whorls may also be shown clearly by connecting the respective parts with lines. For example, FIG. 2 shows that there are altogether ten stamens, of which nine are united into one bundle (cohesion), and the remaining one is free, while FIG. 40 shows that the petals and stamens are united (adhesion). The black dot on the top represents the position of the mother axis (not the pedicel), which bears the flower. The axis lies behind the flower and, therefore, the side of the flower nearest to the axis is called the *posterior* side, and the other side away from the axis the *anterior* side. The floral characteristics of species may be well represented by a floral diagram, while more than one diagram may be necessary to represent a genus or family.

Floral Formula. The different whorls of a flower, their number, cohesion and adhesion may be represented by a formula known as the **floral formula**. In the floral formula K stands for calyx, C for corolla, P for perianth, A for androecium and G for gynoecium. The figures following the letters

 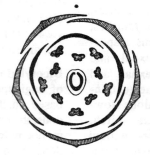 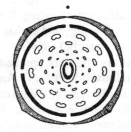

FIG. 2   FIG. 3   FIG. 4

Floral Diagrams (three types). FIG. 2. *Papilionaceae*; FIG. 3. *Caesalpinieae*; FIG. 4. *Mimoseae*

K, C, P, A and G indicate the number of parts of those whorls. Cohesion of a whorl is shown by enclosing the figure within brackets, and adhesion is shown by a line drawn on top of the two whorls concerned. In the case of the gynoecium, the position of the ovary is shown by a line drawn above or below G on the figure. If the ovary is superior, the line should be below it, and if inferior, the line should be on top. Thus, all the parts of a flower are represented in a general way by a floral formula. The floral characteristics of a family may also be represented by one or more formulae, as follows.

Ranunculaceae:	$\oplus \; \text{\Male\Female} \; K_5 C_5 A_\infty \underline{G}_\infty$
Anonaceae:	$\oplus \; \text{\Male\Female} \; K_3 C_{3+3} A_\infty \underline{G}_\infty$
Nymphaeaceae:	$\oplus \; \text{\Male\Female} \; K_4 C_\infty A_\infty \underline{G}_{(\infty)} \text{or}_\infty$
Cruciferae:	$\oplus \; \text{\Male\Female} \; K_{2+2} C_4 A_{2+4} \underline{G}_{(2)}$
Malvaceae:	$\oplus \; \text{\Male\Female} \; K_{(5)} \overline{C_5 A}_{(\infty)} \underline{G}_{(5-\infty)}$
Cucurbitaceae:	$\oplus \; \text{\Male}\,\text{\Female} \; \text{or} \; \text{\Male}-\text{\Female}$
	$\text{\Male} \; K_{(5)} C_{(5)} A_{3 \, or \, 5}$
	$\text{\Female} \; K_{(5)} C_{(5)} \bar{G}_{(3)}$
Solanaceae:	$\oplus \; \text{\Male\Female} \; K_{(5)} \overline{C_{(5)} A}_5 \underline{G}_{(2)}$
Labiatae	$\cdot\vdash \; \text{\Male\Female} \; K_{(5)} \overline{C_{(5)} A}_4 \underline{G}_{(2)}$

Besides, some symbols are used to represent certain features of flowers. Thus $\text{\Male}$ represents male, $\text{\Female}$ female, $\text{\Male\Female}$ hermaphrodite, $\text{\Male\Female}$ dioecious, $\text{\Male}-\text{\Female}$ monoecious, $\text{\Male}\,\text{\Female}\,\text{\Male\Female}$ polygamous, $\oplus$ actinomorphic, $\cdot\vdash$ zygomorphic, ∞ indefinite number of parts, etc.

Features used in descriptions of Angiospermic Plants

Habitat: natural abode of the plant.

Habit: herb (erect, prostrate, decumbent, diffuse, trailing, twining or climbing), shrub (erect, straggling, twining or climbing) or tree or any other peculiarity in the habit.

Root: nature of the root; any special form.

Stem: kind of stem—herbaceous or woody; cylindrical or angular; hairy or smooth; jointed or not; hollow or solid; erect, prostrate, twining or climbing; nature of modification, if any.

Leaf: arrangement—whether alternate, opposite (superposed or decussate) or whorled; stipulate or exstipulate; nature of the stipules, if present, simple or compound; nature of the compound leaf and the number of leaflets; shape and size; hairy or smooth; deciduous or persistent; venation; margin; apex; and petiole.

Inflorescence: type of inflorescence (to be explained).

Flower: sessile or stalked; complete or incomplete; unisexual or bisexual; regular, zygomorphic, or irregular; hypogynous, epigynous or perigynous; bracteate or ebracteate; nature of bracts and bracteoles, if present; shape, colour and size of the flower.

Calyx: polysepalous or gamosepalous; number of sepals or lobes; superior or inferior; aestivation; shape, size and colour.

Corolla: polypetalous or gamopetalous; number of petals or lobes; superior or inferior; aestivation; shape, size colour and scent; corona or any special feature.

(When there is not much difference between the calyx and the corolla, the term **perianth** should be used. It may be sepaloid or petaloid, polyphyllous or gamophyllous, or free or epiphyllous).

Androecium: number of stamens—definite (ten or less) or indefinite (more than ten); free or united; nature of cohesion—monadelphous, diadelphous, polyadelphous, syngenesious or synandrous; nature of adhesion—epipetalous or gynandrous, or any special feature; whether alternating with the petals (or corolla-lobes) or opposite them. Length of stamens—general length; inserted or exerted; didynamous or tetradynamous; position of stamens—hypogynous, perigynous or epigynous; attachment of the anther and its dehiscence; anther lobes or appendages, if any.

Gynoecium or Pistil: number of carpels; syncarpous or apocarpous; nature of style—long or short; stigmas—simple, lobed or branched; their number and nature—smooth or papillose; ovary—superior or inferior; number of lobes; number of chambers (loculi); nature of placen-tation; number and form of ovules in each loculus of the ovary.

Fruit: kind of fruit (to be explained).

Seeds: number of seeds in the fruit; shape and size; albuminous or exalbuminous; nature of endosperm, if present.

CHAPTER 3

SELECTED FAMILIES OF DICOTYLEDONS[1]

Sub-class I Polypetalae

FAMILY 1 RANUNCULACEAE (over 1,200 sp.— 157 sp. in India)

Habit—These are annual or perennial herbs or climbing shrubs, usually with an acrid juice.

Leaves. The leaves are simple or compound, alternate or rarely opposite, radical and cauline, usually with a sheathing base.

Inflorescence. The inflorescence is of the cymose type.

Flowers. These are mostly regular (actinomorphic), and sometimes zygomorphic, as in larkspur (*Delphinium*) and monk's hood (*Aconitum*). They are bisexual and hypogynous, and often showy. The sepals and petals are in whorls, while the stamens and carpels are arranged spirally on the elongated thalamus.

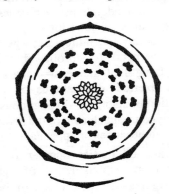

FIG. 5. Floral diagram of *Ranunculaceae*.

Calyx. There are usually 5 sepals, sometimes more. They are free, and often brightly coloured.

Corolla. There are 5 or more petals, which are free. Sometimes petals are absent. They often have nectaries and are imbricate. The perianth leaves (when calyx and corolla are not distinguishable) are free and petaloid.

Androecium. The stamens are numerous, free, and usually spiral.

Gynoecium. The carpels are usually numerous, sometimes a few or even one. They are free (apocarpous), usually spiral, with one or more ovules in each. In *Nigella*, carpels are united at the base.

Fruit. Is an aggregate of achenes or follicles, rarely a berry or capsule. **Seeds** albuminous.

Floral formula $\oplus\ \male\ K_5 C_5 A_\infty \underline{G}_\infty$.

Ranunculaceae, according to Hutchinson, is a most primitive family that originated from some gymnospermic stock and developed parallel with *Magnoliaceae* (see p. 538). The former shows evolutionary progress through herbaceous families like *Nymphaeaceae*, *Papaveraceae*, *Capparidaceae* and *Cruciferae*. Hutchinson also holds that monocotyledonous families like *Alismaceae* and *Hydrocharitaceae* have evolved from Ranalean stock.

EXAMPLES. The larger genera are *Ranunculus* (300 sp.), *Clematis* (250 sp.), *Delphinium* (250 sp.), *Anemone* (120 sp.), *Aconitum* (over 100 sp.), *Thalictrum* (over 100 sp.), and *Aquilegia* (100 sp.). **Useful plants:** monk's hood (*Aconitum ferox*; B. KATBISH; H. BISH)—medicinal, tuberous roots containing a very poisonous alkaloid; black cumin (*Nigella sativa*; B. & H. KALAJIRA)—seeds used as a condiment; *Thalictrum foliolosum*—a tall herb, root powder used as SURMA in eye diseases; *Coptis teeta* (B. MISHMI-TEETA)—a stemless herb in the Mishmi Hills, roots medicinal. **Ornamental plants:** larkspur (*Delphinium ajacis*), wind flower (*Anemone elongata*)— a small, tuberous plant

---

[1]In India, dicotyledons are represented by 173 families and 11,124 species approximately.

Ranunculaceae. FIG. 6. *Ranunculus sceleratus*. *A*, basal portion of the plant with leaves and roots; *B*, upper portion of the same with inflorescence; *C*, flower; *D*, flower cut longitudinally; *E*, a sepal; *F*, a petal; *G*, a stamen; *H*, a carpel; and *I*, a fruit (achene)

with woolly achenes for wind dispersal, virgin's bower (*Clematis*), e.g. *C. gouriana*, *C. cadmia*, etc.—climbing shrubs, columbine (*Aquilegia vulgaris*), etc.

Other common plants: *Ranunculus*, e.g. Indian buttercup (*R. sceleratus*)—usually growing in river and marsh banks, water crowfoot (*R. aquatilis*)—growing in water and showing heterophylly, traveller's joy (*Naravelia zeylanica*)—a climbing shrub, *Thalictrum javanicum*—a perennial herb, etc.

FAMILY-2   MAGNOLIACEAE (250 sp.—30 sp. in India)

Habit. These are mostly ornamental evergreen trees and shrubs. Some are woody climbers.

Leaves. These are simple and alternate. The young leaves are often covered with stipules.

Flowers. These are solitary, terminal (as in *Magnolia*) or axillary (as in *Michelia*). They are often large, showy and fragrant. They are regular, bisexual and hypogynous.

Perianth leaves. These are all alike. They are petaloid and deciduous. They can be either cyclic, being arranged in whorls of 3 (trimerous), or acyclic (spiral). Sometimes the outer whorl is sepaloid.

Androecium. There are many free stamens. The filament is short or absent. The anther-lobes are linear, 4 in number and with prolonged connectives.

Gynoecium. There are many free carpels arranged spirally round the elongated thalamus. There are 1 or a few ovules in each carpel.

Fruit. The fruit is an aggregate of berries or follicles.

Seed. This is albuminous. The endosperm of the seed is non-ruminated.

Floral formula $\oplus$ $\male$ P ∞ A ∞ $\underline{G}$ ∞

Magnoliaceae is related to *Annonaceae*, but the main features that distinguish them from each other are: the presence of big stipules in the former standing as a hood over the bud and the presence of ruminated endosperm in the latter. Hutchinson considers *Magnoliaceae* to be the most primitive family, which closely approaches certain gymnosperms like Bennettitales (e.g. *Bennettites*) because of the spiral arrangement of the free stamens and free carpels, and also the presence of tracheids with bordered pits and unisexual flowers in *Drimys*. *Magnoliaceae* shows evolutionary progress through woody families like *Annonaceae* and *Lauraceae*.

Examples. *Magnolia* (80 sp.), e.g. *M. grandiflora*—a small American tree with large white flowers, *M. pterocarpa* (B. & H. DULEE-CHAMPA)—a tree with large fleshy greenish-white flowers, *M. griffithii* (B. GOURI-CHAMPA)— a tree with large pale-white flowers (about 15 cm. across), *M. fuscata* (B. CHINI-CHAMPA)—a shrub, and *M. pumila* (B. JAHURE-CHAMRA) also a shrub, both commonly planted in gardens, *M. globosa*—a small tree, and *M. campbellii*—a shrub grown at high altitude (the latter planted on Kurseong-Darjeeling road); *Michelia* (50 sp.). e.g.

Schizandra elongata—woody climbers. The family is well-represented in Assam and Meghalaya.

FAMILY 3 ANNONACEAE (850 *sp.*—100 *sp. in India*)

Habit. These are shrubs and trees, sometimes climbers.

Leaves. These are simple, alternate, distichous and exstipulate.

Flowers. These regular, bisexual, and hypogynous. They are often aromatic.

Perianth. This usually occur in three whorls of three members each. There are 3 sepals and 6 petals occurring in two whorls.

Androecium. There are many free stamens arranged spirally round the slightly elongated thalamus. The filament is short or absent. The

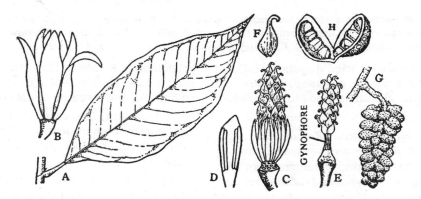

Magnoliaceae. FIG. 7. *Michelia champaca.* A, a leaf; B, a flower; C, stamens and carpels spirally arranged on the thalamus; D, a stamen with four anther lobes; E, carpels (free); F, a carpel; G, aggregate fruit (follicles); and H, a follicle dehiscing

M. champaca (B. SWARNA-CHAMPA; H. CHAMPA)— a tree with golden-yellow flowers, light but durable wood used for cabinet work, *M. alba* (B. & H. CHINA-CHAMPA)—a tree with white flowers, *M. oblonga*—a very tall tree (46 m.) with white flowers, wood used for planking and cabinet work, *Talauma hodgsoni*—a small tree with large red flowers, *T. phellocarpa* (B. TITA-CHAMPA)—a large tree with pale-white flowers, wood used for cabinet work, a few species of *Manglietia*, tulip-tree (*Liriodendron tulipifera*) grown in some gardens as ornamental trees *Kadsura roxburghiana* and

anther lobes are linear, 4 in number, extrorse, with an outgrowth of the connective.

Gynoecium. There are numerous carpels, free or connate, and each has a prolonged appendage. There are one to many ovules in each carpel.

Fruit. The fruit is an aggregate of berries.

Seed. The endosperm is distinctly ruminated, i.e. marked by irregular wavy lines.

Floral formula $\oplus$ ♂ $K_3 C_{3+3} A \propto \underline{G} \propto$

Annonaceae is allied to *Magnoliaceae*, but is distinguished from it by the presence of deeply

FIG. 8. Floral diagram of *Annonaceae* (*Artabotrys*).

ruminated endosperm.

Examples. The larger genera are *Uvaria* (150 sp.), *Annona* (120 sp.), *Polyalthia* (100 sp.), *Xylopia* (100 sp.), and *Artabotrys* (over 50 sp.). Some important species are custard-apple (*Annona squamosa*)—fruit edible, bullock's heart (*A. reticulata*)—fruit edible, sour sop (*A. muricata*)—fruit edible, *Artabotrys hexapetatus* (=*A. odoratissimus*)—flowers very fragrant, *Unona discolor* (B. LAVENDER-CHAMPA)—flowers very fragrant, mast tree (*Polyalthia longifolia*)—an evergreen tall tree, leaves used for decoration, *P. suberosa*—a handsome shrub, *Uvaria hamiltoni* and *Melodorum bicolor*—large woody climbers, *Cananga odorata*—a tall tree, flowers yield Macassar oil (a perfume), and Negro pepper (*Xylopia aromatica*)—an African shrub, fruit (about 5 cm. long) used as a spice.

FAMILY 4. NYMPHAEACEAE (100 sp.—11 sp. in India)

Habit. These are aquatic, perennial herbs.

Leaves. These are usually floating, borne on a long petiole, and cordate or peltate.

Flowers. The flowers are often large, showy and solitary. They are borne on a long pedicel and are usually floating. They are bisexual, regular and usually perigynous, though often hypogynous or even epigynous. The thalamus is fleshy and goblet-shaped.

Perianth. There are several free leaves. There are usually 4 sepals, which gradually merge into the petals. The petals are numerous, and gradually merge into the stamens.

Androecium. The stamens are numerous, free, usually perigynous and adnate to the fleshy thalamus that envelops the carpels.

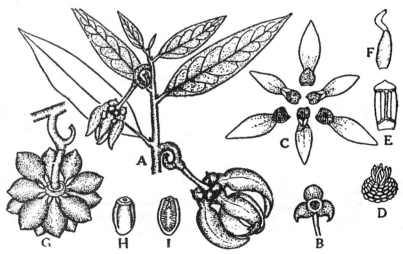

Annonaceae. FIG. 9. *Artabotrys.* *A*, a branch with two flowers; *B*, calyx; *C* petals spread out; *D*, stamens and carpels; *E*, a stamen with four anther lobes; *F*, a carpel; *G*, an aggregate of berries; *H*, a seed; and *I*, the seed cut longitudinally showing the ruminated endosperm

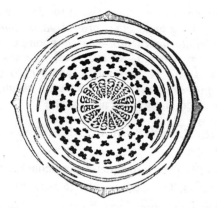

FIG. 10. Floral diagram of *Nymphaeaceae* (*Nymphaea*)

Gynoecium. There are several carpels, which can be either free on the fleshy thalamus, as in lotus, or syncarpous, lying embedded in the thalamus and surrounded by it. The ovary is unilocular with one ovule, or multilocular with many ovules, on superficial placentation. The stigmas are sessile, free or united, radiating, and often with horn-like appendages.

Fruit. The fruit is a berry.

Seeds. These are solitary and exalbuminous, or there can be many with both perisperm and endosperm. A spongy aril is often present, helping the seed float.

Floral formula $\oplus\ \male\ K_4\ C_\infty A_\infty\ \underline{G}(_\infty)\ or\ _\infty$

Nymphaeaceae resembles *Ranunculaceae* and *Magnoliaceae* in that its floral whorls are of a spiro-cyclic nature and the pistil is sometimes apocarpous, as in *Cabomba*. The family also bears an affinity with monocotyledons (e.g. *Alismaceae*) through *Cabomba* which has a typical trimerous symmetry($P_{3+3}A_{3-6}\underline{G}_3$), apocarpous pistil and scattered, closed vascular bundles. It also shows an affinity with *Papaveraceae* with its superficial placentation and radiating stigmas.

Examples. These plants are often cultivated in beautify tanks, pools and ponds. The plants commonly cultivated are : water lilies (*Nymphaea* with 50 sp.), e.g. *N. lotus*, *N. rubra*, *N. stellata*, *N. alba*, etc., *Euryale ferox* (B. & H. MAKHNA), lotus (*Nelumbo nucifera* = *Nelumbium specisum*), and giant water lily (*Victoria amazanica* = *V. regia*; see FIG. IV/I). The giant water lily bears huge tray-like leaves, each measuring 1-2 metres in diameter. Although a native of South America, this plant grows luxuriantly in the Indian Botanical Gardens near Calcutta. Lotus has some distinctive characteristics: (1) the leaves and flowers are raised above the surface of the water; (2) the flowers are hypogynous; (3) there are several carpels, free (apocarpous), and embedded in the upper surface of the top-shaped thallamus; (4) the ovary is unilocular with one ovule; (5) the stigmas are sessile, solitary; and (6) the seeds exalbuminous.

FAMILY 5 PAPAVERACEAE (250 *sp.* —40 *sp. in India*)

Habit. They are mostly herbs with milky or yellowish latex.

Leaves. The leaves are radical and cauline, simple and alternate, often lobed.

Flowers. These are solitary, often showy, regular, bisexual and hypogynous.

FIG. 11. Water lily (*Nymphaea lotus*). *A*, an entire plant; *B*, a flower cut longitudinally (see also FIGS. I/104); *C*, transverse section of the ovary; and *D*, a young fruit

FIG. 12. Floral diagram of *Papaveraceae* (Argemone)

Calyx. The sepals are typically 2, sometimes 3, free, caducous.

Corolla. There are petals 2+2 or 3+3, arranged rarely more, in 2 whorls (rarely 3), large, free, rolled or crumpled in the bud, caducous and imbricate. **Androecium**. Stamens ∞, sometimes 2 or 4. They are free.

Gynoecium. The carpels (2-∞), (4-6) in *Argemone*. It is syncarpous. The ovary is superior, 1-chambered, or spuriously 2- to 4- chambered, with 2-∞ parietal placentae which may project inwards, as in poppy (*Papaver*). The stigmas are distinct or sessile and rayed over the ovary, as in poppy. The ovules are numerous.

Fruit. This is a septicidal capsule dehiscing by valves, or opening by pores. There are many seeds, with oily endosperm.

Floral formula $\oplus$ ♂ $K_{2\text{ or }3} C_{2+2\text{ or }3+3} A_{\infty}$ $\underline{G}_{(2-\infty)}$.

Examples. *Papaver* (110 sp.), e.g. opium poppy (*P. Somniferum*)—opium is the latex obtained from the unripe fruits. The seeds are used as a condiment POSTO and also yield an oil. Garden poppy (*P. orientale*) and Californian poppy (*Eschscholizia*) are cultivated as ornamental flowers. Prickly or Mexican poppy (*Argemone mexicana*) is a prickly weed, bearing yellow flowers in late winter, whose seeds yield an oil. Himalayan poppy (*Meconopsis*; 45 sp.) occurs mainly in Nepal and the Eastern Himalayas.

FAMILY 6 CRUCIFERAE (over 3,000 *sp.*—174 *sp. in India*)

Habit. These are annual herbs.

Leaves. The leaves are radical and cauline, simple, alternate, often lobed, or rarely pinnately compound.

Inflorescence. A raceme (corymbose towards the top).

Flowers. The flowers are regular and cruciform, bisexual and complete hypogynous.

Calyx. They are sepals, 2+2, which are free, and in two whorls.

Corolla—petals 4, free, in one whorl. They alternate with the sepals. They are cruciform. Each petal has distinct limb and claw.

Androecium. There are 6 stamens in two whorls, 2 short outer ones and 4 long inner ones (tetradynamous).

Gynoecium. There are 2 syncarpous carpels. The ovary is superior, at first one-celled, but later 2-celled owing to the development of a *false septum*. There are often many ovules in each cell, sometimes only 2. They are anatropous or campylotropous. The placentation is parietal.

Fruit. The fruit is a long, narrow siliqua or a short, broad silicula.

Seeds. These are exalbuminous. The embryo is curved. The seeds remain attached to a wiry framework, called the *replum* (see p. 105), which surrounds the fruit.

Floral formula $\oplus$ ♂ $K_{2+2} C_4 A_{2+4} \underline{G}_{(2)}$.

Cruciferae is allied to *Capparidaceae* in that

FIG. 13. Floral diagram of *Cruciferae*

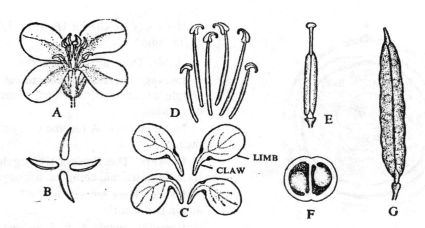

Cruciferae. FIG. 14. Mustard (*Brassica campestris*) flower. *A*, a flower—cruciform; *B*, calyx opened out; *C*, corolla opened out; *D*, androecium showing tetradynamous stamens; *E*, gynoecium showing two carpels united; *F*, ovary in transection showing parietal placentation and replum; and *G*, a fruit—siliqua. (see also FIG. 1 in Introduction)

both have a tetramerous perianth, bicarpellary ovary, parietal placentation, folding of the embryo in various ways, exalbuminous seeds, and often campylotropous ovules. It should be noted, however, that the tetradynamous condition is characteristic of *Cruciferae*, while it is very rare in *Capparidaceae*. The gynophore (sometimes also the androphore) is mostly present in *Capparidaceae*, but altogether absent in *Cruciferae*. The two families may have a common ancestor, or *Cruciferae* may have evolved from some primitive member of *Capparidaceae*.

Examples. The larger genera are *Draba* (about 300 sp. in northern temperate regions and Arctic), *Cardamine* (130 sp.), *Lepidium* (130 sp.), *Alyssum* (130 sp.), *Rorippa* (70 sp.) and *Brassica* (50 sp.). *Useful plants — Oils and condiments:* mustard (*Brassica campestris*), Indian mustard (*B. juncea*), Indian rape (*B. napus*), white mustard (*B. alba*), black mustard (*B. nigra*), etc. *Vegetables:* radish (*Raphanus sativus*), cabbage (*Brassica oleracea* var. *capitata*), cauliflower (*B. oleracea* var. *botrytis*), turnip (*B. rapa*), kohl-rabi or knol-kohl (*B. caulorapa*), *B. rugosa* (B. LAI-SAK), garden cress (*Lepidium sativum*; B. HALIM-SAK; H. HALIM), water cress (*Nasturtium officinale*), etc. **Ornamental plants:** candytuft (*Iberis amara*; H. CHANDNI)—fruit a silicula, alison (*Alyssum mar-*

itimum)—fruit a silicula, wallflower (*Cheiranthus cheiri*), etc.

Other common plants: *Rorippa indica* (=*Nasturtium indicum*), *Eruca sativa*, bitter cress (*Cardamine debilis*), shepherd's purse (*Capsella bursapastoris*)—fruit a silicula, etc.

FAMILY 7 CAPPARIDACEAE (650 sp.—53 sp. in India)

Habit. These are herbs, climbing shrubs, or trees.

Leaves. The leaves are mostly alternate, rarely opposite, and simple or palmately compound. The stipules, if present, are minute or spiny.

Flowers. These are regular (actinomorphic), sometimes zygomorphic, hypogynous or perigynous, and bisexual. The thalamus is elongated in some cases (gynophore) between the stamens and the pistil. Sometimes both the androphore and gynophore develop.

Calyx. There are 2+2 sepals, which are free.

Corolla. There are 4 free petals.

Androecium. There are usually many free stamens, sometimes 6. They are not tetradynamous. There may be a disc between the perianth and the androecium.

Gynoecium. There are usually 2 carpels; rarely

many. They are syncarpous. The gynophore is often present. The ovary is superior, one-celled, or 2-celled due to a false partition wall. The replum can be present or absent. The placentation is parietal. There are many campylotropous ovules.

Fruit. The fruit is an elongated capsule or a berry.

Seeds. These are exalbuminous. The embryo is curved in various ways.

Floral formula $\oplus\ \male\female\ K_{2+2}\ C_4\ A_{\infty\,or\,6}\ \underline{G}\ _{(2)}.$

From the structure of the flower, it appears that *Capparidaceae* stands midway between *Papaveraceae* and *Cruciferae*. Its perianth and pistil resemble those of *Cruciferae* (see p. 547), while its androceum may resemble that of *Papaveraceae*.

Examples. *Polanisia icosandra* (=*Cleome viscosa*), *Gynandropsis gynandra*, *Capparis* (200 sp.), usually with spinous stipules, eg. *C. sepiaria*, *C. horrida* and *C. aphylla* (the whole leaf is modified into a tendril), caperbush (*C. spinosa*)— pickled flower-bud of it is called caper, etc., *Crataeva nurvala* (=*C. religiosa*)—a large tree, and *Roydsia suaveolens*—flowers delightfully scented.

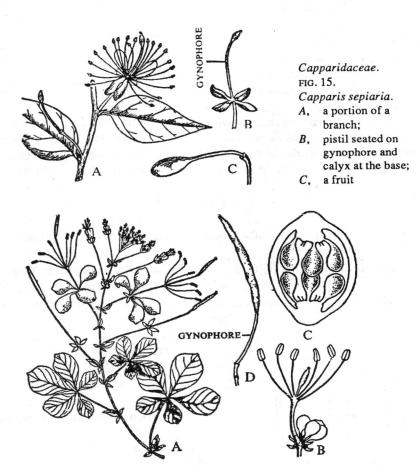

Capparidaceae.
FIG. 15.
Capparis sepiaria.
A, a portion of a branch;
B, pistil seated on gynophore and calyx at the base;
C, a fruit

Capparidaceae. FIG. 16. *Gynandropsis gynandra.* A, a branch with leaves and flowers; B, a flower; C, section of ovary showing parietal placentation; and D, a fruit

FAMILY 8 CARYOPHYLLACEAE (2,000 sp.—106 sp. in India)

Habit. These are annual or perennial herbs, with swollen nodes.

Leaves. These are simple, opposite, sessile, sometimes connate and often stipulate.

Inflorescence. The inflorescence is a cyme (usually dichasial).

Flowers. These are regular, bisexual, hypogynous and caryophyllaceous.

Calyx. There are usually 5, free or slightly connate sepals.

Corolla. There are usually 5 petals. They are free, and usually clawed. Sometimes the androphore develops.

Androecium. There are usually 10, sometimes 8, stamens. They are free or sometimes united at the base and in two whorls, the outer opposite the petals and the inner opposite the sepals.

Gynoecium. There are (5) or (3) carpels. The ovary is one-celled due to the breaking down of the septa at an early stage. The placentation is central. There are usually many ovules and 5 or 3 free styles. The stigma lies along the inner surface of the style.

Fruit. The fruit is a capsule dehiscing by valves.

Seeds. There are usually many, albuminous seeds. The embryo is curved.

Floral formula $\oplus \, \male \, K_5 \, C_5 \, A_{5+5} \, \underline{G}_{(3-5)}$.

Caryophyllaceae is related to *Portulacaceae*. According to Hutchinson, *Amaranthaceae* and *Chenopodiaceae* are derived from Caryophyllaceae, considering the reduction in floral members, while Engler holds the reverse view.

Examples. The larger genera are *Silene* (500 sp.)—a Mediterranean genus, *Dianthus* (ove 300 sp.), *Arenaria* (over 200 sp.)—in northern temperate regions, *Gypsophila* (125 sp.) and *Stellaria* (over 100 sp.). Some important species are *Dianthus*—many cultivated for ornamental flowers, e.g. pink (*D. chinensis*), carnation (*D. caryophyllus*), sweet william (*D. barbatus*), etc., *Drymaria cordata*—a common diffuse weed, soapwort (*Saponaria vaccaria*; B. SABUNI; H. MUSNA)—a weed, *Polycarpon loeflingiae* (B. GIMA; H. SURETA)—a bitter diffuse herb, *Stellaria media*—a weed, *Spergula arvensis*—a weed, *Gypsophila elegans*—flowers in loose sprays and used for table decoration, *Silene* (some species in temperate western Himalayas).

FAMILY 9 DIPTEROCARPACEAE (380 sp.—34 sp. in India)

Habit. These are mostly large, resinous trees.

Leaves. The leaves are simple, usually alternate, entire, leathery, evergreen or deciduous. The stipules are often prominent.

Inflorescence. The pericle an axillary or terminal.

Flowers. These are regular, bisexual, hypogynous or perigynous, and pentamerous.

Calyx. There are 5 sepals (polysepalous) persistent and 2 or more develop into wings.

Corolla. There are 5 petals. They are free or connate at the base. Aestivation is twisted.

Androecium. There are 5, 10, or ∝ stamens, free or connate at the base. The anther is 2-celled, connective, has an appendage.

Gynoecium. There are (3) carpels, syncarpous. The ovary is superior, 3-locular, with 2-∝ pendulous ovules.

Fruit. The fruit is a one-seeded nut, usually winged.

Seed. The seeds are exalbuminous.

Floral formula $\oplus \, \male \, K_5 \, C_5 \, A_{5, \, 10, \, 15 \, or \, \propto} \, \underline{G}_{(3)}$.

Examples. The larger genera are *Vatica* (over 90 sp.), *Hopea* (90), *Shorea* (90 sp.), and

FIG. 17. Floral diagram of *Caryophyllaceae*

Dipterocarpus (70 sp.). Some important species are wood-oil tree (*Dipterocarpus turbinatus*; B. & H. GARJAN; see FIG. I/177*A*)—a moderately hard timber tree, stem yields GARJAN oil and resin; *D. macrocarpus*—a very tall timber tree (46 metres), wood moderately hard; *Shorea robusta* (B. & H. SAL; see FIG. I/177*C*)—a very valuable timber tree; *S. assamica*—wood somewhat softer; *Vatica lancaefolia*—used as firewood and makes good charcoal; *Vateria indica*—yields a gum-resin used for Indian copal varnish; *Hopea odorata* (see FIG. I/176*C*)—a tall tree, etc.

FAMILY 10 MALVACEAE[1] (1,000 sp.—105 sp. in India)

Habit. These are herbs, shrubs or trees.

Leaves. The leaves are simple, alternate and palmately veined. There are 2 free stipules. These are lateral.

Flowers. These are regular, polypetalous, bisexual, hypogynous, and copiously mucilaginous. They have a whorl of bracteoles known as the epicalyx (except in *Abutilon* and *Sida*).

Calyx. There are(5)sepals. They are united and valvate.

Corolla. There are(5)free petals, attached to the base of the staminal tube. The aestivation is twisted.

Androecium. There are many stamens which are monadelphous, i.e. united into one bundle called the staminal column or tube. The androecium is epipetalous (staminal tube adnate to the petals at the base). The anthers are reniform and unilocular. The pollen grains are large and spiny.

Gynoecium. There are usually 5 to ∞ carpels—syncarpous—(2-3 in *Kydia*). The ovary is superior, and 5 to ∞ (locular, usually 5-locular). Each loculus has one to many ovules. The placentation is axile. The style passes through the staminal tube. The stigmas are free, and of the same number as the carpels.

Fruit. The fruit is a capsule, sometimes a

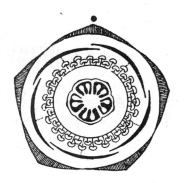

FIG. 18. Floral diagram of *Malvaceae*

schizocarp.

Seed. The seed is endospermic.

Floral formula $\oplus \; \male \; K_{(5)} \overline{C_5 A_{(\infty)}} \underline{G}_{(5-\infty)}$

Malvales may be allied to Guttiferales, considering the various degrees of union of stamens, 5-merous calyx and corolla, and hypogynous flowers. They may have a common origin.

Examples. The larger genera are *Hibiscus* (over 200 sp.), *Sida* (200 sp.), *Abutilon* (100 sp.) and *Malva* (40 sp.). **Useful plants:** *Gossypium* (20 sp.) yields commercial textile cotton, rozelle (*Hibiscus sabdariffa*)—fruits used for a sour jelly, Madras or Deccan hemp (*H. cannabinus*)—a source of strong fibres, musk mallow (*H. abelmoschus*; B. MUSHAKDANA; H. MUSHAK-DANA)—seeds smell like musk and are used as a flavouring agent and as a medicine, mallow (*Malva verticillata*)—cultivated as a winter vegetable, lady's finger (*Abelmoschus esculentus*)— green fruit used as a vegetable. **Ornamental plants:** Several species of *Hibiscus*, e.g. shoe-flower or China rose, (*H. rose-sinensis*), *H. mutabilis* (B. STHAL-PADMA; H. GUL-AJAIB). *H. radiatus*, etc., Chinese lantern (*Achania malvaviscus*; B. LANKAJABA), and hollyhock (*Althaea rosea*). **Shade tree:** Portia tree (*Thespesia populnea*).

Other common plants: *Sida cordifolia, S. rhomboidea, Urena lobata, Hibiscus vitifolius* (B. & H. BAN-KAPAS), Indian mallow (*Abutilon*

---

[1] Malvales of Bentham and Hooker—*Malvaceae, Tiliaceae* and *Sterculiaceae*; the same order of Engler—*Tiliaceae, Malvaceae, Bombacaceae, Sterculiaceae*, and a few more; Hutchinson has split the order into two: Malvales—*Malvaceae*, and Tiliales—*Tiliaceae, Sterculiaceae, Bombacaceae* and a few more.

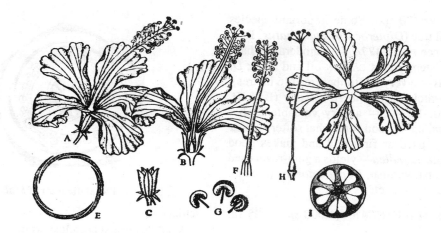

Malvaceae. FIG. 19. China rose (*Hibiscus rosa-sinensis*) flower. *A*, an entire flower; *B*, the same split open longitudinally showing the four whorls, more particularly the staminal column with the style passing through it; *C*, calyx with epicalyx; *D*, corolla opened out; *E*, twisted aestivation of corolla; *F*, androecium showing monadelphous stamens; *G*, one-celled anthers—young and mature (dehiscing*); H*, gynoecium showing five carpels united; and *I*, ovary in transection showing axile placentation

indicum; B. PETARI; H. KANGHI), *Malachra capitata* (B. & H. BAN-BHINDI) and *Malvastrum spicatum*—common weeds of waste places.

FAMILY 11 STERCULIACEAE (700 sp.—75 sp. in India)

Habit. These are shrubs or trees, rarely herbs.

Leaves. The leaves and stipules are like those of *Malvaceae*.

Inflorescence. This is cymose, often complex.

Flowers. (see FIG. I/95C). The flowers are regular and oftens zygomorphic. They are bisexual, rarely unisexual (as in *Sterculia*), and hypogynous.

Calyx and **Corolla.** These are like those of *Malavaceae*, sometimes the corolla is absent. There is no epicalyx.

Androecium. The number of stamens varies from 5-25, though there are usually ∝ stamens. They are mostly arranged in two whorls, the outer whorl opposite to the sepals and often reduced to staminodes or absent, and the inner whorl opposite to the petals, being fertile and often branched. All stamens are more or less united below into a tube,

or sometimes on the gonophore. The anthers are 2-locular.

Gynoecium. There are (5-2) Carpels (often 5); syncarpous. The ovary is superior, and is 5- to 2-locular, with 2-∝ anatropous ovules in each loculus. The style is simple and the stigma lobed.

Fruit. The fruit can be dry or fleshy, and is often a schizocarp.

Seed. This has a fleshy endosperm, sometimes arillate.

Floral formula $\oplus \male$ K$_{(5)}$C$_5$A$_{(\infty)}$$\underline{G}_{(5-2)}$.

Examples. The larger genera are *Sterculia* (over 200 sp.), *Dombeya* (over 100 sp.; African) *Cola* (over 100 sp.; African), *Hermannia* (150 sp.; African), and *Vatica* (over 70 sp.). Some important species are *Sterculia foetida* (B. & H. JANGLI-BADAM)—a tall tree with digitate leaves, *S. villosa* (B. & H. UDAL, ODAL)— a moderately tall tree with deeply-lobed simple leaves, *S. alata*—a very tall handsome tree (46 m. high) with entire simple leaves, etc., *Pterospermum acerifolium* (see FIG. I/95C)—planted as a roadside tree, *Heritiera minor* (B. SUNDRI)—a valuable timber tree of the Sundarbans, *H. macrophylla*—a timber tree of Assam, *Kleinhovia hospita* (B. BOLA)—a tree of the Sundarbans, *Guazuma tomentosa* (B. NEPAL TUNTH)—often planted as a roadside tree, cocoa tree (*Theobroma cacao*)—cocoa and chocolate prepared from roasted seeds, cola-nut tree (*Cola acuminata*) of West Africa—nuts contain much caffeine, devil's cotton (*Abroma augusta*; B. & H. ULATKAMBAL)—a shrub with fruits standing erect on the branches, *Helicteres isora*—a shrub with crimson flowers, *Dombeya mastersii*—an ornamental large shrub (planted in Shillong), *D. angulata*—a much-branched shrub with clusters of pink flowers, noon flower (*Pentapetes phoenicea*)—a tall herb with red flowers, *Melochia corchorifolia* and *Waltheria indica*—common weeds.

FAMILY 12 TILIACEAE (450 *sp.*—72 *sp. in India*)

Habit. These are generally trees or shrubs, and sometimes herbs.

Leaves. The leaves and stipules are like those of *Malvaceae*.

Inflorescence. This is cymose and often complex.

Flowers. These are regular, usually bisexual, hypogynous, pentamerous.

Calyx. There are 5 or (5) sepals. The aestivation valvate. There is no epicalyx.

Corolla. This is polypetalous, with 5 petals. It is rarely absent, and imbricate in the bud.

Androecium. There are usually many stamens, free or polyadelphous. They are arranged at the base of the petals or on the gonophore, as in *Grewia*. The anther is 2-locular.

Gynoecium. This is syncarpous, with 5–2 carpels. The ovary is superior and 10 to 2-locular, with 1 to ∞ anatropous ovules in each chamber. The style is simple, and the stigma capitate or lobed.

Fruit. The fruit can be of different types, usually a capsule, drupe or berry.

Seed. The seed has a fleshy endosperm.

Floral formula $\oplus \; \male \; K_{(5) \, or \, 5} C_5 A_\infty \underline{G}_{(5\text{-}2)}$.

Examples. The larger genera are *Grewia* (150 sp.), *Triumfetta* (over 100 sp.), and *Corchorus*

FIG. 20. Floral diagram of *Tiliaceae* (*Corchorus*)

(40 sp.). Some important species are jute (*Corchorus capsularis* and *C. olitorius*)—bast fibres form commercial jute, *C. aestuans* (B. TITA-PAT)—a common weed, *Grewia asiatica* (B. & H PHALSA)—a tree bearing edible fruits, *G. multiflora*—often grown as a hedge plant, *G. hirsuta*—a shrub, *Brownlowia lanceolata* (B. BOLA-SUNDRI)—a middle-sized tree of the Sundarbans, wood used as a fuel, *Triumfetta rhomboidea*—an undershrub with hooked fruits, and *Tilia europea*—in temperate Himalayas.

FAMILY 13 BOMBACACEAE (180 *sp.*)

Habit. These are large trees.

Leaves. These are simple or digitately compound, with deciduous stipules.

Flowers. The flowers are regular, large, bisexual, and hypogynous.

Calyx. This is gamosepalous, with (5) sepals. It is valvate, often with an epicalyx.

Corolla. This is polypetalous, with 5 petals and imbricate.

Androecium. There are 5-∞ stamens, free or polyadelphous. The anthers are 2-celled (sometimes more). The pollen grains are smooth, and staminodes are often present.

Gynoecium. This is syncarpous, with (2–5) carpels. When 5, the carpels are opposite to the petals. The ovary is superior, multilocular, with 2-∞ ovules in each loculus.

Fruit. The fruit is a capsule.

Seeds. These are smooth, often very hairy, and

Distinguishing Characteristics of Malavales

Malvaceae	Sterculiaceae	Tiliaceae
Herbs, shrubs or trees	trees or shrubs, a few herbs	trees or shrubs, a few herbs
Leaves simple, often palmately lobed	simple or palmately compound	simple, entire or dentate
Flowers regular, bisexual with epicalyx	regular, sometimes zygomorphic, bisexual, rarely unisexual, corolla rarely absent, with no epicalyx	regular, bisexual, rarely unisexual, with no epicalyx
Stamens (∞), monadelphous, epipetalous, anther 1-locular	often many, typically in 2 whorls, the outer staminodial or 0, the inner fertile and branched, connate below, sometimes on gonophore; anther 2-locular	usually many, sometimes 10, free or connate at the base only, developing at the base of the petals or on gonophore, anther 2-locular
Carpels usually(5-∞),ovary 5 to ∞-locular, with 1-∞ anatropous ovules in each chamber	(5-2)(usually 5), ovary 5- to 2-locular, with 2-∞ anatropous ovules in each chamber	(5-2),carpels, ovary 10 to 2-locular, with 1-∞ anatropous ovules in each chamber
Fruit capsular or schizocarpic; seed with scanty endosperm	capsular or schizocarpic, seed with fleshy endosperm	capsular or berry-like; seed with fleshy endosperm
Embryo with folded cotyledons	with flat or folded cotyledons	with large leafy cotyledons

with scanty or no endosperm.

Floral Formula $\oplus\ \male\female\ K_{(5)}C_5A_{5-\infty}\underline{G}_{(2-5)}$

Examples. *Bombax* (60 sp.), e.g. red or silk cotton tree (*Bombax ceiba=Salmalia malabarica*) and *Ceíba* (20 sp.), e.g. white cotton tree or kapok (*Ceiba pentandra=Eriodendron anfractuosum*)—cotton in both used for stuffing pillows and cushions, and wood used for making tea boxes, matchboxes and matchsticks, baobab tree (*Adansonia digitata*)—trunk often reaching a diameter of 9 metres, balsa (*Ocroma pyramidale*)—a South American plant with very light wood, used for making models of boats, ships, etc.

FAMILY 14 RUTACEAE (900 *sp.*— 66 *sp. in India*)

Habit. These are shrubs and trees, (rarely herbs).

Leaves. The leaves are simple or compound, alternate or rarely opposite, and *gland-dotted*.

Flowers. These are regular, bisexual and hypogynous. The disc below the ovary is promi-

FIG. 21. Floral diagram of *Rutaceae*

nent, and ring or cap-like.

Calyx. There are 4 or 5 sepals free or connate below, and imbricate.

Corolla—petals 4 or 5, free, imbricate.

Androecium. The number of stamens varies. They can be as many, or more often twice as many, as the petals (obdiplostemonous), or numerous, as in *Citrus* and *Aegle*. They are free or united in irregular bundles (polyadelphous), and inserted on the disc.

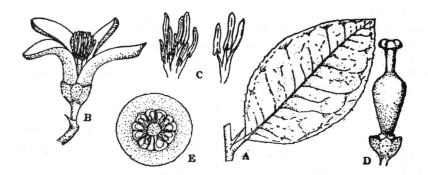

Rutaceae. FIG. 22. Sour lime (*Citrus aurantifolia*). *A,* a leaf; *B,* a flower; *C,* stamens
(polyadelphous); *D,* pistil on a disc, with calyx at the base; and *E,* section of ovary showing axile placentation

Gynoecium. There are generally (4) or (5) carpels, or ∞, as in *Citrus*[1]. They are syncarpous or free at the base and united above, and either sessile or seated on the disc. The ovary is generally 4 or 5-locular, or multilocular as in *Citrus*, with axile placentation (parietal in *Limonia* only). There are usually 2–∞ (rarely 1) ovules in each loculus, arranged in two rows.

Fruit. This is a berry, capsule or hesperidium (see p. 133).

Seeds. The seeds may or may not have an endosperm. Polyembryony is frequent in *Citrus*, e.g. lemon and orange (but not pummelo and citron).

Floral fomula $\oplus$ ♂ $K_{4\text{-}5}C_{4\text{-}5}A_{8,\,10\,or\,\infty}$ $\underline{G}_{(4,5\,or\,\infty)}$.

Rutaceae is similar to *Meliaceae* by virtue of its obdiplostemonous stamens (i.e. stamens in 2 whorls, the outer opposite to the petals), the presence of the disc, and often 5 carpels, the anatropous ovule with ventral raphe, and the types of fruit. Hutchinson has separated the above two families from Geraniales and placed them under two separate orders—Rutales and Meliales, respectively. Rutales is also related to Sapindales (*Sapindaceae, Anacardiaceae,* etc.), but in the latter order, the leaves are not gland-dotted.

Examples. The larger genera are: *Fagara* (over 200 sp.), *Ruta* (60 sp.), *Glycosmis* (60 sp.), and *Evodia* (45 sp.)]. **Useful Plants:** *Citrus* (e.g. lime, lemon, orange, citron and pummelo), wood-apple (*Aegle marmelos*)—the pulp containing *marmelosin* is an effective remedy for chronic dysentery and constipation, elephant-apple (*Limonia acidissima*), Chinese box (*Murraya paniculata*)—wood hard and useful, curry leaf plant (*M. koenigii*)—leaves used for flavouring curries, *Micromelum pubescens*—an evergreen tree, etc.

Other common plants: rue (*Ruta graveolens*; B. ERMUL; H. SADAB)—a strongly smelling small herb, *Glycosmis arborea, Clausena heptaphylla, C. pentaphylla* (B. & H. PAN-KARPUR), *Luvunga scandens*—a large thorny climbing shrub, *Toddalia aculeata* (B. TODALI; H. DAHAN)—a large thorny climbing shrub, *Zanthoxylum budrunga* (B.

[1]Common species of *Citrus:* sour lime (*C. aurantifolia;* B. PATI- OR KAGZI-NEBU; H. NIMBOO), SWEET LIME (*C. limetta;* B. MITHA-NEBU or KAGZI), lemon (*C. limon;* B. NEBU; H. KHATTI), rough lemon (*C. jambhiri;* B. JAMIR; H. JHAMBHIRI), *C assamensis* (B. ADA-JAMIRI)—used for garnishing curries, citron (*C. medica;* B. BARA-NEBU; H. BARA-NIMBOO), pummel or shaddock (*C. Grandis;* B. BATABI-NEBU; H. CHAKOTRA), Mandarin orange (*C. reticulata;* B. KAMALA; H. SANGTRA)—loose skinned commercial orange, sour or bitter orange (*C. aurantium*)—used in preparing marmalade, sweet orange (*C. sinensis*—Malta, Mosambi or Mozambique, and Valentia are varieties of it)—tight-skinned, king orange (*C. nobilis*), wild orange (*C. indica*)—growing wild in Assam, bergamot orange (*C. bergamia*)—bergamot oil is prepared from it, and grape fruit (*C. paradisi*).

BAZINALI; H. BADRANG)—a prickly tree, *Z. alatum* (B. NEPALI-Dhaniya, H. TEJPHAL or TUMRU)—a small aromatic tree, branches used as toothbrushes and fruit as a condiment like coriander, *Z. piperita*—pungent fruit yield Japanese pepper, *Evodia roxburghiana*—a tree, etc.

FAMILY 15 MELIACEAE (1,400 *sp.*—58 *sp. in India*)

Habit. These are mostly trees, rarely shrubs.

Leaves. The leaves are pinnately compound, and the leaflets are oblique.

Inflorescence. This has an axillary panicle.

Flowers. These are regular, often bisexual, sometimes polygamous (as in *Amoora*), and hypogynous.

Calyx. There are (4–5) sepals (gamosepalous).

Corolla. There are 4–5 petals (usually polypetalous) imbricate.

Androecium. There are 8–10 stamens, generally united into a long or short staminal tube.

Gynoecium. There are (2–5) carpels (syncarpous). The ovary is superior. It is 2- to 5-locular, rarely uni-locular, with 1 or 2 ovules in each chamber (seldom more); disc is annular, surrounding the ovary.

Fruit. The fruit is a capsule, berry or drupe.

Seed. This is often winged, and albuminous.

Floral formula $\oplus\ \male\ K_{(4-5)}C_{4-5}A_{(8-10)}\underline{G}_{(2-5)}$.

Examples. The larger genera are *Trichilia* (over 250 sp. in America and Africa), and *Dysoxylum* (about 200 sp.). **Timber trees:** mahogany (*Swietenia mahagoni*), toon (*Cedrella toona*), satinwood (*Chloroxylon swietenia*), *Amoora rohituka*—timber moderately hard, *A. wallichii*—timber hard and suitable for furniture, doors and windows, margosa (*Azadirachta indica = Melia azadirachta*; B. & H. NEEM)—wood dark-red and very hard, also medicinal (NEEM oil extracted from fruit and leaves contains a bitter alkaloid *margosine* which is very efficacious in sores and ulcers), Persian lilac (*Melia azedarach*; B. GHORA-NEEM)—also yields firewood, *Walsura robusta* (B. LALI)—heartwood brown or light red, *Dysoxylum procerum* (B.

LALI)—heartwood bright red, and *Chikrassia tabularis*—wood hard and suitable for planking and furniture.

FAMILY 16 RHAMNACEAE (900 *sp.*—51 *sp. in India*)

Habit. These are trees, shrubs and climbers.

Leaves. The leaves are simple, alternate and rarely opposite. They are stipulate (sometimes spinous).

Inflorescence. There is an axillary cyme (often paniculate).

Flowers. The flowers are small and inconspicuous. They are regular, bisexual or sometimes unisexual, and usually pentamerous (sometimes tetramerous). They are perigynous (with the receptacle cup-shaped) to epigynous (with the receptacle united with the ovary). The disc is well developed (intrastaminal).

Calyx. There are (5–4) sepals, gamosepalous and valvate.

Corolla. It is polypetalous, with 5–4 petals. It is often very small, clawed at the base and hooded above, and sometimes even absent.

Androecium. There are 5–4 stamens opposite to and often enclosed by the petals.

Gynoecium. It is syncarpous, with (3) carpels. The ovary is superior, free or immersed in fleshy disc, 3-locular (sometimes 2 or 1-locular) with 1 basal ovule in each chamber.

Fruit. This can be varying, a drupe, a nut or a dry fruit splitting into mericarps.

Seed. The seed has a thin endosperm.

Floral formula $\oplus\ \male\ K_{(5-4)}C_{5-4}A_{5-4}\underline{G}_{(3)}$.

Rhamnaceae is closely related to *Vitaceae*. *Rhamnaceae* can be distinguished from *Vitaceae* by mainly the following characteristics: simple leaves (sometimes with spines), very small petals, structure of receptacle (free from or united with the ovary), ovary often sunken in receptacle or disc, and fruit sometimes drupaceous.

Examples. The larger genera are *Rhamnus* (over 100 sp.), *Ziziphus* (about 100 sp.), *Gouania* (about 70 sp.), and *Ventilago* (37 sp.). Some important species are Indian plum or jujube (*Zizyphus mauritiana=Z. jujuba*)—a tree with edible fruit, *Z. oenoplia*—a sturdy shrub or undershrub, *Z. nummularia* and *Z. vulgaris*—shrubs, *Gouania leptostachya*—a strong climber with watch-spring-like tendrils, *Rhamnus nepalensis*— a rambling shrub, and *Ventilago maderaspatana*— a strong hook-climber.

FAMILY 17 SAPINDACEAE (1,100 *sp.*—46 *sp. in India*)

Habit. These are trees, shrubs or lianes, climbing by axillary tendrils which are often closely coiled. Balloon vine (*Cardiospermum*), however, is a slender tendril-climber (see FIG. I/37). The family shows anomalous secondary growth.

Leaves. These are alternate, usually pinnately compound, and rarely simple.

Inflorescence. This is racemose or cymose.

Flowers. These are very small, regular or slightly zygomorphic, unisexual, monoecious, or bisexual. They are generally pentamerous, though sometimes tetramerous. The male flowers often have a rudimentary ovary, and the female flowers often have staminodes.

Calyx. There are 5 sepals, sometimes 4. It is usually polysepalous and imbricate.

Corolla. There are 5 petals, often 4, forming regular flowers by the suppression of one petal. They are free and imbricate. The petals often have scales or tufts of hair. An annular disc is often present between the corolla and the androecium.

Androecium. There are 8 stamens (often by the suppression of 2 fewer stamens). They are often inserted within the disc around the ovary.

Gynoecium. There are (3) carpels (syncarpous). The ovary is 3-locular and superior, and has one ovule in each chamber.

Fruit. The fruit is dry (capsule or nut) or fleshy (berry or drupe) or sometimes a schizocarp.

Seed. This is often arillate, exalbuminous; embryo is curved.

Floral formula $\oplus$ or $\cdot | \cdot$ $\male$ − $\female$ $K_{5-4}C_{5-4}A_{4+4}\underline{G}_{(3)}$.

Examples. The larger genera are *Serjania* (over 300 sp., American), *Paullinia* (over 200 sp.,

American)—both are lianes with watch-spring-like tendrils, *Allophylus* (190 sp., tropical), and *Dodonaea* (50 sp.). Some important species are litchi (*Litchi chinensis*)—the edible part is the fleshy aril, longan (*Euphoria longana*)—aril edible, soap-nut (*Sapindus trifoliatus* and *S. mukorossi*)—fruits contain saponin which makes a lather with water and is used for washing silk and woollen fabrics, balloon vine (*Cardiospermum halicacabum*)—a common weed (see FIG. I/37), *Allophylus cobbe*—a shrub or small tree, *Aphania danura*—a small tree common in village shrubberies, *Dodonaea viscosa*—mostly grown as a hedge plant, *Schleichera trijuga*—a deciduous tree, source of the best Mirzapur lac and also a valuable timber tree.

FAMILY 18 ANACARDIACEAE (600 *sp.*—58 *sp. in India*)

Habit. These are shrubs or trees. Many of them are resinous.

Leaves. These are simple or pinnately compound, alternate, and exstipulate.

Inflorescence. This is a panicle of many small flowers.

Flowers. The flowers are small, regular and bisexual. They are sometimes polygamous, hypogynous to epigynous, and usually pentamerous. The disc is present.

Calyx. There are usually 5 sepals, though they vary from 3 to 7. They may be free or united.

Corolla. There are as many petals as sepals. The corolla is sometimes absent. It may be free or connate.

Androecium. There are 10-15 stamens (the number of fertile stamens varies in many cases, as in *Anacardium* and *Mangifera,* where only one stamen is fertile). They are free and inserted on an annular disc.

Gynoecium. There are usually (3−1) carpels and rarely 5 (syncarpous). The ovary is superior or sometimes inferior. It is often 1-celled (rarely 2 to 5-celled) and has one ovule in each chamber. Often only one ovule matures into a seed.

Fruit. The fruit is usually a 1-celled and 1-seeded drupe.

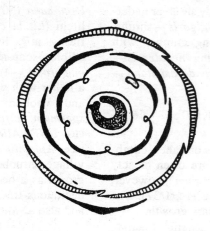

FIG. 23. Floral diagram of Anacardiaceae (*Mangifera*)

Seed. The seed is exalbuminous, with a large, curved embryo.

Floral formula $\oplus\ \male\male\ K_5C_5A_{10-5}\underline{G}_{(3-1)}$.

Examples. The larger genera are *Rhus* (over 300 sp.), and *Semecarpus* (50 sp.). Some important species are Mango (*Mangifera indica*), cashew-nut (*Anacardium occidentale*), Indian hogplum (*Spondias pinnata=S. mangifera*), hogplum (*S. cytherea*), pistachio (*Pistacia vera*), marking-nut (*Semecarpus anacardium*; B. BHELA; H. BHILAWA), *Odina wodier* (B. JIYAL; H. JHINGAN), *Buchanania latifolia* (B. & H. PIYAL), *Tapiria hirsuta*, and *Rhus* (some species are useful while others posionous), e.g. *Rhus parviflora*—fruits sour, *R. semialata*—a common tree of the Khasi Hills, yields extremely sour fruits (sold in the Shillong market as NAGA-TENGA), *R. vernicifera*—the lacquer tree of Japan.

FAMILY 19 LEGUMINOSAE[1] (12,000 *sp.*—951 *sp. in India*)

Habit. These are herbs, shrubs, trees, twiners or climbers.

Roots. The roots of many species, particularly of *Papilionaceae*, have tubercles (see FIG. III/5).

Leaves. These are alternate, pinnately compound, and rarely simple, as in rattlewort (*Crotalaria sericea*), camel's foot tree (*Bauhinia*) and some species of *Desmodium*, e.g *D. gangeticum*, with a swollen leaf-base known as the pulvinus. There are 2, usually free, stipules.

Flowers. These are bisexual and complete, regular or zygomorphic or irregular, and hypogynous or slightly perigynous.

Calyx. There are usually 5 or (5) sepals, with the odd one anterior (away from the axis). Sometimes there are 4 sepals. They may be united or free.

Corolla. There are usually 5 petals, with the odd one posterior (towards the axis). Sometimes there are 4 petals, free or united.

Androecium. There are usually 10 or more

---

[1] According to Bentham and Hooker and also Engler, the order Rosales includes both *Rosaceae* and *Leguminosae*, while Hutchinson has separated *Leguminosae* from Rosales and raised it to the rank of an order with three families—*Caesalpiniaceae*, *Mimosaceae* and *Papilionaceae*. It may also be noted that *Leguminosae* is the biggest family in India.

Distinguishing Characteristics of Leguminosae

	Papilionaceae	Caesalpinieae	Mimoseae
Leaves rarely simple, stipels often present	usually 1-pinnate, rarely simple, stipels absent	1 or 2-pinnate	bipinnate, stipels present or absent
Flowers	papilionaceous	zygomorphic	regular, small
Inflor.	racemose	racemose	spherical head
Calyx	gamosepalous, imbricate	polysepalous sometimes gamo-sepalous, usually imbricate	gamosepalous, usually valvate
Corolla	polypetalous, posterior petal largest and outermost, aestivation vexillary	polypetalous, posterior petal smallest and innermost, aestivation imbricate	gamopetalous, all petals equal, aestivation valvate
Androecium	stamens ten, (9) +1, rarely (10) or 10, pollen grains simple	ten or fewer, free, pollen grains, simple	often many or 10, rarely 4 or 8, free, pollen often compound

Floral formula $\cdot|\cdot \; \male\female \; K_{(5)}C_5A_{(9)+1}\underline{G}_1$ $\quad \cdot|\cdot \; \male\female \; K_5C_5A_{10}\underline{G}_1$ $\quad \oplus \; \male\female \; K_{(5-4)}C_{(5-4)} \; A_{\infty \, or \, 10}\underline{G}_1$

(For floral diagrams see p. 540)

stamens (often less than 10 by reduction) free or united.

Gynoecium. There is one carpel. The ovary is 1-celled, with 1 to many ovules. It is superior and the placentation is marginal. The ovary often borne on a long or short stalk, called the stipe or gynophore.

Fruit. This is mostly a legume or pod (dehiscent), or sometimes a lomentum (indehiscent).

This is the second biggest family among the dicotyledons (being second only to *Compositae*), and has varying characteristics. As such, it has been divided into the following sub-families: *Papilionaceae*, *Caesalpinieae* and *Mimoseae* (see footnote). The division is primarily based on the characteristics of the corolla and the stamens (see FIGS. 2-4). All these sub-families are well represented in India. From an economic standpoint, this is one of the most important families. It probably ranks second to *Gramineae* in the order of importance.

(1) *Papilionaceae* (754 sp. in India). Herbs, shrubs, trees and climbers. **Leaves**—unipinnate, sometimes trifoliate, rarely simple; stipels often present. **Inflorescence**—usually a raceme. **Flowers**—zygomorphic, polypetalous and papilionaceous. **Calyx**—usually 5 sepals, gamosepalous, often imbricate, sometimes valvate. **Corolla**—usually 5 petals, free, of very unequal sizes, the posterior and largest one being the vexillum or standard, the two lateral ones being the wings or alae, and the two innermost ones (apparently united) forming the keel or carina; aestivation vexillary. **Androecium**— stamens 10, diadelphous—(9) + 1, rarely 10, free, as in coral tree (*Erythrina*), or (10), connate, as in rattlewort (*Crotalaria*).

Floral formula $+ \; \male\female \; K_{(5)}C_5A_{(9)+1}\underline{G}_1.$

Examples of Papilionaceae. The larger genera are *Astragalus* (over 1,600 sp.; xerophytic), *Crotalaria* (over 600 sp.), *Desmodium* (over 400 sp.), *Indigofera* (350 sp.), *Trifolium* (300 sp.),

Tephrosia (300 sp.), *Dalbergia* (over 250 sp.), *Phaseolus* (over 200 sp.), *Lupinus* (about 200 sp.), *Lathyrus* (130 sp.) and *Aeschynomene* (over 100 sp.). **Useful plants:** Pulses (rich in protein): Bengal gram (*Cicer arietinum*), lentil (*Lens culinaris*), pigeon pea or red gram (*Cajanus cajan*), pea (*Pisum sativum*), green gram (*Phaseolus aureus*), black gram (*P. mungo*), *Lathyrus sativus* (B. & H. KHESARI), soya-bean (*Glycine max=G. soja*), broad bean (*Vicia faba*), etc. **Vegetables:** country bean (*Dolichos lablab*), cow pea (*Vigna sinensis*), sword bean (*Canavalia ensiformis*), French bean (*Phaseolus vulgaris*), etc. **Natural fertilizers:** *Sesbania cannabina* (B. DHAINCHA), sesban (*S. sesban*; B. JAINTI; H. JAINT), lucerne or alfalfa (*Medicago sativa*)—also an excellent fodder, *Tephrosia candida* and *Derris robusta*—grown in tea gardens, etc. **Timber trees:** Indian redwood (*Dalbergia sissoo*) and Indian rosewood (*D. latifolia*). **Other useful plants:** groundnut or peanut (*Arachis hypogaea*; see FIG. III/49), pith plant (*Aeschynomene aspera*; B. & H. SHOLA), Indian or sun hemp (*Crotalaria juncea*), fenugreek (*Trigonella foenumgraecum*; B. METHI),

indigo (*Indigofera tinctoria*), *Derris elliptica*—a woody climber, roots used as a valuable insecticide and also used for poisoning fish in tanks, Indian liquorice or crab's eye (*Abrus precatorius*), *Psoralea corylifolia*—an erect annual, seeds contain an essential oil used as a remedy for leucoderma, sweet pea (*Lathyrus odoratus*)—ornamental and fragrant, lupin (*Lupinus polyphyllus*)—ornamental and a fodder, red sandalwood (*Pterocarpus santalinus*), *Pongamia pinnata*—a shade tree, etc.

Other common plants: rattlewort (*Crotalaria sericea*), butterfly pea (*Clitoria ternatea*), *Sesbania grandiflora* (B. BAKPHUL; H. AGAST), coral tree (*Erythrina variegata*), flame of the forest (*Butea monosperma*), *Flemingia strobilifera*—a shrub with simple leaves and copious bracts, Indian telegraph plant (*Desmodium gyrans*), *D. gangeticum*, cowage (*Mucuna prurita*)—fruit with stinging hairs, wild pea (*Lathyrus aphaca*), wild indigo (*Tephrosia purpurea*), white clover (*Trifolium repens*)—a common prostrate weed bearing clusters of white flowers (in Shillong), etc.

(2) *Caesalpinieae* (110 sp. in India). Shrubs

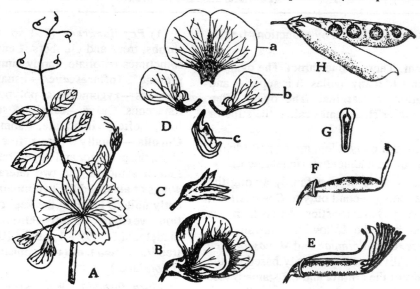

Papilionaceae. FIG. 24. Pea (*Pisum sativum*). *A*, a branch; *B*, a flower—papilionaceous (see also FIG. I/108); *C*, calyx; *D*, corolla—petals opened out (*a*, vexillum, *b*, wing; *c*, keel); *E*, stamens—(9) + 1 and pistil; *F*, pistil—1 carpel (note the ovary, style and stigma); *G*, ovary in transection showing marginal placentation; and *H*, a fruit—legume

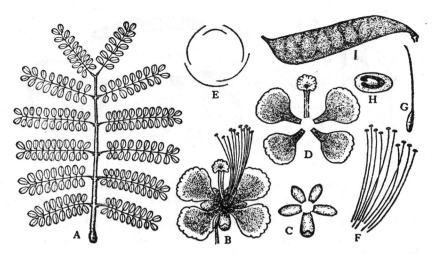

Caesalpinieae. FIG. 25. Dwarf gold mohur (*Poinciana pulcherrima*). *A*, a pinnately compound leaf; *B*, a flower; *C*, calyx; *D*, corolla—petals dissected out; *E*, aestivation (imbricate); *F*, stamens; *G*, pistil (one carpel); *H*, ovary in transection showing marginal placentation; and *I*, a fruit

and trees, rarely climbers or herbs. **Leaves—** unipinnate or bipinnate, rarely simple, as in camel's foot tree (*Bauhinia*): stipels absent. **Inflorescence—** mostly a raceme. **Flowers—** zygomorphic or irregular and polypetalous. **Calyx—**sepals usually 5, polysepalous (sometimes gamosepalous), imbricate. **Corolla—**usually 5 petals, free, subequal or unequal, the odd or posterior one (sometimes very small) always innermost; aestivation imbricate. **Androecium—** 10 stamens, or less by reduction; free.

Floral formula $-\cdot\vdash \oint$ $K_5 C_5 A_{10} \underline{G}_{-1}$.

Examples of *Caesalpinieae.* The larger genera are *Cassia* (450 sp.), *Bauhinia* (250 sp.) and *Caesalpinia* (100 sp.). **Useful plants:** tamarind

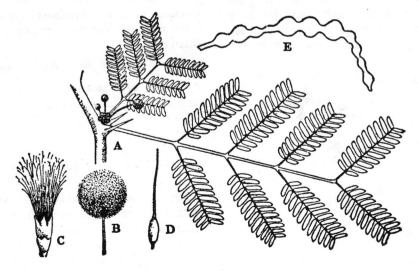

Mimoseae. FIG. 26. Gum tree (*Acacia nilotica*). *A*, a branch with bipinnate compound leaves; *B*, an inflorescence (head); *C*, a flower; *D*, pistil (one carpel); and *E*, a fruit (lomentum)

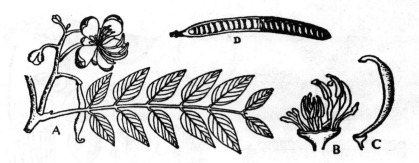

Caesalpinieae. FIG. 27. *Cassia sophera.* A, a branch with inflorescence;
B, stamens and pistil; C, pistil (one carpel); and D, a fruit partially opened up

(*Tamarindus indica*)--fruit widely used for sour preparations, Indian laburnum (*Cassia fistula*)--heartwood very hard and durable, flowers golden yellow, etc. **Medicinal:** Indian senna (*Cassia angustifolia*; B. SONAPAT or SONAMUKHI; H. SANAKKAPAT), *Saraca indica*, fever nut (*Caesalpinia crista= C. bonducella*), etc. **Dyes:** sappan or Brazil wood (*Caesalpinia sappan*; B. & H. BAKAM)--wood yields a valuable red dye used extensively for dyeing silk and wool, starch coloured with this dye forms ABIR used in 'HOLI festival, and pods yield a high percentage of tannin, logwood (*Haematoxylon*), an American plant--wood yields the dye haematoxylin. **Ornamental:** camel's foot tree (*Bauhinia purpurea* and *B. variegata*), gold mohur (*Delonix regia*; see FIG.I/94), dwarf gold mohur or peacock flower (*Poinciana pulcherrima*; FIG. 25),

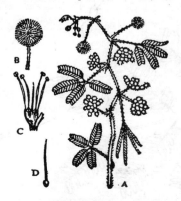

Mimoseae. FIG. 28. Sensitive plant (*Mimosa pudica*).
A, a branch; B, an inflorescence; C, a flower; and
D, pistil (one carpel)

Jerusalem thorn (*Parkinsonia aculeata*) and *Peltophorum ferrugineum*.

Other common plants: *Cassia sophera*, C. *occidentalis*, ringworm shrub (*C. alata*), C. *tora*, C. *auriculata*, etc.

(3) *Mimoseae* (87 sp. in India). Shrubs and trees, sometimes herbs or woody climbers. **Leaves**—bipinnate; stipels present or absent. **Inflorescence**—a head or a spike. **Flowers**—regular, often small and aggregated in spherical heads. **Calyx**—(5)or(4)sepals, generally gamosepalous, valvate. **Corolla**—(5)or 4)petals, mostly gamopetalous; aestivation valvate. **Androecium**—usually ∞ stamens, sometimes 10 (as in *Entada*, *Neptunia*, *Prosopis* and *Parkia*), free, often united at the base; pollen often united in small masses.

Floral formula $\oplus$ ϕ K$_{(5-4)}$C$_{(5-4)}$A$_{\infty \text{ or } 10}$G$_1$.

Examples of *Mimoseae*. The larger genera are *Acacia* (780 sp.), *Mimosa* (over 400 sp.), *Inga* (200 sp.), *Pithecolobium* (120 sp.) and *Albizzia* (100 sp.). **Useful plants:** catechu (*Acacia catechu*)—catechu, a kind of tannin, is obtained by boiling chips of heartwood, *A. nilotica* (=*A. arabica*) and *A. senegal*—yield gum, *A. dealbata*—an evergreen tree common in Shillong, bark rich in tannin, *A. farnesiana*—flowers very fragrant, used in perfumery, *A. pennata*—bark used for poisoning fish, many species of *Acacia* are sources of fuel and tannin, *Albizzia lebbek* (B. & H. SIRISH)—a timber tree, *A. procera*—wood suitable for tea boxes, many species of *Albizzia* are sources of fuel, rain tree (*Pithecolobium saman*)—planted as a shade tree, and *Parkia*—a handsome, rapid-growing, lofty tree. **Other common plants:** sensitive plant (*Mimosa pudica*)—a straggling weed, *M. himalayana* and *M. hamata*—shrubs, etc., *Neptunia oleracea* (B. & H. PANI-LAJUK), *Pithecolobium dulce* (B. & H. DEKANI-BABUL), nicker bean (*Entada gigas* = *E. phaseoloides*; B. & H. GILA)—pod up to a metre in length, and *Prosopis spicigera* (B. & H. SHOMI).

FAMILY 20 ROSACEAE (2,000 *sp.*—244 *sp. in India*)

Habit. These are herbs, shrubs, trees and climbers.

Leaves. The leaves are simple or compound and alternate. There are 2 stipules, often adnate to the petiole.

Inflorescence. The flowers are solitary or in terminal cymes or racemes.

Flowers. (see FIG. I/125*C*) These are regular, bisexual, rosaceous, and usually perigynous. The receptacle is hollowed and cup-shaped. They are rarely epigynous (as in apple and pear). A disc is often present in the form of a ring.

Calyx. There are 5 sepals, adnate to the receptacle. The lobes are free. The *epicalyx* is often present.

Corolla. There are 5 petals (many in cultivated roses). They are free, usually imbricate, and alternate with the sepals. The petals are usually white or pink.

Androecium. There are many stamens incurved in the bud, and arranged in cyclic order.

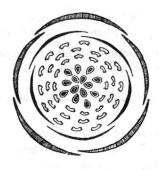

FIG. 29. Floral diagram of *Rosaceae*

Gynoecium. There are many carpels usually. They are free (as in rose) or sometimes (5), united (as in apple and pear). On occasion there is only 1 (as in plum and peach) carpel. The ovary is unilocular or 5-locular in the syncarpous pistil, with usually 2 ovules in each loculus. The ovules are anatropous and pendulous.

Fruit. The fruit varies in forms—drupe, follicle, berry, achene or pome.

Seeds. The seeds are exalbuminous.

Floral formula $\oplus\ \dfrac{\circ}{\varphi}\ K_5C_5A_\infty\ \underline{G}_\infty$ or (5) or 1.

There are wide variations in the floral structure of *Rosaceae*. The flowers may be bisexual or unisexual. There are usually many stamens and sometimes 10. There are many carpels, sometimes 5-10 or even 1 (as in *Prunus*). They are apocarpous or syncarpous. The ovary is superior or inferior and the fruit varying. The family is related to *Leguminosae* by perigyny, and sometimes monadelphy, zygomorphy and simple pistil in some of its members. *Rosaceae* is also related to *Myrtaceae* through *Pyrus*, having (2-5) carpels.

Economically this is an important family. Otto-of-rose (ATTAR) is mostly obtained from *Rosa damascena* and *R. centifolia*. Bulgaria, most famous for its roses, is the world's biggest centre for the distillation of this essential oil. There are many fleshy edible fruits, e.g. plum, peach, prune, apricot, strawberry, apple, pear etc. Several varieties of rose are ornamental garden plants, as also are many species of *Spiraea* (grown in hill stations).

Examples. The larger genera are *Potentilla* (over 300 sp.), *Rubus* (250 sp.), *Rosa* (over 200 sp.), *Prunus* ((150 sp.), *Spiraea* (100 sp.), and *Pyrus* (50 sp.). Some examples are dog rose (*R. canina*), wild rose (*R. gigantea*), wild rose of Bengal (*R. involucrata*), Damask or Bussora rose (*R. damascena* and *R. centifolia*), musk rose (*R. moschata*), *R. indica*, *R. alba*, and several hybrids (*Spiraea cantoniensis*) has white flowers, in clusters (grown as a hedge plant in Shillong), loquat (*Eriobotrya japonica*), plum (*Prunus domestica*)—prune (ALUBUKHRA) is the dried plum, peach (*P. persica*), apricot (*P. armeniaca*), almond (*P.*

amygdalus), cherry (*P. avium*), quince (*Cydonia oblonga*), strawberry (*Fragaria vesca*), wild strawberry (*F. indica*), apple (*Malus sylvestris*), pear (*Pyrus communis* and *P. pyrifolia*), silverweed (*Potentilla fulgens*)—common in the hills, raspberry (*Rubus idaeus*), wild raspberry (*R. moluccanus*), and many other wild species in the hills, and *Photinia notoniana*—a tree in the Khasi Hills.

FAMILY 21 MYRTACEAE (3,000 *sp.*—112 *sp. in India*)

Habit. These are shrubs and trees, rarely herbs. Bicollateral bundles or internal phloem is often present.

Leaves. The leaves are simple, opposite, glanddotted.

Inflorescence. The inflorescence is cymose.

Flowers. The flowers are regular epigynous, bisexual with a disc lining the calyx-tube.

Calyx. The sepals are 4-5, free, or (4-5), connate, persistent or deciduous, valvate or imbricate.

Fruit. The fruit is a berry or capsule, inferior, usually with persistent calyx.

Seed. The seed is exalbuminous.

Floral formula $\oplus \quad \male \quad K_{4\text{-}5 \text{ or } (4\text{-}5)} C_{4\text{-}5} A_\infty \bar{G}_{(2\text{-}5)}$ or (∞).

Examples. The larger genera are: *Eucalyptus* (about 600 sp.), *Syzygium* (500 sp.), *Psidium* (over 100 sp.), *Melaleuca* (100 sp.), and *Myrtus* (about 100 sp.).

Useful plants. *Eucalyptus*—the leaves yield eucalyptus oil, clove (*Syzygium aromaticum*), blackberry (*S. cuminii*), wild berry (*S. fruticosum*), rose-apple (*S. jambos*), Malay apple (*S. malaccense*), guava (*Psidium guayava*), allspice or pimento (*Pimenta officinalis*)—dried unripe fruits form allspice which combines the flavour of cloves, nutmeg and cinnamon, cajeput (*Melaeuca leucadendron*)—leaves yield cajeput oil, and timber useful.

Other common plants: *Barringtonia acutangula* (B. & H. HIJAL), myrtle (*Myrtus commu-*

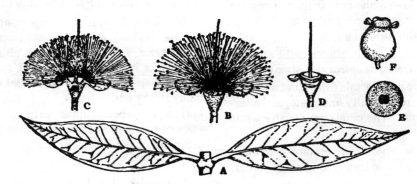

Myrtaceae. FIG. 30. Rose-apple (*Syzygium jambos*). *A*, opposite leaves; *B*, a flower; *C*, a flower cut longitudinally; *D*, pistil; *E*, section of ovary showing axile placentation; and *F*, a fruit

Corolla. The petals are 4-5, free, imbricate.

Androecium. There are many stamens (rarely few), free, sometimes polyadelophous and epigynous.

Gynoecium. The carpels are (2-5) or (∞). They are syncarpous. ovary is crowned by a disc, inferior (or sometimes half-inferior), 1- to 2- locular, sometimes multilocular, with 2 to many ovules in each loculus. The placentation is axile (rarely perietal).

nis)—an ornamental shrub, bottlebrush tree (*Callistemon lanceolatus*), etc.

FAMILY 22 CUCURBITACEAE (750 *sp.*—84 *sp. in India*)

Habit. These are tendril climbers. The tendrils are extra-axillary, simple or branched.

Leaves. The leaves are simple, alternate and palmately veined.

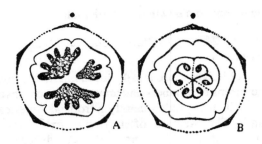

FIG. 31. Floral diagrams of *Cucurbitaceae*.
A, male flower *B*, female flower

Flowers. The flowers are regular, unisexual, epigynous and monoecious or dioecious.

Calyx. The sepals are (5), united, often deeply 5-lobed.

Corolla. The petals are (5), united, often deeply 5-lobed imbricate; inserted on the calyx tube.

Male Flowers—Androecium. There are usually 3 stamens, sometimes 5, varying in character. Sometimes they are free, but more commonly they are united in a pair (or in 2 pairs when stamens 5) throughout their whole length (*synandrous*), the odd one remaining free. In some cases only the anthers are united (*syngenesious*). Each anther is 1-lobed or 2-lobed. Paired stamens have either 2-lobed or 4-lobed anthers. The anther-lobes are variously folded, or *sinuous*, i.e. twisted like a transverse ∽. Rudiments of the pistil are sometimes present.

Female Flowers—Gynoecium—The carpels are syncarpous and (3) in number. The ovary is inferior, unilocular and placentation parietal but often the placentae intrude far into the chamber of the ovary making the latter falsely trilocular. There are many ovules, 1 style and 3 stigmas, which are often forked.

Fruit. The fruit is a pepo.

Floral formulae $\oplus \circlearrowleft \circ$ or $\circlearrowleft \_ \circ$ K$_{(5)}$C$_{(5)}$A$_3$ or $_5\underline{G}_0$ | A$_0\bar{G}_{(3)}$

The systematic position of *Cucurbitaceae* is disputed. There is a controversy regarding the nature of placentation (axile or parietal) and of tendrils, too. Bentham and Hooker placed *Cucurbitaceae* and *Passifloreae* together in the same cohort (order), Passiflorales among polypetalous order, not considering them as advanced, on the basis of the following characters: tendrils, regular flowers (gamopetalous or polypetalous), syncarpous pistil, 1-locular ovary and parietal placentation. *Passifloreae*, however, is distinguished from *Cucurbitaceae* by its stilate leaves, axillary tendrils, mostly bisexual flowers, often androgynophore and corona, free stamens, superior ovary, etc. Engler, however, considered *Cucurbitaceae* as a much advanced family and places it in Sympetalae as an only family of Cucurbitales prior to *Campanulaceae* and close to *Compositae*. Hutchinson separated the two

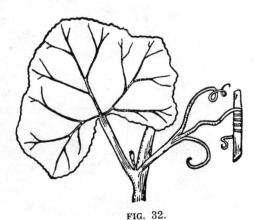

FIG. 32.

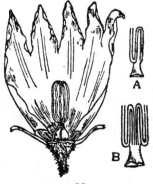

FIG. 33.

Cucurbitaceae. FIG. 32. Gourd (*Cucurbita moschata*). Portion of a branch with a leaf and a tendril. FIG. 33. Male flower of the same. *A*, one stamen; *B*, two stamens united together

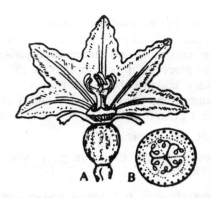

FIG. 34. A, female flower of *Cucurbita moschata*;
B, ovary in transection showing placentation

families into two orders, Cucurbitales and
Passiflorales, but regarding their systematic position he shared the view of Bentham and Hooker.
There is no doubt that *Cucurbitaceae* is closely
related to *Campanulaceae*, the relationship being
based on pentamerous gamopetaly, epigyny,
reduction in the number of stamens and carpels
and syngenesious stamens (sometimes also found
in *Campanulaceae*).

Plants of this family are mostly used as vegetables, a few yield delicious summer fruits, while a
few are medicinal.

Examples. The larger genera are: *Momordica*
(45 sp.), Cyclanthera (40 sp.; American), *Cucumis*
(25 sp.), *Trichosanthes* (25 sp.), and *Cucurbita*
(15 sp.). Some exmples are : sweet gourd or musk
melon (*Cucurbita moschata*), pumpkin or vegetable marrow (*C. pepo*; B. KUMRA; H. HALWAKAD-
DU)—squash is a variety of it, giant pumpkin or
giant gourd (*C. maxima*), bottle gourd (*Lagenaria
siceraria*), cho-cho or chayote (*Sechium
edule*)—commonly grown in hill stations, snake
gourd (*Trichosanthes anguina*), *T. dioica* (B.
PATAL; H. PARWAL), bitter gourd (*Momordica charantia*; B. UCHCHE and KARALA; H. KARELA), *M.
cochinchinensis* (B. KAKROL; H. CHATTHAI), ash or
wax gourd (*Benincasa hispida*), ribbed gourd
(*Luffa acutangula*), bath sponge or loofah (*L.
cylindrica*), *Coccinia indica* (B. TELAKUCHA; H.
KUNDARU), cucumber (*Cucumis sativus*), melon
(*C. melo*), water melon (*Citrullus lanatus*), colocynth (*C. colocynthis*; B. MAKAL: H INDRAYAN)—

medicinal, and *Bryonia*—medicinal.

FAMILY 23 CACTACEAE (about 2,000 *sp.*—6 *sp.*
in India)

Habit. These are mostly succulent herbs, some
are shrubs or climbers and are strongly xerophytic
in habit. It is predominantly a tropical American
family.The stem is often fleshy, exhibiting a
variety of peculiar forms, often modified into
phylloclade. The leaves are often modified into
scales. Axillary spines and sometimes a cluster of
bristles are present. The spines are borne on the
tubercle, often mixed with hairs, usually from a
depressed area at its tip known as the *areole*. The
morphology of the tubercle and the spines is variously interpreted. *Pereskia* is a much-branched
shrub with flat green leaves and strong thorns. The
roots are often very deep. The anatomical characteristics of this family are : abundant water-storing
parenchyma, mucilage-containing cells, thick
cuticle, mechanical tissues in the ridges, sunken
stomata, etc. The flowers are often solitary, sometimes very large, often brightly coloured, but
white in night-blooming cacti. They are regular,
bisexual, epigynous and arise from the areole or
from the axil of a tubercle, as in *Mammillaria*.

Cactaceae. FIG. 35. A, *Cereus triangularis*; B,
Phyllocactus latifrons (see also FIG. I/40B)

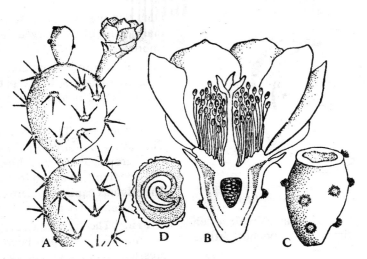

Cactaceae. FIG. 36. Prickly pear (Opuntia dillenii). *A*, plant (portion) with flower, thorns and bristles; *B*, flower cut longitudinally; *C*, fruit; *D*, seed cut longitudinally showing curved embryo

Perianth. There are many tepals, often united to form a tube. They are spirally arranged, showing a gradual transition from sepaloid to petaloid stages.

Androecium. There are many stamens, often epiphyllous.

Gynoecium. The carpels are (3-∞), united. The ovary is inferior, 1-chambered, with 3-∞ parietal placentae, bearing numerous anatropous ovules. The style is simple and stigmas correspond to the number of placentae.

Fruit. The fruit is a many-seeded berry, sometimes edible.

Seed. The seeds can be with or without endosperm.

Floral formula ⊕ ♂ P(∞) A∞Ḡ(3-∞).

The affinity of *Cactaceae* is difficult to trace. Bentham and Hooker placed *Ficoideae* (*Aizoaceae of Engler*) and *Cactaceae* in one cohort. There may be a distant affinity between *Cactaceae* and *Aizoaceae*. Engler separated the two families, and placed *Cactaceae* under the order Opuntiales close to Myrtiflorae, with which the former has some affinity in floral structure, particularly stamens and inferior ovary. Some cacti bear external resemblance with certain species of *Euphorbia* but are readily distinguished from them because they do not have latex.

Examples: The larger genera are: *Opuntia* (over 250 sp.), *Rhipsalis* (60 sp.), *Cereus* (50 sp.), *Echinopsis* (35 sp.), and *Melocactus* (30 sp.). Some examples are: prickly pear (*Opuntia dillenii* : FIG.36)—a troublesome weed, sometimes bearing edible fruit, *Rhipsalis cassytha*—a small fleshy shrub in Madhya Pradesh, *Nopalea*—similar to *Opuntia* but smaller in size, night-blooming cacti (*Cereus*, *Phyllocactus*, etc.), *Cereus grandiflorus*—flowers sweet-scented, *C. giganteus*—largest of all cacti, *C. hexagonus*, C. multangularis *and* C. tetragonus—commonly grown as hedge plants, *C. triangularis* (FIG. 35A)—a climber, *Phyllocactus latifrons*—flat-stemmed (FIG. 35B and I/40B), *Echinocactus*, *Melocatus*, Christmas cactus (*Epiphyllum truncatum*: FIG. I/39C) *Pereskia bleo*—a large, thorny shrub with flat green leaves. Indigenous cacti are very few but a good number of exotic species are grown in Indian gardens as ornamental plants.

FAMILY 24 UMBELLIFERAE (2,900 *sp.*— 176*sp. in India*)

Habit. These are herbs (rarely shrubs). The stem is usually fistular.

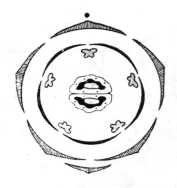

FIG. 37. Floral diagram of *Umbelliferae*

Leaves. The leaves are alternate, simple, often much divided, sometimes decompound; petiole usually sheathing at the base.

Inflorescence. It is an umbel, usually compound or in a few cases simple as in *Centella*.

Flowers. The flowers are regular (actinomorphic) or sometimes zygomorphic, epigynous, bisexual or polygamous. The outer flowers are sometimes rayed; mostly protandrous. The bracts are in the form of an involucre.

Calyx. There are 5 sepals. They are free, adnate to the ovary, often considerably reduced in size.

Corolla. The petals are 5, rarely absent, free, adnate to the ovary and sometimes unequal. The margin is often curved inwards, valvate or imbricate.

Androecium. There are 5 stamens, which are free, alternating with the petals, epigynous. The filaments are bent inwards in the bud; anthers introrse.

Gynoecium. The carpels are (2), syncarpous. The ovary is inferior, 2-celled, antero-posterior, crowned by a 2-lobed, epigynous disc (stylopodium), with two free styles arising from it. The stigmas capitate. There are 2 ovules, solitary in each cell and pendulous.

Fruit. The fruit is a cremocarp consisting of two indehiscent carpels laterally or dorsally compressed, breaking up into two parts, called *mericarps*, which are attached to a slender, often forked axis (*carpophore*). Each mericarp usually shows five longitudinal ridges and oil-canals (*vittae*) in the furrows.

Seeds. There are 2 seeds, one in each mericarp; albuminous.

Floral formula $\oplus$ or $\cdot\vdash \varphi$ $K_5 C_5 A_5 \bar{G}_{(2)}$.

Floral Range. The flowers are commonly in a compound umbel, sometimes in a compact mass (head), as in *Eryngium*, or sometimes in a simple

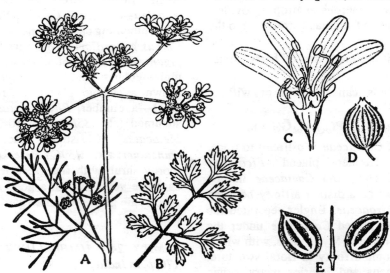

Umbelliferae. FIG. 38. Coriander (*Coriandrum sativum*). *A*, a branch with leaf and compound umbels; *B*, a lower leaf; *C*, a flower; *D*, a fruit; *E*, a fruit split into two mericarps, and the carpophore (central axis)

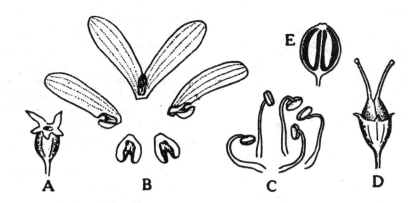

Umbelliferae. (contd.). FIG. 39. Coriander. *A*, calyx with inferior ovary;
B, petals dissected out; *C*, stamens dissected out; *D*, pistil with two styles,
bilobed disc, calyx-teeth and inferior ovary; and *E*, ovary in longitudinal section

umbel, or even single, as in some species of *Hydocotyle* (=*Centella*). They are regular or zygomorphic, bisexual or polygamous, but always epigynous. Flower development is, however, peculiar: the stamens appear first, then the petals followed by the sepals. Last of all appear the two carpels—at first separate but later united; by the rapid ingrowth of the ovary it soon becomes inferior. The disc is variously 2-lobed. The sepals, which adnate to the ovary, are 5-toothed, entire, or reduced to a few scales, or to a narrow circular ridge. There are 5 petals regular or zygomorphic. Some petals of outer flowers are often rayed. Aestivation is imbricate or valvate. The stamens and carpels are more or less constant. The mericarps show a variety of forms and help identification of genera and species. *Umbelliferae* maintains a connection with *Compositae* by the following characters: herbaceous nature of plants, reduction of calyx, presence of involucre, dense inflorescence (a near approach to capitulum of *Compositae*), outer flowers often sterile and rayed, bicarpellate pistil with two distinct styles, inferior ovary, solitary ovule in the ovarian chamber, etc. The fruit characters, however, readily distinguish the two families.

Examples. The larger genera are: *Eryngium* (200 sp.), *Pimpinella* (200 sp.), *Ferula* (over 100 sp.), *Peucedanum* (over 100 sp.), *Hydrocotyle* (100 sp.), *Daucus* (60 sp.), *Centella* (40 sp.),

Oenanthe (40 sp.), and *Carum* (30 sp.)]. **Useful plants:** *Condiments and spices:* coriander (*Coriandrum sativaum*), fennel (*Foeniculum vulgare*; B. PAN-MOURI; H. SAUNF), ajwan or ajowan (*Trachyspermum ammi*=*Carum copticum*; B. JOWAN; H. AJOWAN), *Carum roxburghianum* (B. RANDHANI), caraway (*C. carvi*; B. & H. SHIAJIRA), cumin (*Cuminum cyminum*; B. JIRA; H. SAFED-JIRA), dill (*Anethum graveloens*; B. SULPA; H. SOWA), parsley (*Petroselinum crispum*), anise (*Pimpinella anisum*), etc. *Vegetables:* carrot (*Daucus carota*), parsnip (*Pastinaca sativa*) and celery (*Apium graveolens*). *Medicinal:* asafoetida (*Ferula assa-foetida*; B. & H. HING)—asafoetida (HING) of commerce is obtained from the roots, and Indian pennywort (*Centella asiatica*; B. THULKURI; H. BRAHMI)—leaves used as remedy for dysenteric troubles in children. **Other common plants:** wild coriander (*Eryngium foetidum*), *Centella rotundifolia*, dropwort (*Oenanthe*), e.g. *O. bengalensis* and *O. stolonifera*—common weeds of wet places, *Seseli indicum* (B. BAN-JOWAN)—a common much-branched weed, etc.

Sub-class II. Gamopetalae

FAMILY 25 RUBIACEAE (6,000 *sp.*—489 *sp. in India*)

Habit. These are herbs (erect or prostrate), shrubs, trees and climbers, sometimes thorny.

FIG. 40. Floral diagrams of *Rubiaceae*

Leaves. The leaves are simple, entire, opposite (decussate) or whorled, with interpetiolar (sometimes intrapetiolar) stipules.

Inflorescence. The inflorescence is typically cymose, frequently dichasial and branched, sometimes in globose heads.

Flowers. The flowers are regular, bisexual, epigynous, sometimes dimorphic, as in some species of *Randia* and *Oldenlandia*.

Calyx. There are usually (4) sepals, sometimes (5). It is gamosepalous. The calyx-tube adnates to the ovary.

Corolla. There are usually (4) sometimes (5). It is gamopetalous, generally rotate. The aestivation is valvate, imbricate or twisted.

Androecium. The stamens are as epipetalous, inserted within or at the mouth of the corolla-tube, alternating with the corolla-lobes.

Gynoecium. The carpels are (2), syncarpous. The ovary is inferior, commonly 2-locular, with 1-∞ ovules in each. The disc is usually annular, at the base of the style.

Fruit. The fruit is a berry, drupe or capsule.

Seed. The seed has fleshy or horny endosperm.

Floral formula $\oplus \, \male \, K_{(4-5)} \overline{C_{(4-5)} A_{4-5}} \bar{G}_{(2)}$.

Rubiaceae is related to *Caprifoliaceae*, but in the latter the interpetiolar stipules are wanting and the carpels are (5-3). *Rubiaceae* is also distantly related to *Compositae* by virtue of the head or capitulum, as in *Anthocephalus*, *Uncaria*, *Nauclea*, *Adina*, etc.

Examples. The larger genera are: *Psychotria* (over 600 sp.), *Ixora* (over 300 sp.), *Pavetta* (over 300 sp.), *Galium* (300 sp.), *Gardenia* (250 sp.),

Randia (over 200 sp.), *Oldenlandia* (over 200 sp.), *Mussaenda* (200 sp.). **Useful plants: Medicinal:** *Cinchona* yields quinine which is extracted from root and stem, the bark of the ipecac (*Psychotria ipecacuanha* = *Cephaelis ipecacuanha*) yields emetine, *Paederia foetida*—leaves are a good stomachic, *Oldenlandia corymbosa*—entire plant used as a remedy for jaundice, liver disorders and remittent fever, etc. **Ornamental:** *Ixora coccinea*, *I. parviflora*, *Pavetta indica*, *Gardenia jasminoides* (=*G. florida*), *Anthocephalus indicus* (B. & H. KADAM), *Adina cordifolia* (B. KELI-KADAM; H. HALDU), *Cephalanthus occidentalis* (B. & H. PANI-KADAM), *Randia fasciculata*, *Hamelia patens*, *Mussaenda*—flowers usually yellow or orange and one of the sepals much enlarged (see FIG. I/103), the latter being white in *M. frondosa* and *M. roxburghii*, cream or yellow in *M. incana*, and bright scarlet in *M. erythrophylla*, etc. **Dyes:** madder (*Rubia cordifolia*) and *Morinda tinctoria*. **Beverage:** coffee (*Coffea arabica* and *C. robusta*)—seeds are the source of coffee pwder.

Other common plants: *Coffea bengalensis*, *Oldenlandia diffusa*, *Dentella repens*—all growing wild, *Vangueria spinosa* (B. & H. MOYNA)—a thorny shrub, *Uncaria macrophylla*—a large, woody, hook-climber (see FIG. I/18B), *Galium rotundifolium*—a diffuse herb common in the Khasi Hills, etc.

FAMILY 26 COMPOSITAE OR ASTERACEAE
(14,000 *sp.*—674 *sp. in India*)

Habit. These are herbs and shrubs, rarely twiners, e.g. *Mikarnia scandens*, or trees, e.g. *Vernonia arborea*. They sometimes have internal phloem. Some genera have latex, e.g. *Sonchus*, *Crepis*, *Lactuca*, *Picris*, etc.

Leaves. The leaves are simple, alternate or opposite, rarely compound.

Inflorescence. The inflorescence is a head (or capitulum), with an involucre of bracts.

Flowers (florets). The flowers are of two kinds—the central ones (called *disc florets*) are tubular, and the marginal ones (called *ray florets*) are ligulate. Sometimes all florets are of one kind, either tubular or ligulate. The disc flowers are

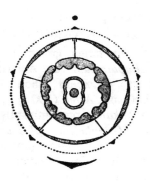

FIG. 41. Floral diagrams of *Compositae* (disc floret)

regular, tubular, bisexual and epigynous, each usually in the axil of a bracteole.

Calyx. The calyx is often modified into a cluster of hairs called pappus, as in *Tridax* and *Ageratum*, or into scales, as in sunflower and *Eclipta*, or absent, as in water cress (*Enhydra*).

Corolla. There are (5) petals. It is gamopetalous and tubular. **Androecium.** The 5 stamens are epipetalous. The filaments are free but the anthers united (syngenesious).

Gynoecium. The carpels are (2), syncarpous. The ovary inferior, 1-celled with one basal, anatropous ovule. There is one style and the stigma is bifid.

Fruit. The fruit is a cypsela.

Floral formula $\oplus\ \male\ $ **Kpappus** or o $\overline{C_{(5)}}A_{(5)}\bar{G}_{(2)}$

The ray florets are zygomorphic, ligulate, unisexual (female), or sometimes neuter, as in sunflower, and epigynous, each usually in the axil of a bracteole. The **Calyx** is usually modified into pappus. Sometimes it is scaly or absent. The **Corolla** has (5) petals, is gamopetalous and ligulate (strap-shaped). The **Gynoecium** is as in the disc florets. The **Fruit** same.

Floral formula $\cdot|\cdot\ \female\ $ **Kpappus** or o $\ \ C_{(5)}\bar{G}_{(2)}$.

Systematic Position of *Compositae*. For its many special characters *Compositae* is assigned an advanced position, the highest according to Engler, in systematic botany. This means that the family is of recent origin; fossils of this family have been traced down to only the Oligocene period (and not further back). Fossil records indicate that the genus *Senecio* came into existence first and other genera developed from it in due course. It is likely that *Compositae* and *Rubiaceae* arose from a common ancestry. The former also maintains a phylogenetic connecion with *Umbelliferae* by virtue of inflorescence and floral mechanism. *Compositae* is remarkable in many respects: it has the maximum number of species among dicotyledons, and some genera with a very large number of

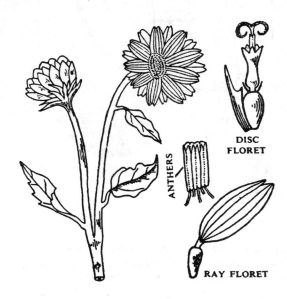

Compositae.
FIG. 42.
Sunflower
(*Helianthus annuus*).
Note the branch with
inflorescences (heads);
disc floret (bisexual),
with a bracteole
at the base; anthers
(syngenesious),
and ray floret
(neuter or female)

species (see below); its worldwide distribution; its variety of forms; and its very effective mechanism for cross-pollination (see p. 102).

Special Features. The special features characterizing *Compositae* as an advanced family are as follows: (1) predominantly herbaceous forms; (2) flowers massed together in a head (a perfect type of inflorescence) with the following decided advantages—(*a*) greater conspicuousness to attract insects for cross-pollination; (*b*) considerable saving of corolla-material and (*c*) achievement of cross-pollination by a single insect within a very short time; (3) very simple but effective type of floral mechanism to achieve cross-pollination without at the same time losing a chance for self-pollination if the former method fails; (4) easy access of insects to the nectary which lies at the base of the style and is protected from rain; (5) flowers typically 5-merous, gamopetalous, bisexual, epigynous with definite number of stamens and carpels—an almost similar type of floral construction throughout the whole family; (6) efficient protection of floral buds by the involucral bracts; (7) very effective mechanism for seed-(fruit-) dispersal by parachute-like pappus (calyx) or by hooks or glands developing on the fruit.

Examples. The larger genera are: *Senecio* (2,500 sp.), *Eupatorium*, an American genus (over 1,000 sp.), *Vernonia* (about 1,000 sp.), *Centaurea* (600 sp.), *Aster* (500 sp.), *Artemisia* (over 300 sp.), *Mikania*, predominantly American (over 200 sp.), *Gnaphalium* (200 sp.), *Bidens* (about 200 sp.), and *Erigeron* (about 200 sp.). **Useful plants:** *Medicinal:* Indian wormwood (*Artemisia nilagirica*=*A. vulgais*; B. NAGDONA; H. NAG-DAMAN), santonin (*A. cina*), *Vernonia anthelminatica* (B. SOMRAJ; H. KALIZIRI), *Eupatorium ayapana* (B. & H. AYAPANA), *Wedelia calendulacea*, *Eclipta alba*, etc. *Vegetables:* chicory (*Cichorium intybus*; B. & H. KASNI)—its carrot-like roots are also roasted, ground and mixed with coffee, endive (*C. endivia*), lettuce (*Lactuca sativa*), *Enhydra fluctuans* (B. HALENCHA; H. HARKUCH), Jerusalem artichoke (*Helianthus tuberosus*; B. & H. HATICHOKE), etc.; *Oils:* safflower (*Carthamus tinctorius*)—the seeds yield a good quality edible oil (about 25%) used for cooking, paint- and soap-making while

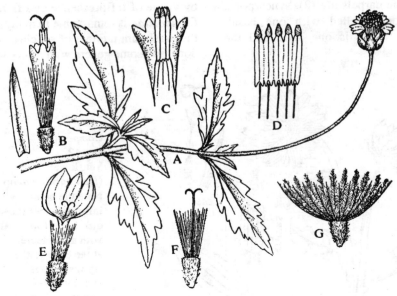

Compositae. FIG. 43. *Tridax procumbens. A*, a branch with capitulum; *B*, a disc floret with a bracteole; *C*, corolla (split open) with epipetalous stamens; *D*, syngernesious stamens (split open); *E*, a ray floret; *F*, pistil and pappus; and *G*, a fruit (cypsela) with pappus (parachute mechanism)

the flowers yield a red dye, sunflower (*Helianthus annuus*; FIG. 42)—seeds yield about 30% of cooking oil, etc. *Insecticides:* a few species of *Chrysanthemum* (*Pyrethrum*), e.g. *C. cinerariefolium* yielding more or less 1% pyrethrin. **Ornamental:** sunflower (*Helianthus annuus*), Mexican sunflower (*Tithonia tagetiflora*), *Zinnia*, *Cosmos*, *Dahlia*, daisy (*Bellis*), tree dahlia (*Montanoa*; in Shillong), *Calendula*, *Aster*, *Chrysanthemum*, *Gerbera*, golden rod or crest (*Solidago virgaurea*), marigold (*Tagetes patula*), everlasting flower (*Helichrysum*), *Centaurea*, e.g. sweet sultan (*C. moschata*), cornflower (*C. cyanus*), etc., *Erigeron mucronatus*—a common small herb growing on hill slopes (in Shillong), etc.

Other common plants: goat-weed (*Ageratum conyzoides*) with purplish heads, *Blumea indicum*, G. *luteo-album* and *Anaphalis contorta*—common weeds in hill-stations, *Eupatorium odoratum*—a common scandent shrub, elephant's foot (*Elephantopus scaber*), *Sonchus asper* and *Launea asplenifolia*—annual weeds with latex, *Tridax procumbens* (FIG. 43), cockle-bur (*Xanthium strumarium*) *Mikania scandens*—a large twiner, *Vernonia cineria* (B. KUKSHIM; H. SAHADEVI)—a herb, and *V. arborea*—a tree.

FAMILY 27 APOCYNACEAE (1,400 sp.—67 sp. in India)

Habit. These are mostly twining or erect shrubs and lianes, a few herbs and trees with latex. Bicollateral bundles or internal phloem often present.

Leaves. The leaves are simple, opposite or whorled, rarely alternate.

Flowers. The flowers are regular, bisexual and hypogynous, in cymes. They are usually salver- or funnel-shaped, often with corona.

Calyx. The sepals are (5), rarely (4), gamosepalous and often united only at the base.

Corolla. There are (5) petals, rarely (4). They are gamopetalous and twisted.

Androecium. There are 5 stamens, rarely 4. They are epipetalous, alternating with the petals,

FIG. 44. Floral diagram of *Apocynaceae*

included within the corolla-tube. The anthers usually connate around the stigma and apparently adnate to it. The disc is ring-like or glandular.

Gynoecium. The carpels are 2 or (2), apocarpous or syncarpous, superior. When apocarpous, each ovary is 1-celled with marginal placentation, and when syncarpous the ovary may be 1-celled with parietal placentation, or 2-celled with axile placentation. There are 2-∞ ovules in each.

Fruit. There are a pair of follicles, berries, or drupes.

Seeds. The seeds often have a crown of long silky hairs and they mostly have endosperm.

Floral formula $\oplus$ $\male$ $K(_5)\overline{C(_5)}A_5\underline{G}_{2\,or\,(2)}$.

Apocynaceae is related to *Asclepiadaceae* in respect of general habit, bicollateral vascular bundles, latex tubes, and general floral and fruit characters. The two families, however, can be easily distinguished from each other by the characters of the androecium and gynoecium. In *Apocynaceae* the stamens are distinct (not united with the stigma), corona (staminal) is absent, the pollen grains are distinct (not in pollinia), and there is one style (not two).

Examples. The larger genera are: *Tabernaemontana* (110 sp.), *Rauwolfia* (about 100 sp.), *Ervatamia* (80 sp.), *Alstonia* (50 sp.), and *Landolphia* (50 sp,)]. **Useful plants:** *Medicinal*: shrubs—*Rauwolfia serpentina* (B. SARPAGANDHA; H. SARPGAND), yellow oleander

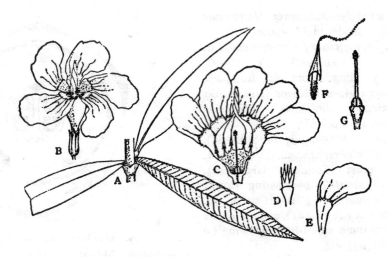

Apocynaceae. FIG. 45. Oleander (*Nerium indicum*). *A*, a whorl of leaves; *B*, a flower;
C, a flower opened out; *D*, calyx; *E*, a petal; *F*, a stamen (connective with hairy appendage); and *G*, pistil

(*Thevetia peruviana*)—seeds very poisonous,
trees—*Holarrhena antidysenterica* (B. KURCHI;
H. KARCHI), *Wrightia tomentosa* (B. DUDHI-
KHOROI; H. DUDHI), devil tree (*Alstonia scholaris*), etc. **Fruits**: *Carissa carandas* (B. KARANJA;
H. KARONDA)—a thorny shrub, and *Willughbeia
edulis* (B. LATA-AM)—a large climber.

Ornamental: herbs—periwinkle (*Lochnera
rosea=Vinca rosea*); shrubs-oleander (*Nerium
indicum=N. oleander*), crepe-jasmine (*Ervatamia
coronaria*; B. TAGAR; H. CHANDNI), temple or
pagoda tree (*Plumeria rubra*); climbers—
Aganosma dichotoma (B. MALATI; H. MALTI);
Vallaris solanacea (B. HAPARMALI; H. RAMSAR),

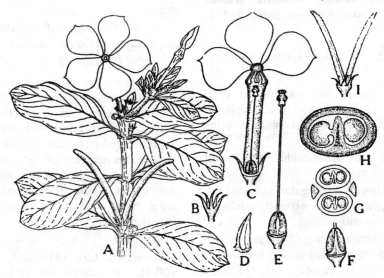

Apocynaceae. FIG. 46. Periwinkle (*Lochnera rosea=vinca rosea*). *A*, a branch; *B*, calyx;
C, a flower split longitudinally; *D*, a stamen; *E*, pistil; *F*, ovaries with disk; *G*, ovaries
with disk (of two glands) in section; *H*, one ovary in section; and *I*, a pair of follicles

Beaumontia grandiflora, *Allamanda catharica* and *Roupellia grata*; tree—*Cerbera odollam*—a tree of the Sundarbans.

Other common plants: *Ichnocarpus frutescens* (B. & H. DUDHI-LATA)—a climber, and *Rauwolfia canescens*—a shrub.

FAMILY 28 ASCLEPIADACEAE (1,800 sp.— 213 sp. in India)

Habit. These are herbs, shrubs or twiners with latex. The leaves are opposite.

Flowers. regular, bisexual and hypogynous.

Calyx. sepals (5), are slightly connate at the base, odd sepal posterior.

Corolla. petals (5), connate; aestivation imbricate, twisted, or valvate.

Androecium. There are (5) stamens, connate in a hollow tube, with horn-like appendages known as the staminal corona, epipetalous; anthers coherent laterally and united with the style and the stigma forming a gynostegium; pollen cohering into two pollen masses known as the pollinia (sing. pollinium), one lying in each lateral anther-lobe.

Gynoecium. There are two carpels, free, superior; styles 2, free but united above forming a large dilated 5-angled stigma; stigma with five receptive surfaces lying on the underside or the edge of it;

FIG. 47. Floral diagram of *Asclepiadaceae* (*Calotropis*)

ovaries 2, free or united at the base only, each unilocular with many ovules in it; placentation marginal on a large intruding ventral placenta.

Fruit. a pair of follicles, or by abortion only one.

Seeds. many, hairy.

Floral formula $\oplus \; \male \; K_{(5)} \; \overline{C_{(5)} \, [A_{(5)} \, \underline{G}_2]}.$

At each angle of the stigma there is a groove which secretes a sticky body called the corpusculum. The sticky secretion extends on either side into a connecting thread (retinaculum) to which each pollinium becomes attached.

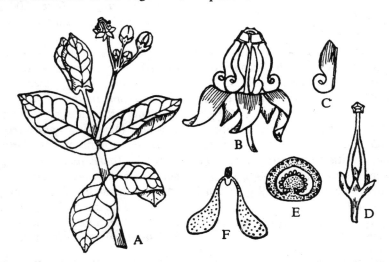

Asclepiadaceae. FIG. 48. Madar (*Calotropis gigantea*). *A*, a branch; *B*, a flower; *C*, staminal corona with the filament (inner side); *D*, apocarpous pistil with the calyx at the base; *E*, section of ovary showing marginal placentation; and *F*, a pair of pollinia (see also FIG. I/118)

Examples. The larger genera are: *Hoya* (about 200 sp.), *Asclepias* (120 sp.), *Ceropegia* (over 100 sp.), *Stapelia* (80 sp.), *Dischidia* (70 sp.), and *Marsdenia* (70 sp.). **Useful plants:** *Medicinal:* Indian sarsaparilla (*Hermidesmus indicus*; B. & H. ANANTAMUL)—a twining shrub. *Tylophora asthmatica*—a twining herb, madar (*Calotropis gigantea* and *C. procera*)—also floss from seeds used for stuffing pillows and cushions; *Ornamental:* *Stephanotis floribunda*—a large climber with white fragrant flowers, *Cryptostegia grandiflora*—a woody climber with large magenta flowers, *Oxystelma esculentum* (B. & H. DUDHIALATA)—a slender perennial twiner with large showy flowers, *Pergularia pallida*—an extensive twiner with fragrant flowers, *Stapelia grandiflora*—a cactus-like pot herb with large red flowers, etc.

FIG. 49. *Left*, a pair of follocles of madar; *right*, a hairy seed of the same

Other common plants: milkweed or bloodflower (*Asclepias curassavica*; B. DUDHIA; H. KAKATUNDI)—an erect herb with orange-red flowers, *Sarcostemma brevistigma* (B. & H. SOMA-LATA)—a leafless shrub with jointed stem and pendulous branches, wax plant (*Hoya parasitica*)—a thick-leaved epiphytic climber, *Dischidia rafflesiana* (see FIG. I/70)—a stout, epiphytic climber with pitchers, *Daemia extensa*—a foetid climbing undershrub, *Dregea volubilis*—a woody climber with small greenish flowers, *Sarcolobus globosus* (B. BAOLI-LATA)—a large climber, *Leptadenia spartium*—a leafless, xerophytic shrub. etc.

FAMILY 29 BORAGINACEAE (1,800 sp.—141 sp. in India)

Habit. These are herbs (annual or perennial),

shrubs or trees, often covered with stiff hairs.

Leaves. The leaves are simple, alternate, rarely opposite, entire.

Inflorescence. It is a scorpioid cyme, sometimes coiled. The flowers are regular, bisexual and hypogynous.

Calyx. There are 5 sepals free or united below into a tube, usually persistent, commonly imbricate.

Corolla. There are (5) petals, gamopetalous, tubular or funnel-shaped, with scales at the throat and imbricate lobes.

Androecium. stamens 5, epipetalous, alternating with the corolla-lobes, commonly inserted at the mouth of the corolla-tube.

Gynoecium. There are (2) carpels. It is syncarpous, on an annular disc. The ovary is superior, 2-locular with 2 ovules in each, or commonly 4-locular with 1 ovule in each. The style gynobasic, rarely terminal. The fruit is a group of 4 nutlets.

Floral formula $\oplus \, \male \quad K_5 C_{(5)} A_5 \underline{G}_{(2)}$.

Examples. The larger genera are: *Cordia* (250 sp.), *Heliotropium* (over 200 sp.), *Tournefortia* (120 sp.), *Cynoglossum* (over 50 sp.). Some examples are: heliotrope (*Heliotropium indicum*)—a diffuse annual weed, *H. strigosum*—a procument, annual weed, hound's tongue (*Cynoglossum lanceolatum*)—an erect annual weed, *Trichodesma indicum*—a diffuse, annual weed, *Coldenia procumbens*—a prostrate weed, forget-me-not (*Myosotis pallustris*) and *Onosma echiodies*—an ornamental herb with blue or pink flowers, *Tournefortia roxburghii*—a rambling shrub, *Cordia myxa* (B. & H. LASORA)—a large shrub with small white flowers, *C. sebestena*—a small tree (planted in gardens) with large, orange flowers, *Ehretia acuminata*—a tree with flowers in dense terminal panicles, etc.

FAMILY 30 CONVOLVULACEAE (over 1,600 sp.—157 sp. in India)

Habit. These are mostly twiners, often with

latex and bicollateral vascular bundles or internal phloem.

Leaves. The leaves are simple, alternate and exstipulate.

Inflorescence. The inflorescence is cymose. The flowers are regular, bisexual, hypogynous, often large and showy.

Calyx. There are 5 sepals, usually free. The odd one is posterior, imbricate and persistent.

Corolla. There are (5) petals. It is gamopetalous, funnel-shaped, twisted in bud, sometimes imbricate.

Androecium. The 5 stamens are epipetalous, alternating with the petals.

Gynoecium. There are (2) carpels, rarely more, connate. The ovary is superior, with a disc at the base. It is 2-celled, with 2 ovules in each cell, or sometimes 4-celled with 1 ovule in each cell. The placentation is axile.

Fruit. The fruit is a berry or a capsule.

Floral formula $\oplus \ \male \ K_5 C_{(5)} A_5 G_{(2)}$.

Convolvulaceae is related to *Solanaceae* by virtue of its persistent calyx, regular gamopetalous corolla, 5 epipetalous stamens, often false septum in the ovary, bicollateral vascular bundles, etc. But it is distinguished from *Solanaceae* by the fact that it has a definite number (1 or 2) of ovules in each chamber of the ovary, the micropyle points downwards, median carpels, etc.

Examples. The larger genera are: *Ipomoea* (=*Pharbitis*; over 400 sp.), *Convolvulus* (200 sp.), *Jacquemontia* (120 sp.), *Cuscuta* (120 sp.), *Evolvulus* (about 100 sp.), *Argyreia* (90 sp.), and *Merremia* (80 sp.).

Useful Plants. Vegetables: sweet potato (*Batatas edulis*=*Ipomoea batatas*), water bindweed (*I. aquatica*=*I. reptans*; B. & H. KALMISAK), *Argyreia nervosa* (in the Khasi Hills), etc. **Medicinal:** *Ipomoea paniculata* (B. & H. BHUIKUMRA), *I. hederacea*, (B. & H. NILKALMI)—seeds sold as KALADANA are used as a purgative, Indian jalap or turpeth (*I. turpethum*=*Operculina turpethum*; B. TEORI or DUDH-KALMI; H. PITOHARI)—roots used as a mild cathartic, jalap (*I. purga*)—turnip-like rhizome used as a strong purgative, elephant climber (*Argyreia speciosa*; B. SAMUDRASOK; H. SAMUNDERPHEN)—roots used in rheumatic afflictions and leaves used in skin diseases and wounds, etc. **Ornamental:** *Ipomoea* (several species), e.g. morning glory (*I. purpurea*)—flowers white, fading to purple, *I. hederacea*—flowers blue or purple, railway creeper (*I. palmata*)—flowers dull violet, moon flower (*I. bona-nox*)—flowers white, opening at dusk, cypress vine (*I. quamoclit* = *Quamoclit pinnata*; B. KUNJALATA)—a slender twiner with scarlet flowers, *I. learii* and *I. nil*—large, very showy flowers, *I. versicolor*—an elegant twiner (in Shillong), *I. carnea*—a much-branched scandent shrub with dull violet flowers, woodrose (*I. tuberosa*)—a liane (in Assam), fruit used for table decoration, etc.; *Convolvulus*

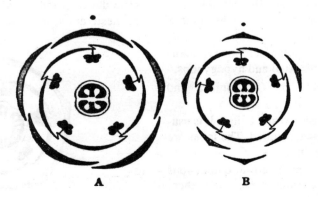

FIG. 50. Floral diagrams of *Convolvulaceae*. A, *Ipomoea*; B, dodder (*Cuscuta*)

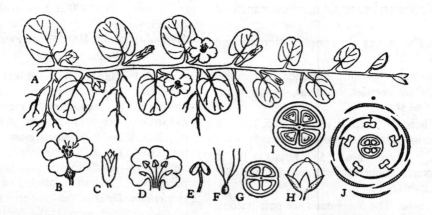

Convolvulaceae. FIG. 51. *Evolvulus nummularius.* A, a branch (prostrate); B, a flower; C, calyx; D, corolla (with epipetalous stamens) opened out; E, a stamen; F, gynoecium; G, ovary in transection with 4 ovules (sometimes 2 or 3); H, a fruit; I, the same in transection; and J, floral diagram

(mostly temperate), e.g. field bindweed (*C. scammonia*), *C. major*, *C. minor*, etc.; *Jacquemontia coerulea*—a garden twiner.

Other common plants: dodder (*Cuscuta reflexa*, see FIG. I/22), bridal creeper (*Porana paniculata*), *Ipomoea pescaprae* (=*I. biloba*)—a creeping perennial plant (sand and mud-binding on the seashore), *Evolvulus nummularius* (FIG. 51)—a prostrate herb with white flowers, and *E. alsinoides*—a diffuse herb with bluish flowers.

FAMILY 31 SOLANACEAE (over 2,000 *sp.*—58 *sp. in India*)

Habit. These are herbs and shrubs; bicollateral bundles or internal phloem are often present.

Leaves. These are simple, sometimes pinnate, as in tomato, and alternate.

Flowers. These are regular, seldom zygomorphic, as in *Brunfelsia*, bisexual and hypogynous.

Calyx. The sepals are (5), united and persistent.

Corolla. The petals are (5) and united. It is usually funnel or cup-shaped, 5-lobed. The lobes are valvate or twisted in the bud.

Androecium. The stamens are 5, epipetalous and alternate with the corolla lobes. The anthers are apparently connate and often open by means of pores.

Gynoecium. The carpels are (2) and syncarpous. The ovary is superior and obliquely placed (FIG. 52). It is 2-celled or sometimes 4-celled, owing to the development of a false septum, as in tomato and thorn-apple. There are many ovules in each chamber. The placentation is axile.

Fruit. The fruit is a berry or capsule with many seeds.

Floral formula $\oplus$ $\male\ K_{(5)}\overline{C_{(5)}}A_5\underline{G}_{(2)}$.

Solanaceae is related to *Convolvulaceae* (see p. 577). It is closely related to *Scrophulariaceae* through *Brunfelsia* and *Schizanthus*, which have a zygomorphic corolla and 4 or 2 stamens. *Solanaceae* is, however, generally distinguished from the latter family by its regular corolla, twisted aestivation, five stamens, obliquely placed

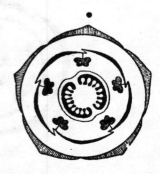

FIG. 52. Floral diagram of *Solanaceae*

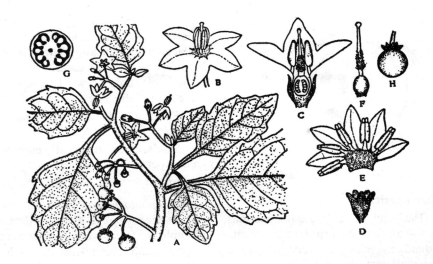

Solanaceae. FIG. 53. Black nightshade (*Solanum nigrum*). *A*, a branch; *B*, a flower; *C*, a flower cut longitudinally; *D*, calyx; *E*, corolla with epipetalous stamens; *F*, pistil; *G*, ovary in transection showing axile placentation; and *H*, a fruit (berry)

carpels, often bicollateral vascular bundles in the stem, etc.

Examples. The larger genera are *Solanum* (1,500 sp.), *Cestrum* (250 sp., mostly American), *Physalis* (100 sp.), *Nicotiana* (100 sp.) and *Capsicum* (50 sp.). **Useful plants:** *Vegetables:* potato (*Solanum tuberosum*), brinjal (*S. melongena*), chilli or red pepper (*Capsicum annuum*)—fruits pungent, mainly used as a condiment, bell-pepper (*C. grossum*)—fruits not pungent, used as a vegetable, and tomato (*Lycopersicum esculentum*); *Medicinal:* deadly nightshade (*Atropa belladonna*), thorn-apple (*Datura stramonium*) and *Datura metel* (=*D. fastuosa*)—seeds narcotic and very poisonous, henbane (*Hyoscyamus niger*), bittersweet (*Solanum dulcamara*; B. & H. MITHA-BISH), *S. indicum* (B. BRIHATI; H. BIRHATTA), *S. surattense* (=*S. xanthocarpum*; B. KANTIKARI; H. KATELI), and *Withania somnifera* (B. ASWAGANDHA; H. ASGAND). *Narcotic:* tobacco (*Nicotiana tabacum*)—commercial tobacco and also a source of nicotine (an insecticide); *Fruit:* gooseberry (*Physalis peruviana*). **Ornamental:** *Petunia hybrida*, queen of the night (*Cestrum nocturnum*; B. HAS-NA-HANA; H. RAT-KI-RANI) and *C. parqui*—both sweet-scent-ed, *Brunfelsia hopeana* (=*Franciscea bicolor*)—flowers white changing to blue, sweet-scented, *Schizanthus pinnatus*—a beautiful garden herb in Shillong, etc.

Other common plants: black nightshade (*Solanum nigrum*; FIG. 53), egg-plant (*S. ferox*), wild gooseberry (*Physalis minima*) and wild tobacco (*Nicotiana plumbaginifolia*).

FAMILY 32 SCROPHULARIACEAE (3,000 sp.— 258 sp. in India)

Habit. These are mostly herbs and undershrubs.

Leaves. These are simple, alternate, opposite or whorled, exstipulate, and sometimes exhibit heterophylly.

Inflorescence. This is usually racemose (raceme or spike), and sometimes cymose (dichasium). It can be axillary or terminal. The flowers are solitary in some species.

Flowers. These are zygomorphic, 2-lipped and sometimes personate. They often have a great diversity of form. They are bisexual and hypogynous. Bracts and bracteoles are generally present.

Calyx. The sepals are (5), gamosepalous, 5-

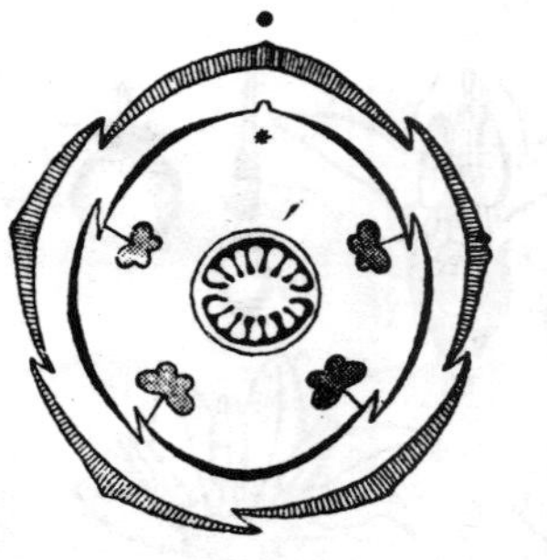

FIG. 54. Floral diagram of *Scrophulariaceae*

lobed and often imbricate.

Corolla. The petals are (5), gamopetalous, often 2-lipped and sometimes spurred or saccate. They are medianly zygomorphic, very rarely regular (as in *Scoparia*), and imbricate.

Androecium. The stamens are 4, didynamous, sometimes 2, arching over in pairs. The posterior stamen is absent or a staminode. The anthers are divaricate.

Gynoecium. The carpels are (2) and syncarpous. The ovary is superior, bilocular and antero-posterior (and not oblique as in *Solanaceae*). The placentation is axile. The stigma is simple or bilobed. There are usually many ovules, though sometimes only a few. The disc is ring-like around the base of the ovary, sometimes unilateral.

Fruit. This is mostly a capsule and sometimes a berry.

Seeds. These are usually numerous, minute and endospermic.

Floral formula ·|· ⚥ $K_{(5)}\overline{C_{(5)}A_{4\ or\ 2}}\underline{G}_{(2)}$.

Scrophulariaceae is closely related to *Solanaceae*, but is distinguished from it by the simple collateral bundles in its stem, zygomorphic corolla, imbricate aestivation, 4 (didynamous) or 2 stamens median position of the ovary, etc. It is distinguished from *Labiatae* and *Verbenaceae* by its inflorescence and fruit. It is also related to *Acanthaceae* (see p. 582).

Examples. The larger genera are *Pedicularis* (over 500 *sp*.), *Veronica* (300 *sp*.), *Scrophularia*

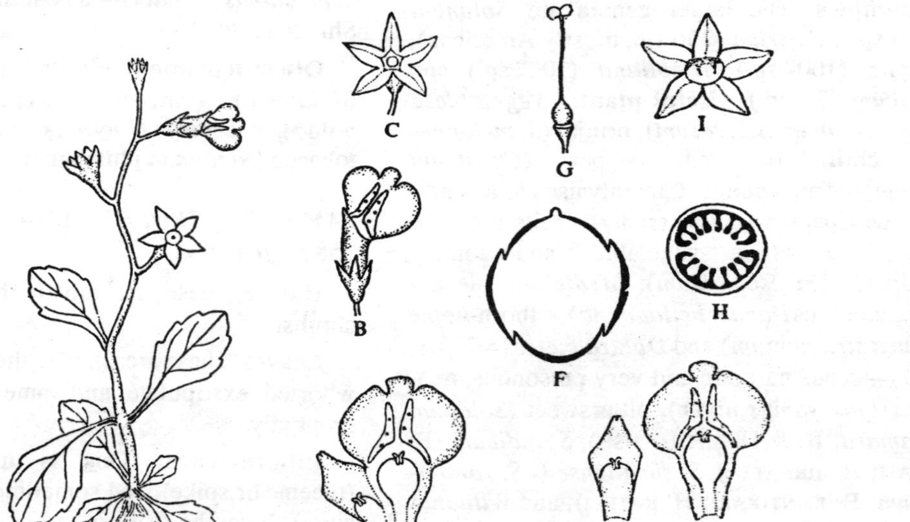

Scrophulariaceae. FIG. 55. *Mazus japonicus*. *A*, an entire plant—a small herb; *B*, a flower—bilabiate; *C*, calyx—gamosepalous and persistent; *D*, corolla split open with epipetalous, didynamous stamens arching over in pairs; *E*, corolla—the two lips separated, each with a pair of epipetalous stamens arching over; *F*, aestivation of corolla—imbricate; *H*, ovary in transection showing axile placentation; and *I*, fruit—capsule (dehiscing) with persistent calyx

(300 *sp.*), *Verbascum* (300 *sp.*) and *Linaria* (150 *sp.*). These occur mostly in northern temperate regions, while *Calceolaria* (about 500 *sp.*) occurs in South America and *Mimulus* (150 *sp.*) in North America. **Useful plants:** *Medicinal:* foxglove (*Digitalis purpurea*)—leaves contain a bitter glycoside, *digitalin*, which acts on the heart and the circulatory system, *Bacopa* (=*Herpestis*) *monnieria* (B. & H. BRAHMI)—a brain and nerve tonic. *Ornamental:* snapdragon (*Antirrhinum majus*), *Torenia fournieri*, fountain plant (*Russelia equisetiformis*=*R. juncea*), *Linaria cymbalaria*, monkey flower (*Mimulus maculosus*), *Veronica speciosa*, *Angelonia salicariaefolia*, *Scrophularia elatior*, etc.

Other common plants: *Weeds: Mazus japonicus* (=*M. rugosus*), *Torenia* (=*Vandellia*) *crustacea*, *Lindernia* (=*Vandellia*) *multiflora*, *L. ciliata* (=*Bonnaya brachiata*), *Limnophila heterophylla*—showing heterophylly, *Hemiphragma heterophyllum* (in Shillong and Darjeeling)—showing heterophylly, *Lindenbergia indica*—a common weed growing on old walls, toad-flax (*Linaria ramosissima*), *Mecardonia dianthera*, *Scoparia dulcis*, *Veronica anagallis*, *Celsia coromandeliana*, *Striga lutea* and a few other species—partial root-parasites, etc.

FAMILY 33 BIGNONIACEAE (750 *sp.*—25 *sp.* in India)

Habit. These are trees, shrubs or climbers (rootlet or tendril-climbers).

Leaves. These are usually pinnately compound, opposite and exstipulate. In *Bignonia* the terminal leaflet is modified into a tendril (branched or unbranched) or into hooks.

Inflorescence. This is often a dichasial cyme.

Flowers. These are bisexual, zygomorphic and hypogynous. Bracts and bracteoles are present.

Calyx. The sepals are (5) and gamosepalous.

Corolla. The petals are (5), gamopetalous and usually obliquely bell or funnel-shaped. The aestivation is imbricate.

Androecium. The stamens are 4, epipetalous and didynamous. The anthers are 2-lobed and the lobes divaricate.

Gynoecium. The carpels are (2), syncarpous and borne on a hypogynous disc. The ovary is superior, usually 2-locular, with many ovules in each chamber. The placentation is axile.

Fruit. This is, a 2-valved capsule, sometimes a berry. The seeds are exalbuminous, usually flattened, with a membranous wing.

Floral formula   ⊕ ♂ $K_{(5)} \overline{C_{(5)} A_4 G_{(2)}}$

Examples. The larger genera are *Bignonia* (150 sp.; now split into several genera), *Tecoma* (90 sp.; now split into several genera), and *Jacaranda* (50 sp.). Some examples are *Bignonia*—usually tendril-climbers, often with showy flowers, e.g. *B. venusta*, *B. unguis-cati* and *B. magnifica*; *Tecoma grandiflora*—a common garden climber, *T. stans*—a garden shrub, Indian cork tree (*Millingtonia hortensis*)—a tall robust tree with sweet-scented flowers, *Stereospermum chelonoides* (=*S. personatum*)—a large tree, *Oroxylum indicum* (see FIG. I/174A)—a small tree, *Spathodea campanulata*—a medium-sized tree with large red flowers, *Jacaranda mimosaefolia* (with 16-20 pairs of pinnae) and *J. acutifolia* (with 6-8 pairs of pinnae)—both planted as roadside or garden trees, with purplish flowers in panicles, calabash (*Crescentia cujete*)—large, gourd-like fruit, *Tecomella undulata*—a small timber tree (commonly called 'desert teak') of Rajasthan and Punjab and candle tree (*Parmentiera cerifera*)—candle-like yellow fruits (35-50 cm. long) hang from the stem and the branches in large numbers.

FAMILY 34 ACANTHACEAE (2,200 *sp.*—409 *sp.* in India)

Habit. These are herbs, shrubs and sometimes climbers. Cystoliths are often present in the stem and leaf.

Leaves. These are simple, opposite and exstipulate.

Inflorescence. This is a spike or a cyme, or sometimes a raceme. In some species, the flowers are in axillary clusters. They are rarely solitary.

Flowers. These are zygomorphic, bilabiate or

oblique, bisexual and hypogynous. They often have conspicuous bracts and bracteoles, the latter often large and sometimes spiny.

Calyx. The sepals are (5), rarely (4), and united.

Corolla. The petals are (5), connate in a two-lipped or oblique corolla, and are twisted or imbricate in the bud.

Androecium. The stamens are 2 or 4 (didynamous), and if epipetalous disc, is often conspicuous.

Gynoecium. This is syncarpous, the carpels being (2). The ovary is 2-celled, superior, with 2 to many ovules in each cell. The placentation is axile. There are 2 stigmas.

Fruit. The fruit is a 2-valved capsule (FIG. 57G).

Seeds. In most cases, these are supported on curved hooks (jaculators). These press the fruit from inside, which bursts with a sudden jerk and scatters the seeds (see FIG. I/182).

Floral formula ⊹ ☿ $K_{(5)}C_{(5)}A_{2 \text{ or } 4}\underline{G}_{(2)}$

Acanthaceae is related to *Scrophulariaceae*, but is distinguished from it by the presence of copious bracts and bracteoles, often unequal posterior sepal, loculicidal capsule dehiscing to the very base, the presence of jaculators, the absence of endosperm, frequent presence of cystolith, etc. It is also related to *Labiatae* (see p. 585) and *Verbenaceae* (see p. 584).

Examples. The larger genera are *Justicia* (250 sp.), *Strobilanthes* (over 200 sp.), *Barleria* (over 200 sp.), *Thunbergia* (about 200 sp.), *Dicliptera*

(150 sp.) and *Hygrophila* (80 sp.). **Useful plants:** *Medicinal: Andrographis paniculata* (B. KALMEGH; H. MAHATITA)—an effective remedy for liver complaints in children, and *Adhatoda vasica* (B. BASAK; H. ADALSA)—an excellent remedy for cough. **Ornamental:** *Barleria*, e.g. *B. prionitis* (B. KANTA-JHANTI; H. KATSAREYA)—spinous, flowers yellow, *B. cristata* (B. JHANTI; H. JHINTI)—flowers white or rose-coloured, *B. strigosa*—flowers blue, *Meyenia erecta*—a pretty shrub with deep blue flowers, *Crossandra undulaefolia*—an undershrub with orange flowers, *Strobilanthes*, e.g. *S. scaber* (with yellow flowers), *S. auriculatus* (with purplish flowers), and many other species common in the Khasi Hills; *Eranthemum* (=*Daedalacanthus*) *nervosus*—flowers bright blue, etc.

Other common plants: *Herbs: Cardanthera triflora*—showing heterophylly (see FIG. I/79A), *Hygrophila polysperma* —a common weed, *Asteracantha longifolia* (=*Hygrophila spinosa*; B. KULEKHARA; H. TALMAKHANA)—an erect spinous herb, *Ruellia tuberosa* (see FIG. I/182), *R. prostrata, Phaylopsis imbricata* (=*P. parviflora*), *Rungia parviflora, R. elegans*—bracts with white margin, *Hypoestis triflora* (in Shillong), *Dicliptera roxburghiana, Justicia simplex* (FIG. 57) and *Ecbolium linneanum* (B. NILKANTHA; H. UDAJATI); *Climbers: Thunbergia alata* (flowers yellow) and *T. grandiflora* (flowers blue). *Shrubs or undershrubs: Justicia gendarussa* (B. JAGAT-MADAN; H. NILI-NARGANDI), *Acanthus ilicifolius* (B. HARGOZA)—a mangrove shrub, *Phlogacanthus curviflorus*— flowers pink, *P. thyrsiflorus*—flowers orange, eaten cooked as a

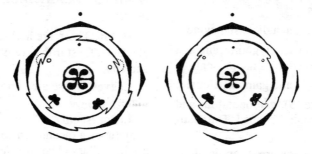

FIG. 56. Floral diagrams (two types) of *Acanthaceae*

Acanthaceae. FIG. 57. *Justicia simplex.* A, a plant with spikes, B, a flower (bilabiate); C, calyx with bracts and bracteoles; D, corolla split open, upper lip with 2 epipetalous stamens; E, stamens—2; F, gynoecium with glandular disc at the base; G, fruit—young, and dehiscent (loculicidal capsule); and H, floral diagram

vegetable, *P. tubiflorus*—flowers red, eaten cooked as a vegetable, leaves rubbed in water give a lather, etc.

FAMILY 35 VERBENACEAE (over 2,600 *sp.*— 107 *sp. in India*)

Habit. These are herbs, shrubs, trees or climbers. They are often prickly and some are xerophytic in habit. They are usually strong-smelling. The stem is sometimes 4-angled.

Leaves. These are simple, opposite or whorled, and sometimes pinnately or palmately compound.

Inflorescence. This is a raceme, panicle or spike (long or condensed), or a dichasial cyme.

Flowers. These are bisexual, medianly zygomorphic, hypogynous and pentamerous. The bracts are sometimes in the form of an involucre, as in *Lantana.*

Calyx. The sepals are usually (5), rarely (4) or more and gamosepalous. The calyx is persistent.

Corolla. The petals are usually (5) and gamopetalous. They are initially 2-lipped and later 5-lobed. The tube may be long or short and the limb oblique is aestivation imbricate.

Androecium. The stamens are 4, didynamous and epipetalous, (very rarely 2 as *Stachytarpheta*, or 5 as in teak). They are often inserted, and sometimes exserted (even far exserted, as in *Clerodendron*), and alternate with the corolla lobes.

Gynoecium. The carpels are mostly (2), rarely (4) as in *Duranta*, and syncarpous. The ovary is superior, entire or lobed, 2-locular with 1 or 2 ovules in each chamber or 4-locular with 1 ovule in each chamber, (8-locular in *Duranta*; FIG. 58G) The style is terminal.

Fruit. This is a drupe (consisting of 2 or 4 pyrenes), and rarely a capsule.

Seed. The seed is exalbuminous.

Floral formula $\cdot | \cdot \; \male \;\; K_{(5)} C_{(5)} A_4 \underline{G}_{(2)}.$

Verbenaceae is closely related to *Labiatae*, both showing zygomorphy in the corolla, often

Verbenaceae. FIG. 58. *Duranta repens* (= *D. plumieri*). *A*, a branch with inflorescence; *B*, a flower; *C*, calyx; *D*, a flower split lengthwise; *E*, stamens (didynamous); *F*, gynoecium—carpels (4); *G*, ovary in transection (8 chambers, each with 1 ovule); *H*, young fruit in transection showing 4 pyrenes (being formed), each 2-chambered with 1 ovule in each; *I*, fruit—a fleshy drupe (the outer envelope is the fleshy persistent calyx); and *J*, floral diagram

extending to the calyx in the latter. It is, however, distinguished from *Labiatae* by the following features: *Verbenacea*—the inflorescence is variously formed; the ovary is 2-locular with 1 or 2 ovules in each chamber, or *later* divided into 4 loculi with 1 ovule in each chamber. The style is terminal. The fruit usually drupaceous, consisting of 2 or 4 pyrenes. Labiatac—the inflorescence is a verticillaster or a cyme; the 2-locular, divided *early* into 4 loculi with 1 ovule in each chamber; the style is gynobasic, the fruit consist of 4 one-seeded nutlets. *Verbenaceae* is distinguished from *Acanthaceae*, another related family, by its 4-chambered ovary (with 1 ovule in each chamber), or 2-chambered ovary (with 1 or 2 ovules in each chamber). The spike of *Acanthaceae*, with the frequently conspicuous bracts and bracteoles, is another distinguishing feature. The fruit is another distinguishing feature.

Examples. The larger genera are *Clerodendrum* (about 400 sp.), *Vitex* (over 250 sp.), *Verbena* (230 sp.), *Lippia* (over 200 sp.), *Premna* (200 sp.), *Lantana* (155 sp.), *Callicarpa* (140 sp.) and *Stachytarpheta* (about 100 sp.). Some examples are Teak (*Tectona grandis*)—a very valuable timber tree, *Gmelina arborea* (B. GAMHAR; H. GAMARI)—a very good timber tree, *Duranta repens* (=*D. plumieri*; FIG. 58)—commonly grown as a hedge plant, *Lantana aculeata* (=*L. camara*)—a strong-smelling straggling shrub with prickly stem, *L. indica*—a strong-smelling, erect shrub stem not prickly, *Clerodendrum infortunatum* (B. & H. BHANT), *C. siphonanthus*, *C. inerme*, *C. thomsonae*—a garden climber with white calyx and red corolla (see FIG. I/143), *Petrea volubilis*—a garden climber with profuse violet flowers in racemes, lady's umbrella or Chinese hat (*Holmskioldia sanguinea*)—a shrub bearing beautiful scarlet flowers (common in the low hills of Assam), *Lippia nodiflora* (=*Phyla nodiflora*)—a prostrate herb in wet places, *L. javanica* (=*L. geminata*)—a scandent shrub on the banks of tanks and canals, *Verbena officinalis*—a small erect weed, *Stachytarpheta indica*—a perennial herb with bluish flowers, often cultivated, *Avicennia officinalis*—a mangrove tree of the Sundarbans, *Premna esculenta*—a shrub, *P. bengalensis*—a tree, *Vitex negundo* (B. NISHINDA; H. SHAMALU)—a shrub, *V. trifolia*—a tree, *Callicarpa arborea*—an evergreen tree, and *C. macrophylla*—a tomentose shrub.

FAMILY 36 LABIATAE OR LAMIACEAE (over 3,000 sp.—391 sp. in India)

Habit. These are herbs and undershrubs with square stems.

Leaves. These are simple, opposite or whorled, exstipulate and have oil-glands.

Flowers. This is a zygomorphic, bilabiate, hypogynous and bisexual.

Inflorescence. This is a verticillaster (see p. 55). It is often reduced to a true cyme, as in sacred

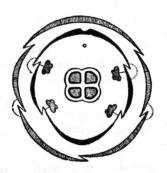

FIG. 59. Floral diagram of *Labiatae*

basil (*Ocimum*; B. & H. TULSI). **Calyx.** The petals are (5), gamopetalous and bilabiate, i.e. 2-lipped. The aestivation is imbricate.

Androecium. The stamens are 4 and didynamous. Sometimes there are only 2, as in sage (*Salvia*; SEE FIG. I/139). They are epipetalous.

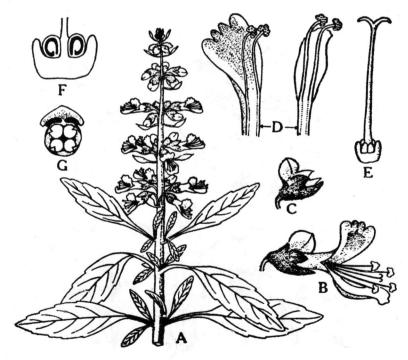

Labiatae. FIG. 60. Basil (*Ocimum basilicum*). *A*, a branch with inflorescences;
B, a flower—bilabiate (note the didynamous stamens); *C*, calyx; *D*, corolla split open with
epipetalous stamens; *E*, pistil (note the gynobasic style); *F*, ovary with the disc (in longi-section);
and *G*, fruit of four nutlets enclosed in the persistent calyx

Gynoecium. The carpels are (2) and syncarpous. The disc is prominent. The ovary is 4-lobed and 4-celled, with one ovule in each cell, ascending from the base of the ovary. The style is gynobasic (FIG. 60 *E-F*), i.e. it develops from the depressed centre of the lobed ovary. The stigma is bifid.

Fruit. This is a group of four nutlets, each with one seed. The seed has only scanty endosperm, or even none.

Floral formula   ⊹ ♂ $K_{(5)}\overline{C_{(5)}A_4\underline{G}_{(2)}}$.

Labitae is closely related to *Verbenaceae* (see p. 584). It may be related to *Boraginaceae* by virtue of the characteristics of its fruit (4 nutlets), but is readily distinguished from it by its inflorescence. *Labitae* is distinguished from *Acanthaceae* and *Scrophulariaceae* by its inflorescence, lobed ovary and fruit structure.

Labiatae abounds in volatile, aromatic soils which are used in perfumery and also as stimulants. Many of them possess a bitter astringent property.

Examples. The larger genera are *Salvia* (over 500 sp.), *Nepeta* (250 sp.), *Stachys* (over 200 sp.), *Teucrium* (over 200 sp.), *Scutellaria* (over 200 sp), *Ocimum* (150 sp.), and *Coleus* (150 sp.). **Useful plants:** *Medicinal:* sacred basil (*Ocimum sanctum*), mint (*Mentha*), e.g. spearmint or garden mint (*M. viridis;* B. PUDINA; H. PODINA)—commonly cultivated and used as a salad, peppermint (*M. piperita*)—yields peppermint oil from which menthol is obtained, Japanese peppermint (*M. arvensis*); garden thyme (*Thymus vulgaris*)—leaves used for flavouring soups and curries, thyme (*T. serpyllum*)—yields thyme oil from which thymol is obtained, patchouli (*Pogostemon heyneanus*)—yields patchouli oil,

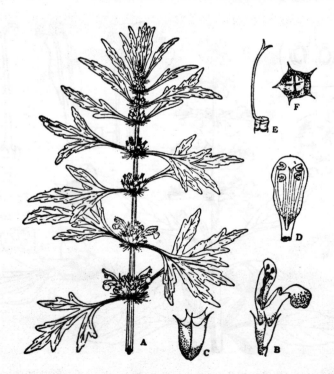

Labiatae. FIG. 61. *Leonurus sibiricus. A,* a branch with opposite leaves and inflorescences; *B,* a flower—bilabiate; *C,* calyx; *D,* stamens—didynamous and epipetalous; *E,* pistil (note the gynobasic style and 4-lobed ovary); *F,* fruit of four nutlets enclosed in persistent calyx

lavender (*Lavandula vera*)—yields lavender oil, and rosemary (*Rosmarinus officinalis*)—yields oil of rosemary. **Ornamental**: sage (*Salvia*), e.g. *S. coccinea* and *S. splendens*—flowers scarlet, cultivated garden herbs or undershrubs, *S. farinacea*—flowers lavender-blue, cultivated, *S. leucantha*—flowers purplish-blue, a scandent shrub, wild and cultivated in the hills, *S. plebeja*—an annual weed; country borage (*Coleus aromaticus*—see FIG. I/6) and marjoram (*Origanum vulgare*)—cultivated for its scented leaves.

Other common plants: *Ocimum gratissimum* (B. & H. RAM-TULSI), basil (*O. basilicum*; B. & H. BABUI-TULSI), wild basil (*O. canum* ; B. & H. BAN-TULSI), *Anisomeles indica*, *Leonurus sibiricus* (FIG. 61), *Leucas lavandulaefolia* (= *L. linifolia*), *L. aspera*, *L. cephalotes*, *L. lanata*—a whitish pubescent herb, *Dysophylla verticillata*—a marsh herb, *Pogostemon plectranthoides*—a common bushy undershrub, *Plectranthus ternifolius*—a bushy, tomentose undershrub, etc.

Sub-class III. Monochlamydeae

FAMILY 37 NYCTAGINACEAE (300 *sp.*—8 *sp.* in India)

Habit. These are herbs, shrubs or climbers, showing anomalous secondary growth.

Leaves. The leaves are simple, opposite, and exstipulate. The leaves of a pair are often unequal.

Inflorescence. This is cymose.

Flowers. These are regular, bisexual or sometimes unisexual (as in *Pisonia*). They are hypogynous. The bracts, usually large and coloured, vary in number (3 petaloid bracts in *Bougainvillea* surrounding a group of 3 flowers; 5 sepal-like bracts in the form of an involucre in *Mirabilis*; in *Boerhaavia*, the involucral bracts are reduced to scales).

Perianth leaves. These are united, tubular or funnel-shaped, 5-lobed and petaloid The lower part of the perianth is persistent in the fruit, enveloping the latter like the pericarp (and known as the anthocarp).

Androecium. There are 5 stamens which alternate with the perianth-lobes. The number of stamens often varies greatly—there can be 1, a few or several (up to 30) by branching. The filaments often unequal.

Gynoecium. There is 1 carpel. The ovary is superior and 1-locular. It has a basal anatropous or campylotropous ovule. The style is long.

Fruit. This is an achene. It is 1-seeded and enclosed by the base of the perianth.

Seed. The seed has a mealy perisperm. The embryo may be straight, folded or curved.

Floral formula $\oplus$ $\male$ $P_{(5)}$ A_5 G_1.

Examples. The larger genera are *Mirabilis* (60 sp.) and *Pisonia* (50 sp.). Some examples are four o'clock plant (*Mirabilis jalapa*)—a garden herb with variously coloured flowers, glory of the garden (*Bougainvillea spectabilis*)—a large climber with petaloid bracts, *Pisonia aculeata*—a large climber elaborately armed with recurved spines, hogweed (*Boerhaavia diffusa*)—a diffuse prostrate herb (medicinal), and *Abronia umbellata*—an annual creeper with pink flowers.

FAMILY 38 AMARANTHACEAE (850 *sp.*—46 *sp. in India*)

Habit. These are mostly herbs, sometimes climbing.

Leaves. These are simple, opposite or alternate, entire and exstipulate.

Inflorescence. This may be an axillary cyme, a simple or branched spike, or a raceme.

Flowers. The flowers are small, regular, bisexual (rarely unisexual), and pentamerous. They often have scarious bracts and bracteoles.

Perianth. There are usually 4-5 tepals. They may be free or united, and are membranous.

Androecium. There are 5 stamens. Some are often reduced to staminodes. They are opposite the perianth leaves and may be free, united to the perianth, or to one another into a membranous tube. Petaloid outgrowths are often present between the stamens. The anthers are 2 or 4-locular.

Gynoecium. This is syncarpous, with (2-3) carpels. The ovary is superior, unilocular, and usually has one campylotropous ovule. Sometimes, as in cock's comb, several ovules are present.

Fruit. The fruit is a utricle (1-seeded small fruit with loose perianth), berry, nut, or dehiscent (capsular).

Seed. The seed is endospermic.

Floral formula $\oplus$ $\male$ P $_{4-5 \, or \, (4-5)}$ A $_5$ $\underline{G}$ $_{(2-3)}$.

Examples. The larger genera are *Amaranthus* (60 sp.) and *Celosia* (60 sp.). **Leafy vegetables:** *Amaranthus caudatus* (B. NATE-SAK; H. CHAULAI), *A. gangeticus* (=*A. tristis*; B. LAL-SAK; H. LAL-SAG), *A. blitum* (=*A. oleraceae*; B. SADANATE; H. CHAULAI)—tall annual, widely cultivated, *A. polygamous* (B.CHAMPANATE). **Ornamental:** *A. tricolor* bearing showy coloured leaves, *A, paniculatus*—a tall plant, long crimson or golden-yellow pendulous spikes, cock's comb (*Celosia cristata*) bearing red fasciated inflorescence with red flowers, *C, argentea* bearing white flowers, *C. plumosa* bearing yellow flowers, button flower or globe amarnth (*Gomphrena globosa*), *Allmania nodiflora*—commonly grown as a garden border, *Deeringia celosioides*—a rambling climber bearing small globose scarlet fruits. **Weeds:** prickly amaranth (*Amaranthus spinosus*; B. KANTA-NATE; H. CHAULAI)—a common spinous weed, *A. viridis*, *A. mangostanus*, *A. tenuifolius*, etc.; chaff-flower (*Achyranthes aspera*; B. APANG; H. LATJIRA)—a common weed with long spinous spikes, *Cyathula prostrata*—a slender erect weed, *C. tomentosa*—a densely tomentose undershrub, *Digera arvensis*—a common weed of fields and roadsides, *Alternanthera amoena*—a very common prostrate weed, *Pupalia atropurpurea*—a climber with hooked fruits, *Aerua scandens*—leaves and branches reddish, *A. lanata* and *A. tomentosa*—having a dense coating of hairs, *A. monsonia*—a much-branched slender herb, etc.

FAMILY 39 CHENOPODIACEAE (1,400 sp.— 40 sp. in India)

Habit. These are mostly herbs and rarely shrubs. They are often fleshy and sometimes covered with hairs. The stem is jointed as in *Salicornia*. They are mostly xerophytic and halophytic.

Leaves. These are simple, usually alternate and rarely opposite. They are often fleshy and often covered with hairs. In some species, the leaves remain undeveloped.

Inflorescence. This is racemose with cymose branches.

Flowers. The flowers are small, greenish and regular. They are bisexual or sometimes unisexual (as in *Spinacea* and *Atriplex*). They may be monoecious or dioecious, and are hypogynous (except in *Beta*).

Perianth. The tepals are 3-5, simple, sepaloid, free and imbricate.

Androecium. There are as many stamens as tepals. They are opposite to the tepals and are free or united at the base. The disc is sometimes present.

Gynoecium. This is syncarpous, with usually (2-3) carpels. The ovary is superior (semi-inferior in *Beta*), unilocular and with one basal campylotropous ovule.

Fruit. This is a small nut, achene or berry.

Seed. This often has mealy endosperm. The embryo may be curved or rolled.

Floral formula $\oplus$ $\male$ P $_{3-5}$ A $_{3-5}$ $\underline{G}$ $_{2-3}$.

Examples. The larger genera are *Atriplex* (about 200 sp.) and *Chenopodium* (ove 100 sp.). **Vegetables:** spinach (*Spinacia oleracea*; B. PALANG; H. PALAK)—a fleshy herb, beet (*Beta vulgaris*)—the sugar-beet, yielding about 18% sugar, is cultivated in Europe, erstwhile Russia and America, while the garden-beet is used extensively in India as a vegetable, Indian spinach (*Basella rubra*; B. PUIN; H. POI)—a large twining, fleshy herb, *Atriplex hortensis*—a succulent herb, goosefoot (*Chenopodium album*; B. & H. BATHUA), etc. **Weeds:** worm-seed (*Chenopodium anthelminticum*)— a roadside weed; essential oil is used as a vermifuge, *C. ambrosioides*—a much-branched weed. **Halophytes:** glasswort (*Salsola foetida*)—a fleshy plant with spinous leaf-apex, saltwort (*Salicornia brachiata*)—a leafless succulent herb with jointed stems; yields barilla (impure sodium carbonate), *Arthrocnemum indicum* (B. JADU-PALANG)—a leafless undershrub with jointed fleshy stem, growing along with *Salicornia*, sea-blite (*Suaeda maritima* and *S. fruticosa*)—herbs with fleshy leaves, etc. **Ornamental:** *Kochia* (90 sp.), e.g. *K. tricophylla*—an ornamental bushy herb, etc.

FAMILY 40 POLYGONACEAE (800 sp.—109 sp. in India)

Habit. These are mostly herbs (sometimes climbing).

Leaves. These are simple, entire, alternate, and opposite or whorled. They have distinct ochreate stipules (a feature characteristic of the family).

Inflorescence. This may be a raceme or spike, with lateral cymes.

Flowers. These are small, regular, bisexual and usually hypogynous. They are trimerous (rarely dimerous), cyclic or acyclic, and sometimes medianly zygomorphic. Several species are dimorphic.

Perianth. There are 3 or 6 tepals (in two whorls). Often there are 5, generally uniform and often persistent.

Androecium. The number of stamens varies. There are usually 5-8 in two series.

Gynoecium. The carpels are (3) or sometimes (2). They are syncarpous. The ovary is superior, unilocular, and contains a single erect (orthotropous) ovule. There are 3 or 2 styles.

Fruit. This is a small, hard, triangular nut.

Seed. The seed is albuminous and often ruminated. The embryo may be curved or straight.

Floral formula $\oplus$ $\male$ $P_{3+3, \text{ or } 5} A_{5-8} \underline{G}_{(3)}$.

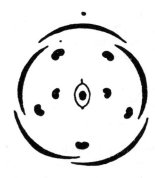

FIG. 62. Floral diagram of *Polygonaceae* (*Polygonum*)

Polygonaceae is related to *Urticaceae* by its unilocular ovary with the single orthotropous ovule. According to Hutchinson it is derived from *Caryophyllaceae*.

Examples. The larger genera are *Polygonum* (275 sp.), *Cocoloba* (150 sp. in America), *Eriogonum* (150 sp. in America), *Rumex* (over 100 sp.) and *Rheum* (50 sp.). Some examples are *Polygonum* (88 sp. in India), e.g. *P. plebejum, P. orientale, P. glabrum, P. hydropiper, P. capitatum* (common in hill slopes in Shillong); dock or sorrel (*Rumex vesicarius*)—cultivated for its sour leaves, *R. maritimus*—a common weed, buckwheat (*Fagopyrum esculentum*)—cultivated in the hills for grains used in making bread, rhubarb (*Rheum*; 7 sp. in alpine and sub-alpine Himalayas), e.g. *Rheum emodi* (Indian rhubarb)—a medicinal (cathartic) herb, and *R. rhaponticum*—cultivated as a vegetable in the Khasi Hills; cocoloba (*Muehlenbeckia platyclados*)—phylloclades (see FIG. I/39B), Sandwich Island climber (*Corculum leptopus=Antigonon leptopus*; see FIG. I/36B)—a common garden climber with pink or white flowers, and *Calligonum polygonodes*—an almost leafless shrub of Rajasthan and Punjab; edible flowers and buds.

FAMILY 41 LORANTHACEAE (1,100 sp.—64 sp. in India)

Habit. These are mostly semi-parasitic shrubs or undershrubs, growing on tree branches and developing sucking roots or haustoria.

Leaves. These are simple, mostly opposite, thick and lathery. They are exstipulate. They are reduced to scales.

Inflorescence. This may be racemose, spicate or cymose. The flowers are often in fascicles.

Flowers. These may be unisexual or bisexual, and regular or slightly zygomorphic. They are greenish or brightly coloured, and epigynous.

Perianth. This grows from the margin of the cup-shaped receptacle, in two whorls. It may be sepaloid (in *Viscum*) or petaloid (in *Loranthus*). The perianth leaves may be free or united into a tubular structure, and are usually 3 to 6-lobed. In

Loranthus, there is a small outgrowth (called **calyculus**) of the axis below the perianth. The calyculus is regarded by some as a calyx.

Stamens. These are opposite the perianth-segments and are the same in number. They are united with the latter.

Carpels. There are (3) or (4) carpels. The ovary is unilocular, inferior and sunken in the receptacle. The ovule is solitary. The placenta is not differentiated from the ovule.

Fruit. This is a drupaceous or berry-like pseudocarp. There is often a very stick substance (viscin) around the seed.

Seed. There is usually 1 seed, sometimes 2 or 3. It is albuminous. On germination, the hypocotyl first forms a swollen sucker, fixing the embryo to the branch of the host plant.

Examples. *With unisexual flowers: Viscum* (60 sp.), e.g. mistletoe (*V. album*)—exhibiting dichasial branching (see FIG. I/24). *With mostly bisexual flowers: Loranthus* (over 500 sp.), now split into a number of genera, e.g. *Dendropthe, Taxillus, Scurrula*, etc., as follows—*Dendropthe falcata* (= *L. longiflorus*), *Taxillus vestitus* (=*L. vestitus*), *Scurrula parasitica* (=*L. scurrula*), *Tolypanthus involucratus* (=*L. involucratus*), *Helixanthera parasitica* (=*L. pentapelalus*), *H. coccinea* (=*L. coccinea*), *Macrosolen cochinchinensis* (=*L. globosus*), etc.; *Phoradendron*, an American genus (about 190 sp.).

FAMILY 42 EUPHORBIACEAE (7,000 sp.—374 sp. in India)

Habit. These are herbs, shrubs and trees. They yield an acrid, milky juice. Many are xerophytic.

Leaves. These are simple and usually alternate. Stipules are usually present.

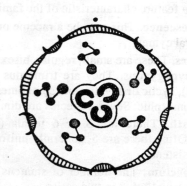

FIG. 63. Floral diagram of *Euphorbiaceae* (*Euphorbia*)

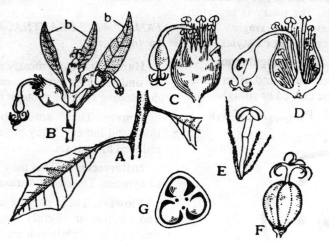

Euphorbiaceae. FIG. 64. Poinsettia (*Euphorbia pulcherrima=Poinsettia pulcherrima*).
A, a portion of a branch; *B*, a branch with three inflorescences; *b*, petaloid bracts;
C, an inflorescence (cyathium); *D*, cyathium cut longitudinally showing the centrally placed
female flower surrounded by numerous male flowers; *E*, a male flower (reduced to a stamen only)
with bract and bracteoles at the base; *F*, female flower (reduced to a pistil only); *G*, ovary in transection

Inflorescence. This may be racemose, cymose, or mixed, or a cyathium (see p. 70), as in spurge (*Euphorbia*) and Jew's slipper (*Pedilanthus*).

Flowers. These are small, bracteate, regular and hypogynous. They are always unisexual and may be monoecious or dioecious. Rudiments of the other sex are often present.

Perianth. This may be in 1 or 2 whorls, and is sometimes altogether absent. It is dissimilar in male and female flowers.

Floral formulae $\oplus \, \male - \female$ or $\male \, \female \, P_{0\,or\,5} A_{1\infty}$ $G_0 | A_0 \underline{G}_{(3)}$

Male Flowers: In spurges (*Euphorbia*) and Jew's slipper (*Pedilanthus*) the flowers are reduced to solitary stamens without any perianth (see p. 54). In other cases, there are usually many stamens, or sometimes only a few. The filaments are either free or connate, in 1 to many bundles. *Female Flowers*: There are (3) carpels (syncarpous). The ovary is 3-celled, 3-lobed and superior, with 1 or 2 ovules in each loculus. It is pendulous. There are 3 styles, each bifid, and 6 stigmas. The fruit is mostly a capsule or a regma. The seed is albuminous.

Euphorbiaceae is closely related to *Sterculiaceae* of the Malvales through the various degrees of the union of stamens and the presence of the pistillode and staminode in the male and female flowers, respectively, (sometimes also the androphore and gynophore). They may have originated from a common stock of the Malvales, but were differentiated by the reduction of the floral parts. *Euphorbiaceae* is also very closely related to Geraniales by the structure of the gynoecium.

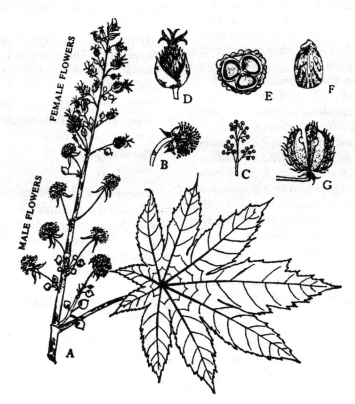

Euphorbicaeae. FIG. 65. Castor (*Ricinus communis*). *A*, a branch with a leaf and an inflorescence; *B*, a male flower; *C*, branched stamens; *D*, a female flower; *E*, ovary in transection; *F*, a seed with caruncle; and *G*, a fruit (regma) splitting

Examples. The larger genera are *Euphorbia* (about 2,000 sp.), *Croton* (700 sp.), *Phyllanthus* (500 sp.), *Acalypha* (430 sp.), *Jatropha* (175 sp.), *Manihot* (170 sp.), etc. **Useful plants:** *Oils*: castor (*Ricinus communis*; FIG. 65)—seeds yield castor oil, *Croton tiglium* (B. JAIPAL; H. JAMOLGOTA) —seeds yield croton oil used as a drastic purgative, Indian walnut (*Aleurites molucana*)—seeds yield a drying oil, sometimes used as candles, *A. cordata* and a few other species—nuts yield 35-40% TUNG oil, used for lacuquering, varnishing, water-proofing and manufacturing oil cloth, etc. *Fruits*: emblic myrobalan (*Emblica officinalis= Phyllanthus emblica*)—fruits rich in vitamins, medicinal and also used for tanning, *Phyllanthus acidus* (=*Cicca acidus*; B. NOAR; H. CHALMERI) —fruits sour but tasty, *Baccaurea sapida* (B. LATKAN; H. LUTKO)—aril, pulpy and edible, etc. **Ornamental:** garden croton (*Codiaeum variegatum*)—with variegated leaves, poinsettia (*Euphorbia pulcherrima = Poinsettia pulcherrima*), *Euphorbia splendens*—a prickly undershrub, each cyathium with two red bracts, *E. tirucalli* (see FIG. I/40A), *Acalypha sanderiana*, *A. tricolor*, Jew's slipper (*Pedilanthus tithymaloides*), tapioca or cassava (*Manihot esculenta*)—tuberous roots yield a valuable starchy food (tapioca), *Jatropha gossypifolia*, purging nut (*J. curcas*)—commonly grown as a hedge plant, *J. multifida*, *J. podogarica*—a xerophyte with gouty stem, *J. panduraefolia*, etc. **Rubber-yielding:** *Manihot glaziovii*— yields ceara rubber, *Hevea brasiliensis* —yields para rubber. **Shade trees:** child life tree (*Putranjiva roxburghii*), *Mallotus philippinensis* —fruit yields a crimson powder used for dyeing silk, etc.

Other common plants: spurges (*Euphorbia*), e.g. *E. antiquorum*, *E. neriifolia*, *E. nivulia*, *E. pilulifera*, *E. heterophylla*, *E. thymifolia*, *E. royleana*, etc., *Croton sparsiflorus*, *Phyllanthus niruri*, *Acalypha indica*, *Chrozophora plicata*, nettle (*Tragia involucrata*)—a twiner with stinging hairs, *Breynia rhamnoides*—a shrub, *Fluggea microcarpa*—a large shrub, *Trewia nudiflora*—a small deciduous tree, wood white and soft, *Biscofia javanica*—a large deciduous tree, wood moderately hard, *Bridelia retusa*—a timber tree, wood cream or brown, very durable, etc.

FAMILY 43 ULMACEAE (180 *sp.*—14 *sp. in India*)

Habit. These are mostly trees with no latex.

Leaves. The leaves are simple, alternate, distichous and often oblique. Stipules are present, being caducous. Mostly, cystoliths are also present.

Inflorescence. This is cymose.

Flowers. These are small, regular, and often solitary. They are unisexual, monoecious (rarely bisexual), and hypogynous.

Perianth. There are 4-5 tepals, which may be free or united. They are sepaloid and imbricate.

Androecium. There are as many stamens as tepals (though sometimes fewer). They are opposite the tepals. The filaments are straight in the bud. The anther splits longitudinally. Rudimentary carpels are often present.

Gynoecium. There are (2) carpels (Syncarpous). The ovary is 1-locular, sometimes 2-locular. The ovule is solitary, and anatropous or amphitropous.

Fruit. This may be a nut, samara or drupe

Seed. The seed is exalbuminous. The embryo may be straight or curved.

Floral formulae $\oplus$ $\male$-$\female$ P$_{4-5}$ or $_{(4-5)}$ A$_{4-5}$ G$_0$ | A$_0$ G$_{(2)}$.

Examples. *Celtis* (60 sp.), e.g. *C. australis*—a middle-sized deciduous tree; *Ulmus* (45 sp.), e.g. *U. lancifolia*—a large deciduous tree; *Trema* (30 sp.), e.g. *T. orientalis*—a fast growing tree, the fibrous bark of which is beaten into a coarse mattress by the Garos.

FAMILY 44 MORACEAE (over 1,000 *sp.*—106 *sp. in India*)

Habit. These are mostly trees. A few are shrubs or herbs, with latex.

Leaves. The leaves are simple, alternate, and may be entire or lobed. The stipules are large and caducous. Cystoliths are present in some genera, e.g. *Ficus* and *Morus*, while absent in others, e.g. *Artocarpus*.

Inflorescence. This is cymose, usually in the form of a raceme, spike, umbel or head. It is a hypanthodium in *Ficus*.

Flowers. These are small, regular, unisexual, and may be monoecious or dioecious. They are hypogynous.

Perianth. There are 4 or (4), tepals, which may be free or united. They are often persistent in the fruit.

Androecium (in ♂ flowers). The stamens are equal in number and opposite to the tepals. They are sometimes reduced to 1 or 2. The filaments are curved in or straight in the bud. The anther is dehiscing.

Gynoecium (in ♀ flowers). There are (2) carpels (syncarpous). They are 1-locular (one carpel usually abortive), and superior to inferior. The ovule is solitary and campylotropous.

Fruit. This may be a drupe, nut or achene. The whole inflorescence sometimes develops into a multiple fruit (sorosis or syconus).

Seed. The seed may or may not have endosperm. The embryo is curved.

Floral formulae $\oplus \male - \female$ or $\male \, \female \, P_{4 \text{ or } (4)}$ $A_{4-1} G_0 \mid A_0 \underline{G}_{(2)}$ or $\bar{G}_{(2)}$.

Examples. Mulberry (*Morus alba*—with short spikes, and *M. nigra*—with long spikes)—fruit edible, wood very valuable, particularly of the latter; silk worms are reared on mulberry; *Ficus* (over 600 sp.), e.g. fig (*F. carica*; B. DUMUR; H. ANJIR), *F. glomerata* (B. JAJNA-DUMUR; H. GULAR), *F. virens* (=*F. infectoria*; B. PAKUR; H. PAKAR), *F. hispida* (B. KAK-DUMUR; H. KONEA-DUMBAR), *F. rumphii* (B. GAI-ASWATTHA; H. KHABAR), banyan (*F. bengalensis*), peepul or bo-tree (*F. religiosa*), india-rubber plant (*F. elastica*), Indian ivy (*F. pumila*; see FIG. I/17), *F. pomifera*—large reddish edible fruit of upper Assam, *F. lanceolata*—large purplish fruit of Khasi Hills, *Artocarpus* (40 sp.), e.g. jack (*A. heterophyllus*)—large summer fruit (sorosis), sweet and edible; wood used for furniture, monkey jack (*A. lakoocha*; B. & H. DEOPHAL)—fruit edible, wood useful, bread-fruit (*A. incisa*)—fruit sliced, roasted and eaten like bread, chaplas (*A. chaplasha*; see FIG. I/79B)—wood valuable; cowtree or milk-tree (*Brosimum galactodendron*) of Venezuela— profuse milky latex used as a substitute for milk, being sweet, tasty and nutritious, *Streblus asper* (B. SHAORA)—a rigid evergreen tree, paper-mulberry (*Broussonetia papyrifera*)—wood very soft and light, bark used for making paper in Japan, *Cudrania javanesis*—a rambling shrub, *Conocephalus suaveolens*—a large evergreen woody climber, *Castilloa elastica*—source of panama-rubber, etc.

Distinguishing Characteristics of Urticales

Urticaceae	Moraceae	Ulmaceae
mostly herbs	trees or shrubs	mostly trees
Latex absent; cystoliths abundant	latex present; cystoliths present or absent	latex absent; cystoliths mostly present
Flowers unisexual, hypogynous	unisexual, hypogynous to epigynous	unisexual, rarely bisexual, hypogynous
Stamens 4-5, anther exploding, filaments incurved in bud straight in bud	4, often reduced to 1 or 2, anther not exploding, filaments incurved or	4-5, anther splitting longitudinally, filaments straight in bud
Carpel 1, style 1 styles 1 or 2	(2), usually 1 aborted,	(2), styles 2
Ovary 1-locular, superior	1-locular, superior to inferior	2-locular or 1-locular, superior
Endosperm oily	fleshy or absent	usually not present
Embryo straight	curved	straight or curved

FAMILY 45 URTICACEAE[1] (600 sp.—104 sp. in India)

Habit. These are mostly herbs (sometimes shrubs) with no latex.

Leaves. These are simple, alternate or opposite, and with three basal nerves. may or may not have stinging hairs. Cystoliths are abundant and in various forms. The stipules are membranous.

Inflorescence. This is cymose (often condensed).

Flowers. These are small, regular, unisexual, and may be monoecious or dioecious.

Perianth. There are usually 4 (sometimes 5) tepals, which may be free or connate. They are sepaloid.

Androecium. The stamens are the same in number as the tepals and are opposite to them. The filaments are incurved in the bud. The anthers are exploding when mature.

Gynoecium. There is 1 carpel. The ovary is superior, 1-locular, and has 1 basal, orthotropous ovule.

Fruit. This is a small achene, nut or drupe.

Seed. The seed usually has oily endosperm. The embryo is straight.

Floral formulae $\oplus \male - \female \text{ or } \male \female \text{ } P_{4 \text{ or } (4)} A_{4 \text{ or } 5}$ $G_0 \mid A_0 \underline{G}_1$.

Examples. *With stinging hairs—nettles:* Urtica (50 sp.), e.g. *U. dioica* (also fibre-yielding), *Laportea* (=*Fleurya*) *interrupta, Girardinia zeylanica* (also fibre-yielding), devil or fever nettle (*Laportea crenulata*), etc. *Without stinging hairs:* Pilea (over 200 sp.), e.g. gunpowder plant (*P. microphylla*), *Boehmeria* (about 100 sp.), e.g. rhea or ramie (*B. nivea*)—cultivated for best fibres (longest, toughest and silkiest), *Pouzolzia indica*—common on roadsides and waste places, *Elatostema*—a herb or undershrub common on hill slopes.

FAMILY 46 CANNABINACEAE (3 sp.—2 sp. in India)

Habit. These are aromatic herbs.

Leaves. The leaves are palmi-nerved and palmately divided. Cystoliths are present. Stipules are present and persistent. There are no latex.

Flowers. These are unisexual, dioecious, and borne in cymes. *In male flowers*, there are 5 perianth leaves and 5 stamens (opposite to the perianth leaves), while *in female flowers*, the perianth is entire and cup-shaped. There are (2) carpels : ovary is 1 celled with 1 pendulous ovule.

Fruit. This may be a nut or an achene.

Seed. The seed may be albuminous or exalbuminous and the embryo curved or spiral.

Examples. There are only 2 genera—*Cannabis* (1 sp.) and *Humulus* (2 sp.). These are hemp (*Cannabis sativa*)—yields valuable bast fibres and is the source of a narcotic resin in three forms: GANJA (resinous flowering shoots of cultivated female plants), CHARAS (resinous exudation from twigs of plants grown in cold climates, particulary in Nepal) and BHANG (mature leaves and flowering shoots with resinous contents of plants growing wild); and hop (*Humulus lupulus*)—fruit used in brewing.

FAMILY 47 CASUARINACEAE (40 sp.—1 sp. in India)

Habit. These are Xerophytic trees. The branches are jointed, and the internodes furrowed.

Leaves. These are alternating whorls of 4-12 minute, scale-like leaves, which are united at the base to form a sheath.

Flowers. These are extremely simple, unisexual and monoecious. They have a bract and two bracteoles. *Male flowers* are borne in terminal, catkin-like spikes at the ends of branches. Each consists of a single stamen, two small perianth leaves, a bract and a pair of lateral bracteoles. The

---

[1] The *Urticaceae* of Bentham and Hooker has been split up by Engler into three families—*Ulmaceae, Moraceae* and *Urticaceae*—under the order Urticales. Hutchinson split the order further into four families—*Ulmaceae, Mordaceae, Urticaceae* and *Cannabinaceae*. The last one has been isolated from *Moraceae*.

flowers are in whorls, and the bracts in a sheath round each whorl. *Female flowers* are borne in a more or less spherical head on a short lateral branch. Each consists of two carpels, a bract and 2 bracteoles which harden in the fruit. The pistil is syncarpous. The ovary is 1-celled (by the suppression of the posterior cell). There are generally 2 ovules, which are orthotropous and ascending, but 1 matures. There are 2 long, protruding stigmas. Pollination takes place through the wind and fertilization is chalazogamic.

Fruit. This is a 1-seeded, winged nut (the whole head, however, becomes woody and cone-like).

Seed. This is exalbuminous and winged.

Examples. *Casuarina*, commonly called beefwood or she-oak, is the only genus of the family (mainly Australian). *C. equisetifolia* is widely grown in India as a roadside or avenue tree.

CHAPTER 4

Selected Families of Monocotyledons

FAMILY 1 HYDROCHARITACEAE (80 *sp.*)

Habit. These are aquatic herbs, usually submerged and sometimes floating. Some are marine.

Leaves. These are simple, radical and clustered, or cauline, entire, ribbon-shaped or flattened.

Flowers. These are often regular. They are trimerous and mostly unisexual (rarely bisexual). They may be dioecious or monocious. They are enclosed in a spathe of 2 or more fused bracts. The female flowers are solitary, sometimes each on a long stalk. The male flowers are in a cluster.

Perianth. There are 3 + 3 segments free and in 2 whorls (1 whorl in *Vallisneria*). The outer whorl (calyx) is often green and the inner (corolla) is petaloid. In ♂ flowers, there are 3-12 stamens, in 1-4 trimerous series. The innermost whorl is often reduced to staminodes. In ♀ flowers there are (2-15), carpels—usually (3) or (6-15). They are connate. The ovary is inferior and unilocular. The placentation is parietal. There are 3-6 placentae which sometimes intrude into the loculus, almost reaching the axis. There are ∞ ovules on each placenta. There is 1 style which is usually divided into 3-12 stigmas.

Fruit. This may be ovoid or oblong, and dry or pulpy.

Seeds. There are a few to ∞ seeds. They are exalbuminous. The embryo is large.

Floral formula $\oplus$ $\male\female P_{3+3} A_{3-12} \bar{G}_{(2-15)}$

Examples. *Dioecious: Vallisneria spiralis*—a stoloniferous submerged herb (see FIG. I/141), *Hydrilla verticillata*—a submerged leafy herb, *Lagarosiphon roxburghii*—a submerged leafy herb, *Blyxa roxburghii*—a submerged tufted herb; *Monoecious: Hydrocharis cellulosa*—a floating herb; *Bisexual: Blyxa griffithii*—a submerged tufted herb, and *Ottelia alismoides*—a partly submerged herb.

FAMILY 2 LILIACEAE (over 3,000 *sp.*)

Habit. These are herbs and climbers, and rarely shrubs or trees, (e.g. *Dracaena* and *Yucca*) with a bulb or rhizome, or with fibrous roots.

Leaves. These are simple, radical or cauline, or both.

Inflorescence. This may be a spike, raceme, panicle or umbel (solitary flowers in *Tulipa*), often on a scape.

Flowers. The flowers are regular, bisexual (rarely unisexual) dioecious, as in *Smilax*). They are trimerous and hypogynous. The bracts are

FIG. 66. Floral diagram of *Liliaceae*

usually small and scarious (thin, dry and membranous).

Perianth. The tepals are petaloid. There are usually 6 in two whorls. They may be 3 + 3 and free (polyphyllous), or (3 + 3), and united (gamophyllous).

Androecium. There are 6 stamens in two whorls—3 + 3, rarely 3 free or united with the perianth (epiphyllous) at the base. The anthers are often dorsifixed.

Gynoecium. There are (3) carpels (syncarpous). The ovary is superior and 3-celled. There are usually ∞ ovules in two rows in each loculus. The placentation is axile. There are (3) or 3 styles.

Fruit. This may be a berry or capsule.

Seeds. The seeds are albuminous.

Floral formula $\oplus \; \mathaccent{\female} \; P_{3+3} A_{3+3} \underline{G}_{(3)}$ or $P_{(3+3)} A_{3+3} \underline{G}_{(3)}$.

Examples. The larger genera are *Allium* (over 400 sp.), *Smilax* (300 sp.), *Asparagus* (300 sp.), *Aloe* (over 200 sp.), *Dracaena* (150 sp.), *Lilium* (70 sp.), *Colchicum* (65 sp.), and *Sansevieria* (60 sp.). **Useful plants:** *Vegetables:* onion (*Allium cepa*), garlic (*A. sativum*)—also medicinal, shallot (*A. ascalonicum*), leek (*A. porrum*), etc. *Medicinal: Asparagus racemosus*—root is tonic and astringent, sarsaparilla (*Smilax zeylanica* and other species; see FIG. I/48)—dried roots form sarasparilla (a blood purifier), Indian aloe (*Aloe vera*), meadow saffron (*Colchicum autumnale*),

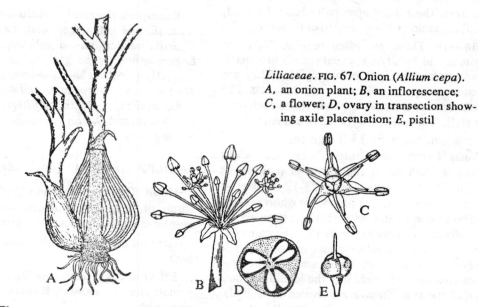

Liliaceae. FIG. 67. Onion (*Allium cepa*).
A, an onion plant; *B,* an inflorescence;
C, a flower; *D,* ovary in transection showing axile placentation; *E,* pistil

It may be noted that *Dracaena, Cordyline, Yucca, Sansevieria* and *Phormium* of *Liliaceae,* and *Agave* and *Polianthes* of *Amaryllidaceae* have now been taken over to a new family *Agavaceae.* Further, *Allium,* having spathaceous involucrate bracts and umbellate inflorescence, has been transferred to *Amaryllidaceae.*

etc. **Ornamental:** lily (*Lilium*), e.g. *L. candidum*—flowers white, *L. bulbiferum*, reproducing through bulbils, etc., glory lily (*Gloriosa superba*; see FIG. I/63C), day lily (*Hemerocallis fulva*), dagger plant or Adam's needle (*Yucca gloriosa*; see FIG. I/81), dragon plant (*Dracaena*), *Sansevieria laurentii*—green foliage with yellow or white margin, *Cordyline australis*—stem erect, cylindrical and *Dracaena*-like, butcher's broom (*Ruscus aculeatus*; see FIG. I/41A), asphodel (*Asphodelus tenuifolium*), *Scilla indica*—propagating through leaf tips, *Asparagus plumosus*, *A. sprengeri*, etc. **Fibre-yielding:** *Phormium tenax*—yielding New Zealand flax, and bowstring hemp (*Sansevieria roxburghii*)—leaves flat and spotted, *S. cylindrica*—leaves cylindrical, *S. zeylanica*—leaves furrowed, etc.

FAMILY 3. AMARYLLIDACEAE (1,100 *sp.*)

Habit. These are often bulbous, sometimes rhizomatous, perennial herbs. The leaves are radical.

Inflorescence. The inflorescence is commonly *umbellate* on a scape, or a solitary flower on a scape, with *spathaceous involucrate* bracts.

Flowers. The flowers are regular, bisexual, epigynous, often showy.

Perianth. The perianth is petaloid, the segments are 3 + 3 or (3 + 3), biseriate, sometimes brightly coloured.

Androecium. There are 3 + 3 stamens in two whorls. Staminodes are sometimes present. The filaments are often dilated at the base. The anthers are erect or versatile. The corona is prominent in some cases, as *Pancratium, Narcissus, Eucharis*, etc.

Gynoecium. There are (3) carpels. It is syncarpous. The ovary is inferior, rarely semi-inferior or even superior, trilocular. The placentation axile, with often numerous anatropous ovules.

Fruit. The fruit is a capsule, or sometimes a berry.

Floral formula $\oplus \; \male \; P_{3+3} \; A_{3+3} \bar{G}_{(3)}$ or

$$\overline{P_{(3+3)}} A_{3+3} \bar{G}_{(3)}$$

Examples. The larger genera are: *Agave* (300 sp., American). *Crinum* (over 100 sp.), and *Zephyranthes* (60 sp., American). Mostly ornamental, e.g. Easter lily (*Amaryllis bella-donna*), spider lily (*Pancratium gloriosa*; FIG. 68), *Crinum asiaticum, C. latifolium*, zephyr lilies, e.g. *Zephyranthes tubispatha*—with white flowers, *Z. carinata*—bright rose flowers *Z. andersoni* — yellow flowers, African lily (*Agapanthus*

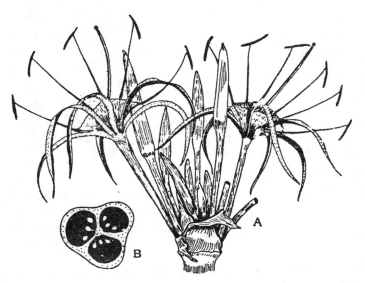

Amaryllidaceae. FIG. 68. Spider lily (*Pancratium*). *A*, inflorescence; and *B*, ovary in transection showing axile placentation

umbellatus)— large bright blue flowers, pin-cushion lily (*Haemanthus multiflororus*), eucharis or Amazon lily (*Eucharis grandiflora*), daffodil (*Narcissus*), tuberose (*Polianthes tuberosa*), American aloe or century plant (*Agave americana*), *Curculigo orchioides* (B. TALMULI; H. MUSLIKAND), etc.

FAMILY 4 COMMELINACEAE (500 *sp.*)

Habit. These are annual or perennial herbs, with 5 jointed stem.

Leaves. The leaves are simple, alternate, with sheathing base.

Flowers. The flowers are more or less regular, commonly blue, sometimes whitish or pinkish, bisexual, hypogynous, in monochasial cyme, enclosed in a distinct spathe.

Perianth. This has 6 segments in two series, distinguishable into the outer sepaloid calyx and the inner petaloid corolla, sepals and petals generally free.

Androecium. There are 6 stamens in two whorls, either all perfect or some reduced to staminodes or absent. The filaments are often bearded with hairs.

Gynoecium. There are (3) carpels. It is syncarpous. The ovary is superior and 3-celled. The placentation is axile. There is solitary ovule, or a few, orthotropous.

Fruit. The fruit is a dehiscent capsule or indehiscent. The seeds are albuminous.

Floral formula $\oplus\ \text{\male\female}\,K_3\,C_3\,A_{3+3}\,\underline{G}(_3)$

Examples. *Commelina* (over 200 sp.), e.g. *C. bengalensis* (see FIG. I/136), *C. salicifolia*, *C. obliqua*, *C. nudiflora*, etc., *Aneilema* (100 sp.), e.g. *A. nudiflorum*, *A. spiratum*, etc., *Cyanotis* (50 sp.), e.g. *C. axillaris*, *C. cristata*, etc., *Floscopa scandens*, *Tradescantia virginiana*, *Rhoeo discolor*, etc.

FAMILY 5 SCITAMINEAE [1] (over 1,200 *sp.*)

Habit. These are generally herbs, rarely woody and tree-like, e.g. traveller's tree (*Ravenala*). The underground stem is usually in the form of a slender or stout rhizome while the aerial stem is distinct or 'false', made of sheathing leaf-bases, and the flowering stem or scape pushing out through the 'false' stem and ending in an inflorescence. The leaves are spiral or distichous, with sheathing.

Inflorescence. The inflorescence is a raceme, spike or spadix, with often large spathes, either terminal or axillary.

Flowers. The flowers are zygomorphic, mostly bisexual and epigynous. The bracts are often spathaceous.

Perianth. The perianth has six segments in two whorls.

Androecium. The stamens vary in number: 1 or 5 (-6) (see sub-families).

Gynoecium. There are 3 carpels. It is syncarpous. The ovary is inferior and trilocular. The placentation is axile, the ovules usually many.

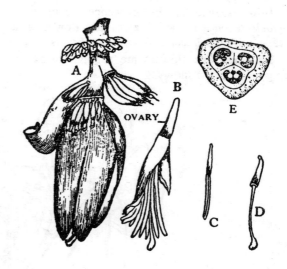

Musaceae. FIG. 69 Banana (*Musa paradisiaca*). *A*, spadix; *B*, a flower; *C*, a stamen; *D*, pistil; and *E*, ovary in transection showing axile placentation (section taken from a wild variety)

---

[1]*Scitamineae* of Bentham and Hooker has been raised by Engler to the rank of an order with four families—*Musaceae, Zingiberaceae, Cannaceae* and *Marantaceae*. Huthchinson renamed the order as *Zingiberales* and divided it into six families.

Fruit. The fruit is a berry or capsule.

Seeds. The seeds have perisperm, often arillate.

Scitamineae has been divided into the following sub-families (later raised to the rank of families), mainly on the basis of the number of stamens.

(1) *Musaceae* (150 sp.). In this family, the leaves are spiral, rarely distichous. They have a sheathing but no ligule: The **Perianth** is petaloid in two series—one with 5 limbs united and the other solitary and free. The **Stamens** are in 2 whorls, 5 perfect and the 6th one sterile or absent. In *Ravenala*, however, there are six stamens and all of them are fertile.

Floral formula $\cdot | \cdot \; \male \; P_{(5)+1} A_{3+2} \bar{G}_{(3)}$

Examples. *Mussa* (35 sp.), e.g. banana (*M. paradisiaca*)—a dessert fruit, plantain (*M. sapientum*)—green fruit used as a vegetable, dwarf plantain of Assam (*M. sanguinea*)—fruit not edible, *M. superba* and *M. nepalensis*— ornamental, fruit not edible, *M. textilis* yields commercial Manila hemp or abaca, *Heliconia* (80 sp. American), traveller's tree (*Ravenala madagascariensis*; B. PANTHAPADAP—see FIG. I/74),—ornamental, and bird of Paradise (*Strelitzia reginae*)—ornamental. [It may be noted that *Ravenala* and *Strelitzia*, which have distichous leaves and flowers in cincinnus, have been separated from *Musaceae* to a new family, *Strelitziaceae*, by Hutchinson.]

(2) *Zingiberaceae* (700 sp.). In this family the leaves are distichous, with sheathing and a distinct ligule. The **Perianth** has segments in 2 whorls, generally distinguishable into calyx and corolla. The **stamens** are in 2 whorls—only 1 perfect. They adnate to corolla-throat (this is the posterior one of the inner whorl), the other 2 stamens of this whorl are united to form a 2-lipped labellum. The anterior stamen of the outer whorl is absent and the remaining 2 are modified into petaloid staminodes or absent. The **style** is slender, and passed through the two anther-lobes.

Floral formula $\cdot | \cdot \; \male \; K_{(3)} C_3 A_1 \bar{G}_{(3)}$

Examples. *Zingiber* (80 sp.), e.g. ginger (*Zingiber*

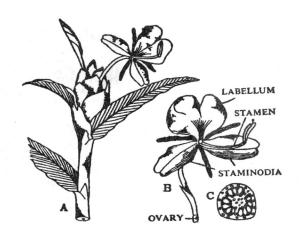

Zingiberaceae. FIG. 70. Butterfly lily (*Hedychium coronarium*). *A*, a branch with inflorescence; *B*, a flower; and *C*, ovary in transection showing axile placentation

officinale), wild ginger (*Z. casumunar*), turmeric (*Curcuma longa*), wild turmeric (*C. aromatica*), mango ginger (*C. amada*), butterfly lily (*Hedychium coronarium*; B. DULAL-CHAMPA), *Kaempferia* (70 sp.), e.g. *K. rotunda* (B. BHUI-CHAMPA), *Costus* (150 sp.), e.g. *Costus speciosus* (B. KUST; H. KEU), *Alpinia* (225 sp.), e.g. *A. allughas* (B. TARA), *A. galanga*—medicinal, *Globba* (100 sp.) e.g. *G. bulbifera* (see FIG. III/58), cardamom (*Elettaria cardamomum*) *Amomum* (150 sp.), e.g. *A. subulatum* (B. BARA-ELAICH), *A. aromaticum* (B. MORAN-HANCHI), etc.

(3) *Cannaceae* (over 40 sp.). In this family the leaves are spiral, with sheathing, but with no ligule. The **Perianth** is in 2 whorls of 3 members each—the outer 3 (sepals) free and the inner 3 (petals) are united. The **Stamens** are in 2 whorls—only 1 anther-lobe of 1 stamen (the posterior one of the inner whorl) is fertile, the other anther-lobe together with the filament is petaloid. One stamen is suppressed and the others are modified into petaloid staminodes, one of which forms the labellum covering the style. All petaloid staminodes together with the petaloid anther-lobe are united below with the corolla into a cylindrical tube. The **style** is petaloid and flattened.

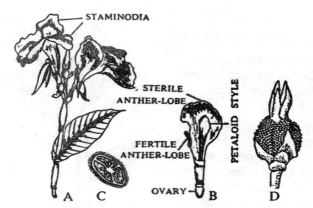

Cannaceae. FIG. 71. Indian shoot (*Canna indica*). *A*, a branch; *B*, a flower (perianth and staminodia cut out); *C*, ovary in transection showing axile placentation; and *D*, a fruit

Floral formula   ⋅⊦⋅ ♀ $K_3 C(_3) A_{\frac{1}{2}} \bar{G}(_3)$

Examples. Only genus is *Canna* in tropical America. Many varieties and hybrids of Indian shot (*Canna orientalis=C. indica*) are grown widely in Indian gardens. *C. edulis*—the starchy rhizome is eaten as a vegetable or ground into flour in the West Indies.

(4) *Marantaceae* (over 350 sp.). In this family the leaves are distichous with sheathing, and ligule. Floral characters are like those of *Cannaceae*. A distinguishing feature of this family is the presence of a joint or swollen pulvinus at the junction of the petiole and the leafblade. It is chiefly a tropical American family.

Floral formula   ⋅⊦⋅ ♀ $P_{3+3} A_{\frac{1}{2}} \bar{G}(_3)$

Examples. *Maranta* (23 sp.), e.g. arrowroot (*Maranta arundinacea*), some ornamental species are *Maranta sanderiana, M. zebrina, M. bicolor, M. viridis*, etc., *Calathea* (about 150 sp.)—several species are ornamental, *C. allouia*—small potato-like tubers, which are eaten as a vegetable in the West Indies, *Clinogyne dichotoma* (B. SITALPATI), and *Phrynium* (30 sp.), e.g. *P. variegatum*—ornamental.

FAMILY 6 ARACEAE (over 1,500 sp.)

Habit. These are herbs, or occasionally climbing shrubs, with two kinds of aerial roots—clinging roots that fix the plant to its support and hanging roots which ultimately grow down into the soil. This plant has an acrid juice or latex, which is poisonous in some cases. The underground stem is in the form of a sympodial rhizome, corm or erect rootstock. In climbing shrubs, the branches are sympodial. Plants of this family grow in moist, shady places.

Leaves. These are alternate, radical and simple. They are often pinnately or palmately divided, sometimes broad, long-petioled and net-veined. In climbing species, the cauline leaves are distinctly alternate, often broad, long-petioled and palmately veined (reticulate). The petiole has a sheathing base.

Inflorescence. This is in the form of a spadix subtended by a large, often brightly coloured spathe. It is usually monoecious with female flowers at the base, a few neuter flowers higher up in some species and a number of closely packed male flowers above. The axis of the spadix is prolonged into a sterile appendix. The flowers are sessile, small and naked. They are unisexual (monoecious or dioecious) or sometimes bisexual, and may be trimerous or dimerous. The perianth is either absent or of 6 or 4 scales.

Androecium. There are (6) stamens in 1 or 2 whorls, or they may be reduced to even 1. The filaments are very short and are often united at the base or into a *synandrium*. The anthers are 2-celled, often dehiscing by the terminal pore.

Gynoecium. The carpels are (1-3) and connate. The ovary is 1 to 3-celled and superior. Each cell

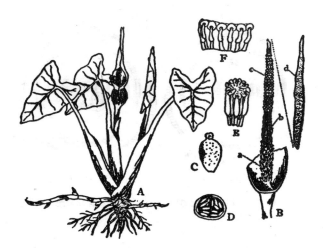

Araceae. FIG. 72. Taro (*Colocasia esculenta*). *A*, a plant; *B*, an inflorescence (spadix)—*a*, female flowers; *b*, neuter flowers; *c*, male flowers; and *d*, appendix; *C*,. pistil; *D*, section of ovary; *E*, synandrium; and *F*, synandrium opened out

has 1 or more ovules. The placentation is often parietal.

Fruit. The fruit is a berry.

Seed. The seed may or may not have endosperm. The flowers are protogynous and pollination is effected mainly by insects. The appendix has a strong, offensive smell, in some species, as in *Arum* and *Amorphophallus* (see p. 101).

Floral Formula $\male - \female$ or $\male\, \female\; P_0 A_{(6-1)} G_0$ | $A_0 \underline{G}_{(1-s)}$

Examples. The larger genera are *Anthurium* (over 500 sp.), *Philodendron* (over 250 sp.), *Arisaema* (over 100 sp.), *Amorphophallus* (about 100 sp.), *Pothos* (75 sp.), *Alocasia* (70 sp.) and *Monstera* (50 sp.). Some examples are Taro (Colocasia esculenta; FIG. 72), *Alocasia indica* (B. MANKACHU; H. MANKANDA), *Typhonium trilobatum* (B. GHETKACHU—see FIG. I/85 trumpet or arum lily (*Richardia africana*), *Amorphophallus Campanulatis* (B. OL; H. ZAMIKAND see FIG. I/137), Portland arrowroot (*Arum maculatum*), snake or cobra plants (*Arisaema consanguineum*; see FIG. I/83; and *A. tortuosum*), sweet flag (*Acorus calamus*; B. BOCH; H. WACH), water lettuce (*Pistia stratiotes*, see FIG. I/34). *Caladium*—ornamental herbs, *Pothos scandens*—a climber, *Scindapsus officinalis* (B. & H. GAJPIPAL)—an epi-

phytic climber, *Monstera* and *Philodendron*—ornamental climbing shrubs, and *Anthurium*—ornamental herbs, dumb-cane or mother-in-law plant (*Dieffenbachia*)—stem fleshy and erect, leaves blotched, juice acrid and poisonous, and causes temporary paralysis and dumbness when in contact with the tongue.

FAMILY 7 PALMAE (over 2,500 *sp.*)

Habit. These are shrubs or trees, sometimes climbing, e.g. cane (*Calamus*).

Stem (caudex) erect, unbranched and woody. It is marked with the scars of shed leaves. It is rarely branched, as in *Hyphaene*. Some palms attain a height of 45 metres or even more. Some canes grow to over 150 metres. A few palms are short-stemmed, e.g. *Phytelephas*, or even apparently stemless, e.g. *Nipa*, and *Phoenix acaulis*. While most palms are polycarpic, usually flowering year after year, a few are monocarpic, flowering only once before dying down, e.g. talipot-palm and sago-palm.

Roots. There are many, adventitious (fibrous) roots developing from the base of the stem.

Leaves. These usually form a crown. They are plaited in the bud. They are often very large (15 m.

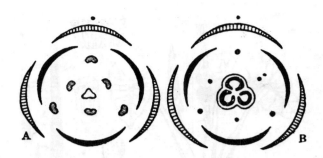

FIG. 73. Floral diagrams of *Palmae*. A, male flower; B, female flower

long and 2.5 m. wide in some species). They are of two types—palmately cut or divided (**fan palms**) or pinnately cut or divided (**feather palms**). The petiole, often has a stout sheathing base.

Inflorescence. This is a spadix, spike or panicle. It is enclosed in one or more large sheathing spathes, often much branched, sometimes very large (as in *Corypha*), often axillary, sometimes terminal.

Flowers. These are sessile, small and inconspicuous. They are sometimes produced in huge numbers presenting an imposing appearance. They are regular, hypogynous and unisexual (rarely bisexual). The male and female flowers may be in the same inflorescence or in two. They may be monoecious or dioecious.

Perianth. This is in two whorls—3 + 3—the outer often being smaller. It is usually free or sometimes connate and may be imbricate or valvate. It is persistent in the female flower.

Androecium. The stamens are usually in two whorls—3 + 3. The filaments may be free or connate. The anthers are versatile and 2-celled. The rudiments of the pistil are often present in the male flower.

Gynoecium. There are (3) carpels (syncarpous) or sometimes 3 (apocarpous). The ovary is superior, unilocular or trilocular, with 1 or 3 ovules.

Fruit. This may be a drupe, berry or nut.

Seed. The seed is albuminous. Pollination is effected by the wind. Pollen is produced in huge quantities. Some palms are pollinated by insects also. The flowers are protandrous and hence, self-pollination is prevented.

Floral formulae $\oplus$ $\male$-$\female$ or $\male$ $\female$ P$_{3+3}$ A$_{3+3}$ G$_0$ | A$_0$ $\underline{G}_{(3)}$ or 3.

Economically, this is one of the most important families since many useful products are obtained from several of its species. Many palms, such as palmyra-palm, toddy-palm, date-palm and are tapped for toddy (fermented country liquor) or for sweet juice from which jaggery or sugar is made. Coconut-palm, date-palm, palmyra-palm, etc. yield edible fruit. The coir fibres of coconut-palm are used for making mats, mattresses and brushes, and also for stuffing cushions. The leaves of many palms are woven into mats, hats and baskets, and also used for thatching. Some palms, e.g. coconut-palm and oil-palm, yield oil. Sago-palms (*Metroxlon* and *Caryota*) yield sago, which is obtained by crushing the pith. Betel nut is chewed with betel leaf. The endosperm of vegetable ivory-palm is very hard and used in making billiard balls. Cane is used for making chairs, sofas, tables and baskets and for a variety of other purposes. Many, sometimes called 'princes of the vegetable kingdom', are ornamental, e.g. fan-palms: (*Livistonia chinensis, Licuala elegans, Sabal palmetto, Pritchardia grandis*, etc.) feather palms (cabbage-palm (*Areca oleracea*), sugar-palm (*Arenga saccharifera*), bottle-palm or royal-palm (*Oreodoxa regia*), *Pinanga spectabilis*, dwarf cane (*Calamus ciliaris*), etc.).

Examples. *Fan-palms:* palmyra-palm (*Borassus flabellifer*), talipot-palm (*Corypha umbraculifera*)—grows to a height of about 24 m., flowers once after about 40 years and then dies; double coconut-palm (*Lodoicea maldivica*)—a native of the Seychelles Islands, bears the largest known seed and fruit; the latter sometimes measuring well over 1 m. (see FIG. I/181), oil-palm (*Elaeis guineensis*), doum-palm (*Hyphaene thebaica*)—exhibits dichotomous branching, etc. *Feather-palms:* Indian sago-palm or fishtail palm or toddy-palm (*Caryota urens*), coconut-palm (*Cocos nucifera*), edible date-palm (*Phoenix dactylifera*), wild date-palm (*P. sylvestris*), *Areca* (over 50 sp.), e.g. areca or betel-nut-palm (*A. catechu*), cane (*Calamus*—over 350 sp.), sago-palm (*Metroxylon rumphii*), nipa-palm (*Nipa fruticans*; B. GOLPATA)—a stemless palm, vegetable ivory-palm (*Phytelephas macrocarpa*), and *Zalacca beccarii*—its large cane-like fruit sold in Shillong.

FAMILY 8 GRAMINEAE OR POACEAE (10,000 sp.)

Habit. These are herbs, rarely woody, as bamboos. They are very widely distributed all over the earth.

Stem. This is cylindrical and has distinct nodes and internodes (sometimes hollow), called *culm.*

Leaves. These are simple, alternate and distichous. They have a sheathing leaf-base which is split open on the side opposite the leaf blade. There is a hairy structure, called the **ligule,** at the base of the leaf blade.

Inflorescence. This is usually a spike or a panicle of spikelets (FIG. 74). Each spikelet consists of one or few flowers (not exceeding 5), and its base bears two empty bracts or *glumes*, (G$_I$, G$_{II}$), one placed a little above and opposite the other. A third glume, called the *lemma* or flowering glume, stands opposite the second glume. The lemma encloses a flower in its axil. It may have a bristle-like appendage, long or short, known as the *awn*. Opposite the flowering glume or lemma, there is a somewhat smaller, 2-nerved glume called the *palea*. The spikelet may be sessile or stalked.

Flowers. These are usually bisexual, sometimes unisexual and monoecious.

Perianth. This is represented by 2 or 3 minute scales, called the **lodicules,** at the base of the flower. These are considered to form the rudimentary perianth.

Androecium. There are 3 stamens, or sometimes 6, as in rice and bamboo. The anthers versatile and pendulous.

Gynoecium. The carpels are generally considered to number (3), reduced to 1 (according to some authors) by their fusion or by the suppression of 2. The ovary is superior and 1-celled, with 1 ovule. The styles usually number 2 (3 in bamboos, and 2 fused into 1 in maize, rarely

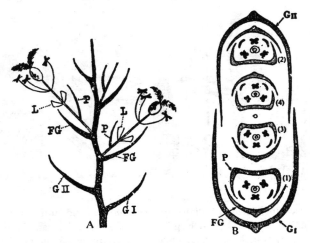

Gramineae. FIG. 74. *A*, spikelet of a grass; *B*, floral diagram of the same; *G$_I$*, first empty glume; *G$_{II}$*, second empty glume; *FG*, flowering glume; *P*, palea; *L*, lodicule; stamens and carpels of the florets are apparent

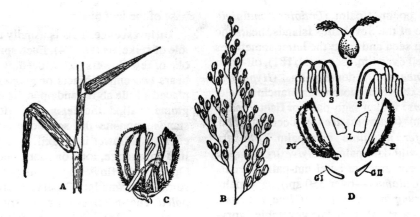

Gramineae. FIG. 75. Rice (*Oryza sativa*). *A*, portion of a branch with sheathing leaves and ligules;
B, a panicle of spikelets; *C*, 1-flowered spikelet (note the glumes and stamens); *D*, spikelets
dissected out: G_I, first empty glume; G_{II}, second empty glume; *FG*, flowering glume;
P, palea; *L*, lodicules; *S*, stamens; and *G*, gynoecium

1). They may be terminal or lateral. The stigmas are feathery.

Fruit. The fruit is a caryopsis.

Seed. This is albuminous. Pollination by the wind is most common. Self-pollination occurs in a few cases, as in wheat.

Floral formula ⚥ P Lodicules$_{2\,or\,3}$ A $_{3\,or\,6}$ $\underline{G}$($_3$) $_{or\,1}$

From an economic standpoint, *Gramineae* is regarded as the most important family as cereals and millets, which constitute the chief foodstuff of mankind, belong to it. Most fodder crops, which are equally important to domestic animals, also belong to this family. So is the importance of bamboo, thatch grass and reed as building materials and of sugarcane as a source of sugar and jaggery. The importance of sabai grass and bamboo as a source of paper pulp is well-known. Some common decorative grasses are ribbon grass (*Phalaris arundinacea*), dwarf bamboo (*Bambusa nana*),

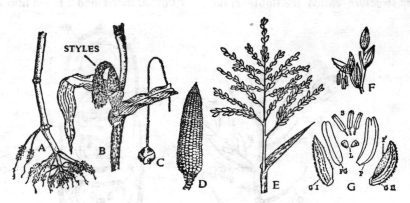

Gramineae. FIG. 76. Maize or Indian corn (*Zea mays*). *A*, adventitious roots; *B*, female
spadix in the axil of a leaf; *C*, female spikelet; *D*, ripe cob; *E*, a panicle of male spikelets;
F, two pairs of male spikelets; and *G*, a male spikelet dissected out; G_I first empty glume;
G_{II}, second empty glume; *P*, palea of the lower flower; *FG*, flowering glume; *P*, palea of the
upper flower; *L*, lodicules; and *S*, three stamens of the upper flower

certain species of *Panicum*, and *Paspalum*. Some common lawn grasses are dog grass (*Cynodon dactylon*) and love thorn (*Chrysopogon aciculatus*).

Examples. The larger genera are *Panicum* (over 500 sp.), *Digitaria* (over 350 sp.), *Aristida* (over 300 sp.), *Eragrostis* (300 sp.), *Paspalum* (250 sp.), *Poa* (over 200 sp.), *Stipa* (over 200 sp.), *Andropogon* (200 sp.). *Agrostis* (over 150 sp), *Sporobolus* (150 sp.), and *Pennisetum* (130 sp.), *Cereals*: rice (*Oryza sativa*—FIG. 75), maize or Indian corn (*Zea mays*— FIG. 76), wheat (*Triticum aestivum*), barley (*Hordeum vulgare*), oat (*Avena sterilis*), etc.; *Millets*: great millet (*Sorghum vulgare*: B. & H. JUAR), Italian millet (*Setaria italica*; KAUN), Indian millet (*Panicum miliaceum* ; B. & H. CHEENA), little millet (*P. miliare*), pearl millet (*Pennisetum typhoideum* ; B & H. BAJRA), *Eleusine coracana* (B. & H. MARUA), etc. Other examples are Job's tears (*Coix lachryma-jobi*)—grains an important food item for poor hill tribes and also made into beads for ornamental purposes, sugarcane (*Saccharum officinarum*), thatch grass (*S. spontaneum*; B. KASH; H. KANS), reed (*Phragmites karka;* B NAL; H. NUDA-NAR), giant reed (*Arundo donax*; B. GABNAL; H. NAL-DURA), bamboo (*Bambusa*), giant bamboo (*Dendrocalamus*), *Melocanna* (B. MULI-BANS)— ripe berries edible, guinea grass (*Panicum maximum*)—a fodder plant, *P. repens*—a mud-binding plant, lemon grass (*Cymbopogon citratus*)—yields lemon oil, *C. nardus*—yields citronella oil, *C. martini*—yields geranium-oil, *Vtiveria zizanioides* (= *Andropogon squarrosus;* B & H. KHUS-KHUS)—fragrant fibrous roots are woven into summer screen and (KHUS-KHUS), sabai grass (*Ischaemum angustifolium*)—paper is manufactured from this grass. **Other common plants**: dog grass (*Cynodon dactylon*), love thorn (*Chrysopogon aciculatus*), *Imperata cylindrica* (B. ULU), several species of *Panicum*, e.g. *P. crusgalli* (B. SHYAMA), and a few species of Paspalum, e.g. *P. scrobiculatum*—common annual grasses.

FAMILY 9 CYPERACEAE (3,500 *sp.*)

Habit. The general habit of *Cyperaceae* is sim-

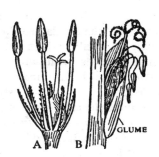

FIG. 77. *A*, flower of *Scirpus; B*, the same of Cyperus

ilar to that of Germineae, but the following points should be noted. The former are herbs, growing mostly in marshy places, pastures and sand beds. The stem is solid and usually triangular. The leaves are simple, alternate and tristichous. The ligule is absent and the sheath is closed.

Inflorescence. This may be a spike or panicle or globose head as a whole, head, but the unit of inflorescence is a spikelet. There may be one or more flowers in each spikelet, each being borne in the axil of a glume. It is minute and may be unisexual or bisexual.

Perianth. This is usually represented by 3 or 6 bristles or scales. It may be altogether absent.

Androecium. There are usually 3 stamens. The anthers are basifixed and linear.

Gynoecium. There are (3) or (2) carpels (syncarpous). The ovary is superior 1-celled, with 1 ovule. These are 3 or 2, and feathery or papillose.

Fruit. This is a small nut or nutlet.

Seed. This is albuminous. Pollination is brought about by the wind.

Examples. The larger genera are *Carex* (over 1,200 sp.), *Cyperus* (700 sp.), *Scirpus* (300 sp.), *Fimbristylis* (over 200 sp.), *Scleria* (200 sp.), *Eleocharis* (150 sp.), *Pycreus* (100 sp.), *Bulbostylis* (100 sp.), and *Kyllinga* (60 sp.). Some examples are Sedge (*Cyperus rotundus*; B. & H. MUTHA), *C. tegetum* (B. MADUR-KATI), *C. difformis*—a weed of rice fields, *C. nutans*—a large sedge, *C. cephalotes*—a floating sedge, umbrella grass (*Cyprus alternifolius*)—ornamental, *Scripus* *grossus* (B. KESHUR)—a tall rush, club rush (*S. littoralis*—a stout rush of the Sundarbans, *S. articulatus* (B. PATPATI)—a small herb in wet places, *Kyllinga*—common weeds with white globose heads, e.g. *K. monocephala, Carex indica*—a short herb, *Juncellus inundatus* (B. PATI)—a stout herb in wet places, *Fimbristylis monostachya* (B. MARMARI) and *F. dichotoma*—small tufted herbs, *Bulbostylis barbata*—a small tufted herb, *Scleria elata*—a tall robust herb, *Eleocharis fistulosa*—a rush-like sedge in ponds, *Pycreus nitens*—a weed of wet places and *Cladium riparium*—a tall stout herb in the Sundarbans. The family is of little economic importance.

Inflorescence. This may be a raceme, panicle or usually a spike (long or short).

Flowers. These are bisexual, epigynous, medianly zygomorphic, often very showy, and fragrant in some species, and come in an endless variety of colours and forms. This is why they are valued and cultivated extensively. Their structure is often very complex.

Perianth. This is in two trimerous whorls. It is epigynous, petaloid and showy. The segments of the outer whorl are almost equal and so are the two lateral segments of the inner whorl. The posterior one of this whorl is the largest and most conspicu-

Distinctions between *Gramineae* and *Cyperaceae*

	Gramineae	Cyperaceae
Stem	cylindrical; solid or hollow	triangular; solid
Leaf	distichous, with ligule; sheath split open	tristichous, without ligule; sheath closed
Inflorescence	spike or panicle of spikelets	spike or panicle or head of spikelets
Glumes	glumes 3, palea 1; lower 2 empty and 3rd one flowering	a flower in the axil of a glume
Perianth	represented by 2 or 3 lodicules	represented by 3 or 6 bristles or scales, or absent
Stamens	usually 3; sometimes 6; anthers versatile	usually 3; rarely 6, anthers basifixed
Carpels	(3) or 1, styles usually 2	(3) or (2), styles 3 or 2
Fruit	caryopsis	nutlet

FAMILY 10 ORCHIDACEAE (about 20,000 *sp*)

Habit. These are perennial herbs, which are mostly epiphytic. Some are terrestrial. A few are saprophytic. Orchids are widely distributed and they are abundant in the tropics. Over 1,700 species have been recorded in India so far, about 400 being in the north-east. Sikkim also abounds in orchids. Mycorrhiza (see p. 16) is common. Epiphytic orchids usually have clinging roots, absorbing roots and hanging roots with velamen (see FIG. I/26). The stems often have pseudobulbs.

Leaves. These are simple, entire and usually thick. They frequently have a sheathing at the base and are variously mottled in a few species.

ous, often being folded, variously shaped and spotted. It encloses the column and is known as the *labellum*. Owing to the twisting of the ovary, the

FIG. 78. Floral diagram of an orchid

labellum, normally posterior, comes round to the anterior side. The labellum is often provided with a spur, long or short, which secretes nectar.

Androecium. The stamens are in two trimerous whorls but undergo a considerable amount of suppression or are modified into staminodes. The majority of orchids bear 1 stamen (anterior one of the outer whorl)—Monandrae, while some bear 2 stamens (two lateral ones of the inner whorl)—Diandrae. The filament and style are united together (gynandrous) and they occur, with a special organ—the rostellum—on a central structure called the *column* (or gymnostemium). The column is an extension of the floral axis and the rostellum is a sterile stigma which aids pollination (see below).

The column with the anther (s) and stigmas stands opposite to and facing the labellum. The anther lies on top of the rostellum and is attached to the column at its back by a short filament. It is usually 2-chambered and has a pair of pollinia. It is sometimes 4 or more-chambered, with as many pollinia. The pollen is often granular. The base of the pollinium often extends into a slender stalk, called the *caudicle*, which may again end in a sticky gland attached to the rostellum.

Gynoecium. There are (3) carpels (syncarpous). There are 3 stigmas —the lateral two are fertile and very sticky and the third one sterile (the rostellum). In Diandrae, three stigmas are fertile (no rostellum). The ovary is inferior, mostly cylindrical and 3-valved. It has 3 ridges (representing the midribs of the three carpels), often twisted, and unilocular (sometimes falsely trilocular). Placentae and numerous extremely minute ovules develop only some time after pollination, as a result of the stimulus caused by the process.

Fruit. This is a loculicidal capsule, mostly cylindrical. It dehiscies by valves and ridges. The fruits and seeds take several months (often a year) to develop and mature. Hygroscopic hairs often develop from the inner walls of the valves, helping in the dispersion of the seeds.

Seeds. These are very numerous, extremely minute and powdery. They are exalbuminous and the embryo is microscopic.

Floral formula $\cdot| \cdot \; \male\female \quad P_{3+3} [A_{1\,or\,2} G_{(3)}]$

Pollination. Orchids are adapted for cross-pollination by insects in a variety of ways. Insects are attracted by the bright colour of the flower, its peculiar form, and sometimes a sweet smell. When an insect visits the flower it sits on the labellum. It moves into the flower, drills its way to get to the nectar which is concealed in the spur at the base. In its effort to get in, it disorganizes a

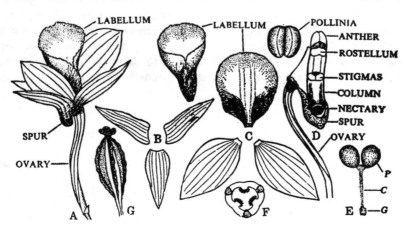

Orchidaceae. FIG. 79. *Dendrobium pierardi. A*, a flower; *B*, outer whorl of perianth; (or gynostemium), ovary and anther; *E*, a pair of pollinia (of *Vanda*)—*P*, pollinium; *C*, caudicle; *G*, gland; *F*, ovary in transection (semi-diagrammatic); *G*, fruit (of *Vanda*)—a capsule dehiscing into 6 valves

part of the restellum from which a sticky substance adheres to the head (or proboscis) of the insect. After collecting the nectar, as the insect crawls out of the flower, it carries the pollinia with it. The pollinia easily fall off from the anther and stick to the insect's head or get attached to it by the caudicle. When the insect visits a second flower, the pollinia on its head point, sometimes by a hygroscopic movement of the caudicle, towards the receptive stigmas. The stigmas, being very sticky, pull away the pollinia from the body of the insect. The relative position of the stigmas and the anther, which are sometimes wide apart, often excludes the possibility of self-pollination. Some orchids are also self-sterile. However, self-pollination is not uncommon among *Orchidaceae*. A few species have cleistogamous flowers. (For details read Darwin's *Fertilization of Orchids*.)

Examples. The larger genera are *Pleurothallis* (1,000 sp. in South America), *Dendrobium* (900 sp. in Asia and Australia), *Bulbophyllum* (900 sp. in the tropics), *Habenaria* (700 sp. in the tropics), *Epidendrum* (400 sp. in tropical America), *Eria* (over 350 sp. in Asia and Australia), *Oncidium* (about 350 sp. in South America), *Oberonia* (over 300 sp. in the tropics), *Microstylis* (=*Malaxis*; 300 sp. cosmopolitan), *Masdevallia* (275 sp. cosmopolitan), *Angraecum* (220 sp. in South Africa and Madagascar), *Eulophia* (200 sp. in the tropics), and *Platanthera* (200 sp. widely distributed). There are several other genera with over 200 sp. **Epiphytic:** *Vanda* (60 sp.), e.g. *V. roxburghii* (B.

& H. RASNA), *V. teres*—branches cylindrical and erect, blue vanda (*V. cerulaea*)—a rare beautiful orchid of the Khasi Hills, *Dendrobium*; (many species in India), e.g. *D. pierardi* (FIG. 79)—pendulous, flowers pink, *D. densiflorum*—pendulous, flowers large and golden yellow, *D. moschatum*—erect, flowers pink, *D. formosum* and *D. nobile*—flowers large, white and showy, *D. multiforum*—flowers red, *D. clavatum*—flowers deep red, *D. chrysanthum*—flowers yellow, profuse, *D. nathanielis*—jointed stem etc.; lady's slipper (*Cypripedium*), *Aerides multiflorum* and *A. odoratum* (flowers scented)—showy epiphytes, *Bulbophyllum* and *Coelogyne*— several species, fox-tail orchid (*Rhynchostylis retusa*)—flowers pink, *Cymbidium aloifolium*—tufted orchid, chain orchid (*Pholidota imbricata*), jewel orchid (*Goodyera*), *Pleione*, *Calanthe*, *Eria*—several species, *Cattleya* (an American genus)—very ornamental, cultivated, etc. **Terrestrial:** *Arundina graminifolia*, butterfly orchid (*Havenaria*)—several species, *Eulophia*, *Zeuxine* (in grassy fields), *Phaius*, *Orchis*, *Pogonia*, *Geodorum*, *Lipparis*, etc. **Saprophytes:** bird's nest orchid (*Neottia nidus-avis*), coral-root orchid (*Corallorhiza*), *Galeola falconeri*—a curious leafless tall orchid of Arunachal, with stout rhizome and upright stout inflorescence axis (3 metres in height), etc. It may be noted that *Vanilla* (90 sp.—climbing orchids) is the only genus of economic importance. Pods of *Vanilla planifolia* yield the essence, *vanillin*, used in perfumery and flavouring confections, and in scenting tobacco. It is cultivated in Mexico and, to some extent, in Sri Lanka.

8 EVOLUTION AND GENETICS

CHAPTER 1

ORGANIC EVOLUTION

It is now an established fact that higher and more complex forms of plants and animals have evolved from earlier and simpler forms. At one time, however, it was believed that the various species of plants and animals were created in the forms in which they exist today. There was also the belief that minute organisms like bacteria develop spontaneously in putrefying material. Louis Pasteur, a French scientist and founder of the science of bacteriology, proved conclusively in 1864 that spontaneous generation is absolutely impossible. Bacteria are present everywhere and they grow wherever they find a suitable medium and favourable conditions. The old view, therefore, is no longer tenable. Moreover, evidence indicates that plants and animals have evolved from pre-existing forms, and have not been created. Fossil records are particularly instructive in this respect (see Part X). It has been possible to trace the gradual changes in the types of plants and animals through the successive periods of the earth. To go back to the earliest stage, the relevant question is, 'What is the origin of life?' or, 'How did the protoplasm, the physical basis of life, first come into being?' But protoplasm once formed has become continuous from the earliest form of life to the present form, through many millions of years.

According to geologists, and also astronomers, the age of the earth may be either 3,440 or 4,550 million years. The *Puranas* say that it is 4,320 million years old. At some early stage, the earth was just a molten mass at an execessively high temperature. Gradually it cooled, and there was spontaneous generation of life. We are not in a position to say with any amount of certainty how and exactly when this happened. According to fossil records, life was already somewhat advanced about 600 million years ago taking the form of bacteria, fungi, blue-green algae and some primitive invertebrates. There is evidence of life in the sedimentary rocks formed about 2,000 millions years ago. Life must have originated much earlier. With the passage of time, newer forms of plants and animals were evolved through successive stages in the earth's history. It is believed that the primitive earth was surrounded by a gaseous atmosphere made of methane (CH_4), ammonia (NH_3), water vapour (H_2O) and hydrogen (H_2). All the elements necessary for the formation of organic molecules were thus present—C, H, O and N. Under special conditions (both chemical and physical) prevailing then, the energy required for their formation was possibly obtained from the ultraviolet rays of the sun, radioactivity, electric discharges, etc., and a soup of organic molecules was possibly formed in the ocean. Some or many of these molecules might have combined to form complex molecules (particularly nucleic acids as the basis of life), and some such molecules acquired the characteristics of life once and for all. Evidently life originated in water (in the ocean), possibly in the form of some aquatic bacteria which could utilize energy by oxidation of iron compounds, sulphur compounds, etc. (and not directly from sunlight) for synthesis of organic compounds. The next phase in evolution was possibly the appearance of blue-green algae. Primitive unicellular animals might have originated at this stage, and forming another line of evolution. Later, with the evolution of green algae, (evidently with the *development of chlorophyll* in organized chloroplasts, which could directly utilize sunlight as a source of energy for manufacture of food), the trend of evolution leading to higher plants became established. This was the **first major event** in the evolution of plants and animals, following separate lines of descent. For millions of years, primitive algae and primitive animals formed the dominant feature of the sea. At the next stage, green plants invaded the land. The *migration of plants* from water (sea) to land (Psilophytales being the earliest land plants) was the **second major event** in the early phase of evolution. It rapidly gave rise to a diversity of forms, such as giant lycopods and horsetails, ferns and two groups of gymnosperms (seed-ferns or Cycadofilicales and Cordaitales), in the early geological age (see Part X, Chapter 2). The colonization of the land by green plants paved the way for the invasion of the land by animals which relied on green plants for food and shelter.

EVIDENCES OF ORGANIC EVOLUTION

1. Geological Evidence. The petrified remains of ancient plants and animals, or impressions left by them in rocks, are called **fossils**. Fossils provide solid evidence of the existence of different types of plants and animals through different geological ages and periods of the earth. They help us trace facts correlated with their origin (first appearance) and evolution, climax of development, relationship, increasing complexity and specialization, extinction of certain groups and so on. The surface of the earth consists of layers or strata of rocks formed in dfifferent ways in various periods. These strata bear fossils of particular types of plants and animals in their increasing complexity. Thus, the rocks formed earlier show fossils of simpler types of plants and animals, while those formed later show fossils of more complex and advanced types (see Part X), maintaing, in many cases, a definite relationship between different groups of plants or animals that appeared through successive stages. Fossil records, therefore, are of considerable importance in elucidating the problem of evolution. These records are, however, incomplete for various reasons. As a result, there are many wide gaps in our knowledge of the evolution of plants and animals. Because of the missing links, the origin of several groups remains a mystery.

2. Taxonomic Evidence. Plants and animals are classified into certain well-marked groups according to the resemblances and differences between them. The members of each group resemble each other more closely. It is difficult to conceive of these similarities in form without postulating the theory of evolution. In addition, it is seen that between two or more species of a particular genus, there are intermediate forms linking such species (*intergrading species*).The occurrence of such forms could not be accounted for if species were constant.

3. Morphological and Anatomical Evidence. The structural similarities between the roots, stems, leaves, flowers and other morphological characteristics of certain groups of plants, and the bones and other organs of certain groups of animals, in addition to the successive stages in the development of such organs from simpler to more complex forms, speak of the evolution of plants and animals towards greater perfection. Equally significant in the question of evolution are the morphological similarities in the type of venation, shape of corolla, cohesion or adhesion of stamens, etc.—between the members of a group of plant. Similarly, the study of types of wood or xylem, development of stele, nature of tracheids and vessels among the higher cryptogams, gymnosperms and angiosperms, and of the development of tissues and nerves among animals lends additional support to the theory of evolution. Sometimes, instead of progressive evolution, certain parts of plants show a reversion to an ancestral type.

4. Embryological Evidence. The study of the nature and development of the embryo reveals a great resemblance between certain groups of plants and of animals. The development indicates the evolutionary changes that have taken place through successive stages. In all cases, at least one fact is common, i.e., the embryo develops from the egg-cell or ovum. Sometimes, some organs of plants or animals bear a striking resemblance with certain forms from which they have possibly been derived. Thus, when a fern spore germinates it resembles a filamentous alga. It then assumes a thalloid form resembling a liverwort. Finally it grows into a fern plant. The frog passes through a tadpole stage, resembling a fish, which is supposed to be its ancestor. Seedlings often resemble plants which may be their ancestors. Thus, the seedling of Australian *Acacia* has bipinnate compound leaves, like other species of Acacia, while the adult Australian *Acacia* has a winged petiole or rachis (phyllode) with or without the compound leaf (see p. 39).

5. Evidence from Geographical Distribution. It has been seen that in their wild state, many allied species of plants remain confined to a particular area. The explanation is that they arose from a common ancestor in that region and could not migrate owing to certain barriers, such as high mountains, seas and deserts. Thus, we find that while double coconut-palm (*Lodoicea*) originated in the Seychelles, traveller's tree (*Ravenala*) in Madagascar, *Eucalyptus* in Australia, cacti in the dry regions of tropical America, cactus-like spurges (*Euphorbia*) in the deserts of Africa, etc., allied species often grow near these species, thereby showing evolution from a common ancestor.

6. Vestigial Structures. Certain parts of plants and animals have degenerated serving no useful purpose. Such parts are known as vestigial structures. It is assumed that those parts were functional and in the course of evolution, they lost their function and degenerated. Thus, in *Asparagus*, the leaves have been reduced to scales with the development of the green branches and the cladodes, the leaves have been reduced to scales. In parasites like broomarape (*Orobanche*) and dodder (*Cuscuta*), the leaves have been reduced to scales in the absence of their normal function of photosynthesis. There are many instances of the reduction of floral organs, particularly stamens, in several families. The presence of vestigial structures is explained on the basis of the early history of the race and the course of evolution.

MECHANISM OF ORGANIC EVOLUTION

Variation. Variation is the rule in nature. No two forms, belonging even to the same species, are exactly alike. The differences between the individuals of a species are spoken of as **variations**. Variations are the basis on which evolution works. They may be of four types: (*a*) Variation due to change in environment is one type. Variation caused by the environment in certain organs of plants or animals is not believed to be inherited by the offspring. (*b*) Slow but continuous variation from generation to generation, according to Darwin, is the basis of organic evolution. (*c*) Discontinuous variation or mutation, on the other hand, means sudden and sharp variation of one or more individuals of the species in respect of one or more characteristics. There are no gradations, as in the previous case; instead, the individuals suddenly assume new forms. Sharp variations of this type are directly inherited by the offspring, and are, according to De Vries, due to change or mutation in genes (see p 623). As mutation occurs suddenly and spontaneously, there is no telling when a new form will appear by this process. There are many cases of mutation on record. Darwin also observed several cases of wide divergences, which he called 'sports'. He thought that sports played only a very minor role in evolution. (*d*) Variation due to hybridization is the fourth type. In this process, a mingling of two sets of contrasting characteristics (paternal and maternal) takes place and, as a result, at least some of the progeny show wider variation.

Adaptation. Adjustment of plants and animals to their environment by means of special structures or functions is spoken of as **adaptation**. There are numerous instances of adaptation in ecology. Adaptation may have an important bearing on evolution. Plants have an inherent capacity to adapt themselves to their environment. Many of them are elastic in nature, and are consequently capable of adapting themselves to changed conditions according to their needs. This is even more true of animals. It is Lamarck's view that adapted structures are fixed and inherited by the offspring, (inheritance of acquired characteristics) at least so long as they remain in the same environment. According to this view, individuals of the species that invade two or more situations will give rise to a corresponding number of new forms.

Heredity. Heredity means transmission of characteristics and qualities of parent forms to their offspring (the term heredity means 'like begets like'). This is evident from the fact that a particular species gives rise through reproduction to the same species and to no other. Although no two forms are exactly alike, the offspring still resemble their parental forms, mostly closely, and also resemble one another most closely with, of course, individual variations. Heredity tends to keep the individuals of a species within specific limits. Variation, on the other hand, tends to separate them from one another by certain differences between them, however minute the differences may be. Variation, no doubt, is responsible for evolution, while heredity is a check on uncontrolled variation and evolution which would have otherwise given rise to a multitude of peculiar forms without any clear distinction between one species and another. However, when heredity is due to cross pollination, a certain amount of variation is inevitable.

Inheritance of Characteristics. In the process of reproduction, we find that two reproductive nuclei (i.e. gametes—male gamete of the pollen-tube and egg-cell of the embryo-sac) of opposite sexes, each with n chromosomes, fuse to give rise to the oospore, the embryo and ultimately the mature plant, each with $2n$ chromosomes. Thus, the inheritance of characteristics takes place through these nuclei. In 1884, Strasburger and Hertwig established the fact that it is through the chromosomes that characteristics are transmitted from generation to generation. It is obvious that particular characteristics of the parent (e.g. colour of flower) cannot be found in the chromosomes; it may be safely assumed that something representing that particular characteristic is present in them. That 'something', obscure though it is, is called the factor or determiner or gene for that particular characteristics. The genes located in the chromosomes of the gametes or reproductive nuclei are responsible for all the characteristics of the parent plants and their transmission to the offspring. The theory of the presence of genes in chromosomes was introduced by Morgan in 1926. Genes are extremely minute bodies, possibly made of a single protein molecule, or at most, very small groups of protein molecules. [For details see pp. 621-2].

THEORIES OF ORGANIC EVOLUTION

PRE-DARWINIAN IDEAS OF EVOLUTION. The idea of evolution dates back to the earliest period of human civilization. The oldest theories discussed the origin of life, but they were based on mere speculation rather than fact. These may be summarized under three heads: (1) theory of eternity of the present conditions, (2) theory of special creation, and (3) theory of catastrophism. The believers of the first theory argued that there was neither beginning nor end to the universe. The life forms which existed millions of years ago remained unchanged and would continue to be the same for eternity. The theory of special creation was preached for many centuries by the Christian Church. Its basis was the account of the creation of the world and everything in it by God. The theory of catastrophism was introduced by Cuvier, a palaeontologist, who carried out research on fossil fauna for a long time in Paris. He believed that at one time, world-wide catastrophes destroyed the old fauna, the extinction of which gave the creation of a new fauna. According to him, this took a long time spanning millions of years, due to the changed environmental conditions.

The idea of organic evolution, although believed to be a modern one, can be traced back to many centuries ago. The idea of evolution emanated from the research of many Greek philosophers, of whom Empedocles was the first. He believed that organisms did not improve through successive generations, but nature tried to produce perfect organisms several times and during this period unfit forms were eliminated. Then came the great philosopher, Aristotle. He believed that organisms in nature had an inherent tendency to attain greater and greater perfection, according to changes in the environment, and that this was the reason why there was a perfect gradation from the lowest to the highest organism evolved in nature. After this period, there was a lull in the speculation on organic evolution, until the coming of such evolutionists as Linnaeus, Buffon, Erasmus Darwin, Lamarck, Charles Darwin and others.

Lamarck's Theory: Inheritance of Acquired Characteristics. The first modern theory of evolution was put forward in 1809 by the French biologist Lamarck (1744-1829). His theory resolves itself into three factors—(*a*) influence of the environment, (*b*) use and disuse of parts and (*c*) inheritance of acquired characteristics. Lamarck held that environment plays the principal part in the evolution of living organisms. He noted many instances where individuals of the same species grown under different environmental conditions showed marked differences. Plants grown in the shade develop larger leaves than those grown in the open. The root system becomes more extensive in dry soil than in wet soil. In darkness, leaves do not develop chlorophyll and the stem becomes weak and drawn out (etiolated). Many plants leading an amphibious life exhibit heterophylly. From such observations, Lamarck concluded that plants react to external conditions, and that new species make their appearance as a result of the cumulative effects of the changed conditions through successive generations. In the case of plants, according to Lamarck, changes in characteristics (or adaptations) arise due to the direct action of the environment and in the case of animals, they are the result of the use and disuse of parts. The use or exercise of certain parts results in the development of those parts, while disuse or want of exercise results in their degeneration. He believed that the new characteristics, however minute, acquired by each generation under changing environmental conditions are preserved and transmitted to the offspring (inheritance of acquired characteristics). The classic example cited in this connection is that of the giraffe. Lamarck's view was that the horse-like ancestors of these animals, living in arid regions in the interior of Africa, had to feed on the leaves of trees. They had to stretch their limbs to reach the leaves. This use or exercise resulted in the lengthening of the neck and the front legs and,

thus, a new type of animal made its appearance. Lamarck's theory is open to certain objections. One objection is that adaptations due to the influence of the environment are very slight and superficial. Another is that the inheritance of acquired characteristics has not been proved yet. In fact, if seeds collected from plants growing away from their original habitat for many years are brought back to their old habitat, the plants lose the acquired characteristics and revert to their original forms.

Darwin's Theory: Natural Selection. The next theory of evolution was put forward in 1859 by the English biologist, Charles Darwin (1809-82), and published in *The Origin of Species by Means of Natural Selection*. His theory, based on a mass of accurate observations and prolonged experiments, led the whole scientific world to believe in the doctrine of evolution. Known as the *theory of natural selection*, his theory is based on three important factors: (*a*) over-production of offspring and a consequent struggle for existence, (*b*) variations and their inheritance, and (*c*) elimination of unfavourable variations (survival of the fittest).

Struggle for Existence. If all the seeds of a particular plant were to germinate and all the seedlings grow into full-sized plants, a very wide area would soon be covered by them in the course of a few years. If other plants (and also animals) were to proliferate at this rate, a keen competition, i.e. a struggle for existence, would ensue because the availability of food, water and space would fall far short of the demand. This struggle would soon result in the destruction of large numbers of individuals.

Variations and their Inheritance. It is known that no two individuals, even of the same parent stalk, are exactly alike. There are always some variations, however minute they may be, from one individual to another. Some variations are suited to the conditions of the environment, while others are not. According to Darwin, these minute variations are preserved and transmitted to the offspring, although he put forward no cause for these variations.

Survival of the Fittest. In the struggle for existence the individuals exhibiting variations in the right directions survive, and these variations are transmitted to the offspring. Others with unfavourable variations perish. Darwin called this the 'survival of the fittest'. The survivors gradually and steadily change from one generation to another, ultimately giving rise to new forms. The new forms are better adapted to the environment.

Darwin's observation of the variations in domestic animals and cultivated plants served as a clue to the elucidation of his theory of natural selection. Sometimes, such extensive changes are found in the course of several generations that it becomes difficult to believe that the first form has given rise to the last. Further, for the purpose of having a desired type, breeders and florists take note of certain variations among individuals, select them for furture generations, rejecting and destroying the rest. They grow the selected types, generation after generation, until the desired result is obtained. New types appear through this process, called *artificial selection*. Many cultivated flowers and vegetables exhibit a number of varieties, and in the course of time, these variations become well-marked.

Natural Selection. Darwin explains natural selection in the following way. Animals and plants multiply at an enormous rate. As we know, no two individuals are exactly alike, and the new forms naturally display certain variations. Some variations are favourable or advantageous so far as adaptation to environmental conditions is concerned, while others are not so. Owing to overcrowding, a keen struggle for existence ensues. In this struggle, those with favourable variations, being better fitted to survive naturally, survive and the rest perish. Through this survival of the fittest the species change steadily owing to preservation and transmission of minute variations, and gradually give rise to newer forms. Darwin called this process 'natural selection' from analogy to artificial selection. It is the environment that selects and preserves the better types and destroys the unsuitable forms.

Pangenesis. This is another theory of Darwin's. It assumes that every cell of the plant body or the animal body produces imaginary particles or units, called *pangenes*, which carry in their body not only the normal parental characteristics, but also those acquired during the life-time of the individual. Pangenes are formed in all parts of the body and gather together to form the germ cells. All the characteristics, normal and acquired, are ultimately transmitted from one generation to another through these cells. Through this theory, Darwin tried to explain how characteristics are carried from the parent to the offspring, assuming that at a certain stage, somatic cells produce germ cells, which in turn produce somatic cells in the next generation. Modern scientists have, however, discarded this theory, since it is now definitely known that only the germ cells are the true bearers of hereditary characteristics, remaining practically unchanged and unaffected by the environment and, thus, passing down intact from generation to generation.

Although Darwin receives full credit for bringing about the final acceptance of the doctrine of evolution, his theory is open to certain doubts. It is true that natural selection is operative in the preservation of certain forms and destruction of others. Yet some doubts have been expressed on whether the process is the cause of the evolution of new species. The following factors are behind these doubts. (a) Are slight variations of any decided advantage in the struggle for existence? It is only the perfected organs that are helpful to organisms, and not the organs during the process of perfection. (b) It is doubtful if slight variations can help the individuals go beyond the boundary of the species.This has never been found possible in artificial selection breeding experiments. (c) There are many organs that are not of any apparent use to the organisms. (d) If only the fittest survive, how is it that many unfit ones still exist? (e) If nature selects suitable forms and features, why were the rest not swept out of existence?

Weismann's Theory: Continuity of Germplasm. An ingenious theory explaining the cause of variation and evolution was put forward in 1895 by the German scientist Weismann (1834-1914), a disciple of Darwin. He divided the protoplasm of the animal or plant body into *somatoplasm*, which gives rise only to somatic or body cells, and *germplasm*, which produces the reproductive cells. His theory states that the two flow as separate streams through the body of the plant or animal. Somatoplasm is responsible for differentiation of tissues, development and growth of the individual plant or animal body, and is exhausted and lost at the end of the life cycle, i.e. it is discontinuous. On the other hand, germplasm is ever-young and immortal, continuous from one generation to another, and is actually the bearer of hereditary characteristics. Somatoplasm may be influenced by the environment and new characteristics acquired during the life-time of an individual, but germplasm is not. Therefore, as is almost universally believed, inheritance of acquired characteristics is not a possibility. Weismann did not believe in Darwin's pangenesis (see p. 614). During reproduction, the fertilized egg gets the parental germplasm from the sperm and the egg-cell, respectively. In nuclei of both somatic and germ cells, there are certain factors which determine the character of the cell. It is believed that each somatic cell has a single factor, whereas a germ cell contains all the factors found in the somatic cells of the adult plant or animal. The inheritance of characteristics by the offspring depends upon the factors contained in only the germ cells. There is always a struggle for existence among these factors, and this results in a *germinal selection*. The stronger factors survive and are readily transmitted from one generation to another. Hence, any mutation in the germplasm or any variation resulting from the struggle among the factors in the germ cells can only be handed down from generation to generation. Weismann's theory supports Darwin's theory of natural selection, but it has been criticized by many scientists as purely speculative. Also, Weismann's assumption that the germplasm is permanently curtained off from the somatoplasm is not a fact. With the advance in knowledge, it has come to light that chromosomes come in direct contact with the somatoplasm during nuclear divisions.

De Vries' Theory: Mutation. Another theory of evolution was advanced in 1901 by the Dutch botanist, Hugo De Vries (1848-1935). He held that small variations, which Darwin regarded as the most important from the standpoint of evolution, are only fluctuations around the specific type. These variations are not inheritable. De Vries held that large variations appearing suddenly and spontaneously in the offspring in one generation are the cause of evolution. He called these variations 'mutations'. That large discontinuous variations are the cause of organic evolution was first advocated by Bateson in 1894. De Vries strongly supported this view on the basis of his extensive observations. He observed an evening primrose (*Oenothera lamarckiana*), introduced from America, growing in a field in Holland. Among numerous plants, he found two types quite distinct from the rest. These new types had not been described before, and since they had bred true, he regarded them as distinct species—*O. brevistylis* and *O. laevifolia*, as he named them. *Oenothera lamarckiana* and the new species were removed to his garden at Amsterdam and cultivated through many generations. It was found that among the thousands of seedlings raised, a few (7 new species) that were different from the rest appeared. When raised generation after generation, these always came true to type. These new forms are known as *mutants*. He propounded a mutation theory as his explanation of evolution. While De Vries agreed with Darwin's view, that natural selection weeds out unsuitable forms, he held that new species are not formed, as Darwin said, by the slow process of continuous variation. Since then, several instances of plant mutations (as well as animal mutations) have been found in nature. Mutation is now known to be caused by changes in genes—loss, degeneration, addition, recombination, etc.—occurring in the gametes, zygote, or somatic cells, ultimately affecting the nature of the mature plant. This is 'gene mutation' (see p. 623). It may also be brought about artificially by treatment with X-rays. The mutation theory of De Vries has been widely accepted.

CHAPTER 2

GENETICS

A considerable amount of experimental work on hybridization of plants was carried out long before Mendel. But it was Mendel who elucidated and formulated for the first time the laws involved in the inheritance of parental characteristics by the offspring. In this connection, the following researchers of the pre-Mendelian period deserve special mention. The first authentic work on artificial hybridization of plants was done by a German botanist, **Joseph Kolreuter**, in 1760. He hybridized two species of tobacco plants (*Nicotiana paniculata* and *N. rustica*). The progeny was a blend of the two parents in respect of many characteristics. This was conclusive evidence to show, for the first time, that the pollen (male) parent also influences the characteristics of the progeny. **John Goss** (1820) in England hybridized two types of pea plants—one with bluish seeds and the other with yellowish-white seeds. In the first generation the seeds were all yellowish-white, but in the second, both bluish and yellowish-white seeds appeared. In 1854, **Naudin** was awarded a prize by the Paris Academy for his valuable work on plant hybridization. He showed that parental characteristics did not actually blend in the offspring of the first generation and that the characteristics reappeared separately in parental forms in the second generation of the cross. He also made reciprocal crosses and proved the identity of the first generation. He almost hit upon the laws of heredity, but failed to crystallize them because he did not count the number of progeny.

GENETICS is the modern experimental study of the laws of inheritance (variation and heredity). The name 'genetics' was proposed by Bateson in 1906. Cytology, dealing with the structure, number, behaviour, etc., of chromosomes, is of immense value in understanding many intricate facts connected with genetics since chromosomes are the bearers of heritable characteristics. It should also be noted that in addition to their characteristic form and individuality, the number of chromosomes is always constant for each species. Scientific studies in genetics were first carried out by Gregor Mendel (1822-84), an Austrian monk. He entered a monastery in Brunn (Austria), where he carried out scientific investigations on hybridization of plants, particularly the garden pea. The results of his eight years' breeding experiments were read before the Natural History Society of Brunn in 1865 and published the following year in the transactions of the society. This publication had only a limited circulation and consequently his work remained unnoticed until 1900, when three distinguished botanists, Hugo De Vries in Holland, Tschermak in Austria and Correns in Germany, working independently along the same lines, discovered its significance and importance. Since then, Mendel's work has formed the basis of studies in genetics, and it has been called Mendelism as a mark of honour to Mendel. Mendel died in 1884 before he could see his work accepted and appreciated. The reason is not far to seek. The internal mechanism in a cell leading to heredity was still unknown; chromosomes and genes directly concerned with the transmission of hereditary characteristics remained undiscovered. Moreover, Mendel's work was overlooked in the excitement caused by the publication of the controversial *The Origin of Species by means of Natural Selection* by Charles Darwin in 1859.

PLANT BREEDING. The subject of plant breeding, although developed in recent times on modern scientific lines after Mendel's discoveries, was known in early times to the Egyptians and Assyrians. During the eighteenth century, several crosses were made by many researchers and interesting results obtained. They produced new varieties by such crosses, but the actual mechanism of fertilization remained undiscovered. Around 1830, the development of the pollen-tube and its approach to the ovule were observed. In 1846, Robert Brown, an English botanist, did considerable work on this problem. But it was in 1884 that

Strasburger clarified the whole process of fertilization and the transmission of hereditary characteristics through the reproductive nuclei, i.e. male gamete and egg-cell, which are directly involved in fertilization. In Germany in the ninteenth century, Gartner made extensive crosses—thousands of them—involving nearly 700 species and obtained about 250 hybrids. His work was published in 1849.

Plant breeding consists of producing offspring by artificially pollenizing the stigma of another flower according to certain principles. Two varieties or species, or even genera, differing from each other in respect of one or more characteristics, may thus be crossed and the results studied. The offspring or hybrids, as they are called, usually show some characteristics of each parent or are a blend of the two parent forms in the first generation. In the subsequent generation, the dormant characteristics are seen to appear in the offspring. The offspring resulting from the crossing of red-flowered and white-flowered plants, of tall and dwarf plants, and of other plants with contrasting characteristics, are said to be **hybrids**. The hybrids are often more vigorous than their parents. This phenomenon is known as **hybrid vigour** or **heterosis**, a term suggested by Shull in 1914. Since the characteristics of parent forms can be combined in the offspring by artificial breeding or **hybridization**, as it is called, it is possible to obtain new varieties with certain desired characteristics. Thus plants of new varieties of economic and ornamental importance can be produced by hybridization. Herein lies the importance of plant breeding (see pp. 625-6).

MENDEL'S EXPERIMENTS. Mendel selected for his work the common garden pea, in which he found a number of contrasting characteristics —purple, red or white flowers, tall dwarf plants, and yellow or green, or smooth or wrinkled seeds. He concentrated his attention on only one pair of characteristics at a time, and traced them carefully through many successive generations. In one series of experiments, he selected tallness and dwarfness of plants. The results he achieved in these experiments were the same in all cases. It did not matter whether he took the dwarf plant as the male one and the tall plant as the female one or vice versa (reciprocal crosses).

Monohybrid Cross. Mendel selected a pea plant, 2 metres in height, and another plant, 0.5 metre in height. He brought about artificial cross-

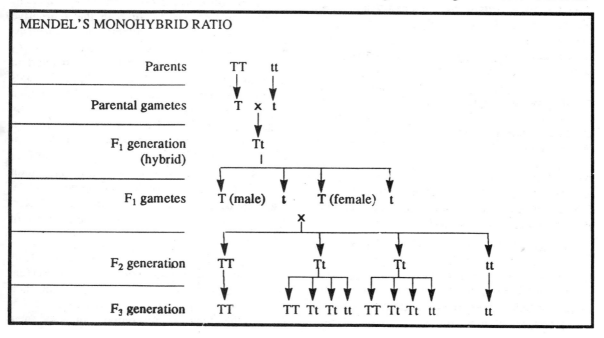

MENDEL'S MONOHYBRID RATIO

Parents	TT tt
Parental gametes	T x t
F₁ generation (hybrid)	Tt
F₁ gametes	T (male) t T (female) t
F₂ generation	TT Tt Tt tt
F₃ generation	TT TT Tt Tt tt TT Tt Tt tt tt

ings between the two. The seeds collected from the crossed plants were sown the next year. The hybrid progeny was, without an exception, tall (with the dwarf characteristic remaining latent and, therefore, impure tall). This generation was called the first filial generation or F_1 generation. Of the two contrasting characteristics, the one that expressed itself in the F_1 generation was termed **dominant** by Mendel, while the other characteristic that remained suppressed (but not absent in the hybrids) was termed **recessive**. All the F_1 plants were inbred, and so were those of the successive generations. Seeds were collected from them and sown, next year. It was seen that they gave rise to a mixed generation of talls—787 plants and dwarfs—277 plants (but no intermediate). This gave an approximate ratio of 3:1, i.e. three-fourths talls and one-fourth dwarfs. This generation was called the second filial generation or F_2 generation. All dwarfs of the F_2 generation bred true, producing only dwarfs in the third and subsequent generations. Seeds were collected separately from the F_2 tall plants and sown separately. They gave rise to the next generation or the F_3 generation. It was seen that one-third of the talls of the F_2 generation bred true to type producing talls only, while the other two-thirds of the talls again split up in the same ratio of 3:1. The F_2 ratio may then be expressed as 1:2:1, i.e. one-fourth pure talls, half mixed talls and one-fourth pure dwarfs. This scheme of inheritance is expressed symbolically in the table on p. 617. It is now the custom to use a capital letter to denote the factor for the dominant characteristic—T in this case, and the corresponding small letter for the recessive characteristic—t in this case.

MENDEL'S LAWS OF INHERITANCE. From the results of his experiments on crossings, Mendel formulated the following laws to explain the inheritance of characteristics.

(1) **Law of Unit Characters.** This means that all the characters of the plant are units by themselves, being independent of one another as far as their inheritance is concerned. There are certain factors or determiners (now called *genes*) of unit characters, which control the expression of these characters during the development of the plant. The factors occur in pairs. This is evident from the fact that the F_1 generation splits into tall and dwarf individuals in the F_2 generation.

(2) **Law of Dominance.** As already mentioned, of the two contrasting characteristics, the one that expresses itself in the F_1 generation is called *dominant*, while the other that remains suppressed in the F_1 generation is called *recessive*. Thus, in the previous experiment tallness is the dominant characteristic, and suppressed dwarfness the recessive characteristic. Mendel reasoned that there must be two factors separately responsible for each pair of contrasting characteristics, i.e. tallness and dwarfness, as in the previous experiment, and that these factors occur in pairs (now known to be arranged in a linear fashion in the chromosome). In the F_1 generation, one factor masks the expression of the other factor and, therefore, one characteristic becomes dominant and the other suppressed or recessive. Later work has shown, however, that dominance does not hold good in all cases. The contrasting pairs of characteristics are called **allelomorphs** (or simply **alleles**). Thus, tallness and dwarfness are allelomorphs.

(3) **Law of Segregation.** It is evident that the F_1 zygote contains factors for both the alternative characteristics, namely, tallness and dwarfness, although tallness has expressed itself in the F_1 generation. These factors remain associated in pairs in the somatic cells of the F_1 individuals throughout their lives. Later, when spores—pollen grains and megaspores (and subsequently gametes)—are formed as a result of reduction division, the factors located in homologous chromosomes are separated out. So each of the four spores (and gametes) will have only one factor (tallness or dwarfness) of the pair and not both, i.e. a gamete becomes *pure* for a particular characteristic. This law is also otherwise called the law of *purity of gametes*.

Phenotype and Genotype. When two individuals are similar in their external appearance (evident from morphological study) but differ in their genetic make-up, they are referred to as phenotypes. When their genetic composition is the same (evident from cytological study), they are referred to as genotypes. In Mendel's previous experiment, TT and Tt individuals of the F_2 generation are externally alike but genetically different. These individuals, therefore, belong to the same phenotype. But due to the differences in their genetic composition they are said to belong to different genotypes—TT to one and Tt to another. It should also be noted that when the individuals have similar gene pairs they are said to be *homozygous*, and when dissimilar they are *heterozygous*. Thus, TT and tt individuals are homozygous and Tt individuals are heterozygous.

Mendel also experimented on other pairs of alternative characteristics and found that in every case, the characteristics followed the same scheme of inheritance. He discovered that in garden pea, the coloured flower was dominant over the white flower, the yellow seed over the green seed, and the smooth seed over the wrinkled seed.

Back Cross. Crossing back F_1 plants (hybrids) to either of the two parental types, normally a recessive type, is called a **back cross**. It is otherwise called **test cross** because, by this method, it is possible to test the purity of the particular race of plants and also the gametic proportion of F_1 hybrids. Back crosses are now extensively employed in experimental plant breeding. It is evident that only two alternative back crosses are recessive types. In the former case, all the progeny would show only the dominant characteristics. The latter, however, is much more important. In such a back cross (i.e. crossing with a recessive type), the dominant characteristic and the recessive characteristic are seen to appear in the ratio of 1:1, i.e. one-half of the total population is dominant and one-half recessive. To take a concrete case, if a tall hybrid (Tt) of F_1, (as in Mendel's experiment with tall and dwarf plants) be crossed back to a parental dwarf (recessive) type (tt), half the progeny will be impure tall (Tt) and half dwarf (tt), i.e. the ratio of tall (dominant) to dwarf (recessive) is 1:1. The explanation is that gametes of the F_1 hybrid are T and t in equal numbers and those of the dwarf parent are t and t in equal numbers. Therefore, only four combinations are possible in such a back-cross,

viz. Tt, Tt, tt and tt, i.e. the ratio of tall (impure Tt) to dwarf (pure tt) is 1:1. This ratio has been verified by thousands of back crosses.

Xenia. The term xenia, first introduced by Focke in 1881, is used to indicate the direct influence of foreign pollen on the endosperm and other seed characteristics of the crossed plant in the same generation, i.e. on the same mother plant in the same year. Such an influence has also been observed on certain maternal tissues outside the embryo and the endosperm—as on the size, colour and flavour of fruits like date-palm, apple and orange. Such a phenomenon was termed *metaxenia* by Swingle in 1926. Swingle further suggested in 1928 that this effect might be due to the secretion of hormones by the embryo and the endosperm. Thus, certain gametic differences have been noticed in some seeds developing directly on the mother plant. In such cases, the dominant factors of the pollen are believed to have been directly introduced through crossing—natural or artificial, and corresponding characteristics have expressed themselves in the seeds directly borne by the mother plant. For instance, the cob with wrinkled grains in maize produces some smooth grains on it at places. These are hybrids which later breed in the Mendelian ratio of 3:1. Similarly, coloured grains are occasionally found on white or golden-grained cob. There are several instances of xenia on record.

Dihybrid Cross. For the dihybrid cross, two pairs of contrasting characteristics are taken into consideration at a time. Mendel selected a tall plant with red flowers—TRTR, and a dwarf one with white flowers—trtr, their respective gametes being TR and tr. Four unit characteristics are, therefore, involved in the dihybrid ratio. Factors for tallness or dwarfness and for red flowers or white are inherited independently. Artificial crossing was brought about between these two plants. In the F_1 generation, all individuals were tall with red flowers—TRtr, because tallness is dominant over dwarfness and coloured flowers dominant over white. Subsequently, their gametes bear factors TR (tall red), Tr (tall white), tR (dwarf red) and tr (dwarf white). When the seeds from the F_1

MENDEL'S DIHYBRID RATIO

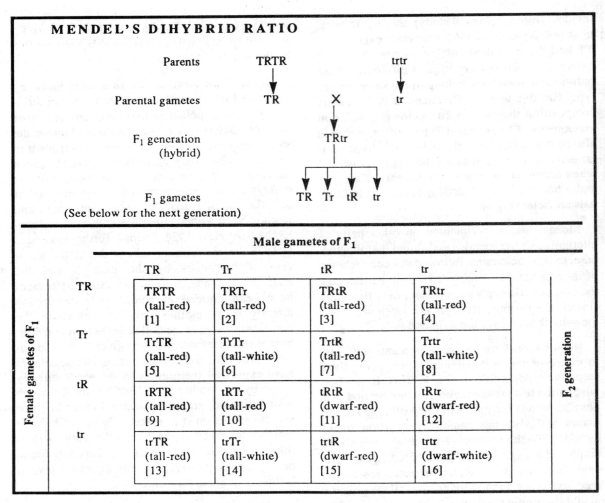

Parents	TRTR		trtr
Parental gametes	TR	X	tr
F₁ generation (hybrid)		TRtr	
F₁ gametes (See below for the next generation)		TR Tr tR tr	

Male gametes of F₁

Female gametes of F₁	TR	Tr	tR	tr
TR	TRTR (tall-red) [1]	TRTr (tall-red) [2]	TRtR (tall-red) [3]	TRtr (tall-red) [4]
Tr	TrTR (tall-red) [5]	TrTr (tall-white) [6]	TrtR (tall-red) [7]	Trtr (tall-white) [8]
tR	tRTR (tall-red) [9]	tRTr (tall-red) [10]	tRtR (dwarf-red) [11]	tRtr (dwarf-red) [12]
tr	trTR (tall-red) [13]	trTr (tall-white) [14]	trtR (dwarf-red) [15]	trtr (dwarf-white) [16]

F₂ generation

generation were grown, a segregation of characteristics showing all possible combinations occurred in the following proportions: 9 red talls, 3 white talls, 3 red dwarfs and 1 white dwarf. This 9:3:3:1 is the dihybrid ratio.

Nos. 1, 2, 3, 4, 5, 7, 9, 10, 13 are tall-red = 9
Nos. 6, 8, 14 .... are tall-white = 3
Nos. 11, 12, 15 ....are dwarf-red = 3
No. 16 .... is dwarf-white = 1

It should also be noted that Nos. 1, 6, 11 and 16 are homozygous (i.e. they have two similar gametes), breeding true, while the rest are heterozygous, (i.e. they have two dissimilar gametes), segregating in the next generation.

No. 1 (TRTR) will breed true for tall-red
No. 6 (TrTr) .... tall-white
No. 11 (tRtR) .... dwarf-red
No. 16 (trtr) .... dwarf-white

Polyhybrid Cross. In this way, Mendel extended the number of characteristics. For example, when three pairs of contrasting characteristics were taken—tall and dwarf, red flower and white, and smooth seed and wrinkled—it was found that in the F₁ generation, all individuals were tall with red flowers and smooth seeds, with the factors TRStrs—three dominant and three recessive. They evidently produced eight kinds of gametes, each with triple factors, e.g. TRS, TRs, TrS, Trs,

tRS, tRs, trS, and trs. When inbred, they formed a possible range of 64 (8 x 8) types of plants in the F_2 generation. When analysed they were found to have split up in the following proportions—27 (tall-red-smooth): 9 (tall-red-wrinkled): 9 (tall-white-smooth): 3 (tall-white-wrinkled): 9 (dwarf-red-smooth): 3 (dwarf-red-wrinkled): 3 (dwarf-white-smooth): 1 (dwarf-white-wrinkled).

Linkage. Chromosomes are regarded as the bearers of hereditary characteristics. Each chromosome is made up of several *genes*, each being generally responsible for a single characteristic. These genes are arranged in a linear fashion. At a certain stage in meiosis we find that homologous chromosomes come in close association in two's and interchange their parts, and while doing so, some of the genes of one chromosome go over to the other chromosome. But some genes of a particular chromosome, whether paternal or maternal, tend to remain together from generation to generation, i.e. these genes are linked together in inheritance even after crossing over (see p. 623). This phenomenon, first noted by Morgan in 1910, is known as *linkage*. For example, as first observed by Bateson and Punnet in 1906 in the sweat pea, there are two flower colours—*purple* and *red*, and two types of pollen—*long* and *round*. The purple colour and long pollen behave as dominants to red and round, respectively, each characteristic being represented by a single gene in inheritance. In a cross between purple long and red round, the F_1 individuals are all purple long. In the F_2 generation, the parental combinations, i.e. purple long and red round, are far more numerous than the expected Mendelian ratio of $9:3:3:1$. The unexpected number is explained by the fact that the genes for purple long as well as red round remain together, i.e. linked in inheritance and hence, more of these parental combinations are produced. There are two factor pairs—Rr and Yy—governing the colour of tomatoes. The R factor produces red flesh and is dominant over the factor which produces yellow flesh. The dominat factor Y produces yellow colour and the recessive factor y

represents colourless fruit. It has been found that the factor pair, Yy, is linked with the size of the fruit. There is a close association of y genes with large fruit. In maize or Indian corn, ten linkage groups have been observed, e.g. coloured and full endosperm, colourless and shrunken endosperm, etc. Generally, the number of linkage groups in any plant or animal is the same as the number of chromosome pairs. Linkage is not, however, always very complete, i.e. a few linked genes break apart and recombinations take place.

GENES[1]

Invisible as they are, genes cannot be properly defined. But from their action, they may be regarded as *functional* units of the chromosome. Genes are highly stable (except when they mutate) and continue as such from generation to generation.

There are several hundreds or thousands of genes in each chromosome, and they are strung together in a linear order. A gene or a group of genes responsible for a particular character is located in a definite position in the chromosome. Genes divide during mitosis and the two cells (subsequently other cells) thus formed receive an identical set of genes to function normally. The gene is a hereditary material in both plants and animals, as has been known for quite some time now.

CHEMICAL BASIS OF GENES. Within the last fifty years or so, intensive work has been done on the chemistry of chromosomes almost throughout the world with the help of electron micrographs, X-ray photographs and radioactive isotopes (particularly S and P). Each chromosome is now known to have a backbone of DNA (deoxyribonucleic acid) molecule, (its short segments being regarded as genes), and some specific proteins. Thus, DNA consists of a large number of genes of different kinds, responsible for the transmission of hereditary characteristics. Much is now known about the function and structure of DNA through the brilliant experimental work of several investigators (see p. 123). Their work has revealed

[1]References: *Elements of Cytology* by N. S. Cohn, the *Scientific American*— 54:1957, 60 & 104:1958, 68:1959, 92:1961, 119 & 123:1962 and 153:1963.

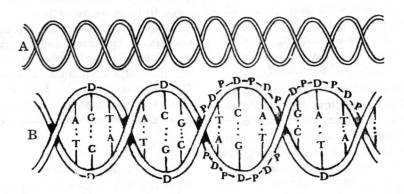

FIG. 1. *A*, Watson-Crick model of DNA molecule—long, double-stranded, wound about each other in a helical fashion; *B*, a portion of the same magnified, showing the distribution of deoxyribose sugar (D) and phosphate (P) in each strand, and cross-links made of thymine-adenine (T-A) and guanine-cytosine (G-C) in infinite sequences; dotted lines indicate linking by hydrogen bonds

that the DNA of the chromosome (and not its proteins) acts in two principal ways: it is the chemical basis of the gene and is the *essential genetic* material, and it controls all the *biosynthetic* processes of the cell, including protein synthesis. It may be noted that most of the work on DNA has been done on viruses and bacteria (see bacteriophage, p. 402) since the results of experiments with them may be observed within 12 to 20 minutes.

DNA Molecule. The model of a DNA molecule (Watson-Crick model; FIG 1), as first worked out by Watson and Crick in 1953, has been described in detail on pp. 124-5. A summary is given here. The two-stranded molecule occurs as a twisted ladder, and its cross-links—2 purines (adenine and guanine) and 2 pyrimidines (thymine and cytosine)—occur as rungs of the ladder. It is the rule that a specific purine always pairs with a specific pyrimidine as alleles (i.e. complementary pairs)—T-A and G-C, loosely linked by hydrogen bonds.

ACTION OF GENE. A gene or DNA, as established on three decades' intensive research, is the 'brain' or 'control' centre of the living cell. It controls all the life processes of the cell by sending

chemical messages or codes to all its parts. The bases, as named above, occur in infinite orders or sequences in a DNA molecule and are used by it to coin an infinite number of codes (messages or information), which are then transmitted to all parts of the cell for necessary biosynthetic processes. Thus, the DNA sends messages to ribosomes in the cytoplasm (see FIG. II/6) through **messenger RNA** and directs the RNA of the ribosomes to make proteins of particular kinds and in particular quantities (see pp. 264-66). In the stepwise reactions of such a synthesis (amino acids to proteins), a specific enzyme is controlled by each gene. This is the familiar 'one gene—one enzyme theory' of Beadle and Tatum (Nobel Prize winners, 1958). DNA controls nuclear divisions and chromosomal changes, and the final distribution of DNA among the newly formed cells, both qualitatively and quantitatively. The importance of DNA or a gene as an essential genetic material, transmitted as such, has been mentioned already.

DUPLICATION OF DNA. The DNA molecule duplicates itself. As stated before, it occurs in two long strands entwined about each other. The two strands unwind, separate lengthwise little by little, and each constructs a new partner. Herbert Taylor of Columbia University elaborated this point in 1958. Briefly speaking, when the two strands are separated, each serves as a template (or mold), forming a new complementary strand or its partner. The new material required for this purpose is obtained from the surrounding cytoplasm. Thus, two molecules appear in place of one and they are exact replicas of the original one. This is called the **template hypothesis.** When the DNA molecule thus divides, the bases also form alleles. A special enzyme, *DNA-polymerase,* (first discovered in 1956 by Arthur Kornberg, a Nobel Prize winner), is responsible for the duplication of DNA.

GENE MUTATION. Genes are the hereditary units present in the chromosomes. They are responsible for various characteristics externally manifested by plants and animals. A single gene may affect one or more characteristics, or a single characteristic may be due to the interaction of several genes. Any change in the gene brings about a change in the characteristics. Although genes are highly stable, one or more of them sometimes (rarely though) mutate. This may occur in the somatic cells, affecting the species only a little. Mutation in gametic cells is, however, of great significance as far as variability among living organisms and evolution are concerned. However, many mutations are harmful, e.g. mutant genes carrying diseases may be passed on to the progeny. In many instances, it has been seen that red-eyed species of *Drosophila* produced white-eyed individuals, or normal *Oenothera* plants produced dwarf species or plants with short styles, and sometimes a red or blue-flowered species suddenly gave rise to a white-flowered species. It was also seen that these individuals with new charactersistics bred true for many generations. It is assumed that in all these cases, gene changes occurred in the parents, evidently causing the appearance of new characteristics in the offspring. These changes are spoken of as **gene mutations.** Their cause is not known yet. On the basis of genetical work on *Neurospora* by Beadle and Tatum (1959) and further work on nucleic acid (DNA and RNA), it may be stated that a gene mutant fails to synthesize a particular enzyme (single gene—single enzyme theory of Beadle and Tatum). This evidently disturbs the sequence of amino acids and leads to the production of altered types of proteins and, therefore, a new type of plant, since each plant has its own specific types of proteins generation after generation through the work of DNA. Thus, gene mutation produces a new strain with new proteins. It is also asserted that evolution itself is primarily due to changes in proteins. Gene mutations can be induced artificially by treatment with X-ray (as shown in 1927 by Hermann J. Muller—a 1946 Nobel Prize winner), exposure to radiation and high temperature. Gene mutations may be due to the complete loss of old genes, or appearance of entirely new genes, or recombination of genes. Direct observation of gene changes is not possible. There are several instances of gene mutation on record.

Crossing Over. Each chromosome consists of a pair of chromatids. At the pachytene stage of meiosis, the homologous chromosomes pair but subsequently, at the diplotene stage, they separate again, remaining attached at one or a few points known as chiasmata. At these points, a break may occur due to the twisting of the chromatids about each other. As a result, a part of a chromatid of one chromosome goes over to a chromatid of the other chromosome. This interchange (of the parts of the chromatids of a pair of chromosomes) is known as **crossing over.** Crossing over brings about parental combinations of linked genes. However, linkage is not always very complete, thus resulting in the separation of a few linked genes and the appearance of new combinations. It must be noted that crossing over normally takes place between only two chromatids of the two homologous chromosomes, while the other two chromatids of the chromosome pair preserve their own identity and pass on to the gametes intact. Temperature, X-ray and radium treatment have a profound influence on the frequency of crossing over.

Sex Chromosomes. Most animals and a good number of plants are dioecious. Sexuality in them is controlled and sex is determined by a definite pair of chromosomes called sex chromosomes. It

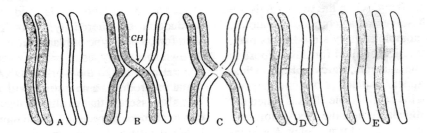

FIG. 2. Diagrammatic representation of crossing over (with one pair of chromosomes).
A, two homologous chromosomes, each with two chromatids (at pachytene); *B*, chiasma (*CH*)
formation (at diplotene); *C*, break of chromatids at chiasma and crossing over (at diakinesis or
at metaphase); *D*, dissociation of two newly-constituted chromosomes (at anaphase); *E*, separation
of four chromatids (at the end of second division), each entering into a daughter nucleus (spore or gamete)

has been observed that, in most cases, both the chromosomes of this pair are identical in the female, whereas one is different in shape from the other in the male. When the pair is similar, the chromosomes are known as X-chromosomes. The other dissimilar chromosome found in the male is known as the Y-chromosome. Except for this pair, all the other chromosomes are identical in both the male and the female. These chromosomes are called *autosomes*, while the sex chromosomes are otherwise called *allosomes*. The chromosome complements in this type may thus be expressed as follows: male—2n + XY, and female—2n + XX. This type is very widespread in both animals and plants. Subsequently, the female yields gametes of one kind (homogametic), each carrying X, while the male yields gametes of two kinds (heterogametic) in equal numbers, i.e. half carrying X and half Y. When fertilization takes place, two combinations are possible: XX (female offspring) and XY (male offspring). Now the question arises whether it is possible by any means to bring about any desired combination at will? The answer is a definite 'no' at the present state of our knowledge. In addition to the common type mentioned above, there are other types. For example, in birds the female has XY, while the male has XX, i.e. the order is seen to be reversed. In liverworts, mosses and some algae, there is an X in the female and a Y in the male. They combine into XY in the zygote and the succeeding

sporophyte. There is another type in which the female has a pair of X-chromosomes, while the male has only one X-chromosome. Thus, one sex is XX (female), while the other is XO (male). Such a type is known as the XO type.

CHROMOSOME MECHANISM IN HEREDITY AND EVOLUTION. On the basis of their recent work on the fruit-fly (*Drosophila melanogaster*), Morgan and his colleagues have put forward the chromosomes theory of heredity. According to this theory, chromosomes are the bearers of hereditary characteristics and the genes responsible for the production of characteristics are arranged in a linear fashion in the chromosomes. The continuity of chromosomes throughout the life cycle of a plant is evident. Plants reproduce by the fusion of the male and female gametes, and the zygote so formed develops into the seedling and the mature plant. So the parental characteristics must be transmited to the offspring through these gametes. The somatic (body) cells of the sporophyte have 2n chromosomes, of which n chromosomes are of paternal origin and n of maternal origin. When the gametes are produced, the sporophytic number (2n) is reduced to half (n) by meiosis so that each gamete has n chromosomes. As soon as the gametes fuse to form the zygote, 2n is regained. The inheritance of parental characteristics by the offspring is carried out by the genes, which are ultra-microscopic particles occurring in pairs (one paternal and one maternal) in a linear series in the chromosomes. When the chromosome splits, the genes are equally apportioned to the two chromatids. A particular plant or animal has a large number of gene pairs but comparatively few chromosomes and, therefore, each chromosome must carry several genes in its body. A gene (or a pair) is a factor or determiner responsible for the production of a particular characteristic, e.g. colour of flower, shape of leaf, size of fruit and so on. The various characteristics of a plant or an animal are, however, always influenced by the interaction of a number of genes. Although some investigators speak of transmission of hereditary characteristics through the cytoplasm of the egg or sperm, it is still regarded as being only of secondary importance. Whether the transmission of characteristics is chromosomal or cytoplasmic, the characteristics of mature plants and animals are modified to a great extent by environmental influences.

Chromosomes play an important role in evolution. New species of plants may arise as a result of changes in or loss or degeneration of genes, or even the appearance of new genes, or due to changes in the proportion of genes, known in all cases as 'gene' mutations. The cause of these changes is as yet unknown. A simple case of 'gene' mutation was observed by De Vries in the evening primrose (*Oenothera lamarckiana*) and it was on this basis that he put forward the mutation theory of evolution. It was observed that now and then, dwarf plants of evening primrose suddenly appeared in the field from normal plants, and these subsequently bred true. These were new species which, according to De Vries, had evolved only by 'gene' mutation. Sometimes, a red or blue-flowered species is seen to suddenly give rise to white-flowered species. It is assumed that the old gene has changed and a new characteristic has developed. New species of plants are also produced by a sudden increase in the number of chromosomes. Thus, there may be $2n$, $3n$, $4n$, $5n$, $6n$, $7n$, $8n$, $9n$, or $10n$, or more or even a variable number. When this increased number is a multiple of haploid, it is expressed as **polyploid** (see pp. 150-3).

ECONOMIC IMPORTANCE OF PLANT-BREEDING.

Plant-breeding has been scientifically developed to such an extent in recent years that it is now recognized as the best practical method for the improvement of various crops—foodgrains, vegetables, pulses, oilseeds, fruit, industrial plants, fodder crops and many other plants of economic importance and aesthetic value. It can improve the productiveness, quality, colour, size, total yield and other useful factors. By the application of this method, it is possible to combine the desired characteristics of parent forms and evolve new types that are far better than the original types in many respects. Babcock, a leading geneticist, even goes so far as to say that plants can almost be made to order. This being so, the subject is considered to be of utmost importance in agriculture and to a great extent, in horticulture. Considerable improvements have already been achieved within the last fifty years through plant-breeding methods. For example, hardy rust-resistant and high-yielding types of wheat has been evolved, and the milling and bread-making qualities of wheat grains considerably improved. Several new varieties of rice with higher yield and of better quality have been brought into existence. In tobacco, the number of leaves per plant has been increased and their size and quality improved. Pea, bean, many vegetables, pulses, oilseeds, etc., have been considerably improved. The same is the case with fruits like apple, grapes, peach, pear, plum, orange and strawberry. In fibre-yielding plants like jute, cotton and flax, better quality fibre (length, strength and fineness) and also higher yields have been achieved. New types of maize, potato and tomato—high-yielding and rust-resistant— evolved in America are also example of the numerous achievements in this direction. In Russian Federation, new varieties of summer and winter wheats and 'perennial' wheat (results of crosses between varieties of wheat and couch-grass), wheat-*Elymus* (result of cross between wheat and *Elymus*—a kind of grass), and barley-*Elymus* (result of cross between barley and *Elymus*) are some of the outstanding features of work in this line. A new hybrid called Triticale—the result of a cross between wheat

(*Triticum*) and rye (*Secale*)—has shown higher production and better nutritional value. In India, too, a considerable amount of work has been done in this line on rice, wheat, millets, maize, sugarcane, pulses, oil-seeds, cotton, tobacco, jute, flax, hemp, etc., and improved strains combining high yield, good quality and resistance to pests and disease evolved by breeding. Pusa wheats deserve a special mention in this connection. Several new Pusa varieties tolerant to rut, resistant to smut and, at the same time, very high-yielding have been evolved at the Indian Agricultural Research Institute[1] and have proved to be an outstanding success. A wheat evolved at Pusa, New Pusa 4 (NP 4), was awarded the first prize in several international exhibitions in America, Australia and Africa. A result of several years' work at ICAR is the production of new types of bread wheat—NP 800, NP 200, NP 400, etc. A variety of rice—GEB 24—evolved at Coimbatore by Ramiah, a pioneer in rice-breeding in India, still remains unsurpassed in quality, productivity and wide adaptability. At the Central Rice Research Institute at Cuttack, new varieties of rice resistant to disease have been evolved. Pusa 33, a hybrid BASMATI rice (a cross between BASMATI 370 and a dwarf type) evolved by IARI in New Delhi, is very high-yielding, aromatic, matures early and is easy to cook. An important achievement of the institute is the development in recent years of hybrid millets and maize strains yielding 50% more than the common varieties. The institute has also evolved some new strains of wheat to suit different climatic regions of India. A hybrid maize, Texas 26, evolved by the same institute, is very high-yielding. In addition, it has developed rust-resistant linseeds, wilt-resistant pigeon peas and late blight-resistant potatoes. Highly improved types of chilli, gram, linseed and mustard evolved through hybridization are some of the special achievements of this institute. A recent success is the production of a sweet-flavoured tomato with a high vitamin content (result of a cross between a cultivated tomato and a wild South American species). New types of sugarcane evolved at Coimbatore have already become world-famous. The improvement of the sugar industry in India can be attributed mainly to these sugarcanes. Although much has already been achieved, there is still ample scope for improvement of several crops for food and industry.

It is evident that plant-breeding has grown so much in economic importance that agricultural and plant breeding stations all over the world have embarked on programmes of artificial plant-breeding to enhance the quality and yield of particular crops, and the power of resistance to pests and diseases.

---

[1] The Indian Agricultural Research Institute (formerly known as the Pusa Institute) was established in 1905 at Pusa in Darbhanga (Bihar) on a liberal donation of £30,000 by an American philanthropist, Mr. Henry Phipps. Early work on the improvement of wheat by selection and breeding was carried out at this institute by the late Sir Alfred Howard with considerable success. The laboratory buildings having been irreparably damaged by the great Bihar earthquake in 1934, the institute was shifted to New Delhi in 1936. At present, it has six sub-stations at Pusa (Bihar), Karnal (east Punjab), Shimla (Himachal Pradesh), Pune (Maharashtra), Indore (Madhya Pradesh) and Willington (Tamil Nadu).

9 ECONOMIC BOTANY

GENERAL DESCRIPTION AND ECONOMIC PLANTS

Economic Botany. This branch deals with the various uses of plants and plant products for the material well-being of mankind. It also includes the various practical methods adopted for their improvement. The economic uses of plants are varied and the scope for improvement to meet man's ever-increasing need is immense. The primary needs of mankind are, of course, food, clothing and shelter, which in their basic forms are supplied by nature and subsequently, improved upon by man through the application of his scientific knowledge. The gifts of nature are almost unlimited and a variety of useful products is obtained from the plant kingdom.

Methods of Improvement. The methods commonly employed for the improvement of the quality, yield, etc. of crops are: (1) pure line selection, (2) breeding (see pp. 617 & 625), (3) improved methods of cultivation, (4) selection and use of 'quality' seeds, (5) proper use of an adequate amount of chemical fertilizers and manures (see p. 224), (6) judicious selection of crops for a particular locality, (7) introduction of high-yielding and disease-resistant varieties, (8) intensive and extensive cultivation, (9) introduction of short-duration and early-maturing crops to avoid flood or drought, (10) protection against diseases and pests (insects, moulds, rats, etc), and against destruction by natural calamities (floods, droughts, hailstorms, etc.) and (11) proper irrigation—*major* by dams and barrages across perennial rivers, diverting the water through canals, and *minor* by wells, tube-wells and tanks with the help of Persian wheels, MOTS and pumps. It may be noted that the loss of crops in India on account of diseases and pests is estimated to be 10-18.6% annually. The use of pesticides in India is meagre. Rats the world over devour about 40 million tonnes a year, enough to feed 250 million people.

There are plenty of economic plants with a variety of uses. Many occur in a natural state, particularly in forests, while a good number of them are cultivated for food and industry. Such plants may be classified under the following heads: (A) food— cereals and millets, (B) pulses, (C) vegetables, (D) oil-seeds, (E) fruits, (F) sugar, (G) spices and condiments, (H) medicinal (drug) plants, (I) beverages, (J) timber, (K) fibres, (L) rubber, and (M) paper. In this context, it is of interest that India is the largest producer of tea, sugarcane, groundnuts and jute; China of rice; U.S.A. of corn and cotton; Brazil of coffee; Ghana of cocoa; and Russian Federation of beet sugar. It may also be noted that the most important exchange earners of India are jute goods, tea and cotton cloth, in their order of importance. These three together represent in value nearly half of India's total exports.

FOOD

Food may be classified into the following groups: (*a*) heat or energy-producing food with high calorific value, such as carbohydrates and fats, (*b*) body-building food such as proteins, (*c*) protective food such as vitamins and some minerals, and (*d*) luxury food such as confectioneries. The energy value of food is expressed in terms of Calories. A Calorie is the amount of heat needed to raise the temperature of 1 kilogram of water through 1 C. It may be noted that 1 gm. of carbohydrate yields about 4 Calories, and 1 gm. of fat about 9 Calories. The daily requirement of a man of average weight, doing moderate work, is about 3,000 Calories, which must be obtained from the food he eats. The average Indian diet produces only about 1,620 Calories. It is evident that food plants must contain sufficiently high percentages of carbohydrates, proteins, and fats and oils, together with vitamins and essential minerals. All cereals and millets are rich in starch and contain vitamins A, B and C. They belong to *Gramineae* and are cultivated as annual crops. Cereals constitute the main foodstuff of human beings all over the world. The major cereals are rice, wheat and maize, and the major millets (smaller-grained ones) are JUAR or CHOLAM (*Sorghum*), RAGI (*Eleusine*) and BAJRA (*Pennisetum*). For proper nutrition, however, a balanced diet consisting of cereals, vegetables, pulses, vegetable oils, sugar, fruit, milk and milk products, and according to habit and custom, fish, meat, eggs, etc., is indispensable. Among the important food crops of India, cereals take up about 60% of the total area under cultivation, pulses about 18% and oil-yielding plants about 8%. After many years of shortages, mainly due to the population explosion, India has now attained self-sufficiency in foodgrains, with an annual production of over 167.06 million tonnes. This has been achieved through improved methods of cultivation, increased use of fertilizers (see p. 224), cultivation of some prolific varieties, arrangements for proper irrigation, and intensive and extensive cultivation of crops.

(A) CEREALS

1. **Rice** (*Oryza sativa*). This is the major agricultural crop in India, occupying about 37% of the total area under cereals. It covers a total area of 42.31 million hectares—the world's largest rice area. The total yield of this vast area, although poor some years back, has now risen to 73.66 million tonnes a year with the cultivation of some special, prolific varieties. However, Asia, as a whole, accounts for 90% of the world's total rice production. Rice is the staple food in India and tropical Asia, and feeds over 60% of the world's population. Its pericarp and embryo contain 70-80% starch, 7% proteins, 1.5% oils, some vitamins (mostly A, B and C) and some essential minerals. In polished rice, however, the pericarp is destroyed, causing the loss of some precious nutrients (proteins, vitamins and minerals). Throwing away the water (gruel) after cooking results in further loss. What finally remains in cooked rice is mainly starch. Rice has been under cultivation in India and China from time immemorial. There are about 7,000 varieties of rice, of which about 4,000 occur in India alone. These are derived from a few old, wild forms that are still found. Although many new better varieties of rice—finer, higher-yielding and disease-resistant—have been evolved in India by the agricultural department and the Central Rice Research Institute at Cuttack (Orissa) by means of selection and hybridization, the annual average yield of the common varieties is very poor. Rice is widely cultivated in India, except in north-west India, where wheat is the main crop. The crop thrives under conditions of moderately high temperature and plenty of rainfall or proper irrigation. Under heavy manuring with cowdung, ashes and tank-earth, and with the use of chemical fertilizers like sulphate of ammonia and bonemeal, the yield increases much above the average. The average yield of rice in India is more or less 1,741 kg. per hectare per year (Tamil Nadu leading with 1,974 kg.) as against 3,117 kg. and 3,406 kg. in Egypt and Japan, respectively, where fields are heavily manured. Rice straw is a fodder for cattle. Rice starch is used in preparing alcoholic beverages.

Cultivation. Two or three croppings are practised in India according to the conditions of the soil and the climate. Indian rice fields generally remain under-manured. Common seasonal varieties are AUS or summer rice, AMAN or winter rice and BORO rice which is grown between the two seasons, with many sub-varieties of each. Some special varieties like Taichung Native 1, Tainan 3, Kalimpong 1, Jaya, Padma, IR 8 and IR 24,—all high-yielding and early-maturing—may be cultivated on the same land, BORO paddy in April, AUS paddy in July and AMAN paddy in October or even earlier. ADT 27, now under cultivation in parts of Madras, yields about 4,257 kg. per hectare per year. Further, two new fine, dwarf, high-yielding varieties, IET 1919 and IET 1039, have shown great promise in several parts of Tamil Nadu.

(*a*) *AUS* or **summer rice** is coarse, difficult to digest and low-yielding, as compared to AMAN. AUS paddy prefers high land without waterlogging. The sandy banks of rivers with silt deposits are ideal for its cultivation. The fields are made ready after ploughing and cross-ploughing. Paddy grains are sown in seed-beds or in the fields in early May and watered regularly. When the seedlings are about 23 cm. high, they are transplanted to water-soaked fields after a few showers of rain. The seedlings are usually planted 15-23 cm. apart in small bunches of 3-5, or even singly. Sometimes, however, they are planted in large bunches of 15 or so in flooded areas. AUS paddy is also broadcast and transplanting is avoided. The yield, however, is low in this case. The time for harvesting is August-September, before the grains fully ripen as they shed very easily. Paddy is threshed out of the stalk by beating or by trampling by cattle.

(*b*) *AMAN* or **winter rice** is better in quality, finer and more easily digestible. AMAN paddy prefers low-lying land with clay soil. The general mode of cultivation is almost the same as that of AUS. Paddy grains are sown in prepared seed-beds (nurseries) in May-June, or sometimes broadcast. Transplantation is done in June-July when sufficient rain water is available. Irrigation is resorted to when necessary. If the season continues to be dry, it is better to grow AUS, maize and millets. AMAN paddy ordinarily requires no manuring, but the addition of manures and fertilizers improves the yield, as in the case of AUS. AMAN paddy is harvested in November-December. It can be stored for months before threshing. Its yield is much heavier that of AUS. The average yield of Kharif rice (i.e. AUS and AMAN together) is 1686 kg. per hectare.

(*c*) *BORO* **paddy** is a minor crop. Two croppings may be practised: (*i*) KHARIF or rain crop sown in June-July and harvested in September-October, and (*ii*) RABI or winter crop sown in October-November and harvested in Mach-April. The grains may be broadcast and the seedlings transplanted later. The yield is 2,712 kg. per hectare per year.

(*d*) **Deep-water paddy** is grown in low-lying areas during the rains, but not widely. It can stand water to a depth of 1.5-3 metres, or even more. A peculiarity is that the plant grows quickly with a rise in the water level—20-30 cm. a day, but it rots if it gets completely submerged. The yield is low.

JHUM cultivation. It is the practice with some hill tribes to select the best fertile areas on hill slopes, cut down and burn forest growths, and then raise crops in these areas for a year or two. After this period, fresh areas are selected and the same practice repeated. Because of the very evil effects of JHUM or shifting cultivation, viz. deforestation, loss of soil fertility, erosion of land, occurrence of floods, etc., this practice is being gradually replaced by ordinary cultivation.

2. Wheat (*Triticum aestivum*). This is the second staple food of people in India and the principal diet in western countries. There are several varieties of wheat. They may be broadly classified into *hard* and *soft*. The former varieties are adapted for making SUJI and ATTA, while the latter varieties are used for making fine flour (MAIDA). Wheat is extensively cultivated in Uttar Pradesh, Madhya Pradesh, Gujarat, Rajasthan, Haryana and Punjab. Soft wheats are grown in the basins of the Ganges and the Indus, and harder varieties elsewhere. The grains are sown in October-December and the crop harvested in March-May. Wheat is a universal crop, i.e. it can be grown successfully in both temperate and tropical countries. The inflorescence usually consists of 15-20 sessile spikelets. Each spikelet bears 1-5 flowers, but all of them are not fertile. The average yield of wheat in India is 2397 kg per hectare. Several new varieties (e.g. SONA 227 evolved by IARI)—hardy, disease-resistant, high-yielding, with better milling and bread-making qualities—have been evolved in India (see p. 626), resulting in a phenomenal increase in yield. Further, with the cultivation of some dwarf Mexican varieties, e.g. Mayo 64, Sonara 63 and

64, and Lerma Rojo 64A, particularly in the Gangetic and Indus plains, the total production is now 55.09 million tonnes a year. Some of the best wheats are grown in Australia, America and Russia. The average chemical composition of wheat is: starch—66-70%, proteins 12% and oils 1.5%. Wheat starch is used in the textile industry and in making alcohol. Wheat straw is a fodder for cattle. Wheat prefers clay loam or sandy loam and a moderately dry climate, and thrives under irrigation. Saltpetre is the best manure for wheat.

3. Maize or Indian Corn (*Zea mays*). This is an important cereal food for poor people. However, it is mainly used for feeding livestock. It is originally a Mexican plant but now grown all over the world. It was introduced into India by the Portuguese in the early part of the 17th century. Maize is now cultivated all over India, both in the hills and the plains, predominantly in Uttar Pradesh, Madhya Pradesh, Punjab, Rajasthan and Bihar. It flourishes both in hot and cold climates. There are several varieties and hybrids. The usual sowing season is April-May and the harvesting season July-August. Each plant usually bears one cob, sometimes two. Some new hybrids of maize which are very high-yielding, disease-resistant, sweetish and nutritious, have evolved in India (see p. 626). The total production of maize in India has now gone up to 7.98 million tonnes a year. Maize cobs may be 15-25 cm. in length, and the grain golden-yellow, dull yellow, red, white, purplish, etc. Maize grains are taken as a substitute for other cereal grains and prepared by boiling. They are also often fried. Usually, they are ground into fine flour called corn-flour. They are also powdered into starch. Maize starch is largely used in making alcoholic beverages. The young tender grains are nutritious and may be taken raw, roasted or boiled in milk. Of all cereals, maize contains the largest amount of oils. The average chemical composition is: starch—68-70%, proteins—10% and oils —3.6-5%. The grains also contain an appreciable quantity of Ca and Fe. Maize prefers high, open land and requires manuring as it exhausts the soil. Its leaves, spathes and stems form a good fodder and the grains a nutritious food for farm animals.

4. *Sorghum vulgare* (=*Andropogon sorghum*; great millet—JUAR or CHOLAM). This is the best of all millets. It affords nutritious food, nearly as good as wheat. It is widely cultivated in India, particularly in south India, and also in Maharashtra and Gujarat. The plants are as tall as 3-4 metres, the stem stout and often sweetish, and the panicle much branched. There are several varieties and hybrids. The average annual yield per hectare is 428 kg., and often double this quantity in properly irrigated black soil. The grains are made into flour, often mixed with wheat, forming a nutritious food. The average chemical composition is: starch—72-%, proteins—9% and oils—2%. The grains are mostly sown in June-July and the crop harvested in October-November. It takes 4-5 months to mature and two croppings are generally practised. JUAR is a good fodder crop.

5. *Eleusine coracana* (African millet—RAGI or MARUA). This is an important food crop of Karnataka. It is extensively cultivated in Karnataka, Tamil Nadu and Andhra and, to some extent, in Maharashtra, Punjab, Uttar Pradesh and Bihar. RAGI being a short duration crop, 2 or 3 croppings are practised a year. The grains are usually sown in June-July and the crop harvested in August-September. The plants are dwarf, being 0.6-1 metre in height, but very hardy. The spikes are short and occur in a whorl. RAGI is a dryland crop. The annual yield per hectare is 1175 kg., and often well over 2,200 kg. in properly irrigated red soil. The grains can be stored for several years without injury. The average chemical composition is: starch—73%, proteins—over 7% and oils—1.5%. The grains are difficult to digest. The straw is a nutritious fodder for cattle.

6. *Pennisetum typhoideum* (pearl millet—BAJRA). This is another important millet, cultivated almost throughout India. The plants are 1-2 metres in height and the dark-brown spikes, 15-23 cm. in length, occur in clusters. The crop takes three months to mature. BAJRA grows in regions with low rainfall on both red and black soils. Generally, two croppings are practised a year. The grains are usually sown in May and the crop harvested in July-August. The average annual yield per hectare is

463 kg., or a little more under irrigation. The total yield a year is over 4.64 million tonnes. The grains often require threshing and husking, like paddy. The average chemical composition is: starch—71-%, proteins—10% and oils—over 3%. The grains are cooked like rice or ground into flour. The straw is not usually used as a fodder for cattle.

(B) *PULSES*

As foodgrains, pulses (family *Papilionaceae*) stand next to cereals. They are cultivated extensively in India as winter crops, in rotation with cereals. Pulses occupy about 13.72% of the total area under cultivation. They are valued as food because of their high protein content, which averages 22-25% (in soya-bean it is as high as 35-42%). The starch content is about 58% and the oil content 2% or more. In gram, however, the oil content may be as high as 5%. Pulses contain vitamins A, B and C, particularly the sprouted seeds. The pulses commonly used in India are Bengal gram, black gram, pea, red gram or pigeon pea, and lentil. With the exception of pigeon pea (which is a shrub), the rest are annuals and form short-duration crops. Pulses are widely used in various culinary preparations, particularly DAL (a kind of soup). The plants form good fodder. Having root-nodules for nitrogen-fixation, they form excellent green manures.

1. Bengal Gram (*Cicer arietium*). This is an important pulse, cultivated extensively all over India. The crop matures in three months. Gram is a nutritious food but somewhat difficult to digest. The split seeds of gram are usually used as a DAL. Grams are also boiled, fried or roasted. Soaked seeds are fed to horses to improve stamina. The dried seeds are ground into flour, which is eaten with relish and widely used in confectioneries. Green seeds are often eaten raw. Apart from its high protein content, it is also rich in oil and is a good source of vitamin A. Because of its nutritious contents, the germinating seeds are specially good for growing children, and also for adults. Its average chemical composition is: starch—58%, proteins—23.5% and oils—5%. The average annual yield per hectare is 652 kg. The straw forms a good fodder.

2. Black Gram (*Phaseolus mungo*). This is one of the best pulses grown throughout India. The plants have a trailing habit. The seeds are usually dark-brown. The average annual yield of the seeds per hectare is 448 kg. Its average chemical composition is: starch—54%, proteins—22% and oils—1%. Apart from their high protein and vitamin content, the seeds are rich in phosphoric acid. The proteins of black gram are more easily digestible and are almost as good as meat. It is prepared as DAL as well as various kinds of pies. PAPPAD (wafer) is made of this pulse. Germinating seeds taken raw are considered nutritious. The husked pods, seeds and straw form a valuable cattle feed.

3. Pea (*Pisum sativum*). This is another common pulse but not very extensively used. It often substitutes for other pulses. The dried split seeds of the field pea are used in the preparation of DAL, while the green seeds of the garden pea are eaten raw or in stews, and commonly used as a vegetable. The latter is sweetish in taste. A large quantity is canned, particularly in America. In India, dehydrated peas are marketed when peas are not in season. The average chemical composition is: starch—55%, proteins—28% and oils—1.5%. The average annual yield per hectare is 902 kg. It is cultivated mainly in northern and eastern India. The leaves and stems are a valuable fodder.

4. Pigeon Pea or **red gram** (*Cajanus cajan*). This is a perennial shrub grown as a pure crop or mixed crop, and is widely cultivated in India. Sowing is done in May-July and it bears pods within six months. The crop is harvested in December-March. Usually, two varieties are distinguished—one with long pods and the other with shorter pods. The average annual yield per hectare is 760 kg. Average chemical composition is: starch—57%, proteins—22% and oils—about 2%. It is widely used in India as DAL, and is one of the important items of a vegetarian diet, particularly in south India. Various sweet cakes are also made of this pulse. Tender green pods are often used as a vegetable. At one time, it was a favourite food with sailors. The leaves form a valuable fodder.

5. Lentil (*Lens culindris*). This is an important

pulse in northern and eastern India. The crop takes only three months to mature and is generally harvested in February-April. The average annual yield per hectare is 641 kg., going up to 900 kg. under irrigation. In eastern India, this nutritious pulse is in almost daily use. Its average chemical composition is: starch—58%, proteins—23-25% and oils—1-1.5%. The dry leaves and stalks are used as a fodder.

6. Soya-bean (*Glycine max = G. soja*). This is a native of China and Japan and is an annual suberect herb. It was introduced into India late in the 19th century but was grown mostly as a garden crop for a long time. Then the government considered extending its cultivation because of its high food value. The seeds, 3 or 4 in each pod, are very rich in protein (35% or more), oils (19%) and also minerals, particularly Ca and Fe, but low in starch and sugar (26%). They are very nutritious, especially useful for diabetics. As a matter of fact, soya-bean is considered to be the richest vegetable food. Though not common in India, it is prepared mainly as DAL or flour. It also makes a good soup. Soya-bean milk is considered a good substitute for cow's milk, is quite suitable for children and invalids, and is much cheaper too. Casein and curd made from this milk are of superior quality. In China and Japan, soya-bean forms a standard food item and it is prepared in various ways. A rather common preparation is a sort of cheese (casein) or paste. Its seeds can also be ground into flour, and biscuits and breads made with it. They yield an edible drying oil which is used in margarine, and also a cooking oil (after refining). Its industrial uses are numerous: soap-making, paints, lacquer, varnish, candle, grease, disinfectant, insecticides, etc. A large quantitiy of seeds and oil is exported annually to Europe from Manchuria. Green plants and oil-cakes (with 40-48% proteins) form an extremely rich cattle food. The crop is ready within three months and is harvested in November-December. The yield of the seeds per hectare per year is about 806 kg. There are several varieties of soya-bean. The annual production of soya-bean in India is near about 1714.6 thousand tonnes, while it is much more in China and America. American varieties have been grown with success since 1967

as a commercial crop in Mysore, Uttar Pradesh, Madhya Pradesh and Rajasthan.

(C) *VEGETABLES*

(*a*) Leafy vegetables like cabbage, lettuce, spinach are rich in vitamins, (usually A, B, C and E) and should, therefore, be included in the daily diet. (*b*) Several fruits (leguminous and non-leguminous) are also used as vegetables. (*c*) Tuber crops are fleshy underground roots or stems, laden with a heavy deposit of food material. Some of the common ones are as follows:

1. Potato (*Solanum tuberosum*—family *Solanaceae*). This much-branched, annual harb is a native of Peru (South America). It was introduced into India by the Portuguese in the early part of the 17th century, and into Europe by Sir Francis Drake late in the 16th century. It started being grown as a commercial crop late in the 18th century. Over 70% of the world's potatoes are grown in Europe and erstwhile USSR. Potato is an underground stem tuber, extensively cultivated in India in the hills as well as in the plains. It is usually grown during the cold months, but can be grown both as a summer crop and a winter crop. Potato is a universal item of food all over the world. It is an excellent food containing easily digestible starch, some essential amino-acids (e.g. lysine), certain useful minerals (e.g. K, Mg and P) and vitamin C. It is used in a variety of culinary preparations. The average yield of potato in India is very low on the whole, being in the neighbourhood of 15934 kg per hectare per year. Under suitable conditions, often double this yield can be achieved. The Central Potato Research Institute in Shimla has evolved some new hybrids and varieties which are very high-yielding and disease-resistant. The *per capita* consumption of potato in India is extremely low, being about 4 kg., as against 117-174 kg. in the European countries. The average yield of tubers per plant in India is 500 gm., varying from 200 gm. to 800 gm. according to the variety. There are a few hundred varieties which may be broadly classified into two—*waxy* and *mealy*. The average chemical composition is: starch—18-20%, proteins—2% and oils—0.1%. Potato starch has a variety of uses, particularly in laundry and in the preparation of alcohol (see p. 137). Sandy loam is the best soil for cultivation of potato. Water-logging is very injurious, while irrigation with proper drainage is very beneficial to the crop. Potato requires 3-4 months to mature, and it is ready to be lifted when the leaves have completely withered—usually in February-March. The yield is generally ten times the seed-potato sown. Late blight of potato (caused by *Phytophthora infestans*) is a serious disease of the crop, particularly in the hills.

2. Sweet Potato (*Ipomoea batatas*—family *Convolvulaceae*). This is an underground tuberous root. The plant, a perennial twiner that trails on the ground is a native of tropical America. It is grown widely in India. It always prefers a moist sandy soil and is usually propagated by branch cuttings or by tuberous roots. There are two common varieties—one with white skin and the other with red skin. Sweet potato is tasty and nutritious, and may be had raw, boiled, fried, or in curries. It also makes delicious CHUTNEY, sweet or sour. Its average chemical composition is: starch and sugar—29%, proteins—2% and oils 0.7%.

3. Tapioca or Cassava (*Manihot esculentus*—family *Euphorbiaceae*). This is the large fleshy root of the plant, a perennial shrub, cultivated mainly in Kerala and only to some extent in other states. The numerous varieties may be broadly classified into *bitter* and *sweet*. The former contains some amount of poisonous hydrocyanic acid which, however, disappears on boiling or roasting. Tapioca makes delicious curries and is very nutritious. Tapioca flour is used in making CHAPATIS, HALWA, puddings and biscuits. Granulated tapioca (called *pearl tapioca*) is sold in the market as a substitute for sago. Tapioca meal may be used as a substitute for arrowroot. Tapioca is a good anti-famine food. The plant is propagated through stem-cuttings. The yield of raw roots may be over 19.61 tonnes per hectare per year. A single plant may produce 11-25 kg. of roots. They lose about 75% of their weight on drying. Tapioca is widely used in America.

4. Yams (Dioscorea—family *Dioscoreaceae*). These are the large underground storage tubers (root tubers or stem tubers, according to the species) of *Dioscorea*, particularly *D. alata*. Yams often weigh as much as 12 kg. or even more. There are also edible bulbils borne in the axils of leaves. Yams are cultivated in all tropical countries (particularly in tropical America) to a greater or lesser extent. Good varieties, when cooked, are tasty and nutritious. They also form a good feed for livestock. They may be ground into flour. *Dioscorea* plants are large twiners, and are easily propagated by means of the bulbils or portions of tubers.

(D) OIL-SEEDS

There are several species of plants yielding oils—edible and industrial—in high percentages. India holds a prominent position in the world market in oil seeds. Oil-yielding plants occupy about 8% of the total cropped area in India and production is rising every year.

1. Groundnut oil. This is obtained from the seeds of *Arachis hypogaea* (family *Papilionaceae*), the yield of oil being 43-46%. Pods develop underground (see FIG. III/49). Groundnut cultivation is now a major agricultural operation in India and occupies the largest area in the world. Tamil Nadu, Andhra, Gujarat (leading in production), Maharashtra, Madhya Pradesh, Punjab and Rajasthan are the principal areas for its cultivation. The average annual yield of pods per hectare is 719 kg., more with some varieties, and the total production is about 18.28 million tonnes. The nuts are nutritious, containing 31% protein. Groundnut proteins are easily assimilated and taste nice. They may supplement milk. The nuts also contain Ca, P and vitamin B. They are eaten raw, fried or roasted, and used in some confectioneries. However, groundnut is cultivated mainly for its edible oil, which is used extensively in cooking. The principal commercial oil of the Vanaspati industry, it is often mixed with soya-bean oil to the extent of 25-30%, and also with sunflower oil. Margarine—an imitation butter— is manufactured from this oil. The oil is also used in making soap, illuminants, lubricants, paints, varnishes, and for tanning. The oil-cake is a good feed for cattle. The volume of export of groundnuts, oil and oil-cakes to France, England and Germany is quite large.

2. Gingelly or sesame oil. This is obtained from the seeds of *Sesamum indicum* (family *Pedaliaceae*), an annual herb 1 metre or so in height. It is mostly grown in Uttar Pradesh, Tamil Nadu and Karnataka. India is the largest producer of this crop. It takes $3\frac{1}{2}$ to $4\frac{1}{2}$ months to mature. The seeds yield 45-50%, or even more, non-drying edible oil. The superior quality gingelly oil is used for cooking in south India. It is also used to oil the body before bathing and as a cooling hair-oil, often perfumed. The inferior quality is usually used for lighting in villages, and also for soap making. The average annual yield of the seeds per hectare is 303 kg., and can go up to 580 kg. The oil-cake makes a good cattle feed, particularly for milch cattle.

3. Mustard oil. This is obtained from the seeds of *Brassica campestris* (family *Cruciferae*) and of a few other species of *Brassica*. Mustard is extensively grown in Uttar Pradesh, Rajasthan, Punjab, Madhya Pradesh, and to some extent in Bihar, Orissa, West Bengal and Assam. It is a winter crop of 5-6 months' duration, mostly harvested in March. The average annual yield of seeds per hectare varies according to the species, but may be taken as 903 kg. The oil content of mustard seeds average 35% or a little more. It is a non-drying edible oil, chiefly used for cooking purposes in northern India. It is also widely used as a bath oil. Mustard powder is a common condiment.

4. Coconut oil. This is obtained from the dry kernel (copra) of the seed of *Cocos nucifera* (family *Palmae*), the yield of oil being 50-60% or even more. It is a very valuable oil used for cooking, lighting, and several toilet preparations such as good quality soap, shampoo, hair-oil, cosmetics and shaving cream. It is also extensively used for making 'margarine'. The oil-cake is a valuable fattening food for cattle. Coconut trees grow luxuriantly along the sea-coasts, extending further in, and on marine islands. A healthy tree bears 60-80 coconuts a year, sometimes even 100, fruiting all the year round. The tree attains a height of 18-20 metres or even more. There are several varieties, including some dwarf ones. Kerala leads in the production of coconut, coconut oil, coir fibres and excellent coir goods.

5. Castor oil. This is obtained from the seeds of *Ricinus communis* (family *Euphorbiaceae*), a quick-growing perennial shrub. It is widely cultivated as an annual crop in Tamil Nadu and Karnataka, and, to some extent, in Bihar and West Bengal. The crop takes 5-8 months to mature. There are two distinct varieties—one with larger seeds and the other with smaller seeds. The former yields an inferior quality of oil, usually 25-30%, while the latter yields a superior quality, usually 36-40% or above. It is a non-drying oil. The yield of seeds per hectare per year varies from 727 kg., and can go up to 1,000 kg. The plant grows well in sandy or clay loam, and also in red soil. Castor oil has a variety of uses. The oil, expressed from the smaller seeds and purified, is used as a medicine. It is a safe purgative, probably because it contains *ricinolic acid*. The oil expressed from the large seeds is widely used for lubricating machinery, particularly the rolling parts of railway carriages. It is also widely used for lighting in villages as it gives out a bright light without soot. It is the main ingredient of copal varnish. It is also used for dressing leather and skin in the tanning industry. Its other uses are soap-making and candle-making. Refined castor oil, often perfumed, is a good (light and non-sticky) cooling and refreshing hair-oil that is in common use. Castor cake is a valuable manure but not a cattle feed since it contains, *ricin*, a poisonous alkaloid. The oil, however, is free from it. ERI silk-worms are reared on castor plants. India is the largest exporter of castor seeds and castor oil. The U.S.A., however, imports castor oil mostly from Brazil and Japan, and only to some extent from India.

(E) *FRUITS*

India abounds in some excellent dessert fruits. Apart from their food value they always contain some vitamins. India's export of fruit, particularly bananas and mangoes, is fairly heavy. Although cold storage methods have not yet been developed extensively in our country for the preservation of fruit in a fresh condition, many are available out of season in the form of various preserves, either as slices or as jams, jellies, pickles, marmalades, chutneys (hot or sweet), etc.

1. **Mango** (*Mangifera indica*—family *Anacardiaceae*). This is regarded as the 'king' of fruits and its edible part is the mesocarp. India is, by far, the world's largest producer of mango (90%). Its cultivation covers an estimated area of 593,520 hectares. It is a mid-summer fruit (drupe) having over 1,000 known varieties, of which about 500 are common. Several of these are good table varieties. The superior ones range in weight from 200-600 gm. or sometimes even more. Mango is possibly the best dessert fruit, specially noted for its very pleasant taste, pulpy flesh and fine flavour, but each variety lasts only for a short time. It makes good chutney, jelly, pickle and tarts. Mango slices and expressed juice spread on plates are also dried in the sun for off-season use. The keeping quality of ripe mangoes is very poor. They are rich in vitamin A, and also contain a little B and C. Mango is considered fattening and energising, and is also a good laxative. The good varieties are propagated through 'inarching' (see FIG. III/65).

Some of the famous varieties of mango are: LANGRA, DASHERI and SAFEDA of Uttar Pradesh; LANGRA, BOMBAI, GULABKHAS, SEPIA and ZARDALU of Bihar; HIMSAGAR, MALDA, FAZLI, KOHINOOR, MOHANBHOG, GOPALBHOG (possibly the best variety) and KISHENBHOG of West Bengal: ALFONSO and PAIRI of Maharashtra; FERNANDIX of Goa; ALFONSO and KESAR of Gujarat; GULABKHAS, HIMSAGAR, KISHENBHOG, DASHERI and SIROLI of north India; SIROLI and TAIMUNSO of Punjab; BANGALORA (or TOTAPURI), BANGANAPALLI, SUBARNAREKHA, JEHANGIR and MALGOA of south India. It may be noted that Uttar Pradesh is the leading mango-producing state in India accounting for nearly one-third the total production. Bihar ranks second.

2. **Pineapple** (*Ananas comosus*—family *Bromeliaceae*). This is the fruit (sorosis), and has a very fine flavour. There are several varieties. The better ones may weigh 1 to 2 kg. and specially large ones (e.g. Singapore variety) may weigh up to 6 kg. or sometimes even more. Pineapple slices and juice are canned on a large scale. The juice contains 8-15% sugar, vitamins A and C, certain minerals—Ca, P and Fe, some fruit acids, and a digestive enzyme *bromelin*. The plant is a native of South America, from where it has spread to all parts of the world. It is a stout perennial herb,

which grows in the plains as well as the low hills. It prefers sandy loam with humus and some amount of lime in it, a little shade and proper drainage. It bears fruit during the rainy season. The plant is propagated through suckers and crowns (see FIG. III/62).

3. **Banana** (*Musa paradisiaca*—family *Musaceae*). This is one of the best dessert fruits and is a berry. The plant is a tall, robust herb, cultivated in most parts of India. It covers an estimated area of 325,700 hectares. The yield of fruit (good varieties) per hectare per year may be 18.60 tonnes. It bears a single, large spadix. The stout scape is cooked and eaten. The ripe fruits are sweet, soft, of a pleasant flavour, nutritious and easily digestible. They make good laxatives. The per capita consumption of this highly nutritious fruit in India is, however, only 58 kg., as compared to 275 kg. or more in other tropical countries. There are 200 varieties, each with its own characteristic taste, size and flavour. Bananas are available throughout the year, specially during the rainy season. They are also used in various sweet preparations. The fruit contains about 20% sugar (but no starch), about 4.7% protein, and vitamins A, B, C, as well as D and E. It is also rich in K, Ca, Fe and P. The green fruit of plantain (*M. sapientum*) is used only as a vegetable. Musa plants are propagated through suckers. The volume of exports of bananas from India is small, Latin America and Jamaica have practically monopolised the European markets.

4. **Orange** (*Citrus reticulata*—family *Rutaceae*). This is a winter fruit (hesperidium)—very juicy, tasty and stomachic. The juice contains citric acid and is rich in vitamin C. The plant is a much-branched, large shrub. It begins to bear fruit within five years of planting. A healthy plant, ten years or so old, often bears 300 to 400 fruits, often more, and presents a spectacular sight. The keeping quality of the ripe fruit is very poor, and a good quantity sheds and is wasted. Orange plantations thrive at low altitudes on hill slopes, with plenty of lime and phosphate in the soil. The climate, too, is an important factor. Assam, West Bengal, Madhya Pradesh, Delhi, Punjab, Madras, Coorg and

Hyderabad are important centres of orange culti-vation in India. Rajasthan is famous for cultivation of sweet orange (*C. sinensis*—MALTA). There are many species and varieties (see p. 555). Good vari-eties are mostly propagated through bud grafting (see FIG. III/66) on a hardy variety, or by gootee (see FIG. III/64). Orange juice contains citric acid (1-2%) and sugar (5-10%), and is rich in vitamin C. Besides, an essential oil is obtained from the peel, as well as bergamot oil (a perfume) from the flow-ers and the peel. Marmalade (a jam) is prepared from the skin and pulp of sour varieties.

5. **Papaw** (*Carica papaya*—family *Caricaceae*). This is a pulpy fruit (berry). It is an excellent dessert fruit—delicious, cooling and refreshing. It serves as a good digestive and laxa-tive too. It contains vitamins A and C. The green fruit is used as a vegetable. The latex obtained from it contains *papain*, a digestive enzyme. The fruit, ripe or green, is available throughout the year, particularly during the rainy season. Some good varieties (e.g. Ranchi variety) may bear fruits weighing up to 3 to 4 kg., particularly when some of the young green fruits are removed early. Each plant may bear 40 to 60 fruits. The plant is monoecious and, therefore, a few male plants in a plantation help pollination and development of large fruits. Proper manuring and watering are also a prerequisite. The plant, originally a native of America, is now extensively grown in all warm countries, including India.

(F) *SUGAR*

Cane-sugar or sucrose ($C_{12}H_{22}O_{11}$) is the main commercial sugar, used universally as a sweetener. Apart from its taste, cane-sugar is one of the best sources of energy available to man. An acre of sugarcane on an average yields more calories of energy than any other field crop covering the same area. But the per capita consumption of sugar in India is the lowest in the world—about 2.7 kg., as against 50.8 kg. in the U.K., 51.7 kg. in Australia, and 58 kg. in Denmark. The per capita consump-tion of GUR (jaggery) in India is about 10 kg. The sugar industry is India's second largest industry next only to textiles. There are two main sources of supply of sugar in the world—sugarcane

in tropical countries and sugar-beet in temperate countries. Maple (*Acer saccharum*) is another source, mostly in the U.S.A. In India, sugar is also obtained from various sugar-palms, mainly in the form of GUR (jaggery).

1. **Sugarcane** (*Saccharum officinarum*—family *Gramineae*). This is a tall, reed-like grass—2.5 to 4 metres or sometimes more in height. It has been in cultivation in India since 300 B.C., possibly much earlier. There are several varieties grown all over India. The major sugarcane-producer states in India are, however, Karnataka, Tamil Nadu, Bihar, Uttar Pradesh and Maharashtra. The plant takes 12 to 20 months to mature. It is propagated through stem cuttings, and the rootstock continues to grow after this operation. The majority of sugar facto-ries are located in Uttar Pradesh and Bihar. India is the largest sugar producing country in the world. Some improved varieties of sugarcane evolved by the Sugarcane Research Station at Coimbatore are now being cultivated extensively in India to feed the numerous sugar mills. Nearly 55% of the national yield of sugarcane is used for making GUR (jaggery) and KHANDSARI (unrefined sugar). These are cottage industries. Aapproximately 25% or a little more is used in mills for the manufacture of white sugar. A small percentage is used for chew-ing. Although India is the largest cane-growing country in the world, the varieties of cane com-monly grown and the yield are the poorest. The average annual yield per hectare in India is nearly 65.83 tonnes, which is much less than that of other cane-growing countries (Java, Hawaii, etc.). The highest yield of nearly 88 tonnes is from Karnataka. Proper irrigation and the use of fertiliz-ers are important factors in the cultivation of sug-arcane. The plants are susceptible to many diseases, particularly 'red rot', caused by *Colleto-trichum*, and to attacks of borers. Although sugar-cane contains 10-15% sugar (18-20% in rich canes and 13% on an average), the actual recovery of sugar from the cane in Indian sugar mills is only about 10%. On an average, 9.5 to 10 tonnes of Indian sugarcane yield one tonne of sugar, where-as in other countries, 8 to 9 tonnes yield one tonne. The average production of sugar in an Indian mill is much less than in other countries (Cuba, Egypt,

etc.). Evidently, there are many uneconomic sugar mills in India.

Manufacturing Process of Cane-sugar. Sugar is not really manufactured in mills, but is extracted from the juicy pith of the stem, crystallised in mills and refined in refineries. The process consists of the following stages (1) **Juice Extraction : Milling.** The cane, cut into short lengths by revolving knives, is passed through a series of rollers to crush and release the juice. It is then strained through perforated metal-sheet strainers to remove the *bagasse* (crushed stalks of sugarcane). The juice thus obtained is turbid and contains many suspended particles. It is acidic (pH 5.1-5.7) in reaction. It is then sent to the boiling house, where the extracted juice is first boiled. (2) **Clarification.** Lime (and sometimes also phosphoric acid) is added continuously to the juice in amounts sufficient to raise the pH to 7 or slightly higher. The juice is then pumped through high-velocity juice-heaters. Impurities are mostly precipitated, and are removed in 'clarifiers'. The clarified juice is bright yellow. The sediment, called press mud, is used as a fertilizer. (3) **Concentration.** The clarified juice is pumped continuously into a multiple-effect evaporator, where it is concentrated into a clear, pale-yellow syrup with soluble solid contents (to the extent of 55-64%). It is then boiled in a single-effect vacuum pan and concentrated further. This operation is carried out in batches. (4) **Crystallization.** The semi-solid mass in the pan is called the *massecuite*. When the pan is full, the massecuite, still hot, is fed into high-speed centrifuges (1,500-1,800 r.p.m.). The centrifugal baskets have closely woven meshes. When the centrifuge is worked, the massecuite is separated into molasses and sugar crystals. The formation of a regular crop of crystals is controlled by an ingenious method. Under centrifugal force, the molasses pass out through the meshes, and are drained off and collected. The sugar thus obtained is still coated with a thin film of molasses. It is called brown sugar. It is widely used in confectioneries because of its special flavour. To obtain white sugar, water is added to the surface of the sugar in the form of a spray while the centrifuge is still revolving. This washes

out the brown film and white sugar is obtained. (5) **Refining.** The sugar thus formed contains 96-97.5% sucrose. The refineries then take over. The sugar is washed, melted and mixed with lime when the pH goes up to 10. The melted sugar is saturated with CO_2 and the pH brought down to 7. It is then heated and passed through charcoal filters. 'Continuous rotary pressure filters' are also used for the purpose. The previous process, described under brown sugar, is repeated and finally, the crystals are dried in a rotary drier.

Utilization of By-products. (1) The *Bagasse* is mostly used as a fuel, as well as in the manufacture of wrapping paper and cardboard. (2) *Press mud* is used on a limited scale as a manure. A good quality wax obtained from it is used as a shoe polish. (3) *Molasses* have a variety of uses, such as manufacture of alcohol, cattle feed, manure, fertilizer and curing tobacco.

2. Sugar-beet (*Beta vulgaris*—family Chenopodiaceae). This is the source of sugar in cold countries (Europe, Russia, Canada and U.S.A.). Sugar is extracted from the fleshy roots, which contain 10-20% sucrose, with an average of 13-14%. Russia is the biggest producer of sugar-beet.

(G) *SPICES AND CONDIMENTS*

Spices are certain aromatic and pungent plant products used for seasoning and flavouring food and various fruit and vegetable preserves. They are used extensively in cookery and confectionery, hot or sweet chutney, and beverages. They may be chewed, with or without betel leaf. They are also used in medicines. India is the only country in the world that produces and exports almost all kinds of spices, particularly pepper, ginger, cardamom and turmeric. India earns a lot of foreign exchange through this export.

1. Cardamom. This is the dried fruit (capsules) of *Elettaria cardamomum* (family *Zingiberaceae*). The plants are tall, perennial herbs growing in clumps from the rhizome. Cardamom cultivation is confined to the low hill of south India: the Western Ghats, Karnatak (Shimoga, Kanara, Hassan and Coorg), Kerala (the Cardamom Hills and the Annamalai Hills) a some southern districts of Tamil Nadu. The main concentration is in the Cardamom Hills. Heavy rainfall and red laterite soil are conducive to their growth. The main picking season is September to January. After picking, the forit is dried in the sun or by different artificial methods. They have a yellowish skin and enclose 15-20 black seeds. The latter contain an aromatic volatile oil—usually 4-6%. The seeds are universally used as an important spice. They also have a medicinal use, as a carminative. The average annual yield of capsules is 74 kg. per hectare. India is the largest producer of cardamom, followed by Sri Lanka, Vietnam, Cambodia and Laos.

2. Pepper. This is the dried berry of pepper wine (*Piper nigrum*—family *Piperaceae*). The dried berry forms commercial black pepper and the seeds form commercial white pepper. Kerala is the principal centre of cultivation. It is also grown in Karnataka, Tamil Nadu, Maharashtra, West Bengal and Assam. It is propagated through stem-cuttings. More or less 1 kg. of cured pepper is obtained from each pepper vine.

3. Red Pepper or **Chilli.** This is the red pod-like fruit (berry) of *Capsicum annuum*—family *Solanaceae*. Chilli is a native of tropical America and the West Indies, and was introduced into India by the Portuguese in the 17th century. The plant is a herb or undershrub, extensively cultivated in all tropical countries and in many Indian states, Maharashtra supplying the largest quantity. Chillies are stomachic, pungent, stimulating and carminative. In small doses, they help secrete of saliva and gastric juice and also induce peristaltic movement. The active ingredient responsible for the pungency is '*capsicin*', which is contained in the skin of the fruit. Chillies are used all over the world as a condiment, in raw, ripe or dried form. They are also used for flavouring curries, chutneys, salads, etc. The dried fruit is ground into a fine powder and sold as Cayenne pepper. Extracts from chillies have many pharmaceutical uses.

4. Camphor. This is obtained from the wood of *Cinnamomum camphora* (family *Lauraceae*), a tall tree of China, Japan and Formosa (Taiwan). It is planted in some gardens in India. Camphor is extracted by steam distillation from old wood cut into chips. Sometimes, as in Florida and Sri Lanka, the young twigs and leaves are used in the same way for extraction of camphor. It has a strong but agreeable odour and is widely used in very small quantities in various food preparations, perfumes and medicines. The camphor industry is practically a monopoly of Japan. Camphor is very slightly soluble in water, but readily so in alcohol and ether. It volatilizes very slowly. Synthetic (artificial) camphor is also in wide use now. It is made from pinene, a derivative of turpentine.

5. Cinnamon. This is the dried brown or dark-brown bark peeled off from the twigs of *Cinnamomum zeylanicum*, a small tree of Sri Lanka. It is grown in parts of south India and Assam, in the plains as well as in the hills. Cinnamon bark contains a volatile oil, tannin, sugar and gum. It is aromatic and tastes sweet. It is extensively used for flavouring foods, various fruit and vegetable preserves and also some sweet preparations. Cinnamon oil is extracted from the bark and the leaf. It is used in combination with certain drugs as an intestinal antiseptic.

6. Bay Leaf. This is the dried leaf of *Cinnamomum tamala*. It is a medium-sized tree that grows in many parts of India, more in the Khasi Hills. The leaves are commonly used as a spice for flavouring various kinds of curries, some sweet preparations, chutney, fruit and vegetable preserves, and often, tea infusion.

7. Nutmeg (*Myristica fragrans*). This is a big evergreen tree of the Moluccas. In India, it grows abundantly in the Western Ghats. Each female tree bears a few thousand oval fruits, each measuring 3 cm. or so in length. The fruit has a hard shell which breaks into two pieces, exposing the seed. The aril of the seed is bright red and deeply lobed, and is known as the mace commercially. The kernel of the seed is commercially known as nutmeg. The mace is aromatic and rich in a volatile oil. The mace and the kernel are important spices used all over India for seasoning and flavouring various curries and confections. It is also used in medicine. Usually, 100 seeds produce about 85 gms. of dried mace. Nutmeg contains a yellowish fat (a fixed oil) called 'nutmeg butter'. Because of its agreeable aroma, it is used in perfumes, hair lotions and ointments.

8. Cloves. These are the dried flower-buds of *Syzygium aromaticum* (family *Myrtaceae*). It is a small tree of the Moluccas, having spread from there to most tropical countries. The green colour of the flower changes to dark-brown on drying. Cloves are very aromatic and are widely used in curries, preserves and medicines. Clove oil is extracted from the unripe fruit and leaves, and is used in certain medicines, for toothaches, and also in certain toilet products. In histological work, its use as a clearing reagent is universal. Cloves are grown in the Western Ghats and in Kerala, but the production is far short of the demand. The main source of supply is Zanzibar, popularly called the 'Island of Cloves', off the east coast of Africa. The yield of dried cloves per plant (after about 20 years of growth) is approximately 2-2.5 kg. per year.

9. Ginger. This is the rhizome of *Zingiber officinale* (family *Zingiberaceae*). The plant is a small, erect, perennial herb. Ginger is considered to be the most important of all spices and condiments, and is used all over the world. It is usually used to lend fragrance and pungency to curries and various fruit and vegetable preserves. An esssential oil contained in ginger is responsible for the aroma. An oleoresin (called *gingerin*) gives it its pungent taste. Medicinally, it is stomachic, digestive and carminative.

10. Garlic (*Allium sativum*—family *Liliaceae*). This is a strong-smelling, whitish bulb, the smell being due to the presence of a sulphur-containing, volatile oil in all parts of the plant. The plant is a small, perennial herb, cultivated throughout India. Garlic is used as a condiment, particularly in fish and meat preparations, and in various fruit and vegetable preserves. It has some important medicinal properties. It is an effective remedy for high blood pressure, rheumatic and muscular pain, giddiness and sore eyes. It is digestive and carminative, and removes pain in the bowels. It heals intestinal and stomach ulcers, and is in fact regarded as Nature's best antiseptic for the alimentary canal. It is highly efficacious in cases of torpid liver and dyspepsia. It is also a good tonic for the lungs.

(H) *MEDICINAL (DRUG) PLANTS*

India's forests abound in medicinal herbs, shrubs and trees. It is estimated that they number over 4,000 species. Of them, 2,500 to 3,000 species are in general use in some form or other. The eastern and western Himalayas and the Nilgiris are known to be the natural abodes of many such plants. A good number of them are now cultivated in various states on an experimental as well as commercial basis. The Central Drug Research Institute in Lucknow has been doing research work on indigenous medicinal plants. The Tropical School of Medicine in Calcutta has also done a good amount of work in this direction, and so have some of the big pharmaceutical concerns. The Medicinal Plants Committee of West Bengal undertook experimental cultivation of certain very valuable medicinal plants at Rongpo in Darjeeling district, with very encouraging results. Some of these plants are ipecac (*Psychotria*), *Digitalis*, *Rauwolfia*, and *Erythroxylum* (cocaine-yielding). Some rare species of *Podophyllum* (for cancer), *Securinega* (for poliomyelitis), *Securigera* (for general debility), *Aralia* (for vigour), etc., have also been introduced.

1. Ipecac (*Psychotria ipecacuanha*—family *Rubiaceae*). This is a herb with closely annulated roots, cultivated at Mungpo (Darjeeling) and in the Khasi Hills. The roots taste bitter and contains 3 or 4 alkaloids, to the extent of 2-3%. Of these, *emetine* is the most important. Earlier, the powdered ipecac root was used in small doses to treat amoebic dysentery. It stimulates the liver, helping secretion of gastric juice, but also produces local irritation. Emetine also makes the heart weak and slow, and lowers the blood pressure. Now emetine hydrochloride is injected for the treatment of amoebic dysentery. Emetine is a highly poisonous drug.

2. Rauwolfia (*Rauwolfia serpentina*—family *Apocynaceae*). This is an evergreen, perennial undershrub found growing extensively in the tropical Himalayas, Assam and the Western Ghats, and to some extent in West Bengal, Orissa and

Bihar. The plant has been named after Leonard Rauwolf, a German botanist of the 16th century. The rauwolfia drug is extensively used all over the world for its hypnotic and sedative properties. It is used in the treatment of insomnia, mental imbalance and insanity. It also has the property of reducing high blood pressure. The roots are cleaned, dried in the sun and then powdered. The powder is strained through a piece of muslin and administered in appropriate doses. It has a bitter taste. It is now known that the dried roots of *Rauwolfia* contain five alkaloids, to the extent of 0.5%. Of them, *serpentine*, *serpentinine* and *rauwolfine* are most powerful. It is on record that the properties of *Rauwolfia* were known to Ayurvedic physicians in ancient India, nearly 3,000 years ago.

3. Nux-vomica (*Strychnos nux-vomica*—family *Loganiaceae*). This is a very valuable drug. The plant is a handsome tree that grows almost throughout tropical India, specially in the Deccan and on the west coast. The seeds, intensely bitter and extremely poisonous, contain a very important alkaloid, *strychnine* (and also another alkaloid, *brucine*), to the extent of 0.5-1.2%. Strychnine is an effective stomachic, a tonic and a stimulant in, of course, very minute doses. It increases secretion of gastric juices, sharpens the appetite and promotes digestion. It helps peristaltic movement of the intestines. It is also used in the treatment of nervous disorders. It increases mental alertness, field of vision and capacity for muscular work. It is also effective in the treatment of paralysis.

4. Cinchona. This is the famous quinine-yielding plant. The bark of the plant (unknown for a long time) was in use as a febrifuge in South America till the late 19th century. The plant yielding this bark was discovered in Peru as late as 1739 by La Condamine. In 1742, Linnaeus named it *Cinchona* after the Countess of Chinchon, wife of a Spanish viceroy in Peru. He was cured of an attack of malarial fever by the use of its bark in 1638. Thereafter, the Jesuits popularized its use. From then on, it was popularly known as 'Countess bark' or 'Jesuit's bark', and also 'Peruvian bark'. In 1858, Markham was deputed by the Secretary of State for India to explore the forests of Peru in search of this plant. After a long, laborious and hazardous journey through dense forests, Markham collected as many as 529 living plants and a quantity of seeds. The small stock that could stand the journey was sent to Kew Gardens, London, in 1861 and some seeds were brought to India. In the meantime, Dr. Anderson, the then Superintendent of the Royal Botanical Gardens, Calcutta, was sent to Jáva and he brought back with him 412 plants and a quantity of seeds. The whole lot was sent in 1861 to Ootacamund in the Nilgiri Hills, where the plants grew luxuriantly. He brought 193 plants from Ootacamund to Calcutta in 1862, but the plantation did not prove to be a success in the plains. So the whole stock was removed to Darjeeling district, where the plantation was finally established in 1864. Dr. Anderson unfortunately died of malarial fever. The work was entrusted to his successor, Dr. King, who made the plantation and the manufacture of quinine a commercial success.

Species. Of about 40 species of *Cinchona* (family *Rubiaceae*), the quinine-yielding ones commonly cultivated are *C. ledgeriana* (yellow bark), *C. officinalis* (brown bark), *C. cordifolia*, *C. succirubra* (red bark), in addition to several varieties and hybrids. Cinchona plants are low trees (6-15 metres high) and prefer cool climate and well-drained soil, as in hill slopes.

Collection of Bark. There are various methods of harvesting the bark—thinning of plantation, uprooting, lopping off branches, coppicing and shaving. There is a rich formation of quinine and other alkaloids in the bark of the root and the stem, 30 cm. below and above the ground, more in the former than in the latter. It gradually decreases and disappears higher up or farther down. The bark is stripped off and dried in the sun or in a drying shed during the rainy season.

Chemistry of Bark. It was in 1820 that quinine was first extracted. About the middle of the century, several alkaloids, particularly quinine, quinidine, cinchonine, cinchonidine, and an amorphous alkaloid were recognized in the bark. In 1888, about 136 kg. of quinine was manufactured for the first time. A crude preparation of the bark powder was used prior to this, under the name 'cinchona febrifuge'. Java bark is the richest in alkaloid contents and over 90% of the world output comes from Java plantations. Bengal bark and Madras bark are rather poor in this respect. The following is an analysis of Bengal bark.

	Quinine	Other alkaloids	Quinine sulphate
C. Ledgeriana	5.49%	2.03%	7.38%
C. officinalis	2.77%	2.62%	3.72%
C. succirubra	1.92%	4.13%	2.75%

All the bark collected in India used to be shipped to Europe for extraction of quinine, the manufactured product subsequently imported back. Around 1875, two factories were established in India—one at Mungpo in Darjeeling district and another at Naduvattam in the Nilgiris.

Manufacture of Quinine. (1) Grinding. This is done by a disintegrator (a heavy circular iron casing) fitted with heavy iron bars, which are made to spin with a tremendous force—2,500 revolutions per minute. The powdered bark is then strained through a fine piece of silk in contact with a spirally wound brush. (2) **Extraction.** 136-227 kg. of powdered bark put into each of the several rows of cylindrical iron vats, called *digestors*, fitted with a spirally-coiled steam-pipe, an oil-pipe and a water-pipe, and a mechanical stirrer. About 900 litres of 20% caustic soda are added to each vat. After continued sitrring and heating for about $3\frac{1}{2}$ hours, the oil released is seen to float, taking up all the alkaloids. It is then skimmed off. Dilute sulphuric acid is added to the alkaloid-bearing oil and the mixture is agitated by jets of steam. This treatment induces the oil to give up the alkaloids to the acid solution. (3) **Purification.** The acid liquor is neutralized with caustic soda solution and poured into long troughs, where the quinine sulphate partially crystallizes out in two days' time as dirty-looking greyish pulp. This is poured into a centrifugal separator, which is a cylindrical copper-gauze basket lined with a piece of calico. The basket is made to revolve at a speed of 1,200 revolutions per minute. All the liquid is strained out. A greyish cake of crystals is left in the basket as crude quinine

sulphate with about 10% of other alkaloids. This is dissolved in boiling water. A precipitate settles and the supernatant liquor now contains practically pure quinine sulphate. It is collected and finally crystallized. The crystals are dried in a drying room. The precipitate forms 'cinchona febrifuge', which is not much in demand these days.

5. Aconite (*Aconitum*—family *Ranunculaceae*). *Aconitum napellus* is the European aconite, while *A. ferox* is the Indian aconite. *Aconitum ferox* is an erect perennial herb, growing wild in the sub-alpine eastern Himalayas. The plant is highly poisonous. Its tuberous roots contain a few alkaloids, of which *aconitine* is the chief active one. Aconite relieves pain in cases of sciatica, neuralgia, rheumatism and inflamed joints. It is used as a tonic, febrifuge, antiperiodic and sedative. It is a highly poisonous drug.

6. Deadly Nightshade (*Atropa belladonna*—family *Solanaceae*). This is a short erect herb, growing wild in the temperate western Himalayas. It is also cultivated as a medicinal plant. The leaves are collected when the plant is in the flowering stage, and dried. The dried leaves contain *atropine* and two other alkaloids to the extent of 0.3%. All parts of the plant are narcotic and poisonous. Atropine is the basis of the drug, *belladonna*, which is used to relieve pain in neuralgia and inflammation of muscles, palpitation of the heart and pain of the cardiac muscles. It has also proved to be very useful in spasms due to bronchitis, asthma and whooping cough, and in spasms of the involuntary muscles. Atropine gives great relief in all such cases. It is an excellent remedy for night sweats, as in phthisis, and is an antidote to certain types of poisoning. Atropine is used to dilate the pupil of the eye in order to facilitate examination.

7. Poppy (*Papaver somniferum*—family *Papaveraceae*). This grows wild in the Himalayas and is also cultivated in Bihar and Uttar Pradesh.

It yields a narcotic drug, which is the latex obtained by incising the unripe capsules. The latex is dried and made into balls or flattened masses, which form the commercial *opium*. Opium contains about 9.5% *morphine*, as well as a number of other alkaloids. Opium and morphine relieve pain and induce sleep. Opium relieves intestinal pain and cures diarrhoea and dysentery, but it reduces the appetite and retards digestion. It removes sensations like hunger, coughing and fatigue. With large doses, the central nervous system becomes depressed. Opium is sedative, astringent and anodyne. The action of morphine is always more definite and less harmful than that of opium. The use of opium in regulated doses is regarded as a panacea for all physical ailments in old age. China is the world's biggest producer of poppy.

(I) *BEVERAGES*

Beverages are mild, agreeable and stimulating liquors meant for drinking. Tea, coffee and cocoa are examples of non-alcoholic beverages.

1. Tea. Tea is the dried and prepared leaves and buds of *Thea* (=*Camellia*) *assamica* and *T. sinensis*, as well as several hybrids of the family *Theaceae*. Tea infusion is now a universal drink. But from the tea garden to the tea cup there is a long history. Tea plants are kept bushy by regular pruning. If left to themselves, they grow to the size of small trees and live for 80-100 years.

A Short History. The plant growing wild and uncultivated was first discovered in north-east Assam by Charles Alexander Bruce, an army man, in 1826. He collected seeds and plants and sent them to the Royal (now Indian) Botanical Gardens near Calcutta. They were grown with success and found to be real tea plants, although distinct from the Chinese species. A tea committee was appointed by Lord Willam Bentinck in 1834 to enquire into the possibility of profitable cultivation of tea plants in India. The committee considered the discovery of tea plants in Assam of far-reaching importance, and strongly recommended their cultivation in Assam and elsewhere in India, particularly because China had monopolized the world tea trade till then. Tea nurseries were immediately established by the Government in Upper Assam, and seeds and plants were also sent to Darjeeling, Dehra Dun, Kangra Valley and the Nilgiri Hills. In 1835, seeds and plants were also obtained from China and in 1836, the first tea garden was started in Upper Assam by Bruce. By 1838, a marketable quantity of tea was produced in Assam. This was sent to England, where it sold for 16-36 shillings per pound. In 1839, the Assam (Tea) Company was floated in England with a capital of £ 500,000. About ten estates were actually growing tea in an area of 1,700 acres by 1859. By this time, tea cultivation was established in Assam, north Bengal and south India (Kerala, Mysore and the Nilgiri Hills). The first public auction of tea was started in 1861. By 1874, there were 11,680 acres of land under tea cultivation. The Indian Tea Association was formed in Calcutta in 1881. Later, it shifted in 1911 to its headquarters at the Tocklai Experimental Station in Jorhat (Assam) for better reseach facilities.

India is the world's major tea-growing country, with over 10,000 gardens, big and small. The principal tea-growing states are Assam, West Bengal, Tamil Nadu and Kerala. Karnataka is a promising one. India continues to be the largest producer and exporter of tea in the world. Foreign exchange earnings on account of tea exports are second only to jute. The production of tea has been increasing annually. More than half the world's output of tea comes from India. Assam monopolises over 50% of India's output, and north Bengal a quarter. In Assam, the annual yield of tea per hectare is over 1,626 kg. (the maximum going up to 2,800 kg.), as against the all-India average of 1,683 kg. There are 750 tea gardens (excluding many small ones) in Assam (mostly in upper Assam) and 350 in West Bengal. The largest buyers of Indian tea are the United Kingdom and Russia. Other countries buying Indian tea in large quantities are the Netherlands, UAR, Germany, France, Afghanistan, Iran, Iraq, Australia, Japan and Canada. Sri Lanka and east Africa also produce and export tea.

Tea Leaves. There are different grades of

manufactured tea. The terminal bud with *two* leaves just next to it forms *fine* tea; the same with *three* leaves forms *coarse* tea. The average yield of manufactured tea in India has now gone up to 1,683 kg. per hectare per year, and 1.8 kg. of green leaves usually make 0.45 kg. of cured tea. The yield of green leaves per plant is more or less 0.9' kg. The plants grow in the plains and hills, up to an altitude of over 2,100 metres. Better tea always grows at higher altitudes. These plants flourish in localities with abundant rainfall. Darjeeling tea is considered to be the world's best quality tea for its very agreeable flavour. But the production of Darjeeling tea per hectare as a whole is very low. Annual pruning after plucking (and the same operation even after the second year of planting) is a very important practice, helping the plant to 'flush' profusely. Regular picking of leaves usually begins from the 7th year, sometimes earlier. The economic utility of tea bushes continues for 50-70 years. Proper irrigation and adequate manuring are required to increase the yield. Chemical fertilizer, like sulphate of ammonia at the rate of 110 kg. per hectare, green manure (growing certain leguminous plants like *Tephrosia*, *Derris*, *Sesbania*, *Cajanus*, etc.), cattle manure and leaf compost are very beneficial.

Chemistry of Tea. Manufactured tea contains 4-5% tannins (catechins), which are responsible for the colour and strength of the infusion, 3.3-4.7% caffeine, which is a stimulant for the heart, a little volatile oil, which gives the tea its aroma, and about 8% resinous matter, which gives the tea infusion its reddish brown, etc. Green tea leaves contain 13-18% of tannins but a greater portion of them is converted into sugar and gallic acid during the process of manufacture. Starch is also converted into sugar during the same process. Caffeine distribution in tea leaves is as follows: 1st leaf and bud—4.7%, 2nd leaf—4.5%, 3rd leaf—3.7%, and 4th leaf—3.3%. The caffeine content is not changed during the process of manufacture. The production of caffeine from tea waste and coffee seeds at the Regional Research Laboratory at Jorhat (Assam) by a new process is under way.

Manufacturing Process. (1) **Plucking.** The quality of cured tea depends to a great extent on the standard of plucking, the proportion of desirable constituents gradually diminishing from the bud to the lower leaves. Plucking season is March to mid-December. (2) **Withering.** After weighing, the leaves are taken to the withering house and spread out thinly on bamboo racks for about 18 hours (by employing heated air, it has been possible to reduce the period to 2 to 3 hours). (3) **Rolling.** The withered leaves, sufficiently flaccid in the previous process, are passed through the rolling machine for half an hour. Rolling twists the leaves. Major chemical changes also take place in this process, and fermentation begins here. (4) **Sifting.** After the first rolling, the sifting is done. Finer meal is taken to the fermentation room, while a second rolling is done with a coarser portion. (5) **Fermentation.** The sifted leaves are spread on the floor of the fermentation room, where the temperature is maintained at 27°C. or so for 3 or 4 hours. The flavour and colour develop during fermentation (actually enzymic oxidation, not bacterial). (6) **Firing.** This usually takes place in two stages—the fisrt one at 93°C. and the second at 82°C. Firing reduces the moisture content to 3-4%, thus ensuring better keeping quality. Firing also arrests further fermentation, and the quality of tea improves further by this process. This is *black tea. Green tea* (largely used in China and Japan) is unfermented tea made by steaming the leaves, then rolling and drying them immediately. It tastes bitter but its use is on the increase because it is known to definitely lower the cholesterol level and prevent heart attacks. The best green tea in India is manufactured in upper Assam and north Bengal, and to some extent in Himachal Pradesh (Kangra Valley) and Uttar Pradesh. It is exported mostly to Afghanistan and some other countries Steps are being taken to produce more green tea in India for bigger export. (7) **Sorting and Grading.** The fired tea is then sorted into grades by automatic devices. Finally, it is packed into plywood chests (specially made for the purpose) for marketing.

2. Coffee. Coffee is a favourite drink in south India, and has become popular all over India. It is regarded as a refreshing drink. Seeds of *Coffea arabica* and *C. robusta* (family *Rubiaceae*), particularly the former, are the sources of coffee. Over 70% of the coffee plantations in India grow *C. arabica*. It is noted for its quality and has already become popular, while *C. robusta* yields more and is resistant to pests and diseases. The seeds are roasted to a desired brown colour and then powdered. The aroma of coffee powder develops only on proper and skilful roasting. Certain chemicals are also added for this purpose. Roasted coffee seeds contain 0.75-1.5% caffeine, several vitamins and a little volatile oil. A coffee bush, 5-6 m. high, bears many red fruit, each with two seeds, and usually yields 0.45-0.9 kg. of cured coffee. It prefers hill slopes with abundant rainfall. The major coffee plantations are in the low hills of south India—Karnataka (particularly Coorg), Kerala and Tamil Nadu. It is also cultivated on a smaller scale in Bihar and Orissa. In Assam, coffee plantation, started in 1954 in the Mikir Hills and North Cachar Hills, has proved to be a success. India's coffee production has now gone up tremendously. More than half this quantity is exported, while the balance is consumed internally. India ranks third in the world in coffee production. The coffee plant, a native of Abyssinia, was first introduced into India by a Muslim pilgrim more than 250 years ago. Regular cultivation of coffee, however, dates back to 1830. Brazil and Kenya are the world's largest suppliers of coffee. America consumes the largest quantity of coffee, well over half the world's supply.

3. Cocoa. Cocoa makes a refreshing and nourishing drink. It is prepared from the seeds of *Theobroma cacao* (family *Sterculiaceae*), a native of tropical America. It is a small tree cultivated more or less extensively in tropical America, the West Indies, Brazil, Ghana and Kenya. The world's supply comes mainly from Brazil, Kenya and Ghana (Ghana supplying the largest quantity). Cocoa is also cultivated in Java and Sri Lanka. Each tree usually bears 70 to 80 fruits, each measuring 15-22 x 7-10 cm. and bearing numerous seeds. The fruit is cut or broken open and the seed dried, roasted and powered. In addition to its use as a drink, cocoa powder is used in making chocolate together with certain ingredients, such as sugar, spices and sometimes milk (milk choco-

late). Considering its protein and fat content, cocoa is also a food. Cocoa seeds contain theobromine and caffeine (1% or less), proteins (15%), starch (15%) and fatty oil (30-50%). On an average, 50 pods with about 30 good seeds each yield over 1 kg. of cured cocoa. Cocoa-butter, an opaque solid oil expressed from warmed seeds, is used in medicine.

(J) *TIMBER TREES*

Timber is the wood (heartwood) used for various building purposes: houses, boats, bridges, ships, etc. It is also used for making furniture, packing boxes, matchsticks, boxes, plywood tea chests, flush doors, partitions, walls, ceilings, shelves, cabinets, prefabricated houses, commercial boards, parts of railway sleepers, etc. In addition, wood chips and shavings are used for making compressed wood, which is in demand for panelled doors, table tops, room partitions, hard blocks, etc. Timber and firewood (fuel), together with many useful forest products, constitute the forest wealth of a country. To be self-sufficient in these, a country should normally have about one-third of the total land area under forests. India, with only 22.7%, lags behind other countries. We consume 240 million cubic metres of wood as fuel every year, and over 200 million cubic metres as timber. According to an estimate, India has already lost nearly 5 million hectares of virgin forests over the past 25 years. At the present rate of deforestation, we will be less and less capable to meet our need for wood. Systematic afforestation is the only means of maintaining a balance between loss and gain. Madhya Pradesh has the largest forest area, while Assam occupies the second place. There are about 75 species of timber trees in Indian forests. The quality of timber depends on its heat, moisture and susceptibility to insect attacks, workability, grains, colour, porosity and capacity to take polish and varnish.

1. Teak (*Tectona grandis*—family *Verbenaceae*). This is the famous timber of the Deccan Plateau, Madras, Kerala, Maharashtra, Bihar and Orissa. It is also grown successfully in Assam. The tree is about 36 metres high. Teak yields a very valuable light golden-brown timber with straight grains. The wood is hard, strong, moderately heavy (720 kg. per cu.m.) and extremely durable, being immune to insect and fungal attacks owing to the presence of an oil and a resinous matter. It does not warp, shrink or expand. This timber is used for making handsome furniture of various designs. It is also used extensively for doors, windows, beams, rafters, staircases and the like as well as in carving. Teak is, however, a very costly wood. Burma (Myanmar) teak is the best. The Deccan Plateau produces the best Indian teak.

2. Indian Redwood (*Dalbergia sissoo*—family *Papilionaceae*). This is a tree of the sub-Himalayan forests extending from Assam to Punjab. It is a very valuable timber with fine to medium grains. It is golden-brown to dark brown. It is hard (harder than teak), strong, very durable and moderately heavy (800-850 kg. per cu.m.). It makes handsome furniture. It is easy to work, takes polish well, and is least susceptible to white ants and borers. This timber is also used for posts, rafters and boards. It makes durable carts, coaches and boats. The wood is widely used for carving.

3. Sal (*Shorea robusta*—family *Dipterocarpaceae*). This is a very valuable timber tree, growing to a height of 20-25 metres, often even 30 metres or more. The SAL tract stretches along the sub-Himalayan region from Assam to Punjab. Tracts of SAL also occur in Madhya Pradesh, Bihar, Orissa and Andhra. The timber is very hard, strong, heavy (900 kg. per cu. m.) and very durable even under water. It is used extensively in the making of railway sleepers, houses, bridges and piles. Posts, rafters, planks, door and window-frames, etc. are made with it. It is also used for the hubs of wheels and bottoms of carts and carriages. It stands heat and water well. *Shorea assamica* of upper Assam and Nagaland is not very durable, but has a variety of other uses. It is suitable for doors, windows, planking and tea chests, and makes good plywood.

4. Jarul (*Lagerstroemia speciosa* = *L. flos-reginae*—family *Lythraceae*). This is a good timber tree common throughout India, particularly in Assam and the west coast. It grows mainly along the banks of rivers and is also cultivated for its ornamental mauve-purple flowers. The timber is hard, durable (even under water), straight-grained and takes a good polish. The wood is light to moderately heavy (640 kg. per cu. m.) and pale red. It is used in making houses, boats, furniture, carts, posts, bridge-piles and bridges. It is also good for general uses.

5. Mahogany (*Swietenia mahagoni*—family *Meliaceae*). This is an evergreen tall tree (18-21 metres high, sometimes even 30 metres). It is a valuable timber tree. Mahogany is an indigenous tree of Central America. In India, it grows in the Deccan Plateau. It is also planted in gardens and forests, and often along roads. The wood is very hard and durable, coarse-grained and takes a good polish. It is dark reddish-brown. It is used for making furniture, boats, ships, caskets and the body of some musical instruments.

6. Pines (*Pinus longifolia* and *P. khasya*—family *Abietaceae*). These are evergreen, tall, straight, coniferous trees. They attain a height of 30-45 metres, and grow abundantly and gregariously at altitudes ranging between 900 to 1,900 metres, or even higher. *Pinus khasya* grows in the Khasi Hills and *P. longifolia* in the western Himalayas. The wood is light (530-610 kg. per cu. m.), moderately hard, easy to work, white to pale brown, with straight but uneven grains, and many dark-coloured resin-ducts and large knots. It is odorous. It seasons well and takes a fairly good polish, and is durable if not exposed. Pine is used extensively in the hills for house-building and furniture-making, and for packing cases. The timber is not susceptible to attacks by white ants.

7. Deodar (*Cedrus deodara*—family *Abietaceae*). This is an evergreen, elegant-looking, cone-shaped, coniferous tree, which can attain a height of 30-60 metres. It grows at altitudes of 1,800 to 2,500 metres. It is a well-known timber tree of the western Himalayas and grows in abundance in Kashmir. The wood is light (560 kg. per cu. m.), moderately hard, extremely durable and seasons well. It is yellowish-brown and odorous. It is easy to work and finishes well, but is not suitable for fine work because of the continuous oozing of resin. On proper treatment, this timber is used for making sleepers, house (beams, rafters and flooring), bridges and light furniture. It is almost immune to white ants. The wood is a source of deodar oil.

Some Common and Useful Timber Trees of Assam. In addition to SAL, AJAR or JARUL, SISSOO and teak, the following may be mentioned: (1) BONSUM (*Phoebe attenuata* and *P. goalparensis*—family *Lauraceae*)—timber very valuable, used extensively for furniture, planks, doors, and windows; (2) GAMHAR (*Gmelina arborea*—family *Verbenaceae*)—wood strong and durable, a good timber for furniture, doors and windows; (3) POMA or toon (*Cedrela toona*—family *Meliaceae*)—wood soft but used for furniture, doors and windows, carriages, tea chests and panelling; (4) BOGA-POMA (*Chickrassia tabularis*—family *Meliaceae*)—wood hard, suitable for planking and furniture; (5) AMARI (*Amoora wallichii*—family *Meliaceae*)—wood hard, used for furniture, doors and windows; (6) LALI (*Dysoxylum procerum*—family *Meliaceae*)—wood bright red, moderately hard, used for doors and windows; (7) GONSOROI (*Cinnamomum glanduliferum*—family *Lauraceae*)—wood soft but durable, scented, it makes fairly strong furniture, cupboards and boxes and is somewhat better than POMA; (8) KHOKAN (*Duabanga sonneratioides*—family *Lythraceae*)—wood soft, used for cheap furniture, suitable for plywood; (9) TITASOPA (*Michelia champaca* and *Talauma phellocarpa*—family *Magnoliaceae*)—wood light but durable, used for furniture; (10) NAHOR (*Mesua ferrea*—family *Guttiferae*)—wood very hard and heavy, used for posts, beams, bridge-piles and railway sleepers.

(K) *FIBRES*

Fibres are thread-like tissues obtained from different parts of the plant body. They are mostly made of sclerenchymatous cells, strongly lignified and thickened. Cotton fibres are, however, made of cellulose. Commercial vegetable fibres may be classified into (*a*) floss fibres or lint, which are the hairy outgrowths of the seed, e.g. cotton, silk-cotton and madar; (*b*) bast fibres, which are the sclerenchymatous tissues of the secondary phloem or bast, e.g. jute, hemp and rhea; (*c*) coir fibres, which are the fibrous husk of the coconut fruit; and (*d*) leaf fibres, which are the sclerenchymatous tissues of the leaf, e.g. bowstring hemp (*Sansevieria*) and American aloe (*Agave*). The quality of the fibres depends on their length, strength, fineness, lustre, reaction to high temperature and water, etc.

1. **Cotton** (*Gossypium sp.*; see p. 533; family *Malvaceae*). This is the most important commercial textile fibre, spun into yarn and woven into various kinds of garments, screens, sheets, canopies, sails, carpets, etc. Cotton fibres are also used for making ropes, twines and threads. Raw cotton is used for stuffing pillows and cushions. Mercerized cotton (treated with caustic soda) is used for finer garments. Pure cotton, properly treated, is used for surgical bandages. Cotton thread is universally used for sewing and stitching. Cotton cultivation and weaving cloth date as far back as 1,800 B.C. The quality of cotton fibres is judged by their length, strength, fineness and silkiness. Indian cottons are poor in respect of length, having a short staple—12.7-25.4 mm. *G. indicum* and Upland American cotton (*G. hirsutum*) have a lint length of 25.4 mm. while of those of Egyptian cotton (*G. peruvianum*) and American cotton (sea island cotton—*G. barbadense*) are 31.7-38 mm. and 38-50.8 mm., respectively. Upland American cotton, naturalized in India, is cultivated extensively in India. *G. arboreum*, a perennial tree cotton, is grown at places in India, while *G. herbaceum,* an annual shrub, has been grown in India from time immemorial. Of all Indian cottons, Broach cotton (*G. herbaceum*) of Gujarat is the finest. The cultivation of long-staple foreign cottons has not yet proved to be a success in India. The Punjab Agricultural University evolved a new strain of cotton, G 27, which yields 50% more than the existing varieties. Although the total area under cotton in India is the largest in the world, its total output is far below that of other cotton-producing countries and it has not yet achieved its target production. The average annual yield of cotton lint (and not seed cotton) in India is only about 217 kg. per hectare. The percentage of lint to seed cotton usually varies from 25-30. Of the total output (9.84 bales of 170 kg. each) of cotton in India, long-staple cotton comprises only

about 7%. Thus, there is ample scope for improvement. Maharashtra, Gujarat, Madhya Pradesh, Tamil Nadu, Karnataka, Andhra, Uttar Pradesh, Punjab and Rajasthan are the important cotton-growing states of India. The indigenous cottons, like *G. herbaceum*, yield 3-10 quintals of seed-cotton per hectare per year; while Upland American cotton (*G. hirsutum*) and hybrid cottons, when properly irrigated, yield 25-30 quintals, sometimes up to 40 quintals. Black soil is most suitable for cotton cultivation. It may be noted that India's first cotton mill was established at Howrah (West Bengal) in 1832.

2. Jute (*Corchorus capsularis* and *C. olitorius*—family *Tiliaceae*). This is a very valuable bast fibre, obtained almost exclusively from the above two species. Jute is cultivated widely in the low-lying areas of West Bengal (mainly), Assam, Bihar and Orissa, and to some extent, Uttar Pradesh, Meghalaya and Tripura. The cultivation of jute in Assam has grown rapidly, so much so that it is now the leading state in jute production. There was record jute cultivation in the then Bengal (West Bengal and Bangladesh) in the early 19th century and 'of the use of fibres in making gunny bags and coarse cloth. With increasing demand for gunny bags for packing foodgrains, etc., the cultivation of jute was rapidly extended. From the middle of the 19th century, several jute mills sprang up in and around Calcutta. Bangladesh produces jute on a large scale. The plant thrives under conditions of heavy rainfall and flooding at a later stage. The sowing season is March or a little later, and the harvesting season is July-September. The fibres mature with the ripening of the fruit. After harvesting, the jute plants are retted in water for 10 to 15 days (sometimes more). The fibres are them stripped off the stalks by hand. Next, they are washed, dried in the sun and finally baled. The annual yield in India usually varies from 1887 kg. per hectare. With the extension of cultivation, the annual production of jute has gone up to 7111.7 lakh bales of 180 kg. each (West Bengal—50.033 lakh bales, Assam—7.94, Bihar—9.57, Orissa—2.77, and the rest—1.62). The Jute Research Institute at Barrackpore (near Calcutta) evolved a new type of jute plant—J.R.

524—which yields 25-32 quintals of fibres per hectare per year. Jute is India's major foreign exchange earner. Jute fibres are used extensively for making gunny bags, cheap rugs, carpets, cordage, hessian (coarse cloth), curtains, etc., but they are much less strong than hemp. The first jute mill in India to manufacture the above goods was established at Rishra (West Bengal) in 1854. There are now 69 jute mills in and around Calcutta and 1 in Assam.

3. Hemp. Hemp obtained from the GANJA plant (*Cannabis sativa*—family *Cannabinaceae*) is the true hemp. But this is an excisable plant and its cultivation is restricted. Its fibres are, however, very strong and durable. Commercial hemp is the sunn hemp or Indian hemp (*Crotalaria juncea*—*Papilionaceae*). Sunn hemp yields very strong fibres used for various kinds of cordage (ropes, twine, fishing nets, coarse sheets, tents, screens, sacks, cigarette paper, tissue paper, etc. Sunn hemp is much stronger than jute and stands water well. It is also used for making strong paper. It is cultivated on a large scale in Uttar Pradesh and also in Bihar and central India. Elsewhere it is cultivated as a green manure crop. It is a monsoon crop that requires about four months to mature. It is harvested in August-September before pod-formation, when the plants usually measure about 2.5 metres in height. The plants are cut or pulled up and steeped in water for a week or so for complete retting. The fibres are then pulled out in strips, beaten and washed in water, so that clean fibres are obtained. Sunn hemp is always grown thickly to discourage the growth of branches and to ensure tallness.

4. Rhea or **Ramie** (*Boehmeria nivea*—family *Urticaceae*). This native of China and Japan is a perennial shrub, yielding very good fibres. Its cultivation in India (since the middle of the 19th century or earlier) has remained restricted mostly to small plots worked by fishermen. However, because of its importance as a fibre crop, efforts have been made to extend its cultivation in Assam, north Bengal and Bihar. The fibres of this plant are known to be the longest, strongest, silkiest and most durable. But they do not take dye very easily. The fibres are usually spun into threads, strings, cords, ropes, belts, nets, and, more particularly, fishing lines and fishing nets. They are also woven into cloths, sails, laces, sheetings, parachutes, hose-pipes, mosquito nets, banknote paper, etc. The fibres adhere to the inner bark of the stem and, therefore, their extraction is problematic. The plant stands 3 or 4 cuttings a year from the second year, each shoot being 1.5 m. in length. The yield of dry fibres from the stem is only 2.5%. The annual yield is low compared to that of jute. Under suitable conditions, the yield may be much higher. The plant prefers rich, sandy loam in highlands. It is propagated through root-cuttings and stem-cuttings, and also through seeds.

5. Flax. This is the fibre of linseed plant (*Linum usitatissimum*—family *Linaceae*). The fibres are fine, very strong and silky, but they are rather short. They are woven into various kinds of valuable fine textiles or linen cloths, mixed or unmixed with cotton. The stem yields fibres, while the seeds yield linseed oil. The same plant cannot, however, be used for both purposes. If required for fibres, the seeds are sown thickly so that the plants may grow erect and unbranched, and the crop is also cut earlier. For extraction of fibres from the stems, the fibres are retted in water for 3 or 4 days, and then beaten on a board. This crop is raised in India mainly for oil, and the major areas of flex cultivation are in Madhya Pradesh, Uttar Pradesh, Maharashtra, Bihar and West Bengal. The stems yield about 15% fibre.

6. Coir. This is the husk fibre obtained from the dry fruit of coconut (*Cocos nucifera*—family *Palmae*). The fibres are short, coarse and rough, but very durable and resistant to water. They are used for making door mats, mattings (to cover floors), mattresses, carpets, rugs, etc. They are also used for making coarse brushes, cords and ropes, in addition to stuffing for sofas and carriage seats. Kerala leads in the production of coconut and in the manufacture of coir goods in India, being second only to the Philippines. Kerala contributes the maximum quantity for export. Other states like Mysore, Madras, Andhra, Orissa and

Maharashtra have also developed this industry. The annual production of coir fibres in India is estimated to be 130,000 tonnes. Sri Lanka is another big centre of fibre production.

(L) *RUBBER*

This is obtained from the latex of *Hevea brasiliensis* (family *Euphorbiaceae*), a big tree, which is the main source of commercial rubber. The yield starts 7 or 8 years after planting, the maximum being obtained in about the 15th year. The latex is collected by tapping the bark. It is then allowed to coagulate with the addition of water and a little acetic acid. The coagulated mass (rubber) is then separated from the liquid portion, washed and dried in the smoke-house. It is then passed through rollers and pressed into blocks, sheets, crepe, etc. Rubber is used to make tyres, tubes for the wheels of various types of vehicles, crepe soles, rubber shoes, rubber sheets, rubber tubings, beltings, insulation of electric wires and various other goods of commercial importance. Indian rubber is mostly consumed within the country itself. The majority of rubber plantations are in Kerala, the rest being in Tamil Nadu and Karnataka. The experimental rubber plantations in the Mikir Hills (Assam) and Garo Hills (Meghalaya) have yielded encouraging results. Kerala accounts for over 90% of the total Indian output. But the demand has been rising and the average annual yield of rubber is only about 1029 kg. per hectare per year. The rubber obtained from *Hevea brasiliensis* is called **para-rubber**, that from *Manihot glaziovii* **ceara-rubber**, that from *Castilloa elastica* **panama-rubber**, and that from *Ficus elastica* **india-rubber**. Synthetic rubber has come into general use. Synthetics and Chemicals Limited at Bareilly is the major unit in India.

(M) *PAPER*

The importance of paper for various essential purposes cannot be overestimated. Printing paper, writing paper, newsprint, wrapping paper, cardboard, poster paper, etc., require an enormous quantity of different grades of paper. The total production of paper in various Indian paper mills does not, however, meet the demand. Paper mills and pulp mills may be separated or both may be integrated.

An Early History. More than 5,000 years ago, the Egyptians first produced a kind of paper from paper-reed (*Cyperus papyrus*—family *Cyperaceae*), a riverside plant abundant on the banks of the Nile. The stem of this plant, split into thin strips, was pressed into stiff sheets, which were then used as a writing material. Much later, about 2,000 years ago, animal skins were specially treated in Asia Minor to make a sort of writing paper (parchment paper). Possibly around this time, the Chinese began to make paper by boiling rags, rice, straw, the bark of paper-mulberry (*Broussonetia papyrifera*) and the stems of certain plants into pulp and finally, beating the pulp into sheets. This was the beginning of the manufacture of the modern type of paper. In 751 A.D., the Arabs learned the secret of paper-making from some Chinese prisoners who were skilled paper-makers, and founded a paper mill at Baghdad. In the 9th century, paper was largely used for writing Arabic manuscripts. Within a few hundred years, the art of paper-making spread to Europe—to Spain in the 12th century, to France in the 14th century and to England in the 15th century. Paper, however, came to be used the world over some time in the middle of the 18th century. In ancient India, the foliated bark of BHURJJAPATRA (*Betula utilis*—family *Betulaceae*), which is easily separable into thin, large, white sheets, was used as a writing material. The plant grows at an altitude of 3,350-3,960 metres, both in western and the eastern Himalayas. The first paper mill was established in India in the year 1820 (see below).

Raw Material. Cellulose is the basic constituent of paper, and the raw material used for paper pulp consists of the wood of coniferous and other trees, different kinds of bamboo (*Bambusa, Melocanna, Dendrocalamus,* etc.), and various grasses like saboi (*Ischaemum*), *Imperata, Erianthus, Phragmites,* etc. Waste paper, cotton and linen rags, straws, etc. are also used in addition to bagasse (see p. 637). The fir and spruce of the Himalayas are considered very suitable for quality newsprint.

The lignin and other non-cellulose components of the raw material are removed by cooking and bleaching. It is the cellulose that finally makes paper.

Paper Mills and Production. The first paper mill in India was started at Serampore in 1820 by Dr William Carey, a missionary, but this venture ended in failure. Between 1867 and 1891, 5 paper mills were established in India—3 in West Bengal, 1 in Lucknow, and 1 in Pune. With the establishment of a large number of paper mills recently, considerable progress has been made in the production of writing and printing paper. Still, India's total annual production falls far short of the estimated demand. The position of newsprint is also far from satisfactory the total production being about 40,000 tonnes a year (or about 109 tonnes daily). The only mill for newsprint in India is at Nepanagar in Madhya Pradesh. The country's annual minimum requirement is more than 225,000 tonnes (or 616 tonnes daily) or so. A huge quantity of newsprint has to be imported, costing the country dearly in foreign exchange. It is imperative to obtain self-sufficiency in this commodity. Production at the NEPA factory has been stepped up to 75,000 tonnes. Besides, four new big projects have been taken up for the exclusive production of newsprint. It may be noted that the average *per capita* consumption of paper in India is only about 0.64 kg., while it is 68 kg. in the United Kingdom, 79 kg. in Canada and over 136 kg in the U.S.A.

Pulp-Making. The raw material cut into small chips is passed through a series of screens of various meshes to obtain uniformity of size. It is then cooked in a huge quantity of water. For chemical pulp required for different grades of paper, three processes are adopted: (*a*) *sulphate process* —sodium sulphate is used for this purpose; this method has become increasingly popular; (*b*) *soda process*—caustic soda is used in this process; and (*c*) *sulphite process*—calcium sulphite is used. Mechanical pulp is obtained by grinding the raw material and adding a sufficient quantity of water. The pulp is screened to remove undigested particles and bleached with hypochlorites, liquid chlorine, milk of lime and sodium peroxide. Rags and waste paper, when used, are first boiled with lime and caustic soda. Different grades of paper are finally made by mixing different pulps in particular proportions. Different chemicals such as rosin, paraffin, wax, alum, sodium aluminate, etc. are used to impart finish and to make it non-absorbent to liquids. The pulp is concentrated to 70% solids or even more before sending it to the mill.

Paper-Making. The de-watered pulp is passed through a series of roll-type presses. The sheet thus obtained is passed through 'driers' or heated cylinders. The dried sheet is then passed through highly polished rolls known as 'calenders' to give the paper a polished surface. To prepare good quality printing paper preventing 'show-through' or 'strike-through' and to improve whiteness, smoothness and fineness, certain materials like china clay, precipitated chalk, titanium dioxide, zinc sulphate, talc, barium sulphate, etc. called fillers are used. The forward-moving sheet, which is continuous, is wound in large rolls, and finally cut to size.

10 PALAEOBOTANY

GENERAL DESCRIPTION

Palaeobotany deals with the study of fossil plants preserved in the rocks of various geological periods. A fossil (*fossilis*, dug out) is any relic or trace of past life (plant or animal) preserved in the earth's crust during the different ages and periods of its formation. The term was formerly used to refer to anything dug out of the earth, but is now used to designate any tangible evidence of former life embedded and preserved in the earth. During the period between the cooling of the earth and modern times, the earth's crust has experienced several revolutions, involving widespread changes in its topography, viz. redistribution of land and water, elevation of submerged land, submergence of elevated land, sedimentation of fragmentary materials and organic remains at the bottom of lakes and oceans. The sediments gradually became transformed to rocks (sedimentary rocks), with the plant and animal remains in them preserved in the form of fossils.

These sedimentary rocks have been divided into different geological periods on the basis of their fossil contents (see table on p. 657). Only certain parts of plants are resistant to decay and these, when properly buried in mud and sand, get transformed to fossils in consolidated sediments, such as shales and sandstone. Pteridophytes and gymnosperms have been found in large numbers in fossil state, while bryophytes, algae and fungi which have delicate parts, are seldom encountered as fossils. Palaeontology, which deals with plant and animal fossils, gives us a glimpse of the occurrence and nature of ancient life—flora and fauna—in past geological ages. It tells us precisely about the period of the earth's history when particular types of plants and animals came into existence, flourished and became extinct, and also their geographical extent. The study of fossils is, thus, of utmost importance in tracing the evolutionary sequence of flora and fauna—appearing, disappearing, and giving rise to more organized forms in successive stages. Palaeontology is directly correlated with the stratigraphy of the earth, i.e. the formation of the earth's strata in the different periods. It has, therefore, been possible to determine the age of the particular strata from the occurrence of fossils in them. The carbon-dating method is used to fix the age of the fossil. Fossils also tell us about the extent of land, lakes and seas in the past ages. This is how it has come to be known that a vast sea called Tethys existed in the region of the present-day Himalayas[1], possibly

---

It may be noted that Birbal Sahni (1891-1949), a student of A.C. Seward, renowned palaeobotanist of Cambridge, was the fountain-head of palaeobotanical work in India. Great advances were made by him in this field of research during the years 1932-48. The Birbal Sahni Institute of Palaeobotany at Lucknow, established by him in 1946, is the centre of palaeobotanical research in this country. Sahni died in 1949, leaving behind a number of enthusiastic workers to continue the work at this Institute. It may further be noted in this connection that the important fossiliferous regions of India lie in Assam, Bihar, Gujarat, South India and Kashmir, which evidently require further exploration.

[1] It may be noted that the upheaval of the Himalayas in the region of the Tethys took place in two phases—one in the Oligocene (about 35 million years ago) age and another in the Pliocene (about 12 million years ago) age—evidently very young in the geological time scale.

with some land bridges across this sea.

Palaeontology has its economic application in the exploration of minerals, specially coal, occurring in freshwater sedimentary formations (Carboniferous), and oil (petroleum) possibly derived from marine, planktonic flora and fauna (in the Eocene age). It is known that an ancient (carboniferous) flora played an important part in the formation of coal. In India, the coal seams of Raniganj and Jharia are of the Permian age. Palynology, dealing with fossil spores and pollen grains, is of great value in determining and corrrelating coal seams and sedimentary beds of both freshwater and marine origin.

Formation of Fossils. Two major factors are involved in the preservation of plant and animal bodies in the form of fossils: rapidity of burial and prevention of normal decay. A combination of these two factors often occurs in the case of burial in stagnant water, complete burial under fine-grained sediment, or rapid infiltration of mineral substances into the cell walls. In any of these cases, the quantity of available oxygen is diminished.

KINDS OF FOSSIL PLANTS

(1) **Petrifaction** (*petra*, rock: *facere*, to make). This means fossilization by cell-to-cell replacement of certain plant parts by a good number of mineral substances, of which carbonates of calcium and magnesium, iron sulphide and silica are the most common. Petrified fossils have shown the external form, internal structure, and sometimes substance of the original plant, often in great detail. In this case, before vertical pressure came into play, the plant fragments were saturated with water, containing mineral substances in solution. The mineral substances infiltrated into the plant body, and gradually separated out from the solution. In due course the water was expelled. Finally, the tissues and cells had a complete filling of solid

materials, and the whole formed a solid, incompressible, hard mass. Coal balls and silicified wood are the best examples of petrification. Coal balls remain embedded in the coal and are of varying sizes, usually about the size of potatoes. They are often very rich in the calcified remains of plant materials. Silicified stumps of wood have often been so well preserved that it has been possible to prepare thin sections of them for microscopic examination. They often reveal minute structures in extraordinary detail.

(2) **Incrustation or Cast.** This is a fossil with the external form as a cast. The internal structure is not preserved. Here the plant substances have disappeared and a cavity has been left. This cavity is subsequently filled with mineral matter, which forms a *cast* of the original plant. The surrounding material, the mould, forms the *incrustation*. Casts of pith cavities of hollow stems have been found. These resulted from the entry of fine sand or mud into the hollow stems. In the course of time the filling material was converted into an internal mould of the hollow stem, e.g. the pith cast of *Calamites*.

(3) **Compression.** In this case, the external form of the plant was modified by the vertical pressure of the sediment in which the plant material was embedded. When a plant is subjected to compression, some of its parts—leaves, seeds, fruits, trunks, etc.—leave impressions on the rock surface. The outline of the plant or its part is left on the rock surface due to compressions.

(4) **Compactions.** These are plants or plant fragments compressed by vertical pressure. Masses of plant fragments without the intervening matrix such as are found in peat and coal are large-scale compactions.

(5) **Impressions.** The forms impressed on a matrix, as on coal and shale, which harden afterwards, are usually termed impressions. The external features of plant parts are thus preserved.

CHAPTER 2

FOSSIL PLANTS

Classification of Fossils

Pteridophytes

(A) Psilophytopsida (or Psilophytinae).

Order 1. Psilophytales, e.g. *Psilophyton, Horneophyton, Rhynia*, etc.

(B) Lycopsida (or Lycopodinae).

Order 2. Lepidodendrales, e.g. *Lepidodendron, Sigillaria*, etc.

(C) Sphenopsida (or Equisetinae).

Order 3. Hyeniales, e.g. *Hyenia, Calamophyton*, etc.

Order 4. Sphenophyllales, e.g. *Sphenophyllum.*

Order 5. Equisetales, e.g. *Equisetites.*

Order 6. Calamitales, e.g. *Calamites.*

(D) Pteropsida or Filicopsida (or Filicinae).

Order 7. Coenopteridales, e.g. *Etapteris* and *Botryopteris.*

Order 8. Marattiales, e.g. *Danaeopsis. Marattia*, and also some other orders.

Gymnosperms

Order 1. Cycadofilicales (or Pteridospermales), e.g. *Glossopteris, Lyginopteris*, etc.

Order 2. Cordaitales, e.g. *Cordaites.*

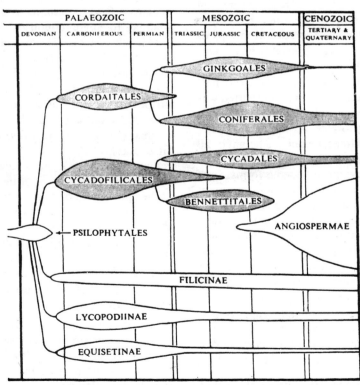

FIG. 1. Diagram showing possible origin, evolution and distribution of pteridophytes, gymnosperms and angiosperms in different geological periods. For time scale see table on p. 657.

Order 3. Bennettitales (or Cycadeoideales), e.g. *Williamsonia, Cycadeoidea* (=*Bennettites*), etc.

Order 4. Ginkgoales, e.g. *Baiera* (fossil) and Ginkgo (living).

Order 5. Cycadales, e.g. cycads (living and fossil).

Order 6. Coniferales, e.g. conifers (living and fossil) such as *Araucaria*, pine, juniper, cypress, yew, etc. *Lebachia, Walchia, Palissya*, etc. are found as fossils only.

The Palaeozoic age. From the standpoint of evolution, this age is immensely interesting inasmuch as it shows many special features of land vegetation. In the early period (Devonian or possibly Silurian) of this age, there was the first invasion of the land by the aquatic flora of the sea. The Psilophytales, which might have evolved from certain green algae, were the first land plants. They were small herbaceous plants (hardly exceeding 0.3 m.), leafless and rootless, but branched, bearing terminal sporangia. They soon became extinct, but before they died out they gave rise to several groups of well-developed plants, which established themselves permanently on the land and dominated the surface of the earth during the Palaeozoic age, particularly the Carboniferous period. This period was warm and humid and naturally favoured luxuriant vegetation. Thus big forests developed, covering wide areas. Many tall trees, reaching a height of 20 to 40 metres, gained prominence in such forests and there were also several herbaceous forms. Such groups were **Lycopodinae** (including giant lycopods), **Equisetinae** (including giant horsetails) and **Filicinae** (particularly Coenopteridales) among the pteridophytes, and **Cycadofilicales** and **Cordaitales** among the primitive gymnosperms. So the Palaeozoic age may be called the 'age of ancient pteridophytes and ancient gymnosperms'. To summarize the above, it may be stated that the five groups (leaving out Psilophytales) appeared in the Devonian, flourished in the Carboniferous, and dwindled rather rapidly, and almost disappeared in the Permian age or a little later in some cases.

The Mesozoic age. Heavy glaciation, upheaval of mountains and redistribution of water and land areas in the late Palaezoic age brought about marked changes in the vegetation of the earth. Palaeozoic ferns and giant lycopods and horsetails disappeared, and so did most of the primitive gymnosperms. In the Mesozoic age the primitive pteriodphytes were replaced by newer herbaceous forms. Some of the common Mesozoic ferns were *Phlebopteris, Todites, Osmundites, Tempskya*, and *Schizaeopsis*. Similarly, the primitive gymnosperms rapidly declined· in the Permian age —Cordaitales became extinct, while some members of Cycadofilicales somehow continued up to the early Mesozoic age. Four new groups of gymnosperms appeared in the late Palaeozoic (the Permian) or the early Mesozoic age, formed from the dying Palaeozoic stock. Thus the Bennettitales (soon, however, altogether extinct) and Cycadales (both living and extinct) made their appearance from the Cycadofilicales stock, while the Coniferales (both living and extinct) and Ginkgoales (now with only one living species—*Ginkgo biloba*, a native of China but planted in some countries) evolved from the Cordaitales stock. These four groups of gymnospersms, particularly the Coniferales, flourished during the Mesozoic age. So the Mesozoic age may be called the 'age of advanced gymnosperms'. In the late Mesozoic age, newer and more modern types of conifers, viz. pine (*Pinus*), cypress (*Cupressus*), yew (*Taxus*), spruce (*Picea*), fir (*Abies*), cedar (*Cedrus*), juniper (*Juniperus*), redwood (*Sequoia*), etc. made their appearance. Another important event of the late Mesozoic age is the appearance of angiosperms. Their ancestry, however, cannot be traced yet. Another event of the Mesozoic age was the appearance of a new group of angiosperm-like plants discovered on the mid-Jurassic rocks of Yorkshire—the Caytoniales—which at one time were regarded as the progenitors of angiosperms (the idea, however, was later discarded).

The Cenozoic age. With the advent of angiosperms and their rapid increase in number, diversification of form, and widespread distribution in the Cretaceous period, ferns and gymnosperms rapidly dwindled and lost their dominant position both numerically and geographically. Angiosperms have dominated the earth's vegetation since then. So the Cenozoic age may be called the 'age of angiosperms'. Among the ancient angiosperms found in the Cretaceous period and later, mention may be made of water lilies, predominantly several arborescent types, such as *Populus*, *Quercus*, *Ficus*, *Juglans*, *Magnolia*, *Fagus*, *Salix*, etc. Among the monocotyledons of that period were several grasses, sedges, aroids, *Typha*, *Smilax*, palms, etc. With the progress of evolution the herbaceous forms outnumbered the woody forms. The former now dominate the surface of the earth.

PTERIDOPHYTES

A. PSILOPHYTOPSIDA or **PSILOPHYTINAE.** Members of this class were the most primitive vascular plants that were abundant during the Devonian period. There are two orders of Psilophytopsida: Psilophytales—an altogether extinct order with *Psilophyton* as the typical genus, and Psilotales—a modern order with two genera, viz. *Psilotum* and *Tmesipteris*.

Order **Psilophytales.** The small plants of this order (hardly exceeding one metre, often much smaller) had a dichotomously branched stem with no leaves, except in *Asteroxylon*. Roots were altogether absent. The underground rhizome bore numerous hairy rhizoids in some genera. The stem was protostelic with the xylem consisting of only tracheids. The plants were sporophytes, reproducing by means of one kind of spores (homosporous). The sporangia were terminal, or in some cases lateral. Nothing is known of the gametophytes yet. Our knowledge of this order began with the discovery of *Psilophyton princeps* in Canada by Sir William Dawson in 1859. But his discovery did not attract much attention. In 1917, Kidston and Lang discovered numerous fossils of other similar plants (*Rhynia*, *Horneophyton*, *Asteroxylon*, etc.) in well-preserved forms in the middle Devonian rocks at Rhynie (Scotland). These discoveries led to the establishment of the order Psilophytales. The members of this order were found in abundance in the lower and middle Devonian rocks in Great Britain, Canada, North America and Australia. Possibly they appeared in the Silurian (early or late) period but disappeared in the later Devonian period. They were the earliest land plants and the oldest and most primitive of all vascular plants. Whatever might have been their origin (probably from some algal stock), they were generally believed to be the ancestors of lycopods, horsetails and ferns in divergent lines.

Psilophyton (20 sp.). Members of *Psilophyton* (family *Psilophytaceae*) were widely distributed in Europe, North America and Canada. They grew in dense clumps in marshy places, and hardly exceeded 60 cm. in height and 1 cm. in diameter. *P. princeps* is the best known species. The plants were slender herbs with short slender rhizome bearing hairy rhizoids but no roots, and unequally dichotomous branches without leaves. There were, however, many small outgrowths (variously described as incipient leaves, spines and thorns) in the lower parts of the aerial shoots. The vegetative shoots were circinate, while the fertile shoots bore small oval sporangia (about 5 mm. long) singly at the tips of curved, bifurcated branches. The sporangia were homosporous. The gametophyte is still unknown. The internal structure of the stem has not been properly assessed except that it was protostelic, with the central xylem consisting of some annular tracheids, and the cortex possibly photosynthetic in nature.

Rhynia (2 sp.). Members of *Rhynia* (family *Rhyniaceae*) were abundant in the middle Devonian period in Scotland. *R. major* was about 50 cm. in height and more or less 6 mm. in diameter at the base. The other species was much smaller. The plants were extremely simple and naked (without leaves), with a slender, branching rhizome and slender, erect aerial shoots, branching dichotomously. The rhizome bore hairy rhizoids, but no roots. Some of the branches ended in solitary sporangia (about 12 mm. long). They were pear-shaped and thick-walled, and homosporous. The gametophyte is still unknown. The stem was protostelic, consisting of the central xylem (made of annular tracheids only), surrounded by phloem (made of some elongated cells). The cortex was thick and carried on photosynthesis. The epidermis had a thick cuticle and some stomata.

B. LYCOPSIDA or LYCOPODINAE. Members of this class had the sporophyte differentiated into the root, stem and leaves—the root and the stem often dichotomously branched, and the leaves mostly small and spirally arranged (ragarded as evolutionary derivatives of Psilotopsida). The vascular system was commonly protostelic. The sporangia were solitary on the upper surface of certain leaves, called sporophylls. Often, sporophylls bearing sporangia were grouped together at the end of branches, forming cones or strobili. The order Lepidodendrales of this class is altogether extinct although other orders (see p. 477) have living representatives.

Order **Lepidodendrales**. The plants of this order, numbering over 200 species, are found only as fossils. Probably they originated from the Psilophytales stock in the late Devonian, or early Carboniferous period, and reached their climax of development in the upper late Carboniferous period. They soon declined and disappeared in the Permian period. They were very tall trees with stout trunks, known as giant lycopods. Some of them reached a height of 40 metres with a diameter of 2 metres, thus showing a considerable amount of secondary growth. They had linear ligulate leaves, spirally arranged, which left characteristic leaf-scars on the stem on falling off. The leaf-scars distinguish the different genera. The stelar structure ranged from protostele to ectophloic siphonostele. They produced spores of two kinds (heterosporous): the microsporangium produced numerous small microspores, while the megasporangium produced 4 to 16 large megaspores. In some cases, only a single megaspore matured. A female gametophyte was produced in the megaspore while it remained within the megasporangium. After fertilization, the entire structure was shed like the seed of a 'flowering' plant. They were the dominant plants of the coal age and hence, important in the formation of coal. *Lepidodendron* and *Sigillaria* (both giant lycopods) are the best known genera.

Lepidodendron. This was a dominant Palaeozoic genus, abundantly found in well-preserved fossilised forms in the Carboniferous coal formations. Most of the species had attained very large sizes (giant lycopods). The single tall trunk (40 m. or so) bore a crown of several dichotomous branches at the top, and had spirally arranged, linear leaves of varying lengths, often up to 20 cm. and sometimes even more. The whole trunk was covered with spirally arranged leaf-scars. Internally, the stem exhibited a considerable amount of secondary growth, consisting mostly of very thick secondary wood with scalariform tracheids. At the base of the stem, there were usually four (sometimes many) very long root-like branches (rhizophores), which forked repeatedly. Their tips bore roots.

Sigillaria. This was another important Palaeozoic genus which held a dominant position in the Carboniferous period. Many species were tall (20 m. or more) and arborescent, like *Lepidodendron*. Some species were, however, much shorter. The stem was unbranched or sparingly branched, and bore long, linear leaves (sometimes about a metre in length) at the top in a cone-like tuft. The leaf-scars were in a *vertical* arrangement. There was a considerable amount of secondary growth in *Sigillaria*, as in *Lepidodendron* and *Sigillaria*, too, bore rhizophores.

C. SPHENOPSIDA or EQUISETINAE. Members of this class also had sporophytes with distinct roots, stems and leaves. The stem was jointed and ribbed, and the leaves were small and simple, occurring in whorls at the nodes and forming a sort of sheath—a feature characteristic of this group and distinguishing it from other pteridophytes. Another characteristic feature of the Sphenopsida was the presence of sporangium-bearing axes (sporangiophores) in whorls. In many forms, these sporangiophores were recurved so that the terminal sporangia were directed towards the axis. Strobili were formed in many genera. This group was contemporaneous with Lycopsida, being abundant in diversified forms during the Carboniferous period, after which it suffered a sharp decline. The order might have evolved from the Psilophytales stock.

Order **Hyeniales**. This order is the oldest of all Sphenopsida, which flourished during the middle

Era	Period (age in million years)	Dominant Plants (& Animals)
CENOZOIC — QUARTERNARY	Recent	Herbaceous plants dominate; forest trees decline. Civilization begins.
	Pleistocene [1-5]	Many large trees die out. Many hardy types of herbs survive and proliferate. Great mammals die out.
	Pliocene [12]	Restricted distribution of forests; rise of herbs. Appearance of man. Upheaval of the Himalayas—2nd phase.
	Miocene [20]	Forest areas decrease; polar flora retreats; grasses increase. Mammals reach zenith.
CENOZOIC — TERTIARY	Oligocene [35]	Tropical forests of angiosperms world-wide. Primitive mammals disappear; higher mammals and birds proliferate. Upheaval of the Himalayas—1st phase.
	Eocene [60]	Pteridophytes continue to flourish; mesozoic gymnosperms disappear except cycads and conifers, which decline; angiosperms dominate; tropical forests in polar regions. Modern birds and higher mammals.
MESOZOIC	Cretaceous [135]	Pteridophytes still thrive; gymnosperms decline rapidly except conifers; new varieties of angiosperms proliferate; modern forests begin. Giant reptiles go extinct. Primitive mammals multiply.
	Jurassic [180]	Luxuriant forest of higher gymnosperms and modern pteridophytes; probable origin of angiosperms. Flying reptiles, dinosaurs abundant; primitive birds; higher insects.
	Triassic [230]	Change in flora due to heavy glaciation in Permian period; most primitive forms disappear; new pteridophytes appear in herbaceous forms; higher gymnosperms (cycads and confers) increase. Origin of mammals and giant reptiles (dinosaurs).
PALAEOZOIC	Permian [280]	Primitive pteridophytes and gynmosperms decline and almost disappear, while advanced groups (cycads, conifers, etc.) appear. Land vertebrates.
	Carboniferous [345]	Pteridophytes: giant lycopods and horsetails (*Calamites*) dominant and widespread; ferns abundant; primitive gymnosperms abundant; luxuriant growth of tall trees, forming dense forests; extensive coal deposits. Amphibians increase; reptiles and insects.
	Devonian [395]	Early land plants. Psilophytales abound but soon disappear; possible origin of gymnosperms (Cycadofilicales and Cordaitales); giant lycopods and horsetails, and ferns. Origin of amphibians; fish dominate.
	Silurian [425]	marine algae dominate; possible origin of land plants: Psilophytales. Higher invertebrates increase. First vertebrates.
	Ordovician [500]	Marine algae abundant. Higher invertebrates.
	Cambrian [600]	Green algae, stoneworts and red algae. Primitive invertebrates: trilobites abundant.
	Proterozoic [2,000]	Bacteria, fungi and blue-green algae.
	Archeozoic [5,000]	No fossil records but unicellular life quite probable.

Devonian period, and resembled the Psilophytales in some respects. *Hyenia* and *Calamophyton* were the typical genera.

Hyenia. The plants of this genus were about 30 cm. in height and the diameter at the base was less than 1 cm. They had a horizontal, stout rhizome with roots, from which arose erect, aerial, dichotomously branched shoots—sterile and fertile. The sterile axis bore several whorls of small, slender leaves, forked repeatedly. The fertile axis bore several whorls of sporangiophores, similarly forked at the apex, and had the appearance of a long, loose cone (strobilus). However, no bracts (sporophylls) were present. Two of the several forks were recurved and each of them ended in a pair of sporangia. They were homosporous.

Order Sphenophyllales. This order was represented by the fossil genus, *Sphenophyllum*, which first appeared in the later Devonian period and continued up to the early Triassic, being very abundant in the Carboniferous period. The plants were small and lay prostrate on the ground. The diameter of the slender stem hardly exceeded 1 cm. The stem bore whorls of leaves at the nodes. They were wedge-shaped and generally lobed, and each whorl consisted of 3 leaves or any multiple of this number. The sporophylls also occurred in whorls, but in long, terminal cones (strobili). The sporangia were homosporous. The solid primary wood (protostele) was triangular and the protoxylem lay at each corner (exarch). There was some amount of secondary growth in the stem.

Order Calamitales. This order consisted of several arborescent species (giant horsetail), closely related to the Equisetales. It appeared in the later Devonian period, became abundant and dominated the swamp forests of the later Carboniferous period, and finally dwindled and disappeared in the later Permian period. The principal family was *Calamitacese*. It was represented by genera like *Protocalamites, Calamites, Calamostachys,* and *Palaeostachya.*

Calamites. Several species of *Calamites* dominated the later Carboniferous period (along with *Lepidodendron*), though their life span extended from the later Devonian to the later Permian. The plants were mostly very tall, some reaching a height of 20-30 m. and a diameter of 60 cm. They had a large, hollow pith cavity. The tall, erect stem developed from an underground rhizome, and was distinctly jointed and rigid. The branches and leaves appeared in whorls from the nodes. The leaves were simple and narrow, but much larger than those of *Equisetum*. They appeared in widely varying numbers (4-60) at the nodes, and were mostly free, or in some species, united into a sheath. Anatomically, the primary bundles were small and arranged in a ring. The protoxylem had a carinal cavity, as in *Equisetum*. The bundles divided at each node and alternated with those of the next internode. But unlike *Equisetum*, there was a considerable amount of secondary growth outside the metaxylem, resulting in the large girth of the stem. Wood rays, often very wide, were present in both the primary and secondary wood, but annual rings were absent. The wood consisted of tracheids with scalariform thickening, or with bordered pits. The strobili (cones) occurred singly at the node or in groups, terminally or on special branches. Each cone was made of whorls of peltate sporangiophores bearing only four pendant sporangia. In several members of Calamitales (e.g. *Calamostachys*), there were whorls of sheathing bracts united at the base into a sort of disc, alternating with the sporangiophores, while in others (e.g. *Calamites*), such bracts were absent. In them, the overlapping sporangiophores afforded the necessary protection to the young sporangia. Most of the species were homosporous,

---

The table on the previous page shows the possible origin and evolution of the main groups of plants (and also animals) in different geological periods. Broadly speaking, the early Palaezoic age was the 'age of algae', and the later Palaezoic was the 'age of pteridophytes', with abundant primitive gymnosperms. The Mesozoic was the 'age of advanced gymnosperms', with abundant advanced pteridophytes and the Cenozoic was the 'age of angiosperms' (herbs dominating the recent period), with modern pteridophytes and modern gymnosperms.

while a few were heterosporous. Apart from their size, *Calamites* resembled Equisetales closely—the *Equisitites* of the Mesozoic age and the *Equisetum* of today.

Order **Equisetales.** This order consists of herbaceous plants closely resemblaning modern *Equisetum.* The order, as represented by the typical fossil genus *Equisetites*, became prominent in the Mesozoic (Triassic), but was also present in the Carboniferous period. The slender, simple leaves of the *Equisetites* were in whorls but had lost their photosynthetic activity. The strobili resembled those of *Equisetum.*

D. PTEROPSIDA or FILICINAE. The ferns are the largest group among the Pteridophyta. They have a stem, well-developed leaves and roots. The sporangia are borne mostly on the leaves in groups or sori. Ferns were no doubt abundant in Palaezoic age, but many of them later proved to be 'seed ferns' or Cycadofilicales. Some of the Palaezoic families of ferns, such as *Gleicheniaceae, Marattiaceae*, and *Schizaeaceae*, still have living representatives. With the close of the Palaezoic era the ferns declined and many of them disappeared altogether. In the Mesozoic age, new ferns appeared in diverse forms and soon became abundant and widespread. The descendants of many Mesozoic ferns thrive even today, in greater numbers and forms. The order, Coenopteridales, belonging to this class became extinct in the Palaeozoic age.

Coenopteridales. The members of this ancient order extended from the Devonian to the Permian periods. They were, however, most abundant in the Carboniferous period, and constituted the most primitive group of ferns (also called the Primofilices). Several species (about 65 sp.) have been found so far. Most of them were distinctly fern-like in appearance. On the one hand, they resembled the Psilophytales with their large terminal sporangia (synangia) and in some cases, by their small undivided leaves. On the other hand, they resembled the ferns with their often pinnately divided, fern-like frond in many cases. The plants of this order were small or medium in size, and often erect or sometimes prostrate. They bore single, large, pyriform sporangia or a group of sporangia united into a synangium. These were borne terminally at the apex of the pinnule of a frond, or sometimes directly on the rachis. The frond was usually branched in many planes, and sometimes in only one plane. The stem, often much-branched, was protostelic, the stele being circular or lobed in outline. All the species were homosporous. *Botryopteris* and *Etapteris* were the two common genera of the order.

GYMNOSPERMS

CYCADOFILICALES (or PTERIDOSPERMALES). The members of this order were distinctly fern-like, with pinnately compound leaves, but they bore seeds. That is why they are called 'seed ferns'. They were the most primitive group of seed plants. They appeared in the later Devonian period, proliferated in the Carboniferous period, declined rapidly in the Permian period, and became extinct in the early or mid-Jurassic period. They were of varied habits. They were usually slender and short, unlike the Cordaitales, and some were like tree-ferns though much smaller. Detached parts of 'seed ferns', more or less perfectly preserved, show roots, stems, leaves, pollen-bearing organs (even pollen grains) and seeds (without, however, any trace of the embryo). They had distinct fern-like fronds, often very large, and for many years they were taken to be ferns. On the basis of their anatomical structure (intermediate between ferns and cycads), this group was named 'Cycadofilicales' by Potonie in 1899. Around 1903, Oliver and Scott found seeds together with the stems and leaves, and they proposed the name 'Pteridosperms' for such seed-bearing, fern-like plants.

The primary xylem in these plants was mostly mesarch (a fern characteristic). They exhibited three kinds of stele—mostly protostele, sometimes polystele, and also ectophloic siphonostele. Cortisal bands of sclerenchyma were a constant feature. There was also some amount of secondary growth, thick or thin. Further, they exhibited gymnospermic tracheids with bordered pits, mostly on the radial wall. They were evidently gymnosperms and their distinct fern-like appearance also suggests a relationship with the ferns. No strobilus was formed in the plants of this group. The microsporangia (pollen-bearing organs) were borne on the margin or lower side of the fertile pinnule, as in many ferns. The ovule (seed) was borne at the end of the frond or modified frond (megasporophyll). A deep pollen-chamber was present in the nucellus, as in gymnosperms. The seeds were like those of other seed-plants but usually enclosed in a cupule.

The Pteridosperms were no doubt the oldest seed plants. Their relationship with the ferns is evident from the nature of the leaves, microsporophylls, primary wood and microsporangia. Their relationship with the Bennettitales and the Cycadales, if not with other gymnosperms, is also close. But the origin of the Pteridosperms is based only on speculation, and cannot be traced with any amount of certainty because of the missing links. Two alternatives are, however, probable. They might have been derived from some unknown Filicinian stock (Primofilices) of the early Palaeozoic age, or they might have descended from the Psilophytalean stock of the Devonian period. Arnold holds that the Pteridosperms with their diverse forms might not have arisen from a single (common) ancestral stock. Whatever their origin, the two groups (Pteridosperms and Filicinae) had developed later in parallel lines.

The order has been divided into seven families—the first three confined to the Palaeozoic age and the last four either confined to the Mesozoic age or extending from the Palaeozoic to the Mesozoic ages.

1. *Lyginopteridaceae*. These had a straggling habit. The stems were usually 1-5 cm. in diameter and protostelic. They had large fronds and a limited amount of secondary growth. The integument was fused with the nucellus, except at the apex. The seed was usually borne in a cupule. Some common genera were *Lyginopteris* (stems—commonly found in coal-balls), *Heterangium* (stem), *Sphenopteris* (frond), *Crossotheca* (pollen-bearing organs), *Lagenostoma* and *Calymmatotheca* (seeds).

2. *Medullosaceae*. The stem was trunk-like but narrow (usually 2-6 cm. in diameter; much thicker in some species). The plants, pollen-bearing organs and seeds were much larger than those of *Lyginopteridaceae*. The stem was polystelic (often with a large number of steles). The secondary growth was wide and distinct. The inner integument was fused with the nucellus. The seed enclosed in a stony cupule. The common genera were *Medullosa* (stems), *Neuropteris* and *Alethopteris* (fronds), *Stephanospermum* and *Codonospermum* (seeds) and *Codonotheca* (pollen-bearing organs).

3. *Calamopityaceae*. Our knowledge of this family is incomplete. The leaves were large and fern-like. The stems ranged from having solid protostele to circum-medullary groups of primary xylem with mixed pith (tracheids and parenchyma). The secondary wood was either manoxylic (soft and sparse with broad rays), or pycnoxylic (dense and compact with very narrow and small rays). The common genera were *Calamopitys* and *Stenomyelon* (stems).

4. *Glossopteridaceae*. Glossopteris flora is characteristic of the Gondwanaland, (see p. 663). The common genera are *Glossopteris* and *Gangamopteris* (leaves), *Vertebraria* (roots), *Ottokaria* and *Scutum* (reproductive organs).

5. *Peltaspermaceae*. Fronds and pollen-bearing organs (but not stems) have been found in the Triassic rocks of Natal, Malagasay, Greenland, Argentina, Australia and China. The common genera were *Lepidopteris* (fronds), *Peltaspermum* (seed-bearing organs) and *Antevsia* (pollen-bearing organs).

6. *Corystospermaceae*. Fronds, pollen-bearing organs and seed-bearing organs have been found in the Triassic rocks of Natal, Australia, Argentina and India. The common genera were *Xylopteris* and *Dicroidium* (fronds), *Umkomasia* (seed-bearing organs) and *Pterucus* (pollen-bearing organs).

7. *Caytoniaceae*. This was a group of angiosperm-like plants (once supposed to be ancestors of angiosperms; see p. 530), first discovered by Thomas in 1925 in the mid-Jurassic rocks of Yorkshire. The leaves (in *Sagenopteris*)—four

leaflets in two pairs—were borne on a slender petiole. They had reticulate venation. The leaves and leaflets were shed by the absciss-layer. The midrib was prominent. The pollen-bearing organs or microsporophylls (in *Caytonanthus*) were borne on a pinnate type of richis, each branch ending in a synangium. There were four pollen sacs, dehiscing except at the apex. The seeds (in *Caytonia*) were borne in the fruit. The pollination mechanism was like that of in gymnosperms. The pollen chamber was present.

Calymmatotheca hoeninghausi. The fossils of these plants, found in the Coal Measures of Europe and America, were not complete. Detached parts of various genera were found, such as the stem of *Lyginopteris oldhamia*, frond of *Sphenopteris sp.*, seed of *Lagenostoma sp.*, root of *Kaloxylon sp.*, etc. These were later assembled together and given the name *Calymmatotheca hoeninghausi*. The plant was upright but reclined against rocks or neighbouring trees. The stem grew to a diameter of 4 cm. and exhibited a ring of mesarch primary bundles, a fair amount of secondary growth, large tracheids with several rows of bordered pits, distinct medullary rays, masses of stone cells in the large pith, and conspicuous leaf-traces and leaf-gaps. The fronds were large, compound (much-divided) and spirally arranged. The rachis had a distinct gland. The fertile pinnule (of *Crossotheca*) was peltate in nature and its undersurface bore a number of bilocular microsporangia or pollen-bearing organs. Ovules were also found attached (terminally) to some of the fertile pinnules. The seed remained enclosed in a seed cup or cupule, which split into 4-6 segments.

BENNETTITALES (or Cycadeoideales). The Bennettitales formed an intermediate group between the Cycadofilicales and the Cycadales. They flourished during the Mesozoic age, reaching their culmination in the Jurassic period when they were distributed world-wide, especially in India, western Europe and North America. They often formed forests in many areas. This order might have evolved from the Pteridospermales in the Triassic period, but it declined and became extinct in the later Cretaceous period. The Bennettitales seem to be closely related to the Cycadales on the one hand and to the Cycadofilicales on the other, going by their pinnate type of compound leaves, circinate venation, type of naked seeds, structure of ovules, loose pattern of secondary wood with large tracheids, numerous medullary rays and large pith. Therefore, these three orders are collectively called 'Cycadophyta'. In the Bennettitales, however, the sporophylls were much more specialized. The cones (flowers) in this order were unisexual or bisexual, with numerous bracts. The microsporophylls, pinnate or entire, bore many microsporangia. The megasporophylls bore many stalked ovules on an elongated receptacle. The seeds had two cotyledons. The plants were of varying habits—most of them were below 1 m. in height, while a few were 2 m. or a little higher. The two principal families of this order were as follows:

1. *Cycadeoideaceae.* This was represented by the only one genus— *Cycadeoidea* (= *Bennettites*)—with over 30 species. It usually had a short, stout and barrel-like or columnar stem. Scales and leaf-scars were present. The internode was short. It had a crown of cycad-like, pinnate leaves and several bisporangiate (bisexual) strobili. Each strobilus was borne on a short axillary branch and consisted of many sterile appendages or perianth-like bracts. These were arranged spirally at the base and overlapped each other. The strobilus had a whorl of 10-12 pinnately divided, leaf-like microsporophylls, each with numerous microsporangia or pollen-sacs, and several megasporophylls intermixed with scales on top of the receptacle, forming a sort of compact cone. Each megasporophyll, highly modified and unlike leaf, was represented by a long stalk with an ovule on its top. The seed was dicotyledonous and had a large embryo (but no endosperm). Thus *Cycadeoidea* had a flower-like appearance and construction, resembling the flower of *Magnolia*. This is why it was once suggested that the Bennettitales might have been the ancestors of the angiosperms. However, considering the other factors, particularly the specialized sporophylls (both micro and mega) it is more reasonable to

suppose that the resemblance is only superficial and reflects parallel development (evolution) rather than any direct relationship.

2. *Williamsoniaceae.* This was represented by the typical genus *Williamsonia.* It had a slender, branched or unbranched stem (tall or short), a dense covering of scales, leaf-scars, short internodes, a crown of cycad-like, pinnate leaves and mostly monosporangiate (unisexual) strobili. A few other genera of this family were *Ptilophyllum, Pterophyllum, Otozamites,* and *Dictyozamites.*

CYCADALES. The extinct Cycadales were a group of cycad-like gymnosperms which flourished during the mid-Mesozoic age. They first appeared in the later Triassic period and reached their peak during the Jurassic-Cretaceous periods, when they were distributed world-wide. Among the 'Cycadophyta,' it is only the Cycadales that have survived until the present day. They were contemporaneous with the Bennettitales and closely related to them. Both groups might have been derived from the Cycadofilicales, though independently of each other. Some of the extinct genera of the Cycadales are *Nilssonia, Beania,* and *Palaeocycas,* while the living Cycadales are represented by nine genera consisting about 100 species.

CORDAITALES. The members of this extinct group of gymnosperms appeared in the late Devonian period, reached the peak of their development during the later Carboniferous period, and became practically extinct by the end of the Permian period. The Cordaitales and Cycadofilicales were comtemporaneous, but the former soon died out completely, while the latter survived for some time more (see FIG. 1). Both orders were, however, abundant in diverse forms during the Carboniferous period, the Cordaitales dominating the gymnospermic forests. Detached parts of roots, shoots, leaves, strobili, and seeds (but no embryo) found in well-preserved fossil forms were initially given different names, but later Williamson (1851), Renault (1879), Scott (1900) and others brought them together under the order Cordaitales. The order is divided into two

families, viz. (*a*) *Cordaitaceae,* e.g. *Cordaites* (a characteristic genus), and (*b*) *Poroxylaceae,* e.g. *Poroxylon.* The Cordaitales were mostly tall trees (unlike the Pteridosperms) reaching a height of 30 m., but their appearance and the nature of their leaves were not fern-like. On the other hand, they approached the coniferales in habit and in the structure of the secondary wood. They are thus regarded as their ancestors. The Cordaitales bore a crown of branches at the top and also many large, simple, parallel, veined leaves (often 1 m. long and 15 cm. wide). The leaves were internally differentiated into palisade and spongy tissues and several ribs of sclerenchyma. The stem anatomy was very much like that of modern *Araucaria,* a coniferous genus. It exhibited a considerable amount of secondary growth, having well-developed tracheids with many rows of bordered pits on the radial walls, medullary rays which had a single-cell thickness, and a large pith. The plants were monoecious, evidently bearing monosporangiate (unisexual) strobili. Several strobili were borne on special branches developing from the axis, giving them the appearance of inflorescences. Each strobilus (male or female) consisted of several spirally arranged sterile bracts and some sporophylls (micro or mega). The male strobilus consisted of a few long-stalked microsporophylls or stamens, each with 4-6 terminal microsporangia or pollen-sacs. The female (ovulate) strobilus consisted of a few (1-4) ovules bore on short (dwarf) branches.

The Cordaitales were an ancient group of 'seed' plants as old as the Cycadofilicales. Like the latter, the Cordaitales were abundant during the later Carboniferous period, forming extensive forests. Two alternatives are probable regarding their origin: both groups might have originated from some extinct fern-like plants (maybe the Psilophytales), or the Cordaitales might be an early offshoot of the Cycadofilicales. Many share the former view. Whatever their origin, it is assumed for valid reasons that before they died out in the Permian period, the Cordaitales gave rise to two well-known groups of gymnosperms—the Coniferales and the Ginkgoales—which flourished during the Mesozoic period.

GINKGOALES. The members of this order were abundant and were distributed world-wide during the Mesozoic age. Some of the Mesozoic genera were *Baiera*, *Ginkgoites*, and *Windwardia*. The only living representative of the order is the maiden-hair tree (*Ginkgo biloba*), which is referred to as the 'living fossil'. The order might have been derived from the Cordaitales.

CONIFERALES. The members of this order can be traced back to the Permian period, but they were abundant and widely distributed during the Mesozoic age when they appeared in diverse forms. They reached the peak of their development during the Cretaceous period. They might have been derived from the Cordaitales. The order still thrives with 500 species. As in the Mesozoic age, this is the largest order of gymnosperms. The earliest known Coniferales were *Lebachia*, *Walchia*, etc. (Permian period) and *Volziopsis*, *Pseudovoltzia*, etc. (Triassic period). Some of the modern conifers can be traced back to the Jurassic period.

The Gondwana System. In the early Carboniferous period, the flora of the southern hemisphere was very similar to that of the northern homisphere. But by the later Carboniferous period and early Permian times, the two hemispheres became separated by a vast sea called the Tethys (see p. 651). The land mass of the southern hemisphere, comprising Africa, Maalagasay, India, Australia, South America and Antarctica, formed one huge southern continent, which geologists call the Gondwanaland. Possibly from the Jurassic period, the Gondwanaland began to break up into separate components which gradually drifted to their present locations. According to this 'continental drift' theory the northern part of the Gondwanaland, which has become the Indian sub-continent, collided with the Asian continent with such tremendous force that it pushed up huge land masses forming the present-day Himalayas. Further, according to the same theory, its southern part—Antarctica—drifted all the way down to the South Pole. The name Gondwana was first introduced by Medlicott in 1872 after the kingdom of the Gond, an ancient tribe of central India, while he was studying the geological formations

of the area. The Gondwana had developed in India mostly in a triangular area: (*a*) from the Godavari valley to the Rajmahal Hills, (*b*) the Damodar, Sone and Narmada valleys, extending east to west, and (*c*) along the Godavari, extending north-west to south-east. Other formations have been found along the foothills of the Himalayas (Nepal, Bhutan and Assam), and isolated formations have been found in Salt Range, Kashmir, Garhwal, Kutch, Saurashtra and Madhya Pradesh. At that time, the flora was similar in both the northern and southern hemispheres. During the later Carboniferous period and the early Permian period, however, there was extensive glaciation (known as the Permo-Carboniferous Ice Age) in the Gondwanaland. The heavy glaciation in the southern hemisphere resulted in the destruction of most of the older vegetation, the redistribution of land and sea, and the upheaval of mountains. After this, the climate became humid and warmer. Under these conditions, an almost entirely new type of vegetation sprang up from the meagre flora that survived the catastrophe—the **Glossopteris Flora**. This flora was entirely different from that of North America and Europe. It was characterized by a small number of species and scarcity of woody plants. Many fossils of leaves have been found and these have been named *Glossopteris*. The leaves were simple and mostly tongue-shaped but were of varying shapes and sizes (some even 30 cm. or more in length) venation was always reticulate and the mid-rib distinct. There were two types of leaves, viz. (*a*) foliage leaves, as described above, and (*b*) small scale-leaves. *Glossopteris* probably belonged to the order Pteridospermales. *Gangamopteris*, another constitutent of the Glossopteris flora, resembled *Glossopteris*, except that it had no mid-rib. The other constitutents were some lycopods and horsetails, and several ferns and gymnosperms. The glossopteris flora was characteristic of the Lower Gondwana (Permo-Carboniferous period) of the Gondwanaland continent. The Upper Gondwana (Mesozoic period), on the other hand, was dominated by the **Ptilophyllum flora**, the main constituents were *Ptilophyllum* order Bennettitales) and *Thinnfeldia* (order Pteridospermales), together with several advanced ferns and gymnosperms. The Gondwanaland has been divided into two main divisions—Lower Gondwana and Upper Gondwana—on the basis of fossil flora. These have been further sub-divided into series and stages. During the Permo-Triassic transition, the Glossopteris flora of the Lower Gondwana suffered a decline and a break, and was succeeded by the Ptilophyllum flora of the Upper Gondwana (Mesozoic period). The Gondwana, as a whole, extended from the later Carboniferous period to the Jurassic or early Cretaceous period, and in the Tertiary period, angiospermic vegetation began to dominate (as we find in the present times).

Fossils of the Main Gondwana Rocks of India[1]. The Lower Gondwana (Upper Carboniferous to Upper Permian or Lower Triassic) comprises the following series in the ascending order of formations: (1) Talchir, (2) Damuda (Raniganj and Barakar) and (3) Panchet. The Upper Gondwana (Middle Triassic to Upper Jurassic or Lower Cretaceous) comprises the following series: (1) Mahadeva, (2) Rajmahal and (3) Jabalpur. The following is an account of the fossil contents of these series.

Lower Gondwana. (1) Talchir Series (Upper Carboniferous): **Pteridospermales**—*Glossopteris*, *Gangamopteris, Vertebraria*, etc.; **Cordaitales**—*Noeggerathiopsis*; **Incertae**—*Samaropsis*.

(2) Damuda Series (Permian): A good number of fossils have been found in Raniganj and Jharia coalfields: **Lycopodiales**—*Bothrodendron*; **Equisetales**—*Schizoneura* (a few species), *Phyllotheca*, etc; **Sphenophyllales**—*Sphenophyllum*; **Filicales**—*Alethopteris, Actinopteris*, etc.; **Pteridospermales**—*Glossopteris* (several species), *Gangamopteris, Sphenopteris, Vertibraria*, etc.; **Cordaitales**—*Noeggerathiopsis*

and *Dadoxylon*; **Cycadeoideales**—*Taeniopteris*; **Incertae**—*Dictyopteridium, Cordaicarpus* and *Samaropsis*.

(3) Panchet Series (Upper Permian to Lower Triassic): The lower beds of the Panchet Hill lying to the north-west of Asansol contain many animal fossils but few plant fossils, such as *Glossopteris, Schizoneura*, and also *Pecopteris* and *Cyclopteris*.

Upper Gondwana. These fossils represent more advanced types of plants.

(1) Mahadeva Series (Middle to Upper Triassic): This series has been named after the Mahadeva Hills near Panchmari. Plant fossils are not common in this series although some leaf impressions have been found in clayey soil.

(2) Rajmahal Series (Lower to Middle Jurassic): This series is rich in plant fossils and a good number of them have already been collected and identified. They are: **Lycopodiales**—*Lycopodites* and *Lycoxylon*; **Equisetales**—*Equisetites*; **Filicales**—*Marattiopsis, Gleichenites,* Pecopteris; etc.; **Pteridospermales**—*Thinnfeldia, Danaeopsis* and *Sphenopteris*; **Cycadeoideales**—*Ptilophyllum, Otozamites, Dictyozamities, Taeniopteris* (a few species), *Nilssonia* (several species), etc.; **Coniferales**—*Elatocladus,* *Brachyphyllum, Pagiophyllum*, etc.; several gymnospermic stems and cones; **Caytoniales**—*Sagenopteris*; **Incertae**—*Rajmahalia* and *Podozamites*.

(3) Jabalpur Series (Upper Jurassic to Lower Cretaceous): **Filicales** —*Gleichenites, Cladophlebis*, etc.; **Pteridospermales**— *Thinnfeldia*; **Cycadeoideales**—*Ptilophyllum, Otozamites, Williamosonia, Dictyozamites, Taeniopteris, Nilssonia* (a few species); **Coniferales**—*Elatocladus, Brachyphyllum, Pagiophyllum, Araucarites*, (a few species), etc.; **Ginkgoales**—*Ginkgoites*; **Incertae**—*Podozamites*.

---

[1] Mainly based on *Geology of India and Burma* by M. S. Krishnan, 1960 edition, and *Fifty Years of Science in India* (Indian Science Congress Association, 1963): *Progress of Botany* by P. Maheshwari and R. N. Kapil, and *Progress of Geology* by S. Ray.

APPENDIX I (a)

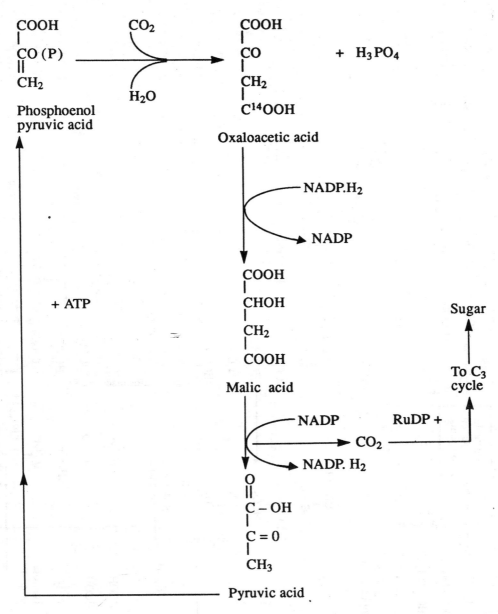

Mesophyll chloroplasts
(C$_4$ cycle)

Bundle sheath
chloroplasts
(C$_3$ cycle)

C$_4$ MECHANISM (see p. 252)

APPENDIX I (b)

C₃ MECHANISM (See p. 252)

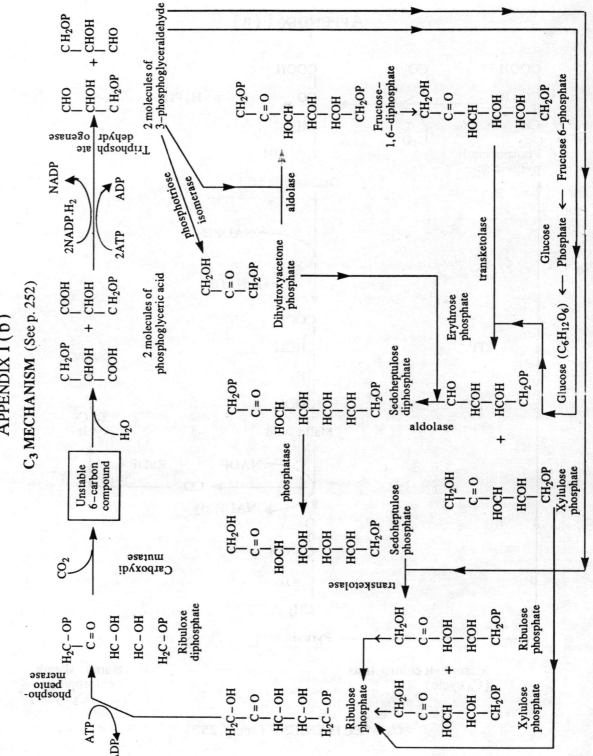

APPENDIX II

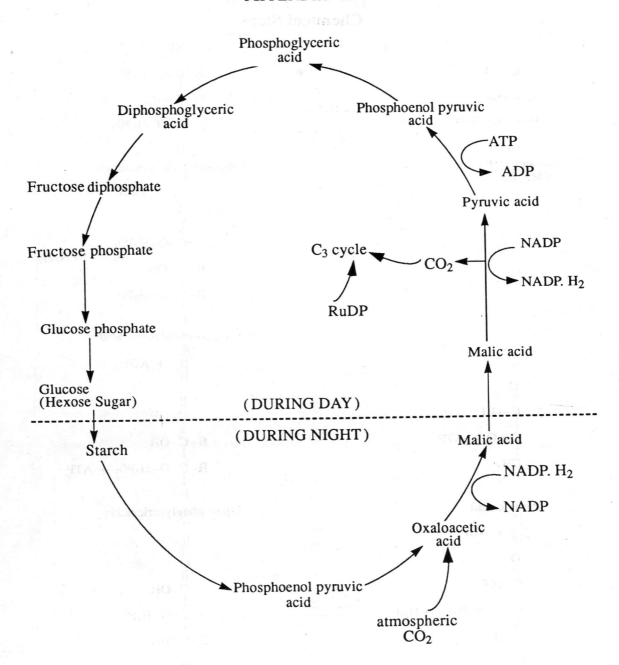

CAM MECHANISM (See p. 261)

Appendix III (a)
Chemical Steps

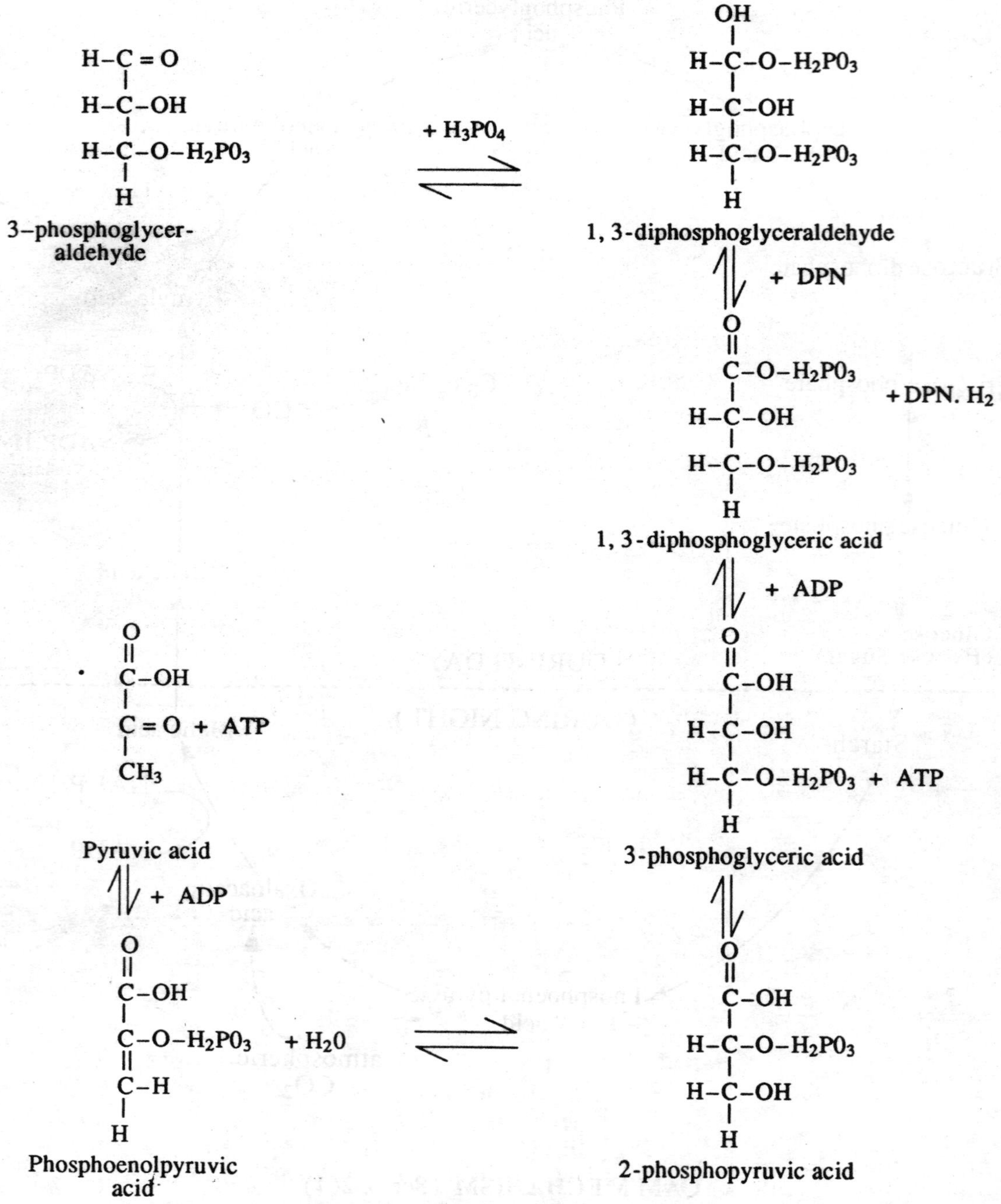

$$H-C = O$$
$$H-C-OH$$
$$H-C-O-H_2P0_3$$
$$H$$

3-phosphoglycer-
aldehyde

$+ H_3P0_4$ ⇌

$$OH$$
$$H-C-O-H_2P0_3$$
$$H-C-OH$$
$$H-C-O-H_2P0_3$$
$$H$$

1, 3-diphosphoglyceraldehyde

↑↓ $+ DPN$

$$O$$
$$\|$$
$$C-O-H_2P0_3$$
$$H-C-OH$$
$$H-C-O-H_2P0_3$$
$$H$$

$+DPN. H_2$

1, 3-diphosphoglyceric acid

↑↓ $+ ADP$

$$O$$
$$\|$$
$$C-OH$$
$$H-C-OH$$
$$H-C-O-H_2P0_3 + ATP$$
$$H$$

3-phosphoglyceric acid

$$O$$
$$\|$$
$$C-OH$$
$$C = O + ATP$$
$$CH_3$$

Pyruvic acid

↑↓ $+ ADP$

$$O$$
$$\|$$
$$C-OH$$
$$C-O-H_2P0_3 \quad + H_2O$$
$$\|$$
$$C-H$$
$$H$$

Phosphoenolpyruvic
acid

⇌

↑↓

$$O$$
$$\|$$
$$C-OH$$
$$H-C-O-H_2P0_3$$
$$H-C-OH$$
$$H$$

2-phosphopyruvic acid

FIG : GLYCOLYSIS (See p. 285)

APPENDIX III (b)

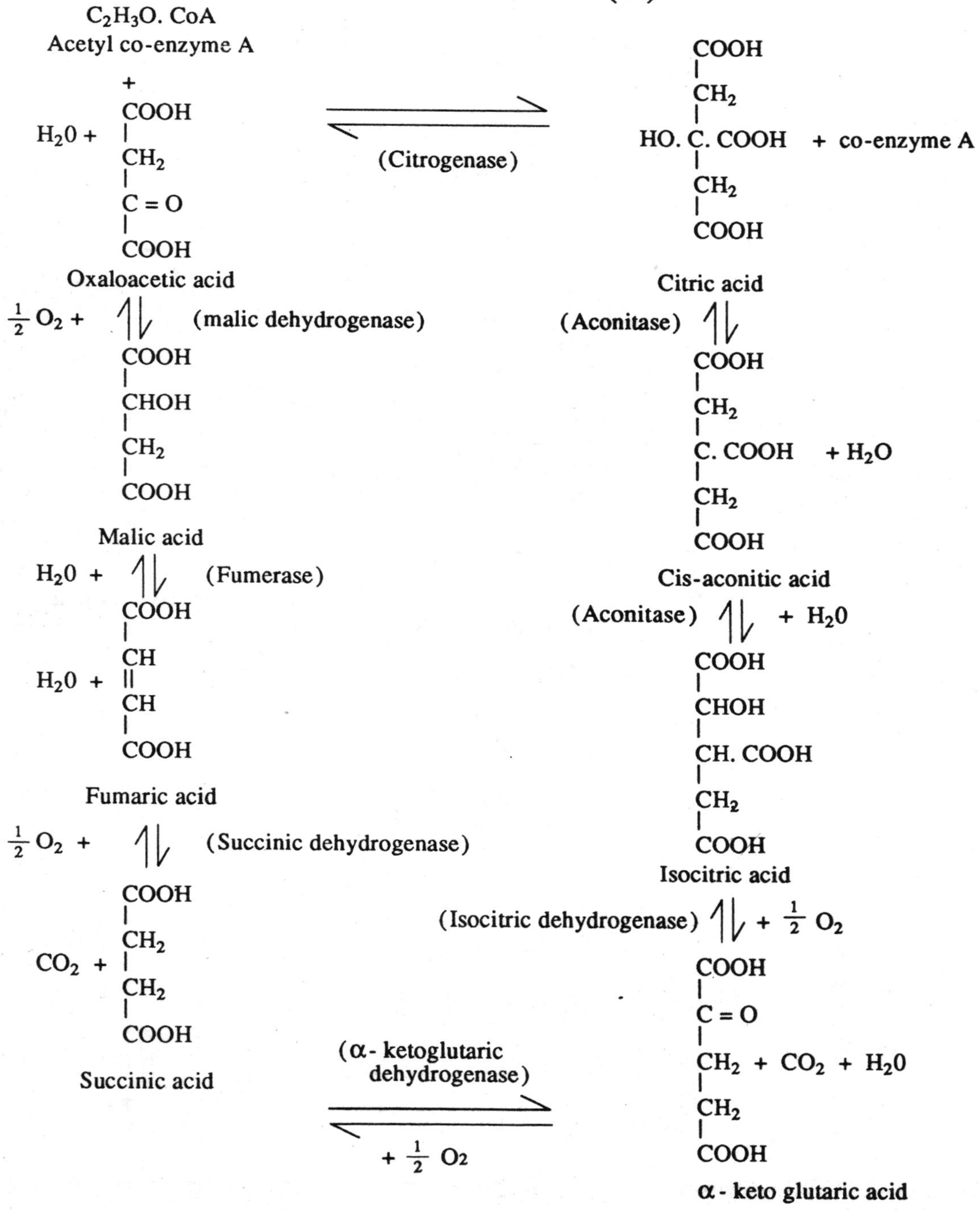

$C_2H_3O \cdot CoA$
Acetyl co-enzyme A

$$+$$

$$\text{COOH}$$
$$|$$
$H_2O + \quad \text{CH}_2$
$$|$$
$$C = O$$
$$|$$
$$\text{COOH}$$

Oxaloacetic acid

$\frac{1}{2} O_2 + \quad \uparrow\downarrow$ (malic dehydrogenase)

$$\text{COOH}$$
$$|$$
$$\text{CHOH}$$
$$|$$
$$\text{CH}_2$$
$$|$$
$$\text{COOH}$$

Malic acid

$H_2O + \quad \uparrow\downarrow$ (Fumerase)

$$\text{COOH}$$
$$|$$
$$\text{CH}$$
$H_2O + \quad ||$
$$\text{CH}$$
$$|$$
$$\text{COOH}$$

Fumaric acid

$\frac{1}{2} O_2 + \quad \uparrow\downarrow$ (Succinic dehydrogenase)

$$\text{COOH}$$
$$|$$
$$\text{CH}_2$$
$CO_2 + \quad \text{CH}_2$
$$|$$
$$\text{COOH}$$

Succinic acid

(Citrogenase)

$$\text{COOH}$$
$$|$$
$$\text{CH}_2$$
$$|$$
$HO \cdot C \cdot COOH \quad + \text{ co-enzyme A}$
$$|$$
$$\text{CH}_2$$
$$|$$
$$\text{COOH}$$

Citric acid

(Aconitase) $\uparrow\downarrow$

$$\text{COOH}$$
$$|$$
$$\text{CH}_2$$
$$|$$
$C \cdot COOH \quad + H_2O$
$$|$$
$$\text{CH}_2$$
$$|$$
$$\text{COOH}$$

Cis-aconitic acid

(Aconitase) $\uparrow\downarrow \quad + H_2O$

$$\text{COOH}$$
$$|$$
$$\text{CHOH}$$
$$|$$
$$\text{CH} \cdot \text{COOH}$$
$$|$$
$$\text{CH}_2$$
$$|$$
$$\text{COOH}$$

Isocitric acid

(Isocitric dehydrogenase) $\uparrow\downarrow \quad + \frac{1}{2} O_2$

$$\text{COOH}$$
$$|$$
$$C = O$$
$$|$$
$CH_2 + CO_2 + H_2O$
$$|$$
$$\text{CH}_2$$
$$|$$
$$\text{COOH}$$

α - keto glutaric acid

(α - ketoglutaric dehydrogenase)

$+ \frac{1}{2} O_2$

FIG : KREBS CYCLE (See p. 285)

APPENDIX III (c)

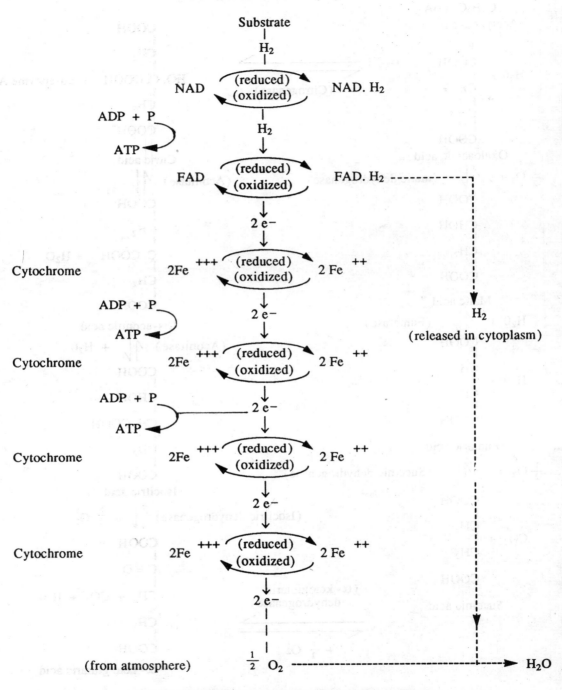

ELECTRON TRANSPORT SYSTEM (See p. 285)

GLOSSARY OF NAMES OF PLANTS

Botanical name in *italics*; English name in Roman; Indian name in CAPITALS. A. for Assamese; B. for Bengali; G. for Gujarati; H. for Hindi; K. for Kannada; M. for Malayalam; M'. for Marathi; O. for Oriya; P. for Punjabi; T. for Tamil; and T'. for Telugu.

Abelmoschus esculentus—lady's finger; A., O. & M'. BHENDI; B., H. & P. BHINDI; G. BHINDA; K. BHENDE KAYI; M. & T. VENDAKKA; T'. BENDA

Abroma augusta—devil's cotton; A. BONKOPAHI; B. & H. ULATKAMBAL; G. GUMCHI; K. DEVVA HATHI; M'. OLAKTAMBOL; P. ULTKAMBAL; T. SIVAPPUTTUTTI

Abrus precatorius—crab's eye or Indian liquorice; A. LATUMMONI; B. KUNCH; H. & P. RATTI; K. GULAGANJI; M. KUNNI; M'. GUNJ; O. KAINCHA, GUNJA; T. KUNDOOMONY; T'. GURUGINJA

Abutilon indicum—A. JAPAPETARI; B. PETARI; G. DABALI; H. KANGHI; K. THURUBI GIDA, SHREE-MUDRE GIDA; KISANGI; M. & T. PERINTHOTTY; M'. MUDRA; O. PEDIPEDIKA; P. PILIBUTI; T'. THUTIRIBENDA

Acacia nilotica (=*A. arabica*)—gum tree; A. TORUKADAM; B. BABLA; G. KALOABAVAL; H. BABUL, KIKAR; K. KARI JALI; M. & T. KARUVELAM; M' BABHUL; O. BABURI; P. KIKAR; T'. NALLATUMMA

Acacia catechu—catechu; A., B. & M'. KHAIR; G. KHER; H. & P. KATHA, KHAIR; K. KAGGALI, KACHU; M. KADARAM; O. KHAIRA; T. KADIRAM; T'. KHADIRAMU

Acalypha indica—B. MUKTOJHURI; G. VANCHI KANTO; H. KUPPI; K. KUPPI GIDA, TUPPAKEERE; M. & T. KUPPAMANI; M'. KHOKALI; O. INDRAMARISHA; P. KOKALI KUPPAMANI

Achras zapota—sapota or sapodilla plum; A. SAPHEDA; B. SHABEDA; H. & M. SAPOTA; K. CHIKKU, SAPOTA; M'. CHIKKU; O. SAPETA; P. CHIKU; T. SIMAIYILUPPAI; T'. SIMAIPPA

Achyranthes aspera—chaff-flower; A. UBTISATH; B. APANG; G. SAFED AGHEDO; H. LATJIRA; K. UTTARNI; M. KATALADY; M'. AGHADA; O. APAMARANGA; P. PUTH KANDA, KUTRI; T. NAHIROORVY; T'. ATTARENI

Acorus calamus—sweet flag; A., B. & H. BOCH; G. GODAVAJ; K. BAJE; M. VAYAMBU; M'. WEKHAND; O. BACHA; P. WARCH, BOJ, BARI; T. VASAMBOO; T'. VASA

Adhatoda vasica—A. BANHAKA; B. BASAK; G. ADALSO; H. ADALSA; K. ADUSOGE, KURCHI GIDA, ADDALASA; M. ADALODAKAM; M'. ADULSA; O. BASANGA; P. BANSA SUBJ, BASUTI; T. ADATODAY; T'. ATARUSHAMMU

Aegle marmelos—wood-apple; A. & B. BAEL; G. BILIVAPHAL; H. SIRIPHAL; K. BILVA PATRE; M. KOOVALAM; M'. BEL; O. BELA; P. BIL; T. VILVAMARAM; T'. BILAMBU

Aeschynomene indica—pith plant; A. KUNHILA; B., H. & P. SHOLA; K. BENDU KASA; M. KADESU ATTUKEDESU; O. SOLA; T. ATTUNETTEE; T'. JILUGA

Agave americana—American aloe or century plant; B. & H. KANTALA; G. JANGLI-KANVAR; K. KATTALE; M. NATTUKAITA; M'. GHAYPAT; O. BARABARASIA; P. WILAYATI KANTALA; T. ANAKUTTILAI; T'. BONTHARAKASI

Albizzia lebbek—siris tree; A., B., H., M'. & P. SIRISH; G PITOSARSHIO; K. SHIRISHA BAGE, HOMBAGE; M. VAGA; O. SIRISA; T. VAGAI; T'. DIRISANA

Allium cepa—onion; A. PONORU; B., H. & P. PIYAZ; G. DUNGARI; K. NEERULLI, ULLAGADDI; M. ULLI; M'. KANDA; O. PIAJA; T. VENGAYAM; T'. NEERULLI

Allium sativum—garlic; A. NAHARU; B. RASUN; G. LASAN; H. & P. LAHSUN; K. BELLULLI; M. VELUTHULLI; M'. LASUN; O. RASUNA; T. VELLAIPOONDU; T'. VELLULLI

Alocasia indica—A. & B. MANKACHU; G. ALAVU; H. MANKANDA; K. MANAKA; M'. ALU; O. MANASARU; P. ARVI

Aloe vera—Indian aloe; A. CHALKUNWARI; B. GHRITAKUMARI; G. KUNVAR; H. GHIKAVAR; K. LOLESARA; M. KATTARVAZHA; M'. KORPHAD; O. GHEEKUANRI; P. KAWARGANDAL, GHIKUAR; T. KUTTILAI; T'. KALABANDA

Alpinia allughas—A. TORA; B. TARA; K. DUMPARASME; M. CHITTARATHTHA; M'. TARAKA; O. GHODAGHASA; P. KALANJAN; T. PERIYARATHTHA

Alstonia scholaris—devil tree; A. CHATIAN; B. CHHATIM; H. SATIAN, SAPTAPARNA; K. SAPTA PARNA, MADDALE, KODALE; M. EZHILAMPALA; M'. SATVIN; O. CHHATIANA, CHHANCHANIA; P. SATONA; T. ELILAIPILLAI; T'. EDAKULAPALA

Alternanthera amoena—B. SENCHI; G. JALAJAMBO; K. HONAGANE SOPPU; M. KOZHUPPA; M'. KANCHARI; O. MADARANGA; P. CHURA; T. PONNAN KANNI KEERAI; T'. PONA-GANTIKURA

Amaranthus spinosus—prickly amaranth; A. KATAKHUTURA; B. KANTANATE; G. TANJALJO; H. & P. CHULAI; K. MULLU KEERE (or HARIVE SOPPU); M. MULLANCHEERA; M'. KATE MATH; O. KANTANEUTIA, KANTAMARISHA; T. MULLUKKERAI; T'. MUNDLA THOTAKURA

Amorphophallus campanulatus—A. & B. OL; G. & M'. SURAN; H. ZAMIKAND, KANDA; K. SUVARNA (or CHURNA), GEDDE; M. CHAENA; O. OLUA; P. ZAMIN KANDA; T. KARUNAKILANGU; T'. THIYA KANDHA

Anacardium occidentale—cashewnut; A. KAJUBADAM; B. HIJLIBADAM; G., H., M'. & P. KAJU; K. GODAMBI, GERUPAPPU; M. KASHUMAVU; O. LANKA BADAM; T. MUNDIRI; T'. JIDIMAMIDI

Ananas comosus—pineapple; A. MATI-KOTHAL; B. ANARAS; G., H. & M' ANANAS; T. ANASSAPPALAM; T'. ANASAPANDU

Andrographis paniculata—A. KALPATITA; B. & H. KALMEGH, MAHATITA; G. KIRYATO; K. NELA BEVU, KALA MEGHA; M. KIRIYATHTHU; M'. PALEKIRAIET; O. BHUINIMBA; P. CHARAITA; T. NELAVEMBU

Anisomeles indica—B. GOBRA; K. MANGA MARI SOPPU, HENNU KARI THUMBE; M. POOTHACHETAYAN; M'. GOPALI; O. BHUTA-AIRI; T. PEYAMERATTI

Annona reticulata—bullock's heart; A. ATLAS; B. NONA; G., H., M'. & P. RAMPHAL; K. RAMA PHALA; M. ATHA; O. NEUA, BADHIALA; T. & T'. RAMSITA

Annona squamosa—custard-apple; A. ATLAS; B. ATA; G & M'. SITAPHAL; H. & P. SHARIFA, SITAPHAL; K. SEETHA PHALA; M. SEEMA-ATHA; T. & T' SEETHA

Anthocephalus indicus—A., B., H. & P. KADAM; G. & O. KADAMBA; K. KADAMBBA MARA, KADAVALA; M. KADAMBU; M'. KADAMB

Arachis hypogaea—groundnut or peanut; A., B. & O. CHINABADAM; G MAFFALI; H. & P. MUNGPHALI; K. NELAGADALE, SHENGA, KALLEKAI; M. & T. NILAKKADALAI; M'. BHUIMUG; T'. VERU SANAGA

Areca catechu—areca- or betel-nut; A. TAMBUL; B., G., M'. & P. SUPARI; H. KASAILI; K. ADIKE; M. ADAKKA; O. GUA; T. PAKKU; T'. POKA

Argemone mexicana—prickly or Mexican poppy; A. KUHUMKATA; B. SHEALKANTA; G. DARUDI; H. PILADHUTURA; K. DATTURADA GIDA, ARISINA UMMATTI; M. SWARNAKSHEERI; M'. PIWALA DHOTRA; O.AGARA; P. KANDIARI; T. BRAHMADANDU; T'. BRAHMADANDI

Aristolochia gigas—pelican flower; A., B. & O. HANSHALATA; K. KURI GIDA; M. GARUDAKKODI; M'. POPAT VEL; P. BATAKH PHUL; T. ADATHINAPALAI

Aristolochia indica—Indian birthwort; A. ISWERMUL; B. ISHERMUL; G. & M'. SAPSAN; H. ISHARMUL; K. ESHWARI BERU TOPPALU; M. ISVARAMUULI; O. GOPOKORONI; P. ANANTMUL, ISHARMUL; T'. ESWARI

Artabotrys hexapetatus (=*A. adoratissmus*)—A. KOTHALICHAMPA; B., G. & H. KANTALICHAMPA; K. MANORANJINI, KANDALA SAMPIGE; M. & T. MANORANJINI; M'. HIRWA CHAPHA; O. CHINICHAMPA; P. CHAMPA; T'. MANORANJITHAM

Artocarpus heterophyllus—jack tree; A. KOTHAL; B. KANTHAL; G. MANPHANASA; H. KATAHAR; K. HALASU; M. & T. PILA; M'. O. PANASA; P. KATAR

Artocarpus lakoocha—monkey jack; A. CHAMA, DEWA; B. DEO, DEOPHAL; H. DEOPHAL, BARHAL; K. WATE GIDA; M'. LAKUCH; O. JEUTA; P. DEHEO

Asparagus racemosus—A. SHATMUL; B. SATAMULI; H. & P. SATAWAR; K. SHATAVARI; O. CHHATUARI; M., M'., & T. SATHAVARI; T'. SADAVARI

Asteracantha longifolia—B. KULEKHARA; G. EKHARO; H. GOKULA-KANTA; M'. KOLSHINDA; O. KANTAKALIA KOILKHIA; P. TALMAKHANA; T. NIRMULLI

Averrhoa carambola—carambola; A. KORDOITENGA; B. KAMRANGA; G. KAMARAKHA; H. & P. KAMARAKH; K. KAMARAXI; KAMARAK; M. IRIMPANPULI; M'. CAMARANGA; O. KARMANGA; T. KAMARANKAI; T'. TAMARTA

Azadirachta indica—margosa; A. MOHA-NIM; B., H. & P. NIM, MIMBA; G. LIMBA; K. OLLE BEVU; M. VEPPU; M'. KADU LIMB; O. NIMBA; T. VEMBU; T'. VFPA

Bacccaurea sapida—A. LETEKU; B. LATKAN; H. LUTKO; K. KOLI KUKKE; P. KALA BOGATI

Balanites aegyptiaca—A. HINGOOL; B. HINGAN; G. HINGER; H. & P. HIINGOL, HINGU; K. INGALADA MARA, INGLIKA; M. MANJUNTA; M'. HINGANBET; O. HINGU; T. NANJUNDAN

Bambusa tulda—bamboo; A. BANH; B., H. & P. BANS; G. KAPURA; K. HEBBIDIRU, UNDE BIDIRU; M. MULAH; M'. BAMBOO; O. BAUNSA; T. MULAI

Barleria prionitis—A. NILBAGI; B. KANTAJHANTI; G. KANTAASHERIO; H. VAJRADANTI; K. MULLU GORANTI; M. KANAKABARAM; M'. KORANTI; O. DASKARANTA; P. PILA BANSA, GAT SARIYA; T. CHEMMULLI

Barringtonia acutangula—A. HIDOL; B. & H. HIJAL; G. SAMUDARPHAL; K. NEERU GANIGALU, DHATRI PHALA; M. & T. SAMUNDRAKSHAM; M' DHATRIPHAL; O. HINJALA; P. SAMUNDURAPHAL

Basella rubra—Indian spinach; A. PURAI; B. PUIN; H., O. & P. POI; K. KEMPU BAYI BASALE; M. SAMPARCHEERA; M'. VELBONDI; T. SAMBARKEERAI

Bassia latifolia—see *Madhuca latifolia*

Batatas edulis—see *Ipomoea batatas*

Bauhinia variegata—camel's foot tree; A., B. & M'. KANCHAN; G. KOVIDARA; H. & P. KACHNAR; K. ULIPE, BILI MANDARA; M. MANDARUM; O. KANCHANA; T. TIRUVATTI; T'. ADAVIMANDARA

Benincasa hispida—ash gourd; A. KOMORA; B. CHALKUMRA; G. KOHWLA; H. & P. PETHA; K. BOODU GUMBALA; M. KUMPALAM; M'. KOHALA; O. PANIKAKHARU; T. KUMPALY; T'. PULLA GUMMUDI

Beta vulgaris—beet; A. BEET-PALENG; B. BEET-PALANG; G. & M'. BEET; H. & P. CHUKANDAR; K. BEET ROOT; O. PALANGA SAGA, BEET

Biophytum sensitivum—sensitive wood-sorrel; A. & B. BAN-NARANGA; G. JAHARERA; H. LAJALU; K. HORA MUNI; M. MUKKUTTI, THINDANAZHI; M'. LAJARI

Blumea lacera—A. KUKURSHUTA; B. KUKURSONGA; G. KALARA; H. & P. KOKRONDA; K. GANDHARI GIDA; M'. BURANDO; O. POKASUNGA; T. KATUMULLANGI; T'. KARUPOGAKU

Boerhaavia diffusa—A. PONONUA; B. & M'. PUNARNA-VA; G. GHETULI; H. THIKRI, GADHAPURVA; K. BAL-AVADIKE, GONAJALI, RAKTA PUNARNAVA; M. THAZHUTHAMA; O. GHODAPURUNI; P. BISKHAPPA, ITSIT; T. MUKKARATAI; T'. PUNARNABA

Bombax ceiba—(=*Salmalia malabarica*)—silk cotton tree; A. SIMALU; B. SIMUL; G. ʀATOSHEMALO; H. & P. SIMAR, SIMBAL; K. BOORUGA, KEMPUBOORUGA; M. & T'. ELAVU, MULLILAVU; M'. KATE SAVAR; O. SIMULI; T'. KONDABURAGA, SALMALI

Borassus flabellifer—palmyra-palm; A. & B. TAL; G. & M'. TAD; H. & P. TAR; K. TALE MARA, TATI NUNGU; M. KARIMPANA; O. TALA; T. PANAI; T'. THADI

Boswellia serrata—incense tree; A. DHUNA; B. DHUP, GUGGUL; G. DHUP GUGALI; H. GUGUL; K. CHILAKA DHUPA, CHILAKADI, MADDI; M. MUKUNDAM; M'. DHUP; P. SALAI, SALER; T. ATTAM; T'. ANDUGA

Brassica campestris—mustard; A. SARIAH; B. SARISHA; G. SAFED-RAI; H. & P. SARON; K. SASIVE; M. KATUKU; M'. MOHORI; O. SOROSHA; T. KARUPPUKKADUGU; T'. AAVA

Bryophyllum pinnatum—sprout-leaf plant; A. PATEGAZA, DUPORTENGA; B. PATHURKUCHI; H. ZAKHM-I-HAYAT; K. KADU BASALE; M'. PANPHUTI; O. AMAR-POI; P. PATHURCHAT; T. RANAKALLI; T'. SIMAJAMUDU

Butea monosperma—flame of the forest or parrot tree; A., B. & M'. PALAS; G. KHAKARA; H. & P. DHAK; K.

MUTTUGA; M. CHAMATHA; O. PALASA; T. SAMITHU, PALASAM; T'. MODUGA,

Caesalpinia crista (=*C. bonducella*)—fever nut; A. LETAGUTI; B. NATA; G. KAKACHIA; H. KATKARANJ; K. GAJJIGA; M. KAZHANCHIKKUROO; M' SAGARGOTA; O. GILA; P. BEL KARANJWA; T. KALAKKODI

Caesalpinia pulcherrima—dwarf gold mohur or pea-cock flower; A. KRISHNACHURA; B. RADHACHURA; G. SANDHESHARO; H. GULETURA; K. KENJIGE GIDA, RATNA GANDHI; M. RAJMALLI; M'. SHANKASUR; O. KRUSH-NACHUDA, GODIBANA; P. KRISHANACHURA; T. MAYIRKONRAI; T'. TURAYI

Caesalpinia sappan—sappan or Brazil wood; B., H. & P. BAKAM; G. PATANG; K. PATHANGA; SAPPANGA; M. PATRANGAM; M'. PATANG; T. PATANGAM; T'. PATANGA

Cajanus cajan—pigeon pea or red gram; A. RAHAR-MAH; B. ARAHAR; G. TUVARE; H. RAHAR; K. THOGARI KALU; M. THUVARA; M'. TUR; O. HARADA; T. THO-VARAY; T'. KANDULU

Calamus viminalis—cane; A. BAT; B., H. & P. BET; K. NEERU HAMBU, BETTA; M. CHOORAL; M'. VET; O. BETA; T. SURAI; T'. BETTAMU

Calophyllum inophyllum—Alexandrian laurel; B. & H. SULTANA-CHAMPA, PUNNAG; K. SURA HONNE, PINNE KAI, PUNNAGA; M. & P. PUNNA; M'. UNDI; O. POLAN-GA; T. PUNNAGAM; T'. PUNNAGA

Calotropis gigantea—madar; A. AKON; B. AKANDA; G. AKADO; H. & P. AK; K. EKKADA GIDA; M. & T. ERUKKU; M'. RUI; O. ARKA; T'. JILLEDU

Canavalia ensiformis—sword bean; A. KANTAL-URAHI; B. MAKHAN-SHIM; H. BARA-SEM; K. THAMATE BALLI, SHAMBE; M. & T. VAALAVARAKKAI; M'. ABAI; O. BADA SIMBA, MAHARADA; P. BARASEM, TALWAR PHALI; T'. TUMBATTAN KAYA

Canna orientalis (=*C. indica*)—Indian shot; A. PARIJAT-PHUL; B. & O. SARBAJAYA; G. KARDALI; H. SABBA-JAYA; K. KYANA GIDA; M. KATIUVAZHA; M'. KARDAL; P. HAKIK; T. KALVAALAI

Cannabis sativa—hemp; A., B., H. & P. BHANG, GANJA; G., P. & T. GANJA : K. GANJA GIDA, BHANGI; M. KAN-CHAVU; M'. BHANG; O. BHANGA, GANJEI; T'. GANJA CHETTU

Capparis sepiaria—B. KANTA-GURKAMAI; G. KAN-THARO; H. HIUN; K. OLLE UPPI GIDA, KADU KATTARI; M. THORATTI; M'. BASHINGI, KAKADANI; O. KANTIKA-PALI; P. HIUS, HIUNGARNA; T. KARINDU; T'. NALLUPPI

Capsicum annuum—chilli; A. JOLOKIA; B. LANKA, MARICH; G. LALMIRICHI; H. & P. LAL-MIRCH; K.

MENASINA KAI; M. MULAGU; M'. MIRCHI; O. LANKA-MARICHA; T. MILAGU; T'. MIRAPAKAYA

Cardiospermum halicacabum—balloon vine; A. KOPALPHOTA; B. KAPALPHUTKI, SHIBJHUL; G. KARODIO; K. BEKKINA BUDDE GIDA, ERUMBALLI; M. VALLIYUZHINJA; M'. KAPALPHODI; O. PHUTPHUTKIA; P. HAB-UL-KULKUL; T. MODAKATHAN; T'. BUDDAKAKKIRA, KASARITIGE

Carica papaya—papaw; A. AMITA; B. PAYPAY; G. PAYPAYI; H. & P. PAPITA; K. PARANGI, PAPAYA, PAPALI; M. KARUTHA; M'. POPAI; O. AMRUTABHANDA; T. PAPALI; T'. BOPPAYI

Carissa carandas—A. KORJA-TENGA; B. KARANJA; H. KARAUNDA; K. KAVALI GIDA, KARANDA; M. ELIMULLU; M'. KARVANDA; O. KHIRAKOLI; P. GARANDA; T. KALAKKAI; T'. KALIVI VARA

Carthamus tinctorius—safflower; A. & B. KUSUMPHUL; G. KUSUMBO; H. & P. KUSAM; K. KUSUBI, KUSUME; M. SINDOORIM; M'. KARDAI; O. KUSUMA; T. KUSUMBA; T'. AGNISIKHA

Carum copticum—see *Trachyspermum ammi*

Cassia fistula—Indian laburnum; A. SONARU; B. SHONDAL; G. GARMALA; H. & P. AMALTASH; K. KAKKE GIDA, HONNAVARIKE; M. & T. KONNAI; M'. BAHAWA; O. SUNARI

Cassia sophera—A. MEDELUA; B. KALKASUNDE; G. KASUNDARI; H. & P. KASUNDA; K. KASAMARDA; M. PONNARAN or PONNAMTHAKARA; M'. KALAKASBINDA; O. KUSUNDA; T. PONNAVEERAN

Cassytha filiformis—B. AKASHBEL; H. AMARBELI; K. AKASHA BALLI, MANGANA VIDIDARA; M. AKASAVALLI; M'. AKASHVALLI; O. AKASHA BELA; P. AMIL, AMARBELI

Casuarian equisetifolia—beef-wood tree or she-oak; A., B., H. & P. JHAU; G. VILIYATI SARU; K. SARVE MARA, GALI MARA; M. CHOOLAMARUM; KATTADIMARUM; M'. KHADSHERANI; O. JHAUN; T. SAVUKKU; T'. SARAVU

Cayratia carnosa—see *Vitis trifolia*

Cedrela toona—toon; B., H. & P. TOON; K. NANDI URUKSHA, NANDURI, BELANDI; M. CHUVANNAGIL; M'. MAHANIM; T. MALAVEMBU; T'. GALIMANU

Celosia cristata—cock's comb; A. KUKURA-JOA-PHUL; B. MORAG-PHUL; G. LAPADI; H. JATADHARI; K. MAYURA SHIKHI; M. KOZHIPULLU; M'. KOMBADA; O. GANJACHULIA; P. KUKUR-PHUL

Centella asiatica—Indian pennywort; A. MANIMUNI; B. THULKURI; G. KARBRAHMI; H. & P. BRAHMI-BOOTI; K. ONDELAGA, BRAHMI SOPPU; M. KODANGAL, KOTAKAN; M'. BRAHMI; O. THALKUDI; T. VULLARAI

Cestrum nocturnum—queen of the night; A. & B. HASNA-HANA; H. RAT-KI-RANI; K. RATRI RANI HOOVU

Chenopodium album—A. JILMIL-SAK; B. & H. BATHUA-SAK; G. CHEEL; K. HUNCHIK POLYA; M'. CHAKAVAT; O. BATHU SAGA; P. BATHU; T. PARUPAKKIRAI

Chrysanthemum coronarium—A. & B. CHANDRAMALLIKA; G. & H. GULDAUDI; K. SHAVANTIGE, SEVANTIGE; M. SHEVANTI; O. SEBATI; P. GULDADU; T. SHAMANTIPPU; T'. CHAMANTI

Chrysopogon aciculatus—love thorn; A. BONGUTI; B. CHORKANTA; K. GANJIGARIKE HULLU; O. GUGUCHIA; P. CHORKANDA

Cicer arietinum—gram; A. BOTMAH; B. CHHOLA; G., H. & P. CHANA; K. KADALE, CHANA; M. & T. KADALAI; M'. HARABHARA; O. BUTA; T. SANIKALU

Cinnamomum camphora—camphor; A. & B. KARPUR; G., H. & M'. KAPUR; K. KARPURADA GIDA; M. KARPPURAVRIKSHAM; O. KARPURA; P. KAFUR; T. KARUPPURAM; T'. KAPPURAMU

Cinnamomum tamala—bay leaf; A. TEJPAT, MAHPAT; B. TEZPATA; G. & H. TEZPAT; K. KADU DALCHINNI; M'. TAMAL; O. & P. TEJPATRA; T. TALISHAPPATTIRI; T'TALLISHAPATRI

Cinnamomum zeylanicum—cinnamon; A., B., G., M'., O. & P. DALCHINI; H. DARCHINI; K. DALCHINNI, LAVANGA CHAKKE; M. & T. ILLAVANGAM; T'. DALCHINA CHEKKA

Cissus quadrangularis—A., B. & H. HARHJORA; K. MANGARA VALLI, SANDU BALLI; M. PIRANTA; M'. KANDAWEL; O. HADAVANGA; P. GIDAR-DAK, DRUKRI; T. PIRANDAI; T'. NALLERU

Citrullus colocynthis—colocynth; A. KOABHATURI; B. MAKAL; G. & H. INDRAYAN; K. DODDA HALMEKKE, INDRAVARUNI; M. & T. KUMMATHIKKAI, PEYKUMMATTY; M'. KAVANDAL; O. INDRAYANA; P. TUMMA; T'PATSAKAYA

Citrullus lanatus—water melon; A. KHORMUJA; B. TARMUZ; G. KARIGU; H. & P. TARBUZA; K. KALLANGADI BALLI; M. & T. KUMMATTIKKAI; M'. KALINGAD; O. TARABHUJA

Citrus aurantifola—sour lime; A. NEMU-TENGA; B. KAGJI-NEBU; G. LIMBU; H. NIMBOO; K. NIMBE; M. CHERUNARAKAM; M'. KAGADI LIMBU; O. LEMBU; P. GALGAL; T. ELIMICHCHAM; T'.NARINJA

Citrus grandis—pummelo or shaddock; A. REBABTENGA; B. BATABI-NEBU; G. OBAKOTRU; H. & P.

CHAKOTRA; K. CHAKKOTHA; M. BAMBLEENARAKAM; M'. PAPANAS; O. BATAPI; T. BAMBALMAS

Citrus reticulata—orange; A. KAMALA-TENGA; B. KAMALA; G. SUNTRA; H. NARANGI; K. KITTALE; M. NARAKAM; M'. SANTRA; O. KAMALA; P. SANGTRA; T. NARANGAM; T'. NARANJI

Cleome—see *Polanisia*

Clerodendrum infortunatum—A. BHETTITA; B. & H. BHANT, GHENTU; K. MADARASA MALLIGE, IBBANE; M. PERU-VALLEM; G. & M'. KARI; O. KUNTI; P. KARU; T. KARUKANNI; T'. BASAVANAPADU

Clitoria ternatea—butterfly pea; A., B. & O. APARAJITA; G. GARANI; H. APARAJIT, GOKARNA; K. GIRI KARNIKE, SATUGARA GIDA; M. SANKHUPUSHPAM; M'. GOKARNA; P. APARAJIT, NILI LOEL; T. KAKKATAN; T'. SANGAPUSH-PAM

Coccinia indica—(=*C. cordifolia*)—A. BELIPOKA; B. TELAKUCHA; H. KUNDARU, BHIMBA; K. THONDE KAYI, KAGE DONDE; M. KOVEL; M. KOVEL; M'. TONDALE; O. KUNDURI, KAINCHI-KAKUDI; P. GHOL; T. KOVARAI; T'. KAKIDONDA

Cocos nucifera—coconut-palm; A. NARIKOL; B. NARIKEL; G., H. & P. NARIYAL; K. TENGU; M. THENGU, NALIKERAM; M'. NARAL; O. NADIA; T. THENGU; T'. TENKAYA

Coix lachryma-jobi—job's tears; A. KAURMONI; B. & P. KALA-KUNCH, GURGAR; G. KASAI; H. SANKRU; K. KALMATTU BEEJA, KOTHI BEEJA; M'. RAFI JONDHALA; O. GARAGADA; T. KATTU KUNDUMANI

Colocasia esculenta—taro; A. & B. KACHU; H. & P. KACHALU; K. KESAVINA GEDDE, SAVE GEDDE; M. CHEMPU; M'. KASALU; O. SARU; T. SAMAKILANGOO; T'. CHEMA

Commelina bengalensis—A. KONASIMOLU; B. KANSHI-RA; G. MHOTUNSHUSHMULIYUN; H. KANKIYA; K. GUB-BACHI BALE, KANNE SOPPU; O. KANSIRI

Coriandrum sativum—coriander; A., B., H., O. & P. DHANIA; G. DHANE; K. KOTHAMBARI, HAVEEJA; M. & T. KOTTAMALLI; M'. KOTHIMBIR; T'. DHANIYALU

Crataeva nurvala—(=*C. religiosa*)—A. & B. BARUN; G. VAYAVARNA; H. & P. BARNA; K. ADIRAJA, MAVALIN-GA, NERVALA; M. NIRMATHALAM; M'. WAYAWARNA; O. BARUNA; T. MAVALINGAM; T'. VOOLEMERI

Crinum asiaticum—B. & P. SUKHDARSHAN; M. POLATHALI; G. & M'. NAGDAUNA; H. PINDAR; K. VISHA MOONGILI, VISHA BIDURU; O. ARISA; T. VESHAMOONGHEE

Crocus sativus—saffron; A., B. & O. JAFRAN; G. & M'.

KESHAR; H. & P. ZAFRAN; K. KUMKUMA KESARI; T. KUNGUMAPU; T'. KUNKUMAPUVU

Crotalaria juncea—Indian or sunn hemp; A. SHON; B. SHONE; G., H. & P. SAN; K. APSENA-BU, SANNA SENABU; M. THANTHALAKOTTI; M'. KHULKHULA; O. CHHANAPATA; T. SANAPPAI; T'. JANNAMU

Crotalaria sericea—rattlewort; A. GHANTAKORNA; B. ATASHI; H. JHUNJHUNIA; K. GIJIGIJI GIDA; M. THANTHALAKOTTI; M'. GHAGRI; O. JUNKA; P. JHAN-JHANIAN

Croton tiglium—A. JOYPAL; B. JAIPAL; G. JAMAL GOET; H., M'. & P. JAMALGOTA; K. JAPALA; M. & T. NIR-VALEM; O. BAKSA GACHHA

Cucumis melo—melon; A. BANGI; B. PHUTI; G. TAR-BUCH; H. & P. KHARBUZA, PHUTI & KAKRI; K. KARABU-JA, KEKKARIKE; M. & T. THANNIMATHAI; M'. KHARBUJ; O. KHARBUJA

Cucumis sativus—cucumber; A. TIANH; B. SASHA; G. KAKRI; H., M'. & P. KHIRA; K. SOUTHE KAYI; M. MUL-LENVELLARI; O. KAKUDI; T. MULLUVELLARI

Cucurbita moschata—sweet gourd; A. RONGALAU; B. MITHAKUMRA; H. MITHAKADDU; K. SEEGUMBALA; M. MATHANGAI; M'. KALA BHOPALA; O. MITHA KOKHARU; P. HALWA-KADDU; T. POOSANIKAI

Curcuma amada—mango ginger; A. & B. AMADA; G. AMBA-HALDAR; H. AM-HALDI; K. MAVINA SHUNTI; KARPURA ARISINA; M'. AMBE HALAD; O. AMBA KASSIA ADA; P. AMBA HALDI; T'. MAMIDIALLAM

Curcuma longa—turmeric; A. HOLODHI; B. HALOOD; G. & M'. HALAD; H. & P. HALDI; K. ARISINA; M. MAN-GAL; O. HALADI; T. MANJAL; T'. PASUPU

Cuscuta reflexa—dodder; A. AKASHILOTA, RAVA-NARNARI; B. SWARNALATA; G. AKASWEL; H. AKASH-BEL, AMARBEL; K. BADANIKE, BANDALIKE, MUDITALE; M'. AMAR VEL; O. NIRMULI; P. AMARBEL

Cynodon dactylon—dog grass; A. DUBORIBON; B. DURBAGHAS; G. DURVA, H. & P. DOOB; K. GARIKE HULLU, KUDIGARIKE; M. & T. ARUGAMPULLU; M'. HARALI; O. DUBA GHASA; T'. GERICHA GADDI

Cyperus rotundus—sedge; A. MOTHA; B. & H. MUTHA; G. BARIK-MOTHA; K. TUNGE HULLU, KONNARI GEDDE; M. KORA; M'. & P. NAGAR-MOTHA; O. MUTHA GHASA; T. KORAI; T'. PURA GADDI

Dalbergia latifolia—Indian rosewood; B. SITSAL; G. SISAM; K. BEETE MARA, TODEGATTI; M. & T. ITTI; M'. SISSU; O. PAHADI SISU; T'. JITTEGI

Dalbergia sissoo—Indian redwood; A. SHISHOO; B. SISsoo; G. SHISHAM; H. & P. SHISHAM, TAHLI; K. BIRADI, BINDI, SHISSU; M. VEETI; M'. SHISAVI; O. SISSU

Datura stramonium—thorn-apple; A. DHOTURA; B. DHUTRA; G. DHATOORA; H. & P. DHUTURA; K. DATTURA, UMMATTI; M. UMMAM; M'. DHOTRA; O. DUDURA; T. OOMMATHAI; T'. UMMATHA

Delonix regia—gold mohur; A. RADHACHURA; B. KRISHNACHURA; G., H., M. & P. GULMOHR; K. SEEME SANKESWARA, KEMPU TURAI; M. MARAMANDARAM; O. RADHACHUDA; T. MAYILKONNAI

Dendropthoe falcata (=*Loranthus longiflorus*)—A. ROGHUMALA; B. MANDA; G. VANDO; H. BANDA; K. SIGARE BANDANIKE; M. ITHTHIL; M'. BANDGUL; O. MALANGA, MADANGA; P. PAND; T. PULLURUVI; T'. BAJINNIKI, BADANIKA

Desmodium gangeticum—B. SALPANI; G. SALVAN; H. SALPAN; K. SALAPARNI, KOLAKU NARU; M. PULLATI; M'. SALPARNI; O. KURSOPANI; P. SHALPURHI; T. PULLADI; T'. GITANARAM

Desmodium gyrans—Indian telegraph plant; A. & B. BANCHANDAL, GORACHAND; H. BAN-CHAL; K. NAGATAGARE, TELEGRAPH GIDA; O. GORA CHANDA, TELEGRAPH GACHHA; P. PAUDA TAR

Dillenia indica—A. OU-TENGA; B., H. & P. CHALTA; G. CARAMBAL; K. MUCHHILU, KALTEGA; M. VALLAPUNNA; M'. KARAMAL; O. OU; T. UVATTEKU; T'. UVVA

Dioscorea alata—white yam; A. KATH-ALOO, PATNI-ALOO; B. & H. CHUPRIALOO, KHAM-ALOO; K. MUDI GENASU, TOONA GENASU; M'. KONA; O. KHAMBO-ALOO P. KNISS; T. KAYAVALLI; T'. GUNAPENDALAMU

Dioscorea bulbifera—wild yam; A. GOCH-ALOO; B. GACHH-ALOO; G. SAURIYA; H. & P. ZAMINKHAND; K. HEGGENASU, KUNTA GENASU; M. KATTUKACHIL M'. KADU KARANDA; O. DESHI-ALOO, PITA-ALOO; T. KATTUKKILANGU; T'. PENDALAMU

Diospyros ebenum—Indian ebony; B. ABLOOSH; H. TENDU; K. BALE MARA; M. KARU; M'. & P. ABNUS; T. KAKKAYITALI; T'. NALLAVALLUDU

Diospyros peregrina—wild mangosteen; A. & O. KENDU; B. & P. GAB; G. TEMRU; H. TENDU; M. VANANJI; M'. TEMBURNI; T. TUVARAI; T'. TUMMIKA

Dolichos lablab—country bean; A. UROHI; B. SHIM; G. AVRI; H. & P. SEM; K. AVARE BALLI; M. SIMA-PAYARU; M'. PAVATA; O. SIMA; T. AVARAI; T'. CHIKKUDI

Duranta repens (=*D. plumieri*)—A. JEORA-GOCH; B. DURANTA-KANTA; H. & P. NILKANTA; K. DURANTHA KANTI; M'. DURANTA; O. BILATI KANTA, BENJUATI

Ecobolium linneanum—B. NILKANTHA; H. & P. UDAJATI; K. KAPPUKARNI, KAPPUBOBLI; M. KURANTA; M'. RAN ABOLI; O. NILAKANTHA; T. NILAMBARI

Eclipta alba—A. KEHORAJI; B. KESARAJ; G. BHANGRA; H. & P. SAFED BHANGRA; K. GARUGADA GIDA, GARUGALU; M. & T. KAYYANYAM, KAITHONNI; M'. MAKA; O. KESHDURA

Elephantopus scaber—elephant's foot; B. & H. HASTIPADA, GOBHI; G. BHOPA THARI; K. HASTIPADA, HAKKARIKE; M. & T. ANACHUVADI; M'. HASTI PAD; O. GOBI; P. GAOZBAN

Eleusine coracana—B. & H. MARUA; G. NAVTO; K. & T'. RAGI; M. PANJAPPULLU; M'. NACHANI; O. MANDIA; P. KODRA, MANDWA; T. KOLVARAKU

Emblica officinalis—emblic myrobalan; A. AMLOKI; B. AMLA, AMLAKI; G. AMBALA; H. AMLA, AMLIKA; K. NILLI-BETTADA NELLI, NELLI-ISNELLI; M. & T. NELLIKKAI; M'. AWALA; O. ONLA; P. AMLA; T'. USIRI

Enhydra fluctuans—A. HELACHI-SAK, MONOA-SAK, B. & P. HALENCHA; H. HARUCH; M'. HARKUCH; O. HIDIMICHI, PANI SAGA

Entada gigas (=*E. phaseoloides*)—nicker bean; A. GHILA; B., H., O. & P. GILA; G. SUVALI-AMLI; K. GARDALA, HALLEKAYI BALLI; M. KAKKUVALLY; M'. GARBI; T. CHILLU; T'. GILLATIGAI

Enterolobium saman—see *Pithecolobium saman*

Ervatamia coronaria—crepe-jasmine; A. KOTHONA-PHUL; B. & M'. TAGAR; H. & P. CHANDNI; K. NANDI BATLU, NANJA BATLU; M. & T. NANTHIAR VATTAM; O. TAGARA

Erythrina variegata—coral tree; A. MODAR; B. MANDAR; G. PANARAWAS; H. PANJIRA; K. HARIVANA, VARJIPE; M. & T. MURUKKU; M'. PANGARA; O. PALDHUA; P. DARAKHT FARID, PANGRA

Euphorbia antiquorum—B. BAJBARAN or TESHIRA-MANSHA; G. TANDHARI; K. BONTE GALLI, CHADARA GALLI; M. CHATHIRAKKALLI; M'. CHAUDHARI NIWDUNG; O. DOKANA SIJU; P. DANDA THOR, TIDHARA SEHUD; T. SHADRAIKALLI; T'. BONTHAKALI

Euphorbia neriifolia—A. SIJU; B. MANSHASIJ; G. THOR; H. SIJ; K. ELE GALLI; M. & T. ILAKKALLI; M'. CHAUDHARI NIWDUNG; O. PATARA SIJU; P. GANGICHU; T'. AKUJEMUDU

Euphorbia nivulia—A. SIJU; B. SIJ; G. THOR KANTALO; H. SIJ, THOR; K. GOOTA GALLI; M. & T. ILAKKALLI; M'. NIWDUNG; O. SIJU; T'. AKUJEMUDU

Euphorbia (=*Poinsettia*) *pulcherrima*—poinsettia; A.

LALPAT; B., M'. & P. LALPATA; K. POINSETTIA GIDA; O. PANCHUTIA; P. LAL-PATTI; T. MAYILKUNNI

Euryale ferox—A. NIKORI; B., H. & P. MAKHNA; M'. PADMA KANT, MAKHAN; O. KANTA PADMA

Evolvulus alsinoides—G. JHINKIPHUDARDI; H. SANKHAPUSHPI, VISHNUKRANTA; K. VISHNUKRANTHI; M. VISHNUKTANTHI, KRISHNAKTANTHI; M'. VISHNUKRANT; O. BICHHAMALIA; P. SHANKH-HOLI; T. VISHNUKIRANDI; T'. VISHNUKRANTHI

Feronia limonia—see *Limonia acidissima*

Ferula assa-foetida—asafoetida; A., B., G., H., M'. & P. HING; K. INGU; HINGU; M. KAYAM; O. HENGU; T'. INGUVA

Ficus bengalensis—banyan; A. BORGOCH; B. BOT; H. & P. BARH; G. & M'. WAD; K. AALADA MARA; M. PEERALU; O. BARA; T. AALUMARAM; T'. MARRI

Ficus glomerata—A. DIMORU; B. JAJNYA-DUMUR; G. UMBARO; H. & P. GULAR; K. ATHI; M. & T. ATHTHIMARAM; M'. UMBAR; O. DIMURI; T'. BODDA

Flacourtia jangomas (=*F. cataphracta*)—A. PONIAL; B. & H. PANIALA; G. TALISPATRA; K. GORAJI, CHANCHALLI, TALISAPATRE; M. & T. TALISAM; M'. JUGGUM; O. PANIONLA; P. PANIALA, PANIAUNLA; T'. TALISAPATRA-MU

Flacourtia ramontchi & *F. indica*—B. BOINCHI; H. BOWCHI, BILANGRA; K. GAJABIRA, MULLUTARE, KUDAVALE, M'. BHEKAL; O. BAINCHA KOLI; P. KATAL, KUKAI; T. MALUKKARAI; T'. KANAREGU

Foeniculum vulgare—anise or fennel; A. GUAMOORI; B. PANMOURI; G. WARIARI; H. & P. SAUNF; K. DODDA JEERIGE, DODDA SOMPU; M'. BADISHEP; O. PAN MOHURI

Garcinia mangostana—mangosteen; B., H. & M'. MANGUSTAN; G. & K. MANGOSTEEN; M. SULAMPULI; O. MANGOSTEEN, SITAMBU; T. SULAMBULI

Gardenia jasminoides—cape jasmine; A. TOGOR; B., H. & P. GANDHARAJ; G. DIKAMALI; K. SUVASANE MALLE; M'. GANDHRAJ; O. SUGANDHARAJ

Girardinia zeylanica—A. SHORUCHORAT; B. BICHUTI; M. AANACHORIYANAM; O. BICHHUATI; P. BICHUTI, BHABHER

Gloriosa superba—glory lily; A. & B. ULATCHANDAL; G. & M'. KHADYANAG; H. KALIARI, KULHARI; K. SHIVASHAKTI, LANGULIKA; M. MANTHONNI, PARAYANPOOVA; O. PANCHAANGULIA; P. GURHPATNI, KULHARI; T. KALAPAIKILANGU; T'. AGNISIKA

Glycosmis arborea—A. CAULDHOA; B. ASHHOURA; H. BANNIMBU; M. PANAL; O. CHAULADHUA

Gossypium sp.—cotton; A. KOPAH; B., H. & P. KAPAS; G. RUI; K. HATHI; M. KURUPARATHY; M'. KAPUS; O. KOPA; T. PARATHY

Gynandropsis gynandra—A. BHUTMULA; B. HURHURE; G. ADIYA-KHARAM; H. HURHUR; K. NARAMBELE SOPPU; M. KATTUKATUKU; M'. TILVAN; O. ANASORISIA, SADA HURHURIA; P. HULHUL; T. NAIKADUGU; T'. VAMINTA

Helianthus annuus—sunflower; A. BELIPHUL; B. & O. SURJYAMUKHI; G. SURYAMUKHI; H. & P. SURAJMUKHI; K. SURYAKANTHI; M., T. & T'. SURIYAKANTI; M'. SURYAPHUL

Heliotropium indicum—heliotrope; A. & B. HATISUR; G. HATHISUNDHANA; H. HATTASURA; K. CHELUKONDI GIDA, CHELUMANI GIDA; M. TEKKADA; M'. BHURUNDI; O. HATISUNDA; P. UNTH-CHARA

Hemidesmus indicus—Indian sarsaparilla; A. & B. ANANTAMUL; G. DURIVEL; H. ANANTAMUL, SALSA; K. SUGANDHI BERU, SOGADE BERU; M'. ANANTMUL; O. ANANTAMULA, KAPRI; P. DESI SARVA; T. NANNARI; T' SUGANDIPALA

Hibiscus cannabinus—Madras or Deccan hemp; B. NILITA; G. BHINDI; H. AMBARI; K. PUNDI, GOGU; M. KANJARU; M'. AMBADI; O. KAUNRIA, NALITA; P. SANKUKRA; T. KACHURAI

Hibiscus esculentus—see *Abelmoschus esculentus*

Hibiscus mutabilis—A. & B. STHALPADMA; G. UPALASARI; H. GULIAJAIB; K. BETTA DAVARE, KEMPUSURYAKANTHI; M. CHINAPPARATTI; M'. GULABI BHENDI; O. THALAPADMA; P. GUL-I-AJAIB; T. SEMBARATTAI

Hibiscus rosa-sinensis—China rose or shoe-flower; A. JOBA; B. JABA; G. JASUNT; H. GURHAL, JASUM; K. KEMPU DASAVALA; M. CHEMPARATHY; M'. JASWAND; O. MANDARA; P. GURHAL, JIA PUSHPA; T. SAMBATHOOCHEDI; T'. DASANI

Hibiscus sabdariffa—rozelle; A. MESEKA-TENGA; B. MESTA; H. & P. PATWA; K. KEMPU PUNDRIKE; M. PULICHI; M'. LAL-AMBADI; O. KHATA KAUNRIA

Hiptage bengalensis (=*H. madablota*)—A. MADHOILOTA; B. & O. MADHABILATA; G. MADHAVI; H. MADHULATA; K. MADHABI LATHE; M. SITAPU; M'. MADHUMALATI; P. MADHULATA, BANKAR; T. KURUKKATTI, MADAVI

Holarrhena antidysenterica—A. DUDKHORI; B. KURCHI; G. INDRAJAVANU; H. KUTAJ, KARCHI; K. KODACHAGA, KODAMURUKA, KORJU; M. KODAKAPPALA, M'. KUDA; O. PITA KORUA; P. INDER JAU, KAWAR

Hordeum vulgare—barley; A. & B. JOB; G. BAJRI; H. JAWA; K. BARLEY, JAVE GODHI; M'. SATU; O. BARLEY, JABA; P. JAU; T. BARLIYARISI; T'. YAVAKA

Hydrocotyle—see *Centella*

Hygrophila spinosa—see *Asteracantha longifolia*

Impatiens balsamina—balsam; A. DAMDEUKA; B. DOPATI; H. GULMENDI; K. GOURI HOOVU, BASAVANA PADA; M. & T. BALSAM; M'. TERADA; O. HARAGOURA; P. MAJITI, BANTIL, PALLU

Indigofera tinctoria—indigo; A., B., H. & P. NIL; G. GALI; K. OLLE NEELI, HENNU NEELI; M. AMARY; M'. NEEL; O. NILA; T. AVARY; T'. AVIRI

Ipomoea batatas—sweet potato; A. & B. MITHA-ALOO; G. SHAKKARIA; H. & P. SHAKARKAND; K. GENASU; M. MADHURAKI ZHANGU; M'. RATALA; O. CHINI-ALOO, KANDAMULA; T'. KANDAMOOLA

Ipomoea aquatica (=*I. reptans*)—water bindweed; A. KALMAU; B. & H. KALMI-SAK; G. NALINIBHAJI; K. BILI HAMBU; M'. KALAMBI, NAL; O. KALAMA SAGA; P. NALI, KALMI SAG; T'. TUTICURA

Ipomoea pes-tigridis—B. LANGULI-LATA; K. ADAMBALLI; M. VELLATAMPU; O. KANSARINATA; P. ISHOPECHAN

Ixora coccinea—A. & B. RANGAN; H. GOTAGANDHAL, RANJAN; K. MALE HOOGIDA, KEPALE; M. & T. CHETHTHY, THETTY; M'. MAKADI; O. KHADIKA PHULA, RANGANI; P. RUNGAN

Jasminum sambac—jasmine; A. JUTIPHUL; B. BELA; G. BATMOGRI; H. MUGRA; K. GUNDU MALLIGE; M. MULLA; M'. MOGARA; O. MALLI

Jatropha curcas—physic or purging nut; A. BONGALI-ARA; B. BAGHBHARENDA; G. JEPAL; H. JANGLI-ARANDI; K. KADU HARALU; M. KATALAVANAKKU; M'. MOGALI ERAND; O. BAIGABA; P. JAMALGOTA, JABLOTA, JAPHROTA

Jatropha gossypifolia—A. BHOTERA; B., H. & P. LAL-BHARENDA; K. CHIKKA KADU HARALU, HATHI YELE HARALU; M'. VILAYATI ERAND; O. NALI BAIGABA, VERENDA; T. ADALAI; T'. NEPALEMU

Jussiaea repens—A. TALJURIA; B. KESSRA; K. NEERU DANTU, KAVAKULA; M. NIRGRAMPU; M'. PAN LAWANG; T. NIRKIRAMPU; T'. NIRUYAGNIVENDRAMU

Lagenaria siceraria—bottle gourd; A. JATI-LAU; B. & O. LAU; H. LAUKI; K. EESUGAYI BALLI, HALU GUMBALA; M. & T. CHORAKKAI; M'. DUDHYA BHOPALA; P. GHIYA; T'. ANAPA

Lagerstroemia speciosa (=*L. flos-reginae*)—A. AJAR; B., H. & P. JARUL; K. HOLE DASAVALA, CHELLA, BEN-DEKA; M. NIRVENTEKKU; M'. TAMAN; O. PATOLI; T. PUMARUTHU

Lantana aculeata & *L. indica*—lantana; G. GHANIDALIA; K. LANTAVANA GIDA; M. PUCHEDI; M'. GHANERI; O. NAGA-AIRI; P. DESI LANTANA; T. ARIPPU; T'. LANTANA

Laportea crenulata—devil or fever nettle; A. DOM-CHOR-AT; M. CHORIYANAM; M'. & P. CHORPATTA; T'. OTTA-PLAVU

Lathyrus aphaca—wild pea; A. & B. BAN-MATAR; G. JANGLI VATANA; H. JANGLI MATAR; M'. VANMATAR; O. JANGALI MATAR; P. JANGLI MATAR, RAWARI

Lathyrus sativus—A. KOLA-MAH; B., H. & O. KHESARI; G. MATER; K. CHIKKA TOGARI, VISHA TOGARI, KESARI BELE; M'. LAKH; P. KISARI DAL

Lemna paucicostata—duckweed; A. SORUPUNI; B. KHUDI-PANA; K. NEERU HASARU CHUKKE; M'. TIK-LICHE SHEWALE; O. CHUNIDALA, BILATI DALA; P. BUR

Lens culinaris—lentil; A. MOSOORMAH; B., H., M'. & P. MASUR; G. MASURIDAL; K. MASURU BELE, LENTEL GIDA; O. MASURA

Leonurus sibiricus—A. RONGA-DORON; B. DRONA; H. HALKUSHA, GUMA; O. KOILEKHIA; T'. ENUGUTUMMI

Lepidium sativum—garden cress; A. & B. HALIM-SAK; G. ASALIYA; H. HALIM; K. KURTHIKE, KURATHIRUGI; M'. ALIV; O. HIDAMBA SAGA; P. HALON

Leucas lavandulaefolia (=*L. linifolia*) A. DORON, DURUM-PHUL; B. SWET-DRONA; G. JHINA-PANNI KUBO; H. CHOTA-HALKUSA; K. GANTU THUMBE, KARJALI GIDA; M. THUMPA; M'. DRONAPUSHPI, GUMA; O. GAISA; P. GULDODA; T. THUMBAI; T'. TAMMA CHETTU

Limonia acidissima—elephant-apple; A. & B. KATH-BAEL; G. KOTHA; H. & P. KAITHA; K. KADU BILVA PATRE, NAYI BELA; M. BLANKA; M. KAWATH; O. KAINTHA; T. VELAMARUM; T'. VELAGA

Linum usitatissimum—linseed; A. TICHI; B. TISHI; G. JAVA; H. & P. ALSHI; K. SEEME AGASE BEEJA; M'. JAWAS; O. PESI; T. AALIVIRAI

Lochnera rosea (=*Vinca rosea*)—periwinkle; A. & B. NAYANTARA; H. SADABAHAR; K. KEMPUKASI-KANI-GALU, TURUKU MALLIGE; M. KASITHUMPA; M'. SADA-PHULI; O. SADABIHARI; P. RATTAN JOT

Loranthus longiflorus—see *Dendropthoe falcata*

Luffa acutangula—ribbed gourd; A. JIKA; B. JHINGA; G. SIROLA; H. & P. KALITORI; K. HEERE BALLI; M. PEECHIL. PEECHINGAI; M'. DODAKA; O. JAHNI; T. PEECHANKA

Luffa cylindrica—bath sponge or loofah; A. BHOL; B. D. IUNDUL; H. & P. GHIYATORI; M'. GHOSALE; O. PITA TARADA

Lycopersicum sulentum—tomato; A. BELAHI-BENGENA; B. BILATI-BEGOON; H. & P. TAMATAR; G. TAMETA, TOMATO, RAKTAVURNTTANK; K. TOMATO; M. & T. THAKKALIKKAI; M'. TAMBETA; O. BILATI BAIGANA; T'. THAKKALI

Madhuca latifolia (= *Bassia latifolia*)—A., B. & H. MAHUA; G. MAHUDA; K. HIPPE, ALIPPE, M'. MOHA; O. MAHULA; P. MOHWA; T. ILLUPAI; T'. IPPA

Malva verticillata—mallow; A. & B. LAFFA; H. & P. SONCHAL; K. KADU KADDALE

Marsilea quardrifolia—A. PANI-TENGECHI; B. SUSHNI-SAK; K. NEERU PULLAM PARACHI-ELE GIDA; M. NALILAKKOTAKAN; O. SUNSUNIA; P. CHAUPATI; T. ARAKKODAI

Martynia annua (= *M. diandra*)—tiger's nail; A. & B. BAGHNAKHI; G. VICHCHIDA; H. SHERNUI; K. HULI NAKHA, GARUDA MOOGU; M. & T. KAKKACHUNDU, PULINAGAM; M'. WINCHAURI; O. BAGHA NAKHI; P. HATHAJORI; T'. GARUDA MUKKU

Mentha viridis—spearmint or garden mint; A. PODINA; B., G., H. & M'. PUDINA; M. PUTIYINA

Mesua ferrea—iron-wood; A. NAHOR; B. NAGESWAR; H. NAGKESAR; K. NAGA KESARI, NAGA SAMPIGE; M. & T. IRUMPARATHTHAN; M'. NAGCHAMPAKA; O. NAGC-SWARA; P. NAGAR KESAR; T'. NAGAKESARI

Michelia champaca—A. & P. champa-phul; B. CHAMPA or SWARNACHAMPA; G. RAE CHAMPAC; H. CHAMPAK; K. SAMPIGE; M. & T. CHEMPAKAM; M'. SONCHAPHA; O. CHAMPA; T'. SAMPAKA

Millingtonia hortensis—Indian cork tree; B., H., M. & P. AKASNIM; K. SEESE BIRATO MARA; O. RIALI

Mimosa pudica—sensitive plant; A. LAJUKILOTA; B. LAJ-JABATILATA; G. LAJJAWANTI; H. LAJWANTI, CHHUIMUI; K. MUTTIDARE MUNI, MUDUGU DAVARE; M. THOTTAL-VADI; M'. LAJALU; O. LAJAKULI, LAJKURI; P. LAJWANTI; T. THOTTASINIGI; T'. PEDDA NIDRAKANTHA

Mirabilis jalapa—four o'clock plant or marvel of Peru; A. GODHULIGOPAL; B. KRISHNAKOLI; H. GULABBAS; K. SANJE MALLIGE, GULBAKSHI, BHADRAKSHI; M. NALUMANICHEDI; M'. GULBAKSH; O. RANGANI, BAD-HULI; P. GUL-E-ABBASI; T. ANDIMANDARAI; T'. CHAN-DRAKANTA

Momordica charantia—bitter gourd; A. TITA-KERALA; B. KARALA, UCHCHE; G., H. & P. KARELA; K. HAGALA KAYI; M. & T. PAVAL, PAVAKKAI; M'. KARLE; O. KALARA; T'. KAKARA

Moringa oleifera—drumstick or horse radish; A. & O. SAJANA; B. SAJINA; G. SARAGAVA; H. SAINJNA; K. NUGGE MARA, MOCHAKA MARA; M. MURINGA; M'. SHEVAGA; P. SAONJNA; T. MURUNGAI; T'. MUNAGA

Morus alba & *M. nigra*—mulberry; A. NOONI; B. TOONT; G. TUTRI; H. & P. SHAH-TOOT; K. KAMBALI GIDA, RESHME HIPPALI GIDA; M. MALBERRY; M'. TUTI; O. TUTAKOLI; T'. POOTIKAPALLU

Mucuna prurita—cowage; A. BANDARKEKOA; B. ALKUSHI; G. KIVANCH; H. & P. KAWANCH; K. NASA-GUNNI, NAYI SONKU BALLI; M. NAIKORUNA; M'. KHAJ KUIRA; O. BAIDANKA

Murraya paniculata (= *M. exotica*)—chinese box; A. KAMINIPHUL; B. & O. KAMINI; H. MARCHULA; K. KADU KARI BEVU, ANGARAKANA GIDA; M. MARAMULLA; M'. PANDHARI KUNTI; P. MARUA; T. KATTUK'ARUVEPPILAI; T'. NAGAGOLUGI

Musa paradisiaca—banana; A. KOL; B. KALA; G. & H. KELA; K. BALE GIDA, BALE HANNU; M. VAZHA; M'. KADALI, KEL; O. KODOLI, ROMBHA; T. VAZHAI; T'. ARATI, KADALI

Myristica fragans—nutmeg; B., H., M'. & P. JAIPHAL; G. JAYIPHAL; K. JATIKAYI, JAPATRE; M. & T. JATHIKKAI; O. JAIPHOLO; T'. JAJIKAYA

Nelumbo nucifera (= *Nelumbium speciosum*)—lotus; A. PODUM; B. & O. PADMA; G. & M'. KAMAL; H. & P. KANWAL; K. KAMALA, TAVARE; M. THAMARA; T. THAMARAI; T'. TAMARA

Nerium indicum—oleander; A. KORBIPHUL; B. KARAVI; G. & M'. KANHER; H. & P. KANER; K. KANIGALU; M. & T. ARALY; O. KARABI; T'. GANNERU

Nicotiana tabacum—tobacco; A. DHOPAT; B. TAMAK; G., H., M'. & P. TAMBAKU; K. HOGE SOPPU, TAMBAKU; M. & T. PUKAYILA; O. DHUANPATRA; T'. POGAKU

Nigella sativa—black cumin; B. & O. KALA-JIRA; G. KADU-JEEROO; H. KALOUNJI; K. KARI JEERIGE; M. & T. KARUN-JIRAGAM; M'. KALA JIRE; P. KALONGI, KALAJIRA

Nyctanthes arbor-tristis—night jasmine; A. SEWALI; B. SHEWLI, SHEPHALI; G. RATRANE; H. HARSHINGAR; K. PARIJATA; M. PAVIZHAMULLA; M'. PARIJATAK; O. SIN-GADAHARA; P. HARSANGHAR; T. PAVELAM; T'. PARI-JATHAM

Nymphaea lotus—water lily; A. BHET; B. SHALOOK; G. NILOPAL; H. & P. NILOFAR; K. KENDAVARE, KAN-NAIDILE; M. & T. AMPAL; M'. LALKAMAL; O. KAIN, KUMUDA; T'. KALUVA

Ocimum sanctum—sacred basil; A. TULASHI; B., G., H. & P. TULSI; K. SREE TULSI, VISHNU TULSI; M. & T. THULASI; M'. TULAS; O. TULASI; T'. ODDHI.

Oldenlandia corymbosa—B. & P. KHETPAPRA; G. PARPAT; H. DAMANPAPPAR; K. HUCHHU NELA BEVU, KALLU SABBASIGE; M'. PITPAPADA; O. GHARPODIA

Opuntia dillenii—prickly pear; A. SAGORPHENA; B. PHANIMONSHA; G. NAGNEVAL; H. NAGPHANI; K. PAPAS KALLI, CHAPPATE KALLI; M. ELAKKALLI; M'. PHADYA NIWDUNG; O. NAGAPHENI; P. CHITAR-HOR; T. SAPPATHTHIKKALLI; T'. NAGADALI

Orobanche indica—broomrape; B. BANIABAU; H. & P. SARSON-BANDA; K. BENKI GIDA, BODU GIDA; T. POKAYILAI-KALAN

Oroxylum indicum—A. BHATGHILA; B. SONA; G. PODVAL; H. ARLU; K. PATAGANI, SONEPATTA, TIGUDU; M. PATHIRI; M'. TETU; O. PHANPHANIA, PHAPANI; P. SANNA; T. PAYYALANTHA; T'. PAMPINI

Oryza sativa—paddy; A., B. & H. DHAN; G. CHOKHA; K. BHATHA, NELLU; M. ARI; M'. BHAT; O. DHANA; P. CHAWAL; T. ARISHI; T'. VARI

Oxalis repens (= *O. corniculata*)—wood-sorrel; A. SENGAITENGA, TENGECHI; B. AMRULSAK; H. CHUKATRIPATI, KHATTIPATTI; K. PUTTAM PURALE; M. PULIYARILA; M'. AMBOSHI; O. AMBILITI, AMLITI; P. KHATTIBUTI

Paederia foetida—A. BHEDAILOTA; B. GANDHAL; G. GANDHANA; H. GANDHALI; M. TALANILI; M'. PRASARUM; O. PASARUNI; P. GUNDALI; T'. SAVIRELA

Paederia tectorius (= *P. odoratissimus*)—screwpine; A. KETEKI; B. & G. KETAKY; H. & P. KEORA; K. TALE HOOVU, KEDIGE; M. KAITHA; M'. KEWADA; O. KIA; T. THAZHAI; T'. MOGIL

Panicum miliaceum—Indian millet; B., H., O. & P. CHEENA; G. SAMLI; K. BARAGU; M. THENA; M'. WARAI; T. VARAGU; T'. VARAGI

Papaver somniferum—opium poppy; A. AFUGOCH; B. AFING; G. APHIM; H. & P. POST; K. GASA GASE, APPEEMU GIDA; M. & T. GASHAGASHA; M'. APHU; O. APHIMA

Passiflora foetida—passion flower; A. JUNUKA; B., H. & P. JHUMKALATA:K. KUKKI BALLI; M. KRISTHUPAZHAM; M'. KRISHNA KAMAL; O. JHUMUKA LATA; T. SIRUPPUNAIKKALI; T'. JUKAMALLE

Pedilanthus tithymaloides—jew's slipper; B. RANGCHITA; H. NAGDAMAN; M. VERAKKODI; M'. VILAYATI SHER; O. BILATI SIJU, CHITA SIJU; P. NAG DAUN

Pennisetum typhoideum—pearl millet; B., H., O. & P.

BAJRA; K. SAJJE, KAMBU; M. & T. KAMPU, BAJRA; M'. BAJARI; T'. SAJJA, SAJJALU

Pentapetes phoenicea—noon flower; B. DUPOHRIA; G. DUPORIO; H. & P. GULDUPAHARIA; K. BANDURE; M'. DUPARI; O. DIPAHARIA

Phaseolus aureus—green gram; A. MOGU-MAH; B. & H. MOONG; G. MUGA; K. MESARU; M. CHERUPAYARU; M'. HIRAVE MUG; O. JHAIN-MUGA; P. MUNG; T. PACHAPAYARU; T'. PESALU

Phaseolus mungo—black gram; A. MATI-MAH; B. MASH, KALAI; G. UDAD; H. URID; K. UDDU; M. UZHUNNU; M'. UDID; O. MUGA; P. MASH; T. ULUNNU; T'. UDDULU

Phoenix sylvestris—date-palm; A. & B. KHEJUR; G., H. & P. KHAJUR; K. EECHALU, KHARJURA; M. ITTA; M'. KHARIK; O. KHAJURI; T. ICHCHAM; T'. ITHA

Phragmites karka—A. KHAGRA; B. & P. NAL; H. NUDANAR; K. HULUGILA HULLU; O. JANKAI

Phyllanthus acidus—A. HOLPHOLI, PORAMLOKHI; B. NOAR; H. CHALMERI; HARFARAURI; K. NELLI-KIRUNELLI; M. NELLIPULI, ARINELLI; M'. RAY AWALI; O. NARAKOLI; T. ARUNELLI; T'. RATSAVUSIRIKI

Phyllanthus emblica—see *Emblica officinalis*

Piper betle—betel; A., B., G., H. & P. PAN; K. VEELE DELE, YELE BALLI; M. & T. VETHILA; M'. NAGWELI; O. PANA; T'TAMALAPAKU

Piper cubeba—cubeb; B., H. & O. KABAB-CHINI; G. TADAMIRI; K. BALA MENASU; M. & T. THIPPLI; M'. KABAB CHINI, KANKOL; T'. TOKAMIRIYALU

Piper longum—long pepper; A. PIPOLI; B. PIPOOL; G. PIPARA; H. PIPLI; K. HIPPALI; M. THIPPALI; M'. PIMPALI; O. PIPALI; P. DARFILFIL, MAGHAN

Piper nigrum—black pepper; A. JALUK; B. GOLMARICH; G. KALOMIRICH; H. GOLMIRCH; K. KARI MENASU; M. KURUMULAGU; M'. KALI MIRI; O. GOLA MARICHA; P. KALI MARCH; T. MILAGOO; T'. SAVYAMU

Pistia stratiotes—water lettuce; A. BORPUNI; B. PANA; G. ALAKUMBHI; H. & P. JALKHUMBI; K. ANTARA GANGE; M. MUTTAPPAYAL; M'. GANGAVATI; O. BORA JHANJI; T. AGASATHAMARAI; T'. AKASATAMARA

Pisum sativum—pea; A. MOTOR; B., H., O. & P. MATAR; G. VATANA; K. BATANI, VATAGI; M. PAYARU; M'. WATANE; P. PATTANI; T'. GUNDUSANI GHELU

Pithecolobium saman—rain tree; A. SIRISH GOCH; K. MALE MARE; M. URAKKAM-THOONGIMARAM; M'. SAMAN; O. BADA GACHHA CHAKUNDA, BANA SIRISHA

Plantago ovata—flea seed; A., B. & O., ISOBGUL; G. UTHAMUJEERUM; H., M'. & P. ISOBGOL; K. ISPHA

GOLU, ISAMGOLU; M. KARKATASRINGI; T'. ISHAP-
PUKOL

Plumbago zeylanica—A. AGYACHIT; B. CHITA; G.
CHITRAMULA; H., M'. & P. CHITRAK; K. BILI CHITRA
MOOLA; M. & T. KODUVELI; O. DHALACHITA

Plumeria rubra—temple or pagoda tree; A. GULANCHI;
B. KATGOLAP; G. RHAD CHAMPO; H. & P. GOLAINCHI;
K. HALU SAMPIGE; M. EEZHAVA-CHEMPAKAM; M'.
KHUR CHAPHA; O. KATHA CHAMPA; P. GULCHIN

Polanisia icosandra—B. HALDE-HURHURE; G. TILVAN; H.
HULHUL; M. & T. NAIKADUGU; M'. PIWALI TILVAN; O.
ANASORISIA; P. BUGRA, GANDHULI; T. KUKKA VAVINTA

Polianthes tuberosa—tuberose; A., B. & O. RAJANI-
GANDHA; H. & P. GULSHABO; K. SUGANDHA RAJA; M'.
GULCHHADI; T. NILASAMPANGI; T'. SUKANDARAJI

Polyalthia longifolia—mast tree; A. & O. DABADARU;
B. DEBDARU; G. ASHOPALO; H. & M'. ASHOK; K.
PUTRAJEEVI, KAMBADA MARA; M. ARANAMARAM; P.
DEVIDARI; T. NETTILINGAM; T'. DEVADARU

Polygonum sp.—A. BIHLONGONI; B. PANI MARICH; H.
NARI; M. MOTHALAMOOKA; O. MUTHI SAGA; P. NARRI;
T. AATALARIE

Portulaca oleracea—purslane; A. HANHTHENGIA; B.
NUNIA-SAK; G. LONI; H. & P. KULFA SAG; K. DODDA
GONI SOPPU; M. KARICHEERA; M'. GHOL; O. BAL-
BALUA; T. KARIKEERAI; T'. PEDDAPAVILIKURA

Pothos scandens—A. HATILOTA; G. MOTO PIPAR; K.
ADKE BEELU-BALLI, AGACHOPPU; M. ANAPPARUVA; M'.
ANJAN VEL; O. GAJA PIPALI; P. GAZPIPAL

Prosopis spicigera—A. SOMIDH; B., H., M'. & O.
SHOMI; G. KANDO; K. VUNNE, PERUMBE; M. PARAMPU;
P. JAND; T. PERUMBAI; T'. JAMBI

Psidium guayava—guava; A. MODHURI-AM; B. PAYARA;
G. JAMFAL; H. & P. AMRUD; K. SEEBE, CHEPE, PERALA;
M. PERAKKA; M'. PERU; O. PIJULI; T. KOYYA; T'. JAMA

Pterospermum acerifolium—A. KONOKCHAMPA; B.
MOOCHKANDA; H. KANAKCHAMPA; K. MUCHUKUNDA
GIDA; M'. MUCHKUND; O. MOOCHKUNDA; T. VENNAN-
GU; T'. MUSHKANDA

Punica granatum—pomegranate; A. & B. DALIM; G.
DADAM; H. & P. ANAR; K. DALIMBE; M. MATALAM; M'.
DALIMB; O. DALIMBA; T. MADULAM

Quamoclit pinnata—(=*Ipomoea quamoclit*)—A. KUN-
JALOTA; B. KUNJALATA, TORULATA; H. & P. KAMLATA;
K. KAMALATHE; M'. GANESH PUSHPA; O. KUNJALATA;
T'. KASIRATNAM

Quisqualis indica—Rangoon creeper; A. MADHA-

BILOTA; B. SANDHYAMALATI; G. BARMA SINIVEL; H. &
P. LAL MALTI; K. RANGOON KEMPUMALLE; M'. LAL
CHAMELI; O. MODHUMALATI; T. RANGOON MALLI

Raphanus sativus—radish; A., B., M'. & O. MULA; H. &
P. MULI; K. MOOLANGI; M. MULLANKI; T. & T'. MUL-
LANGI

Rauwolfia serpentina—A. CHANDO; B., G. & T. SARPA-
GANDHA; H., M'. & P. SARPGANDH; K. SARPAGANDHI;
SHIVANABHI BELLI; SUTRANABHI; M. AMALPORIYAN; O.
PATALA GARUDA

Richinus communis—castor; A. ERIGOCH; B. & P. ARAN-
DA; G. ERANDI; H. RENDI; K. HARALU; M. & T.
AVANAKKU; M'. ERAND; O. JADA; P. RENDI, ARANDA;
T'. AMUDAMU

Rumex vesicarius—sorrel; A. CHUKA-SAK; B. CHUKA-
PALANG; H. CHUKA, KHATTA-PALAK; K. CHUKKI SOPPU,
SUKKE SOPPU; M'. CHUKA; O. PALANGA; P. KHATTA-
MITHA; T. CHUKKAKURA

Saccharum officinarum—sugarcane; A. KUNHIAR; B.
AKH; G. SHERDE; H. GUNNA; K. KABBU; M. & T.
KARIMPU; M'. USA; O. AKHU; P. GUNNA; T'. CHERUKU

Saccharum spontaneum—A. KANHIBON; B. KASH; G. &
H. KANS; K. DHARBE, KADU KABBU; M. NAINKANA;
M'. BAGBERI; O. KASHATANDI; P. KAHI

Salmalia malabarica—see *Bombax ceiba*

Sansevieria roxburghiana—bowstring hemp; A. GUMU-
NI; B. MURGA, MURVA; H. MARUL, MURVA; K. MANJINA
NARU, GODDUMANJI; M. PAMPINPOLA; O. MURUGA; T.
MARUL

Santalum album—sandalwood; A., B., H., M'. & P.
CHANDAN; G. SUKHADA; K. SREEGANDHA; M. & T.
CHANNANAMARAM; O. CHANDANA; T'. CHANDANAMU

Sapindus mukorossi & *S. trifoliatus*—soap-nut; A.
MONICHAL, HAITAGUTI; B., H., M'. & P. RITHA; G.
ARITHA; K. ANTUVALA, NOREKAYI; M. URVANJI; O.
RITHA, MUKTAMANJI; T. PONNANKOTTAI; T'. KUNKUDU

Saraca indica—asoka tree; A., B., & P. ASOKA; G. ASU-
PALA; H. SEETA ASOK; K. ASHOKADA MARA, KENKALI,
ACHANGE; M. & T. ASOKAM; M'. SITECHA ASHOK; O.
ASOKA; T'. ASAKAMU

Sesamum indicum—gingelly; A. TISI; B., H., M'. & P.
TIL; G. MITHO TEL; K. YELLU; M. & T. ELLU; O. KHASA,
RASHI; T. NUVVULU

Sesbania grandiflora—A. & B. BAKPHUL; G. AGATHIO;
H. & P. AGAST; K. AGASE, CHOGACHI; M. AGATHI; M'.
AGASTA; O. AGASTI; T. AGATHYKKEERAI; T'. AVISI

Sesbania sesban—A. JOYANTI; B. JAINTI; G. RAYSAN-

GANI; H. & P. JAINT; M. SHEMPA; M'. SEVARI; O. JAYANTI; T. SITHAGATHI

Setaria italica—Italian millet; A. KONIDHAN; B. KAUN; G. KANG; H. CHEENA, KAUNI; K. NAVANE, KONGU; M. NAVANA; M'. RALE; O. TANGUN; P. KANGNI; T. TENNAI; T'. KORRA KORALU

Shorea robusta—sal tree; A., B., H. & P. SAL; G. RAL; K. BILE BHOGE, AASINA MARA, ASCHA KARNA; M. MARA-MARAM; M'. SHALA, RALVRIKSHA; O. SALA; T. SHA-LAM; T'. GUGGILAMU

Sida cordifolia—A. BARIALA; B. BERELA; G. JANGLI METHI; H. BARIARA; K. HETHUTHI; M. KURUMTHOTTI; M'. CHIKANA; O. BISIRIPI; P. KHARENTI; T. KARUMTHOTTEE; T'. CHERUBENDA

Smilax zeylanica—sarsaparilla; A. HASTIKARNA LOTA; B. KUMARIKA; H. CHOBCHINI; M'. GHOT VEL; O. KUMBHATUA, KUMARIKA; P. USHBA

Solanum ferox—A. BON BENGENA; B. RAM BEGOON; K. ANE SUNDE GIDA, HALADI GULLA; M. ANACHCHUNTA; M'. BHAJICHE WANGE; O. BHEJI BAIGANA; ANAICHUNDAI; T'. MULAKA

Solanum indicum—A. BHEKURI GOCH, TIT-BHEKURI; B. BRIHATI; G. UBHIRINGANI; H. BIRHATTA; K. KEMPU GULLA, HABBU GULLA; M. KATTUCHUNDA; M'. DORLI; O. KANTARA; P. BARI KANDIARI

Solanum melongena—brinjal; A. BENGENA; B. BEGOON; G. & O. BAIGANA; H. BAIGON; K. BADANE KAYI; M. VAZHUTHANA; M'. WANGE; P. BENGAN; T. KAththIRI; T'. VANGA

Solanum nigrum—black nightshade; A. POKMOU; B. GURKI; G. PILUDU; H. GURKAMAI, MAKOI; K. KARI KACHI GIDA, KEMPU KACHI, KAKA MUNCHI; M. MULAGUTHAKKALI; M. KANGANI; O. NUNNUNIA; P. MAKO; T. MANATHAKKALI; T'. KAMANCHICHETTU

Solanum surattense—A. KANTAKARI; B. KANTIKARI; G. BHOYARINGANI; H. KATELI, KATITA; K. RAMA GULLA; M. KANDAKARYCHUNDA; M'. KATERINGANI; O. ANKARANTI; P. KANDIALI; T. KANDANKAththIRI; T'. NELAVAKUDU

Solanum tuberosum—potato; A., B., H., O. & P. ALOO; G. PAPETA; K. ALUGEDDE; M. & T. URULAKKIZHANGU; M'. BATATA; T'. URULAGADDA

Sorghum vulgare—great millet; A. JOUDHAN; B. & G. JUAR; H. & P. JOWAR; K. BILI JOLA; M. & T. CHOLAM; M'. JAWAR; O. BAJARA; T'. JONNALU

Spinacia oleracea—spinach; A. MITHA-PALENG; B. PALANG, MITHA-PALANG; H., M. & M'. PALAK

Sterculia foetida—A. BAN-BADAM; B., H., M'. & P. JAN-GLI BADAM; G. NARKAYA-UDA; K. PEE NARI, PATHALA MARA, BHETALA; M. ANAThThONDI; O. JANGALI BADAM; T. PAEMARAM; T'. GUTTAPUBADAMU

Syzyzium aromaticum—clove; A., H. & P. LAUNG; B. LAVANGA; G. LAVANG; K. NAGE, LAVANGA; M. GRAAM-PU; M'. LAWANG; O. LABANGA

Syzygium cuminii—A. JAMU; B. KALA-JAM; G. JAMDU-DO; H. & P. JAMAN; K. NERILE; M. & T. NAAVAL; M'. JAMBUL; O. JAMUKOLI

Syzygium jambos—rose-apple; A. GOLAPI JAMU; B. GOLAP-JAM; H. & P. GULÀB-JAMAN; K. JAMBU NERILE; M. PANINIRCHAMPA; M'. GULAB JAMB; O. GOLAP JAMU; T. NAAVAL; T'. NEEREDU

Syzygium malaccense—Malay apple; A. PANI-JAMU; B. JAMRUL; H. MALAY JAMAN; K. PANNERILE; M'. SAFED JAMB; P. MALAY KA SEB

Tagetes patula—marigold; A. NARJIPHUL; B. & H. GENDA; K. CHENDU HOOVA, SEEME SHAVANTIGE; M'. GULJAPHIRI; O. GENDU; P. GENDA, GUTTA

Tamarindus indica—tamarind; A. TETELI; B. TENTUL; G. AMIL; H. & P. IMLI; K. HUNISE MARA; M. & T. PULI; M'. CHINCH; O. KAINYA, TENTULI; T'. CHINTHA

Tamarix dioica—A. JHAU-BON; B. & H. BON-JHAU; K. SEERE GIDA; M'. JAO; O. DISHI-JHAUN, THARTHARI; P. PILCHI

Tectona grandis—teak; A. & B. shegoon; G. & H. SHAG-WAN; K. TEGADA MARA, SAGUVANI; M. & T. THEKKU; M'. SAG; O. SAGUAN; P. SAGWAN; T'. TEKU

Tephrosia purpurea—wild indigo; A. BON-NIL; B. & H. JANGLI-NIL; G. JHILA; K. VAJRA NEELI, KOGGILI, KOLIN-JI; M. KOJHINGIL; M'. SHARAPUNKHA; O. BANA NILA; P. JHANA; T. KOLINGI; T'. VEMPALI

Terminalia arjuna—A. ARJUN GOCH; B. & H. ARJUN; G. SAJADAN; K. BILI MATHI, HOLE MATHI, TORA MATHI; M. VELLI-LAVU; M'. ARJUN-SADADA; O. ARJUNA; P. ARJAN; T. MARUTHU; T'. TELLA MADOI

Terminalia belerica—beleric myrobalan; A. BHOMRA-GUTI; B. & P. BAHERA; G. BERANG; H. BHAIRAH; K. TARE MARA, SHANTHI MARA; M. & T. THANNIKKAI; M'. BEHADA; O. BAHADA

Terminalia catappa—country almond; A. BADAM-GOCH; B., G., H., M'., O. & P. DESHI-BADAM; M. ADAMARAM; T. NATTUVADUMAI. T'. BADAMI

Terminalia chebula—chebulic myrobalan; A. SHILIKHA; B. HARITAKI; G. PILO-HARDE; H. & P. HARARA; K. ALALE KAYI; M. & T. KADUKKAI; M'. HIRDA; O. HARI-DA; T'. KARAKA

Thespesia populnea—portia tree; B. PARAS; G. PURUSA-PIPALO; H. & P. PARAS-PIPAL; K. BUGURI, HOOVARISI, JOGIYARALE; M. & T. POOVARASU; M'. BHENDICHA JHAR; O. HABALI; T'. GANGARAVI

Thevetia peruviana—yellow oleander; A. KARABI; B. KALKE-PHUL; G., H. & P. PILA-KANER; K. KADUKASI KANAGALU; M. & T. SIVANARALI; M'. PIWALA KANHER; O. KANIARA, KONYAR PHULA; T'. PACHCHAGANNERU

Tinospora cordifolia—A. AMORLOTA, AMOILOTA; B. GULANCHA; G. GADO; H. GURCHA; K. AMRUTA BALLI, MADHU PARNI; M. AMRITHU; M'. GULVEL; O. GULUCHI; P. GALO; T. SINDHILKODI; T'. TIPPATIGE

Trachyspermum ammi—ajowan or ajwan; A. JONI-GUTI; B. JOWAN; G. AJAMO; H. & P. AJOWAN; K. OMU, AJAWANA; M. AYAMODAKAM; M'. OWA; O. JUANI; T. OMAM; T'. OMAMU

Tragia involucrata—nettle; A. CHORAT; B. BICHUTI; H. & P. BARHANTA; K. TURACHI BALLI, CHELURI GIDA; M. CHORIYANAM; M'. KHAJAKOLTI; O. BICHHUATI; T. KANJURI; T'. DULAGONDI

Trapa natans—(=*T. bispinosa*)—water chestnut; A. SHINGORI; B. PANI-PHAL; G. SHENGODA; H. & P. SINGARHA; K. MULLU KOMBU BEEJA, SINGARA BEEJA; M. KARIMPOLA; M'. & O. SINGADA; T. SINGARAKOTTAI; T'. KUBYAKAM

Trewia nudiflora—A. BHELKORA; B. PITULI; H. BHILLAURA; K. KADU GUM BALA, KATAKAMBA, HEELAGA; M. THAVALA; M'. PITARI; O. JANDAKHAI, PANIGAMBHAR; P. TUMARI, KHAMARA; T. AATTARASU

Tribulus terrestris—B. GOKHRIKANTA; G. GOKHARU; H. GOKHRU; K. SANNA NEGGILU; M. NERUNJIL; M'. KATE GOKHRU; O. GOKHARA; P. BHAKHRA; T. NERINJI; T'. PALLERU

Trichosanthes anguina—snake gourd; A. DHUNDULI; B. CHICHINGA; G. PADAVALI; H. CHACHINDA; K. PADAVALA; M. PADAVALAM; M'. PADVAL; O. CHHACHINDRA; P. PAROL; T. PUDALAI; T'. POTLA

Trichosanthes dioica—A. & B. PATAL; H. & P. PARWAL; K. KADU PADAVALA; M. PATOLAM; G. & M'. PARWAR; O. PATALA; T. KOMBUPPUDALAI; T. KOMMUPOTLA

Trigonella foenum-graecum—fenugreek; A. MITHIGUTI; B., G., H., O., M'. & P. METHI; K. MENTHYA SOPPU, MENTHYA PALYA; M. VENTHIAM; T. VENDAYAM

Triticum aestivum—wheat; A. GHENHU; B. GOM; G. GAHUN; H. & P. GEHUN; K. GODHI; M. KOTHAMPU; M'. GAHU; O. GAHAMA; T. GHODUMAI; T'. GOTHI, GODUMULU

Typha elephantina—elephant grass or bulrush; B. HOGLA; G. GHABAJARIN; H. PATER; K. ANEJONDA, APU, NARI BALA; M'. PAN KANIS; O. HAUDAGHASA, HOGOLA; P. PATIRA; T. CHAMBU

Typhonium trilobatum—A. SAMAKACHU; B. GHETKACHU; K. KANDA GEDDE; H. GHEKUL; M. CHENA; T. KARUNKARUNAI, ANAIKKORAI; T'. JAMMU-GADDI

Urena lobata—A. BON-AGARA; B. BAN-OKRA; H. & P. BACHATA; K. DODDA BENDE, KADU THUTHI; M. OORPUM; M'. VAN-BHENDI; O. JATJATIA; T. OTTATI

Utricularia sp.—B. JHANJI; K. NEERU GULLE GIDA, SEETHASRU BEEJA; M. MULLANPAYAL, KALAKKANNAN; M'. GELYACHI VANASPATI; O. BHATUDIA DALA

Vanda roxburghii—orchid; A. KOPOUPHUL; B., H. & P. RASNA; G. RASNA-NAI; K. VANDAKA GIDA; M. MARAVAZHA; M'. BANDE; O. RASHNA, MADANGA

Vangueria spinosa—A. KOTRORA, MOYENTENGA; B. & H. MOYNA; K. CHEGU GADDE, ACHHURA MULLU; M'. ALU; O. GURBELI; T. MANAKKARAI; T'. SEGAGADDA

Vernonia cineria—B. KUKSHIM; G. SADORI; H. & M'. SAHADEVI; K. KARE HINDI, GAYA DOPPALU, SAHADEVI; M. POOVAN-KURUNTHILA; O. POKASUNGA, JHURJHURI; P. SAHDEVI, KUKSHIM; T. PUVAMKURUNDAL; T'. GARITIKAMMA

Vigna sinensis—cow pea; A. NESERA MAH; B. BARBATI; H. BORA; K. ALASANDI, TADAGANI; M'. CHAVLI; O. BARGADA; P. RAUNG; T. THATTAPAYERU; T'. ALACHANDALU

Vinca rosea—see *Lochnera rosea*

Viscum monoicum—mistletoe; A. ROGHUMALA; B. BANDA; H. & P. BHANGRA, BANDA; K. HASARU BADANIKE; M. ITHTHIL; M'. JALUNDAR; O. MALANGA; T. OTTU

Vitis trifolia (=*Cayratia carnosa*)—B. AMAL-LATA; G. KHAT-KHATUMBO; H. & P. AMALBEL; K. NEERGUNDI, NOCHHI, NEERLAKKI; M. SORIVALLI; M'. AMBATVEL; O. AMARLATA

Vitis vinifera—grape vine; A., B., H. & P. ANGOOR; G. MUDRAKA; K. DRAKSHI BALLI; M. & T. MUNTHIRYVALLY; M'. DRAKSHA-VEL; O. ANGURA; T'. DRAKSHA

Wedelia calendulacea—A. BHIMRAJ; B. BHIMRAJ, BHRINGARAJ; G., H. & P. BHANGRA; K. KESHARAJA, GARGARI; M. PEE-KAYYANNYAM; M'. PIVALABHANGRA; O. BHRUNGA-RAJA

Withania somnifera—A. LAKHANA; B. ASWAGANDHA; G. ASUNDHA; H. & P. ASGANDH; K. ASWAGANDHI, PEN-

NERU, HIRE MADDINA GIDA; M. & T. AMUKKIRAM; M'. ASKANDH; O. AJAGANDHA; T'. ASVAGANDHI

Wrightia tomentosa—A. DUDHKHOROI; B. INDRAJOB; G., H. & P. DUDHI; K. BILI GANAGALA, KADU JANAGALU; M. & T. NILAM-PALA; M'. KALA-INDERJAW; O PHAOKURNI; T'. PALA

Xanthium strumarium—cockle-bur; A. AGARA; B. & H. OKRA; G. GADIYAN; K. MARALU UMMATHI; M'. SHANKESHVAR; O. CHOTA GOGHURU; P. GOKHRU KALAN; T. MARLUMUTTA; T'. MARULAMATHANGI

Zanthophyllum budrunga—A. BROJONALI; B. BAZINALI; H. BADRANG; K. MARALU MATHANGI; M. KAT-TUMURIKKU; M'. BUDRANJ; T. IRATCHAI; T'. RACHAMAM

Zea mays—Indian corn or maize; A. MAKOI-JOHA; B. BHUTTA; G. & P. MAKAI; H. MAKKA, BHUTTA; K. MUSUKINA JOLA, GOVINA JOLA; M. & T. MAKKA CHOLAM; M'. & O. MAKKA; T'. MOKKA JONNA

Zingiber officinale—ginger; A., B. & O. ADA; G. ADHU; H. ADRAK; K. SHUNTI, ALLA; M. INCHI; M'. ALE; P. ADARAK; T. INJI; T'. ALLAM

Zizyphus mauritiana—(=*Z. jujuba*)—Indian plum; A. BAGARI; B. KUL; G. BORADI; H. & P. BER; K. ELACHI, BORE HANNU; M. & T. ELINTHAI; M'. BOR; O. BARKOLI; T'. REGU

Zizyphus oenoplia—A. BAN-BAGARI, B. SHIAKUL; K. SURI MOLLU, SONDLI GIDA; M. THODALI; M'. BURGI; O. BHUNKOLI; P. MAKOH; T. SOORAI; T'. BANKA

GLOSSARY OF ARABIC (A) AND NEPALI (N) NAMES OF PLANTS

Sincere and grateful thanks of the author are due to Dr P. K. Mukherjee and Saeed Abdo Gabali, Head, Department of Biology, Higher College of Education, Khormaksar, Aden (PDRY), for kindly furnishing Arabic names of plants, and to Dr G. S. Yonzone and his colleague, Professor K. K. Tamang, Darjeeling Government College, Darjeeling, for Nepali names of plants.

Abelmoschus esculentus—lady's finger; A. BAMIA; N. BHENDI. *Abroma augusta*—devil's cotton; N. SANU KAPASI. *Abrus precatorius*—crab's eye or Indian liquorice; N. LAL GERI. *Abutilon indicum*—N. GHANTI PHUL. *Acacia catechu*—catechu; A. KAAT; N. KHAIR. *Acacia nilotica* (=*A. arabica*)—gum tree; A SANAT ARABI; N. BABUL. *Achras zapota*—sapota or sapodilla plum; A. ABBASI; N. SAPHEDA. *Acorus calamus*—sweet flag; N. BOJHO. *Adhatoda vasica*—N. ASURU. *Aegle marmelos*—wood-apple; N. BEL. *Aeschynomene indica*—pith plant; N. GUDI RUKH. *Agave americana*—American aloe or century plant; A. SABER; N. HATI BAR, *Albizzia lebeek*—siris tree; A. LEBBAKH; N. HARRA SIRISH. *Allium cepa*—onion; A. BASAL; N. PYAZ. *A. sativum*—garlic; A. THOMA; N. LAHSUN. *Alocasia indica*—A. KAIKAS; N. MANE, *Aloe vera*—N. GHIU KUMARI. *Amaranthus spinosus*—prickly amaranth; N. KANRAY. *Ananas comosus*—pineapple; A. ANANAS; N. BHUI KATAHAR. *Annona reticulata*—bullock's heart; N. RAM PHAL. *A. squamosa*—custard-apple; A. ATT; N. SARIFA. *Arachis hypogaea*—groundnut or peanut; A. LOAZE or PHOOL SUDANEE; N. BADAM. *ARECA CATECHU*—areca-nut or betel-nut; A. PHOPHAL; N. SUPARI. *Artocarpus heterophyllus*—jack tree; N. RUKH KATA-HAR. *A. lakoocha*—monkey jack; N. RORHAR. *Asparagus racemosus*—A. KOSHK-ALMAZ; N. SAT MULI. *Averrhoa carambola*—carambola; N. KAMARAK. *Azadirachta indica*—margosa; A. MOREMIRA; N. NIM.

Baccauria sapida—N. KUSUM. *Bambusa tulda*—bamboo; A. GHAB or BAMBOO; N. RARANTI BANS. *Barringtonia acutangula*—N. HIJAL. *Basella rubra*—Indian spinach; N. POL. *Bauhinia variegata*—camel's foot tree; N. KOIRALO. *Benincasa hispida*—ash gourd; N. SETO PHARSI. *Beta vulgaris*—beet; A. BHANGAR; N. BEET. *Blumea lacera*—N. BABURI. *Bombax ceiba*—silk cotton tree; N. SIMAL. *Borassus flabellifer*—palmyra palm; N. TAL. *Bougainvillea spectabilis*—glory of the garden; A. GAHANNAMIYA. *Brassica campestris*—mustard; A. KHARDAL; N. SETO RAYO. *Butea monosperma*—flame of the forest or parrot tree; N. PALAS.

Caesalpinia crista (=*C. bonducella*)—fever nut; N. YANGKUP. *C. pulcherima*—dwarf gold mohur or peacock flower; N. GOLMOHUR. *Cajanus cajan*—pigeon pea; N. RAHAR. *Calamus viminalis*—cane; A. KHAIZARAN; N. BET. *Calotropis gigantea*—madar; A. OSHAR; N. AUK. *Canna orientalis* —(=*C. indica*)Indian shot; A. KANA. *Cannabis sativa*—hemp; A. KENNAB; N. BHANG. *Capsicum annuum*—chilli; A. BISBAS. *Carica papaya*—papaw; A. AMBA BABAL; N. MEWA. *Cassia fistula*—Indian laburnum; N. RAJBRIKSH. *C. sophera*—N. TAPRE. *Cassytha filiformis*—N. AMAR BEL. *Casuarina equisetifolia*—beef-wood tree or she-oak; A. KASARINA; N. KUR KURE RUKH. *Celosia cristata*—cock's comb; N. BHALE KO SIR. *Centella asiatica*—Indian pennywort; N. MADHESI DUNGRI JHAR; *Cestrum nocturnum*—queen of the night; N. RAAT KO RANI. *Chrysanthemum coronarium*—N. GADWARI. *Cicerarietenum*—gram; A. SOMBRA; N. CHANA; *Cinnamomun camphora*—camphor; N. KAPUR. *C. tamala*—bay leaf; N. TEZPATA. *C. zeylanicum*—cinnamon; A. KIRFA; N. DALCHINI. *Cissus quadrangularis*—A. HALAS; N. PANI LAHARA. *Citrullus colo cynthis*—colocynth; A. HANDAL; N. INDRAYAN. *C. lanatus*—water melon; A. HABHAB; N. TARMUZA. *Citrus aurantifolia*—sour lime; A. LEIMONN; N. KAGATI NIMBU. *C. grandis*—pummelo or shaddock; N. SANGKATRA. *C. reticulata*—orange; A. PORTUKAL; N. SUNTALA. *Clitoria ternatea*—butterfly pea; N. APARAJITA. *Cocos nucifera*—coconut-palm; A. NARGEEL; N. NARIWAL. *Colocasia esculenta*—taro; N. MANE. *Cariandrum sativum*—coriander; A. KABZARA; N. DHANIA. *Crotalaria juncea*—Indian or sunn hemp; N. SAN. *C. sericea*—rattlewort; N. SUHUTUNG RUNG. *Croton tiglium*—A. KROTON; N. JAIPHAL. *Cucumis melo*—melon; A. SHAMMAM; N. KHARBUZA. *C. sativus*—cucumber; N. KAKRA. *Cucurbita pepo*—vegetable marrow; A. DUBBA; N. PHARSI. *Curcuma amada*—mango ginger; N. ANP HARDI. *C. longa*—turmeric; N. HARDI. *Cuscuta reflexa*—dodder; A. HAKOOL; N. SWARNALATA. *Cynodon dactylon*—dog grass; A. NAGEEL; N. DUBO.

Dalbergia latifolia—Indian rosewood; N. SATISAL.

D. sissoo—Indian red-wood; N. SISSAU. *Datura stramonium*—thorn -apple; N. DHUTURA. *Daucas carota*—carrot; A. GUZAR. *Delonix regia*—gold mohur; N. KRISHAN CHURA. *Desmodium gyrans*—Indian telegraph plant; N. SARKINU. *Dillenia indica*—N. PANCHAPHAL. Dioscorea alata—white yam; N. GHAR TARUL. *D. bulbifera*—wild yam; N. BANTARUL. *Dolichos lablab*—COUNTRY BEAN; A. PHOOL. *Duranta repens* (=*D. plumieri*)—A. & N. DURANTA.

Eleusine coracana—N. MARUA. *Emblica officinalis*—emblic myrobalan; N. AMALA. *Enttada gigas*—nicker bean; N. PANGRA. *Ervatamia coronaria*—N. TAGAR. *Erythrina variegata*—coral tree; N. PHALEDO. *Euphorbia antiquorum*—N. SHIV RUKH. *E. neriifolia*—N. SIJ. *E.* (=*Poinsettia*) *pulcherrima*—poinsettia; N. LAL PATTA. *Euryale ferox*—N. MAKHNA.

Ferula assa-foetida—asafoetida; A. ALTIT; N. HING. *Ficus bengalen-sis*—banyan; A. TEEN BENGALI; N. BAR. *F. glomerata*—fig; N. DUMRI. *F. religiosa*—peepul; N. PIPUL. *Foeniculum vulgare*—anise or fennel; A. SHAMAR; N. MAURI.

Garcinia mangostana—mangosteen; N. CHUNYEL. *Gardenia jasmi-noides*—cape jasmine; N. GANDHA RAJ. *Gloriosa superba*—glory lily; N. KULHARI. *Gossypium sp.*—cotton; N. KAPAS. *Gynandropsis gynandra*—N. BAHU PATE.

Helianthus annuus—sunflower; A. ABBAD-AS-SHAMS; N. SURYA MUKHI. *Heliotropium indicum*—heliotrope; N. HATI SUR. *Hibiscus cannabinus*—Madras or Deccan hemp; N. AMBARI. *H. rosa-sinensis*—China rose or shoe flower; A. ABESCHUS; N. JAVA KUSUM. *H. sabadariffa*—rozelle; N. PATWA. *Holarrhena antidysenterica*—N. KHIRRA. *Hordeum vulgare*—barley; A. SHAIER; N. JAW.

Impatiens balsamina—balsam; N. PHAT PHATE. *Ipomoea batatas*—sweet potato; A. SHUKARIAKAND; N. SAKARKHANDA. *Ixora coccinea*—N. CHIWRIPAT.

Jasminum sambac—jasmine; A. YASMIN; N. HARE LAHARA. *Jatropha curcas*—N. BHARENDA. *J. gossypifolia*—N. CHAP CHAPE.

Lagenaria siceraria—bottle gourd; N. LAUKA. *Lagerstroemia speciosa* (=*L. flos-reginae*)—N. BORDERI. *Laportea crenulata*—devil or fever nettle; N. MORINGE. *Lawsonia alba*—A. HENNA. *Lens culinaris* (=*L. esculenta*)—lentil; A. AADAS; N. MASUR. *Lochnera rosea*—(=*Vinca rosea*)—periwinkle; N. TARA PHUL. *Luffa acutangula*—ribbed gourd; A. TORI; N. JHINGENI. *L. cylindrica*—bath sponge or luffa; A. LUFA;

N. JHUTRA. *Lycopersicum esculentum*—tomato; A. TAMATA; N. RAMBHERA.

Marsilea quadrifolia—N. PANI SAK. *Martynia annua* (=*M. diandra*)—tiger's nail; N. BAGH NANGRE. *Mentha viridis*—spearmint or garden mint; N. PODINA. *Mesua ferrea*—iron wood; N. NAGESURI. *Michelia champaca*—N. AULE CHANP. *Mimosa pudica*—sensitive plant; A. ALMUSTAHIYA; N. BUHARI JHAR. *Mirabilis jalapa*—four o'clock plant; N. KRISHNA KALI. *Moringa oleifera*—drumstick or horse radish; N. SAJANI. *Morus alba* & *M. nigra*—mulberry; N. KIMBU. *Mucuna prurita*—cowage; N. KUACH. *Murraya paniculata*—Chinese box; N. KAMINI PHUL. *Musa paradisiaca*—banana; A. MOSZE; N. KERA.

Nelumbo nucifera (=*Nelumbium speciosum*)—lotus; N. KAMAL. *Nerium indicum* (=*N. oleander*)—oleander; A. DAFLA; N. KARAVI. *Nicotiana tabacum*—tobacco; A. TUMBAK; N. SURTI. *Nigella sativa*—black cumin; A. HABBAT ASSODA; N. KALO JIRA. *Nyctanthes arbor-tristis*—night jasmine; N. RAT GANDHA. *Nymphaea lotus*—water lily; N. SANO KAMAL.

Ocimum sanctum—sacred basil; N. TULSI. *Opuntia dillenii*—prickly pear; A. TEEN SHOKI; N. KARE SIWARI. *Oroxylum indicum*—N. TOTALA. *Oryza sativa*—paddy; A. ROZZ; N. DHAN. *Oxalis repens*—wood-sorrel; N. CHARI AMILO.

Paederia foetida—N. GANDHALI. *Pandanus tectorius* (=*P. odoratissimus*)—screwpine; A. KADI; N. TARIKA. *Papaver somniferum*—opium poppy; A. KHASKHAS; N. APHIM. *Passiflora foetida*—passionflower; N. GARANDEL PHUL. *Pennisetum typhoides*—pearl millet; N. BAJRA. *Pentapetes phoenicea*—noon flower; N. DEWSE. *Phaseolus aureus*—N. MOONG. *P. mungo*—N. KALO DAL. *Phoenix dactytifera*—date; A. TAMR; N. KHAJUR. *Phyllanthus acidus*—N. amale. *Piper betle*—betel; A. TUMBOL; N. pan. *P. longum*—long pepper; N. PIPLA. *P. nigrum*—black pepper; A. PHIL-PHIL; N. GOLOMARICH. *Pistia stratiotes*—water lettuce; N. PANIKUMBI. *Pisum sativum*—pea; A. ATAR; N. MATAR. *Pithecolobium dulce*—A. DAIMEN; *P. saman*—rain tree; N. JHARE RUKH. *Plumeria rubra*—temple tree or pagoda tree; N. MANDIRE. *Polyalthia longifolia*—mast tree; N. DEBDARU. *Portulaca oleracea*—purslane; A. REGNA. *Psidium guayava*—guava; A. ZAITOON; N. AMBAK. *Pterospermum acerifolium*—N. HATIPAILA. *Punica granatum*—pomegranate; A. RUMMMAN; N. DARIM.

Quamoclit pinnata (=*Ipomoea quamoclit*)—N. KUNJALATA. *Quisqualis indica*—Rangoon creeper; N. RANGOON LAHARA.

Raphanus sativus—radish; A. BAKL; N. MULA.
Ricinus communis—castor; A. KHARWA; N. REFI.
Rumex vesicarius—sorrel; N. MADISE HAL HALE.

Saccharum officinarum—sugarcane; A. SUKKAR; N. UKHU. *Saraca indica*—asoka tree; N. ASOK RUKH. *Sesamum indicum*—gingelly, A. GIL-GIL; N. TIL. *Sesbania grandiflora*—N. BAKULE. *S. sesban*—N. JAINTI. SHOREA ROBUSTA—*N. sal. Smilax zeylanica*—sarsaparilla; N. KUKUR DAINE. *Solanum indicum*—N. BIHI. *S. melongana*—brinjal; A. BEEDINGAN; N. BAIGOON. *S. nigrum*—black nightshade; N. KALE BIHI. *S. tuberosum*—potato; A. BATATA; N. ALU. *Sorghum vulgare*—great millet; N. JAWAR. *Spinacia oleraceea*—spinach; N. PALANG SAK. *Syzygium aromaticum*—clove; A. KORON PHUL; N. LWANG. *S . cuminii*—N. JAMUNA. *S. jambos*—rose-apple; N. JAMUNA. *S. malaccense*—Malay apple; N. PANI JAMUNA.

Tagetes patula—marigold; A. MARIGOLD; N. SAYAPATRI. *Tamarindus indica*—tamarind; A. HOMAR; N. TITERI. *Tamarix dioica*—A. ETHL; N. JANGALI JHAU. *Tectona grandis*—teak; N. SHAHGOON. *Terminalia arjuna*—N. PANISAJ. *T. belerica*—N. BARRA. *T. catappa*—N. DESHIBADAM. *T. chebula*—N. HARRA.

Thes-pesia populnea—portia tree; A. LAKEED; N. KAPHAIMUK. *Thevetia peruviana*—yellow oleander; A. TEVETIA; N. PAHELE BIKHU. *Tinospora cordifolia*—N. GURJO. *Trachyspermum ammi*—ajowan or ajwan; A. NAKHWA; N. JUWANO. *Tragia involucrata*—nettle; N. MADESHI SHISHNU. *Trapa natans*—N. PANI PHAL. *Trichosanthes anguina*—snake gourd; N. CHICHINDA. *T. dioica*—N. POTAL. *Trigonella foenum-graccum*—fenugreek; A. HULBA; N. METHI. *Triticum aestivum*—wheat; A. KAMHH; N. GAHU. *Typha elephantina*—N. PATAR.

Utricularia sp.—N. SHIM PHAKUNDE.

Vanda roxburghii—N. VANDASUNAKHARI. *Vangueria spinosa*—N. TIKHE. *Vicia faba*—broad bean; A. PHOOL. *Vigna sinensis*—cow pea; A. DUGGRA; N. BORI. *Viscum monoicum*—mistletoe; N. HARCHUR. *Vitis vinifera*—grape vine; A. ENAP; N. ANGOOR.

Withania somnifera—N. ASGANDHA. *Wrightia tomentosa*—N. KHIRRA.

Xanthium strumarium—N. OKRE.

Zea mays—maize; A. DURRA HINDI: N. MAKAI. *Zingiber officinale*—ginger; N. ADUWA. *Zizyphus mauritiana* (=*Z. jujuba*)—A. DOME; N. BAER.

INDEX

(Numbers followed by 'f' refer to illustration pages)